When a school seeks provisional approval, the final decision on the school's application is made by the Council. The Accreditation Committee's findings of fact are binding on the Council unless those findings are not supported by substantial evidence in the record, but the Accreditation Committee's conclusions and recommendations are not binding on the Council.

If the decision of the Council is to grant provisional approval, that decision is final and effective immediately upon notice to the school. If the decision of the Council is to deny provisional approval, the school has the right to appeal to the ABA House of Delegates and ask the House to refer the matter back to the school. If the House refers the matter back to the Council, the application process continues with the Accreditation Committee and the Council again reviewing the school to determine whether it meets the standards for provisional approval. In the event of a second referral back by the House, the Council's decision after the second referral back is final.

A school that is provisionally approved is entitled to all the rights of a fully approved law school. Similarly, graduates of provisionally approved law schools are entitled to the same recognition that is accorded graduates of fully approved schools.

Obtaining Full Approval
Once a school has obtained provisional approval, it remains in provisional status for at least three years. Unless extraordinary circumstances justify an extension, a school may not remain in provisional status for more than five years. In order to be granted full approval, a school must demonstrate that it is in full compliance with each of the Standards; substantial compliance does not suffice. Again, the burden is upon the school to establish full compliance.

During a school's provisional status, the progress of the school is closely monitored. A visit to the school by a full site evaluation team is conducted in years two, four, and five after provisional approval, and a limited site evaluation by one or two site evaluators is conducted during years one and three. After each such site visit, a site evaluation report is submitted to the school and the Accreditation Committee. The Committee reviews the site report and the school's response and sends the school a letter that indicates any areas where the Committee concludes the school does not yet fully comply with the Standards.

In the year in which a school is considered for full approval, the process is identical to that undertaken in connection with an application for provisional approval. Decisions on full approval are made only by the Council, by reviewing the findings, conclusions, and recommendations of the Accreditation Committee. The role of the House of Delegates in reviewing Council decisions on full approval is identical to the House's role concerning decisions on provisional approval.

Oversight of Fully Approved Schools
After a school is granted full approval, it undergoes a full site evaluation in the third year after full approval, and then a full sabbatical site evaluation every seven years.

Each law school is required to complete a comprehensive Annual Questionnaire, which inquires into facts relevant to continued compliance with accrediting Standards. The questionnaire elicits information regarding significant changes in curriculum, facilities, fiscal and administrative capacity, student retention, bar passage rates, and student placement data. Information obtained is reported to the Accreditation Committee on a fact sheet prepared by the Consultant's Office. For schools undergoing a sabbatical review, similar information is reported on a Site Evaluation Questionnaire and both questionnaires are reviewed as well by the site evaluation team.

The Accreditation Committee's actions upon review of a site report on a fully approved school are likely to take one of three forms. If the Committee concludes that the school fully complies with all the Standards, it writes the school with that conclusion and indicates that the school remains on the list of approved schools. In the remainder of the cases, the Committee will conclude either that the school does not appear to comply with one or more of the Standards, or that the Committee lacks sufficient information to determine whether or not the school complies. In either case, the Committee's action letter will indicate with specificity the Standard or Standards with which the school does not comply, or to which Standard or Standards the Committee lacks sufficient information to determine compliance. The school will then be required, by a specific time, to indicate what steps the school has taken to bring itself into compliance or to provide the information necessary to enable the Committee to determine compliance.

If facts indicating possible noncompliance are presented from any source, the Accreditation Committee may, in its discretion, send a special fact finder to ascertain facts for the Accreditation Committee's consideration on whether the school is in compliance. In addition, major changes in the program or organizational structure of the school may constitute grounds for a special site visit and action by the Accreditation Committee.

Once a finding of noncompliance is made under Rule 13(b), the school is required to appear at a show cause hearing and demonstrate that it complies with the Standards and that no remedial action is necessary. If the Accreditation Committee finds that the school is, in fact, out of compliance, then it gives the school no more than two years to come into compliance, absent a finding of good cause for extending the time period. If the school fails to come into compliance during that two-year period, the Accreditation Committee initiates action to remove the school from the list of approved law schools.

Site Evaluation Process
The Office of the Consultant appoints a site evaluation team of six or seven persons to undertake a site evaluation of the school. The team chairperson is always an experienced site evaluator and often—but not always—a present or former law school dean. The team usually consists of one or two academic law school faculty members, a law librarian, one faculty member with an expertise in professional skills instruction (clinic, simulation skills, or legal writing), one judge or practitioner, and, except on teams visiting a law school that is not affiliated with a university or college, one university administrator who is not a member of a law faculty. The site team is responsible for submitting to the Accreditation Committee a report that addresses the factual information

relevant to each of the Standards so that the Accreditation Committee can determine whether a school is in compliance with the Standards.

The Section conducts annual workshops to train evaluators and chairs of site evaluation teams. Workshops are also conducted to prepare schools for site evaluation visits.

The site evaluation team carefully reviews the materials the school has provided and visits the school for a three-day period, often from Sunday afternoon through Wednesday morning following the schedule as outlined in the Section's Conduct Memo and on the Section website (*www.abanet.org/legaled*). During that visit, the team meets with the dean and other leaders of the faculty and law school administration, with the president and other university administrators (or, in the case of a free-standing law school, with the leadership of the board of trustees), and tries to have one member of the team meet individually with every member of the faculty. The team also visits as many classes as it can during its visit in order to make judgments concerning the quality of instruction, holds an open meeting with students, and meets with student leaders. In addition, the team meets with alumni and members of the bar and judiciary who are familiar with the school.

At the end of the visit (usually on Wednesday morning), the team meets with the dean and the president (or board chair) to provide an oral report of the team's findings. Shortly after

leaving the school, the team drafts and finalizes an extensive written site evaluation report. The report covers all aspects of the school's operation as outlined in the Format Memo, including faculty and administration, the academic program, the student body and its success on the bar examination and in placement, student services, library and information resources, financial resources, and physical facilities and technological capacities.

The site evaluation team does *not* make judgments or reach conclusions as to whether the school complies with the Standards. Those judgments are made by the Accreditation Committee and, ultimately, the Council. The role of the site evaluation team is to provide a factual report that accurately and completely describes the situation of the school and that provides a comprehensive basis for the judgments that must be made by the Accreditation Committee and the Council.

The site evaluation report is sent to the Office of the Consultant. Then, the report is sent to the school, which is given the opportunity to provide written corrections of any factual errors and other comments on the site report.

Confidentiality
The Rules of Procedure for the Approval of Law Schools makes clear that, in general, all matters relating to the accreditation of a law school are confidential.

Chapter 9: Financing Your Legal Education

■ The Cost of a Legal Education

Legal education is an investment. It can be an expensive one. The cost of a three-year law school education could exceed $150,000. Tuition alone can range from a few thousand dollars to more than $50,000 a year. When calculating the total cost of attending law school, you also have to include the cost of housing, food, books, transportation, and personal expenses. Law schools will determine the student expense budget for you. Today, approximately 80 percent of law school students rely on education loans as their primary but not exclusive source of financial aid for law school. Loans from governmental and private sources at low and moderate interest rates may be available to qualified students.

Financial Aid: A Student's Responsibility

The first step in applying for financial aid for law school is to complete the Free Application for Federal Student Aid (FAFSA), available online at *fafsa.ed.gov*, from your college or university financial aid office, or from the law school to which you are applying. This is a free form and you need not pay to file it. The FAFSA is a need analysis tool developed by the US Government, Department of Education. It asks for information about your income, assets, and other financial resources. The information you provide on the financial aid form will be used to compute how much you (and your spouse) should contribute toward your legal education. Most schools require copies of your actual tax return to verify financial information, so be sure to keep a photocopy for your files; some schools also require students to fill out a supplemental form to be considered for institutional aid. Once the analysis is completed, the financial aid officer at the school can determine what types of aid you will need—such as scholarships, grants, loans, or work-study—to pay your law school expenses.

A brochure published by the Law School Admission Council, *Financial Aid for Law School: A Preliminary Guide*, is available at most law school financial aid offices and at *www.LSAC.org*. For complete and individualized information on financing your law school education, contact the financial aid office at the individual law school(s) to which you apply.

Determining How You Will Pay

There are three basic types of financial aid:

- **Scholarships, Grants, and Fellowships**—Depending on the school's policies, these types of awards—which do not have to be repaid—are given according to need or merit. Their availability is quite limited, and they are usually awarded by the law schools themselves. The law schools' admission and financial aid offices can give you more information.

- **Federal Work Study**—Federal Work Study is a program that provides funding for students to work part time during the school year and full time during the summer months. Students sometimes work on campus in a variety of settings or in off-campus nonprofit agencies. Additional information is available from any law school financial aid office. Not all law schools participate in the Federal Work-Study Program.

- **Loans**—Education loans may be awarded directly by the school or through other private agencies. The largest student loan programs are funded or guaranteed by the federal government. Some are awarded on a need basis, while others are not need based. Federal student loans are usually offered at interest rates lower than consumer loans, and the repayment of principal and interest usually begins after the end of your educational program. Private education loans are offered at market rates. Private loans are approved on the basis of your credit.

Debt Management

An education loan is a serious financial obligation that must be repaid. Dealing with this long-term financial obligation can be made easier through the implementation of sound debt management practices—both while you are in law school and following your graduation.

Credit History

Lenders will analyze your credit report before they approve the loan. Most offer prequalification services on the Internet or by phone. If you have a poor credit history, you may be denied a loan. If there is a mistake on your credit report—and there are often mistakes—you will want adequate time to correct the error. It would be wise to clear up errors or other discrepancies before you apply for a private loan.

You may want to obtain a copy of your credit report so that you can track and clear up any problems. You can order your free copy from one or all of the major credit reporting agencies by calling 1.877.322.8228, or go to *www.annualcreditreport.com*. You may also mail a request to Annual Credit Report Request Service, PO Box 105281, Atlanta, GA 30348-5281.

Living on the Student Expense Budget

While loans may be available to students with good credit histories, the question of how much to borrow is often asked. The maxim "Live like a student now or you will live like a student later" is a good one to remember. Although students may borrow up to the limit of the school-determined student expense budget, loans do have to be paid back. Consider tracking your current spending habits and comparing them to the budgets at schools of your choice. Look into having a roommate. Learn to cook; food expenses are often budget-busters. For example, $5 a day for lunch totals $25 weekly, $100 monthly, and so on. If you have to borrow to pay for lunch, the real cost is in the neighborhood of $8 a day. Bring a lunch rather than buying one. While law school may be an excellent long-term investment, paying loans in the short term can be a real burden. Remember, not all lawyers will earn the highest reported salaries.

If possible, you should pay off any outstanding consumer debt before entering law school. Student expense budgets do not allow the use of education loan funds to pay for prior consumer debt. Entering law school with no credit card debt will make living on your budget easier. Most federal and private education loans allow you to defer payment while you attend law school at least half time. Interest on subsidized

loans does not accrue, while unsubsidized and private loans accrue interest while you are in law school. Be sure to inform your prior lenders that you have returned to school.

Loan Default or Delinquency

These two terms are often confused: neither is good. Delinquency occurs when you have begun repayment on a loan or other obligation and have missed one or more payment dates; default generally occurs when a delinquency goes beyond 150–180 days.

Delinquencies appear on credit records and may hinder you from qualifying for an education loan that requires a credit check. Defaults are even more serious and are likely to prevent you from receiving federal financial aid as well as disqualifying you for most other education loans. If you are in a default status, you must take steps to change your status if you wish to apply for a federally guaranteed loan for law school. Contact the servicer of your loan(s) for more information on this subject.

Planning Ahead: Repayment of Your Loan

Your income after law school is an important factor in determining what constitutes manageable payments on your education loans. Although it may be difficult to predict what kind of job you will get (or want) after law school, or exactly what level of salary you will receive, it is important that you make some assessment of your goals for the purpose of sound debt management. In addition to assessing expected income, you must also create a realistic picture of how much you can afford to pay back on a monthly basis while maintaining the lifestyle that you desire. You may have to adjust your thinking about how quickly you can pay your loans back, or how much money you can afford to borrow, or just how extravagantly you expect to live in the years following your graduation from law school.

Your education loan debts represent a serious financial commitment that must be repaid. A default on any loan engenders serious consequences, including possible legal action against you by the lender or the government, or both.

Law school graduate debt of $100,000 amounts to almost $1,187 a month on a standard repayment plan. Most lenders offer graduated and income-sensitive repayment plans that lower monthly payment amounts but increase the number of years of repayment. Federal Loan Consolidation allows students to repay their Federal Stafford, Ford Federal Direct Loans, and Graduate PLUS loans on an extended repayment schedule, lasting up to 30 years. Stafford and Direct Loan lenders also now offer income-based repayment options (IBR). This repayment will allow borrowers to pay a small amount monthly toward their loans, depending on income and the loan amounts. There also may be forgiveness after 25 years, and federal loan forgiveness for government and nonprofit employees after 10 years. The federal government (www.ed.gov), and many lenders have websites with loan repayment and budget calculators.

Strategies for Graduates Seeking Public Interest Careers

Students who seek to work in public service or the public interest sector of the profession face special challenges in financing their legal educations. Salaries for such jobs are comparatively low. Students graduating from law school with the average amount of indebtedness may find that the average entry-level public service or public interest salary ($44,000 for 2008 graduates) will not provide the resources needed to repay their law school loans and cover their basic living expenses.

Students can employ a number of strategies to make it easier (or possible) to pursue a career in the public service or interest sectors. First, students can borrow less during law school (e.g., attend a lower tuition institution; follow some of the debt management strategies mentioned in this chapter). Students may also take advantage of programs developed at some law schools to relieve the debt burden for those interested in public interest careers, including fellowships, scholarships, and loan repayment assistance programs (LRAPs). LRAPs provide financial assistance to law school graduates working in the public interest sector, government, or other lower-paying legal fields. In most cases, this aid is given to graduates in the form of a forgivable loan to help them repay their annual educational debt. Upon completion of the required service obligation, schools will forgive or cancel these loans for program participants.

The number of law schools sponsoring LRAPs is limited: as of December 2006, approximately 106 law schools sponsored such programs. The funding for these programs is limited, so that most schools are unable to provide assistance to all applicants.

LRAPs are also administered by state bar foundations, public interest legal employers, and federal and state governments to assist law graduates in pursuing and remaining in public interest jobs. The federal government offers some options to assist graduates seeking legal careers in public service, including the new Income-Based Repayment (IBR) option for federal loan repayment and the Federal Loan Forgiveness Program, both beginning in 2009. The IBR will allow any federal education loan borrower the opportunity to make low monthly payments on their federal loans. The payments are equal to 15 percent of the difference between the borrower's earnings and 150 percent of the federal poverty level. The Federal Government Loan Forgiveness Program allows borrowers who work in government or nonprofits the opportunity to make payments under the IBR, then have their outstanding balances forgiven after 120 eligible payments. Please check with your school or directly with the Department of Education for details on these new programs.

For more information about loan repayment assistance programs or the income-based repayment program, visit www.abalegalservices.org/lrap or www.equaljusticeworks.org.

*All figures and calculations are based on current interest rates, loan terms, and fees, and are subject to change.

Chapter 10: Finding a Job

■ Employment Prospects

Because the number of practicing lawyers in the United States continues to increase, it may become more difficult for recent graduates to find jobs in some fields and in certain parts of the country. Opportunities will vary from locality to locality and among legal disciplines. Future lawyers may have to devote considerable time and energy to secure a first job that they consider acceptable. Competition for certain positions will continue to be intense, while opportunities in other fields may expand.

Future demand for people with legal training is almost impossible to predict. Demand for legal services is substantially influenced by the state of the economy. Rising caseloads in the nation's courts and continuing federal and state regulations suggest that the need for lawyers is growing. Whether this expanding need will match or fall short of the parallel growth in the number of practicing lawyers is a question no one can answer with certainty. Lawyers with outstanding academic credentials will continue to obtain desirable positions.

The legal profession itself may adapt to changing job markets by encouraging the entry of lawyers into relatively new fields of law, such as environmental law, intellectual property law, immigration law, and other fields. In addition, certain parts of the country are underrepresented by lawyers.

Career Satisfaction

A job search strategy requires careful self-assessment in much the same way as a school search strategy does. A legal career should meet the interests, abilities, capacities, and priorities of the individual lawyer. Career satisfaction is a result of doing what you like to do, and being continually challenged by it. It is up to you to determine what skills you are comfortable using, and to discern which skills are required in the specialties or types of practice you are considering.

Gathering Information

Take advantage of any programs and workshops offered by the career services office at your law school. (See page 20 for more on the role of the career services office.) Place your name on file in the office, and be sure to maintain contact with the staff even after you leave school. NALP—The Association for Legal Career Professionals is an important source of information (see page 887 for details). Both employers and students are guided in the employment process by NALP's Principles and Standards for Law Placement and Recruitment Activities. These guidelines are promulgated to ensure that students have an adequate opportunity to make decisions about offers of employment without undue pressure and that employers will receive responses from students in a timely manner. Copies of the Principles and Standards are available through each law school or by contacting NALP.

This chapter includes a number of charts and graphs compiled by NALP that provide current information relating to employment of law school graduates.

■ Graduates Acquire Jobs at Various Times

The search for a full-time job is a process that is dictated not only by the effort and commitment of the candidate but also by the unique recruiting practices of various types of employers. Large firms tend to be more structured and predictable than smaller firms.

Summer Clerkship May Lead to First-Year Associate Offer

Some law firms (typically large firms, which can predict their needs well in advance) interview on campus in the fall to hire students for the following summer. If a student's performance is acceptable and the hiring needs of the firm have remained consistent with the size of the summer class, the student may receive an offer for a full-time job following graduation. Students receiving such offers make a decision on whether to accept such an offer during the fall of their third year of law school. Some government agencies (typically the Department of Justice and other large agencies) have honors programs that work in a similar manner, although few of those agencies actually conduct on-campus interviews.

Employers Hire in Spring from Third-Year Class

Smaller private practice employers and a significant number of public interest and government agencies interview and hire third-year law students during the spring of the student's third year. This timetable enables them to predict more accurately their hiring needs and offers both employers and students an additional semester of law school for hiring/career decisions.

Judicial Clerkships Are a Source of Postgraduation Employment

Jobs as clerks for judges at the local, state, or federal level provide postgraduate employment for about 10 percent of law graduates. These job offers typically encompass one or two years and provide invaluable experience in the court system. Judicial clerks balance the advantages of the clerkship experience with the delay of entering full-time practice.

■ Graduates Choose Jobs According to Interests

Members of each graduating class acquire full- and part-time jobs with an array of public and private, legal and nonlegal organizations. Although most graduates obtain jobs as attorneys, not all do. One kind of nonattorney job is a "JD preferred" position, requiring a Juris Doctor and substantial use of legal skills and training. Examples of jobs for which a JD is preferred (and may even be required) include corporate contracts administrator, alternative dispute resolution specialist, government regulatory analyst, FBI special agents, jobs with legal publishers, and jobs in law school career services offices. Other professional but nonlegal jobs do not require a Juris Doctor and may or may not make specific use of legal skills and background. Law graduates have in the past obtained legal, nonlegal, and full- and part-time jobs from the following general types of employers:

- **Private Practice**—includes all positions within a law firm, including solo practitioner, associate, law clerk, paralegal, and administrative or support staff.

- **Public Interest**—includes positions funded by the Legal Services Corporation and others providing civil, legal, and indigent services. Also includes public defenders as well as positions with unions, nonprofit advocacy groups, and cause-related organizations.

- **Government**—includes all levels and branches of government, including prosecutor positions, positions with the military, and all other agencies, such as the US Small Business Administration, state or local transit authorities, congressional committees, law enforcement, and social services.

- **Judicial Clerkship**—a one- or two-year appointment clerking for a judge on the federal, state, or local level.

- **Business and Industry**—includes positions in accounting firms; insurance companies; banking and financial institutions; corporations, companies, and organizations of all sizes, such as private hospitals, retail establishments, and consulting and public relations firms; political campaigns; and trade associations.

- **Academic**—includes work as a law professor, law librarian, administrator, or faculty member in higher education or other academic settings, including elementary and secondary schools.

- **Nonlegal Careers for Lawyers**—Law-trained individuals pursue a wide variety of careers, and the skills discussed in the first section of this chapter provide excellent training for law school graduates who pursue directions outside the practice of law itself. Lawyers work in the media; as teachers of college, graduate school, and law school; and in law enforcement, public relations, foreign service, politics, and administration.

■ *Jobs & JD's*—Research From NALP

The charts, tables, and text in this section were adapted with permission from *Jobs & JD's: Employment and Salaries of New Law Graduates, Class of 2008* (NALP). More than 93 percent of all 2008 graduates from ABA-accredited law schools reported employment status; and salary information was reported for 67 percent of those employed full time.

■ Types of Employment

Class of 2008[†]
(as of February 15, 2009)

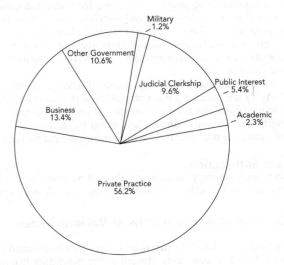

[†]Based on 36,497 jobs.
Note: The category for unknown employer type, representing 1.2% of jobs, is not shown.

■ Salary as an Employment Factor

The national median salary for the class of 2008 was $72,000, up more than $6,000 over the class of 2007. The median has more than doubled since 1985, when a national median was first compiled.

The highest-paying jobs were the exception rather than the rule: Although salaries of more than $75,000 accounted for 47 percent of the salaries reported, salaries of $55,000 or less accounted for 34 percent of salaries. This is despite the fact that, since 1997, the share of salaries of more than $75,000 has increased from 14 percent to 47 percent, while the proportion of salaries that were $40,000 or less decreased from 53 percent to less than 10 percent.

The vast majority of 2008 graduates—89.9 percent of those for whom employment status was known—were employed as of February 15, 2009. However, this rate—down from a 20-year high of 91.9 percent in 2007—was the first decrease since 2003. The employment market for new law school graduates remained relatively strong and remarkably stable for the classes of 1997 through 2008, with the employment rate close to or above 89 percent. This contrasts with the

early- and mid-1990s, when employment rates were in the 84 to 85 percent range.

Median Starting Salaries

	Private Practice	Business	Government
Atlanta	$145,000	$77,500	$52,250
Boston	$160,000	$70,000	$40,000
Chicago	$160,000	$66,000	$55,361
Houston	$160,000	$70,000	$55,000
Los Angeles	$160,000	$75,000	$60,000
New York City	$160,000	$82,500	$57,000
Philadelphia	$145,000	$71,000	$49,000
San Diego	$140,000	$85,000	$58,552
San Francisco	$160,000	$76,000	$63,000
Washington, DC	$160,000	$72,400	$58,206

Note: Figures reflect full-time jobs only.

Note: The median is the midpoint in a ranking of salaries reported. However, because so many reported salaries are identical and especially cluster at round dollar amounts, such as $50,000, the median should generally be interpreted as the point at which half the salaries are at or above that figure and half are at or below it.

Differences in Salary Medians by Job and Employer Type

	Bar Passage Required	JD Preferred	Other Professional
All Types	$75,000	$60,000	$65,000
Academic	$50,000	$45,550	$48,500
Business	$70,000	$70,000	$75,000
Private Practice	$125,000	$40,000	$51,250
Government	$52,712	$50,000	$60,000
Public Interest	$43,500	$44,500	$45,900

Note: Figures reflect full-time jobs only.

■ Geography as an Employment Factor

Geographic considerations provide yet another perspective on the placement of new law graduates.

Jobs by City

The 20 cities reporting the largest number of jobs accounted for about 44 percent of all jobs with a known location. Of these 20 cities listed in the table at right, 11 correspond to the 20 largest cities in terms of population. The three largest cities in the country—New York, Los Angeles, and Chicago—continue to be major employment centers for new law graduates.

Nine of the 20 cities providing the most jobs, however, are not among the largest cities in the country. Even though Washington, DC, does not rank as one of the 20 largest cities in terms of population, its importance in the legal job market is unlikely to diminish. Not surprisingly, New York City accounts for by far the largest number of jobs with location reported, more than 10 percent of the total.

Jobs by State

States vary widely in the number of jobs each provides, again reflecting the distribution of the total population. However, the top 10 states in terms of total reported jobs taken by law graduates have remained the same over the past six years,

Number of Jobs by Region*—Full- and Part-Time Jobs
Number of Jobs = 35,990

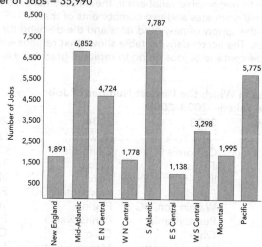

Note: Jobs in foreign locations—286 jobs—are not shown.
*See page 42 for US Census Bureau Regions.

with New York and California consistently ranked first and second, respectively. In 2007, however, Georgia replaced New Jersey as number 10 on the list.

Cities with the Largest Number of Jobs Reported

City	Number of Jobs
New York	3,631
Washington, DC	2,189
Chicago	1,582
Los Angeles	1,084
Boston	853
Houston	708
San Francisco	645
Atlanta	609
San Diego	532
Philadelphia	507
Dallas	473
Minneapolis/St. Paul	427
Miami	414
Seattle	364
Denver	339
Phoenix	299
Cleveland	292
Austin	277
Indianapolis	258
New Orleans	249

Place of Work Versus Place of School

Nationally, about 75 percent of jobs were accepted by graduates who had attended law school in the same region. Comparing the location of graduates' law school training with the location of their first job provides an understanding of the extent to which each geographic market attracts and absorbs graduates from within that market. The data collected here (see page 41) do not allow for various factors (such as the perceived attractiveness of each market and individual

preferences) to be isolated. Nonetheless, the data can provide insights into geographic variations in the employment market for new law graduates and two components of that market—the supply of new graduates and the demand for new graduates. The accompanying table shows that regions with the highest percentage of jobs going to regional graduates are also among the regions where the total supply of graduates exceeded the number of jobs taken by the largest margin. This finding suggests that there is a correlation between a region's supply of graduates and the extent to which employers hired from that supply.

States in Which the Largest Number of Jobs Were Taken—2003–2008

Rank	2003	2004	2005	2006	2007	2008
1	New York	New York	New York	New York	New York	New York
2	California	California	California	California	California	California
3	Texas	Illinois	Texas	Illinois	Washington, DC	Texas
4	Illinois	Texas	Illinois	Texas	Illinois	Washington, DC
5	Florida	Washington, DC	Florida	Florida	Florida	Florida
6	Washington, DC	Florida	Washington, DC	Washington, DC	Texas	Illinois
7	Pennsylvania	Pennsylvania	Pennsylvania	Pennsylvania	Pennsylvania	Massachusetts
8	Ohio	Ohio	Ohio	Massachusetts	Massachusetts	Pennsylvania
9	Massachusetts	Massachusetts	Massachusetts	Ohio	Ohio	Ohio
10	New Jersey	New Jersey	New Jersey	New Jersey	Georgia	Georgia

Jobs and Graduates by Region of Law School

	New England	Mid-Atlantic	East North Central	West North Central	South Atlantic	East South Central	West South Central	Mountain	Pacific	Total
Graduates with Known Employment Status	3,191	6,308	6,722	2,505	8,960	1,468	3,812	1,581	6,035	40,582
Graduates with Known Job Location[†]	2,849	5,541	5,888	2,189	7,788	1,306	3,299	1,419	5,245	35,524
Jobs Reported in Region	1,891	6,852	4,724	1,778	7,787	1,138	3,298	1,995	5,775	35,238
Graduates Staying in Region	1,494	4,555	3,964	1,493	5,785	824	2,743	1,135	4,506	26,499
Percentage of Jobs to Region Graduates	79.0	66.5	83.9	84.0	74.3	72.4	83.2	56.9	78.0	75.2
Percentage of Graduates Staying in Region	52.4	82.2	67.3	68.2	74.3	63.1	83.1	80.0	85.9	74.6
Ratio of Graduates to Jobs	1.69	0.92	1.42	1.41	1.15	1.29	1.16	0.79	1.05	1.15

[†]Includes locations outside the US.

US Census Bureau Regions

Region	States Included
New England	CT, ME, MA, NH, RI, VT
Mid-Atlantic	NJ, NY, PA
East North Central	IL, IN, MI, OH, WI
West North Central	IA, KS, MN, MO, NE, ND, SD
South Atlantic	DE, DC, FL, GA, MD, NC, SC, VA, WV
East South Central	AL, KY, MS, TN
West South Central	AR, LA, OK, TX
Mountain	AZ, CO, ID, MT, NV, NM, UT, WY
Pacific	AK, CA, HI, OR, WA

Career Placement and Bar Passage Chart

| | Career Placement | | | | | | | | | | | | | Bar Passage* | | |
| | Employment Status | | | | Type of Employment | | | | | | Location | | | | | |
	% Employment Status Known	% Employed	% Pursuing Graduate Degree	% Unemployed - Seeking, Not Seeking, or Studying for the Bar	% in Law Firms	% in Business & Industry	% in Government	% in Public Interest	% in Judicial Clerkships	% in Academia	% Employed in State	% Employed in Foreign Nations	# States Where Employed	State Where Most Take Exam	% Pass Rate for First-time Test Takers	% State's Overall Pass Rate for First-time Test Takers
Alabama																
Alabama	98.7	87.7	3.9	1.9	53.7	12.5	15.4	4.4	11.8	1.5	61.0	2.2	18	AL	97	89
Faulkner	100.0	90.0	3.3	5.0	68.5	7.4	11.1	3.7	7.4	1.9	90.7	0.0	2	AL	93	89
Samford	100.0	83.6	9.4	6.3	72.9	11.3	10.5	0.0	3.0	2.3	57.9	0.8	17	AL	96	89
Arizona																
Arizona	99.3	92.3	1.4	2.1	47.0	9.1	21.2	2.3	18.2	2.3	65.2	0.8	15	AZ	92	84
Arizona State	99.6	92.9	2.9	0.0	52.9	10.3	17.5	9.0	7.2	2.7	72.6	0.0	21	AZ	90	84
Phoenix	100.0	88.2	5.9	2.9	60.0	16.7	3.3	10.0	3.3	6.7	93.3	0.0	3	AZ	97	84
Arkansas																
Arkansas	98.5	85.3	9.3	3.1	62.7	17.3	10.9	4.5	2.7	1.8	63.6	0.0	14	AR	82	83
Arkansas-Little Rock	100.0	92.5	2.5	4.2	51.4	14.4	12.6	3.6	12.6	4.5	84.7	0.0	12	AR	81	83
California																
California-Berkeley	100.0	96.2	2.4	1.4	72.2	3.9	5.0	10.0	8.9	0.0	69.0	2.1	23	CA	88	78
California-Davis	98.9	95.2	2.7	1.1	52.8	7.3	10.7	11.8	7.3	3.4	87.1	0.0	12	CA	80	78
California-Hastings	99.7	84.1	1.3	6.6	63.1	8.4	8.7	6.0	6.0	7.8	87.1	0.3	19	CA	81	78
California-Los Angeles	100.0	95.8	1.5	0.9	63.8	6.8	7.7	8.7	10.5	1.9	87.0	0.3	16	CA	89	78
California Western	90.2	82.2	3.5	8.7	60.3	12.7	14.3	6.9	4.8	1.1	76.2	0.5	15	CA	84	78
Chapman	99.5	84.1	3.8	2.7	56.9	9.2	10.5	0.7	2.6	19.6	89.5	0.0	12	CA	75	78
Golden Gate	94.6	84.9	6.8	5.7	51.5	12.3	14.7	7.4	4.3	9.2	85.9	1.2	11	CA	72	78
La Verne	100.0	76.6	1.3	6.5	72.9	16.9	5.1	3.4	0.0	1.7	93.2	0.0	5	CA	61	78
Loyola Marymount	100.0	95.2	1.0	2.5	58.9	18.0	6.9	11.9	2.4	1.3	95.2	0.0	9	CA	85	78
Pacific, McGeorge	99.0	90.6	3.0	3.7	50.4	8.9	25.6	8.5	2.6	3.3	89.6	0.4	14	CA	80	78
Pepperdine	98.6	93.7	3.9	2.4	66.1	17.2	5.7	3.6	4.7	2.6	81.2	1.0	21	CA	87	78
San Diego	100.0	90.5	4.0	1.5	55.4	18.2	13.2	6.4	4.1	2.0	87.8	0.0	17	CA	79	78
San Francisco	94.3	95.8	0.5	2.8	49.0	23.8	9.7	10.2	1.5	1.0	85.4	0.5	9	CA	86	78
Santa Clara	99.7	81.8	1.4	6.4	56.6	26.4	9.1	3.7	1.7	1.2	89.3	0.0	13	CA	78	78
Southern California	98.1	97.6	1.0	1.5	75.6	6.5	4.0	5.5	5.0	3.0	85.6	0.0	13	CA	90	78
Southwestern	96.1	93.8	0.7	1.5	59.9	19.1	8.9	3.5	1.9	2.7	91.4	0.0	8	CA	70	78
Stanford	99.4	98.3	0.6	1.1	61.0	4.7	3.5	6.4	23.3	1.2	43.6	1.7	22	CA	96	78
Thomas Jefferson	96.9	86.4	4.1	5.5	47.4	22.1	8.9	3.2	5.8	2.6	71.1	1.1	18	CA	70	78
Western State	99.0	69.2	0.0	27.9	76.4	12.5	5.6	1.4	0.0	4.2	80.6	0.0	12	CA	65	78
Whittier	99.4	91.9	3.1	3.1	61.9	22.4	8.2	2.7	2.0	2.7	76.9	3.4	17	CA	83	78
Colorado																
Colorado	96.5	92.7	0.6	1.2	39.2	4.6	13.1	8.5	23.5	3.3	73.9	2.0	8	CO	93	83
Denver	99.7	87.5	3.8	5.4	52.2	17.2	13.9	3.6	9.9	0.7	77.4	0.7	22	CO	80	83
Connecticut																
Connecticut	96.8	92.2	1.7	3.4	58.2	13.9	10.3	2.4	12.7	2.4	66.1	0.6	13	CT	92	88
Quinnipiac	97.5	94.9	0.0	1.7	30.4	25.0	20.5	1.8	9.8	0.9	63.4	0.0	13	CT	93	88
Yale	99.5	96.0	2.0	1.5	41.4	7.3	5.2	8.4	35.1	2.6	6.3	3.1	28	NY	96	89
Delaware																
Widener	78.8	89.8	1.9	7.0	43.5	21.2	6.7	2.6	23.8	2.1	24.9	0.0	12	PA	86	87

| | Career Placement | | | | | | | | | | | | | Bar Passage* | | |
| | Employment Status | | | | Type of Employment | | | | | | Location | | | | | |
	% Employment Status Known	% Employed	% Pursuing Graduate Degree	% Unemployed - Seeking, Not Seeking, or Studying for the Bar	% in Law Firms	% in Business & Industry	% in Government	% in Public Interest	% in Judicial Clerkships	% in Academia	% Employed in State	% Employed in Foreign Nations	# States Where Employed	State Where Most Take Exam	% Pass Rate for First-time Test Takers	State's Overall Pass Rate for First-time Test Takers
District of Columbia																
American	99.6	88.9	2.8	4.1	47.5	12.0	14.1	11.5	12.5	1.2	43.6	1.2	31	NY	92	89
Catholic	98.5	91.1	1.5	7.1	42.0	13.1	26.5	2.4	12.2	2.4	45.7	0.4	23	MD	88	86
District of Columbia	83.8	75.4	10.5	8.8	27.9	16.3	18.6	18.6	11.6	4.7	53.5	0.0	11	MD	92	86
George Washington	99.8	97.3	1.5	0.9	65.6	6.8	11.7	4.1	9.5	2.1	52.1	1.0	26	NY	95	89
Georgetown	98.8	96.1	1.3	2.0	74.0	4.6	6.2	5.4	7.8	1.1	35.3	2.0	33	NY	97	89
Howard	86.8	93.9	0.8	5.3	50.0	9.7	16.1	3.2	16.1	0.0	34.7	0.0	21	MD	64	86
Florida																
Ave Maria	92.2	79.2	4.7	13.2	46.4	19.0	17.9	7.1	7.1	2.4	36.9	1.2	25	MI	80	82
Barry	97.2	66.3	2.9	26.7	57.9	15.8	14.9	7.0	0.9	2.6	84.2	0.0	13	FL	76	81
Florida A&M	93.6	81.8	6.8	8.0	55.6	8.3	15.3	8.3	1.4	4.2	52.8	0.0	6	FL	66	81
Florida Coastal	96.4	91.4	3.4	1.8	48.5	13.1	15.5	17.5	2.7	2.4	73.7	0.3	33	FL	83	81
Florida	100.0	87.3	8.3	3.3	64.8	8.1	13.1	4.8	4.5	2.9	74.6	1.4	23	FL	89	81
Florida International	93.5	92.0	1.1	6.9	40.0	13.7	7.5	3.7	1.2	0.0	97.5	0.0	3	FL	88	81
Florida State	98.1	95.1	1.9	1.0	48.1	9.6	25.3	10.9	2.0	4.1	77.8	0.3	20	FL	87	81
Miami	96.8	91.7	4.1	1.1	66.0	10.2	9.9	3.3	5.4	1.2	66.6	0.3	26	FL	91	81
Nova Southeastern	98.8	81.6	4.3	13.7	68.3	9.6	10.1	7.2	3.4	1.4	88.0	0.5	14	FL	84	81
St. Thomas	100.0	68.3	4.8	26.9	48.6	26.1	12.0	7.7	1.4	1.4	74.6	0.7	13	FL	79	81
Stetson	98.0	93.5	2.4	3.4	60.7	10.9	10.9	6.5	3.3	3.3	80.7	0.4	19	FL	82	81
Georgia																
Atlanta's John Marshall	100.0	94.3	0.9	3.8	64.0	15.0	10.0	4.0	5.0	2.0	87.0	1.0	15	GA	88	89
Emory	97.1	93.3	0.8	2.5	67.6	9.5	5.0	2.3	8.1	0.0	40.1	0.9	29	GA	94	89
Georgia	98.5	96.5	3.0	0.5	57.5	7.3	11.4	5.7	17.1	1.0	76.7	0.5	18	GA	99	89
Georgia State	98.9	97.3	1.6	0.5	55.9	18.1	9.6	6.2	3.4	4.0	90.4	0.6	9	GA	94	89
Mercer	100.0	86.9	1.4	7.6	65.9	4.8	18.3	3.2	7.9	0.0	81.0	0.0	12	GA	96	89
Hawai'i																
Hawai'i	100.0	91.8	3.1	0.0	36.7	8.9	18.9	4.4	24.4	6.7	82.2	3.3	8	HI	86	88
Idaho																
Idaho	97.1	84.8	3.0	10.1	36.9	6.0	21.4	8.3	23.8	2.4	64.3	0.0	13	ID	81	80
Illinois																
Chicago	100.0	96.2	1.4	0.9	81.3	3.0	2.0	0.5	12.8	0.0	34.5	0.5	22	IL	95	91
Chicago-Kent	91.2	90.3	3.8	4.1	54.6	17.2	13.0	8.0	5.0	2.3	80.2	0.0	23	IL	96	91
DePaul	99.7	89.5	0.7	5.6	55.1	20.1	13.1	3.3	1.5	5.5	81.4	0.4	21	IL	89	91
Illinois	99.1	89.5	3.8	2.4	60.1	13.8	13.8	2.7	6.9	2.7	64.4	1.1	22	IL	91	91
John Marshall	96.6	89.1	1.5	8.7	54.9	22.8	15.0	2.2	1.7	3.3	83.8	0.0	23	IL	88	91
Loyola-Chicago	100.0	87.9	1.7	6.0	61.8	17.2	12.7	3.9	2.9	1.5	81.9	0.5	22	IL	94	91
Northern Illinois	95.5	87.7	1.9	7.5	58.1	12.9	19.4	5.4	2.2	2.2	80.6	2.2	11	IL	96	91
Northwestern	100.0	97.4	1.8	0.0	74.1	4.5	1.5	5.3	12.0	1.9	41.0	0.8	25	IL	98	91
Southern Illinois	100.0	80.4	3.7	15.0	46.5	14.0	26.7	7.0	2.3	3.5	67.4	0.0	14	IL	95	91
Indiana																
Indiana-Bloomington	100.0	92.5	2.8	3.8	45.4	16.8	16.8	5.6	11.2	4.1	31.6	1.0	31	IN	95	84
Indiana-Indianapolis	99.6	94.7	0.0	3.5	51.9	19.4	17.9	5.2	1.1	4.1	79.9	0.4	20	IN	84	84
Notre Dame	98.9	97.8	1.6	0.5	60.6	5.6	11.7	6.7	14.4	1.1	6.7	0.0	34	IL	100	91
Valparaiso	100.0	83.5	0.8	10.5	60.4	12.6	11.7	0.0	11.7	3.6	45.0	0.0	23	IN	83	84
Iowa																
Drake	100.0	90.8	3.1	3.1	50.8	20.3	11.9	5.9	9.3	1.7	62.7	0.0	21	IA	90	90
Iowa	100.0	94.6	4.4	0.0	51.5	13.9	16.5	3.1	11.9	3.1	34.0	0.0	30	IA	94	90

	Career Placement													Bar Passage*		
	Employment Status				Type of Employment						Location					
	% Employment Status Known	% Employed	% Pursuing Graduate Degree	% Unemployed - Seeking, Not Seeking, or Studying for the Bar	% in Law Firms	% in Business & Industry	% in Government	% in Public Interest	% in Judicial Clerkships	% in Academia	% Employed in State	% Employed in Foreign Nations	# States Where Employed	State Where Most Take Exam	% Pass Rate for First-time Test Takers	% State's Overall Pass Rate for First-time Test Takers
Kansas																
Kansas	98.2	85.1	6.8	5.0	56.2	14.6	17.5	3.6	7.3	0.7	44.5	2.2	21	KS	94	89
Washburn	95.3	90.1	3.5	2.8	42.5	12.6	23.6	9.4	9.4	0.8	65.4	0.0	15	KS	89	89
Kentucky																
Kentucky	100.0	93.7	2.5	1.9	57.3	7.3	9.3	5.3	19.3	1.3	69.3	0.0	24	KY	94	83
Louisville-Brandeis	97.6	93.5	3.2	3.2	56.9	16.4	10.3	7.8	5.2	3.4	79.3	2.6	15	KY	88	83
Northern Kentucky	100.0	87.0	0.6	7.1	52.2	20.9	10.4	6.7	8.2	0.7	44.0	0.0	9	OH	86	88
Louisiana																
Louisiana State	98.4	91.9	3.2	2.7	51.2	11.2	14.7	2.4	17.6	1.8	80.0	0.0	13	LA	81	67
Loyola-New Orleans	95.1	91.9	3.8	1.7	62.3	10.7	12.1	3.7	10.2	0.9	69.3	2.8	19	LA	67	67
Southern	98.4	81.8	1.7	16.5	56.6	9.1	16.2	3.0	8.1	7.1	87.9	0.0	8	LA	57	67
Tulane	97.5	90.3	2.5	7.2	57.3	9.9	9.9	8.9	12.2	1.9	37.6	2.3	32	LA	76	67
Maine																
Maine	98.6	87.1	5.7	7.1	54.1	11.5	11.5	6.6	16.4	0.0	70.5	1.6	9	ME	92	91
Maryland																
Baltimore	98.3	95.1	1.4	2.4	31.1	17.9	20.1	7.3	20.5	2.6	82.1	0.4	11	MD	85	86
Maryland	96.5	94.0	1.6	2.8	39.7	15.4	14.5	6.0	18.4	6.0	58.1	0.0	27	MD	90	86
Massachusetts																
Boston College	100.0	96.4	0.0	2.6	67.8	4.5	7.2	3.0	13.6	3.8	50.0	1.1	24	MA	94	92
Boston	99.3	96.7	2.9	0.4	68.5	5.2	5.2	6.0	5.6	7.1	45.7	1.5	24	MA	98	92
Harvard	100.0	97.5	1.0	0.7	65.9	4.3	3.7	6.1	19.0	1.0	11.0	4.0	35	NY	96	89
New England	87.3	84.4	5.1	10.1	39.1	26.6	15.0	4.3	13.3	1.7	62.7	0.4	28	MA	91	92
Northeastern	97.0	90.1	0.5	7.3	33.5	26.6	8.1	15.6	13.3	2.9	68.8	1.7	21	MA	94	92
Suffolk	98.9	86.5	2.8	9.4	40.2	28.3	13.2	3.2	11.2	3.0	80.9	0.2	22	MA	93	92
Western New England	90.6	81.7	4.8	12.7	48.5	16.5	9.7	7.8	15.5	1.9	35.0	1.0	16	CT	77	88
Michigan																
Detroit Mercy	98.1	74.4	0.5	19.3	57.1	22.1	5.2	4.5	5.8	5.2	57.8	16.9	19	MI	71	82
Michigan	99.7	97.7	1.6	0.0	72.6	5.1	2.7	5.3	13.6	0.8	10.1	1.9	31	NY	91	89
Michigan State	97.5	87.1	5.1	6.8	47.6	22.9	10.0	3.0	9.2	5.9	54.6	4.1	32	MI	84	82
Thomas M. Cooley	87.8	78.8	3.6	13.9	53.4	16.8	15.2	4.1	4.5	3.6	33.2	1.0	39	MI	81	82
Wayne State	96.9	86.0	2.3	10.4	66.0	13.1	11.5	5.8	2.1	1.6	89.5	0.0	9	MI	96	82
Minnesota																
Hamline	93.0	88.2	2.1	4.3	40.6	26.7	8.5	7.3	15.2	0.6	73.9	0.6	18	MN	93	91
Minnesota	99.6	90.1	4.4	3.2	59.9	7.5	11.0	4.4	16.7	0.0	52.0	1.3	28	MN	97	91
St. Thomas-Minneapolis	100.0	87.0	2.1	8.9	44.1	21.3	11.8	6.3	14.2	1.6	71.7	0.0	17	MN	90	91
William Mitchell	99.7	91.2	0.9	2.8	50.9	26.0	7.6	3.5	9.3	1.4	84.4	0.0	15	MN	90	91
Mississippi																
Mississippi	95.5	90.5	0.6	7.1	50.0	11.2	13.8	4.6	17.1	3.3	59.2	0.0	17	MS	90	88
Mississippi College	100.0	90.1	4.3	5.6	52.1	19.9	15.1	0.0	12.3	0.7	66.4	1.4	17	MS	94	88
Missouri																
Missouri-Columbia	98.6	89.1	3.6	5.1	53.7	11.4	13.8	4.9	13.0	1.6	79.7	0.8	13	MO	92	92
Missouri-Kansas City	98.7	88.7	6.0	3.3	57.9	8.3	16.5	4.5	11.3	0.8	73.7	0.8	15	MO	98	92
St. Louis	100.0	89.5	2.0	7.0	62.0	16.6	7.4	10.5	3.1	0.4	62.0	0.0	23	MO	94	92
Washington University	97.4	95.0	1.5	3.1	61.8	10.2	10.6	2.0	10.6	2.0	22.8	3.7	30	MO	100	92
Montana																
Montana	96.3	87.3	6.3	5.1	46.4	4.3	10.1	10.1	24.6	0.0	72.5	0.0	11	MT	88	92

	% Employment Status Known	% Employed	% Pursuing Graduate Degree	% Unemployed - Seeking, Not Seeking, or Studying for the Bar	% in Law Firms	% in Business & Industry	% in Government	% in Public Interest	% in Judicial Clerkships	% in Academia	% Employed in State	% Employed in Foreign Nations	# States Where Employed	State Where Most Take Exam	% Pass Rate for First-time Test Takers	% State's Overall Pass Rate for First-time Test Takers
Nebraska																
Creighton	100.0	89.0	2.7	7.5	48.5	20.8	23.1	1.5	5.4	0.0	48.5	0.0	27	NE	88	89
Nebraska	95.1	90.5	6.0	2.6	41.0	15.2	25.7	3.8	10.5	3.8	65.7	0.0	15	NE	91	89
Nevada																
Nevada	100.0	93.6	1.4	2.1	55.0	12.2	9.9	3.8	16.0	2.3	83.2	0.8	11	NV	81	77
New Hampshire																
Franklin Pierce	99.2	90.6	0.9	5.1	59.4	16.0	5.7	6.6	8.5	2.8	21.7	0.9	24	NH	93	88
New Jersey																
Rutgers-Camden	95.0	92.1	0.0	6.4	40.6	9.4	6.6	2.0	39.8	0.4	55.3	0.4	18	NJ	85	85
Rutgers-Newark	98.0	93.0	2.1	2.9	46.0	15.5	10.6	4.9	21.7	1.3	62.4	1.3	15	NJ	87	85
Seton Hall	100.0	94.7	0.7	3.3	39.9	12.5	5.6	1.0	39.2	1.0	70.5	0.0	13	NJ	90	85
New Mexico																
New Mexico	100.0	93.3	1.9	3.8	34.7	14.3	17.3	16.3	13.3	3.1	78.6	1.0	11	NM	92	92
New York																
Albany	100.0	93.9	0.0	6.1	48.3	18.4	15.9	5.5	9.0	2.0	81.1	0.0	16	NY	81	89
Brooklyn	98.1	87.0	0.9	5.9	57.4	11.7	18.0	5.5	6.2	1.0	86.0	1.5	21	NY	89	89
Buffalo	93.6	90.8	3.7	4.1	61.1	11.1	10.6	7.1	4.5	4.0	81.8	0.5	20	NY	81	89
Cardozo	97.8	92.1	1.1	3.9	57.8	19.3	8.0	10.4	4.6	0.0	81.3	1.5	16	NY	92	89
CUNY	90.2	84.9	1.7	11.8	21.8	6.9	16.8	34.7	17.8	2.0	63.4	0.0	15	NY	84	89
Columbia	100.0	99.3	0.2	0.5	81.7	2.0	1.7	3.0	10.9	1.0	66.2	3.5	23	NY	97	89
Cornell	100.0	97.8	0.5	1.6	85.7	0.0	1.6	3.3	8.8	0.5	59.9	2.2	21	NY	99	89
Fordham	99.2	92.9	1.3	4.3	75.9	9.7	5.1	3.4	4.4	0.7	84.4	0.2	14	NY	94	89
Hofstra	99.7	93.6	2.0	3.5	48.1	25.9	12.8	2.8	5.6	3.1	84.1	0.0	18	NY	86	89
New York Law	97.2	90.9	2.0	5.3	43.0	23.0	13.9	6.1	4.2	3.9	70.7	0.5	14	NY	91	89
New York	100.0	94.6	3.7	0.8	75.1	2.2	2.2	9.2	10.5	0.9	68.8	2.8	28	NY	97	89
Pace	91.5	91.8	2.6	2.1	44.4	17.4	17.4	6.7	5.1	7.3	62.4	0.0	11	NY	83	89
St. John's	100.0	87.3	3.6	4.0	58.1	14.9	16.6	3.3	4.1	2.9	90.0	0.0	11	NY	91	89
Syracuse	96.4	89.4	5.1	1.9	46.6	24.4	14.0	5.7	8.8	0.5	39.9	1.0	26	NY	84	89
Touro	94.0	71.8	0.0	23.4	57.8	14.1	19.3	3.0	5.2	0.7	90.4	0.0	5	NY	78	89
North Carolina																
Campbell	95.4	94.2	2.9	2.9	66.3	5.1	22.4	1.0	3.1	1.0	90.8	1.0	6	NC	95	83
Charlotte	0.0	0.0	0.0	0.0	0.0	0.0	0.0	0.0	0.0	0.0	0.0	0.0	0			
Duke	100.0	98.1	0.5	0.0	75.4	3.0	1.5	3.0	16.3	1.0	9.4	0.0	30	NY	96	89
Elon	0.0	0.0	0.0	0.0	0.0	0.0	0.0	0.0	0.0	0.0	0.0	0.0	0			
North Carolina	98.6	90.3	1.4	4.1	63.3	8.7	7.1	8.7	9.7	1.5	55.1	0.0	22	NC	90	83
North Carolina Central	84.0	82.6	5.8	8.3	53.0	6.0	22.0	7.0	6.0	1.0	68.0	0.0	9	NC	81	83
Wake Forest	98.0	96.6	0.7	2.7	69.5	6.4	8.5	0.0	9.2	3.5	55.3	0.0	20	NC	96	83
North Dakota																
North Dakota	100.0	81.2	4.7	9.4	43.5	17.4	10.1	5.8	21.7	1.4	63.8	0.0	14	ND	91	85
Ohio																
Akron	98.0	82.1	1.4	10.3	47.9	22.7	19.3	5.0	4.2	0.8	79.8	0.0	15	OH	91	88
Capital	81.6	87.0	0.7	11.6	56.7	16.5	19.7	3.9	0.8	2.4	87.4	0.0	12	OH	95	88
Case Western	96.3	94.2	1.5	1.9	47.4	17.0	17.0	11.3	4.6	2.1	45.4	3.1	28	OH	88	88
Cincinnati	100.0	91.0	2.5	4.1	50.5	12.6	11.7	12.6	6.3	5.4	68.5	0.0	17	OH	82	88
Cleveland State	97.6	89.5	1.0	7.0	53.1	23.5	12.3	2.8	5.0	3.4	88.8	0.6	15	OH	90	88
Dayton	96.8	93.4	0.8	5.7	57.9	13.2	13.2	4.4	8.8	2.6	62.3	0.0	26	OH	94	88
Ohio Northern	81.9	89.6	6.5	3.9	53.6	5.8	30.4	1.4	2.9	4.3	43.5	0.0	17	OH	94	88

| | Career Placement | | | | | | | | | | | | | Bar Passage* | | |
| | Employment Status | | | | Type of Employment | | | | | | Location | | | | | |
	% Employment Status Known	% Employed	% Pursuing Graduate Degree	% Unemployed - Seeking, Not Seeking, or Studying for the Bar	% in Law Firms	% in Business & Industry	% in Government	% in Public Interest	% in Judicial Clerkships	% in Academia	% Employed in State	% Employed in Foreign Nations	# States Where Employed	State Where Most Take Exam	% Pass Rate for First-time Test Takers	% State's Overall Pass Rate for First-time Test Takers
Ohio State	99.5	93.5	2.8	1.4	53.7	14.4	17.9	3.0	6.0	5.0	63.2	1.0	24	OH	90	88
Toledo	97.9	95.0	2.1	2.1	42.9	13.5	24.8	8.3	3.8	4.5	61.7	0.8	18	OH	88	88
Oklahoma																
Oklahoma	100.0	88.6	1.8	4.2	56.8	14.9	20.3	2.0	2.7	3.4	76.4	0.0	11	OK	96	93
Oklahoma City	97.8	83.0	2.3	5.7	62.3	14.4	15.1	5.5	0.0	2.7	65.8	0.7	17	OK	90	93
Tulsa	92.2	92.9	3.9	1.9	58.7	21.0	11.2	4.9	1.4	2.8	56.6	0.7	21	OK	93	93
Oregon																
Lewis & Clark	94.3	92.6	3.7	1.4	44.5	20.0	17.0	11.0	6.0	1.5	64.0	2.0	19	OR	81	79
Oregon	98.4	89.4	0.6	8.3	45.3	10.6	15.5	11.2	13.7	3.7	62.1	1.2	17	OR	85	79
Willamette	94.4	94.1	1.0	5.0	48.4	18.9	17.9	6.3	6.3	1.1	66.3	0.0	14	OR	84	79
Pennsylvania																
Duquesne	90.3	87.1	2.2	7.9	57.0	17.4	10.7	0.8	12.4	1.7	71.9	0.0	18	PA	96	87
Earl Mack, Drexel	0.0	0.0	0.0	0.0	0.0	0.0	0.0	0.0	0.0	0.0	0.0	0.0	0			
Penn State	95.8	87.3	3.9	6.1	39.2	10.8	22.2	2.5	20.3	2.5	45.6	0.6	24	PA	85	87
Pennsylvania	100.0	98.8	0.4	0.4	76.8	3.9	0.0	2.8	16.5	0.0	16.1	2.0	22	NY	98	89
Pittsburgh	99.6	90.4	3.3	5.4	61.6	16.7	9.7	4.2	7.4	0.5	62.5	0.9	24	PA	91	87
Temple	98.0	88.9	1.3	7.0	45.7	14.7	14.0	6.8	16.2	2.6	69.4	0.8	20	PA	89	87
Villanova	99.6	90.2	1.8	5.3	55.7	17.2	5.9	6.4	14.8	0.0	60.1	0.5	15	PA	93	87
Widener	98.4	90.1	1.7	2.5	39.4	16.5	22.0	6.4	13.8	1.8	77.1	0.0	10	PA	91	87
Puerto Rico																
Inter American	98.4	91.3	1.6	7.1	43.5	20.8	23.2	0.6	8.9	3.0	96.4	0.0	0	PR	48	54
Pontifical Catholic	100.0	35.1	3.6	61.3	30.8	56.4	5.1	0.0	2.6	5.1	100.0	0.0	1	PR	44	54
Puerto Rico	36.7	76.4	0.0	8.3	58.2	12.7	14.5	1.8	10.9	1.8	98.2	0.0	0	PR	69	54
Rhode Island																
Roger Williams	90.8	86.2	5.9	5.3	43.8	21.0	13.0	8.0	13.0	0.6	43.2	1.2	23	MA	86	92
South Carolina																
Charleston	93.3	67.8	4.6	23.7	42.7	6.8	13.6	3.9	31.1	1.9	89.3	0.0	9	SC	73	82
South Carolina	93.9	91.0	4.5	4.5	51.4	9.3	14.8	4.4	19.1	1.1	72.7	0.5	13	SC	91	82
South Dakota																
South Dakota	98.8	91.8	1.2	4.7	32.1	14.1	21.8	7.7	17.9	3.8	64.1	0.0	13	SD	95	95
Tennessee																
Memphis	97.7	88.2	2.4	4.7	69.6	10.7	8.9	3.6	5.4	1.8	88.4	0.0	12	TN	93	88
Tennessee	96.5	91.3	2.2	2.2	58.7	6.3	15.9	4.0	12.7	2.4	68.3	0.8	17	TN	90	88
Vanderbilt	99.1	95.5	3.2	0.9	73.8	2.9	6.2	1.9	14.8	0.5	18.1	1.4	32	TN	96	88
Texas																
Baylor	95.4	95.9	2.1	2.1	65.0	9.3	12.1	0.7	10.0	2.1	89.3	0.0	12	TX	93	85
Houston	99.3	96.0	1.0	2.3	57.6	21.2	10.1	4.2	3.8	2.1	90.6	0.7	15	TX	91	85
St. Mary's	99.6	89.0	1.8	8.3	61.6	10.8	18.2	2.0	4.9	2.5	88.7	0.0	10	TX	87	85
SMU Dedman	100.0	91.5	1.7	1.4	65.8	22.7	5.2	1.5	2.2	2.6	94.1	0.0	12	TX	94	85
South Texas	89.1	90.1	0.7	7.3	62.3	16.8	12.5	2.6	4.8	1.1	92.7	0.0	8	TX	89	85
Texas	100.0	94.6	0.5	1.8	62.8	9.6	10.3	3.1	12.9	0.7	66.7	1.2	24	TX	89	85
Texas Southern	95.0	71.1	2.6	11.1	57.0	23.7	9.6	0.7	1.5	3.0	64.4	0.7	15	TX	60	85
Texas Tech	91.7	90.5	2.3	6.4	54.3	17.1	20.6	2.5	4.5	0.5	82.4	1.0	5	TX	87	85
Texas Wesleyan	87.5	77.0	2.5	15.5	58.1	29.0	10.5	0.8	1.6	0.0	81.5	0.0	9	TX	78	85
Utah																
Brigham Young	98.7	98.7	0.6	0.0	56.6	12.5	12.5	0.7	15.8	1.3	40.1	2.6	27	UT	92	87
Utah	100.0	98.5	0.8	0.0	59.7	7.0	14.7	5.4	10.1	3.1	77.5	0.8	13	UT	86	87

	Career Placement										Location			Bar Passage*		
	Employment Status				Type of Employment											
	% Employment Status Known	% Employed	% Pursuing Graduate Degree	% Unemployed - Seeking, Not Seeking, or Studying for the Bar	% in Law Firms	% in Business & Industry	% in Government	% in Public Interest	% in Judicial Clerkships	% in Academia	% Employed in State	% Employed in Foreign Nations	# States Where Employed	State Where Most Take Exam	% Pass Rate for First-time Test Takers	% State's Overall Pass Rate for First-time Test Takers
Vermont																
Vermont	100.0	84.2	7.6	4.7	34.7	18.7	16.0	15.3	14.6	0.7	14.6	0.0	29	NY	83	89
Virginia																
Appalachian	73.7	75.7	1.4	17.1	62.3	11.3	11.3	5.7	5.7	0.0	20.8	0.0	17	VA	83	83
George Mason	99.6	96.8	0.0	0.5	47.0	9.8	17.2	8.4	12.6	5.1	42.8	0.9	18	VA	88	83
Liberty	89.2	78.8	6.1	15.2	38.5	23.1	15.4	7.7	7.7	7.7	46.2	0.0	12	VA	89	83
Regent	96.9	90.9	3.2	3.2	42.9	11.4	19.3	8.6	11.4	5.0	44.3	0.7	25	VA	73	83
Richmond	96.5	87.2	4.3	6.7	53.1	7.7	11.9	2.1	17.5	0.0	68.5	0.0	19	VA	91	83
Virginia	100.0	98.8	0.7	0.5	76.6	1.3	4.5	3.8	13.6	0.3	11.3	2.0	34	NY	97	89
Washington and Lee	97.9	89.9	0.7	9.4	57.3	7.3	8.9	5.6	20.2	0.8	27.4	1.6	23	VA	84	83
William & Mary	99.5	92.3	2.4	2.9	60.1	6.7	15.0	4.1	14.0	0.0	36.8	0.5	25	VA	89	83
Washington																
Gonzaga	96.9	85.4	8.2	3.8	51.9	11.9	14.8	7.4	8.1	2.2	62.2	0.7	13	WA	82	74
Seattle	100.0	91.7	2.5	3.3	45.2	31.0	11.7	4.5	6.6	0.9	84.3	0.3	20	WA	79	74
Washington	100.0	93.6	2.9	1.7	53.7	7.4	13.6	8.0	16.0	1.2	62.3	1.9	16	WA	85	74
West Virginia																
West Virginia	99.3	91.7	4.9	1.4	45.5	22.7	7.6	5.3	15.9	3.0	72.7	0.0	16	WV	76	79
Wisconsin																
Marquette	97.9	92.7	1.6	5.8	63.8	14.1	9.6	5.1	4.0	3.4	74.0	0.6	16	WI	100	92
Wisconsin	100.0	96.2	0.7	1.7	58.1	12.2	15.4	6.8	5.7	1.8	50.9	2.9	26	WI	99	92
Wyoming																
Wyoming	98.6	84.3	4.3	10.0	40.7	15.3	16.9	6.8	13.6	1.7	59.3	0.0	9	WY	76	67

*Bar Passage data for first-time bar exam takers in the 2008 calendar year.

New England

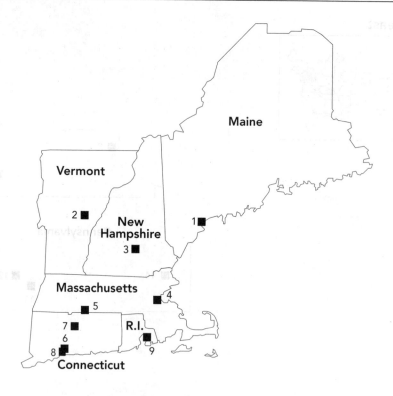

Maine
1. **Portland—Population: 64,249**
   Maine—Enrollment: 264/0

Vermont
2. **South Royalton—Population: 750**
   Vermont—Enrollment: 567/0

New Hampshire
3. **Concord—Population: 40,687**
   Franklin Pierce—Enrollment: 429/1

Massachusetts
4. **Boston—Population: 589,141**
   Boston College—Enrollment: 812/2
   Boston University—Enrollment: 827/3
   Harvard (Cambridge, MA)—Enrollment: 1,765/0
   New England—Enrollment: 737/359
   Northeastern—Enrollment: 602/2
   Suffolk—Enrollment: 1,079/603
5. **Springfield—Population: 152,082**
   Western New England—Enrollment: 389/149

Connecticut
6. **Hamden—Population: 53,200**
   Quinnipiac—Enrollment: 291/124
7. **Hartford—Population: 121,578**
   Connecticut—Enrollment: 450/191
8. **New Haven—Population: 123,626**
   Yale—Enrollment: 613/0

Rhode Island
9. **Bristol—Population: 22,469***
   Roger Williams—Enrollment: 550/0

"Enrollment" represents the numbers of total full-time/total part-time students unless otherwise indicated.

*Population information is derived from the US Bureau of the Census, Population Division, Washington, DC. Data are accurate as of the 2000 Census. City populations reflect the number of people residing in the city proper, not the metropolitan area, which would include outlying suburbs as well. Donald P. Racheter, previously director of the prelaw program at Central College and now president of the Public Interest Institute in Iowa, also contributed data for these regional maps.

Northeast

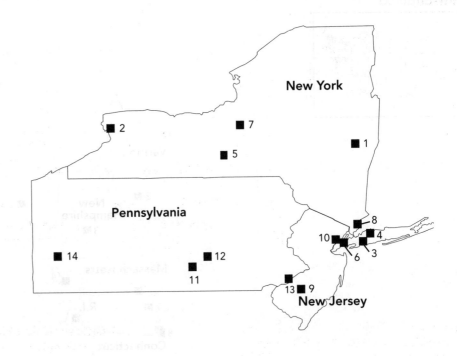

New York

1. **Albany—Population: 95,658**
   Albany—Enrollment: 712/37
2. **Buffalo—Population: 292,648**
   Buffalo—Enrollment: 718/8
3. **Hempstead—Population: 56,554**
   Hofstra—Enrollment: 939/170
4. **Huntington—Population: 18,403**
   Touro—Enrollment: 553/233
5. **Ithaca—Population: 29,287**
   Cornell—Enrollment: 622/0
6. **New York City—Population: 8,008,278**
   Brooklyn—Enrollment: 1,278/180
   Cardozo, Yeshiva University—Enrollment: 1,020/101
   CUNY—Enrollment: 406/0
   Columbia—Enrollment: 1,309/1
   Fordham—Enrollment: 1,160/309
   New York Law School—Enrollment: 1,408/448
   New York University—Enrollment: 1,427/0
   St. John's (Jamaica, NY)—Enrollment: 737/178
7. **Syracuse—Population: 147,306**
   Syracuse—Enrollment: 598/5
8. **White Plains—Population: 53,077**
   Pace—Enrollment: 562/185

New Jersey

9. **Camden—Population: 79,904**
   Rutgers–Camden—Enrollment: 619/191
10. **Newark—Population: 273,546**
    Rutgers–Newark—Enrollment: 593/242
    Seton Hall—Enrollment: 723/367

Pennsylvania

11. **Carlisle—Population: 17,970**
    Penn State, Dickinson—Enrollment: 586/11
12. **Harrisburg—Population: 48,950**
    Widener—Enrollment: 358/103
13. **Philadelphia—Population: 1,517,550**
    Earl Mack, Drexel—Enrollment: 410/0
    Pennsylvania—Enrollment: 790/1
    Temple—Enrollment: 784/192
    Villanova (Villanova, PA)—Enrollment: 754/0
14. **Pittsburgh—Population: 334,563**
    Duquesne—Enrollment: 446/258
    Pittsburgh—Enrollment: 682/0

Midsouth

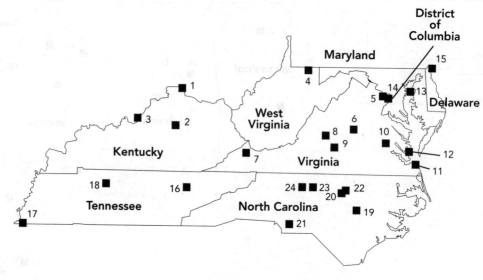

Kentucky

1. **Highland Heights—Population: 6,554**
   Northern Kentucky—Enrollment: 374/235
2. **Lexington—Population: 260,512**
   Kentucky—Enrollment: 406/0
3. **Louisville—Population: 530,000**
   Louis D. Brandeis—Enrollment: 368/67

West Virginia

4. **Morgantown—Population: 26,809**
   West Virginia—Enrollment: 412/6

Virginia

5. **Arlington—Population: 189,453**
   George Mason—Enrollment: 480/217
6. **Charlottesville—Population: 45,049**
   Virginia—Enrollment: 1,122/0
7. **Grundy—Population: 1,105**
   Appalachian—Enrollment: 334/0
8. **Lexington—Population: 6,867**
   Washington and Lee—Enrollment: 390/0
9. **Lynchburg—Population: 65,269**
   Liberty—Enrollment: 267/0
10. **Richmond—Population: 197,790**
    Richmond—Enrollment: 465/0
11. **Virginia Beach—Population: 425,257**
    Regent—Enrollment: 394/23
12. **Williamsburg—Population: 11,998**
    William & Mary—Enrollment: 626/0

Maryland

13. **Baltimore—Population: 651,154**
    Baltimore—Enrollment: 672/431
    Maryland—Enrollment: 723/230

District of Columbia

14. **Washington, DC—Population: 572,059**
    American—Enrollment: 1,195/290
    Catholic—Enrollment: 574/316
    District of Columbia—Enrollment: 266/27
    George Washington—Enrollment: 1,328/304
    Georgetown—Enrollment: 1,628/354
    Howard—Enrollment: 468/0

Delaware

15. **Wilmington—Population: 72,664**
    Widener—Enrollment: 612/363

Tennessee

16. **Knoxville—Population: 173,890**
    Tennessee—Enrollment: 471/0
17. **Memphis—Population: 650,100**
    Memphis—Enrollment: 392/28
18. **Nashville—Population: 545,524**
    Vanderbilt—Enrollment: 594/0

North Carolina

19. **Buies Creek—Population: 2,215**
    Campbell—Enrollment: 405/0
20. **Chapel Hill—Population: 48,715**
    North Carolina—Enrollment: 765/0
21. **Charlotte—Population:**
    Charlotte—Enrollment: 380/101
22. **Durham—Population: 187,035**
    Duke—Enrollment: 626/35
    North Carolina Central—Enrollment: 480/121
23. **Greensboro—Population:**
    Elon—Enrollment: 315/0
24. **Winston-Salem—Population: 185,776**
    Wake Forest—Enrollment: 463/13

Southeast

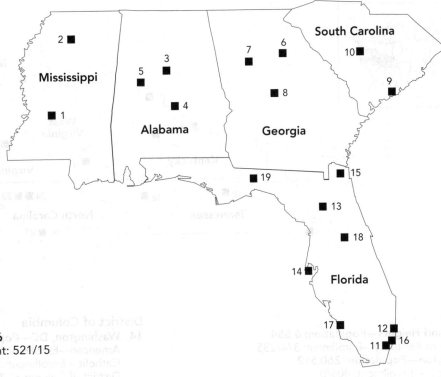

Mississippi
1. **Jackson—Population: 184,256**
   Mississippi College—Enrollment: 521/15
2. **Oxford—Population: 11,756**
   Mississippi—Enrollment: 495/0

Alabama
3. **Birmingham—Population: 242,820**
   Samford—Enrollment: 493/0
4. **Montgomery—Population: 201,568**
   Faulkner—Enrollment: 323/18
5. **Tuscaloosa—Population: 77,906**
   Alabama—Enrollment: 527/20

Georgia
6. **Athens—Population: 100,266**
   Georgia—Enrollment: 694/0
7. **Atlanta—Population: 416,474**
   Atlanta's John Marshall—Enrollment: 371/184
   Emory—Enrollment: 715/0
   Georgia State—Enrollment: 480/193
8. **Macon—Population: 97,255**
   Mercer—Enrollment: 431/0

South Carolina
9. **Charleston—Population: 96,650**
   Charleston—Enrollment: 459/200
10. **Columbia—Population: 116,278**
    South Carolina—Enrollment: 685/0

Florida
11. **Coral Gables—Population: 42,249**
    Miami—Enrollment: 1,351/33
12. **Ft. Lauderdale—Population: 152,397**
    Nova Southeastern—Enrollment: 903/189

13. **Gainesville—Population: 95,447**
    Florida—Enrollment: 1,106/0
14. **Gulfport—Population: 12,527**
    Stetson—Enrollment: 876/208
15. **Jacksonville—Population: 735,617**
    Florida Coastal—Enrollment: 1,539/66
16. **Miami—Population: 362,470**
    Florida International—Enrollment: 294/329
    St. Thomas—Enrollment: 682/0
17. **Naples—Population: 20,976**
    Ave Maria—Enrollment: 375/0
18. **Orlando—Population: 185,951**
    Barry—Enrollment: 609/162
    Florida A&M—Enrollment: 385/228
19. **Tallahassee—Population: 150,624**
    Florida State—Enrollment: 763/0

Puerto Rico
20. **Ponce—Population: 186,475**
    Pontifical Catholic—Enrollment: 474/222
21. **San Juan—Population: 434,374**
    Inter American—Enrollment: 430/418
    Puerto Rico—Enrollment: 527/213

South Central

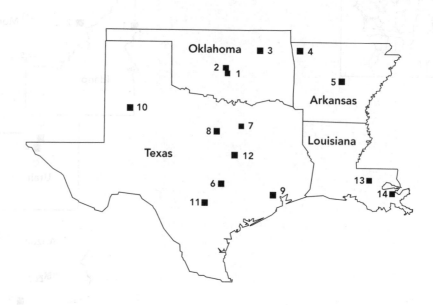

Oklahoma

1. **Norman—Population: 95,694**
   Oklahoma—Enrollment: 550/0
2. **Oklahoma City—Population: 506,132**
   Oklahoma City—Enrollment: 533/90
3. **Tulsa—Population: 393,049**
   Tulsa—Enrollment: 382/40

Arkansas

4. **Fayetteville—Population: 58,047**
   Arkansas–Fayetteville—Enrollment: 398/0
5. **Little Rock—Population: 183,133**
   Arkansas–Little Rock—Enrollment: 316/155

Texas

6. **Austin—Population: 656,562**
   Texas—Enrollment: 1,182/0
7. **Dallas—Population: 1,188,580**
   SMU Dedman—Enrollment: 524/379
8. **Fort Worth—Population: 534,694**
   Texas Wesleyan—Enrollment: 522/271
9. **Houston—Population: 1,953,631**
   Houston—Enrollment: 715/183
   South Texas—Enrollment: 973/305
   Texas Southern—Enrollment: 542/0

10. **Lubbock—Population: 199,564**
    Texas Tech—Enrollment: 637/0
11. **San Antonio—Population: 1,144,646**
    St. Mary's—Enrollment: 681/182
12. **Waco—Population: 113,726**
    Baylor—Enrollment: 465/0

Louisiana

13. **Baton Rouge—Population: 227,818**
    Louisiana State—Enrollment: 587/11
    Southern—Enrollment: 431/167
14. **New Orleans—Population: 484,674**
    Loyola–New Orleans—Enrollment: 726/156
    Tulane—Enrollment: 771/3

Mountain West

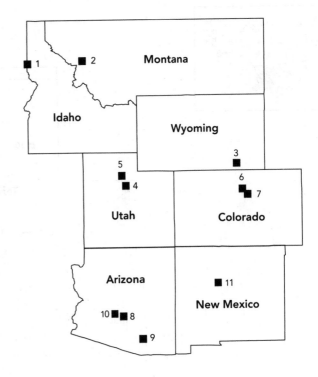

Idaho
1. **Moscow—Population: 21,291**
   Idaho—Enrollment: 319/3

Montana
2. **Missoula—Population: 57,053**
   Montana—Enrollment: 248/0

Wyoming
3. **Laramie—Population: 27,204**
   Wyoming—Enrollment: 225/0

Utah
4. **Provo—Population: 105,166**
   Brigham Young—Enrollment: 447/0
5. **Salt Lake City—Population: 181,743**
   Utah—Enrollment: 381/19

Colorado
6. **Boulder—Population: 94,673**
   Colorado—Enrollment: 547/0
7. **Denver—Population: 554,636**
   Denver—Enrollment: 786/232

Arizona
8. **Tempe—Population: 158,625**
   Arizona State—Enrollment: 576/0
9. **Tucson—Population: 486,699**
   Arizona—Enrollment: 475/0
10. **Phoenix—Population: 1,321,045**
    Phoenix—Enrollment: 352/185

New Mexico
11. **Albuquerque—Population: 448,607**
    New Mexico—Enrollment: 351/0

Far West

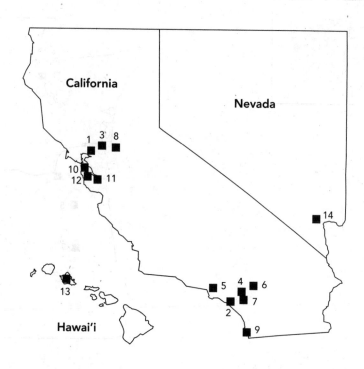

California

Nevada

Hawai'i

California

1. **Berkeley—Population: 102,743**
   California–Berkeley—Enrollment: 892/0
2. **Costa Mesa—Population: 108,724**
   Whittier—Enrollment: 450/141
3. **Davis—Population: 60,308**
   California–Davis—Enrollment: 606/0
4. **Fullerton—Population: 126,003**
   Western State—Enrollment: 276/141
5. **Los Angeles—Population: 3,694,820**
   California–Los Angeles—Enrollment: 1,011/0
   Loyola Marymount—Enrollment: 1,002/285
   Pepperdine—Enrollment: 667/0
   Southern California—Enrollment: 618/0
   Southwestern—Enrollment: 729/323
6. **Ontario—Population: 158,007**
   La Verne—Enrollment: 275/117
7. **Orange—Population: 128,821**
   Chapman—Enrollment: 510/37
8. **Sacramento—Population: 407,018**
   Pacific, McGeorge—Enrollment: 660/377

9. **San Diego—Population: 1,223,400**
   California Western—Enrollment: 791/101
   San Diego—Enrollment: 816/184
   Thomas Jefferson—Enrollment: 648/241
10. **San Francisco—Population: 776,733**
    California–Hastings—Enrollment: 1,292/7
    Golden Gate—Enrollment: 529/108
    San Francisco—Enrollment: 574/132
11. **Santa Clara—Population: 102,361**
    Santa Clara—Enrollment: 749/252
12. **Stanford—Population: 13,315**
    Stanford—Enrollment: 557/0

Hawai'i
13. **Honolulu—Population: 371,657**
    Hawai'i—Enrollment: 285/41

Nevada
14. **Las Vegas—Population: 478,434**
    Nevada–Las Vegas—Enrollment: 366/118

Northwest

Washington

1. **Seattle—Population: 563,374**
   Seattle—Enrollment: 808/228
   Washington—Enrollment: 530/0
2. **Spokane—Population: 195,629**
   Gonzaga—Enrollment: 516/10

Oregon

3. **Eugene—Population: 137,893**
   Oregon—Enrollment: 544/0
4. **Portland—Population: 529,121**
   Lewis & Clark—Enrollment: 521/194
5. **Salem—Population: 136,924**
   Willamette—Enrollment: 421/5

Midwest

North Dakota
1. **Grand Forks—Population: 49,321**
    North Dakota—Enrollment: 247/0

South Dakota
2. **Vermillion—Population: 9,765**
    South Dakota—Enrollment: 202/2

Nebraska
3. **Lincoln—Population: 225,581**
    Nebraska—Enrollment: 394/0
4. **Omaha—Population: 390,007**
    Creighton—Enrollment: 471/13

Iowa
5. **Des Moines—Population: 198,682**
    Drake—Enrollment: 451/16
6. **Iowa City—Population: 62,220**
    Iowa—Enrollment: 590/0

Kansas
7. **Lawrence—Population: 80,098**
    Kansas—Enrollment: 499/0
8. **Topeka—Population: 122,377**
    Washburn—Enrollment: 441/0

Missouri
9. **Columbia—Population: 84,531**
    Missouri–Columbia—Enrollment: 441/4
10. **Kansas City—Population: 441,545**
    Missouri–Kansas City—Enrollment: 489/26
11. **St. Louis—Population: 348,189**
    St. Louis—Enrollment: 771/196
    Washington University—Enrollment: 851/5

Great Lakes

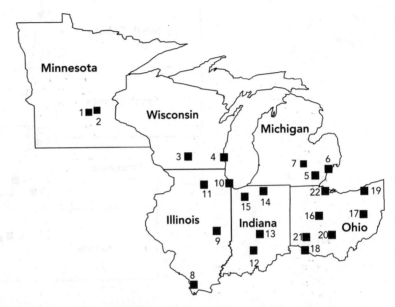

Minnesota

1. **Minneapolis—Population: 382,618**
   Minnesota—Enrollment: 766/0
   St. Thomas—Enrollment: 457/2
2. **St. Paul—Population: 287,151**
   Hamline—Enrollment: 468/182
   William Mitchell—Enrollment: 603/374

Wisconsin

3. **Madison—Population: 208,054**
   Wisconsin—Enrollment: 792/33
4. **Milwaukee—Population: 596,974**
   Marquette—Enrollment: 563/180

Michigan

5. **Ann Arbor—Population: 114,024**
   Michigan—Enrollment: 1,117/0
6. **Detroit—Population: 951,270**
   Detroit Mercy—Enrollment: 586/144
   Wayne State—Enrollment: 457/112
7. **Lansing—Population: 119,128**
   Michigan State—Enrollment: 892/65
   Thomas M. Cooley—Enrollment: 586/3,141

Illinois

8. **Carbondale—Population: 20,681**
   Southern Illinois—Enrollment: 382/1
9. **Champaign—Population: 67,518**
   Illinois—Enrollment: 617/0
10. **Chicago—Population: 2,896,016**
    Chicago—Enrollment: 590/0
    Chicago-Kent—Enrollment: 769/179
    DePaul—Enrollment: 772/255
    John Marshall—Enrollment: 1,038/339
    Loyola–Chicago—Enrollment: 652/188
    Northwestern—Enrollment: 814/0
11. **DeKalb—Population: 39,018**
    Northern Illinois—Enrollment: 298/11

Indiana

12. **Bloomington—Population: 69,291**
    Indiana–Bloomington—Enrollment: 620/2
13. **Indianapolis—Population: 781,870**
    Indiana–Indianapolis—Enrollment: 625/319
14. **South Bend—Population: 107,789**
    Notre Dame—Enrollment: 548/0
15. **Valparaiso—Population: 27,428**
    Valparaiso—Enrollment: 541/41

Ohio

16. **Ada—Population: 5,582**
    Ohio Northern—Enrollment: 307/0
17. **Akron—Population: 217,074**
    Akron—Enrollment: 279/238
18. **Cincinnati—Population: 331,285**
    Cincinnati—Enrollment: 391/0
19. **Cleveland—Population: 478,403**
    Case Western Reserve—Enrollment: 618/22
    Cleveland State—Enrollment: 482/157
20. **Columbus—Population: 711,470**
    Capital—Enrollment: 461/187
    Ohio State—Enrollment: 669/0
21. **Dayton—Population: 166,179**
    Dayton—Enrollment: 500/0
22. **Toledo—Population: 313,619**
    Toledo—Enrollment: 346/147

Chapter 12: Key Facts About ABA-Approved Law Schools

Admission Data

	Application Fee ($)	Full-time									Part-time									Total							
Admission Fall 2009		75% GPA	Median GPA	25% GPA	75% LSAT	Median LSAT	25% LSAT	# of Applicants	# of Offers	# of Matriculants	75% GPA	Median GPA	25% GPA	75% LSAT	Median LSAT	25% LSAT	# of Applicants	# of Offers	# of Matriculants	75% GPA	Median GPA	25% GPA	75% LSAT	Median LSAT	25% LSAT	Total # of Offers	Total # of Matriculants
Alabama																											
Alabama	40	3.91	3.77	3.42	166	164	160	1,403	433	164	3.75	3.19	3.02	165	158	153	0	26	20	3.90	3.76	3.32	165	164	159	459	184
Faulkner	30	3.33	3.07	2.76	152	149	147	747	405	150	0.00	0.00	0.00	0	0	0	0	0	0	3.33	3.07	2.76	152	149	147	405	150
Samford	50	3.59	3.31	3.01	157	155	153	980	506	178	0.00	0.00	0.00	0	0	0	0	0	0	3.59	3.31	3.01	157	155	153	506	178
Arizona																											
Arizona	65	3.71	3.51	3.34	163	161	159	2,214	738	155	0.00	0.00	0.00	0	0	0	0	0	0	3.71	3.51	3.34	163	161	159	738	155
Arizona State	50	3.78	3.60	3.34	163	161	158	2,400	667	184	0.00	0.00	0.00	0	0	0	0	0	0	3.78	3.60	3.34	163	161	158	667	184
Phoenix	50	3.39	3.14	2.79	154	151	148	1,557	1,090	211	3.35	3.15	2.79	154	150	147	249	131	61	3.39	3.15	2.79	154	151	148	1,221	272
Arkansas																											
Arkansas	0	3.74	3.49	3.16	158	155	153	1,167	395	139	0.00	0.00	0.00	0	0	0	0	0	0	3.74	3.49	3.16	158	155	153	395	139
Arkansas-Little Rock	0	3.70	3.36	2.92	158	154	150	1,372	334	99	3.61	3.22	2.86	156	151	148	198	68	62	3.67	3.29	2.90	157	153	150	402	161
California																											
California-Berkeley	75	3.95	3.83	3.68	170	168	165	7,960	803	292	0.00	0.00	0.00	0	0	0	0	0	0	3.95	3.83	3.68	170	168	165	803	292
California-Davis	75	3.72	3.51	3.23	165	163	160	3,189	1,026	213	0.00	0.00	0.00	0	0	0	0	0	0	3.72	3.51	3.23	165	163	160	1,026	213
California-Hastings	75	3.71	3.58	3.39	165	164	161	6,150	1,454	469	0.00	0.00	0.00	0	0	0	0	0	0	3.71	3.58	3.39	165	164	161	1,454	469
California-Los Angeles	75	3.88	3.75	3.57	169	168	164	8,255	1,383	320	0.00	0.00	0.00	0	0	0	0	0	0	3.88	3.75	3.57	169	168	164	1,383	320
California Western	55	3.50	3.28	3.05	155	153	150	2,683	1,276	322	3.56	3.33	2.93	154	151	148	239	72	18	3.50	3.28	3.04	155	153	150	1,348	340
Chapman	65	3.56	3.41	3.11	159	158	156	2,615	839	178	3.82	3.46	2.85	160	158	151	268	52	3	3.56	3.43	3.11	159	158	156	891	181
Golden Gate	60	3.43	3.20	2.88	155	153	151	2,419	1,257	199	3.18	2.90	2.63	155	154	151	350	115	44	3.39	3.14	2.84	155	153	151	1,372	243
La Verne	50	3.31	3.14	2.86	155	151	149	1,335	576	114	3.27	2.90	2.60	154	151	149	316	89	33	3.31	3.06	2.77	155	151	149	665	147
Loyola Marymount		3.68	3.54	3.33	163	160	157	4,994	1,602	339	3.66	3.44	3.20	163	159	155	2,485	110	57	3.67	3.53	3.31	163	160	157	1,712	396
Pacific, McGeorge	50	3.60	3.41	3.07	160	158	155	2,657	1,138	236	3.51	3.29	3.05	157	155	151	378	149	85	3.58	3.38	3.05	159	157	153	1,287	321
Pepperdine	60	3.79	3.61	3.43	163	162	160	3,244	872	230	0.00	0.00	0.00	0	0	0	0	0	0	3.79	3.61	3.43	163	162	160	872	230
San Diego	50	3.60	3.46	3.24	162	160	158	4,010	1,416	281	3.56	3.25	3.10	160	158	156	394	88	40	3.59	3.44	3.22	162	160	158	1,504	321
San Francisco	60	3.57	3.41	3.15	160	158	156	3,391	1,247	227	3.61	3.47	2.96	160	156	153	485	104	45	3.57	3.41	3.12	160	158	155	1,351	272
Santa Clara	75	3.61	3.39	3.11	161	160	157	4,099	1,826	235	3.41	3.21	2.88	159	157	156	481	129	76	3.59	3.35	3.03	161	159	157	1,955	311
Southern California	75	3.71	3.60	3.47	167	167	165	6,024	1,322	215	0.00	0.00	0.00	0	0	0	0	0	0	3.71	3.60	3.47	167	167	165	1,322	215
Southwestern	60	3.56	3.29	3.10	157	155	153	2,994	926	284	3.41	3.18	2.89	155	153	151	500	179	111	3.51	3.26	3.06	156	154	152	1,105	395
Stanford	75	3.97	3.88	3.77	172	170	167	4,082	373	180	0.00	0.00	0.00	0	0	0	0	0	0	3.97	3.88	3.77	172	170	167	373	180
Thomas Jefferson	50	3.22	3.00	2.71	153	151	149	2,587	1,339	305	3.10	2.86	2.63	152	149	147	395	194	90	3.19	2.96	2.70	153	151	148	1,533	395
Western State	50	3.40	3.16	2.83	154	151	149	1,266	663	130	3.36	3.18	2.81	154	150	148	374	131	58	3.38	3.16	2.81	154	151	149	794	188
Whittier	60	3.35	3.10	2.82	153	151	149	1,914	906	245	3.40	3.09	2.85	153	151	149	370	134	61	3.35	3.10	2.83	153	151	149	1,040	306
Colorado																											
Colorado	65	3.78	3.68	3.42	165	163	160	3,059	709	166	0.00	0.00	0.00	0	0	0	0	0	0	3.78	3.68	3.42	165	163	160	709	166
Denver	60	3.69	3.52	3.27	161	159	156	2,587	862	237	3.67	3.43	3.15	158	156	154	338	99	63	3.69	3.51	3.23	160	159	155	961	300

	Application Fee ($)	Full-time									Part-time									Total							
		75% GPA	Median GPA	25% GPA	75% LSAT	Median LSAT	25% LSAT	# of Applicants	# of Offers	# of Matriculants	75% GPA	Median GPA	25% GPA	75% LSAT	Median LSAT	25% LSAT	# of Applicants	# of Offers	# of Matriculants	75% GPA	Median GPA	25% GPA	75% LSAT	Median LSAT	25% LSAT	Total # of Offers	Total # of Matriculants
Connecticut																												
Connecticut	60	3.59	3.43	3.22	163	162	160	2,268	582	120	3.59	3.29	3.06	160	158	156	992	255	62	3.59	3.38	3.20	162	161	158	837	182
Quinnipiac	40	3.63	3.32	3.10	160	158	156	2,686	1,093	113	3.51	3.29	3.01	154	153	151	679	85	47	3.60	3.31	3.09	159	157	154	1,178	160
Yale	75	3.96	3.90	3.82	176	173	170	3,363	270	214	0.00	0.00	0.00	0	0	0	0	0	0	3.96	3.90	3.82	176	173	170	270	214
Delaware																												
Widener	60	3.42	3.11	2.83	154	153	151	2,055	1,139	249	3.53	3.16	2.79	152	150	148	534	240	134	3.46	3.13	2.82	154	152	150	1,379	383
District of Columbia																												
American	70	3.59	3.39	3.14	164	163	158	7,649	1,715	385	3.52	3.28	3.06	162	161	159	1,018	216	96	3.56	3.36	3.13	164	162	158	1,931	481
Catholic		3.55	3.38	3.17	160	158	157	2,517	845	178	3.48	3.23	3.03	158	156	154	782	233	90	3.55	3.33	3.13	160	158	156	1,078	268
District of Columbia	35	3.28	3.06	2.83	153	151	149	1,601	336	96	3.21	3.01	2.60	154	151	149	0	0	27	3.26	3.05	2.80	153	151	149	336	123
George Washington	80	3.86	3.77	3.45	168	167	163	8,906	2,929	456	3.83	3.53	3.16	167	165	162	686	116	50	3.86	3.77	3.41	168	167	163	2,145	506
Georgetown	80	3.81	3.68	3.42	172	170	168	10,731	2,459	463	3.78	3.62	3.42	168	166	163	922	186	127	3.79	3.65	3.42	171	169	167	2,645	590
Howard	60	3.51	3.20	2.92	156	153	150	2,000	443	160	0.00	0.00	0.00	0	0	0	0	0	0	3.51	3.20	2.92	156	153	150	443	160
Florida																												
Ave Maria	50	3.53	3.22	2.91	155	150	147	1,775	885	210	0.00	0.00	0.00	0	0	0	0	0	0	3.53	3.22	2.91	155	150	147	885	210
Barry	50	3.26	2.90	2.58	152	150	148	1,773	1,019	214	3.25	2.90	2.57	154	150	149	216	98	39	3.25	2.90	2.58	152	150	148	1,117	253
Florida A&M	30	3.36	3.06	2.78	149	146	144	1,519	452	165	3.25	3.09	2.67	150	147	145	288	107	69	3.32	3.07	2.75	150	146	144	559	234
Florida Coastal	0	3.42	3.21	2.95	153	150	147	6,274	4,118	702	3.38	3.00	2.57	153	148	147	57	33	20	3.42	3.20	2.94	153	150	147	4,151	722
Florida	30	3.85	3.69	3.42	163	161	158	3,170	780	307	0.00	0.00	0.00	0	0	0	0	0	0	3.85	3.67	3.42	163	161	158	780	307
Florida International	20	3.67	3.45	3.18	156	154	152	1,957	515	168	3.48	3.24	2.90	155	153	150	486	117	82	3.62	3.40	3.13	156	154	151	632	250
Florida State	30	3.74	3.53	3.23	162	160	159	3,316	860	244	0.00	0.00	0.00	0	0	0	0	0	0	3.74	3.53	3.23	162	160	159	860	244
Miami	60	3.66	3.46	3.25	159	157	155	4,605	2,409	530	0.00	0.00	0.00	0	0	0	0	0	0	3.66	3.46	3.25	159	157	155	2,409	530
Nova Southeastern	50	3.47	3.23	3.02	152	149	147	2,122	969	374	3.45	3.20	2.94	151	148	145	421	126	56	3.47	3.22	3.01	152	149	147	1,095	430
St. Thomas	60	3.19	2.90	2.90	153	150	150	2,352	1,071	263	0.00	0.00	0.00	0	0	0	0	0	0	3.19	2.90	2.90	153	150	150	1,071	263
Stetson	55	3.65	3.46	3.21	158	156	153	2,845	1,099	335	3.59	3.39	3.12	156	153	151	621	134	60	3.65	3.44	3.19	158	156	153	1,233	395
Georgia																												
Atlanta's John Marshall	50	3.26	2.96	2.67	153	151	149	1,436	580	145	3.31	3.01	2.64	153	150	149	353	132	66	3.28	2.97	2.67	153	151	149	712	211
Emory	70	3.68	3.57	3.37	167	166	165	4,562	1,149	248	0.00	0.00	0.00	0	0	0	0	0	0	3.68	3.57	3.37	167	166	165	1,149	248
Georgia	50	3.80	3.70	3.40	165	164	161	3,076	857	241	0.00	0.00	0.00	0	0	0	0	0	0	3.80	3.70	3.40	165	164	161	857	241
Georgia State	50	3.80	3.60	3.20	162	161	159	2,493	410	168	3.73	3.52	3.10	161	159	158	321	81	49	3.78	3.60	3.20	162	161	159	491	217
Mercer	50	3.67	3.43	3.13	158	156	153	1,571	600	157	0.00	0.00	0.00	0	0	0	0	0	0	3.67	3.43	3.13	158	156	153	600	157
Hawai'i																												
Hawai'i	60	3.68	3.51	3.21	160	157	155	1,098	224	87	3.61	3.43	3.02	154	151	147	318	45	37	3.68	3.45	3.18	158	156	153	269	124
Idaho																												
Idaho	50	3.64	3.35	3.09	157	155	152	743	355	114	0.00	0.00	0.00	0	0	0	0	0	0	3.64	3.35	3.09	157	155	152	355	114
Illinois																												
Chicago	75	3.84	3.76	3.63	173	171	169	5,403	982	191	0.00	0.00	0.00	0	0	0	0	0	0	3.84	3.76	3.63	173	171	169	982	191
Chicago-Kent	60	3.69	3.53	3.21	163	161	157	3,141	1,383	246	3.59	3.25	2.96	160	158	155	348	133	52	3.67	3.50	3.11	163	161	156	1,516	298
DePaul	60	3.57	3.40	3.11	162	159	158	4,366	1,658	252	3.41	3.26	3.04	157	156	154	702	330	112	3.53	3.35	3.09	161	158	154	1,988	364
Illinois		3.90	3.80	3.20	167	166	160	3,516	1,031	232	0.00	0.00	0.00	0	0	0	0	0	0	3.90	3.80	3.20	167	166	160	1,031	232
John Marshall	60	3.53	3.25	3.00	156	153	150	2,728	1,328	394	3.44	3.20	2.88	154	152	149	617	225	125	3.51	3.22	2.98	155	153	150	1,553	519
Loyola-Chicago	0	3.62	3.50	3.29	162	160	158	3,565	1,133	203	3.50	3.31	3.06	158	155	153	671	151	65	3.60	3.47	3.24	161	160	156	1,284	268
Northern Illinois	50	3.51	3.23	2.93	156	154	153	1,169	472	105	3.74	3.65	3.57	153	151	150	14	2	2	3.51	3.23	2.93	156	154	153	474	107
Northwestern	100	3.81	3.72	3.40	172	170	166	5,205	952	271	0.00	0.00	0.00	0	0	0	0	0	0	3.81	3.72	3.40	172	170	166	952	271

	Application Fee ($)	Full-time 75% GPA	Median GPA	25% GPA	75% LSAT	Median LSAT	25% LSAT	# of Applicants	# of Offers	# of Matriculants	Part-time 75% GPA	Median GPA	25% GPA	75% LSAT	Median LSAT	25% LSAT	# of Applicants	# of Offers	# of Matriculants	Total 75% GPA	Median GPA	25% GPA	75% LSAT	Median LSAT	25% LSAT	Total # of Offers	Total # of Matriculants
Southern Illinois	50	3.52	3.25	3.01	157	153	151	753	362	137	0.00	0.00	0.00	0	0	0	0	0	0	3.52	3.25	3.01	157	153	151	362	137
Indiana																											
Indiana-Bloomington	50	3.83	3.70	3.26	165	164	156	2,524	805	220	0.00	0.00	0.00	0	0	0	0	0	0	3.83	3.70	3.26	165	164	156	805	220
Indiana-Indianapolis	50	3.73	3.59	3.23	160	158	154	1,513	570	195	3.56	3.33	3.04	155	152	147	253	140	102	3.70	3.50	3.15	159	156	151	710	297
Notre Dame	60	3.74	3.60	3.36	167	166	163	3,178	810	186	0.00	0.00	0.00	0	0	0	0	0	0	3.74	3.60	3.36	167	166	163	810	186
Valparaiso	60	3.59	3.34	3.08	152	150	148	1,440	889	191	3.22	2.95	2.82	151	149	147	135	45	12	3.59	3.34	3.08	152	150	148	934	203
Iowa																											
Drake	50	3.64	3.42	3.12	158	155	153	1,069	575	150	3.93	3.41	3.10	159	156	155	36	9	6	3.64	3.42	3.10	158	155	153	584	156
Iowa	60	3.81	3.61	3.43	164	161	158	1,291	566	195	0.00	0.00	0.00	0	0	0	0	0	0	3.81	3.61	3.43	164	161	158	566	195
Kansas																											
Kansas	55	3.71	3.50	3.25	160	157	155	1,098	387	163	0.00	0.00	0.00	0	0	0	0	0	0	3.71	3.50	3.25	160	157	155	387	163
Washburn	40	3.68	3.31	2.95	157	154	152	957	453	159	0.00	0.00	0.00	0	0	0	0	0	0	3.68	3.31	2.95	157	154	152	453	159
Kentucky																											
Kentucky	50	3.82	3.60	3.33	161	159	156	1,080	414	152	0.00	0.00	0.00	0	0	0	0	0	0	3.82	3.60	3.33	161	159	156	414	152
Louisville-Brandeis	50	3.75	3.50	3.15	159	157	154	1,162	432	118	3.67	3.45	3.04	155	154	151	93	33	23	3.73	3.50	3.14	159	156	153	465	141
Northern Kentucky	40	3.64	3.39	3.16	157	154	152	1,029	439	135	3.41	3.27	3.07	154	152	150	196	87	59	3.56	3.35	3.19	157	153	151	526	194
Louisiana																											
Louisiana State	50	3.66	3.44	3.22	159	157	155	1,408	527	233	0.00	0.00	0.00	0	0	0	0	0	0	3.66	3.44	3.22	159	157	155	527	233
Loyola-New Orleans	40	3.52	3.29	3.05	155	153	151	1,671	825	254	3.46	3.14	2.84	155	152	149	156	103	69	3.51	3.26	3.01	155	153	150	928	323
Southern	25	3.31	2.86	2.60	149	146	143	849	369	156	3.10	2.72	2.41	148	144	142	276	92	83	3.21	2.84	2.55	148	145	143	461	239
Tulane	60	3.75	3.60	3.34	164	162	160	2,990	894	284	0.00	0.00	0.00	0	0	0	0	0	0	3.75	3.60	3.34	164	162	160	894	284
Maine																											
Maine	50	3.61	3.37	3.06	158	154	152	705	341	90	0.00	0.00	0.00	0	0	0	0	0	0	3.61	3.37	3.06	158	154	152	341	90
Maryland																											
Baltimore	60	3.67	3.34	3.03	158	156	153	1,990	803	245	3.40	3.16	2.80	154	152	150	758	322	134	3.59	3.29	2.97	157	155	151	1,125	379
Maryland	70	3.67	3.50	3.29	167	162	161	3,073	588	226	3.61	3.31	3.12	161	158	154	535	111	72	3.66	3.46	3.21	166	161	159	699	298
Massachusetts																											
Boston College	75	3.68	3.53	3.34	167	166	163	7,166	1,431	264	0.00	0.00	0.00	0	0	0	0	0	0	3.68	3.53	3.34	167	166	163	1,431	264
Boston	75	3.83	3.70	3.50	167	166	164	7,659	1,801	271	0.00	0.00	0.00	0	0	0	0	0	0	3.83	3.70	3.50	167	166	164	1,801	271
Harvard	85	3.96	3.89	3.76	176	173	171	7,391	833	559	0.00	0.00	0.00	0	0	0	0	0	0	3.96	3.89	3.76	176	173	171	833	559
New England	65	3.45	3.24	3.00	154	152	151	2,678	1,599	296	3.40	3.13	2.80	155	151	149	765	391	107	3.45	3.22	2.97	154	152	150	1,990	403
Northeastern	75	3.63	3.40	3.20	163	161	155	3,798	1,280	214	0.00	0.00	0.00	0	0	0	0	0	0	3.63	3.40	3.20	163	161	155	1,280	214
Suffolk		3.60	3.30	3.30	159	157	154	2,630	1,333	339	3.50	3.20	2.90	156	153	151	631	363	192	3.50	3.30	3.00	158	156	153	1,696	531
Western New England	50	3.55	3.23	2.94	156	153	151	1,423	769	131	3.40	3.19	3.09	151	148	147	273	132	50	3.51	3.22	2.99	155	152	150	901	181
Michigan																											
Detroit Mercy	50	3.38	3.15	2.93	154	150	147	1,707	772	243	3.31	3.17	2.91	149	147	144	219	87	39	3.38	3.16	2.93	153	150	146	859	282
Michigan	60	3.84	3.70	3.55	170	169	167	5,414	1,178	371	0.00	0.00	0.00	0	0	0	0	0	0	3.84	3.70	3.55	170	169	167	1,178	371
Michigan State	60	3.61	3.37	3.09	159	156	153	2,547	1,214	264	3.53	2.90	2.67	153	148	144	189	52	24	3.61	3.36	3.07	159	155	153	1,266	288
Thomas M. Cooley	0	3.42	3.06	2.80	152	148	146	4,986	3,622	221	3.34	2.97	2.58	149	145	143	789	948	1,289	3.35	2.99	2.62	150	146	144	4,570	1,510
Wayne State	50	3.69	3.53	3.25	159	156	153	1,364	537	163	3.70	3.36	3.11	160	156	154	146	31	22	3.69	3.51	3.17	159	156	153	568	185
Minnesota																											
Hamline	35	3.68	3.47	3.27	159	155	151	1,331	628	147	3.51	3.23	2.95	155	150	147	175	116	60	3.66	3.42	3.16	158	154	150	744	207
Minnesota	75	3.85	3.64	3.30	168	167	160	3,594	911	213	0.00	0.00	0.00	0	0	0	0	0	0	3.85	3.64	3.30	168	167	160	911	213

	Application Fee ($)	Full-time									Part-time									Total							
		75% GPA	Median GPA	25% GPA	75% LSAT	Median LSAT	25% LSAT	# of Applicants	# of Offers	# of Matriculants	75% GPA	Median GPA	25% GPA	75% LSAT	Median LSAT	25% LSAT	# of Applicants	# of Offers	# of Matriculants	75% GPA	Median GPA	25% GPA	75% LSAT	Median LSAT	25% LSAT	Total # of Offers	Total # of Matriculants
St. Thomas-Minneapolis		3.59	3.34	3.07	161	157	153	1,551	785	174	0.00	0.00	0.00	0	0	0	0	0	0	3.59	3.34	3.07	161	157	153	785	174
William Mitchell	50	3.67	3.49	3.29	159	156	154	1,268	602	197	3.48	3.26	2.95	154	150	147	424	190	103	3.60	3.40	3.19	158	155	150	792	300
Mississippi																											
Mississippi	40	3.71	3.49	3.27	157	154	151	1,164	472	173	0.00	0.00	0.00	0	0	0	0	0	0	3.71	3.49	3.27	157	154	151	472	173
Mississippi College		3.53	3.30	3.01	153	150	148	1,315	744	193	0.00	4.01	0.00	0	153	0	1	1	1	3.53	3.30	3.01	153	150	148	745	194
Missouri																											
Missouri-Columbia	55	3.70	3.47	3.24	161	158	156	914	400	147	0.00	0.00	0.00	0	0	0	0	0	0	3.70	3.47	3.24	161	158	156	400	147
Missouri-Kansas City	50	3.58	3.30	3.03	156	154	152	914	437	155	3.54	2.88	2.70	161	154	148	36	14	9	3.58	3.30	2.99	157	154	152	451	164
St. Louis	55	3.64	3.41	3.21	160	157	154	2,140	1,024	243	3.45	3.25	3.02	155	153	152	480	171	88	3.61	3.37	3.16	159	156	153	1,195	331
Washington University	70	3.80	3.70	3.30	168	167	161	3,690	987	261	0.00	0.00	0.00	0	0	0	0	0	0	3.80	3.70	3.30	168	167	161	987	261
Montana																											
Montana	60	3.69	3.44	3.26	157	154	151	396	199	84	0.00	0.00	0.00	0	0	0	0	0	0	3.69	3.44	3.26	157	154	151	199	84
Nebraska																											
Creighton	50	3.64	3.43	3.15	156	153	151	1,314	753	173	3.10	2.92	2.79	152	149	147	52	18	4	3.64	3.43	3.13	156	153	151	771	177
Nebraska	25	3.82	3.55	3.29	158	156	154	712	369	137	0.00	0.00	0.00	0	0	0	0	0	0	3.82	3.55	3.29	158	156	154	369	137
Nevada																											
Nevada	50	3.67	3.50	3.19	160	158	156	1,511	333	122	3.64	3.43	3.13	158	155	152	226	48	36	3.66	3.48	3.18	160	158	155	381	158
New Hampshire																											
Franklin Pierce	55	3.62	3.35	3.06	155	152	149	1,336	671	158	0.00	0.00	0.00	0	0	0	0	0	0	3.62	3.35	3.06	155	152	149	671	158
New Jersey																											
Rutgers-Camden	65	3.70	3.53	3.21	162	161	159	N/A	N/A	227	3.70	3.41	3.05	161	160	157	N/A	N/A	41	3.70	3.46	3.18	162	161	158	619	268
Rutgers-Newark	65	3.60	3.39	3.13	161	158	155	2,761	821	191	3.60	3.25	2.95	159	157	154	704	127	68	3.60	3.36	3.09	161	158	155	948	259
Seton Hall	65	3.68	3.48	3.21	161	160	158	2,804	1,453	240	3.47	3.24	3.00	156	153	150	588	226	117	3.64	3.40	3.13	160	158	154	1,679	357
New Mexico																											
New Mexico		3.67	3.51	3.12	158	155	152	1,039	254	117	0.00	0.00	0.00	0	0	0	0	0	0	3.67	3.51	3.12	158	155	152	254	117
New York																											
Albany	60	3.56	3.30	3.03	157	155	153	2,215	972	255	0.00	0.00	0.00	0	0	0	0	0	0	3.56	3.30	3.03	157	155	153	972	255
Brooklyn	0	3.64	3.47	3.26	164	163	160	4,909	1,470	406	3.55	3.41	3.28	160	158	157	977	182	90	3.63	3.46	3.26	164	162	159	1,652	496
Buffalo	50	3.73	3.52	3.19	159	157	153	2,104	678	208	0.00	0.00	0.00	0	0	0	0	0	0	3.73	3.52	3.19	159	157	153	678	208
Cardozo	70	3.75	3.60	3.39	166	164	161	4,645	1,204	268	3.71	3.56	3.28	161	160	158	625	166	102	3.73	3.59	3.37	165	162	160	1,370	370
CUNY	50	3.54	3.31	3.10	156	153	151	2,165	575	158	0.00	0.00	0.00	0	0	0	0	0	0	3.54	3.31	3.10	156	153	151	575	158
Columbia	75	3.81	3.72	3.60	175	172	170	8,505	1,235	400	0.00	0.00	0.00	0	0	0	0	0	0	3.81	3.72	3.60	175	172	170	1,235	400
Cornell	80	3.80	3.63	3.48	168	167	165	4,207	900	205	0.00	0.00	0.00	0	0	0	0	0	0	3.80	3.63	3.48	168	167	165	900	205
Fordham	70	3.77	3.64	3.44	167	166	164	7,294	1,635	318	3.66	3.42	3.28	165	163	161	1,549	269	158	3.74	3.59	3.37	167	165	162	1,904	476
Hofstra	75	3.70	3.56	3.27	159	157	155	4,573	1,853	391	3.67	3.41	3.08	158	156	152	320	38	10	3.70	3.56	3.27	159	157	155	1,891	401
New York Law	65	3.48	3.25	3.02	157	154	152	3,403	1,936	569	3.46	3.07	2.79	155	152	149	785	310	167	3.48	3.23	2.96	157	154	152	2,246	736
New York	75	3.86	3.72	3.57	173	171	169	7,272	1,644	450	0.00	0.00	0.00	0	0	0	0	0	0	3.86	3.72	3.57	173	171	169	1,644	450
Pace	65	3.61	3.39	3.20	157	154	152	2,527	1,035	204	3.43	3.27	3.08	155	153	149	489	138	58	3.60	3.36	3.15	157	154	152	1,173	262
St. John's	60	3.70	3.48	3.16	163	161	156	3,232	1,260	231	3.77	3.62	3.12	155	153	147	804	219	84	3.73	3.53	3.16	162	160	154	1,479	315
Syracuse	70	3.51	3.32	3.13	157	155	153	2,518	960	223	0.00	0.00	0.00	0	0	0	0	0	0	3.51	3.32	3.13	157	155	153	960	223
Touro	60	3.41	3.17	2.88	153	151	149	1,610	793	234	3.33	3.09	2.81	152	150	149	485	169	81	3.39	3.14	2.86	153	151	149	962	315
North Carolina																											
Campbell	50	3.59	3.37	3.12	159	156	154	1,514	460	159	0.00	0.00	0.00	0	0	0	0	0	0	3.59	3.37	3.12	159	156	154	460	159

| | | Admission Fall 2009 | | | | | | | | | | | | | | | | | | | | | | | | | |
| | | Full-time | | | | | | | | | Part-time | | | | | | | | | Total | | | | | | | |
School	Application Fee ($)	75% GPA	Median GPA	25% GPA	75% LSAT	Median LSAT	25% LSAT	# of Applicants	# of Offers	# of Matriculants	75% GPA	Median GPA	25% GPA	75% LSAT	Median LSAT	25% LSAT	# of Applicants	# of Offers	# of Matriculants	75% GPA	Median GPA	25% GPA	75% LSAT	Median LSAT	25% LSAT	Total # of Offers	Total # of Matriculants
Charlotte	50	3.40	3.11	2.76	153	151	149	2,025	1,118	234	3.40	3.15	2.73	153	150	147	257	91	42	3.40	3.11	2.76	153	151	148	1,209	276
Duke	70	3.84	3.76	3.60	171	169	167	6,334	1,161	228	0.00	0.00	0.00	0	0	0	0	0	0	3.84	3.76	3.60	171	169	167	1,161	228
Elon	50	3.49	3.21	2.99	156	154	152	761	316	121	0.00	0.00	0.00	0	0	0	0	0	0	3.49	3.21	2.99	156	154	152	316	121
North Carolina	75	3.73	3.58	3.43	164	162	157	2,905	426	262	0.00	0.00	0.00	0	0	0	0	0	0	3.73	3.58	3.43	164	162	157	426	262
North Carolina Central	40	3.43	3.21	2.99	148	145	142	2,013	353	169	3.67	3.48	3.16	155	151	148	806	127	35	3.49	3.24	3.02	150	145	143	480	204
Wake Forest	60	3.70	3.60	3.20	164	162	160	2,775	905	154	0.00	0.00	0.00	0	0	0	0	0	0	3.70	3.60	3.20	164	162	160	905	154
North Dakota																											
North Dakota	35	3.73	3.30	3.00	155	152	149	534	187	86	0.00	0.00	0.00	0	0	0	0	0	0	3.73	3.30	3.00	155	152	149	187	86
Ohio																											
Akron	0	3.70	3.45	3.16	159	156	152	1,541	585	117	3.60	3.27	3.05	153	151	148	335	162	85	3.67	3.39	3.12	157	153	150	747	202
Capital	40	3.51	3.23	2.96	156	153	151	1,174	693	182	3.47	3.16	2.86	155	152	150	260	120	66	3.50	3.23	2.96	156	153	150	813	248
Case Western	40	3.64	3.47	3.21	161	159	157	2,667	1,126	195	3.57	3.31	3.20	157	154	150	275	38	15	3.63	3.46	3.20	160	158	156	1,164	210
Cincinnati	35	3.79	3.60	3.29	161	160	156	1,322	666	138	0.00	0.00	0.00	0	0	0	0	0	0	3.79	3.60	3.29	161	160	156	666	138
Cleveland State	0	3.68	3.46	3.19	158	156	153	1,513	543	158	3.59	3.44	3.25	158	155	151	309	79	45	3.64	3.44	3.19	158	156	153	622	203
Dayton	50	3.40	3.16	2.87	153	151	148	2,097	1,214	202	0.00	0.00	0.00	0	0	0	0	0	0	3.40	3.16	2.87	153	151	148	1,214	202
Ohio Northern		3.65	3.49	2.96	157	154	149	1,286	464	113	0.00	0.00	0.00	0	0	0	0	0	0	3.65	3.40	2.90	157	154	149	464	113
Ohio State	60	3.81	3.64	3.49	164	162	158	2,521	857	225	0.00	0.00	0.00	0	0	0	0	0	0	3.81	3.64	3.49	164	162	158	857	225
Toledo	0	3.59	3.35	3.07	158	155	152	639	367	99	3.36	2.98	2.60	152	150	149	229	154	82	3.54	3.23	2.92	156	153	150	521	181
Oklahoma																											
Oklahoma	50	3.72	3.51	3.29	161	158	155	1,137	355	199	0.00	0.00	0.00	0	0	0	0	0	0	3.72	3.51	3.29	161	158	155	355	199
Oklahoma City	50	3.47	3.22	2.90	152	150	148	1,214	675	200	3.30	3.11	2.87	153	148	148	120	46	24	3.47	3.20	2.88	152	150	148	721	224
Tulsa	30	3.55	3.22	2.83	157	155	152	1,304	659	140	0.00	0.00	0.00	0	0	0	0	0	0	3.55	3.22	2.83	157	155	152	659	140
Oregon																											
Lewis & Clark	50	3.72	3.52	3.21	164	161	158	2,946	1,034	176	3.68	3.48	3.12	160	157	153	235	73	55	3.71	3.52	3.20	164	161	157	1,107	231
Oregon	50	3.56	3.34	3.12	161	159	157	2,093	888	182	0.00	0.00	0.00	0	0	0	0	0	0	3.56	3.34	3.12	161	159	157	888	182
Willamette	50	3.51	3.23	3.05	157	154	153	1,532	598	148	0.00	0.00	0.00	0	0	0	0	0	0	3.51	3.23	3.05	157	154	153	598	148
Pennsylvania																											
Duquesne	60	3.67	3.43	3.25	155	153	152	852	397	161	3.59	3.42	3.13	154	150	149	212	99	63	3.63	3.42	3.19	154	151	150	496	224
Earl Mack, Drexel	0	3.70	3.42	3.09	163	160	156	2,862	937	156	0.00	0.00	0.00	0	0	0	0	0	0	3.70	3.42	3.09	163	160	156	937	156
Penn State	60	3.68	3.48	3.28	160	158	157	4,047	1,157	206	0.00	0.00	0.00	0	0	0	0	0	0	3.68	3.48	3.28	160	158	157	1,157	206
Pennsylvania	75	3.90	3.82	3.57	171	170	166	6,205	895	255	0.00	0.00	0.00	0	0	0	0	0	0	3.90	3.82	3.57	171	170	166	895	255
Pittsburgh	55	3.63	3.42	3.18	161	159	157	2,177	811	235	0.00	0.00	0.00	0	0	0	0	0	0	3.63	3.42	3.18	161	159	157	811	235
Temple	60	3.60	3.43	3.14	163	161	160	4,194	1,737	239	3.65	3.28	2.89	161	159	156	457	132	64	3.61	3.41	3.11	163	161	159	1,869	303
Villanova	75	3.63	3.44	3.17	163	162	160	3,254	1,401	255	0.00	0.00	0.00	0	0	0	0	0	0	3.63	3.44	3.17	163	162	160	1,401	255
Widener	60	3.44	3.18	2.78	151	150	148	1,442	800	143	3.67	3.38	2.83	154	151	148	249	114	40	3.47	3.20	2.80	152	150	148	914	183
Puerto Rico																											
Inter American	63	3.59	3.38	3.30	144	139	138	585	217	127	3.55	3.34	2.95	142	138	136	459	145	111	3.74	3.37	3.46	146	139	142	362	238
Pontifical Catholic		3.54	3.16	2.93	138	135	133	414	227	187	3.53	3.31	2.93	138	135	132	148	91	79	3.54	3.22	2.93	138	135	133	318	266
Puerto Rico		3.83	3.65	3.33	150	145	141	389	163	145	3.67	3.45	3.32	147	144	141	180	58	55	3.79	3.60	3.33	149	145	141	221	200
Rhode Island																											
Roger Williams	60	3.49	3.26	2.99	157	152	150	1,489	871	210	0.00	0.00	0.00	0	0	0	0	0	0	3.49	3.26	2.99	157	152	150	871	420
South Carolina																											
Charleston	50	3.43	3.20	2.95	156	154	151	1,710	785	189	3.30	2.92	2.51	152	151	147	352	110	52	3.40	3.14	2.87	156	153	151	895	241

	Application Fee ($)	Full-time									Part-time									Total							
		75% GPA	Median GPA	25% GPA	75% LSAT	Median LSAT	25% LSAT	# of Applicants	# of Offers	# of Matriculants	75% GPA	Median GPA	25% GPA	75% LSAT	Median LSAT	25% LSAT	# of Applicants	# of Offers	# of Matriculants	75% GPA	Median GPA	25% GPA	75% LSAT	Median LSAT	25% LSAT	Total # of Offers	Total # of Matriculants
South Carolina	60	3.70	3.46	3.14	160	158	156	1,973	730	240	0.00	0.00	0.00	0	0	0	0	0	0	3.70	3.46	3.14	160	158	156	730	240
South Dakota																											
South Dakota	35	3.65	3.44	3.13	155	152	149	382	217	78	0.00	0.00	0.00	0	0	0	0	0	1	3.65	3.44	3.13	155	151	149	217	79
Tennessee																											
Memphis	25	3.68	3.43	3.17	158	156	153	905	293	136	3.69	3.44	3.22	156	154	150	46	10	7	3.68	3.43	3.16	158	156	153	303	143
Tennessee	15	3.77	3.55	3.28	161	160	157	1,468	398	158	0.00	0.00	0.00	0	0	0	0	0	0	3.77	3.55	3.28	161	160	157	398	158
Vanderbilt	50	3.86	3.71	3.50	169	168	164	4,850	1,181	195	0.00	0.00	0.00	0	0	0	0	0	0	3.86	3.71	3.50	169	168	164	1,181	195
Texas																											
Baylor	40	3.80	3.62	3.40	162	160	156	3,659	1,090	197	0.00	0.00	0.00	0	0	0	0	0	0	3.80	3.62	3.40	162	160	156	1,090	197
Houston	70	3.63	3.37	3.08	164	162	160	3,021	817	205	3.54	3.28	3.02	161	160	156	631	86	51	3.62	3.34	3.08	163	161	159	903	256
St. Mary's	55	3.50	3.21	2.88	156	154	151	1,647	712	231	3.44	3.00	2.67	155	153	150	253	94	61	3.49	3.18	2.82	156	154	151	806	292
SMU Dedman	75	3.87	3.76	3.30	165	164	158	2,056	465	178	3.76	3.60	3.17	160	159	153	699	143	78	3.84	3.66	3.24	165	162	155	608	256
South Texas	55	3.56	3.30	3.04	156	153	151	2,076	989	350	3.26	3.02	2.70	155	152	150	301	129	84	3.51	3.25	2.99	156	153	151	1,118	434
Texas	70	3.87	3.71	3.54	168	167	164	5,275	1,224	379	0.00	0.00	0.00	0	0	0	0	0	0	3.87	3.71	3.54	168	167	164	1,224	379
Texas Southern	55	3.21	2.98	2.66	148	146	144	2,003	684	219	0.00	0.00	0.00	0	0	0	0	0	0	3.21	2.98	2.66	148	146	144	684	219
Texas Tech		3.75	3.57	3.34	157	154	151	1,768	652	213	0.00	0.00	0.00	0	0	0	0	0	0	3.62	3.43	3.13	158	156	153	652	213
Texas Wesleyan	55	3.46	3.21	2.93	156	153	151	1,606	757	170	3.33	3.03	2.73	154	152	151	371	115	63	3.44	3.17	2.88	155	153	151	872	233
Utah																											
Brigham Young	50	3.85	3.74	3.52	165	163	160	733	218	147	0.00	0.00	0.00	0	0	0	0	0	0	3.85	3.74	3.52	165	163	160	218	147
Utah		3.76	3.60	3.41	163	160	156	1,277	375	129	0.00	0.00	0.00	0	0	0	0	0	0	3.76	3.60	3.41	163	160	156	375	129
Vermont																											
Vermont	60	3.57	3.32	3.05	158	155	152	884	590	233	0.00	0.00	0.00	0	0	0	0	0	0	3.57	3.32	3.05	158	155	152	590	233
Virginia																											
Appalachian	60	3.31	2.94	2.61	152	148	147	1,617	784	129	0.00	0.00	0.00	0	0	0	0	0	0	3.31	2.94	2.61	152	148	147	784	129
George Mason	35	3.83	3.65	3.20	165	163	158	4,624	1,144	190	3.81	3.72	3.25	163	161	157	1,787	156	56	3.83	3.72	3.21	165	163	158	1,300	246
Liberty	50	3.53	3.15	2.80	154	151	148	466	201	119	0.00	0.00	0.00	0	0	0	0	0	0	3.53	3.15	2.80	154	151	148	201	119
Regent	50	3.71	3.36	3.00	157	153	150	749	351	152	3.67	3.44	2.96	153	150	148	37	17	10	3.71	3.37	3.00	156	152	150	368	162
Richmond	35	3.63	3.48	3.19	163	161	159	2,036	584	149	0.00	0.00	0.00	0	0	0	0	0	0	3.63	3.48	3.19	163	161	159	584	149
Virginia	75	3.92	3.85	3.54	171	170	165	7,880	1,166	368	0.00	0.00	0.00	0	0	0	0	0	0	3.92	3.85	3.54	171	170	165	1,166	368
Washington and Lee	0	3.78	3.53	3.28	167	166	160	3,416	873	135	0.00	0.00	0.00	0	0	0	0	0	0	3.78	3.53	3.28	167	166	160	873	135
William & Mary	50	3.77	3.66	3.42	166	165	161	4,980	1,109	209	0.00	0.00	0.00	0	0	0	0	0	0	3.77	3.66	3.42	166	165	161	1,109	209
Washington																											
Gonzaga	50	3.51	3.30	3.05	157	155	153	1,513	649	188	0.00	0.00	0.00	0	0	0	0	0	0	3.51	3.30	3.05	157	155	153	649	188
Seattle	60	3.63	3.37	3.16	160	158	155	2,374	895	268	3.55	3.26	2.99	159	156	153	252	103	64	3.63	3.35	3.15	160	157	155	998	332
Washington	50	3.80	3.66	3.47	166	163	160	2,448	622	181	0.00	0.00	0.00	0	0	0	0	0	0	3.80	3.66	3.47	166	163	160	622	181
West Virginia																											
West Virginia	50	3.70	3.41	3.12	156	153	151	648	327	153	0.00	0.00	0.00	0	0	0	0	0	0	3.70	3.41	3.12	156	153	151	327	153
Wisconsin																											
Marquette	50	3.61	3.40	3.09	159	157	155	1,905	868	185	3.60	3.35	2.88	158	154	151	179	59	34	3.61	3.39	3.07	159	157	154	927	219
Wisconsin	56	3.76	3.60	3.31	163	162	156	2,936	697	278	0.00	0.00	0.00	0	0	0	0	0	0	3.76	3.60	3.31	163	162	156	697	278
Wyoming																											
Wyoming	50	3.68	3.44	3.25	157	153	150	583	198	83	0.00	0.00	0.00	0	0	0	0	0	0	3.68	3.44	3.25	157	153	150	198	83

Students, Faculty, Tuition

| | Admission Fall 2009 | | | | | | | | | | | | | | |
| | Student Body | | | | | Faculty | | | Tuition ($) | | | | Other | |
	# Full-time	# Part-time	% Men	% Women	% Minorities	# Full-time and Other	% Men	% Women	Student/Faculty Ratio	Resident, Full-time	Nonresident, Full-time	Resident, Part-time	Nonresident, Part-time	Official Guide Page #	Grid included •
Alabama															
Alabama	527	20	58.0	42.0	14.4	46	60.9	39.1	10.2	14,675	26,785			80	•
Faulkner	323	18	62.2	37.8	11.4	21	71.4	28.6	12.8	30,870				288	
Samford	493	0	54.8	45.2	7.9	22	68.2	31.8	18.0	31,698	31,698	18,814	18,814	656	•
Arizona															
Arizona	475	0	52.6	47.4	26.7	36	55.6	44.4	10.7	20,895	35,807			96	•
Arizona State	576	0	56.6	43.4	21.0	52	65.4	34.6	8.5	19,225	32,619			100	•
Phoenix	352	185	47.9	52.1	19.6	25	52.0	48.0	12.4	15,781	15,781	12,763	12,763	596	•
Arkansas															
Arkansas	398	0	59.0	41.0	17.3	28	53.6	46.4	12.3	10,772	21,439			104	
Arkansas-Little Rock	316	155	52.4	47.6	20.0	24	50.0	50.0	17.0	11,456	23,538	7,557	15,108	108	•
California															
California-Berkeley	892	0	48.4	51.6	34.6	88	56.8	43.2	11.3	35,907	48,152			152	
California-Davis	606	0	46.7	53.3	35.8	48	54.2	45.8	11.6	33,949	44,895			156	•
California-Hastings	1292	7	48.9	51.1	32.4	67	59.7	40.3	16.5	32,468	43,693			160	•
California-Los Angeles	1011	0	51.5	48.5	32.5	85	63.5	36.5	11.3	35,327	45,967			164	•
California Western	791	101	45.0	55.0	27.9	41	63.4	36.6	18.3	38,500	38,500	27,100	27,100	168	•
Chapman	510	37	51.6	48.4	22.5	53	67.9	32.1	8.9	38,046	38,046	30,336	30,336	192	•
Golden Gate	529	108	43.5	56.5	30.8	37	54.1	45.9	15.2	36,860	36,860	25,880	25,880	340	•
La Verne	275	117	55.4	44.6	30.6	18	50.0	50.0	16.4	36,320	36,320	27,450	27,450	408	•
Loyola Marymount	1002	285	50.4	49.6	40.1	68	52.9	47.1	14.8	40,530	40,530	27,165	27,165	428	•
Pacific, McGeorge	660	377	49.7	50.3	28.1	48	64.6	35.4	14.0	38,629	38,629	25,705	25,705	580	•
Pepperdine	667	0	50.4	49.6	16.3	31	67.7	32.3	17.1	39,340	39,340			592	•
San Diego	816	184	54.5	45.5	27.4	59	62.7	37.3	14.3	40,014	40,014	28,904	28,904	660	•
San Francisco	574	132	45.2	54.8	35.1	37	54.1	45.9	15.2	37,310	37,310	26,645	26,645	664	•
Santa Clara	749	252	55.2	44.8	43.1	52	50.0	50.0	17.9	38,040	38,040	26,628	26,628	668	•
Southern California	618	0	49.7	50.3	39.3	41	63.4	36.6	12.4	46,264	46,264			696	•
Southwestern	729	323	46.1	53.9	35.9	56	60.7	39.3	14.3	36,950	36,950	22,250	22,250	708	•
Stanford	557	0	52.8	47.2	35.7	70	64.3	35.7	8.0	44,121	44,121			712	
Thomas Jefferson	648	241	54.6	45.4	33.0	37	45.9	54.1	18.0	36,300	36,300	24,000	24,000	756	
Western State	276	141	50.1	49.9	34.1	16	68.8	31.3	22.6	32,870	32,870	22,070	22,070	832	•
Whittier	450	141	45.5	54.5	27.6	35	48.6	51.4	17.6	37,060		24,720		836	
Colorado															
Colorado	547	0	50.1	49.9	20.3	43	58.1	41.9	11.5	25,399	33,463			224	•
Denver	786	232	52.8	47.2	17.7	65	53.8	46.2	15.5	35,700	35,700	26,244	26,244	248	•

| | Admission Fall 2009 | | | | | | | | | | | | | | |
| | Student Body | | | | | Faculty | | | | Tuition ($) | | | | Other | |
	# Full-time	# Part-time	% Men	% Women	% Minorities	# Full-time and Other	% Men	% Women	Student/Faculty Ratio	Resident, Full-time	Nonresident, Full-time	Resident, Part-time	Nonresident, Part-time	Official Guide Page #	Grid included •
Connecticut															
Connecticut	450	191	54.6	45.4	20.6	51	60.8	39.2	11.4	20,374	42,094	14,246	29,406	232	•
Quinnipiac	291	124	48.9	51.1	12.8	32	59.4	40.6	11.2	40,780	40,780	28,780	28,780	612	•
Yale	613	0	52.2	47.8	27.6	81	75.3	24.7	7.3	48,340	48,340			866	•
Delaware															
Widener	612	363	55.8	44.2	13.6	52	57.7	42.3	18.6	33,540	33,540	24,620	24,620	840	•
District of Columbia															
American	1195	290	44.6	55.4	35.9	106	53.8	46.2	13.4	41,406	41,406	29,027	29,027	88	
Catholic	574	316	48.7	51.3	18.8	56	50.0	50.0	12.8	37,985	37,985	29,005	29,005	188	•
District of Columbia	266	27	42.3	57.7	49.5	25	48.0	52.0	12.2	7,980	15,330	6,130	11,630	260	
George Washington	1328	304	58.0	42.0	21.3	105	55.2	43.8	14.2	42,205	42,205	32,648	32,648	324	•
Georgetown	1628	354	54.7	45.3	22.4	127	62.2	37.8	12.4	43,750	43,750	38,280	38,280	328	
Howard	468	0	39.3	60.7	87.2	31	54.8	45.2	16.5	24,490	24,490			368	•
Florida															
Ave Maria	375	0	57.3	42.7	17.1	21	71.4	28.6	17.5	35,380	35,380			116	
Barry	609	162	55.1	44.9	16.6	28	50.0	50.0	26.7	31,700		23,920		124	•
Florida A&M	385	228	45.4	54.6	61.5	41	48.8	48.8	19.4	9,036	28,302	6,627	20,755	292	•
Florida Coastal	1539	66	52.4	47.6	27.0	63	42.9	57.1	21.0	32,662	32,662	26,442	26,442	296	•
Florida	1106	0	52.0	48.0	23.4	60	50.0	50.0	15.9	14,228	33,593			300	•
Florida International	294	329	52.3	47.7	55.7	26	53.8	46.2	16.2	12,800	26,584	9,682	20,021	304	
Florida State	763	0	58.8	41.2	17.2	43	55.8	44.2	14.2	14,239	31,250			308	•
Miami	1351	33	56.9	43.1	23.2	65	63.1	36.9	16.5	38,012	38,012			460	•
Nova Southeastern	903	189	46.1	53.9	30.3	57	50.9	49.1	17.7	31,672	31,672	23,878	23,878	552	•
St. Thomas	682	0	53.4	46.6	44.9	28	50.0	46.4	21.1	31,616	31,616			652	•
Stetson	876	208	47.4	52.6	19.6	55	58.2	41.8	15.8	31,640	31,640	21,920	21,920	716	•
Georgia															
Atlanta's John Marshall	371	184	48.8	51.2	25.8	30	30.0	70.0	12.7	31,970	31,970	19,682	19,682	112	•
Emory	715	0	52.2	47.8	30.6	60	55.0	45.0	10.5	41,376	41,376			284	•
Georgia	694	0	52.6	47.4	17.9	51	58.8	41.2	12.2	14,448	30,226			332	•
Georgia State	480	193	52.7	47.3	19.6	54	51.9	48.1	10.7	11,838	32,862	10,980	25,032	336	•
Mercer	431	0	53.4	46.6	16.5	29	65.5	34.5	13.0	34,330	34,330			456	•
Hawai'i															
Hawai'i	285	41	42.3	57.7	61.0	42	45.2	54.8	7.8	15,581	28,565	13,055	23,869	356	•
Idaho															
Idaho	319	3	59.9	40.1	12.1	21	47.6	52.4	16.5	11,776	21,856			372	•

| | | Admission Fall 2009 | | | | | | | | | | | | |
| | Student Body | | | | | Faculty | | | Tuition ($) | | | | Other | |
	# Full-time	# Part-time	% Men	% Women	% Minorities	# Full-time and Other	% Men	% Women	Student/Faculty Ratio	Resident, Full-time	Nonresident, Full-time	Resident, Part-time	Nonresident, Part-time	Official Guide Page #	Grid included •
Illinois															
Chicago	590	0	55.3	44.7	28.3	69	71.0	29.0	9.5	44,757				204	
Chicago-Kent	769	179	54.0	46.0	19.2	67	62.7	37.3	11.0	38,152	38,152	27,910	27,910	208	•
DePaul	772	255	49.2	50.8	24.1	62	58.1	41.9	13.4	37,975	37,975	24,830	24,830	252	•
Illinois	617	0	57.9	42.1	22.5	45	66.7	33.3	13.1	36,420	43,420			376	
John Marshall	1038	339	54.6	45.4	22.7	73	64.4	35.6	14.4	35,380	35,380	25,300	25,300	396	•
Loyola-Chicago	652	188	47.1	52.9	16.4	54	59.3	40.7	14.3	36,770	36,770	27,720	27,720	432	•
Northern Illinois	298	11	54.4	45.6	24.9	16	50.0	50.0	20.3	14,847	27,351			536	•
Northwestern	814	0	53.8	46.2	33.9	90	53.3	46.7	8.8	47,472	47,472			544	
Southern Illinois	382	1	62.4	37.6	8.4	27	51.9	48.1	11.7	14,137	33,040			700	•
Indiana															
Indiana-Bloomington	620	2	58.4	41.6	18.0	58	70.7	29.3	9.5	24,891	40,691			380	•
Indiana-Indianapolis	625	319	55.1	44.9	15.1	41	53.7	46.3	17.7	18,163	38,478	14,065	29,640	384	•
Notre Dame	548	0	57.8	42.2	23.4	41	73.2	26.8	11.0	39,320	39,320			548	
Valparaiso	541	41	52.4	47.6	16.3	33	66.7	33.3	16.4	35,230	35,230	22,010	22,010	780	
Iowa															
Drake	451	16	55.5	44.5	10.3	29	65.5	34.5	14.5	31,186	31,186			264	•
Iowa	590	0	55.8	44.2	15.4	39	66.7	33.3	15.5	21,432	39,138			392	
Kansas															
Kansas	499	0	60.1	39.9	16.4	35	54.3	45.7	12.4	14,478	25,375			400	•
Washburn	441	0	59.4	40.6	12.9	28	57.1	42.9	12.9	16,150	25,150			804	•
Kentucky															
Kentucky	406	0	55.7	44.3	13.8	23	69.6	30.4	16.9	16,020	27,758			404	•
Louisville-Brandeis	368	67	54.7	45.3	8.3	26	50.0	50.0	15.5	14,632	29,172	7,412	15,172	424	•
Northern Kentucky	374	235	53.5	46.5	9.7	29	72.4	27.6	15.1	14,812	32,232	5,740	12,440	540	•
Louisiana															
Louisiana State	587	11	55.0	45.0	13.4	32	68.8	31.3	17.5	14,350	25,446			420	•
Loyola-New Orleans	726	156	51.1	48.9	27.6	48	56.3	43.8	17.1	34,166	34,166	23,096	23,096	436	•
Southern	431	167	44.8	55.2	60.7	35	45.7	54.3	12.4	7,978	12,580	6,668	11,268	704	
Tulane	771	3	59.4	40.6	16.3	54	59.3	40.7	14.1	40,644	40,644			768	•
Maine															
Maine	264	0	57.6	42.4	8.3	17	70.6	29.4	14.2	20,702	31,202			440	•
Maryland															
Baltimore	672	431	48.4	51.6	14.3	58	60.3	39.7	15.9	23,992	35,988	17,916	25,440	120	•
Maryland	723	230	50.1	49.9	31.5	66	42.4	57.6	11.7	23,762	35,041	18,053	26,512	448	

| | Admission Fall 2009 | | | | | | | | | | | | | | |
| | Student Body | | | | | Faculty | | | | Tuition ($) | | | | Other | |
	# Full-time	# Part-time	% Men	% Women	% Minorities	# Full-time and Other	% Men	% Women	Student/Faculty Ratio	Resident, Full-time	Nonresident, Full-time	Resident, Part-time	Nonresident, Part-time	Official Guide Page #	Grid included •
Massachusetts															
Boston College	812	2	52.9	47.1	22.6	53	56.6	43.4	13.5	39,600	39,600			132	•
Boston	827	3	50.2	49.8	22.8	65	60.0	40.0	12.2	39,658				136	
Harvard	1765	0	52.7	47.3	28.6	152	73.7	26.3	11.0	45,026				352	
New England	737	359	44.5	55.5	9.9	36	69.4	30.6	23.2	38,580	38,580	28,960	28,960	504	•
Northeastern	602	2	40.6	59.4	31.5	36	50.0	50.0	15.5	39,866				532	
Suffolk	1079	603	52.7	47.3	14.1	79	60.8	39.2	16.6	39,670	39,670	29,754	29,754	720	•
Western New England	389	149	47.4	52.6	11.5	39	43.6	56.4	12.7	35,612	35,612	26,328	26,328	828	•
Michigan															
Detroit Mercy	586	144	54.1	45.9	17.7	39	53.8	46.2	14.1	16,085	16,085	12,884	12,884	256	•
Michigan	1117	0	56.5	43.5	22.9	84	69.0	31.0	11.4	43,250	46,250			464	
Michigan State	892	65	60.9	39.1	13.3	51	56.9	43.1	16.6	33,054	33,054	27,394	27,394	468	•
Thomas M. Cooley	586	3141	52.4	47.6	23.0	99	59.6	40.4	23.5	28,740	28,740	18,490	18,490	752	
Wayne State	457	112	49.7	50.3	15.3	39	51.3	48.7	14.4	23,713	25,919	12,815	13,992	820	•
Minnesota															
Hamline	468	182	46.3	53.7	13.1	37	59.5	40.5	14.8	32,014	32,014	23,078	23,078	348	•
Minnesota	766	0	58.4	41.6	15.9	55	54.5	45.5	12.0	28,203	37,605			472	•
St. Thomas- Minneapolis	457	2	54.7	45.3	13.5	23	60.9	39.1	17.7	34,756				648	•
William Mitchell	603	374	50.3	49.7	9.6	37	48.6	51.4	20.1	32,340	32,340	23,400	23,400	854	•
Mississippi															
Mississippi	495	0	56.6	43.4	14.5	29	75.9	24.1	18.2	9,350	20,440			476	•
Mississippi College	521	15	58.0	42.0	11.8	25	44.0	56.0	18.2	26,300				480	•
Missouri															
Missouri-Columbia	441	4	61.6	38.4	13.7	22	72.7	27.3	17.9	16,017	30,519			484	•
Missouri-Kansas City	489	26	59.6	40.4	12.6	33	60.6	39.4	14.1	14,242	27,262	10,248	19,548	488	•
St. Louis	771	196	52.8	47.2	15.7	60	48.3	51.7	17.1	34,362	34,362	25,047	25,047	640	•
Washington University	851	5	58.2	41.8	24.2	66	43.9	56.1	10.7	42,330				816	•
Montana															
Montana	248	0	55.2	44.8	8.1	18	55.6	44.4	12.3	10,620	24,333			492	•
Nebraska															
Creighton	471	13	57.6	42.4	10.1	25	72.0	28.0	17.6	30,294	30,294	17,670	17,670	240	•
Nebraska	394	0	60.2	39.8	7.4	25	84.0	16.0	13.6	12,154	26,600			496	•
Nevada															
Nevada	366	118	53.7	46.3	28.9	23	43.5	56.5	16.8	18,838	30,838	12,328	20,032	500	
New Hampshire															
Franklin Pierce	429	1	62.1	37.9	18.4	31	58.1	41.9	14.3	36,980	36,980	27,755	27,755	316	

| | Admission Fall 2009 | | | | | | | | | | | | | | |
| | Student Body | | | | | Faculty | | | | Tuition ($) | | | | Other | |
	# Full-time	# Part-time	% Men	% Women	% Minorities	# Full-time and Other	% Men	% Women	Student/Faculty Ratio	Resident, Full-time	Nonresident, Full-time	Resident, Part-time	Nonresident, Part-time	Official Guide Page #	Grid included •
New Jersey															
Rutgers-Camden	619	191	59.5	40.5	18.9	54	64.8	35.2	11.8	23,860	34,360	19,198	27,938	628	•
Rutgers-Newark	593	242	57.0	43.0	36.8	35	65.7	34.3	17.6	23,676	33,740	15,470	22,174	632	•
Seton Hall	723	367	54.4	45.6	15.5	55	52.7	45.5	15.4	42,980	42,980	32,430	32,430	676	•
New Mexico															
New Mexico	351	0	45.9	54.1	44.7	30	40.0	60.0	11.3	12,620	28,235			508	•
New York															
Albany	712	37	56.1	43.9	12.0	46	50.0	50.0	13.1	39,050	39,050	29,325	29,325	84	
Brooklyn	1278	180	51.3	48.7	26.3	68	55.9	44.1	18.4	44,015	44,015	33,099	33,099	144	
Buffalo	718	8	54.4	45.6	14.9	51	62.7	37.3	15.3	17,577	25,827			148	•
Cardozo	1020	101	49.9	50.1	20.5	59	64.4	35.6	15.6	45,170	45,170	45,170	45,170	180	•
CUNY	406	0	37.4	62.6	30.8	38	39.5	60.5	10.4	10,612	16,512	370	620	216	•
Columbia	1309	1	51.5	48.5	28.7	112	70.5	29.5	10.1	48,004	48,004			228	
Cornell	622	0	48.2	51.8	30.4	46	67.4	32.6	10.0	49,020	49,020			236	
Fordham	1160	309	51.3	48.7	22.1	81	58.0	42.0	13.6	44,996	44,996	33,816	33,816	312	•
Hofstra	939	170	51.3	48.7	26.9	61	70.5	29.5	15.4	41,780	41,780	31,259	31,259	360	
New York Law	1408	448	49.6	50.4	19.9	61	68.9	31.1	23.6	44,800	44,800	34,500	34,500	512	•
New York	1427	0	56.0	44.0	23.3	150	68.7	31.3	9.4	46,196				516	
Pace	562	185	41.5	58.5	17.5	48	62.5	37.5	12.7	39,794	39,794	29,858	29,858	576	•
St. John's	737	178	53.0	47.0	24.0	50	54.0	46.0	14.6	42,200	42,200	31,650	31,650	636	•
Syracuse	598	5	58.5	41.5	20.9	64	59.4	40.6	10.9	44,856	44,856	39,088	39,088	724	•
Touro	553	233	51.9	48.1	21.6	39	51.3	46.2	15.9	39,130	39,130	29,330	29,330	764	
North Carolina															
Campbell	405	0	50.4	49.6	10.6	22	77.3	22.7	18.0	30,850	30,850			172	•
Charlotte	380	101	50.1	49.9	17.3	21	47.6	52.4	18.0	33,166	33,166	26,816	26,816	200	
Duke	626	35	57.0	43.0	22.4	62	69.4	30.6	9.7	45,271	45,271			268	•
Elon	315	0	54.9	45.1	11.1	17	64.7	35.3	17.3	30,750	30,750			280	•
North Carolina	765	0	47.2	52.8	23.9	42	64.3	35.7	15.4	16,014	29,332			520	
North Carolina Central	480	121	39.4	60.6	55.7	35	40.0	60.0	16.5	8,097	20,835	8,097	20,835	524	•
Wake Forest	463	13	58.2	41.8	17.0	41	56.1	43.9	9.8	36,166	36,166			800	•
North Dakota															
North Dakota	247	0	54.7	45.3	10.1	12	75.0	25.0	21.7	9,461	20,476			528	•
Ohio															
Akron	279	238	54.5	45.5	14.5	33	57.6	42.4	11.2	19,570	30,850	15,958	24,962	76	•
Capital	461	187	54.5	45.5	11.7	31	64.5	35.5	15.8	31,146	31,146	20,406	20,406	176	•
Case Western	618	22	57.7	42.3	12.7	48	64.6	33.3	12.2	38,679	38,679			184	•
Cincinnati	391	0	57.8	42.2	16.1	31	48.4	51.6	9.9	19,942	34,776			212	•

| | Admission Fall 2009 | | | | | | | | | | | | | | |
| | Student Body | | | | | Faculty | | | | Tuition ($) | | | | Other | |
	# Full-time	# Part-time	% Men	% Women	% Minorities	# Full-time and Other	% Men	% Women	Student/Faculty Ratio	Resident, Full-time	Nonresident, Full-time	Resident, Part-time	Nonresident, Part-time	Official Guide Page #	Grid included •
Cleveland State	482	157	58.5	41.5	14.6	37	54.1	45.9	13.2	16,764	22,996	12,895	17,689	220	•
Dayton	500	0	58.0	42.0	14.0	27	55.6	44.4	16.2	32,684	32,684			244	•
Ohio Northern	307	0	58.0	42.0	13.4	21	61.9	38.1	12.8	28,900	28,900			556	•
Ohio State	669	0	57.2	42.8	21.4	47	66.0	34.0	13.3	22,433	37,383			560	•
Toledo	346	147	59.8	40.2	9.7	29	55.2	44.8	13.4	19,137	29,553	14,343	22,155	760	•
Oklahoma															
Oklahoma	550	0	56.7	43.3	20.9	32	56.3	43.8	14.2	16,976	26,904			564	•
Oklahoma City	533	90	59.4	40.6	16.4	30	60.0	40.0	17.6	31,870	31,870	21,270	21,270	568	•
Tulsa	382	40	61.1	38.9	16.1	29	51.7	48.3	12.0	29,040	29,040			772	•
Oregon															
Lewis & Clark	521	194	51.5	48.5	19.6	53	56.6	43.4	10.0	31,984	31,984	23,998	23,998	412	•
Oregon	544	0	55.3	44.7	18.2	31	45.2	54.8	16.4	22,328	27,818			572	•
Willamette	421	5	57.3	42.7	16.7	26	57.7	42.3	15.0	29,680	29,680			846	
Pennsylvania															
Duquesne	446	258	48.6	51.4	6.4	27	66.7	33.3	19.5	30,866	30,866	23,874	23,874	272	
Earl Mack, Drexel	410	0	52.4	47.6	17.8	27	44.4	55.6	16.4	32,921	32,921			276	•
Penn State	586	11	60.0	40.0	20.4	58	58.6	41.4	9.4	34,462	34,462			584	•
Pennsylvania	790	1	52.8	47.2	27.9	70	65.7	34.3	10.7	46,514	46,514			588	
Pittsburgh	682	0	54.4	45.6	15.8	44	63.6	36.4	12.9	25,098	33,094			600	
Temple	784	192	53.8	46.2	22.6	57	59.6	40.4	13.0	17,226	29,516	13,908	23,744	728	•
Villanova	754	0	56.0	44.0	17.2	45	55.6	44.4	17.3	35,250	35,250			792	
Widener	358	103	52.1	47.9	10.4	27	51.9	48.1	19.4	33,540	33,540	24,620	24,620	842	•
Puerto Rico															
Inter American	430	418	45.9	54.1	100.0	23	60.9	39.1	25.9	13,491	13,491	10,481	10,481	388	
Pontifical Catholic	474	222	46.6	53.4	100.0	20	75.0	25.0	28.3	13,806		10,526		604	
Puerto Rico	527	213	45.3	54.7	99.6	26	69.2	30.8	23.0	6,345	8,105	5,125	7,397	608	•
Rhode Island															
Roger Williams	550	0	49.1	50.9	10.4	29	55.2	44.8	16.7	35,570	35,570			624	•
South Carolina															
Charleston	459	200	55.5	44.5	8.3	31	61.3	38.7	18.2	34,618	34,618	27,824	27,824	196	•
South Carolina	685	0	58.4	41.6	11.8	39	61.5	38.5	14.9	19,034	38,014			684	•
South Dakota															
South Dakota	202	2	49.5	50.5	7.4	15	73.3	26.7	12.3	10,695	20,575	5,508	10,607	688	•
Tennessee															
Memphis	392	28	57.9	42.1	14.0	19	57.9	42.1	17.7	13,570	35,442	12,800	32,680	452	•
Tennessee	471	0	52.9	47.1	20.4	27	74.1	25.9	13.8	13,118	31,862			732	•
Vanderbilt	594	0	51.5	48.5	17.0	32	59.4	40.6	14.4	44,074	44,074			784	•

| | Admission Fall 2009 | | | | | | | | | | | | | | |
| | Student Body | | | | | Faculty | | | | Tuition ($) | | | | Other | |
	# Full-time	# Part-time	% Men	% Women	% Minorities	# Full-time and Other	% Men	% Women	Student/Faculty Ratio	Resident, Full-time	Nonresident, Full-time	Resident, Part-time	Nonresident, Part-time	Official Guide Page #	Grid included •
Texas															
Baylor	465	0	52.9	47.1	20.9	27	77.8	22.2	15.2	38,408				128	•
Houston	715	183	56.0	44.0	28.5	68	63.2	36.8	11.8	21,029	28,439	15,125	20,065	364	•
St. Mary's	681	182	57.2	42.8	34.4	38	65.8	34.2	20.9	27,904	27,904	18,864	18,864	644	•
SMU Dedman	524	379	53.2	46.8	23.8	49	65.3	34.7	15.0	38,406	38,406	28,805	28,805	680	•
South Texas	973	305	51.6	48.4	26.0	49	65.3	34.7	20.0	25,710	25,710	17,340	17,340	692	•
Texas	1182	0	55.4	44.6	29.0	107	59.8	40.2	11.3	27,177	42,814			736	•
Texas Southern	542	0	47.6	52.4	80.8	35	40.0	60.0	13.0	13,235	16,985			740	•
Texas Tech	637	0	58.2	41.8	25.0	34	61.8	38.2	15.3	15,194	22,110			744	•
Texas Wesleyan	522	271	49.4	50.6	24.7	29	69.0	31.0	24.3	26,000	26,000	18,650	18,650	748	•
Utah															
Brigham Young	447	0	65.3	34.7	15.7	22	77.3	22.7	17.3	9,980	19,960			140	•
Utah	381	19	59.0	41.0	13.3	40	72.5	27.5	8.1	16,666	33,084			776	•
Vermont															
Vermont	567	0	49.9	50.1	8.6	46	58.7	41.3	13.5	40,420	40,420			788	•
Virginia															
Appalachian	334	0	62.9	37.1	9.6	19	68.4	31.6	15.8	26,825	26,825			92	•
George Mason	480	217	58.2	41.8	17.1	41	78.0	22.0	13.2	20,556	34,220	16,921	28,145	320	•
Liberty	267	0	62.9	37.1	15.0	18	72.2	27.8	12.1	27,847				416	•
Regent	394	23	51.3	48.7	15.1	25	68.0	32.0	16.2	29,852	29,852	23,027	23,027	616	•
Richmond	465	0	52.3	47.7	16.6	32	68.8	31.3	15.9	32,450	32,450			620	•
Virginia	1122	0	55.9	44.1	19.7	76	71.1	28.9	12.6	38,800	43,800			796	
Washington and Lee	390	0	56.9	43.1	18.7	37	73.0	27.0	9.4	38,062	38,062			812	•
William & Mary	626	0	50.8	49.2	15.8	40	62.5	37.5	15.7	21,646	31,846			850	•
Washington															
Gonzaga	516	10	60.5	39.5	8.4	29	48.3	51.7	15.3	31,460	31,460			344	•
Seattle	808	228	49.1	50.9	25.2	65	60.0	40.0	12.3	35,406	35,406	29,494	29,494	672	•
Washington	530	0	45.1	54.9	22.1	54	57.4	42.6	10.1	22,267	32,777			808	•
West Virginia															
West Virginia	412	6	59.6	40.4	7.9	28	82.1	17.9	12.9	10,644	24,010			824	•
Wisconsin															
Marquette	563	180	56.0	44.0	14.7	39	53.8	46.2	20.5	32,410	32,410	19,425	19,425	444	•
Wisconsin	792	33	53.9	46.1	23.8	58	51.7	48.3	12.8	16,426	36,350	1,372	3,032	858	
Wyoming															
Wyoming	225	0	52.0	48.0	10.2	16	75.0	25.0	12.4	9,966	21,156			862	•

Chapter 13: ABA-Approved Law Schools

This chapter is designed to provide consumers with basic information in a simple format that will facilitate the consideration of ABA-approved law schools. Please note that applicants should not use this information as the sole source regarding application and admission. Rather, this book should supplement other avenues of evaluating respective schools, including making direct contact with admission officers, professors, students, alumni, or prelaw advisors.

The following section includes four pages of text and numerical data from 198 ABA-approved law schools that confer the first degree in law (the JD degree). The two pages of numerical data about each school were compiled from questionnaires completed during the fall 2009 academic semester and submitted by ABA-approved law schools to the ABA's Consultant on Legal Education as part of the accreditation process. The completed questionnaires provided to the Consultant's Office are certified by the dean of each law school. Each certification is submitted to the Consultant's Office as an assurance that the information provided accurately reflects prevailing conditions at the law school for which the certification is given. The Consultant's Office, however, does not directly audit the information submitted by the respective institutions on an annual basis.

The information contained in this book is only a small portion of what is collected in the questionnaire for accreditation purposes. Each page is divided into different segments as discussed below. In addition, many of the same data are displayed on the charts in chapters 10, 11, and 12 and in Appendix A to facilitate side-by-side comparisons.

In addition to the two pages of numerical data, each law school provides two pages of descriptive text to LSAC. LSAC edits these text pages for style and formatting, but does not verify the descriptive information provided by the schools. As part of this two-page spread, most schools provide applicant profile grids that illustrate admission prospects based on a combination of LSAT score and GPA. The data in these grids are based on 2008–2009 academic year admission decisions as reported by the schools to LSAC. The grids are intended to be indicative of the applicant profile of last year's entering law school classes; they should not be interpreted as predictors of the likelihood of admission for any applicant.

LSAC collects applicant profile data and school descriptions each fall as a service to its member schools and to prospective law school applicants. The information provided by the law schools to LSAC in no way affects the ABA accreditation process.

■ School Name

The law schools are arranged in alphabetical order by each institution's primary name. Please note that some schools are known by more than one name. Adjacent to the law school's name and contact information is the date that the school was granted ABA-approval. In some cases, that approval may be designated as provisional. A law school that has completed at least one full year of successful operation may apply for provisional approval. A law school is granted provisional approval when it establishes that it substantially complies with the Standards and Rules of Procedure for Approval of Law Schools and gives assurances that it will be in full compliance with all of the Standards within three years after receiving provisional approval. A designation of "Probation" means that the school is in substantial noncompliance with the Standards and is at risk of being removed from the list of approved law schools. It is the ABA's view that students at provisionally approved law schools or those on probation and persons who graduate while a school is provisionally approved or on probation are entitled to the same recognition as students and graduates of fully approved law schools.

Multiple campuses: Some schools have multiple campuses. Contact the admission office of those schools for more information about curriculum offerings and application processes.

The Basics
The Basics section contains a variety of general information, sorted into the categories listed below.

Type of school: All ABA-approved law schools are either public or private. *Public* means that the school receives money from the state in which the school is located. *Private* indicates the school is not operated by the state.

Term: Indicates whether the school operates on a semester, quarter, or trimester system.

Application deadline: Not all schools have specific deadlines for admission applications. If the item was left blank in the questionnaire completed by the school, it generally means that the school considers applications on a continual basis until the class is filled.

Application fee: Fee charged by most law schools for processing an application for admission.

Financial aid deadline: Indicates the deadline for the school's financial aid form. (The school deadline may not be the same as federal and state deadlines.) If the item was left blank in the questionnaire completed by the school, it generally means that the school considers financial aid applications on a continuing basis.

Can first year start other than fall? Indicates whether the school has an entering class other than in the fall term.

Student-to-faculty ratio: Indicates the number of students relative to the number of instructors for the calendar year. The ratio is calculated by comparing faculty full-time equivalency (FTE) to FTE of JD enrollment. A general definition of faculty FTE is as follows: total full-time faculty plus additional instructional resources. Additional instructional resources include administrators who teach, as well as part-time faculty. Teaching administrators and part-time faculty are included in the faculty FTE at differing weighted factors ranging from .2 to .7. FTE of JD enrollment is calculated as follows: full-time JD enrollment plus two-thirds of part-time JD enrollment less enrollment in semester-abroad programs. For a detailed definition of the ABA's student-to-faculty ratio, please consult the ABA's *Standards and Rules of Procedure for Approval of Law Schools* at *www.abanet.org/legaled.*

...dent housing: Indicates the number of housing spaces available restricted to law students and number of graduate housing spaces for which law students are eligible.

Faculty and Administrators
This section of the two-page spread contains detailed information on the number, gender, and race of the teachers at the school for both semesters. It should be noted that some schools may have lower part-time numbers in the fall semester because at their school most of the part-time instruction occurs in the spring semester. The five categories of faculty are mutually exclusive. Teachers on leave or sabbatical are not included in the full-time faculty count for the term they are on leave. The *Full-time* row indicates tenured or tenure-track faculty. *Other full-time* indicates nontenured professional skills instructors and nontenured legal writing instructors. *Deans, librarians, & others who teach* are law school administrators who teach at least halftime. Administrators who neither teach nor hold faculty rank are not included in these numbers. Administrators who teach are typically at the school and available to students during the entire year. For this reason, they are counted in fall and spring regardless of their teaching load. *Part-time* during the fall semester includes adjuncts, permanent part time, faculty from another unit, part-time professional skills, and emeritus part time. The *Total* row combines figures from the *Full-time* row through the *Part-time* row.

JD Enrollment and Ethnicity
This section represents the JD enrollment by ethnic category, gender, first-year student, and full-time/part-time status. Students are classified for purposes of enrollment statistics on the basis of whether they are carrying a full load in the division in which they are enrolled. Minority group enrollment is the total enrollment of students who classify themselves as African American; American Indian or Alaska Native; Asian or Pacific Islander; Mexican American; Puerto Rican; or other Hispanic American. Although Puerto Rican law students enrolled in the three approved law schools in Puerto Rico are not classified as minority students in the "Survey of Minority Group Students Enrolled in JD Programs in Approved Law Schools," they are counted as minorities in all other areas. Nonresident alien students (foreign nationals) and students whose ethnicity is unknown or unspecified are not included as minority students.

JD Degrees Awarded: This indicates the total number of JD degrees awarded during the 2008–2009 academic year.

Curriculum
All information in this category is based on the 12-month period beginning at the close of the prior academic year (e.g., June 2008 through May 2009). In courses where there was enrollment by both full-time and part-time students, schools were asked to classify each of those courses as full time or part time based on time of day and relative enrollment of full-time and part-time students. Some schools that have a part-time program experienced difficulty providing curriculum information that distinguished between full time and part time. In those cases, the part-time column contains zeros. A *small section* means a section of a substantive law course, which may include a legal writing component; small section

does not mean a legal writing section standing alone. The *number of classroom course titles beyond first-year curriculum* refers only to classroom courses offered the previous year, not to clinical or field placement possibilities. If a title is offered in both the full-time program and part-time program, the school could count it once in each column. *Seminars* are defined as courses requiring a written work product and having an enrollment limited to no more than 25. A *simulation course* is one in which a substantial portion of the instruction is accomplished through the use of role-playing or drafting exercises (for example, trial advocacy, corporate planning and drafting, negotiations, and estate planning and drafting). *Faculty supervised clinical courses* are those courses or placements with other agencies in which full-time faculty have primary professional responsibility for all cases on which students are working. *Field placements* refer to those cases in which someone other than full-time faculty has primary responsibility to the client; these placements are frequently called externships or internships. Schools were also asked not to double count a single course by classifying it both as full time and part time. *Number involved in law journals* and *Number involved in interschool competitions* reflect those students beyond the first year who participated in those activities during the previous year regardless of whether they received credit.

Transfers
This section refers to the number of students who transferred in and transferred out of the law school in the 2008–2009 academic year.

Tuition and Fees

- *Full-time*: Represents the full-time tuition (plus annual fees) for the academic year for a typical first-year student.

- *Part-time*: Represents the part-time tuition (plus annual fees) for the academic year for a typical first-year student. Please note that some schools elected to report part-time tuition on a "per-credit-hour" basis.

- *Tuition Guarantee Program*: Indicates if the law school has a tuition policy that guarantees all entering students the same tuition rate throughout their enrollment.

Living Expenses
This represents the 2009–2010 academic year total living expenses (room, board, etc.) and book expenses for full-time, single, resident students *Living on campus*, *Living off campus*, and *Living at home*. Tuition and fee charges are not included. The figures are used in analyzing law student budgets for loan purposes. Many schools use the same budget amount for all three categories.

GPA and LSAT Scores
This section of the two-page spread contains statistics on the 2009 entering class. All persons in this particular category, regardless of whether they were admitted through any special admission program rather than through the normal admission process, were included. The admission year was calculated

from October 1, 2008, through September 30, 2009. Schools that admit in the spring and/or summer were to include those students in the totals. Figures on matriculants include all students who attended at least one class during the first week of the term in which they were admitted. For a small number of schools, applications and admitted applicants are not identified by the school as full time or part time. Therefore, "N/A" appears under the full-time and part-time columns, and the total application and admission offers are entered under the total column.

Percentiles of GPA and LSAT: The GPA and LSAT scores represent the 75th percentile, 25th percentile, and the median scores of the entering class. For example, one quarter (25 percent) of the first-year class has credentials that are *below* the number given for the 25th percentile. Three quarters (75 percent) of the first-year class have credentials that are below the number given for the 75th percentile. One half (50 percent) of the first-year class has credentials that are *below* the number given for the median. For example, if a school reports a 25th percentile/median/75th percentile GPA— 3.01/3.25/3.47, then 25 percent of this first-year class had a GPA of *less than* 3.01, 50 percent of this class had a GPA of *less than* 3.25, and 75 percent of this class had a GPA of *less than* 3.47. The same principle holds for the 25th percentile/median/75th percentile LSAT score.

Grants and Scholarships (from prior year)
This indicates the number and percentage of students receiving internal grants or scholarships from law school or university sources. External grants such as state grants are not included. The percentages for full time and part time are based on the total number of full-time and part-time JD students, respectively. The total column percentage is based on total JD enrollment. Zeros are reported in those areas where a school did not provide data. The data represent information from the previous academic year.

Informational and Library Resources
This section of the two-page spread contains basic information about the law library. In addition, it contains brief information about the physical size of the school and the number of networked computers available.

- *Total amount spent on library materials:* Total expenditures for serial subscriptions (print, microforms, and nonprint), monographs (print, microforms, and nonprint), electronic resources purchased during the fiscal year, and electronic resources licensed for the fiscal year.

- *Study seating capacity inside the library:* Number of study seats available for library users.

- *Number of full-time equivalent professional librarians:* The number of full-time equivalent professional librarians who teach or hold faculty rank plus the number of full-time equivalent librarians who do not teach or hold faculty rank.

- *Hours per week library is open:* Number of hours per week that professional staff are on duty in the library.

- *Number of open, wired connections available to students:* Number of open, wired, network connections available to students or, if the library has a wireless network, the number of simultaneous users accommodated within.

- *Number of networked computers available for use by students:* Number of workstations in law school or library computer labs, plus workstations in the library for users that are not in computer labs.

- *Has wireless network:* Indicates the school has a wireless network.

- *Require computer:* Indicates whether the school requires students entering the law school to have a computer.

JD Attrition (from prior year)
Attrition percentages were based on fall 2008 enrollment. *Academic* attrition, for this purpose, refers to those students not continuing their legal studies between October 1, 2008, and October 1, 2009. *Other* attrition may include transfers and students who leave for other reasons.

Employment (nine months after graduation)
This section represents statistics on the employment status of the 2008 graduating class nine months after graduation. The employment percentages are based on the graduates whose employment status was "known." Hence, for the schools reporting a large percentage of graduates for whom the employment status is unknown, the percentage reported may not be a very accurate reflection of the actual percentage of the class as a whole. *Type of Employment* and *Geographic Location* percentages are based on the number of students employed.

Bar Passage Rates
This section refers to numbers and percentages of law school graduates who took the bar for the first time during calendar year 2008. The pass rates for each jurisdiction were obtained from the National Conference of Bar Examiners. In reporting their first-time bar passage rates, each school must account for at least 70 percent of its first-time takers in the year reported. For some schools, in order to reach this 70 percent threshold, they need to report data for only a single jurisdiction. Other schools may have to report pass rates for multiple jurisdictions in order to account for at least 70 percent of first-time takers in the reporting year. Note that pass rates can vary widely from jurisdiction to jurisdiction; similarly, pass rates among schools can also vary widely. In instances where a school's pass rate is 15 or more points below the states' pass rates, applicants are encouraged to contact the school and obtain data for their ultimate pass rates (i.e., pass rates of repeat takers). Note that Wisconsin permits graduates of the University of Wisconsin Law School and Marquette University Law School to exercise the "diploma privilege" and be admitted to the bar without taking the examination.

■ Applicant Profiles

Applicant profiles are provided by some schools to give candidates information about the number of applicants and admitted applicants in each cell. For various reasons, the total number of applicants and admitted applicants does not equal the official totals that appear on the ABA data pages in this book.

The purpose of the applicant profiles is to provide information about the LSAT/GPA credentials of applicants and admitted applicants to the schools that provide the profiles. You will note that some schools provide alternatives to the grid format for their profile or no profile at all.

The University of Akron School of Law

302 Buchtel Common
Akron, OH 44325-2901
Phone: 800.425.7668 or 330.972.7331; Fax: 330.258.2343
E-mail: lawadmissions@uakron.edu; Website: www.uakron.edu/law

The Basics

Type of school	Public
Term	Semester
Application deadline	3/1
Application fee	$0
Financial aid deadline	3/1
Can first year start other than fall?	No
Student to faculty ratio	11.2 to 1
# of housing spaces available restricted to law students	
graduate housing for which law students are eligible	

Faculty and Administrators

	Total		Men		Women		Minorities	
	Spr	Fall	Spr	Fall	Spr	Fall	Spr	Fall
Full-time	28	33	18	19	10	14	4	4
Other full-time	0	0	0	0	0	0	0	0
Deans, librarians, & others who teach	5	6	3	3	2	3	0	0
Part-time	27	19	19	15	8	4	3	1
Total	60	58	40	37	20	21	7	5

Curriculum

		Full-Time	Part-Time
Typical first-year section size		41	49
Is there typically a "small section" of the first-year class, other than Legal Writing, taught by full-time faculty		Yes	Yes
If yes, typical size offered last year		24	24
# of classroom course titles beyond first-year curriculum		92	
# of upper division courses, excluding seminars, with an enrollment:	Under 25	92	
	25–49	47	
	50–74	21	
	75–99	1	
	100+	1	
# of seminars		37	
# of seminar positions available		799	
# of seminar positions filled		243	127
# of positions available in simulation courses		646	
# of simulation positions filled		286	128
# of positions available in faculty supervised clinical courses		221	
# of faculty supervised clinical positions filled		75	16
# involved in field placements		53	14
# involved in law journals		46	20
# involved in moot court or trial competitions		25	10
# of credit hours required to graduate		88	

JD Enrollment and Ethnicity

	Men		Women		Full-Time		Part-Time		1st-Year		Total		JD Degs. Awd.
	#	%	#	%	#	%	#	%	#	%	#	%	
African Amer.	16	5.7	20	8.5	11	3.9	25	10.5	17	8.4	36	7.0	12
Amer. Indian	2	0.7	1	0.4	1	0.4	2	0.8	0	0.0	3	0.6	0
Asian Amer.	9	3.2	9	3.8	14	5.0	4	1.7	7	3.4	18	3.5	11
Mex. Amer.	0	0.0	0	0.0	0	0.0	0	0.0	0	0.0	0	0.0	0
Puerto Rican	0	0.0	0	0.0	0	0.0	0	0.0	0	0.0	0	0.0	0
Hispanic	8	2.8	10	4.3	11	3.9	7	2.9	10	4.9	18	3.5	1
Total Minority	35	12.4	40	17.0	37	13.3	38	16.0	34	16.7	75	14.5	24
For. Nation.	0	0.0	0	0.0	0	0.0	0	0.0	0	0.0	0	0.0	0
Caucasian	214	75.9	179	76.2	211	75.6	182	76.5	144	70.9	393	76.0	100
Unknown	33	11.7	16	6.8	31	11.1	18	7.6	25	12.3	49	9.5	20
Total	282	54.5	235	45.5	279	54.0	238	46.0	203	39.3	517		144

Transfers

Transfers in	2
Transfers out	9

Tuition and Fees

	Resident	Nonresident
Full-time	$19,570	$30,850
Part-time	$15,958	$24,962
Tuition Guarantee Program	N	

Living Expenses

Estimated living expenses for singles

Living on campus	Living off campus	Living at home
$15,404	$15,404	$15,404

The University of Akron School of Law

ABA
Approved
Since
1961

GPA and LSAT Scores

	Total	Full-Time	Part-Time
# of apps	1,876	1,541	335
# of offers	747	585	162
# of matrics	202	117	85
75% GPA	3.67	3.70	3.60
Median GPA	3.39	3.45	3.27
25% GPA	3.12	3.16	3.05
75% LSAT	157	159	153
Median LSAT	153	156	151
25% LSAT	150	152	148

Grants and Scholarships (from prior year)

	Total		Full-Time		Part-Time	
	#	%	#	%	#	%
Total # of students	488		246		242	
Total # receiving grants	187	38.3	117	47.6	70	28.9
Less than 1/2 tuition	56	11.5	37	15.0	19	7.9
Half to full tuition	39	8.0	23	9.3	16	6.6
Full tuition	2	0.4	0	0.0	2	0.8
More than full tuition	90	18.4	57	23.2	33	13.6
Median grant amount			$14,006		$10,000	

Informational and Library Resources

Total amount spent on library materials	$865,909
Study seating capacity inside the library	287
# of full-time equivalent professional librarians	7
Hours per week library is open	105
# of open, wired connections available to students	16
# of networked computers available for use by students	82
Has wireless network??	Y
Require computer?	N

JD Attrition (from prior year)

	Academic	Other	Total	
	#	#	#	%
1st year	9	22	31	19.6
2nd year	3	4	7	4.4
3rd year	0	0	0	0.0
4th year	0	0	0	0.0

Employment (9 months after graduation)

	Total	Percentage
Employment status known	145	98.0
Employment status unknown	3	2.0
Employed	119	82.1
Pursuing graduate degrees	2	1.4
Unemployed (seeking, not seeking, or studying for the bar)	15	10.3
Type of Employment		
# employed in law firms	57	47.9
# employed in business and industry	27	22.7
# employed in government	23	19.3
# employed in public interest	6	5.0
# employed as judicial clerks	5	4.2
# employed in academia	1	0.8
Geographic Location		
# employed in state	95	79.8
# employed in foreign countries	0	0.0
# of states where employed	15	

Bar Passage Rates

First-time takers	118	Reporting %	100.00
Average school %	90.68	Average state %	88.09
Average pass difference	2.59		

Jurisdiction	Takers	Passers	Pass %	State %	Diff %
Ohio	118	107	90.68	88.09	2.59

The University of Akron School of Law

302 Buchtel Common
Akron, OH 44325-2901
Phone: 800.425.7668 or 330.972.7331; Fax: 330.258.2343
E-mail: lawadmissions@uakron.edu; Website: www.uakron.edu/law

■ Introduction

Located in the heart of downtown Akron and just 45 minutes south of Cleveland, the University of Akron (UA) is one of the 50 largest universities in the country. UA is a comprehensive research and teaching university with degree programs ranging from the associate to the doctoral level. Founded in 1870, UA has celebrated nearly 140 years of academic excellence while forging ahead to meet the complex needs of today's students.

The Akron School of Law was founded in 1921 and merged with UA in 1959. More than 6,000 students have graduated from the law school. Akron Law alumni practice throughout the US and abroad.

More than 160 Akron Law alumni have been or currently are judges in 13 states and the District of Columbia, as well as in the federal court system.

■ Admission

In order to be considered for admission, the applicant must submit the application form and personal statement. The $35 fee is waived for online applications. The applicant must also take the LSAT and register for LSAC's Credential Assembly Service before the file may be sent to the Admission Committee. An applicant may apply during his or her final year of undergraduate studies. The bachelor's degree coursework must be completed prior to law school matriculation. Decisions are made on a rolling basis as soon as the files are complete. The priority deadline is March 1, but applications are accepted throughout the spring and summer months. For more details on admission, please see our website at *www.uakron.edu/law.*

Students enrolled in an American Bar Association (ABA)-accredited law school may apply for transfer or transient status. A law student who has completed neither more nor less than one year (approximately 30 semester credit hours) and is in good academic standing may apply for transfer. A law student who has the dean's permission to visit for one or two semesters may apply for transient status. Consult *www.uakron.edu/law* for details.

■ Tuition/Fees and Financial Aid (Annual)

First-year students are considered for full or partial scholarships. No application is required. Upper-division students may apply for merit-based and need-based scholarships. Students also have access to Stafford, Graduate PLUS, and alternative loans, as well as federal work-study funds (summer term only).

■ Flexible Scheduling

Akron Law offers a traditional full-time JD program, which law students may complete in two and one-half or three years. Akron Law also offers a flexible part-time program, which allows students to attend classes during daytime or evening hours. Part-time students may complete the JD program in as few as three and one-half years or as many as six years. A few upper-division classes are also offered at 7:30 AM to allow students to attend classes before work. Students may transfer from full time to part time (or vice versa) as their needs dictate.

■ Physical Facilities

The law building includes a 1987 addition to the library and a 1993 addition to the original structure. The university's $200 million New Landscape for Learning campus improvement program includes a new Student Union, Student Recreation and Wellness Center, Student Affairs Building, academic buildings, and parking decks. Approximately 30 acres of new green space were added to campus to create a more park-like setting. The law school is within one block of the Akron Municipal Court, the court of common pleas, and the Ninth District Court of Appeals. The federal court is a few blocks from campus. While the law school is in the downtown Akron area, the campus is a green one bordered by grassy areas, decorative plantings, and fountains.

■ Intellectual Property Center

Patent, trademark, trade secret, copyright, licensing, and cyber law are among the many topics covered in the Intellectual Property (IP) Law program. Staffed by three full-time faculty, and supplemented by three full-time and additional part-time faculty with special expertise, Akron's IP program is one of the most extensive in the nation. Twenty-two IP courses are offered either every year or every other year, and more than six additional courses are planned.

In addition, Akron offers an LLM degree in Intellectual Property Law. This full-time or part-time graduate program provides law graduates with an opportunity to begin or continue a specialization in IP.

■ Curriculum/Special Programs

The first-year curriculum is traditional in content, using traditional and innovative interactive pedagogies. The upper-class curriculum is varied between basic courses and specialty courses, and also focuses on interactive learning pedagogies and development of crucial lawyering skills. All law students are eligible to participate in the programs offered and the services provided by the Academic Success Office. The director of academic success programs counsels students on study techniques, learning styles, time management, and other topics related to academic success. A comprehensive writing program designed to enhance students' skills in research, exposition, drafting, and argumentation is an integral part of the curriculum.

Specialized Studies: Business, Criminal, Intellectual Property, International, Litigation, Public, and Tax.

Joint Degrees: JD/Master in Business Administration, JD/Master of Science and Management in Human Resources, JD/Master in Taxation, JD/Master in Public Administration, and JD/Master in Applied Politics.

Certificate Programs: Intellectual Property and Litigation.

Study Abroad: Akron Law offers a five-week program in **Geneva, Switzerland**, in which law students may earn up to six hours of elective credit studying comparative law.

LLM Graduate Law Degree: Intellectual Property.

■ Competition Teams

Students have many opportunities to sharpen their litigation skills by participating in regional and national mock trial, moot court, and negotiation competitions. Our litigation teams have had almost unparalleled success in competitions throughout the United States and Europe. Each year, the National Institute of Trial Advocacy (NITA) ranks law school trial programs based on three-year averages of their performance in the three major national tournaments; Akron has been in the top 16 trial programs 17 times in the last 19 years. In 2007, Akron finished second in the NITA Tournament of Champions, third in the National Criminal Trial Competition, and first in the National Civil Trial Competition.

■ Legal Clinic

Students represent clients in court, at trial, and on appeal. A variety of opportunities for clinical training are offered. Programs offered include Appellate Review; Clinical Seminar; Criminal, Judicial, and Public External Placement clinics; Prisoner Legal Assistance Clinic; Street Law; New Business Legal Clinic; Civil Litigation Clinic; Trial Litigation Clinic; and pro bono opportunities.

■ Student Activities and Leadership

Our more than 20 law student organizations include the *Akron Law Review*, Black Law Students Association, Asian-Latino Law Students Association, Environmental Law Society, Gay/Straight Law Alliance, Intellectual Property and Technology Law Association, International Law Society, Law Association for Women, Akron Public Interest Law Society, Student Bar Association, and more. Elections for leadership positions are held each year for day and evening students.

■ Library and Technology

UA's campus is wireless, allowing for Internet and network access in any building on campus. The law library contains 287,000 volumes. Students have access to 47.6 million library items, 11 million unique titles that may be delivered through OhioLINK, 3.8 million library items through UA Libraries Catalog, and many full-text resources including 6,000 journals, more than 7.5 million articles, and 40,000 e-books. Law students also receive free access to LexisNexis and Westlaw.

■ Career Planning and Placement

The Career Planning and Placement Office (CPPO) director counsels law students on résumé writing, job searching, interviewing skills, and preparing for entrance into the legal profession. On-campus interviews, a minority clerkship program, an attorney-student mentor program, employment-related seminars, and career fairs are offered. Akron's extensive law alumni database enables the CPPO to assist students with networking opportunities nationwide. This office assists in the placement of students in law-related positions during summer sessions and upper-division years. Graduates receive placement assistance, on request, throughout their careers. Akron's reputation for excellence in legal education and a subsequent high bar passage rate facilitates competitive placements for students and graduates in all areas of practice.

■ Visiting Akron Law

Several programs are offered throughout the year for prospective and admitted students to interact with law students, alumni, faculty, and administration at the School of Law. In addition, guests are welcome to schedule an appointment to visit a class, take a tour, or meet with an admission representative. Prospective students may request additional information at *www.uakron.edu/law*. For those unable to visit Akron Law, our representatives can also be met on the recruitment road each fall. Consult our website for our national recruitment schedule.

Applicant Profile

The University of Akron School of Law

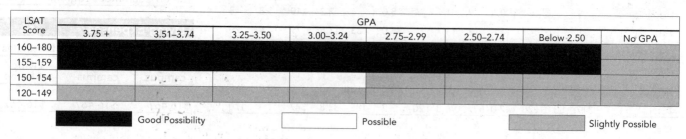

LSAT Score	GPA							
	3.75 +	3.51–3.74	3.25–3.50	3.00–3.24	2.75–2.99	2.50–2.74	Below 2.50	No GPA
160–180								
155–159								
150–154								
120–149								

Good Possibility   Possible   Slightly Possible

The University of Alabama School of Law

Box 870382
Tuscaloosa, AL 35487
Phone: 205.348.5440; Fax: 205.348.5439
E-mail: admissions@law.ua.edu; Website: www.law.ua.edu

ABA
Approved
Since
1926

The Basics

Type of school	Public
Term	Semester
Application deadline	
Application fee	$40
Financial aid deadline	
Can first year start other than fall?	No
Student to faculty ratio	10.2 to 1
# of housing spaces available restricted to law students	
graduate housing for which law students are eligible	

Faculty and Administrators

	Total Spr	Total Fall	Men Spr	Men Fall	Women Spr	Women Fall	Minorities Spr	Minorities Fall
Full-time	42	41	28	27	14	14	5	5
Other full-time	5	5	1	1	4	4	0	0
Deans, librarians, & others who teach	13	13	9	9	4	4	0	0
Part-time	22	25	18	23	4	2	1	3
Total	82	84	56	60	26	24	6	8

JD Enrollment and Ethnicity

	Men #	Men %	Women #	Women %	Full-Time #	Full-Time %	Part-Time #	Part-Time %	1st-Year #	1st-Year %	Total #	Total %	JD Degs. Awd.
African Amer.	19	6.0	31	13.5	44	8.3	6	30.0	22	11.9	50	9.1	11
Amer. Indian	3	0.9	1	0.4	4	0.8	0	0.0	0	0.0	4	0.7	1
Asian Amer.	7	2.2	8	3.5	15	2.8	0	0.0	7	3.8	15	2.7	5
Mex. Amer.	0	0.0	0	0.0	0	0.0	0	0.0	0	0.0	0	0.0	0
Puerto Rican	0	0.0	0	0.0	0	0.0	0	0.0	0	0.0	0	0.0	0
Hispanic	9	2.8	1	0.4	9	1.7	1	5.0	4	2.2	10	1.8	3
Total Minority	38	12.0	41	17.8	72	13.7	7	35.0	33	17.8	79	14.4	20
For. Nation.	0	0.0	0	0.0	0	0.0	0	0.0	0	0.0	0	0.0	1
Caucasian	279	88.0	189	82.2	455	86.3	13	65.0	172	93.0	468	85.6	149
Unknown	0	0.0	0	0.0	0	0.0	0	0.0	0	0.0	0	0.0	0
Total	317	58.0	230	42.0	527	96.3	20	3.7	185	33.8	547		170

Curriculum

	Full-Time	Part-Time
Typical first-year section size	63	0
Is there typically a "small section" of the first-year class, other than Legal Writing, taught by full-time faculty	No	No
If yes, typical size offered last year		
# of classroom course titles beyond first-year curriculum	149	
# of upper division courses, excluding seminars, with an enrollment: Under 25	106	
25–49	44	
50–74	7	
75–99	3	
100+	2	
# of seminars	17	
# of seminar positions available	204	
# of seminar positions filled	173	0
# of positions available in simulation courses	567	
# of simulation positions filled	501	0
# of positions available in faculty supervised clinical courses	109	
# of faculty supervised clinical positions filled	108	0
# involved in field placements	89	0
# involved in law journals	84	0
# involved in moot court or trial competitions	88	0
# of credit hours required to graduate	90	

Transfers

Transfers in	17
Transfers out	2

Tuition and Fees

	Resident	Nonresident
Full-time	$14,675	$26,785
Part-time		
Tuition Guarantee Program	N	

Living Expenses

Estimated living expenses for singles

Living on campus	Living off campus	Living at home
$16,467	$16,467	$16,467

The University of Alabama School of Law

ABA Approved Since 1926

GPA and LSAT Scores

	Total	Full-Time	Part-Time
# of apps	1,403	1,403	0
# of offers	459	433	26
# of matrics	184	164	20
75% GPA	3.90	3.91	3.75
Median GPA	3.76	3.77	3.19
25% GPA	3.32	3.42	3.02
75% LSAT	165	166	165
Median LSAT	164	164	158
25% LSAT	159	160	153

Grants and Scholarships (from prior year)

	Total #	Total %	Full-Time #	Full-Time %	Part-Time #	Part-Time %
Total # of students	495		481		14	
Total # receiving grants	236	47.7	227	47.2	9	64.3
Less than 1/2 tuition	88	17.8	80	16.6	8	57.1
Half to full tuition	50	10.1	49	10.2	1	7.1
Full tuition	61	12.3	61	12.7	0	0.0
More than full tuition	37	7.5	37	7.7	0	0.0
Median grant amount			$12,564		$2,540	

Informational and Library Resources

Total amount spent on library materials	$1,297,008
Study seating capacity inside the library	506
# of full-time equivalent professional librarians	20
Hours per week library is open	100
# of open, wired connections available to students	73
# of networked computers available for use by students	81
Has wireless network?	Y
Require computer?	N

JD Attrition (from prior year)

	Academic #	Other #	Total #	Total %
1st year	2	8	10	6.5
2nd year	0	0	0	0.0
3rd year	0	0	0	0.0
4th year	0	0	0	0.0

Employment (9 months after graduation)

	Total	Percentage
Employment status known	155	98.7
Employment status unknown	2	1.3
Employed	136	87.7
Pursuing graduate degrees	6	3.9
Unemployed (seeking, not seeking, or studying for the bar)	3	1.9
Type of Employment		
# employed in law firms	73	53.7
# employed in business and industry	17	12.5
# employed in government	21	15.4
# employed in public interest	6	4.4
# employed as judicial clerks	16	11.8
# employed in academia	2	1.5
Geographic Location		
# employed in state	83	61.0
# employed in foreign countries	3	2.2
# of states where employed	18	

Bar Passage Rates

First-time takers	136	Reporting %	77.21
Average school %	97.15	Average state %	88.96
Average pass difference	8.19		

Jurisdiction	Takers	Passers	Pass %	State %	Diff %
Alabama	98	95	96.94	89.02	7.92
Tennessee	7	7	100.00	88.10	11.90

The University of Alabama School of Law

Box 870382
Tuscaloosa, AL 35487
Phone: 205.348.5440; Fax: 205.348.5439
E-mail: admissions@law.ua.edu; Website: www.law.ua.edu

■ Introduction

The University of Alabama School of Law, the only public law school in Alabama, offers students a nationally recognized, progressive legal education. The law school has served as the training ground for state and national leaders in the legal profession, business, and government. Law students are provided with an abundance of cultural, academic, and athletic opportunities through the university. The curriculum is traditional but diverse. The law school is student-centered; faculty and administration are accessible to students. Although the faculty's first priority is teaching, the professors are actively engaged in scholarly research and writing. Alabama is accredited by the ABA and the AALS.

■ Library and Physical Facilities

The law school building, which sits on 23 acres of the University of Alabama's campus in Tuscaloosa, was designed by Edward Durell Stone, the architect for the Museum of Modern Art in New York, the US Embassy in New Delhi, and the Kennedy Center for the Performing Arts. Construction on a new wing and renovations to the existing building were completed in 2006. The wing includes new classrooms, the clinical offices, a cafeteria, a career services suite, meeting rooms, and a 24-hour computer lab. The Bounds Law Library provides users with a substantial research collection, student study carrels, the Hugo Black Study, the Howell Heflin Conference Room, and the Payne Special Collections Room. The school is on a wireless network.

■ Special and Summer Programs

Clinical programs enable law students to gain valuable practical experience in interviewing clients, preparing cases, and participating in courtroom presentations. During the second and third years, students can choose to participate in the Elder Law, Domestic Violence, Civil, Community Development, Capital Defense, Mediation Law, or Criminal Defense clinics. Alabama guarantees every interested student the opportunity to participate in at least one clinic before graduating.

The externship program offers students practical experience while receiving credit. Externships are available during the summers and the second and third academic years. The law school's Public Interest Institute awards grants to encourage students to participate in the area of public interest and honors students who perform public interest work. The institute also has a full-time dean to assist students.

The joint JD/MBA program offers select students an opportunity to earn both an MBA and JD. Students may select from programs designed for them to earn both degrees within three or four years. The graduate program for international students provides international lawyers an opportunity to earn an LLM degree. The law school also offers a part-time LLM in Taxation Program for JD degree holders.

The law school's two summer programs at the University of Fribourg, in Fribourg, Switzerland, and the Australian National University in Canberra provide a unique international experience. Both programs include a course surveying the host country's national law and a comparative law doctrinal course. In addition, Alabama Law recently announced the opportunity for current students to study abroad for a semester at Tel Aviv University in Israel and the National Law University of New Delhi in India.

Summer school is open to students who have completed the first year.

■ Admission

A student must obtain a bachelor's degree at an accredited institution before enrolling, but may apply during his or her senior year. Applicants must take the LSAT, preferably in June or October in the year preceding enrollment, and register for the Credential Assembly Service (CAS). Transcripts must show all schools attended. Application materials are available in the summer each year and accepted in early fall. Applications are processed on a rolling basis. The two most significant factors for admission are the undergraduate GPA and LSAT score. However, the school believes that the law school experience is enriched by a diverse group of students. The Admissions Committee also considers other factors, such as honors, activities, unique work or service experience, difficulty of undergraduate courses, writing ability, trends in academic performance, leadership roles, travel experience, exceptional talents, career achievements, graduate school performance, and history of overcoming adversity. One letter of recommendation is required. The law school recommends that letters be submitted to the Credential Assembly Service. Students are admitted only for the fall semester.

■ Student Activities

A broad range of student activities adds to the students' law school experience. Student organizations represent diverse interests. These include the Student Bar Association, Black Law Students Association, Public Interest Law Association, Civil Rights Law Students Association, Dorbin Association (women's group), Law Students for Choice, Gay-Straight Alliance, Environmental Law Society, International Law Society, Just Democracy, Labor and Employment Law Society, Law Democrats, Law Republicans, Business Law Society, Criminal Law Association, Defense Lawyers Association, Future Trial Lawyers Association, Christian Legal Society, Sports and Entertainment Law Society, and Latin American Law Association.

The School of Law also offers numerous writing opportunities. The *Alabama Law Review*, a nationally recognized law journal, is edited by students and devotes substantial space to national and state issues. The *Journal of the Legal Profession, Law and Psychology Review,* and our newest journal, *Alabama Civil Rights and Civil Liberties Law Review,* are also student-edited law journals.

Moot court and trial advocacy teams have enjoyed exceptional success over the years. The law school sponsors teams in several moot court, specialty, and trial advocacy competitions. The moot court and trial advocacy teams have

won many team and individual awards in both regional and national competitions.

■ Expenses and Financial Aid

The majority of students enrolled in the School of Law finance their legal education through loans, savings, earnings, or family contributions. Applicants are considered automatically for first-year scholarships, which are typically based on factors such as GPA and LSAT performance. Scholarships sometimes are renewable during the second and third years—depending upon funding, the student's need, and whether the recipient maintains stated levels of academic achievement. Following acceptance by the law school, each admitted student who applies for federal aid through the Free Application for Federal Student Aid (FAFSA) receives a financial aid packet from the university's Financial Aid Office. Information on loans can be obtained by contacting Student Financial Aid, the University of Alabama, Box 870162, Tuscaloosa, AL 35487-0162. Phone: 205.348.6756; *www.financialaid.ua.edu.* Applicants should complete the FAFSA form as soon after January 1 as possible, and may apply online at *www.fafsa.ed.gov.*

■ Career Services

The Career Services Office assists students in their efforts to find employment. The office provides individual career counseling, group presentations, speaker programs, and library and database resources. Seminars are presented on résumé writing, interviewing techniques, job-search techniques, judicial clerkships, and nontraditional legal jobs, to name a few. Extensive on-campus interviewing occurs. The law school also participates in job fairs in Atlanta, New York City, Chicago, and Washington, DC. The employment rate within nine months of graduation was 97.4 percent for the Class of 2008 with approximately 40 percent practicing outside of Alabama. Our national bar passage rate was 95 percent and the in-state bar passage rate was 97 percent.

■ Housing

The University of Alabama maintains residence halls and units for students; however, most law students live off campus. The cost of living in Tuscaloosa for a single law student ranges from approximately $500 to $1,100 per month. For information on university housing, students must contact the Office of Residential Life at the University of Alabama at *housing@sa.ua.edu.*

Applicant Profile

The University of Alabama School of Law
This grid includes only applicants who earned 120–180 LSAT scores under standard administrations.

LSAT Score	GPA								
	3.75 +	3.50–3.74	3.25–3.49	3.00–3.24	2.75–2.99	2.50–2.74	2.25–2.49	2.00–2.24	Below 2.00
175–180									
170–174									
165–169									
160–164									
155–159									
150–154									
145–149									
140–144									
135–139									
130–134									
125–129									
120–124									

Good Possibility   Possible   Unlikely

Reflects 99% of the total applicant pool; average LSAT data reported.

Albany Law School of Union University

80 New Scotland Avenue
Albany, NY 12208-3494
Phone: 518.445.2326; Fax: 518.445.2369
E-mail: admissions@albanylaw.edu; Website: www.albanylaw.edu

ABA
Approved
Since
1930

The Basics

Type of school	Private
Term	Semester
Application deadline	3/1
Application fee	$60
Financial aid deadline	
Can first year start other than fall?	No
Student to faculty ratio	13.1 to 1
# of housing spaces available restricted to law students	
graduate housing for which law students are eligible	

Faculty and Administrators

	Total		Men		Women		Minorities	
	Spr	Fall	Spr	Fall	Spr	Fall	Spr	Fall
Full-time	45	46	21	23	24	23	7	9
Other full-time	0	0	0	0	0	0	0	0
Deans, librarians, & others who teach	6	6	4	4	2	2	1	1
Part-time	46	30	32	20	13	10	3	3
Total	97	82	57	47	39	35	11	13

Curriculum

	Full-Time	Part-Time
Typical first-year section size	65	0
Is there typically a "small section" of the first-year class, other than Legal Writing, taught by full-time faculty	No	No
If yes, typical size offered last year		
# of classroom course titles beyond first-year curriculum	129	
# of upper division courses, excluding seminars, with an enrollment: Under 25	73	
25–49	29	
50–74	19	
75–99	5	
100+	4	
# of seminars	42	
# of seminar positions available	798	
# of seminar positions filled	627	0
# of positions available in simulation courses	480	
# of simulation positions filled	272	0
# of positions available in faculty supervised clinical courses	128	
# of faculty supervised clinical positions filled	121	0
# involved in field placements	164	0
# involved in law journals	144	0
# involved in moot court or trial competitions	23	0
# of credit hours required to graduate	87	

JD Enrollment and Ethnicity

	Men		Women		Full-Time		Part-Time		1st-Year		Total		JD Degs. Awd.
	#	%	#	%	#	%	#	%	#	%	#	%	
African Amer.	8	1.9	10	3.0	16	2.2	2	5.4	10	3.9	18	2.4	9
Amer. Indian	2	0.5	3	0.9	5	0.7	0	0.0	1	0.4	5	0.7	3
Asian Amer.	12	2.9	24	7.3	35	4.9	1	2.7	7	2.7	36	4.8	19
Mex. Amer.	0	0.0	3	0.9	3	0.4	0	0.0	1	0.4	3	0.4	1
Puerto Rican	3	0.7	4	1.2	6	0.8	1	2.7	4	1.6	7	0.9	3
Hispanic	14	3.3	7	2.1	21	2.9	0	0.0	10	3.9	21	2.8	4
Total Minority	39	9.3	51	15.5	86	12.1	4	10.8	33	12.8	90	12.0	39
For. Nation.	5	1.2	10	3.0	14	2.0	1	2.7	4	1.6	15	2.0	5
Caucasian	333	79.3	231	70.2	534	75.0	30	81.1	168	65.4	564	75.3	165
Unknown	43	10.2	37	11.2	78	11.0	2	5.4	52	20.2	80	10.7	10
Total	420	56.1	329	43.9	712	95.1	37	4.9	257	34.3	749		219

Transfers

Transfers in	2
Transfers out	7

Tuition and Fees

	Resident	Nonresident
Full-time	$39,050	$39,050
Part-time	$29,325	$29,325
Tuition Guarantee Program	N	

Living Expenses

Estimated living expenses for singles

Living on campus	Living off campus	Living at home
N/A	$17,700	$8,800

Albany Law School of Union University

ABA
Approved
Since
1930

GPA and LSAT Scores

	Total	Full-Time	Part-Time
# of apps	2,215	2,215	0
# of offers	972	972	0
# of matrics	255	255	0
75% GPA	3.56	3.56	0.00
Median GPA	3.30	3.30	0.00
25% GPA	3.03	3.03	0.00
75% LSAT	157	157	0
Median LSAT	155	155	0
25% LSAT	153	153	0

Grants and Scholarships (from prior year)

	Total		Full-Time		Part-Time	
	#	%	#	%	#	%
Total # of students	735		707		28	
Total # receiving grants	235	32.0	226	32.0	9	32.1
Less than 1/2 tuition	133	18.1	130	18.4	3	10.7
Half to full tuition	77	10.5	71	10.0	6	21.4
Full tuition	23	3.1	23	3.3	0	0.0
More than full tuition	2	0.3	2	0.3	0	0.0
Median grant amount			$18,000		$13,500	

Informational and Library Resources

Total amount spent on library materials	$1,759,951
Study seating capacity inside the library	432
# of full-time equivalent professional librarians	7
Hours per week library is open	104
# of open, wired connections available to students	1,142
# of networked computers available for use by students	110
Has wireless network?	Y
Require computer?	N

JD Attrition (from prior year)

	Academic	Other	Total	
	#	#	#	%
1st year	5	0	5	1.9
2nd year	0	7	7	2.8
3rd year	0	0	0	0.0
4th year	0	0	0	0.0

Employment (9 months after graduation)

	Total	Percentage
Employment status known	214	100.0
Employment status unknown	0	0.0
Employed	201	93.9
Pursuing graduate degrees	0	0.0
Unemployed (seeking, not seeking, or studying for the bar)	13	6.1
Type of Employment		
# employed in law firms	97	48.3
# employed in business and industry	37	18.4
# employed in government	32	15.9
# employed in public interest	11	5.5
# employed as judicial clerks	18	9.0
# employed in academia	4	2.0
Geographic Location		
# employed in state	163	81.1
# employed in foreign countries	0	0.0
# of states where employed		16

Bar Passage Rates

First-time takers	212	Reporting %	96.70
Average school %	81.47	Average state %	88.93
Average pass difference	-7.46		

Jurisdiction	Takers	Passers	Pass %	State %	Diff %
New York	193	156	80.83	88.98	-8.15
Connecticut	8	7	87.50	88.28	-0.78
Pennsylvania	2	2	100.00	86.69	13.31
Maine	1	1	100.00	90.74	9.26
Maryland	1	1	100.00	85.51	14.49

Albany Law School of Union University

80 New Scotland Avenue
Albany, NY 12208-3494
Phone: 518.445.2326; Fax: 518.445.2369
E-mail: admissions@albanylaw.edu; Website: www.albanylaw.edu

■ Introduction

The only law school in the capital of New York State, Albany Law School is the oldest private, independent law school in North America. Our location, in the center of state government, provides unprecedented opportunities for internships, field placements, clinical experience, and career opportunities. Our world-class faculty is dedicated and accessible. Students have access to New York's highest court, federal courts, and the state legislature, as well as to a thriving tech-based economy. The employment rate for our graduates has been well above the national average for law schools for over 25 years.

■ The Academic Experience

From your first day at Albany Law School you will be challenged by a rigorous academic curriculum. You will get a firm foundation in fundamental areas of law plus opportunities to shape your learning to fit your professional interests.

As a first-year student, you begin to acquire the skills that will become the foundation of your legal career. As part of our innovative Introduction to Lawyering course, you will represent a plaintiff or defendant in a simulated case where you conduct legal research, draft motions and memoranda, and participate in client interviews and negotiations. The class culminates with each student presenting an oral argument before some of the state's most notable attorneys.

As a second- and third-year student, you can focus your studies in one of 14 concentrations to complement coursework. Opportunities include seven clinical projects and more than 150 field placement internships in the Albany region, many of them in state and federal government positions as well as in law firms and high-tech companies. Students also participate in real-world work through the Government Law Center, the Center for Law and Innovation, the Clinic and Justice Center, and study-abroad programs. Some students choose to pursue a joint-degree program with an area graduate school, earning a master's degree while working toward a Juris Doctor (JD) degree.

■ Real-Life Experience

Our groundbreaking legal centers and award-winning clinical programs provide the valuable hands-on experience that employers find highly desirable. You work alongside committed clinical faculty and practicing attorneys to assist low-income clients with real legal issues relating to health law, HIV/AIDS, disabilities, domestic violence, disputes with the Internal Revenue Service, and financial investments. You will also work with prosecutors, judges, and experienced attorneys through our field placement program.

Because of our unique location, you interact with the leaders in New York state government—countless Albany Law alumni—and visionaries building New York's high-technology base through the programs at the Government Law Center and the Center for Law and Innovation.

In the Government Law Center you conduct research, contribute to publications, and participate in conferences and special projects that promote the study of the issues facing government, public policy, and public service.

You can provide legal services to start-up ventures and early-stage technology companies in the Tech Valley, New York City, and throughout New York by working and studying with attorneys at the Center for Law and Innovation.

■ Your Career

From your first week at school, our Career Center helps you develop a career plan and supports you throughout your job search. Professional career counselors help you define career goals, craft résumés and cover letters, prepare you for interviews, and compare employment offers.

The Career Center is a state-of-the-art facility with multiple interview rooms set aside for professionals to conduct on-campus interviews. These rooms are equipped with all the amenities of a law office and are extremely popular with employers. Our job search software, which works like a private *Monster.com*, is exclusive to Albany Law students and alumni. Some 4,000 employers currently post jobs on the private system.

Job fairs, information sessions, workshops, and panel discussions on a variety of employment–related topics occur almost daily. The Career Center hosts more than 1,200 interviews each year and conducts off-campus interview programs in metropolitan areas, including New York City; Chicago; Washington, DC; and Boston, exclusively for Albany Law School students. Our alumni are avid supporters of these efforts and participate enthusiastically in center activities.

Our graduates find jobs in law firms, government agencies, public interest organizations, and business and industry throughout the country. About one-third of Albany Law School graduates work in the New York City metropolitan area, with large groups of alumni in Boston; Washington, DC; and business centers along the eastern seaboard as far as Florida.

The employment rate for the Class of 2008 was 94 percent—above the national average of 89 percent, and consistently above national rates for over 25 years.

■ Our Community

The Albany Law School community of approximately 650 students, 55 full-time faculty, and 54 part-time faculty is intimate, respectful, and supportive. We welcome students and faculty with diverse backgrounds and talents, and provide an outstanding environment for the pursuit of scholarship, teaching, and public service.

The small size of our student body fosters an environment that encourages camaraderie and frequent contacts between students and faculty.

Nearly 12 percent of our students graduated five or more years before entering law school and had careers in other professions prior to beginning their legal studies. Nearly 50 percent of our students are women, over a third are from outside New York State, and 25 percent are members of a minority group.

■ Our Campus

Albany Law School's facilities honor our 158-year history, while supporting a twenty-first century legal education. The open design of the 53,000-square-foot Schaffer Law

Library—a federal depository library—provides an inviting environment with seating for hundreds of students. Book and microfilm collections number more than half a million volumes, and the library supplements its collection with online databases and legal research systems, including LexisNexis and Westlaw. The library also houses technological devices for the hearing and visually impaired.

The main building of Albany Law School is known as the 1928 Building, acknowledging its year of construction. The building has been recently renovated and houses contemporary lecture halls, seminar-style classrooms, two modern moot courtrooms, and "smart" classrooms with wireless Internet access and advanced audio, video, computing, and conferencing systems.

A 45,000-square-foot building built in 2000 houses the Albany Law School clinic, law centers, and administrative offices, as well as several classrooms, including a high-tech distance learning classroom. Our new bookstore and student center opened last year, along with a new state-of-the-art fitness center.

Student Life

You have dozens of opportunities to participate in student organizations and activities around specific academic, professional, social, cultural, or athletic interests.

Three student-edited journals, the *Albany Law Review*, the *Albany Law Journal of Science and Technology*, and the *Albany Government Law Review* offer cocurricular research and writing opportunities.

Our nationally recognized Moot Court Program enables you to develop skills in trial advocacy, appellate advocacy, client counseling, and negotiating while competing in both intramural and interscholastic competitions.

The Capital Region is home to 16 colleges and universities and boasts museums, galleries, restaurants, shops, theaters, nightclubs for every taste, venues that host professional sporting events, and performing arts centers that attract national acts. The Adirondack, Berkshire, and Catskill mountains offer skiing, camping, hiking, and water sports, as well as the Saratoga Race Course for thoroughbred and harness racing. Metropolitan centers in New York City, Boston, and Montreal are all within an easy drive and about 10 trains provide daily service to New York City. All major air carriers operate from the Albany International Airport and provide daily nonstop service to most eastern US cities, with connections worldwide.

Admission and Financial Aid

Albany Law School commits close to $5 million annually to scholarship assistance. Over 30 percent of first-year students receive awards that average $20,000 for each year of study. We offer grants based on academic merit, ranging from $5,000 to full-tuition scholarships.

When evaluating each individual application, the Admissions Committee takes a highly personalized, holistic approach, reviewing LSAT score, undergraduate grade-point average, strength of the undergraduate program, rigor of the undergraduate curriculum, and life experience. The committee seeks to enroll a student body that enriches the educational experience of all of its members. Albany Law School also seeks to provide future members of the bar who reflect the diversity and sensibilities of our society.

Approximately 90 percent of our students qualify for financial aid, via federal, state, and private loans, or for part-time employment to assist in meeting educational expenses.

We encourage you to visit Albany Law School—meet our faculty, speak with our students, and tour our beautiful facilities. We look forward to meeting you.

Applicant Profile

Albany Law School attracts talented, diverse students from a wide spectrum of backgrounds and experiences. Applicants come from the highest ranks of their prior graduate and undergraduate institutions. LSAT scores and prior academic performance are important in assisting our Admissions Committee in offering seats to applicants. Those indicators are, however, not the sole factors weighed when admission decisions are made. Interested applicants are encouraged to explore how their careers can be enhanced by an Albany Law School education. Contact the Admissions Office at 518.445.2326 to discuss your individual qualifications.

American University, Washington College of Law

4801 Massachusetts Avenue NW, Suite 507
Washington, DC 20016
Phone: 202.274.4101; Fax: 202.274.4107
E-mail: wcladmit@wcl.american.edu; Website: www.wcl.american.edu

ABA
Approved
Since
1940

The Basics

Type of school	Private
Term	Semester
Application deadline	3/1
Application fee	$70
Financial aid deadline	3/1
Can first year start other than fall?	No
Student to faculty ratio	13.4 to 1
# of housing spaces available restricted to law students	
graduate housing for which law students are eligible	25

Faculty and Administrators

	Total		Men		Women		Minorities	
	Spr	Fall	Spr	Fall	Spr	Fall	Spr	Fall
Full-time	83	86	52	50	31	36	17	18
Other full-time	23	20	10	7	13	13	6	8
Deans, librarians, & others who teach	13	13	5	5	8	8	2	2
Part-time	124	107	92	71	31	35	13	11
Total	243	226	159	133	83	92	38	39

Curriculum

		Full-Time	Part-Time
Typical first-year section size		98	93
Is there typically a "small section" of the first-year class, other than Legal Writing, taught by full-time faculty		Yes	No
If yes, typical size offered last year		41	
# of classroom course titles beyond first-year curriculum		295	
# of upper division courses, excluding seminars, with an enrollment:	Under 25	189	
	25–49	61	
	50–74	32	
	75–99	13	
	100+	0	
# of seminars		135	
# of seminar positions available		2,103	
# of seminar positions filled		1,018	542
# of positions available in simulation courses		1,478	
# of simulation positions filled		597	559
# of positions available in faculty supervised clinical courses		222	
# of faculty supervised clinical positions filled		202	20
# involved in field placements		238	26
# involved in law journals		336	19
# involved in moot court or trial competitions		93	2
# of credit hours required to graduate		86	

Transfers

Transfers in	24
Transfers out	25

Tuition and Fees

	Resident	Nonresident
Full-time	$41,406	$41,406
Part-time	$29,027	$29,027
Tuition Guarantee Program	N	

Living Expenses

Estimated living expenses for singles

Living on campus	Living off campus	Living at home
$21,384	$21,384	$21,384

JD Enrollment and Ethnicity

	Men		Women		Full-Time		Part-Time		1st-Year		Total		JD Degs. Awd.
	#	%	#	%	#	%	#	%	#	%	#	%	
African Amer.	36	5.4	107	13.0	102	8.5	41	14.1	52	10.8	143	9.6	48
Amer. Indian	7	1.1	10	1.2	14	1.2	3	1.0	3	0.6	17	1.1	4
Asian Amer.	67	10.1	100	12.2	133	11.1	34	11.7	54	11.3	167	11.2	34
Mex. Amer.	13	2.0	22	2.7	31	2.6	4	1.4	11	2.3	35	2.4	10
Puerto Rican	12	1.8	2	0.2	11	0.9	3	1.0	8	1.7	14	0.9	7
Hispanic	72	10.9	85	10.3	132	11.0	25	8.6	61	12.7	157	10.6	44
Total Minority	207	31.3	326	39.6	423	35.4	110	37.9	189	39.4	533	35.9	147
For. Nation.	12	1.8	30	3.6	36	3.0	6	2.1	12	2.5	42	2.8	18
Caucasian	396	59.8	412	50.1	662	55.4	146	50.3	215	44.8	808	54.4	269
Unknown	47	7.1	55	6.7	74	6.2	28	9.7	64	13.3	102	6.9	20
Total	662	44.6	823	55.4	1195	80.5	290	19.5	480	32.3	1485		454

American University, Washington College of Law

ABA
Approved
Since
1940

GPA and LSAT Scores

	Total	Full-Time	Part-Time
# of apps	8,667	7,649	1,018
# of offers	1,931	1,715	216
# of matrics	481	385	96
75% GPA	3.56	3.59	3.52
Median GPA	3.36	3.39	3.28
25% GPA	3.13	3.14	3.06
75% LSAT	164	164	162
Median LSAT	162	163	161
25% LSAT	158	158	159

Grants and Scholarships (from prior year)

	Total		Full-Time		Part-Time	
	#	%	#	%	#	%
Total # of students	1,461		1,235		226	
Total # receiving grants	373	25.5	361	29.2	12	5.3
Less than 1/2 tuition	332	22.7	320	25.9	12	5.3
Half to full tuition	15	1.0	15	1.2	0	0.0
Full tuition	23	1.6	23	1.9	0	0.0
More than full tuition	3	0.2	3	0.2	0	0.0
Median grant amount			$12,000		$3,675	

Informational and Library Resources

Total amount spent on library materials	$1,974,848
Study seating capacity inside the library	596
# of full-time equivalent professional librarians	10
Hours per week library is open	119
# of open, wired connections available to students	2,160
# of networked computers available for use by students	166
Has wireless network?	Y
Require computer?	N

JD Attrition (from prior year)

	Academic	Other	Total	
	#	#	#	%
1st year	1	25	26	5.5
2nd year	0	0	0	0.0
3rd year	0	0	0	0.0
4th year	0	0	0	0.0

Employment (9 months after graduation)

	Total	Percentage
Employment status known	469	99.6
Employment status unknown	2	0.4
Employed	417	88.9
Pursuing graduate degrees	13	2.8
Unemployed (seeking, not seeking, or studying for the bar)	19	4.1
Type of Employment		
# employed in law firms	198	47.5
# employed in business and industry	50	12.0
# employed in government	59	14.1
# employed in public interest	48	11.5
# employed as judicial clerks	52	12.5
# employed in academia	5	1.2
Geographic Location		
# employed in state	182	43.6
# employed in foreign countries	5	1.2
# of states where employed	31	

Bar Passage Rates

First-time takers	485	Reporting %	98.76
Average school %	88.76	Average state %	85.46
Average pass difference	3.30		

Jurisdiction	Takers	Passers	Pass %	State %	Diff %
New York	138	127	92.03	88.98	3.05
Maryland	120	106	88.33	85.51	2.82
Virginia	60	51	85.00	82.70	2.30
California	52	36	69.23	78.07	−8.84
Others (21)	109	105	96.33		

American University, Washington College of Law

4801 Massachusetts Avenue NW, Suite 507
Washington, DC 20016
Phone: 202.274.4101; Fax: 202.274.4107
E-mail: wcladmit@wcl.american.edu; Website: www.wcl.american.edu

■ Introduction

American University Washington College of Law (WCL) offers an opportunity for the study of law in the center of the nation's legal institutions. The law school is minutes from downtown Washington, yet offers the facilities and ambience of a campus environment in one of the city's most beautiful residential neighborhoods. Founded in 1896 by two women, the law school is national in character. WCL offers renowned programs in experiential learning (clinics and externships), international law, law and government, intellectual property, business, environmental law, health law, and gender. It is committed to the development of the intellectual abilities, professional values, and practical skills required to prepare lawyers to practice in an increasingly complex and transnational world.

■ Library and Physical Facilities

The John Sherman Myers and Alvina Reckman Myers Law Center houses the Pence Law Library, two courtrooms, classrooms, faculty offices, and administrative offices of the Washington College of Law. The two-story law library is the heart of the complex and seats over 600 students. The entire law school facility has wireless access, and most of the law library seating has wired access as well. The library has more than 600,000 volumes, access to multiple databases, and 14 group-study rooms in addition to individual study carrels and seating. There are a number of research stations and network printing is available to the community. The library collection includes European Community and US government depositories and the Baxter Collection in International Law. Students also have access to the university's library, the Library of Congress, specialized agency libraries, and other area law libraries to which the school is electronically linked. The law school also encompasses more than 12 program offices, several faculty offices, and conference rooms in two neighboring buildings.

■ Curriculum

The law school offers full- and part-time programs leading to the JD degree, which is awarded after satisfactory completion of 86 credit hours, 32 of which are prescribed. All degree candidates must also fulfill an upper-level writing requirement. While a modified version of the Socratic method is the dominant form of teaching in the first year, faculty increasingly employ such methodologies as role-playing, simulations, and small-group collaborative exercises. The goal is to develop the skills of critical analysis, provide perspectives on the law and lawyering, and deepen understanding of fundamental legal principles. In the Legal Rhetoric Program, basic legal research and writing skills are taught to groups of students by full-time faculty (23 students per section) and practicing attorneys (12 students per section). During the spring semester of the first year, students enroll in an elective first-year course in addition to their required courses. Examples of first-year elective courses are International Law, Introduction to Intellectual Property Law and Policy, and Introduction to Public Law. In the second and third years, students elect a course of study drawing from advanced courses, seminars, independent research, externships, and clinical programs. JD students take upper-level courses with LLM students, learning side by side with more than 180 practicing attorneys from around the world. Students are exposed to a variety of teaching approaches by the law school's distinguished full-time tenured and tenure-track faculty and adjunct professors.

■ Special Programs

While many of the advanced courses are taught in a traditional classroom setting, a variety of other innovative teaching modes are available to enhance research skills and provide professional training.

- **Clinical Program**—The Washington College of Law was one of the first law schools to develop modern clinical legal education. Typically, more than 200 second- and third-year students participate in one of the 10 law clinics each academic year—making the Clinical Program one of the largest in the nation. All ten clinics are open to third-year students and seven are open to second-year students. Full-time faculty and practitioners-in-residence work collaboratively to teach students about client-centered, ethical practices. The Clinical Program serves a diverse clientele including immigrants and refugees; victims/survivors of domestic violence; juveniles; criminal defendants; low-income taxpayers; individuals seeking help with family law, consumer, disability, and intellectual property issues; community groups; and nonprofit organizations. The 10 clinics include: General Practice Clinic, Community and Economic Development Law Clinic, Criminal Justice Clinic, DC Law Students in Court Clinic, Disability Rights Law Clinic, Domestic Violence Law Clinic, Janet R. Spragens Federal Tax Clinic, Glushko-Samuelson Intellectual Property Law Clinic, International Human Rights Law Clinic, and Women and the Law Clinic.
- **Dual-Degree Programs**—American University offers five domestic dual-degree programs for students seeking to enhance their law degree with additional graduate coursework. These programs are a JD/MA in International Affairs with the School of International Service, JD/MBA with the Kogod School of Business, and JD/MPA; JD/MPP; and JD/MS in Justice, Law, and Society programs with the School of Public Affairs. In addition to our domestic dual-degree programs, the law school offers three international dual-degree programs with law schools in Melbourne, Australia; Ottawa, Canada; and Paris, France. These programs provide students more opportunities to practice law in the international arena.
- **Externship Program**—The program places upper-level students in many governmental, nonprofit, and public interest entities throughout the DC metropolitan area, the US, and abroad. More than 300 students participate in an externship each year.
- **Trial Advocacy Program**—The nationally recognized Stephen S. Weinstein Trial Advocacy Program prepares about 300 students each year to enter the legal community with solid trial litigation skills. The program emphasizes basic skills training, development of case theory and themes, analysis of strategies, and professional ethics.

- **Graduate Study**—Graduate study is available leading to either an LLM or SJD degree in International Legal Studies or Law and Government.
- **Summer Programs**—In addition to our summer session courses, the law school offers five intensive summer institutes at our DC location in the areas of international arbitration, human rights, health law, law and government, and environmental law.
- **Study Abroad**—Students have the opportunity to study law for a semester in more than 18 different countries or through one of the law school's five summer abroad programs in Chile, Europe (London/Paris/Geneva), The Hague, Turkey, and Israel.

■ Admission

Applicants to the law school are admitted based on the strength of their entire academic and related record. The Committee on Admissions gives primary emphasis to the undergraduate record, LSAT scores, and major accomplishments and achievements, whether academic, work-related, or extracurricular. The committee considers the benefits from having racial, ethnic, cultural, economic, and geographic diversity among its students. Admission to the law school is highly selective and operates both a binding Early Decision Option and a modified rolling admission process, so early application is strongly encouraged.

■ Student Activities

The law school has four journals and several publications edited and published by students. Journals include *Administrative Law Review; American University Law Review; American University International Law Review;* and *American*

University Journal of Gender, Social Policy, and the Law. Publications include *American Jurist, Business Law Brief, Criminal Law Brief, Health Law and Policy, Human Rights Brief,* the *Modern American,* and *Sustainable Development Law and Policy.* The Moot Court Honor Society sponsors appellate competitions for first-year and upper-level students and prepares students for a number of national and international interschool appellate competitions. The Mock Trial Honor Society sponsors a closing argument competition for first-year students and prepares student teams for national interschool mock trial competitions. There are more than 50 active student organizations, including the Asian-Pacific American Law Students Association, Black Law Students Association, Latino/a Law Students Association, South Asian Law Students Association, Lambda Law Society, Environmental Law Society, Equal Justice Foundation, Federalist Society, International Trade Law Society, Intellectual Property Law Society, and Law and Government Society.

■ Career Services

Staffed by seven attorney counselors, the Office of Career and Professional Development provides individual career and professional development counseling to students and alumni on all aspects of the job search process, and sponsors dozens of educational and job-related programs throughout the year. The office coordinates both on- and off-campus recruitment for summer, academic year, and postgraduate positions, including regional interview programs in Atlanta, Boston, Chicago, New York, and the West Coast. Students also participate in a wide variety of hiring consortia, including the Boston Lawyers Group, the Patent Law Interview Program, the New Hampshire Job Fair, the Delaware Minority Job Fair, the WMACCA Corporate Scholars Program, and regional Black Law Students Association fairs.

Applicant Profile

The Committee on Admissions considers a number of factors when evaluating a candidate for admission; therefore we elected not to include a grid based on undergraduate GPA and LSAT scores. Many applicants have similar scores, but each applicant has a unique background of academic, cultural, and professional experiences and achievements. The committee weighs all of these factors when determining a candidate's suitability for admission.

Appalachian School of Law

1169 Edgewater Drive, PO Box 2825
Grundy, VA 24614
Phone: 800.895.7411 (toll free) or 276.935.4349; Fax: 276.935.8496
E-mail: admissions@asl.edu; Website: www.asl.edu

ABA
Approved
Since
2001

The Basics

Type of school	Private
Term	Semester
Application deadline	7/1
Application fee	$60
Financial aid deadline	7/1
Can first year start other than fall?	No
Student to faculty ratio	15.8 to 1
# of housing spaces available restricted to law students	
graduate housing for which law students are eligible	

Faculty and Administrators

	Total		Men		Women		Minorities	
	Spr	Fall	Spr	Fall	Spr	Fall	Spr	Fall
Full-time	20	19	13	13	7	6	4	4
Other full-time	0	0	0	0	0	0	0	0
Deans, librarians, & others who teach	3	3	2	2	1	1	0	0
Part-time	0	2	0	2	0	0	0	0
Total	23	24	15	17	8	7	4	4

JD Enrollment and Ethnicity

	Men		Women		Full-Time		Part-Time		1st-Year		Total		JD Degs. Awd.
	#	%	#	%	#	%	#	%	#	%	#	%	
African Amer.	4	1.9	12	9.7	16	4.8	0	0.0	5	3.9	16	4.8	1
Amer. Indian	1	0.5	1	0.8	2	0.6	0	0.0	0	0.0	2	0.6	1
Asian Amer.	1	0.5	5	4.0	6	1.8	0	0.0	2	1.6	6	1.8	1
Mex. Amer.	0	0.0	0	0.0	0	0.0	0	0.0	0	0.0	0	0.0	0
Puerto Rican	0	0.0	0	0.0	0	0.0	0	0.0	0	0.0	0	0.0	0
Hispanic	5	2.4	3	2.4	8	2.4	0	0.0	3	2.4	8	2.4	3
Total Minority	11	5.2	21	16.9	32	9.6	0	0.0	10	7.9	32	9.6	6
For. Nation.	1	0.5	1	0.8	2	0.6	0	0.0	0	0.0	2	0.6	0
Caucasian	172	81.9	93	75.0	265	79.3	0	0.0	101	79.5	265	79.3	90
Unknown	26	12.4	9	7.3	35	10.5	0	0.0	17	13.4	35	10.5	20
Total	210	62.9	124	37.1	334	100.0	0	0.0	128	38.0	334		116

Curriculum

	Full-Time	Part-Time
Typical first-year section size	129	0
Is there typically a "small section" of the first-year class, other than Legal Writing, taught by full-time faculty	Yes	No
If yes, typical size offered last year	45	
# of classroom course titles beyond first-year curriculum		46
# of upper division courses, excluding seminars, with an enrollment: Under 25		18
25–49		7
50–74		8
75–99		0
100+		9
# of seminars		7
# of seminar positions available		140
# of seminar positions filled	97	0
# of positions available in simulation courses	427	
# of simulation positions filled	417	0
# of positions available in faculty supervised clinical courses	0	
# of faculty supervised clinical positions filled	0	0
# involved in field placements	127	0
# involved in law journals	45	0
# involved in moot court or trial competitions	35	0
# of credit hours required to graduate		90

Transfers

Transfers in	3
Transfers out	3

Tuition and Fees

	Resident	Nonresident
Full-time	$26,825	$26,825
Part-time		
Tuition Guarantee Program		Y

Living Expenses

Estimated living expenses for singles

Living on campus	Living off campus	Living at home
N/A	$19,610	N/A

Appalachian School of Law

ABA Approved Since 2001

GPA and LSAT Scores

	Total	Full-Time	Part-Time
# of apps	1,617	1,617	0
# of offers	784	784	0
# of matrics	129	129	0
75% GPA	3.31	3.31	0.00
Median GPA	2.94	2.94	0.00
25% GPA	2.61	2.61	0.00
75% LSAT	152	152	0
Median LSAT	148	148	0
25% LSAT	147	147	0

Grants and Scholarships (from prior year)

	Total		Full-Time		Part-Time	
	#	%	#	%	#	%
Total # of students	350		350		0	
Total # receiving grants	86	24.6	86	24.6	0	0.0
Less than 1/2 tuition	28	8.0	28	8.0	0	0.0
Half to full tuition	22	6.3	22	6.3	0	0.0
Full tuition	36	10.3	36	10.3	0	0.0
More than full tuition	0	0.0	0	0.0	0	0.0
Median grant amount			$15,582		$0	

Informational and Library Resources

Total amount spent on library materials	$827,882
Study seating capacity inside the library	232
# of full-time equivalent professional librarians	5
Hours per week library is open	86
# of open, wired connections available to students	730
# of networked computers available for use by students	30
Has wireless network?	Y
Require computer?	N

JD Attrition (from prior year)

	Academic	Other	Total	
	#	#	#	%
1st year	9	5	14	11.1
2nd year	10	5	15	13.9
3rd year	0	0	0	0.0
4th year	0	0	0	0.0

Employment (9 months after graduation)

	Total	Percentage
Employment status known	70	73.7
Employment status unknown	25	26.3
Employed	53	75.7
Pursuing graduate degrees	1	1.4
Unemployed (seeking, not seeking, or studying for the bar)	12	17.1
Type of Employment		
# employed in law firms	33	62.3
# employed in business and industry	6	11.3
# employed in government	6	11.3
# employed in public interest	3	5.7
# employed as judicial clerks	3	5.7
# employed in academia	0	0.0
Geographic Location		
# employed in state	11	20.8
# employed in foreign countries	0	0.0
# of states where employed	17	

Bar Passage Rates

First-time takers	97	Reporting %	100.00	
Average school %	79.35	Average state %	84.24	
Average pass difference	−4.89			

Jurisdiction	Takers	Passers	Pass %	State %	Diff %
Virginia	18	15	83.33	82.70	0.63
North Carolina	17	11	64.71	82.61	−17.90
Tennessee	13	12	92.31	88.10	4.21
Kentucky	10	5	50.00	83.08	−33.08
Others (21)	39	34	87.18		

Appalachian School of Law

1169 Edgewater Drive, PO Box 2825
Grundy, VA 24614
Phone: 800.895.7411 (toll free) or 276.935.4349; Fax: 276.935.8496
E-mail: admissions@asl.edu; Website: www.asl.edu

■ Introduction

The Appalachian School of Law (ASL) opened its doors in 1997 and is fully approved by the ABA. ASL's location, nestled in the mountains of southwestern Virginia, provides a peaceful and scenic setting for the study of law. The small size assures an individualized education and creates the opportunity for students to make their own contributions to building a young institution. ASL's commitment to community service is a special and important feature that reinforces and gives context to the academic program.

The following statement of purpose was written by representatives of the students, faculty, staff, and administration of ASL: *The Appalachian School of Law exists to provide opportunity for people from Appalachia and beyond to realize their dreams of practicing law and bettering their communities. We attract a qualified, diverse, and dedicated student body, many of whom will remain in the region after graduation and serve as legal counselors, advocates, judges, mediators, community leaders, and public officials. We offer a nationally recruited, diverse, and well-qualified faculty; a rigorous program for the professional preparation of lawyers; and a comprehensive law library. The program emphasizes professional responsibility, dispute resolution, and practice skills. The ASL community is an exciting, student-centered environment that emphasizes honesty, integrity, fairness, and respect for others. We also emphasize community service, and staff and faculty development. At the same time, we are a full participant in our community, serving as a resource for the people, the bar, and other institutions of the region.*

■ Curriculum

The curriculum at ASL is structured to give students the skills and knowledge to succeed. Students receive intensive instruction in legal research, writing, analysis, and other skills essential to the practice of law through ASL's Legal Process program and required upper-level skills courses. The academic program for the first year has been intentionally designed by the faculty to facilitate the transition to the unique requirements of law studies, to foster collegiality and the traditions of professionalism among first-year students, and to minimize or ameliorate the stress of peer competition during that crucial initial transitional year. During the summer between the first and second years, each student will serve an externship with a judge, prosecutor, or other government lawyer, or legal services organization. Recent placements have included externships in the chambers of justices of the supreme courts in North Carolina, Tennessee, and Virginia, and with the United States Department of Justice and Environmental Protection Agency. The second-year curriculum provides required courses in the subject areas that law students are typically expected to master and lawyers are universally expected to understand. The third-year curriculum will provide additional required courses in critical subject areas mixed with skill courses in a wide array of subjects. Alternative dispute resolution and professional responsibility are infused throughout the curriculum.

ASL also offers an Academic Success program, designed to assist students with the development and refinement of the skills necessary to make a successful transition to the study of law.

■ Community Service

ASL's vision is to educate community leaders. We emphasize community service as a central aspect of professional responsibility and provide a variety of service opportunities to our students. To demonstrate the commitment of the legal profession to public service, as well as to enhance the program of legal education at ASL, our students are required to complete 25 hours of community service each semester in a project of their choosing.

Although students are able to structure their community service to meet their own individual preferences and schedules, ASL assists students in making time for these projects by scheduling one afternoon each week that they may devote to community service projects. Projects sponsored by ASL in recent years have included a conflict resolution program taught by our students in public elementary schools; a county mapping project in which our students engaged in property research and mapping; work with Buchanan Neighbors United, a group that provides housing repairs to improve substandard housing; a community recycling project; and a gender-bias study of the Virginia state court system. Students also are invited to develop alternative projects to satisfy their service obligations.

■ Faculty

ASL's expanding faculty currently consists of approximately 22 full-time professors and a talented group of adjunct professors drawn from the region's bench and bar. The full-time faculty offers an unusual depth of private and governmental practice experience, as well as experience teaching at other law schools. The ranks of the faculty include professionals ranging from former law clerks to federal and state court judges, government officials, and partners in small and large private law firms. In addition to being dedicated classroom professors, the ASL faculty also has published a variety of scholarly works in areas ranging from constitutional law to legal ethics to business and commercial matters.

■ Students and Student Organizations

ASL enjoys the support and enthusiasm of a dedicated student body. The entering class usually numbers around 140. Students come to Grundy not only from the immediate region but from across the country.

The student body elects a Student Bar Association. Students may also participate in numerous student organizations, in the *Appalachian Journal of Law* and the *Appalachian Natural Resources Law Journal*, and on moot court, trial advocacy, and alternate dispute resolution competition teams. ASL has a family resource network for the spouses, partners, and families of law students. ASL also has a speaker series that brings a number of distinguished speakers to campus.

Facilities

ASL is housed in four buildings on a 3.5-acre campus located near the town center of Grundy. The classroom and office building was extensively renovated for the law school in 1997 into a state-of-the-art law school facility and has won an award from the American Institute of Architects. The classroom building is constructed around an open quadrangle that serves as an informal gathering place for the ASL community. The library was extensively renovated in 1998 and provides a modern, well-organized, and technologically advanced facility. A third building houses student organizations and a coffee shop. The law school also occupies 10,600 square feet of classroom and office space in the Booth Center for higher education adjacent to the ASL campus.

Students have access to the Internet through connections to the ASL network that are available in most of ASL's classrooms and at all tables and carrels in the library. ASL also has wireless Internet access.

Admission and Financial Aid

ASL accepts for admission those students who will benefit from a challenging curriculum in a caring environment. Admission decisions are not based on a single criterion, but rather, each item will be considered in relation to the applicant's total qualifications. Besides the usual undergraduate transcripts and LSAT score, other considerations include an applicant's graduate work, character, work history, professional promise, personal commitment, recommendations, life experience, and other nonacademic achievements. We are happy to discuss our admission process and criteria with potential applicants at any time.

In accordance with current admission goals, ASL may offer a Pre-Admission Summer Opportunity (PASO) program for students who may have the potential to succeed as law students and lawyers, but whose skills and talents may not be reflected fully by the traditional measures of the LSAT and undergraduate performance. PASO provides participants an opportunity to experience law school coursework and gives an opportunity for the faculty to evaluate the students' performances to assess their ability to succeed in law school. Participants who fail to demonstrate potential to successfully complete ASL's three-year legal education program will not be offered admission. In most years, between 20 and 40 percent of PASO participants are offered admission to the fall entering class.

While most students will depend on federal student loans to finance a legal education, ASL does offer both merit- and need-based scholarships. Merit-based scholarships are based on entering LSAT and GPA credentials; the application for admission serves as the application for a merit scholarship.

Applicant Profile

Appalachian School of Law

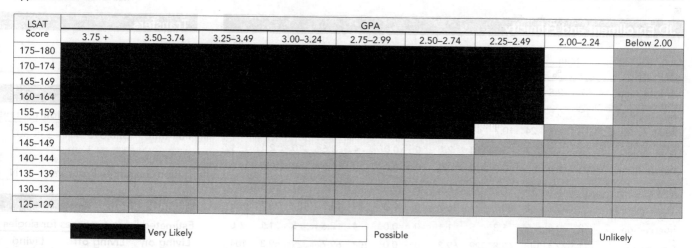

LSAT Score	GPA 3.75 +	3.50–3.74	3.25–3.49	3.00–3.24	2.75–2.99	2.50–2.74	2.25–2.49	2.00–2.24	Below 2.00
175–180									
170–174									
165–169									
160–164									
155–159									
150–154									
145–149									
140–144									
135–139									
130–134									
125–129									

■ Very Likely   □ Possible   ▨ Unlikely

This grid represents data for 100 percent of the applicant pool for fall 2009 admission. It does not reflect the possibility of invitation to participate in the Pre-Admission Summer Opportunity program. This chart is to be used as a general guide only. Nonnumerical factors are strongly considered for all applicants.

The University of Arizona James E. Rogers College of Law

PO Box 210176, 1201 E. Speedway
Tucson, AZ 85721-0176
Phone: 520.621.7666; Fax: 520.626.3436
E-mail: eric.eden@law.arizona.edu; Website: www.law.arizona.edu

ABA
Approved
Since
1930

The Basics

Type of school	Public
Term	Semester
Application deadline	2/15
Application fee	$65
Financial aid deadline	3/1
Can first year start other than fall?	No
Student to faculty ratio	10.7 to 1
# of housing spaces available restricted to law students	
graduate housing for which law students are eligible	319

Faculty and Administrators

	Total		Men		Women		Minorities	
	Spr	Fall	Spr	Fall	Spr	Fall	Spr	Fall
Full-time	39	35	21	19	18	16	8	7
Other full-time	0	1	0	1	0	0	0	0
Deans, librarians, & others who teach	13	12	4	5	9	7	2	2
Part-time	45	29	32	18	13	11	4	2
Total	97	77	57	43	40	34	14	11

Curriculum

	Full-Time	Part-Time
Typical first-year section size	77	0
Is there typically a "small section" of the first-year class, other than Legal Writing, taught by full-time faculty	Yes	No
If yes, typical size offered last year	26	
# of classroom course titles beyond first-year curriculum	120	

# of upper division courses, excluding seminars, with an enrollment:		
Under 25	108	
25–49	16	
50–74	6	
75–99	0	
100+	3	

	Full-Time	Part-Time
# of seminars	39	
# of seminar positions available	679	
# of seminar positions filled	466	0
# of positions available in simulation courses	324	
# of simulation positions filled	235	0
# of positions available in faculty supervised clinical courses	114	
# of faculty supervised clinical positions filled	76	0
# involved in field placements	137	0
# involved in law journals	108	0
# involved in moot court or trial competitions	38	0
# of credit hours required to graduate	85	

JD Enrollment and Ethnicity

	Men #	Men %	Women #	Women %	Full-Time #	Full-Time %	Part-Time #	Part-Time %	1st-Year #	1st-Year %	Total #	Total %	JD Degs. Awd.
African Amer.	7	2.8	8	3.6	15	3.2	0	0.0	2	1.3	15	3.2	3
Amer. Indian	15	6.0	15	6.7	30	6.3	0	0.0	6	3.9	30	6.3	6
Asian Amer.	17	6.8	24	10.7	41	8.6	0	0.0	13	8.4	41	8.6	11
Mex. Amer.	3	1.2	7	3.1	10	2.1	0	0.0	4	2.6	10	2.1	1
Puerto Rican	0	0.0	0	0.0	0	0.0	0	0.0	0	0.0	0	0.0	0
Hispanic	17	6.8	14	6.2	31	6.5	0	0.0	4	2.6	31	6.5	17
Total Minority	59	23.6	68	30.2	127	26.7	0	0.0	29	18.7	127	26.7	38
For. Nation.	2	0.8	3	1.3	5	1.1	0	0.0	4	2.6	5	1.1	0
Caucasian	181	72.4	148	65.8	329	69.3	0	0.0	108	69.7	329	69.3	104
Unknown	8	3.2	6	2.7	14	2.9	0	0.0	14	9.0	14	2.9	0
Total	250	52.6	225	47.4	475	100.0	0	0.0	155	32.6	475		142

Transfers

Transfers in	4
Transfers out	4

Tuition and Fees

	Resident	Nonresident
Full-time	$20,895	$35,807
Part-time		
Tuition Guarantee Program	N	

Living Expenses

Estimated living expenses for singles

Living on campus	Living off campus	Living at home
N/A	$19,166	$11,206

The University of Arizona James E. Rogers College of Law

ABA
Approved
Since
1930

GPA and LSAT Scores

	Total	Full-Time	Part-Time
# of apps	2,214	2,214	0
# of offers	738	738	0
# of matrics	155	155	0
75% GPA	3.71	3.71	0.00
Median GPA	3.51	3.51	0.00
25% GPA	3.34	3.34	0.00
75% LSAT	163	163	0
Median LSAT	161	161	0
25% LSAT	159	159	0

Grants and Scholarships (from prior year)

	Total #	Total %	Full-Time #	Full-Time %	Part-Time #	Part-Time %
Total # of students	469		469		0	
Total # receiving grants	325	69.3	325	69.3	0	0.0
Less than 1/2 tuition	189	40.3	189	40.3	0	0.0
Half to full tuition	83	17.7	83	17.7	0	0.0
Full tuition	16	3.4	16	3.4	0	0.0
More than full tuition	37	7.9	37	7.9	0	0.0
Median grant amount			$10,000		$0	

Informational and Library Resources

Total amount spent on library materials	$1,015,474
Study seating capacity inside the library	379
# of full-time equivalent professional librarians	10
Hours per week library is open	99
# of open, wired connections available to students	0
# of networked computers available for use by students	32
Has wireless network?	Y
Require computer?	N

JD Attrition (from prior year)

	Academic #	Other #	Total #	Total %
1st year	1	0	1	0.6
2nd year	0	5	5	3.1
3rd year	0	2	2	1.4
4th year	0	0	0	0.0

Employment (9 months after graduation)

	Total	Percentage
Employment status known	143	99.3
Employment status unknown	1	0.7
Employed	132	92.3
Pursuing graduate degrees	2	1.4
Unemployed (seeking, not seeking, or studying for the bar)	3	2.1
Type of Employment		
# employed in law firms	62	47.0
# employed in business and industry	12	9.1
# employed in government	28	21.2
# employed in public interest	3	2.3
# employed as judicial clerks	24	18.2
# employed in academia	3	2.3
Geographic Location		
# employed in state	86	65.2
# employed in foreign countries	1	0.8
# of states where employed		15

Bar Passage Rates

First-time takers	137	Reporting %	86.13
Average school %	91.53	Average state %	82.49
Average pass difference	9.04		

Jurisdiction	Takers	Passers	Pass %	State %	Diff %
Arizona	90	83	92.22	84.03	8.19
California	24	21	87.50	78.07	9.43
Washington	4	4	100.00	74.40	25.60

The University of Arizona James E. Rogers College of Law

PO Box 210176, 1201 E. Speedway
Tucson, AZ 85721-0176
Phone: 520.621.7666; Fax: 520.626.3436
E-mail: eric.eden@law.arizona.edu; Website: www.law.arizona.edu

■ Introduction

Founded in 1915, the University of Arizona James E. Rogers College of Law is the oldest law school in Arizona and has a rich and distinguished history. The college is an integral part of the University of Arizona, one of the nation's leading research institutions and most spirited campuses. Arizona Law has a national reputation for providing its students with an exceptional education in a collegial and intellectually challenging atmosphere. The college is located in Tucson, a vibrant, environmentally unique, and culturally rich city of one million people that is home to an active legal and judicial community. The college is approved by the ABA, has been a member of the AALS since 1931, and has a chapter of the Order of the Coif.

■ The College

Five core values are the foundation of the college's culture: justice, professional integrity, educational excellence, public leadership, and community service. The environment of the college is further shaped by several key components. First, its size enables students and faculty to learn in a congenial atmosphere. Approximately 150 1L students join upperclass students, 36 full-time faculty, and many visiting scholars and lecturers in an intellectually stimulating community. Arizona Law offers a favorable student-faculty ratio (11:1) that enables full-time faculty to teach first-year classes in sections of 25 students. Second, the college has an outstanding, diverse faculty of gifted teachers and nationally recognized scholars. Third, the college offers 11 dual-degree programs in conjunction with world-class departments at the University of Arizona. Fourth, the college's generous financial aid program enables students to pursue a legal education without assuming an overwhelming debt burden. Fifth, the college attracts students of intelligence, energy, and commitment. The JD student body of 470 represents more than 160 undergraduate and graduate schools, many nationalities, diverse ethnic and cultural groups, and unique work, volunteer, and personal achievements. Finally, the college nurtures an ethic of public service and community involvement through volunteer activities for students, faculty, and staff organized by the College Community Service Board and various student organizations.

■ Library and Physical Facilities

In the fall of 2008, the Rogers College of Law opened a newly renovated state-of-the-art building and library—the Law Commons—designed to enhance student learning and engagement. The Rountree Hall clinical facility is adjacent to the Law Commons, and both are part of the 390-acre campus of the University of Arizona, located in central Tucson. The law library is one of the foremost legal research facilities in the Southwest. In addition to a strong Anglo-American collection, the library has nationally recognized collections in Mexican, Latin American, and water law. Students have access to the resources of the Arizona Health Sciences Library and university libraries, with collections exceeding 11 million volumes. The law library is a fully networked, technologically sophisticated facility that is constantly evolving to meet research needs.

■ Curriculum

Arizona Law has committed substantial faculty resources to the first-year curriculum and the development of research and writing skills. Each 1L meets in a section of 25 in one of the first-semester courses and shares all other classes with that group of students. Students enroll in a three-unit Legal Analysis, Writing, and Research class of 13 in the second semester. Students must also complete a special writing seminar during the second or third year.

After completing the first-year requirements, students have considerable flexibility in determining upper division coursework. The college offers a rich variety of courses and provides opportunities to pursue a general curriculum or to focus studies in specialized areas of concentration, including Indigenous Peoples Law and Policy, Environmental Law, International Trade and Business, Criminal Law, Intellectual Property, Tax, Estates and Trusts, and Corporate Law.

In 2004, Arizona Law's nationally recognized Trial Advocacy Program won the Emil Gumpert Award from the American College of Trial Lawyers, awarded annually to the best trial advocacy program in the United States. The college also has numerous clinical opportunities that combine classroom instruction and field placements in child advocacy, domestic violence, immigration, indigenous peoples law, criminal defense and prosecution, and the judicial clerking program. The Arizona Supreme Court convenes annually at the college and hears arguments on cases under review. The college awards academic credit for congressional and executive agency internships in Washington, DC; a state legislative internship; an Arizona Governor's Office internship; a university attorney internship; and internship programs with several tribal governments.

The JD degree is normally completed in six semesters of full-time study; a total of 85 units and a cumulative grade-point average of 2.0 are required to graduate.

■ Dual-Degree, LLM, and SJD Programs

The College of Law offers the following dual degrees: JD/PhD programs in Philosophy, Psychology, and Economics; JD/MA programs in American Indian Studies, Latin American Studies, Women's Studies, and Information Resources and Library Science; a JD/MBA; a JD/MPA; a JD/MS in Economics, Law, and Environment; and a JD/MMF in Management/Finance. Law students with a 2.75 GPA or better may take six units of coursework in another department and transfer that work to the College of Law for elective credit. The college offers two, one-year LLM programs in International Trade Law and in Indigenous Peoples Law and Policy, and a Doctor of Juridical Science (SJD) program.

■ Admission

Admission to the College of Law is very selective. All applications are reviewed in a holistic manner. In making decisions, all information submitted by applicants is

The University of Arizona James E. Rogers College of Law

considered, with significant focus on the strength of the candidate's undergraduate academic record, LSAT score, personal statement, résumé, and letters of recommendation. Additional factors include the nature and rigor of the undergraduate experience; graduate education; work and travel experience; unique talents, interests, or accomplishments; significant extracurricular activities; leadership, strength of character, and integrity; substantial community or public service; distinctive ethnic or cultural background; or other circumstances that have influenced the candidate's life or given him/her direction. The college fosters a dynamic learning community and welcomes students who bring diverse perspectives, ideas, and varied life experiences to the educational process. The deadline for applications is February 15. To complete a timely application, applicants must take the LSAT no later than February of the year of expected enrollment.

■ Tuition and Financial Aid

The tuition structure and generous financial aid program of the University of Arizona afford students the opportunity to pursue a legal education of outstanding quality with less debt burden than is typical of other fine law schools. Tuition and fees for JD students for the 2009–2010 year was $20,895 for Arizona residents and $35,807 for nonresidents. The College of Law awarded more than $3 million in merit- and need-based scholarships to JD students in 2009–2010.

■ Student Activities

The student body is self-governing through the Student Bar Association and there are more than 25 law student

organizations that are an important part of institutional and student life. Students also participate in school governance by serving as voting members of student-faculty committees. The *Arizona Law Review* and the *Arizona Journal of International and Comparative Law* are well-known student operated and edited scholarly journals on current legal problems. The students in the moot court and trial advocacy programs excel in national and state appellate advocacy competitions. College-sponsored community service projects are an important element in cultivating collaboration among students, faculty, and staff.

■ Career and Professional Development

Each 1L student is paired with an attorney mentor. Special programs on résumé, cover letter, and interviewing techniques are offered for 1Ls. Our on-campus Sonoran Desert Public Sector Career Fair, designed in particular for 1Ls, provides over 150 paid summer jobs, volunteer and for credit. Arizona Law students clerk nationally and throughout Arizona. In 2009, 92 percent of the 1L class had summer legal experience in 10 states and 9 foreign countries. The 2008 after-graduation employment rate was 93 percent, with 19.5 percent in judicial clerkships. Typically, one-third of our graduates practice in 15–20 states. Arizona Law graduates took the bar exam in 23 states in July 2009 with a 92 percent pass rate. Ninety-three percent of first-time takers passed the Arizona Bar, the highest of all law schools in Arizona and far exceeding the average pass rate of 84 percent. Average law firm salary was $104,535.

Applicant Profile

The University of Arizona James E. Rogers College of Law
This grid includes only applicants with 120–180 LSAT scores earned under standard administrations.

LSAT Score	3.75 +		3.50–3.74		3.25–3.49		3.00–3.24		2.75–2.99		2.50–2.74		2.25–2.49		2.00–2.24		Below 2.00		No GPA		Total	
	Apps	Adm	Apps	Adm	Apps	Adm	Apps	Adm	Apps	Adm	Apps	Adm	Apps	Adm	Apps	Adm	Apps	Adm	Apps	Adm	Apps	Adm
175–180	6	5	3	3	1	0	2	2	0	0	1	1	1	0	1	0	0	0	0	0	15	11
170–174	9	9	8	8	5	5	5	3	2	2	0	0	0	0	0	0	0	0	0	0	29	27
165–169	40	38	47	41	33	29	20	14	19	11	9	0	4	0	0	0	0	0	0	0	172	133
160–164	130	115	146	121	123	90	58	23	24	4	21	3	7	1	1	0	0	0	7	4	517	361
155–159	114	40	191	56	164	37	98	7	51	5	18	1	9	0	3	1	1	0	7	2	656	149
150–154	71	8	94	6	112	11	103	4	40	0	18	1	3	0	2	0	0	0	5	1	448	31
145–149	24	3	46	2	48	2	45	1	23	0	23	0	16	0	1	0	0	0	4	0	230	8
140–144	7	0	8	0	31	0	19	1	15	0	12	0	8	0	4	0	0	0	4	0	108	1
135–139	0	0	4	0	6	0	7	0	7	0	11	0	3	0	2	0	0	0	0	0	40	0
130–134	0	0	4	0	0	0	0	0	2	0	0	0	1	0	1	0	0	0	2	0	10	0
125–129	0	0	0	0	0	0	0	0	0	0	0	0	0	0	0	0	1	0	0	0	1	0
120–124	0	0	0	0	0	0	0	0	0	0	0	0	0	0	0	0	0	0	0	0	0	0
Total	401	218	551	237	523	174	357	55	183	22	113	6	52	1	15	1	2	0	29	7	2226	721

Apps = Number of Applicants   Adm = Number Admitted   Reflects 99% of the total applicant pool; average LSAT data reported.

Arizona State University—Sandra Day O'Connor College of Law

Armstrong Hall, 1100 S. McAllister Avenue, PO Box 877906
Tempe, AZ 85287-7906
Phone: 480.965.1474; Fax: 480.727.7930
E-mail: law.admissions@asu.edu; Website: www.law.asu.edu

ABA Approved Since 1969

The Basics

Type of school	Public
Term	Semester
Application deadline	11/1 2/1
Application fee	$50
Financial aid deadline	3/15
Can first year start other than fall?	No
Student to faculty ratio	8.5 to 1
# of housing spaces available restricted to law students	
graduate housing for which law students are eligible	

Faculty and Administrators

	Total		Men		Women		Minorities	
	Spr	Fall	Spr	Fall	Spr	Fall	Spr	Fall
Full-time	57	51	38	34	19	17	8	7
Other full-time	1	1	0	0	1	1	0	0
Deans, librarians, & others who teach	8	8	5	5	3	3	0	0
Part-time	31	34	26	27	5	7	5	6
Total	97	94	69	66	28	28	13	13

JD Enrollment and Ethnicity

	Men		Women		Full-Time		Part-Time		1st-Year		Total		JD Degs. Awd.
	#	%	#	%	#	%	#	%	#	%	#	%	
African Amer.	7	2.1	5	2.0	12	2.1	0	0.0	4	2.1	12	2.1	8
Amer. Indian	20	6.1	17	6.8	37	6.4	0	0.0	14	7.5	37	6.4	11
Asian Amer.	5	1.5	14	5.6	19	3.3	0	0.0	8	4.3	19	3.3	11
Mex. Amer.	10	3.1	14	5.6	24	4.2	0	0.0	13	7.0	24	4.2	8
Puerto Rican	2	0.6	0	0.0	2	0.3	0	0.0	1	0.5	2	0.3	0
Hispanic	15	4.6	12	4.8	27	4.7	0	0.0	4	2.1	27	4.7	15
Total Minority	59	18.1	62	24.8	121	21.0	0	0.0	44	23.5	121	21.0	53
For. Nation.	6	1.8	5	2.0	11	1.9	0	0.0	2	1.1	11	1.9	2
Caucasian	225	69.0	168	67.2	393	68.2	0	0.0	123	65.8	393	68.2	104
Unknown	36	11.0	15	6.0	51	8.9	0	0.0	18	9.6	51	8.9	18
Total	326	56.6	250	43.4	576	100.0	0	0.0	187	32.5	576		177

Curriculum

	Full-Time	Part-Time
Typical first-year section size	63	0
Is there typically a "small section" of the first-year class, other than Legal Writing, taught by full-time faculty	Yes	No
If yes, typical size offered last year	30	
# of classroom course titles beyond first-year curriculum	121	
# of upper division courses, excluding seminars, with an enrollment: Under 25	90	
25–49	22	
50–74	5	
75–99	3	
100+	0	
# of seminars	45	
# of seminar positions available	675	
# of seminar positions filled	600	0
# of positions available in simulation courses	321	
# of simulation positions filled	307	0
# of positions available in faculty supervised clinical courses	134	
# of faculty supervised clinical positions filled	119	0
# involved in field placements	234	0
# involved in law journals	91	0
# involved in moot court or trial competitions	144	0
# of credit hours required to graduate	88	

Transfers

Transfers in	31
Transfers out	3

Tuition and Fees

	Resident	Nonresident
Full-time	$19,225	$32,619
Part-time		
Tuition Guarantee Program	N	

Living Expenses

Estimated living expenses for singles

Living on campus	Living off campus	Living at home
$20,044	$20,044	$20,044

Arizona State University—Sandra Day O'Connor College of Law

*ABA
Approved
Since
1969*

GPA and LSAT Scores

	Total	Full-Time	Part-Time
# of apps	2,400	2,400	0
# of offers	667	667	0
# of matrics	184	184	0
75% GPA	3.78	3.78	0.00
Median GPA	3.60	3.60	0.00
25% GPA	3.34	3.34	0.00
75% LSAT	163	163	0
Median LSAT	161	161	0
25% LSAT	158	158	0

Grants and Scholarships (from prior year)

	Total		Full-Time		Part-Time	
	#	%	#	%	#	%
Total # of students	539		539		0	
Total # receiving grants	273	50.6	273	50.6	0	0.0
Less than 1/2 tuition	210	39.0	210	39.0	0	0.0
Half to full tuition	34	6.3	34	6.3	0	0.0
Full tuition	8	1.5	8	1.5	0	0.0
More than full tuition	21	3.9	21	3.9	0	0.0
Median grant amount			$3,000		$0	

Informational and Library Resources

Total amount spent on library materials	$940,402
Study seating capacity inside the library	570
# of full-time equivalent professional librarians	7.0
Hours per week library is open	111
# of open, wired connections available to students	186
# of networked computers available for use by students	76
Has wireless network?	Y
Require computer?	N

JD Attrition (from prior year)

	Academic	Other	Total	
	#	#	#	%
1st year	1	7	8	4.3
2nd year	0	6	6	3.7
3rd year	0	1	1	0.5
4th year	0	0	0	0.0

Employment (9 months after graduation)

	Total	Percentage
Employment status known	240	99.6
Employment status unknown	1	0.4
Employed	223	92.9
Pursuing graduate degrees	7	2.9
Unemployed (seeking, not seeking, or studying for the bar)	0	0.0
Type of Employment		
# employed in law firms	118	52.9
# employed in business and industry	23	10.3
# employed in government	39	17.5
# employed in public interest	20	9.0
# employed as judicial clerks	16	7.2
# employed in academia	6	2.7
Geographic Location		
# employed in state	162	72.6
# employed in foreign countries	0	0.0
# of states where employed	21	

Bar Passage Rates

First-time takers	200	Reporting %	86.00
Average school %	89.53	Average state %	84.03
Average pass difference	5.50		

Jurisdiction	Takers	Passers	Pass %	State %	Diff %
Arizona	172	154	89.53	84.03	5.50

Arizona State University—Sandra Day O'Connor College of Law

Armstrong Hall, 1100 S. McAllister Avenue, PO Box 877906
Tempe, AZ 85287-7906
Phone: 480.965.1474; Fax: 480.727.7930
E-mail: law.admissions@asu.edu; Website: www.law.asu.edu

■ Introduction

Founded in 1967, the Arizona State University—Sandra Day O'Connor College of Law combines the best traditions of American legal education with innovative programs supported by strong community partnerships. Our vision includes excellence in all we do, while reaching out to all parts of the university and the community, striving for inclusion, and having a meaningful impact on contemporary problems through teaching, research, and collaborative problem-solving. Students are attracted by the quality of the legal education, commitment to innovative teaching and scholarship, reasonable tuition, breadth and depth of the curriculum, numerous opportunities for experiential learning, and excellent student-to-faculty ratio. A busy calendar of conferences, seminars, and speakers enriches the student experience and fosters a strong sense of community. Committed to excellence, the college has an outstanding faculty, many opportunities for interdisciplinary learning, extensive pro bono opportunities, an exceptional legal writing program, and clinics of significant variety. Our students benefit greatly from the fact that Phoenix is the fifth largest metropolitan area in the country and a state capital.

■ Admission

Every completed application receives full review and consideration by the Admissions Committee prior to a decision. Among the factors influencing the admission decision are undergraduate and previous graduate education, LSAT performance, quality and grading patterns of undergraduate institutions, demonstrated commitment to public service, work experience, leadership experience, extracurricular or community activities, history of overcoming economic or other disadvantages, personal experiences with discrimination, overcoming disability, geographic diversity, uniqueness of experience and background, maturity, ability to communicate, foreign language proficiency, honors and awards, service in the armed forces, publications, and exceptional personal talents. Students from minority groups are encouraged to apply. Students from diverse backgrounds enrich the College of Law community and ultimately further efforts to diversify the bench and bar.

■ Curriculum

The College of Law offers one of the best student-to-faculty ratios in the country and a wide variety of courses. Because we have a large, nationally acclaimed faculty with high standards in both teaching and research, we have unusual depth in our course offerings. More than 70 percent of the classes in the second and third year have fewer than 20 students. As part of a large, premier research institution, the opportunities for interdisciplinary work are extensive. Concurrent degrees are offered with the MBA program, the PhD in Psychology, the PhD in Justice and Social Inquiry, the MHSM in Health Management and Policy, and the MD with Mayo Medical School. Further, the college takes full advantage of its unique location in Phoenix by offering over 150 externships and countless opportunities to do pro bono work. Students also have wonderful opportunities to develop their legal writing skills because of our commitment to maintaining an excellent legal writing program.

■ Clinical Programs

The law school's Clinical Program offers students unparalleled opportunities to practice law in a variety of settings with people who have real legal problems. We offer eleven separate clinics—civil justice, criminal practice, domestic violence, immigration, Indian law, healthcare entrepreneurship, mediation, patent litigation, post-conviction, public defender, and technology ventures—a greater variety of clinics than most law schools of any size. Under the supervision of faculty members who are experts in their subject matter, students manage real cases and represent clients in hearings and trials before courts and administrative agencies, assist in the commercialization and monetization of new technologies, and mediate cases pending in the judicial system. Because of our small student body, we are able to accommodate nearly every student who expresses an interest in the experiential learning offered through the Clinical Program.

■ Library and Physical Facilities

The College of Law is composed of Armstrong Hall and the John J. Ross-William C. Blakley Law Library and is set on the eastern edge of the university's beautiful, 700-acre Tempe campus. The Willard H. Pedrick Great Hall serves not only as a courtroom for annual visits from the Ninth Circuit Court of Appeals, the Arizona Supreme Court, the Navajo Supreme Court, and the Arizona Court of Appeals, but also as a location for campus events. Armstrong Hall also houses the legal clinic; the Center for Law, Science, and Innovation; the Indian Legal Program; the Center for Law and Global Affairs; the Philosophy, Politics, and Law Workshop; the ABA *Jurimetrics* journal; and the Cohen Student Center and Sidebar Café. The Ross-Blakley Law Library is a stunningly beautiful work of architecture with lots of windows to allow natural light in. It has three computer labs, a well-staffed help desk, and numerous study rooms for groups or individuals. Both Armstrong Hall and the Ross-Blakley Law Library are fully equipped with a wireless network.

■ Center for Law, Science, and Innovation

Founded in 1984, the Center for Law, Science, and Innovation is the oldest, largest, and most comprehensive law and science center in the country. Through the Center, students may receive a certificate in Law, Science, and Technology, specializing in environmental law, genomics and biotechnology law, health law, intellectual property law, or law and psychology. Every year, 10 students in each class are named Center Scholars and participate in special activities designed for those with significant interest in law and science. Center faculty and students edit and copublish, along with the American Bar Association, the prestigious, peer-refereed *Jurimetrics: The Journal of Law, Science, and Technology*, the oldest and most widely circulated journal in the field of law and science.

Arizona State University—Sandra Day O'Connor College of Law

■ Indian Legal Program

The Indian Legal Program enjoys a position of national preeminence. This preeminence is due to the large Native American student population, the Indian Law Certificate program, well-respected faculty, the Indian law curriculum, well-placed alumni, scholarly conferences, and the Indian Legal Clinic. An extraordinary faculty and long-term partnerships with tribal governments contribute to the strength and reputation of the College of Law in this critical area.

■ Student Activities

To prepare proactive, socially conscious attorneys and leaders, we enhance the traditional classroom experience with many extracurricular and cocurricular activities. We have over 50 active student groups, from the ASU Bar Association and 30 professional affiliations to 24 pro bono groups. Plus, we grow and change with the interests of our students. On average, about 70 percent of our students participate in pro bono work of some kind, with about one third of the student body graduating with Pro Bono Distinction. Students are active in ASU student governance and in our communities with public service. Our students are competitive in moot court competitions, both regionally and internationally. Two formal law journals, the *Arizona State Law Journal* and *Jurimetrics*, allow additional professional development opportunities for students.

■ Career Services and Professional Development

Our graduates have proven success in the legal employment market and hold prominent positions and leadership roles throughout the international, national, and Arizona legal communities in business, politics, government, the judiciary, and private firms. A broad range of employers interview our students on campus, at regional interview programs sponsored by the Career Services and Professional Development Office, and at job fairs. Through attorney-student mentor programs, speaker series and panels, networking events, career fairs, and a large on-campus recruitment program, the Career Services professional staff serves students in all phases of their professional development and job search. Career Services acts as a bridge between the students' academic and professional careers by offering extensive programming and individual career counseling.

■ LLM Programs

The Master of Laws (LLM) program allows one year of post-JD study tailored to the scholarly and practice interests of participating students. The concentration in US Law and Legal Institutions is designed for foreign lawyers who wish to learn about the US legal system. Two other, more specialized LLM programs are offered by the College of Law. The groundbreaking Master of Laws in Biotechnology and Genomics is the first degree of its kind in the nation. It provides students with in-depth study of the scientific and policy aspects of genomics. Through classroom instruction and guided independent study, students explore the laws that enable and constrain the development, control, and application of biotechnology and genomics, including areas such as public health law, agricultural law and policy, and intellectual property. Because of the strength of our Indian Legal Program, the LLM in Tribal Policy, Law, and Government was also established. It allows lawyers interested in teaching or practice related to Native American issues to further their career goals through a one-year practicum track or a two-year thesis track.

Applicant Profile

Arizona State University—Sandra Day O'Connor College of Law
This grid includes only applicants with 120–180 LSAT scores earned under standard administrations.

LSAT Score	3.75 +		3.50–3.74		3.25–3.49		3.00–3.24		2.75–2.99		2.50–2.74		2.25–2.49		2.00–2.24		Below 2.00		No GPA		Total	
	Apps	Adm	Apps	Adm	Apps	Adm	Apps	Adm	Apps	Adm	Apps	Adm	Apps	Adm	Apps	Adm	Apps	Adm	Apps	Adm	Apps	Adm
175–180	4	3	1	1	1	1	2	2	0	0	0	0	0	0	0	0	0	0	0	0	8	7
170–174	5	5	2	2	1	1	2	2	2	2	2	2	0	0	0	0	0	0	0	0	14	14
165–169	23	23	17	17	18	18	11	11	6	6	8	6	3	2	1	0	0	0	0	0	87	83
160–164	90	89	93	88	78	59	59	31	27	6	20	4	4	0	1	0	0	0	1	0	373	277
155–159	120	78	197	85	193	34	127	8	70	9	18	0	9	1	4	0	1	0	6	3	745	218
150–154	94	17	118	13	142	8	123	8	53	3	22	0	18	0	5	0	2	0	11	2	588	52
145–149	28	3	53	3	69	5	66	1	45	1	27	0	14	0	5	0	3	0	5	0	315	13
140–144	3	0	25	0	33	0	32	0	28	0	19	0	16	0	8	0	2	0	3	0	169	0
135–139	2	0	8	0	5	0	12	0	7	0	10	0	5	0	9	0	1	0	0	0	59	0
130–134	1	0	3	0	0	0	0	0	2	0	2	0	4	0	2	0	0	0	3	0	17	0
125–129	0	0	0	0	0	0	0	0	2	0	2	0	1	0	1	0	0	0	0	0	6	0
120–124	0	0	0	0	0	0	0	0	0	0	0	0	0	0	0	0	0	0	1	0	1	0
Total	370	218	517	209	540	126	434	63	242	27	130	13	74	3	36	0	9	0	30	5	2382	664

Apps = Number of Applicants   Adm = Number Admitted   Reflects 99% of the total applicant pool; average LSAT data reported.

University of Arkansas School of Law

Robert A. Leflar Law Center
Fayetteville, AR 72701
Phone: 479.575.3102; Fax: 479.575.3937
Website: http://law.uark.edu

ABA
Approved
Since
1928

The Basics

Type of school	Public
Term	Semester
Application deadline	4/1
Application fee	$0
Financial aid deadline	4/1
Can first year start other than fall?	No
Student to faculty ratio	12.3 to 1
# of housing spaces available restricted to law students	
graduate housing for which law students are eligible	

Faculty and Administrators

	Total		Men		Women		Minorities	
	Spr	Fall	Spr	Fall	Spr	Fall	Spr	Fall
Full-time	26	27	15	15	11	12	2	2
Other full-time	1	1	0	0	1	1	0	0
Deans, librarians, & others who teach	11	10	4	4	7	6	2	1
Part-time	20	18	18	12	2	6	1	0
Total	58	56	37	31	21	25	5	3

JD Enrollment and Ethnicity

	Men		Women		Full-Time		Part-Time		1st-Year		Total		JD Degs. Awd.
	#	%	#	%	#	%	#	%	#	%	#	%	
African Amer.	17	7.2	20	12.3	37	9.3	0	0.0	12	8.7	37	9.3	19
Amer. Indian	7	3.0	4	2.5	11	2.8	0	0.0	3	2.2	11	2.8	1
Asian Amer.	9	3.8	1	0.6	10	2.5	0	0.0	4	2.9	10	2.5	4
Mex. Amer.	1	0.4	1	0.6	2	0.5	0	0.0	1	0.7	2	0.5	0
Puerto Rican	0	0.0	0	0.0	0	0.0	0	0.0	0	0.0	0	0.0	0
Hispanic	5	2.1	4	2.5	9	2.3	0	0.0	5	3.6	9	2.3	3
Total Minority	39	16.6	30	18.4	69	17.3	0	0.0	25	18.1	69	17.3	27
For. Nation.	1	0.4	0	0.0	1	0.3	0	0.0	1	0.7	1	0.3	0
Caucasian	194	82.6	133	81.6	327	82.2	0	0.0	112	81.2	327	82.2	94
Unknown	1	0.4	0	0.0	1	0.3	0	0.0	0	0.0	1	0.3	1
Total	235	59.0	163	41.0	398	100.0	0	0.0	138	34.7	398		122

Curriculum

	Full-Time	Part-Time
Typical first-year section size	70	0
Is there typically a "small section" of the first-year class, other than Legal Writing, taught by full-time faculty	No	No
If yes, typical size offered last year		
# of classroom course titles beyond first-year curriculum	88	
# of upper division courses, excluding seminars, with an enrollment: Under 25	92	
25–49	22	
50–74	6	
75–99	3	
100+	0	
# of seminars	9	
# of seminar positions available	135	
# of seminar positions filled	97	0
# of positions available in simulation courses	231	
# of simulation positions filled	206	0
# of positions available in faculty supervised clinical courses	132	
# of faculty supervised clinical positions filled	117	0
# involved in field placements	76	0
# involved in law journals	72	0
# involved in moot court or trial competitions	46	0
# of credit hours required to graduate	90	

Transfers

Transfers in	7
Transfers out	6

Tuition and Fees

	Resident	Nonresident
Full-time	$10,772	$21,439
Part-time		
Tuition Guarantee Program		N

Living Expenses

Estimated living expenses for singles

Living on campus	Living off campus	Living at home
$12,062	$12,062	$7,954

University of Arkansas School of Law

ABA Approved Since 1928

GPA and LSAT Scores

	Total	Full-Time	Part-Time
# of apps	1,167	1,167	0
# of offers	395	395	0
# of matrics	139	139	0
75% GPA	3.74	3.74	0.00
Median GPA	3.49	3.49	0.00
25% GPA	3.16	3.16	0.00
75% LSAT	158	158	0
Median LSAT	155	155	0
25% LSAT	153	153	0

Grants and Scholarships (from prior year)

	Total		Full-Time		Part-Time	
	#	%	#	%	#	%
Total # of students	403		403		0	
Total # receiving grants	161	40.0	161	40.0	0	0.0
Less than 1/2 tuition	97	24.1	97	24.1	0	0.0
Half to full tuition	57	14.1	57	14.1	0	0.0
Full tuition	0	0.0	0	0.0	0	0.0
More than full tuition	7	1.7	7	1.7	0	0.0
Median grant amount			$6,000		$0	

Informational and Library Resources

Total amount spent on library materials	$1,197,095
Study seating capacity inside the library	413
# of full-time equivalent professional librarians	6.0
Hours per week library is open	98
# of open, wired connections available to students	73
# of networked computers available for use by students	48
Has wireless network?	Y
Require computer?	N

JD Attrition (from prior year)

	Academic	Other	Total	
	#	#	#	%
1st year	4	15	19	14.2
2nd year	0	0	0	0.0
3rd year	0	0	0	0.0
4th year	0	0	0	0.0

Employment (9 months after graduation)

	Total	Percentage
Employment status known	129	98.5
Employment status unknown	2	1.5
Employed	110	85.3
Pursuing graduate degrees	12	9.3
Unemployed (seeking, not seeking, or studying for the bar)	4	3.1
Type of Employment		
# employed in law firms	69	62.7
# employed in business and industry	19	17.3
# employed in government	12	10.9
# employed in public interest	5	4.5
# employed as judicial clerks	3	2.7
# employed in academia	2	1.8
Geographic Location		
# employed in state	70	63.6
# employed in foreign countries	0	0.0
# of states where employed		14

Bar Passage Rates

First-time takers	123	Reporting %	72.36
Average school %	82.02	Average state %	82.53
Average pass difference −0.51			

Jurisdiction	Takers	Passers	Pass %	State %	Diff %
Arkansas	89	73	82.02	82.53	−0.51

University of Arkansas School of Law

Robert A. Leflar Law Center
Fayetteville, AR 72701
Phone: 479.575.3102; Fax: 479.575.3937
Website: http://law.uark.edu

■ Introduction

The University of Arkansas School of Law is located on the main university campus at Fayetteville, a city of approximately 67,000 in northwest Arkansas. The School of Law was established in 1924 and has continuously sought to provide high-quality legal education in a university community. In 1926, the School of Law was approved by the ABA, and, in 1927, the school became a member of the AALS.

■ Enrollment/Student Body

Although approximately 75–80 percent of the students are Arkansas residents, others are from every part of the United States. Since the school has no undergraduate course prerequisites, the academic backgrounds and nonacademic experiences of students are varied.

■ Library and Physical Facilities

The law library has over 314,000 volumes and volume equivalents. Students are trained in the techniques of computer-assisted legal research as well as in the traditional research methods. The law library is a federal and state depository for government documents.

■ Curriculum

The primary function of the University of Arkansas School of Law is to prepare lawyers who will render the highest quality of professional service to their clients, who are interested in and capable of furthering legal process and reform, and who are prepared to fill the vital role of the lawyer as a community leader. The school offers a full-time, three-year program leading to the JD degree. The degree is conferred upon satisfactory completion of 90 semester hours, including 42 hours of required courses. The first-year curriculum is required. A broad selection of elective second- and third-year courses is available. Students who have completed the first year of law school may earn up to 12 semester hours of credit in summer school, and graduation can be accelerated one semester by summer coursework.

The School of Law offers a joint JD/MBA program with the College of Business Administration. If a student is accepted into both programs, a maximum of six hours of approved upper-level elective law courses may be used on duplicative credit toward the MBA degree, and a maximum of six hours of approved graduate courses in business administration may be used as duplicative credit toward the JD degree.

The Department of Political Science, the graduate school, and the School of Law cooperate in offering a dual-degree program that allows a student to pursue the MPA and the JD degrees concurrently. Students must be admitted to the MPA program, the School of Law, and the dual-degree program.

The School of Law and the Department of Political Science provide a dual JD/MA in International Law and Politics. This program's students must be admitted both to the School of Law and the Graduate School, Department of Political Science. The Graduate Program in Agriculture Law provides opportunities for advanced study, creative research, and specialized professional training in this rapidly developing area of law. The program is designed to prepare a small number of carefully selected attorneys as specialists in the legal problems of agriculture production, distribution, and marketing.

Applicants for admission as candidates for the Master of Laws (LLM) in Agricultural Law must have earned a JD or LLB degree from a fully accredited law school in the United States. Graduates from a law school in another country may be admitted upon the approval of the Agricultural Law Programs Committee.

■ Admission

First-year students are admitted in the fall and only for full-time study. Prior to enrolling in the School of Law, applicants must have completed all requirements for an undergraduate degree from an accredited four-year college. Admission is based on the applicant's LSAT score and undergraduate GPA. In a small percentage of cases, additional criteria such as age; gender; cultural, ethnic, and racial background; geographic origin; socioeconomic background and status; undergraduate major; graduate studies; career objectives; nonacademic work; and other life experiences are considered by a faculty admission committee. Preference is given to Arkansas residents; for the current status of this preference, contact the school. A nonrefundable tuition deposit is required of all admitted candidates.

The law school's application deadline is April 1 of the year in which admission is sought. Applicants must take the LSAT no later than February. Applications completed after April 1 will be considered only on a space-available basis.

■ Housing

Housing for single students is available in campus dormitories. For more information about housing, please contact the Housing Office, University of Arkansas, Fayetteville, AR 72701, 479.575.3951. Information is also available at *http://housing.uark.edu*. A variety of private off-campus housing options are available in Fayetteville and surrounding communities, within easy commuting distance of the law school. For more information, please visit *http://offcampushousing.uark.edu/*.

■ Student Activities

The *Arkansas Law Review* is a legal periodical published quarterly by the students of the School of Law in cooperation with the Arkansas Bar Association. Candidates for the *Law Review* are selected on the basis of scholarship and writing ability. The *Journal of Food Law and Policy* is a legal periodical published twice a year by students of the School of Law. Candidates for the journal are selected from the second- and third-year law classes by the editorial board on the basis of scholarship and writing ability.

Students in their second and third years are encouraged to compete in an intramural moot court competition, and Arkansas students participate in national moot court competitions. The University of Arkansas School of Law also

participates in the ABA Law Student Division Client Counseling Competition. The law school operates a legal aid clinic providing counseling and representation for university students and indigent persons seeking legal assistance. An Arkansas Supreme Court Rule permits senior law students, upon certification and under supervision, to appear in court on a no-fee basis.

The Student Bar Association sponsors a variety of academic and social activities. All students are also eligible for membership in the Law Student Division of the Arkansas Bar Association. Three of the largest national legal fraternities, Delta Theta Phi, Phi Alpha Delta, and Phi Delta Phi, maintain active chapters at the school. The Women's Law Student Association was organized to provide an opportunity for women to discuss and work with common professional interests and problems. Members of the Arkansas Chapter of the Black Law Students Association work as a collective body to inform black students of the availability and advantages of a legal education, to promote the academic success of black law students at Arkansas, and to increase the awareness and commitment of the legal profession to the black community. Other organizations include the Christian Legal Society, Lambda, the Federalist Society, the Asian Pacific American Law Student Association, and Equal Justice Works.

■ Expenses and Financial Aid

Students are expected to make sufficient financial arrangements for the first year of study without the necessity of seeking employment. All law students are required to be full-time students. All financial aid in the form of Perkins Loans (formerly NDSL), higher education loans, and work-study grants is processed by the University of Arkansas Office of Student Financial Aid, University of Arkansas, Fayetteville, AR 72701. Merit scholarships are awarded to some entering students. Applications for a limited number of other scholarships are distributed following fall registration in August.

■ Career Planning and Placement

The law school maintains an Office of Career Planning and Placement with a full-time, highly qualified director and staff to assist and advise students and graduates. Services offered by the office include on-campus interviews for permanent and summer employment; individual career counseling sessions; workshops and handbooks regarding résumé preparation, interviewing skills and techniques, and job searches; panels of lawyers who present programs on a variety of topics; a job bulletin; and a comprehensive placement library. The office also maintains employment and bar passage statistics.

Applicant Profile Not Available

University of Arkansas at Little Rock, William H. Bowen School of Law

1201 McMath Avenue
Little Rock, AR 72202-5142
Phone: 501.324.9903; Fax: 501.324.9909
E-mail: lawadm@ualr.edu; Website: www.law.ualr.edu

ABA
Approved
Since
1969

The Basics

Type of school	Public
Term	Semester
Application deadline	4/15
Application fee	$0
Financial aid deadline	3/1
Can first year start other than fall?	No
Student to faculty ratio	17.0 to 1
# of housing spaces available restricted to law students	
graduate housing for which law students are eligible	

Faculty and Administrators

	Total		Men		Women		Minorities	
	Spr	Fall	Spr	Fall	Spr	Fall	Spr	Fall
Full-time	19	21	10	11	9	10	5	6
Other full-time	2	3	0	1	2	2	0	0
Deans, librarians, & others who teach	11	11	1	1	10	10	5	5
Part-time	39	43	27	28	12	14	4	1
Total	71	78	38	41	33	36	14	12

Curriculum

	Full-Time	Part-Time
Typical first-year section size	93	61
Is there typically a "small section" of the first-year class, other than Legal Writing, taught by full-time faculty	No	No
If yes, typical size offered last year		
# of classroom course titles beyond first-year curriculum		83
# of upper division courses, excluding seminars, with an enrollment: Under 25		91
25–49		28
50–74		7
75–99		24
100+		2
# of seminars		16
# of seminar positions available		237
# of seminar positions filled	128	106
# of positions available in simulation courses	431	
# of simulation positions filled	242	140
# of positions available in faculty supervised clinical courses		64
# of faculty supervised clinical positions filled	43	5
# involved in field placements	42	6
# involved in law journals	38	1
# involved in moot court or trial competitions	21	4
# of credit hours required to graduate		90

JD Enrollment and Ethnicity

	Men		Women		Full-Time		Part-Time		1st-Year		Total		JD Degs. Awd.
	#	%	#	%	#	%	#	%	#	%	#	%	
African Amer.	18	7.3	39	17.4	38	12.0	19	12.3	21	12.7	57	12.1	16
Amer. Indian	4	1.6	1	0.4	5	1.6	0	0.0	2	1.2	5	1.1	2
Asian Amer.	6	2.4	6	2.7	7	2.2	5	3.2	0	0.0	12	2.5	0
Mex. Amer.	5	2.0	3	1.3	6	1.9	2	1.3	2	1.2	8	1.7	4
Puerto Rican	0	0.0	0	0.0	0	0.0	0	0.0	0	0.0	0	0.0	0
Hispanic	6	2.4	6	2.7	4	1.3	8	5.2	4	2.4	12	2.5	0
Total Minority	39	15.8	55	24.6	60	19.0	34	21.9	29	17.6	94	20.0	22
For. Nation.	6	2.4	4	1.8	6	1.9	4	2.6	4	2.4	10	2.1	3
Caucasian	197	79.8	157	70.1	239	75.6	115	74.2	127	77.0	354	75.2	102
Unknown	5	2.0	8	3.6	11	3.5	2	1.3	5	3.0	13	2.8	0
Total	247	52.4	224	47.6	316	67.1	155	32.9	165	35.0	471		127

Transfers

Transfers in	4
Transfers out	2

Tuition and Fees

	Resident	Nonresident
Full-time	$11,456	$23,538
Part-time	$7,557	$15,108
Tuition Guarantee Program		N

Living Expenses

Estimated living expenses for singles

Living on campus	Living off campus	Living at home
$14,173	$14,173	$14,173

University of Arkansas at Little Rock, William H. Bowen School of Law

ABA
Approved
Since
1969

GPA and LSAT Scores

	Total	Full-Time	Part-Time
# of apps	1,570	1,372	198
# of offers	402	334	68
# of matrics	161	99	62
75% GPA	3.67	3.70	3.61
Median GPA	3.29	3.36	3.22
25% GPA	2.90	2.92	2.86
75% LSAT	157	158	156
Median LSAT	153	154	151
25% LSAT	150	150	148

Grants and Scholarships (from prior year)

	Total #	Total %	Full-Time #	Full-Time %	Part-Time #	Part-Time %
Total # of students	456		311		145	
Total # receiving grants	164	36.0	127	40.8	37	25.5
Less than 1/2 tuition	81	17.8	64	20.6	17	11.7
Half to full tuition	50	11.0	36	11.6	14	9.7
Full tuition	28	6.1	23	7.4	5	3.4
More than full tuition	5	1.1	4	1.3	1	0.7
Median grant amount			$2,750		$1,250	

Informational and Library Resources

Total amount spent on library materials	$925,626
Study seating capacity inside the library	347
# of full-time equivalent professional librarians	6.0
Hours per week library is open	99
# of open, wired connections available to students	1
# of networked computers available for use by students	51
Has wireless network?	Y
Require computer?	N

JD Attrition (from prior year)

	Academic #	Other #	Total #	Total %
1st year	3	4	7	4.4
2nd year	2	12	14	9.4
3rd year	0	0	0	0.0
4th year	0	0	0	0.0

Employment (9 months after graduation)

	Total	Percentage
Employment status known	120	100.0
Employment status unknown	0	0.0
Employed	111	92.5
Pursuing graduate degrees	3	2.5
Unemployed (seeking, not seeking, or studying for the bar)	5	4.2
Type of Employment		
# employed in law firms	57	51.4
# employed in business and industry	16	14.4
# employed in government	14	12.6
# employed in public interest	4	3.6
# employed as judicial clerks	14	12.6
# employed in academia	5	4.5
Geographic Location		
# employed in state	94	84.7
# employed in foreign countries	0	0.0
# of states where employed	12	

Bar Passage Rates

First-time takers	124	Reporting %	86.29
Average school %	81.31	Average state %	82.53
Average pass difference −1.22			

Jurisdiction	Takers	Passers	Pass %	State %	Diff %
Arkansas	107	87	81.31	82.53	−1.22

University of Arkansas at Little Rock, William H. Bowen School of Law

1201 McMath Avenue
Little Rock, AR 72202-5142
Phone: 501.324.9903; Fax: 501.324.9909
E-mail: lawadm@ualr.edu; Website: www.law.ualr.edu

■ About the UALR Bowen School of Law

The William H. Bowen School of Law is located in the heart of Little Rock, within a five-minute drive of state and federal courts as well as some of Arkansas's largest law firms and corporations. Established in 1975, the law school is fully accredited by the ABA and is a member of the AALS. In addition to being the seat of state government, Little Rock is Arkansas's legal, business, and financial center. The city's vibrant legal community affords students and alumni many professional opportunities.

■ Admission

Bowen seeks to enroll approximately 150 students each year. The law school takes a holistic approach to admission, as the Admissions Committee assesses a wide array of applicant factors. The law school values inclusion and is committed to enrolling students of diverse ethnicities and backgrounds. The application deadline is April 15, though candidates are strongly encouraged to apply by January 15. First-year students are admitted for the fall semester only.

Bowen hosts prospective students throughout the year. In addition to attending scheduled events, prospective students may contact the Admissions Office for individual tours, class visits, and meetings with faculty members and current students.

■ Juris Doctor Curriculum

The Juris Doctor (JD) curriculum seeks to provide students with strong foundations in the traditional areas of law, while providing a diverse selection of electives. To receive the JD, students must complete 90 credit hours with a cumulative GPA of 2.0 (on a 4.0 scale) or better. Courses are prescribed during the first year of full-time study (or the first two years of part-time study). After that, most of the curriculum is elective, allowing students to explore their interests in many areas. Course descriptions and further information about the Bowen curriculum can be found at *www.law.ualr.edu/academics/curriculum.asp.*

■ Concurrent Degrees

Bowen allows students to pursue law degrees while concurrently pursuing master's degrees in business administration (JD/MBA), public administration (JD/MPA), public health (JD/MPH), or public service (JD/MPS). A concurrent degree in law and medicine is also offered (JD/MD). In order to be eligible for one of the concurrent degree programs, students must be offered admission into both the law school and the school offering the other desired degree.

■ Enrollment Divisions

Bowen offers both full-time and part-time divisions. Full-time study generally takes three years to complete. Part-time study is generally completed in four years. In both divisions, study may be accelerated by attending summer school.

The environment for full-time students is one of a traditional "academy," where students spend significant portions of their days on campus engaging in various curricular and extracurricular activities.

Bowen is one of the few law schools in the country that is statutorily mandated to offer a part-time division. The division attracts many successful professionals, including state legislators and business executives.

■ Faculty

The faculty is made up of an outstanding group of scholars, practitioners, and teachers. Full-time professors teach virtually all required courses in both the full-time and part-time divisions. Experienced adjunct professors teach upper-level courses in their areas of specialty. The quality and accessibility of professors are often cited by Bowen students as "favorite things" about the school.

■ Academic Support

Bowen provides a comprehensive academic support program. This support begins prior to the first class during the week-long orientation program. Once classes begin, the principles taught in orientation are reinforced through a series of relevant workshops and seminars. The assistant dean for academic support also provides advising services to all students, helping them develop study plans, choose courses, and prepare for exams. Finally, Bowen helps ease the transition from law student to lawyer by offering an in-house bar exam prep course.

■ Clinical Programs

Bowen has three legal clinics that help students bridge the gap between theory learned in the classroom and practice. Through their clinic work, students practice law under the supervision of a faculty member, while at the same time helping to fill unmet legal needs in the community.

Litigation Clinic: Students represent clients involved in many types of cases within the broad areas of juvenile delinquency and family law. Qualified students receive special licenses to practice law in Arkansas.

Mediation Clinic: Students gain valuable experience in the rapidly expanding area of alternative dispute resolution. After extensive training, clinic students act as mediators in disputes relating to child abuse and neglect, juvenile delinquency, custody and visitation, special education, and small claims.

Tax Clinic: Students represent taxpayers involved in disputes with the IRS. Clinic students gain litigation and negotiation experience while acquiring significant knowledge of tax law.

■ Externships

The Public Service Externship provides students with another opportunity to gain hands-on experience and make significant professional contacts. Externships consist of field placements in government agencies, nonprofit legal services organizations, judiciary offices, and the Arkansas Legislature. Externship students earn academic credit for their participation.

■ Facilities and Library

Bowen is housed in a historic building originally constructed in the 1930s to house the state's medical school. The

University of Arkansas at Little Rock, William H. Bowen School of Law

spacious facility contains over 150,000 square feet and is compliant with the Americans with Disabilities Act.

The six-story structure has modern classrooms and courtrooms. A renovation was completed recently to install smart technology in the classrooms and courtrooms and wireless Internet throughout the building. The Lecture Capture system allows professors to record lectures (video and audio) and make them available to students via the Web.

Wrapped around a four-story atrium, the library seats over 300 and houses two computer labs. The library is open seven days a week, and librarians are available on weekdays and Saturdays.

■ Cost and Financial Aid

With full-time resident tuition around $11,000, Bowen is an exceptional value. In addition, most nonresident students at Bowen earn scholarships that lower their tuition to no more than the resident rate. The law school participates in the Federal Stafford Loan Program, the Federal Graduate PLUS Loan Program, and the Federal Work-Study Program, as well as major private loan programs.

■ Scholarships

The Bowen School of Law automatically considers all admitted applicants for three scholarships.

Bowen scholarships cover full tuition and fees for up to 90 credit hours. Recipients have exceptional academic credentials, strong LSAT scores, and demonstrated leadership qualities.

Merit scholarships are awarded in amounts up to $21,000. These scholarships are awarded based on an array of factors, including academic achievement, LSAT scores, diversity, and

quality of application materials. Personal statements are critical to the selection of merit scholarship recipients.

Nonresident scholarships are awarded in an amount that equals the out-of-state fees required to attend Bowen. All nonresident students are eligible for these scholarships.

■ Bowen Fellowship Program

Applicants who submit all required materials by January 1 and meet the criteria listed below may be considered for a Bowen Fellowship. Bowen Fellows receive a scholarship of up to full tuition and are given first choice of faculty research assistantships. In addition to the earlier application deadline, Bowen Fellowship applicants must have

- an LSAT score of 159 or higher;
- an undergraduate GPA of 3.3 or higher; and
- a sincere desire to attend Bowen full time.

Applicants interested in a Bowen Fellowship should e-mail Assistant Dean for Admissions Aaron N. Taylor at *antaylor@ualr.edu*.

■ Student Life

The relatively small student body at Bowen lends itself to a supportive and engaging community. On the curricular side, the *UALR Law Review* and the Moot Court Board are highly sought-after activities. Extracurricular organizations include the ABA, ACLU, Arkansas Bar Association, Arkansas Association of Women Lawyers, Asian Pacific American Law Students Association, Black Law Students Association, Lambda, Christian Legal Society, Hispanic Law Students Association, International Law Society, Part-time Students Association, Student Animal Defense Fund, and Student Bar Association.

Applicant Profile

University of Arkansas at Little Rock, William H. Bowen School of Law
This grid includes only applicants who earned 120–180 LSAT scores under standard administrations.

LSAT Score	3.75 +		3.50–3.74		3.25–3.49		3.00–3.24		2.75–2.99		2.50–2.74		2.25–2.49		2.00–2.24		Below 2.00		No GPA		Total	
	Apps	Adm	Apps	Adm	Apps	Adm	Apps	Adm	Apps	Adm	Apps	Adm	Apps	Adm	Apps	Adm	Apps	Adm	Apps	Adm	Apps	Adm
175–180	0	0	0	0	0	0	0	0	0	0	0	0	0	0	0	0	0	0	0	0	0	0
170–174	0	0	0	0	0	0	0	0	0	0	1	1	0	0	0	0	0	0	0	0	1	1
165–169	3	3	1	1	1	1	4	3	0	0	1	0	0	0	2	2	0	0	0	0	12	10
160–164	9	7	14	12	10	8	7	4	1	1	8	3	4	3	2	0	2	0	1	1	58	39
155–159	24	21	34	23	24	14	32	23	25	12	26	12	7	5	4	3	0	0	3	0	179	113
150–154	41	28	57	35	66	32	62	24	54	12	49	16	17	3	10	2	3	0	2	0	361	152
145–149	43	18	46	13	76	15	95	12	67	9	48	6	23	1	9	1	4	0	6	1	417	76
140–144	13	3	25	0	45	5	54	5	57	1	41	0	26	0	16	0	1	0	10	0	288	14
135–139	3	0	7	0	23	1	23	1	25	0	31	0	21	1	12	0	2	0	10	0	157	3
130–134	2	0	2	0	8	0	11	0	11	0	11	0	7	0	7	0	0	0	4	0	63	0
125–129	0	0	0	0	0	0	1	0	2	0	3	0	2	0	1	0	0	0	1	0	10	0
120–124	0	0	0	0	0	0	0	0	0	0	1	0	0	0	0	0	0	0	0	0	1	0
Total	138	80	186	84	253	76	289	72	242	35	220	38	107	13	63	8	12	0	37	2	1547	408

Apps = Number of Applicants   Adm = Number Admitted   Reflects 99% of the total applicant pool; average LSAT data reported.

Atlanta's John Marshall Law School

1422 W. Peachtree Street NW
Atlanta, GA 30309
Phone: 404.872.3593; Fax: 404.873.3802
E-mail: admissions@johnmarshall.edu; Website: www.johnmarshall.edu

ABA
Approved
Since
2005

The Basics

Type of school	Private
Term	Semester
Application deadline	8/15
Application fee	$50
Financial aid deadline	7/1
Can first year start other than fall?	No
Student to faculty ratio	12.7 to 1
# of housing spaces available restricted to law students	
graduate housing for which law students are eligible	

Faculty and Administrators

	Total		Men		Women		Minorities	
	Spr	Fall	Spr	Fall	Spr	Fall	Spr	Fall
Full-time	32	30	11	9	21	21	7	7
Other full-time	0	0	0	0	0	0	0	0
Deans, librarians, & others who teach	4	4	3	3	1	1	1	1
Part-time	15	12	11	9	4	3	4	2
Total	51	46	25	21	26	25	12	10

Curriculum

		Full-Time	Part-Time
Typical first-year section size		49	45
Is there typically a "small section" of the first-year class, other than Legal Writing, taught by full-time faculty		No	No
If yes, typical size offered last year			
# of classroom course titles beyond first-year curriculum		51	
# of upper division courses, excluding seminars, with an enrollment:	Under 25	95	
	25–49	36	
	50–74	6	
	75–99	0	
	100+	0	
# of seminars		4	
# of seminar positions available		103	
# of seminar positions filled		32	31
# of positions available in simulation courses		332	
# of simulation positions filled		250	82
# of positions available in faculty supervised clinical courses		0	
# of faculty supervised clinical positions filled		0	0
# involved in field placements		82	17
# involved in law journals		23	12
# involved in moot court or trial competitions		24	5
# of credit hours required to graduate		88	

JD Enrollment and Ethnicity

	Men		Women		Full-Time		Part-Time		1st-Year		Total		JD Degs. Awd.
	#	%	#	%	#	%	#	%	#	%	#	%	
African Amer.	35	12.9	69	24.3	52	14.0	52	28.3	53	22.7	104	18.7	21
Amer. Indian	0	0.0	3	1.1	3	0.8	0	0.0	1	0.4	3	0.5	1
Asian Amer.	13	4.8	7	2.5	11	3.0	9	4.9	12	5.2	20	3.6	5
Mex. Amer.	0	0.0	0	0.0	0	0.0	0	0.0	0	0.0	0	0.0	0
Puerto Rican	11	4.1	5	1.8	11	3.0	5	2.7	7	3.0	16	2.9	7
Hispanic	0	0.0	0	0.0	0	0.0	0	0.0	0	0.0	0	0.0	0
Total Minority	59	21.8	84	29.6	77	20.8	66	35.9	73	31.3	143	25.8	34
For. Nation.	1	0.4	0	0.0	1	0.3	0	0.0	0	0.0	1	0.2	0
Caucasian	202	74.5	181	63.7	269	72.5	114	62.0	147	63.1	383	69.0	87
Unknown	9	3.3	19	6.7	24	6.5	4	2.2	13	5.6	28	5.0	5
Total	271	48.8	284	51.2	371	66.8	184	33.2	233	42.0	555		126

Transfers

Transfers in	12
Transfers out	20

Tuition and Fees

	Resident	Nonresident
Full-time	$31,970	$31,970
Part-time	$19,682	$19,682
Tuition Guarantee Program		N

Living Expenses

Estimated living expenses for singles

Living on campus	Living off campus	Living at home
N/A	$51,720	N/A

Atlanta's John Marshall Law School

ABA
Approved
Since
2005

GPA and LSAT Scores

	Total	Full-Time	Part-Time
# of apps	1,789	1,436	353
# of offers	712	580	132
# of matrics	211	145	66
75% GPA	3.28	3.26	3.31
Median GPA	2.97	2.96	3.01
25% GPA	2.67	2.67	2.64
75% LSAT	153	153	153
Median LSAT	151	151	150
25% LSAT	149	149	149

Grants and Scholarships (from prior year)

	Total		Full-Time		Part-Time	
	#	%	#	%	#	%
Total # of students	496		319		177	
Total # receiving grants	12	2.4	8	2.5	4	2.3
Less than 1/2 tuition	3	0.6	3	0.9	0	0.0
Half to full tuition	5	1.0	4	1.3	1	0.6
Full tuition	4	0.8	1	0.3	3	1.7
More than full tuition	0	0.0	0	0.0	0	0.0
Median grant amount			$0		$0	

Informational and Library Resources

Total amount spent on library materials	$572,403
Study seating capacity inside the library	212
# of full-time equivalent professional librarians	5.0
Hours per week library is open	87
# of open, wired connections available to students	181
# of networked computers available for use by students	24
Has wireless network?	Y
Require computer?	N

JD Attrition (from prior year)

	Academic	Other	Total	
	#	#	#	%
1st year	2	25	27	15.9
2nd year	0	4	4	2.6
3rd year	0	0	0	0.0
4th year	0	0	0	0.0

Employment (9 months after graduation)

	Total	Percentage
Employment status known	106	100.0
Employment status unknown	0	0.0
Employed	100	94.3
Pursuing graduate degrees	1	0.9
Unemployed (seeking, not seeking, or studying for the bar)	4	3.8
Type of Employment		
# employed in law firms	64	64.0
# employed in business and industry	15	15.0
# employed in government	10	10.0
# employed in public interest	4	4.0
# employed as judicial clerks	5	5.0
# employed in academia	2	2.0
Geographic Location		
# employed in state	87	87.0
# employed in foreign countries	1	1.0
# of states where employed		15

Bar Passage Rates

First-time takers	106	Reporting %	100.00
Average school %	88.67	Average state %	88.63
Average pass difference	0.04		

Jurisdiction	Takers	Passers	Pass %	State %	Diff %
Georgia	93	82	88.17	89.27	−1.10
Tennessee	5	5	100.00	88.10	11.90
Washington	2	2	100.00	74.40	25.60
Colorado	1	1	100.00	83.29	16.71
Others (4)	4	3	75.00		

Atlanta's John Marshall Law School

1422 W. Peachtree Street NW
Atlanta, GA 30309
Phone: 404.872.3593; Fax: 404.873.3802
E-mail: admissions@johnmarshall.edu; Website: www.johnmarshall.edu

■ The Dean's Introduction

Atlanta's John Marshall Law School has been educating lawyers and leaders in Georgia since 1933 and now attracts students from around the country. We provide a rigorous, high-quality program of legal education that produces competent and ethical lawyers who are dedicated to helping people, especially in underserved communities. We intentionally instill in our students a sense of obligation to the community and to the legal profession—an obligation to pursue justice, rather than mere personal gain, and to improve society, rather than to solely advance personal ambition. Whether our graduates remain in law practice, become judges, enter politics, or succeed in business, these rich values stay with them.

■ The Mission

The mission of the Law School is to prepare highly competent and professional lawyers who possess a strong social conscience, continually demonstrate high ethical standards, and are committed to the improvement of the legal system and society. The school is dedicated to providing a quality educational opportunity to nontraditional or adult learners, and to other significantly underserved segments of the community. We emphasize the highest standards of ethical and professional conduct. As Supreme Court Justice Thurgood Marshall once said, "There's only one kind of reputation a young lawyer gets in a hurry." Graduates of this law school are trained to do the right thing.

■ Atlanta Living

The Law School campus is centrally located in midtown Atlanta, the social, cultural, and economic hub of the South. It is in close proximity to Atlanta's largest law firms, as well as government offices, state and federal courts, and nonprofit legal organizations. Atlanta also boasts an extensive array of arts, music, sports, and recreational events, making it an exciting place to live.

■ Facilities, Library, and Modern Technology

The Law School is housed in a modern, nine-story building located on one of the major streets in Atlanta. Recently, the facility underwent major renovations, including the addition of new classrooms and new trial and appellate courtrooms.

The Law School has made the inclusion of new technologies throughout the school a priority. All students and faculty enjoy direct and unlimited access to wireless internet, massive online legal databases, as well as new state-of-the-art technology in multiple classrooms that allows for interactive learning experiences. Students can take both midterm and final exams on their laptops and download them to the school's network.

Our library spreads over three floors, contains over 200,000 total volumes and equivalents, and provides students and faculty with access to all legal materials necessary to learn the skill of legal research.

■ Dedicated Faculty

The John Marshall faculty makes the difference in the student experience and is committed to students' success throughout their legal education and beyond. The faculty is dedicated to providing an intellectually rigorous academic program while instilling the highest sense of professional, ethical, and moral responsibilities that are required of members of the legal profession. All of our faculty members have extensive practical experience in their respective fields of expertise, bringing real-world experience into the classroom. Our low student-to-faculty ratio is one of the best among American law schools. All first-year and required courses are taught in small classes, and professors are easily accessible to their students outside of class. Our small class sizes and low faculty-to-student ratio create a supportive environment where students can enjoy learning and express their views.

■ Commitment to Diversity

Because John Marshall's educational environment focuses on an interactive learning process, a diverse student body is essential to providing a broad range of perspectives in the classroom and the Law School community. The fall 2009 entering class of 211 students was made up of 49 percent women and 36 percent minorities. The student body is not only ethnically diverse, but it is varied in life experience and professional backgrounds. In the 2009 entering class, the median age of full-time students was 23, and the median age of part-time students was 29.

■ The Legal Program

John Marshall's rigorous program of study is designed toward the development of intellectual, analytical, and lawyering skills. From the first-year curriculum, with its predetermined set of core courses, through the third year, with courses that emphasize practical skill development, the degree program is designed to promote analytical reasoning, precision in both oral and written communication, and problem-solving skills. Upper-class students can pursue their areas of interest through a broad variety of elective courses.

Full-Time and Part-Time Law Study. John Marshall remains dedicated to providing access to legal education to both traditional and nontraditional students by offering both full-time and part-time law programs. Individuals who are unable to devote themselves to the study of law full time may attend either the part-time evening or part-time day program.

The **Legal Skills and Professionalism Program** takes a holistic approach to preparing students for success during and after law school. Beginning with writing, the program teaches legal skills and professionalism. The same tools that students use to draft documents in their writing classes are employed to solve legal problems in Negotiations, Mediation, Trial Advocacy, Client Interviewing and Counseling, and other skills courses. In addition, a professionalism component is built into every course in the program, preparing students to confront and resolve real-world professionalism issues as they learn to solve legal problems and meet client goals. The Law School faculty come with diverse law practice backgrounds,

including criminal defense and prosecution, administrative law, domestic relations practice, and corporate/transactional work.

Academic Support. Tools for academic growth and professional success are not only fostered through interactive classroom teaching, but also through individual advisement and group workshops. The director of academic achievement meets individually with students and also plans lectures and special programs to assist in the development of students' legal writing, studying, and exam skills, including the bar exam.

Pro Bono and Externship Programs. The director of pro bono and externships encourages students to be involved in pro bono work, both legal and nonlegal. The director also supervises students in externships throughout Atlanta, including externships for academic credit. Externship placements include the ACLU, Atlanta City Council, Atlanta Legal Aid Society, Department of Homeland Security, district attorney and public defender offices throughout the city, the Georgia Recording Artist Association, the Landlord/Tenant Mediation Project, the Georgia Innocence Project, the Georgia Court of Appeals, and the Southern Center for Human Rights, among others. In 2007, John Marshall established the Micronesian Externship Program, which places students in judicial chambers and government law offices in Guam, the Commonwealth of the Northern Marianas, the Federated States of Micronesia, and Palau.

■ Career Development

The Office of Career Development offers individualized, professional advice to students about their personal career goals and tailors strategies to assist students in reaching those goals. In addition to providing résumé and interview workshops to facilitate job searches, John Marshall also participates in the Georgia Law School Consortium to plan job fairs and other state-wide recruiting efforts, such as judicial clerkships; placement with prosecutors, public interest agencies, and public defenders; and minority recruiting. As a member of the National Association of Law Placement, John Marshall allows its students the opportunity to attend regional hiring consortia that attract private and government recruiters throughout the Southeast.

■ Admission

The Admissions Committee is committed to finding a well-rounded and diverse group of students. In addition to the candidate's academic record and standardized test results, the Admissions Committee will examine with particular care those factors that indicate a high probability for success in law study. Such factors include life experiences, personal or family hardships overcome, demonstrated personal and professional achievements, ability to overcome life's obstacles, the capacity for rigorous intellectual study, the self-discipline demanded by the profession, and a commitment to be of service to the profession and society as a whole.

■ Law School Visits

The Office of Admissions makes numerous college visits and holds open houses throughout the year to provide prospective students with information and guidance about the law school admission process. Please visit our website for additional information regarding the dates and times of events. We also invite you to contact us for a personalized tour, to sit in on a class, or to meet personally with an admission professional.

Applicant Profile

Atlanta's John Marshall Law School
This grid includes only applicants who earned 120–180 LSAT scores under standard administrations.

LSAT Score	GPA								
	3.75 +	3.50–3.74	3.25–3.49	3.00–3.24	2.75–2.99	2.50–2.74	2.25–2.49	2.00–2.24	Below 2.00
155–180									
150–154									
145–149									
120–144									

■ Likely   ■ Possible   □ Unlikely

Ave Maria School of Law

1025 Commons Circle
Naples, FL 34119-1376
Phone: 239.687.5300; Fax: 239.687.5340
E-mail: info@avemarialaw.edu; Website: www.avemarialaw.edu

ABA
Approved
Since
2002

The Basics

Type of school	Private
Term	Semester
Application deadline	6/10
Application fee	$50
Financial aid deadline	6/1
Can first year start other than fall?	No
Student to faculty ratio	17.5 to 1
# of housing spaces available restricted to law students	111
graduate housing for which law students are eligible	

Faculty and Administrators

	Total		Men		Women		Minorities	
	Spr	Fall	Spr	Fall	Spr	Fall	Spr	Fall
Full-time	15	17	11	13	4	4	0	0
Other full-time	4	4	2	2	2	2	0	0
Deans, librarians, & others who teach	6	6	4	5	2	1	1	1
Part-time	22	14	18	11	4	3	0	0
Total	47	41	35	31	12	10	1	1

Curriculum

	Full-Time	Part-Time
Typical first-year section size	63	0
Is there typically a "small section" of the first-year class, other than Legal Writing, taught by full-time faculty	No	No
If yes, typical size offered last year		
# of classroom course titles beyond first-year curriculum		77
# of upper division courses, excluding seminars, with an enrollment: Under 25		59
25–49		15
50–74		6
75–99		0
100+		0
# of seminars		17
# of seminar positions available		242
# of seminar positions filled	176	0
# of positions available in simulation courses	148	
# of simulation positions filled	119	0
# of positions available in faculty supervised clinical courses		51
# of faculty supervised clinical positions filled	46	0
# involved in field placements	50	0
# involved in law journals	32	0
# involved in moot court or trial competitions	19	0
# of credit hours required to graduate		90

JD Enrollment and Ethnicity

	Men		Women		Full-Time		Part-Time		1st-Year		Total		JD Degs. Awd.
	#	%	#	%	#	%	#	%	#	%	#	%	
African Amer.	1	0.5	12	7.5	13	3.5	0	0.0	10	4.8	13	3.5	1
Amer. Indian	1	0.5	1	0.6	2	0.5	0	0.0	1	0.5	2	0.5	1
Asian Amer.	13	6.0	4	2.5	17	4.5	0	0.0	5	2.4	17	4.5	8
Mex. Amer.	4	1.9	10	6.3	14	3.7	0	0.0	6	2.9	14	3.7	3
Puerto Rican	2	0.9	0	0.0	2	0.5	0	0.0	1	0.5	2	0.5	0
Hispanic	9	4.2	7	4.4	16	4.3	0	0.0	10	4.8	16	4.3	3
Total Minority	30	14.0	34	21.3	64	17.1	0	0.0	33	15.9	64	17.1	16
For. Nation.	6	2.8	3	1.9	9	2.4	0	0.0	2	1.0	9	2.4	0
Caucasian	178	82.8	120	75.0	298	79.5	0	0.0	170	81.7	298	79.5	71
Unknown	1	0.5	3	1.9	4	1.1	0	0.0	3	1.4	4	1.1	0
Total	215	57.3	160	42.7	375	100.0	0	0.0	208	55.5	375		87

Transfers

Transfers in	2
Transfers out	27

Tuition and Fees

	Resident	Nonresident
Full-time	$35,380	$35,380
Part-time		
Tuition Guarantee Program		N

Living Expenses

Estimated living expenses for singles

Living on campus	Living off campus	Living at home
$20,399	$20,399	$20,399

Ave Maria School of Law

ABA Approved Since 2002

GPA and LSAT Scores

	Total	Full-Time	Part-Time
# of apps	1,775	1,775	0
# of offers	885	885	0
# of matrics	210	210	0
75% GPA	3.53	3.53	0.00
Median GPA	3.22	3.22	0.00
25% GPA	2.91	2.91	0.00
75% LSAT	155	155	0
Median LSAT	150	150	0
25% LSAT	147	147	0

Grants and Scholarships (from prior year)

	Total #	Total %	Full-Time #	Full-Time %	Part-Time #	Part-Time %
Total # of students	302		302		0	
Total # receiving grants	193	63.9	193	63.9	0	0.0
Less than 1/2 tuition	97	32.1	97	32.1	0	0.0
Half to full tuition	70	23.2	70	23.2	0	0.0
Full tuition	26	8.6	26	8.6	0	0.0
More than full tuition	0	0.0	0	0.0	0	0.0
Median grant amount			$15,000		$0	

Informational and Library Resources

Total amount spent on library materials	$890,875
Study seating capacity inside the library	103
# of full-time equivalent professional librarians	4
Hours per week library is open	104
# of open, wired connections available to students	0
# of networked computers available for use by students	28
Has wireless network?	Y
Require computer?	N

JD Attrition (from prior year)

	Academic #	Other #	Total #	Total %
1st year	4	35	39	30.7
2nd year	1	2	3	3.4
3rd year	0	0	0	0.0
4th year	0	0	0	0.0

Employment (9 months after graduation)

	Total	Percentage
Employment status known	106	92.2
Employment status unknown	9	7.8
Employed	84	79.2
Pursuing graduate degrees	5	4.7
Unemployed (seeking, not seeking, or studying for the bar)	14	13.2
Type of Employment		
# employed in law firms	39	46.4
# employed in business and industry	16	19.0
# employed in government	15	17.9
# employed in public interest	6	7.1
# employed as judicial clerks	6	7.1
# employed in academia	2	2.4
Geographic Location		
# employed in state	31	36.9
# employed in foreign countries	1	1.2
# of states where employed	25	

Bar Passage Rates

First-time takers	119	Reporting %	77.31
Average school %	77.16	Average state %	83.67

Average pass difference –6.51

Jurisdiction	Takers	Passers	Pass %	State %	Diff %
Michigan	44	35	79.55	82.13	–2.58
California	8	4	50.00	78.07	–28.07
Florida	7	5	71.43	80.76	–9.33
Illinois	5	4	80.00	90.94	–10.94
Others (9)	28	23	82.14		

Ave Maria School of Law

1025 Commons Circle
Naples, FL 34119-1376
Phone: 239.687.5300; Fax: 239.687.5340
E-mail: info@avemarialaw.edu; Website: www.avemarialaw.edu

■ Introduction

Ave Maria School of Law offers students a distinctive legal education that focuses on professional excellence, the moral foundations of the law, and the harmony of faith and reason. As a national Catholic law school, Ave Maria is committed to producing highly competent graduates who are able to reflect critically on the law, the principles that undergird it, and their role within the legal system.

With a student-to-faculty ratio of approximately 20 to 1, Ave Maria students benefit from ready access to experienced faculty members who prepare students to practice at the highest level and to succeed on bar exams throughout the country. The quality of Ave Maria's academic program is recognized by judges throughout the nation who have hired graduates as judicial clerks—with 57 clerkships secured by members of the 2003–2009 graduating classes, most of these federal clerkships.

In the summer of 2009, Ave Maria School of Law relocated to southwest Florida, just 7 miles inland of the Gulf of Mexico. The new location will enhance the school's ability to fulfill its distinctive mission as a Catholic law school dedicated to professional excellence. In the new location, students have found employment and externship opportunities with courts and law firms in nearby Naples and Fort Myers, while the law school's clinical programs have found new opportunities as well. With no other law school serving this rapidly developing region, which is expected to double its population in the next two decades, the School of Law has been both a catalyst and a beneficiary of the area's dynamic growth.

Ave Maria School of Law encourages applications from students of all faiths who seek a distinctive legal education enriched by the Catholic intellectual tradition.

■ Curriculum

Ave Maria School of Law awards the Juris Doctor degree after three years (90 credits) of full-time residential study. The required curriculum of 60 credits ensures that all students develop those skills that are fundamental to the effective practice of law—analysis, reasoning, problem solving, research, writing, oral advocacy, and others. Through elective courses, students have the opportunity to focus on specific subject areas of interest, such as commercial law, employment law, international law, and intellectual property law. A central tenet of the educational philosophy at Ave Maria is that law and morality are inherently intertwined.

■ Faculty

At the core of the Ave Maria School of Law education is the faculty who teach and mentor students. Faculty members bring to the classroom their experience as attorneys in private practice, judicial clerks, and teachers and administrators at other law schools. In hiring faculty, the law school administration has sought individuals who would be able to translate the mission of the School of Law in the classroom, in their scholarship, and in their service. Ave Maria faculty members actively contribute to the profession through their legal research, writing, and involvement in professional and civic organizations. Our faculty includes 34 full-time professors. Select upper-level courses are taught by adjunct faculty members drawn from area law firms, corporations, and the judiciary.

■ Enrollment/Student Body

While many of Ave Maria's students come to the School of Law directly from their undergraduate institutions, others have earned postgraduate degrees and have work experience in fields including business, medicine, engineering, the military, and education. More than 170 different undergraduate colleges are represented at the School of Law, including Brigham Young University, Christendom College, Franciscan University, Hillsdale College, University of Notre Dame, Princeton University, Thomas Aquinas College, the University of Michigan, and many other fine schools.

■ Career Services/Placement

Ave Maria School of Law graduates accept employment with an array of employers in all regions of the country, including national and regional law firms such as Akin Gump, Sidley Austin, Butzel Long, Reed Smith, Roetzel and Andress, Skadden Arps, and Holland and Hart. Graduates have also been successful in obtaining employment with state and federal governmental agencies, including the US Departments of Justice, Homeland Security, and Defense, as well as multiple prosecutors' offices nationwide.

The Career Services Office uses a proactive and individualized approach to assist students during each stage of the career-search process—counseling, strategizing, résumé and cover letter preparation, interviewing, and consideration of employment offers. The full-time staff of three, two of whom are attorneys, is dedicated to expanding employment opportunities for students through the cultivation of relationships with legal employers throughout the region and the nation.

■ Library/Physical Facilities

The Ave Maria Law School Library is housed in an environment that is both welcoming and conducive to research and study. Materials are available in all formats; the collection is particularly strong in digital resources. Apart from a fine compilation of US and international primary and secondary legal materials, the Ave Maria Law Library's collection emphasizes the areas of canon law, bioethics and biotechnology, natural law, and related philosophy, history, political science, and economics titles. Seating in the library includes a variety of carrel, table, group study, and soft seating. Leisure reading in the form of magazines and daily newspapers is provided.

■ Admission

Ave Maria School of Law enrolls talented individuals from diverse backgrounds who seek a rigorous and distinctive legal education. To this end, Ave Maria evaluates applicants from a whole-person perspective and considers many factors,

including work experience, activities, background, obstacles overcome, accomplishments, undergraduate and graduate school records, Law School Admission Test (LSAT) scores, letters of reference, and the applicant's personal statement. Ave Maria recognizes that a diverse student body, drawn from throughout the United States and internationally, enriches the educational experience.

■ Student Activities

By providing opportunities for interaction among students, faculty, and the legal community, Ave Maria School of Law ensures a vibrant professional atmosphere and a constructive law school experience. A five-day orientation program, a Distinguished Speaker Series, conferences, and the Board of Visitor Mentor Program, together with a challenging and comprehensive curriculum, provide Ave Maria students with an exceptional law school experience. A multitude of student organizations offers students the opportunity to

pursue their specific areas of interest and augment their law school education.

■ Housing

Ave Maria School of Law's campus in Naples, Florida, offers on-site housing as well as close-by apartments, condominiums, and single-family homes. The law school provides assistance to students during their search for housing and, if applicable, roommates.

■ Expenses/Financial Aid

Ave Maria School of Law offers a generous scholarship program that annually provides as many as 50 full- and three-quarter tuition scholarships to members of the entering class. Additionally, the School of Law annually awards as many as 15 scholarships to entering students who have a record of service and leadership in select areas. Tuition for members of the fall 2009 entering class is $34,900.

Applicant Profile

Ave Maria School of Law has chosen not to provide an admission profile grid. This reflects our commitment to consider every applicant from a whole-person perspective. Every component of the application is carefully reviewed,

and, while qualifications as measured by LSAT and GPA are important, equal consideration is also given to the applicant's background, letters of recommendation, and personal statement.

University of Baltimore School of Law

1420 North Charles Street
Baltimore, MD 21201
Phone: 410.837.4459; Fax: 410.837.4450
E-mail: lwadmiss@ubalt.edu; Website: http://law.ubalt.edu

ABA
Approved
Since
1972

The Basics

Type of school	Public
Term	Semester
Application deadline	7/15
Application fee	$60
Financial aid deadline	3/1
Can first year start other than fall?	No
Student to faculty ratio	15.9 to 1
# of housing spaces available restricted to law students	
graduate housing for which law students are eligible	

Faculty and Administrators

	Total		Men		Women		Minorities	
	Spr	Fall	Spr	Fall	Spr	Fall	Spr	Fall
Full-time	47	49	28	30	19	19	8	8
Other full-time	9	9	4	5	5	4	1	2
Deans, librarians, & others who teach	7	5	3	2	4	3	1	0
Part-time	75	70	52	45	22	24	7	9
Total	138	133	87	82	50	50	17	19

Curriculum

		Full-Time	Part-Time
Typical first-year section size		58	43
Is there typically a "small section" of the first-year class, other than Legal Writing, taught by full-time faculty		No	No
If yes, typical size offered last year			
# of classroom course titles beyond first-year curriculum			150
# of upper division courses, excluding seminars, with an enrollment:	Under 25		184
	25–49		39
	50–74		20
	75–99		8
	100+		0
# of seminars			36
# of seminar positions available			721
# of seminar positions filled		415	98
# of positions available in simulation courses		996	
# of simulation positions filled		548	220
# of positions available in faculty supervised clinical courses		180	
# of faculty supervised clinical positions filled		154	29
# involved in field placements		184	26
# involved in law journals		345	55
# involved in moot court or trial competitions		78	12
# of credit hours required to graduate		87	

JD Enrollment and Ethnicity

	Men		Women		Full-Time		Part-Time		1st-Year		Total		JD Degs. Awd.
	#	%	#	%	#	%	#	%	#	%	#	%	
African Amer.	22	4.1	46	8.1	27	4.0	41	9.5	20	4.7	68	6.2	33
Amer. Indian	1	0.2	2	0.4	2	0.3	1	0.2	2	0.5	3	0.3	1
Asian Amer.	22	4.1	40	7.0	42	6.3	20	4.6	24	5.7	62	5.6	23
Mex. Amer.	0	0.0	0	0.0	0	0.0	0	0.0	0	0.0	0	0.0	0
Puerto Rican	0	0.0	0	0.0	0	0.0	0	0.0	0	0.0	0	0.0	0
Hispanic	11	2.1	14	2.5	13	1.9	12	2.8	14	3.3	25	2.3	5
Total Minority	56	10.5	102	17.9	84	12.5	74	17.2	60	14.2	158	14.3	62
For. Nation.	5	0.9	2	0.4	3	0.4	4	0.9	6	1.4	7	0.6	0
Caucasian	391	73.2	387	68.0	488	72.6	290	67.3	299	70.7	778	70.5	207
Unknown	82	15.4	78	13.7	97	14.4	63	14.6	58	13.7	160	14.5	37
Total	534	48.4	569	51.6	672	60.9	431	39.1	423	38.4	1103		306

Transfers

Transfers in	11
Transfers out	23

Tuition and Fees

	Resident	Nonresident
Full-time	$23,992	$35,988
Part-time	$17,916	$25,440
Tuition Guarantee Program		N

Living Expenses

Estimated living expenses for singles

Living on campus	Living off campus	Living at home
N/A	$20,930	$7,830

University of Baltimore School of Law

*ABA
Approved
Since
1972*

GPA and LSAT Scores

	Total	Full-Time	Part-Time
# of apps	2,748	1,990	758
# of offers	1,125	803	322
# of matrics	379	245	134
75% GPA	3.59	3.67	3.40
Median GPA	3.29	3.34	3.16
25% GPA	2.97	3.03	2.80
75% LSAT	157	158	154
Median LSAT	155	156	152
25% LSAT	151	153	150

Grants and Scholarships (from prior year)

	Total		Full-Time		Part-Time	
	#	%	#	%	#	%
Total # of students	1,077		633		444	
Total # receiving grants	167	15.5	135	21.3	32	7.2
Less than 1/2 tuition	83	7.7	68	10.7	15	3.4
Half to full tuition	67	6.2	54	8.5	13	2.9
Full tuition	0	0.0	0	0.0	0	0.0
More than full tuition	17	1.6	13	2.1	4	0.9
Median grant amount			$14,000		$10,147	

Informational and Library Resources

Total amount spent on library materials	$864,948
Study seating capacity inside the library	317
# of full-time equivalent professional librarians	11
Hours per week library is open	94
# of open, wired connections available to students	29
# of networked computers available for use by students	36
Has wireless network?	Y
Require computer?	N

JD Attrition (from prior year)

	Academic	Other	Total	
	#	#	#	%
1st year	14	30	44	10.7
2nd year	3	1	4	1.3
3rd year	0	0	0	0.0
4th year	0	0	0	0.0

Employment (9 months after graduation)

	Total	Percentage
Employment status known	287	98.3
Employment status unknown	5	1.7
Employed	273	95.1
Pursuing graduate degrees	4	1.4
Unemployed (seeking, not seeking, or studying for the bar)	7	2.4
Type of Employment		
# employed in law firms	85	31.1
# employed in business and industry	49	17.9
# employed in government	55	20.1
# employed in public interest	20	7.3
# employed as judicial clerks	56	20.5
# employed in academia	7	2.6
Geographic Location		
# employed in state	224	82.1
# employed in foreign countries	1	0.4
# of states where employed	11	

Bar Passage Rates

First-time takers	287	Reporting %	83.97
Average school %	84.65	Average state %	85.51
Average pass difference	−0.86		

Jurisdiction	Takers	Passers	Pass %	State %	Diff %
Maryland	241	204	84.65	85.51	−0.86

University of Baltimore School of Law

1420 North Charles Street
Baltimore, MD 21201
Phone: 410.837.4459; Fax: 410.837.4450
E-mail: lwadmiss@ubalt.edu; Website: http://law.ubalt.edu

■ Introduction

Founded in 1925, the University of Baltimore is one of 13 institutions in the University System of Maryland. The school bears the name of the city of Baltimore and is an integral part of the city's life and that of the Mount Vernon Cultural District, which immediately surrounds it. Although UB is the sixth largest public law school in the country with approximately 1,000 JD students, the school prides itself on excellent classroom teaching, small law school sections, and personalized service.

The School of Law remains committed to its traditional values of community involvement, public interest, access, and diversity. Regardless of a graduate's area of practice, the school believes that all of its students should be exposed to the traditional obligation of lawyers to serve the poor and the common good. Finally, the school values a diverse faculty, staff, and student body as an essential part of its pedagogical mission. The School of Law is accredited by the ABA and AALS.

■ Admission

The School of Law has established an admission policy designed to obtain a diverse and well-qualified student body. In evaluating applicant files, the Admission Committee considers not only the cumulative undergraduate grade-point average and the LSAT score, but also nontraditional factors that may be relevant in determining an applicant's ability to succeed in law school. Applicants are encouraged to discuss fully in a personal statement any such factors they wish the committee to consider in evaluating their application.

■ Enrollment/Student Body

The University of Baltimore School of Law provides three options for pursuing a law degree: a full-time day program, a part-time evening program, and a part-time day program. Approximately a third of the student body is part time, making the part-time division one of the largest in the nation. Over 88 percent of the classes are composed of 50 students or less. The School of Law typically offers between 60 and 65 classes a semester.

■ Curriculum

The School of Law provides a rich curriculum in both day and evening divisions, offering a wide variety of specialized courses in addition to a solid core curriculum. Our legal skills offerings are especially strong as the School of Law is one of the national leaders in "narrowing the gap" between legal education and the legal profession. Our skills programs begin with the first-year courses in legal analysis, research, and writing and culminate with one of the best legal clinics in the nation. Students also have the opportunity to select an area of law in which to concentrate their upper-class studies. Upper-level courses offer students a range of in-depth concentrations that provide students with a sophisticated understanding of a particular area of law.

■ Library

The library's permanent collection contains approximately 354,000 books and bound volume equivalents. The collection includes the published reports of federal and state courts, statutes, administrative materials, and secondary materials such as treatises, legal encyclopedias, digests, citators, form books, looseleaf services, and law reviews. The library staff believes that technology should not be considered separate from the study and practice of law: professional reference librarians are available to students seven days a week to show students how to use the computer-assisted legal systems, as well as how to access the library's many Web-based resources. The library's two computer labs are open to law students during library hours and, along with the wireless network, provide access to word processing, LexisNexis, Westlaw, the Internet, online catalogs, and other resources.

■ Joint Degrees

The School of Law offers six joint degrees: JD with MBA, MPA, MS in Criminal Justice, MS in Negotiations and Conflict Management, LLM in Taxation, and the PhD in Policy Science.

■ Special Programs

Areas of Concentration—The School of Law has an innovative curriculum that allows students the opportunity to develop an in-depth knowledge in a particular area of the law. Students may take courses in one of nine areas of concentration: business law, criminal practice, estate planning, family law, intellectual property, international and comparative law, litigation and advocacy, public and governmental service, and real estate practice.

The Center for Families, Children, and the Courts focuses on the development and implementation of family court planning and reform initiatives throughout the country.

The Center for International and Comparative Law promotes the study and understanding of international and comparative law and the political and economic institutions that support the international legal order. The center places special emphasis on environmental law, human rights, intellectual property, and international business transactions.

The Center on Applied Feminism serves as a bridge between feminist legal theory and the law. The Center examines how feminist theory can benefit legal practitioners in representing clients, shape legal doctrine, and play a role in policy debates and implementation.

The Stephen L. Snyder Center for Litigation Skills supports and enhances the acclaimed litigation skills training of the School of Law through a variety of programs and activities, including lectures by prominent lawyers and judges, special conferences, and litigation research.

Clinical, Advocacy, and Internship Programs—Professional development is fostered through clinics in which students represent individuals and organizations in litigation and transactional matters. Clinics include the **Appellate Practice Clinic**, which enables students to brief and argue a case in the Maryland Court of Special Appeals; the **Civil Advocacy Clinic**, which focuses on such issues as consumer protection, public

benefits cases, and landlord-tenant disputes; the **Community Development Clinic**, which represents nonprofit community organizations in a variety of housing, economic, social, and cultural development areas; the **Criminal Practice Clinic**, in which students handle misdemeanor and felony matters in the district and circuit courts; the **Disability Law Clinic**, which provides representation to patients in involuntary commitment hearings; the **Family Law Clinic**, where students represent low-income clients seeking child custody, support, divorce, and protection from domestic violence; the **Family Mediation Clinic**, which permits students to co-mediate family law disputes and engage in projects designed to improve the practice of family mediation; the **Immigrant Rights Clinic**, which enables students to represent low-income immigrants in Immigration Court and in District Court of Maryland, as well as work with immigrant advocates to develop programs that increase access to justice for immigrant communities; the **Innocence Project Clinic** provides students with the opportunity to review records, interview clients and witnesses, conduct legal research, devise investigative strategies, draft pleadings, and argue motions in cases involving claims of wrongful conviction; and the **Tax Clinic**, which enables students to represent low-income clients before the Internal Revenue Service and the US Tax Court. **Internship Programs** give students experience clerking for academic credit in the public and private sector, including positions in the executive, legislative, and judicial branches of state and local governments.

Law Reviews, Journals, and Other Periodicals give students an opportunity to hone their skills in research, analysis, and writing. The *University of Baltimore Law Review*, the *Journal of Environmental Law*, and the *Intellectual Property Law Journal* offer in-depth analysis of issues of current concern to practitioners and judges alike. The *Law Forum* specializes in articles that trace developing trends in the law.

■ Financial Aid

The university's Financial Aid Office administers federal, state, and institutional loan programs. First-year and transfer applicants are advised to apply for financial aid well in advance of the March 1 deadline. Students are automatically considered for merit-based scholarships. The School of Law awarded more than $1.3 million in scholarships to students matriculating in 2009.

■ Career Services

The professional staff of the Law Career Development Office (LCDO) works individually and collectively to establish effective, dynamic relationships with law students and graduates seeking to articulate, develop, and achieve their career goals. By forging cooperative relationships with a host of employers, regionally and nationally, in the public and private sectors, the LCDO and the School of Law have demonstrated significant success in meeting the needs of our law students who are competing in a challenging and evolving market. Through a host of services, including individual counseling, career workshops, mock interviews, on-campus and off-campus recruitment programs, as well as a detailed and extensive library of resources, the LCDO seeks to provide each and every law student and graduate with job search strategies and the tools to succeed in their professional careers. In addition, through the innovative EXPLOR Program, the LCDO guarantees all first-year students an opportunity to gain substantive legal experience their first summer, thereby establishing a solid foundation on which to build for future success.

Applicant Profile

University of Baltimore School of Law
This grid includes only applicants who earned 120–180 LSAT scores under standard administrations.

LSAT Score	GPA								
	3.75 +	3.50–3.74	3.25–3.49	3.00–3.24	2.75–2.99	2.50–2.74	2.25–2.49	2.00–2.24	Below 2.00
175–180									
170–174									
165–169									
160–164									
155–159									
150–154									
145–149									
140–144									
Below 140									

Good Possibility   Possible   Unlikely

Average LSAT data reported.

Barry University Dwayne O. Andreas School of Law

6441 East Colonial Drive
Orlando, FL 32807
Phone: 321.206.5600
E-mail: krupert@mail.barry.edu; Website: www.barry.edu/law

ABA Approved Since 2002

The Basics

Type of school	Private
Term	Semester
Application deadline	4/1
Application fee	$50
Financial aid deadline	4/15
Can first year start other than fall?	No
Student to faculty ratio	26.7 to 1
# of housing spaces available restricted to law students	
graduate housing for which law students are eligible	

Faculty and Administrators

	Total		Men		Women		Minorities	
	Spr	Fall	Spr	Fall	Spr	Fall	Spr	Fall
Full-time	18	24	10	13	8	11	1	4
Other full-time	2	4	0	1	2	3	0	1
Deans, librarians, & others who teach	11	12	5	5	6	7	2	2
Part-time	41	38	33	29	8	9	3	4
Total	72	78	48	48	24	30	6	11

Curriculum

		Full-Time	Part-Time
Typical first-year section size		100	55
Is there typically a "small section" of the first-year class, other than Legal Writing, taught by full-time faculty		No	Yes
If yes, typical size offered last year			61
# of classroom course titles beyond first-year curriculum		172	
# of upper division courses, excluding seminars, with an enrollment:	Under 25	92	
	25–49	18	
	50–74	16	
	75–99	7	
	100+	4	
# of seminars		20	
# of seminar positions available		400	
# of seminar positions filled		236	37
# of positions available in simulation courses		511	
# of simulation positions filled		325	95
# of positions available in faculty supervised clinical courses		40	
# of faculty supervised clinical positions filled		27	4
# involved in field placements		15	16
# involved in law journals		42	11
# involved in moot court or trial competitions		40	13
# of credit hours required to graduate		90	

JD Enrollment and Ethnicity

	Men		Women		Full-Time		Part-Time		1st-Year		Total		JD Degs. Awd.
	#	%	#	%	#	%	#	%	#	%	#	%	
African Amer.	9	2.1	20	5.8	21	3.4	8	4.9	8	3.1	29	3.8	8
Amer. Indian	0	0.0	0	0.0	0	0.0	0	0.0	0	0.0	0	0.0	1
Asian Amer.	16	3.8	16	4.6	30	4.9	2	1.2	14	5.4	32	4.2	6
Mex. Amer.	0	0.0	0	0.0	0	0.0	0	0.0	0	0.0	0	0.0	0
Puerto Rican	0	0.0	0	0.0	0	0.0	0	0.0	0	0.0	0	0.0	0
Hispanic	32	7.5	35	10.1	54	8.9	13	8.0	14	5.4	67	8.7	11
Total Minority	57	13.4	71	20.5	105	17.2	23	14.2	36	14.0	128	16.6	26
For. Nation.	0	0.0	0	0.0	0	0.0	0	0.0	0	0.0	0	0.0	0
Caucasian	291	68.5	221	63.9	399	65.5	113	69.8	163	63.4	512	66.4	117
Unknown	77	18.1	54	15.6	105	17.2	26	16.0	58	22.6	131	17.0	30
Total	425	55.1	346	44.9	609	79.0	162	21.0	257	33.3	771		173

Transfers

Transfers in	4
Transfers out	21

Tuition and Fees

	Resident	Nonresident
Full-time	$31,700	
Part-time	$23,920	
Tuition Guarantee Program		N

Living Expenses

Estimated living expenses for singles

Living on campus	Living off campus	Living at home
N/A	$22,710	$22,710

Barry University Dwayne O. Andreas School of Law

ABA
Approved
Since
2002

GPA and LSAT Scores

	Total	Full-Time	Part-Time
# of apps	1,989	1,773	216
# of offers	1,117	1,019	98
# of matrics	253	214	39
75% GPA	3.25	3.26	3.25
Median GPA	2.90	2.90	2.90
25% GPA	2.58	2.58	2.57
75% LSAT	152	152	154
Median LSAT	150	150	150
25% LSAT	148	148	149

Grants and Scholarships (from prior year)

	Total #	Total %	Full-Time #	Full-Time %	Part-Time #	Part-Time %
Total # of students	763		612		151	
Total # receiving grants	648	84.9	532	86.9	116	76.8
Less than 1/2 tuition	598	78.4	497	81.2	101	66.9
Half to full tuition	50	6.6	35	5.7	15	9.9
Full tuition	0	0.0	0	0.0	0	0.0
More than full tuition	0	0.0	0	0.0	0	0.0
Median grant amount			$6,000		$6,500	

Informational and Library Resources

Total amount spent on library materials	$938,564
Study seating capacity inside the library	338
# of full-time equivalent professional librarians	11
Hours per week library is open	106
# of open, wired connections available to students	0
# of networked computers available for use by students	38
Has wireless network?	Y
Require computer?	N

JD Attrition (from prior year)

	Academic #	Other #	Total #	Total %
1st year	11	24	35	13.1
2nd year	17	4	21	7.0
3rd year	3	0	3	1.9
4th year	0	0	0	0.0

Employment (9 months after graduation)

	Total	Percentage
Employment status known	172	97.2
Employment status unknown	5	2.8
Employed	114	66.3
Pursuing graduate degrees	5	2.9
Unemployed (seeking, not seeking, or studying for the bar)	46	26.7
Type of Employment		
# employed in law firms	66	57.9
# employed in business and industry	18	15.8
# employed in government	17	14.9
# employed in public interest	8	7.0
# employed as judicial clerks	1	0.9
# employed in academia	3	2.6
Geographic Location		
# employed in state	96	84.2
# employed in foreign countries	0	0.0
# of states where employed	13	

Bar Passage Rates

First-time takers	166	Reporting %	92.17
Average school %	76.47	Average state %	80.76
Average pass difference	−4.29		

Jurisdiction	Takers	Passers	Pass %	State %	Diff %
Florida	153	117	76.47	80.76	−4.29

Barry University Dwayne O. Andreas School of Law

6441 East Colonial Drive
Orlando, FL 32807
Phone: 321.206.5600
E-mail: krupert@mail.barry.edu; Website: www.barry.edu/law

■ A Growing Presence in Higher Education

Founded in early 1993, the University of Orlando School of Law admitted its first class in 1995. In March of 1999, the School of Law became a part of Barry University, a Catholic international university located in Miami Shores, Florida. The affiliation is an extremely positive one, since both administrations have the same focus—to offer quality academics grounded in a strong ethical foundation with the goal of preparing qualified, competent practicing attorneys.

The School of Law is situated on a charming 20-acre campus in East Orlando, about 15 minutes from downtown. The School of Law facilities include a two-story, 20,000-square-foot Law Center building; a 9,000-square-foot Administration and Moot Court building; a 9,000-square-foot classroom and faculty office building; and a 36,000-square-foot law library.

The Barry Law mission guides everything the law school does, from awarding and maintaining scholarships to arranging mentors, to providing career service and academic success guidance and bar prep programs. The School of Law is proud of the quality education provided, with an emphasis on social justice and a spiritual dimension, all within a caring environment. Candidates who choose to study at Barry Law will enjoy the benefits of a mission-centered university where students get the attention they need to succeed.

■ The Perfect Venue for Your Legal Education

Central Florida is one of the fastest growing areas in the country. A host of attractions bring millions of visitors to central Florida each year. Just an hour away are Kennedy Space Center and the beaches of the Atlantic.

Orlando is a major commercial center; many national corporations have headquarters in the city. The area is fast becoming a television and motion picture production center.

Central Florida provides a wealth of first-hand exposure to the practice of corporate and entertainment law, as well as juvenile and criminal law. The Advisory Board is composed of many prominent central Florida attorneys, judges, government officials, and others in the community. Their community affiliations enhance the networking and career opportunities available to Barry's students.

Central Florida enjoys a year-round subtropical climate and offers a wide range of cultural and recreational activities. Accommodations in the immediate area include fully furnished or unfurnished apartments as well as a wide range of single-family dwellings. Orlando has a large number of hotels and executive lodges that offer reduced rates on a weekly or monthly basis.

Orlando is the ideal venue to pursue your legal education.

■ Mission and Goals of the School of Law

Barry University School of Law seeks to offer a quality legal education in a caring environment that will enable its graduates to apply the skills and knowledge they have acquired to their own personal development, and to the good of society, through the competent and ethical practice of law. The School of Law seeks to provide a learning environment that challenges students to accept intellectual, personal, ethical, spiritual, and social responsibilities. The school commits itself to assuring a religious dimension in an atmosphere of religious freedom and to providing community service.

■ An Overview

The School of Law teaches students to become responsible lawyers, trained to assume an active role in the legal community. Students are trained to act in strict accord with the highest ethical standards and to exercise their professional skills competently, with sensitivity to the needs and concerns of their clients.

The School of Law offers a three-year daytime program structured for full-time students. The School of Law also offers a four-year extended studies program in the evening to accommodate working adults or anyone who is unable to pursue full-time study.

Students at the School of Law have many opportunities to experience the "law-in-action" concept, both in the classroom and through practical application. The law school offers a collegial student/professor relationship indicative of legal education at its best.

Through the in-house Children and Families Clinic, Barry students gain solid practical experience working on actual cases involving disadvantaged children in need of legal services. The School of Law also offers an Immigration Clinic and the Earth Justice Clinic, focusing on environmental law. Additionally, Barry Law offers a wealth of externship opportunities that allow students to further develop their skills as emerging attorneys while working in various venues. Externship placement currently includes opportunities in the following areas: civil government, civil poverty, judicial, mediation, public defender, and state attorney.

■ Juris Doctor

The School of Law offers the Juris Doctor (JD) degree. All students in the program must complete 90 semester hours of study in areas that are essential to the understanding and practice of law. Students in the fall entering class must complete required courses in subjects that provide a common core of understanding in the law. Students may choose from a wide variety of electives to meet the remaining requirements necessary for graduation.

■ Scholarship Program

The School of Law proudly offers a merit-based scholarship program. Generally, between 80 and 90 percent of the entering class receive a Barry Law scholarship between $1,000 and $23,000. Admitted candidates are automatically considered for scholarships and do not need to complete any additional forms. If a scholarship is offered to a candidate, notice will be sent within three to four weeks of the official acceptance letter.

Scholarships are offered for three years for full-time students and four years for part-time students. The law GPA required to maintain an institutional scholarship ranges from 2.6 to 3.0. The majority of enrolled students are able to meet the fair and reasonable renewal requirements; for those who do not meet the law GPA, the scholarship can be prorated in

some situations and then adjusted to initial levels once the requisite law GPA is achieved. Contact the financial aid office for more questions in this regard.

Barry Law also offers a Scholarship Bonus Program to second- and third-year students. Students who rank in the top 10 percent and hold at least a 3.2 grade-point average after the first and second year of law school are offered a 75 percent scholarship. What great motivation to rank in the top 10 percent, among other obvious reasons!

■ Program Objective

The School of Law combines traditional and innovative teaching methods to provide a dynamic, professional program. The JD curriculum is designed to develop students' analytical ability, communication skills, and understanding of the codes of professional responsibility and ethics that are central to the practice of law. The faculty utilizes a variety of teaching methods, including simulations and role-playing.

Seminars and advanced courses in the second and third year of study provide close interaction with faculty.

Barry Law emphasizes research and writing proficiency from the first day of class. Armed with a strong foundation in research and writing, Barry Law students gain an advantage in the legal marketplace.

■ Graduation Requirements

To be eligible to receive the degree of JD, a student must (1) complete 90 academic credits of instruction with a cumulative grade-point average of 2.0 or above, (2) earn a cumulative grade-point average of 1.8 for all required courses and a passing grade in each of the required courses, (3) successfully complete the writing requirement, (4) complete a minimum of 60 out of 90 academic credits in residence at Barry University School of Law, (5) successfully complete the pro bono requirement, (6) satisfy all financial obligations to Barry University, and (7) be approved by the faculty for graduation.

Applicant Profile

Barry University Dwayne O. Andreas School of Law

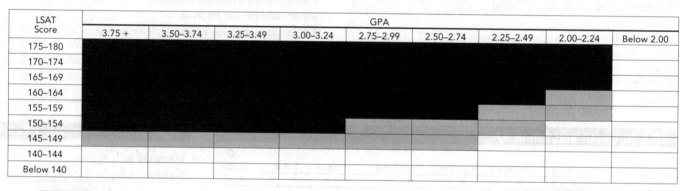

LSAT Score	GPA								
	3.75 +	3.50–3.74	3.25–3.49	3.00–3.24	2.75–2.99	2.50–2.74	2.25–2.49	2.00–2.24	Below 2.00
175–180									
170–174									
165–169									
160–164									
155–159									
150–154									
145–149									
140–144									
Below 140									

Good Possibility   Possible   Unlikely

Baylor University School of Law

1114 South University Parks Drive, One Bear Place #97288
Waco, TX 76798-7288
Phone: 254.710.2529; Fax: 254.710.2316
E-mail: BaylorLaw@baylor.edu; Website: http://law.baylor.edu

ABA
Approved
Since
1931

The Basics

Type of school	Private
Term	Quarter
Application deadline	11/1 2/1 3/1
Application fee	$40
Financial aid deadline	2/1
Can first year start other than fall?	Yes
Student to faculty ratio	15.2 to 1
# of housing spaces available restricted to law students	
graduate housing for which law students are eligible	48

Faculty and Administrators

	Total		Men		Women		Minorities	
	Spr	Fall	Spr	Fall	Spr	Fall	Spr	Fall
Full-time	24	27	19	21	5	6	3	3
Other full-time	0	0	0	0	0	0	0	0
Deans, librarians, & others who teach	6	6	4	4	2	2	0	0
Part-time	16	13	14	11	2	2	1	1
Total	46	46	37	36	9	10	4	4

Curriculum

	Full-Time	Part-Time
Typical first-year section size	66	0
Is there typically a "small section" of the first-year class, other than Legal Writing, taught by full-time faculty	Yes	No
If yes, typical size offered last year	52	
# of classroom course titles beyond first-year curriculum		81
# of upper division courses, excluding seminars, with an enrollment: Under 25		82
25–49		30
50–74		14
75–99		9
100+		0
# of seminars		6
# of seminar positions available		96
# of seminar positions filled	96	0
# of positions available in simulation courses	1,031	
# of simulation positions filled	1,031	0
# of positions available in faculty supervised clinical courses		52
# of faculty supervised clinical positions filled	52	0
# involved in field placements	91	0
# involved in law journals	65	0
# involved in moot court or trial competitions	56	0
# of credit hours required to graduate		126

JD Enrollment and Ethnicity

	Men		Women		Full-Time		Part-Time		1st-Year		Total		JD Degs. Awd.
	#	%	#	%	#	%	#	%	#	%	#	%	
African Amer.	3	1.2	9	4.1	12	2.6	0	0.0	8	4.2	12	2.6	2
Amer. Indian	1	0.4	0	0.0	1	0.2	0	0.0	0	0.0	1	0.2	0
Asian Amer.	18	7.3	24	11.0	42	9.0	0	0.0	18	9.4	42	9.0	6
Mex. Amer.	8	3.3	4	1.8	12	2.6	0	0.0	0	0.0	12	2.6	4
Puerto Rican	0	0.0	0	0.0	0	0.0	0	0.0	0	0.0	0	0.0	0
Hispanic	14	5.7	16	7.3	30	6.5	0	0.0	25	13.1	30	6.5	2
Total Minority	44	17.9	53	24.2	97	20.9	0	0.0	51	26.7	97	20.9	14
For. Nation.	0	0.0	0	0.0	0	0.0	0	0.0	0	0.0	0	0.0	0
Caucasian	202	82.1	166	75.8	368	79.1	0	0.0	140	73.3	368	79.1	116
Unknown	0	0.0	0	0.0	0	0.0	0	0.0	0	0.0	0	0.0	0
Total	246	52.9	219	47.1	465	100.0	0	0.0	191	41.1	465	100.0	130

Transfers

Transfers in	0
Transfers out	2

Tuition and Fees

	Resident	Nonresident
Full-time	$38,408	
Part-time		
Tuition Guarantee Program		N

Living Expenses

Estimated living expenses for singles

Living on campus	Living off campus	Living at home
$17,301	$16,821	$10,608

Baylor University School of Law

ABA
Approved
Since
1931

GPA and LSAT Scores

	Fall	Spring	Summer	Total
# of apps	2,360	881	418	3,659
# of offers	763	204	123	1,090
# of matrics	86	77	34	197
75% GPA	3.89	3.71	3.73	3.80
Median GPA	3.76	3.52	3.53	3.62
25% GPA	3.45	3.31	3.28	3.40
75% LSAT	164	159	161	162
Median LSAT	162	156	159	160
25% LSAT	160	155	157	156

Grants and Scholarships (from prior year)

	Total #	Total %	Full-Time #	Full-Time %	Part-Time #	Part-Time %
Total # of students	418		418		0	
Total # receiving grants	382	91.4	382	91.4	0	0.0
Less than 1/2 tuition	232	55.5	232	55.5	0	0.0
Half to full tuition	77	18.4	77	18.4	0	0.0
Full tuition	55	13.2	55	13.2	0	0.0
More than full tuition	18	4.3	18	4.3	0	0.0
Median grant amount			$3,331		$0	

Informational and Library Resources

Total amount spent on library materials	$1,366,591
Study seating capacity inside the library	279
# of full-time equivalent professional librarians	4
Hours per week library is open	108
# of open, wired connections available to students	733
# of networked computers available for use by students	39
Has wireless network?	Y
Require computer?	N

JD Attrition (from prior year)

	Academic #	Other #	Total #	Total %
1st year	0	16	16	9.0
2nd year	1	4	5	3.5
3rd year	1	0	1	1.0
4th year	0	0	0	0.0

Employment (9 months after graduation)

	Total	Percentage
Employment status known	146	95.4
Employment status unknown	7	4.6
Employed	140	95.9
Pursuing graduate degrees	3	2.1
Unemployed (seeking, not seeking, or studying for the bar)	3	2.1
Type of Employment		
# employed in law firms	91	65.0
# employed in business and industry	13	9.3
# employed in government	17	12.1
# employed in public interest	1	0.7
# employed as judicial clerks	14	10.0
# employed in academia	3	2.1
Geographic Location		
# employed in state	125	89.3
# employed in foreign countries	0	0.0
# of states where employed	12	

Bar Passage Rates

First-time takers	150	Reporting %	95.33
Average school %	93.01	Average state %	85.00
Average pass difference	8.01		

Jurisdiction	Takers	Passers	Pass %	State %	Diff %
Texas	143	133	93.01	85.00	8.01

Baylor University School of Law

1114 South University Parks Drive, One Bear Place #97288
Waco, TX 76798-7288
Phone: 254.710.2529; Fax: 254.710.2316
E-mail: BaylorLaw@baylor.edu; Website: http://law.baylor.edu

■ Introduction

Baylor University School of Law is a private, ABA-approved law school and is a member of the Association of American Law Schools. Formally organized in 1857, Baylor law school is the oldest law school in Texas and is located on the campus of Baylor University in Waco, Texas. Waco is located in central Texas, has a population of over 220,000, and offers a diverse and rich array of cultural and recreational opportunities, as well as very moderate living costs.

Baylor law school stands at the forefront of practice-oriented law schools nationally. Baylor is clear about its mission—to equip students upon graduation to practice law effectively and ethically. That is the key difference. Students are trained and mentored in all facets of law, including theoretical analysis, practical application, legal writing, advocacy, professional responsibility, and negotiation and counseling skills.

■ Enrollment/Diversity

Baylor law school is small by choice, with entering classes of approximately 70 students in the spring, 30 in the summer, and 70 in the fall. Baylor law school has a target student population of 400. We keep our program small because we are interested in producing quality, not quantity.

Baylor is deeply committed to enrolling classes that are rich in diversity. Indeed, diversity is an important element of our educational mission. Baylor's minority enrollment for the spring, summer, and fall 2009 entering classes was 26 percent. While the Law School Admission Test (LSAT) score and undergraduate grade-point average are strong indicators for academic ability, Baylor is committed to considering carefully all factors of every applicant's application file, including socioeconomic disadvantage, bilingual language skills, work experience, community involvement, leadership roles, and communication skills. These factors enable us to enroll classes that are well qualified and especially distinctive.

■ Faculty

Baylor law school is committed to providing its students with a classroom and courtroom experience that will prepare them fully for the practice. Faculty members, committed to the dual mission of teaching and scholarship, hold degrees from law schools and universities throughout the nation and include former law clerks for various appellate courts throughout the nation.

Faculty members are experts in their areas and have substantial practical experience. They produce a significant amount of legal scholarship, which results in their demand as speakers at legal institutes and civic functions. One of the distinctive features of the faculty is that professors maintain unrestricted hours for student consultation. Every professor is available for lending advice and guidance in all academic, professional, and other matters of concern to students.

■ Facilities and Technology

The home of Baylor law school, the award-winning Sheila and Walter Umphrey Law Center, was dedicated in 2002. At every stage of the design of the Law Center, the most important goal was to put teaching first. The building houses every facility a modern law school requires: classrooms that are unsurpassed as teaching facilities; an advocacy suite, including state-of-the-art courtrooms that provide the optimum environment for advocacy training—Baylor's centerpiece of excellence; a large, two-story appellate advocacy courtroom/classroom; a library with comfortable study and seating space in several impressive reading rooms overlooking the Brazos River; and faculty offices that support faculty mentoring, which is the hallmark of our program.

Technology permeates the Law Center, including data and electric ports at virtually every seat in the building, along with a concurrent wireless network. Classrooms are equipped with cutting-edge technology, including audio, video, and Internet access. The automatic cameras in the courtrooms can be aimed at a desired location in the room through use of joystick controllers mounted in the console tabletops. The law school uses a sophisticated course-management system that allows the faculty to post assignments, syllabi, and course announcements, and provides discussion boards.

■ Trial Advocacy Program

Procedure is the tool of the trial lawyer, and the bedrock of Baylor's nationally ranked advocacy program is Practice Court—an ultra-intensive study of civil procedure. In addition to the science of procedure, students will learn the art of trial advocacy in a rigorous and tough six-month program of skills training during the third year of law school. Students try lawsuits from beginning to end. This course prepares students to be competent, responsible, and ethical lawyers.

Baylor has a long record of successfully competing at the national and regional levels in both moot court and mock trial interscholastic competitions. In 2009, Baylor's mock trial team was crowned the national champions at the National Trial Competition sponsored by the American College of Trial Lawyers and the Texas Young Lawyers Association.

■ Curriculum and Special Programs

The required curriculum is structured to provide a logical progression for legal study from fundamental legal doctrine in first-year courses to increasingly more sophisticated and complex second- and third-year courses. The challenging curriculum, along with providing students the opportunity to perform specialized lawyering tasks under the direct supervision of accomplished lawyers, also prepares them for the rigors of any type of modern legal practice. Additionally, students have the opportunity to complete a more concentrated course of study and training in seven areas of interest: general civil litigation, business litigation, business transactions, criminal practice, estate planning, administrative practice, and intellectual property.

There are three joint degrees: JD/MBA, JD/MTax, and JD/MPPA.

■ Scholarships and Financial Aid

Baylor law school has an extraordinarily generous scholarship program. Scholarships are awarded to entering students based primarily on undergraduate GPA and LSAT scores. These scholarships are automatically awarded to students who qualify. Scholarship awards generally range from one half to full tuition. The law school also participates in nationally recognized financial aid programs. Texas residents are eligible for the Texas Tuition Equalization Grant.

■ Admission

The law school has three entering classes—spring (February), summer (May), and fall (August)—with completely separate application processes. Each class has far more applications than seats available; however, admission to the spring or summer classes is slightly less competitive than admission to the fall class.

The Admission Committee considers each application in its entirety and considers many factors beyond test scores and undergraduate GPA. Such factors include employment experience, demonstrated leadership potential, cocurricular and extracurricular activities, ethnicity, academic performance trends, undergraduate major, caliber of undergraduate school, life experience, circumstances of particular disadvantage, and any other relevant information submitted by the applicant. Any factors the applicant would like the Admission Committee to take into consideration should be addressed in a personal statement.

■ Student Life

Students will find a stimulating variety of enjoyable student activities and organizations that will enhance their legal education. Students can compete interscholastically on Baylor's nationally recognized mock trial and moot court teams. Students can hone their writing and legal scholarship abilities by being a member of the Baylor Law Review, which is a legal periodical published quarterly by the students under the supervision of faculty. Baylor law school also offers a wide array of "special interest" student organizations focused on particular areas of law.

■ Career Services and Bar Passage

The Career Services Office is committed year-round to providing students with the support and resources they need in pursuing their chosen career paths. Shortly after graduation, over 97 percent of our 2008 graduates seeking employment were employed or enrolled in graduate-degree programs. Baylor graduates find positions throughout the nation in private practice in large and small firms, government agencies, judicial clerkships, public interest organizations, and public and private corporations.

The Career Services Office provides extensive one-on-one training on job-search techniques, interview skills, job strategies, and résumé- and cover letter-writing techniques. The office coordinates an on-campus interview program and posts job listings from employers around the country. The office also hosts regular seminars to foster professional development for students.

Our record of success on the Texas bar exam is unsurpassed by any other Texas law school. In July 2009, 94.12 percent of Baylor graduates passed the Texas bar exam the first time. The overall state pass rate was 89.41 percent. Baylor Law School has had the highest pass rate 12 times since 2001. Graduates taking other state bar exams have been exceptionally successful as well.

Applicant Profile

Baylor University School of Law
This grid includes only the fall 2009 entering class and includes applicants who earned 120–180 LSAT scores under standard administrations.

LSAT Score	3.75 +		3.50–3.74		3.25–3.49		3.00–3.24		2.75–2.99		2.50–2.74		2.25–2.49		2.00–2.24		Below 2.00		No GPA		Total	
	Apps	Adm	Apps	Adm	Apps	Adm	Apps	Adm	Apps	Adm	Apps	Adm	Apps	Adm	Apps	Adm	Apps	Adm	Apps	Adm	Apps	Adm
175–180	1	1	1	1	3	3	0	0	0	0	0	0	0	0	0	0	0	0	0	0	5	5
170–174	11	11	12	12	14	14	10	10	1	1	1	1	1	0	0	0	0	0	0	0	50	49
165–169	72	71	48	46	52	49	29	23	7	5	6	4	5	1	0	0	0	0	0	0	219	199
160–164	188	181	155	124	109	66	64	15	24	10	14	2	2	0	2	0	0	0	5	2	563	400
155–159	180	42	207	39	142	18	74	2	35	0	14	0	8	0	4	0	1	0	6	0	671	101
150–154	63	3	91	1	77	0	71	0	47	0	22	0	12	0	1	0	0	0	3	0	387	4
145–149	24	0	36	0	66	0	42	0	38	0	15	0	11	0	6	0	0	0	4	0	242	0
140–144	8	0	16	0	24	0	25	0	13	0	8	0	12	0	4	0	0	0	1	0	111	0
135–139	1	0	6	0	10	0	10	0	7	0	7	0	3	0	2	0	1	0	0	0	47	0
130–134	2	0	1	0	4	0	0	0	4	0	2	0	1	0	1	0	0	0	2	0	17	0
125–129	0	0	0	0	0	0	1	0	1	0	2	0	1	0	0	0	1	0	0	0	6	0
120–124	0	0	0	0	0	0	0	0	0	0	0	0	1	0	0	0	0	0	0	0	1	0
Total	550	309	573	223	501	150	326	50	177	16	91	7	57	1	20	0	3	0	21	2	2319	758

Apps = Number of Applicants   Adm = Number Admitted   Reflects 98% of the total applicant pool.

Boston College Law School

Office of Admissions, 885 Centre Street
Newton, MA 02459
Phone: 617.552.4351; Fax: 617.552.2917
E-mail: bclawadm@bc.edu; Website: www.bc.edu/law

ABA Approved Since 1932

The Basics

Type of school	Private
Term	Semester
Application deadline	3/1
Application fee	$75
Financial aid deadline	3/15
Can first year start other than fall?	No
Student to faculty ratio	13.5 to 1
# of housing spaces available restricted to law students	
graduate housing for which law students are eligible	32

Faculty and Administrators

	Total		Men		Women		Minorities	
	Spr	Fall	Spr	Fall	Spr	Fall	Spr	Fall
Full-time	49	51	28	30	21	21	9	9
Other full-time	2	2	0	0	2	2	0	0
Deans, librarians, & others who teach	13	13	3	3	10	10	1	1
Part-time	46	37	33	27	12	8	3	1
Total	110	103	64	60	45	41	13	11

JD Enrollment and Ethnicity

	Men		Women		Full-Time		Part-Time		1st-Year		Total		JD Degs. Awd.
	#	%	#	%	#	%	#	%	#	%	#	%	
African Amer.	12	2.8	17	4.4	28	3.4	1	50.0	8	3.0	29	3.6	10
Amer. Indian	2	0.5	4	1.0	6	0.7	0	0.0	3	1.1	6	0.7	1
Asian Amer.	42	9.7	52	13.6	94	11.6	0	0.0	37	13.9	94	11.5	25
Mex. Amer.	2	0.5	6	1.6	8	1.0	0	0.0	3	1.1	8	1.0	3
Puerto Rican	3	0.7	1	0.3	4	0.5	0	0.0	2	0.8	4	0.5	2
Hispanic	30	7.0	13	3.4	43	5.3	0	0.0	17	6.4	43	5.3	7
Total Minority	91	21.1	93	24.3	183	22.5	1	50.0	70	26.3	184	22.6	48
For. Nation.	2	0.5	10	2.6	12	1.5	0	0.0	1	0.4	12	1.5	4
Caucasian	296	68.7	242	63.2	537	66.1	1	50.0	168	63.2	538	66.1	169
Unknown	42	9.7	38	9.9	80	9.9	0	0.0	27	10.2	80	9.8	21
Total	431	52.9	383	47.1	812	99.8	2	0.2	266	32.7	814		242

Curriculum

	Full-Time	Part-Time
Typical first-year section size	88	0
Is there typically a "small section" of the first-year class, other than Legal Writing, taught by full-time faculty	Yes	No
If yes, typical size offered last year	30	
# of classroom course titles beyond first-year curriculum	149	

# of upper division courses, excluding seminars, with an enrollment:		
	Under 25	73
	25–49	32
	50–74	12
	75–99	10
	100+	2

# of seminars	42	
# of seminar positions available	588	
# of seminar positions filled	471	0
# of positions available in simulation courses	593	
# of simulation positions filled	473	0
# of positions available in faculty supervised clinical courses	121	
# of faculty supervised clinical positions filled	121	0
# involved in field placements	54	0
# involved in law journals	173	0
# involved in moot court or trial competitions	46	0
# of credit hours required to graduate	85	

Transfers

Transfers in	13
Transfers out	15

Tuition and Fees

	Resident	Nonresident
Full-time	$39,600	$39,600
Part-time		
Tuition Guarantee Program	N	

Living Expenses

Estimated living expenses for singles

Living on campus	Living off campus	Living at home
N/A	$18,390	N/A

Boston College Law School

ABA Approved Since 1932

GPA and LSAT Scores

	Total	Full-Time	Part-Time
# of apps	7,166	7,166	0
# of offers	1,431	1,431	0
# of matrics	264	264	0
75% GPA	3.68	3.68	0.00
Median GPA	3.53	3.53	0.00
25% GPA	3.34	3.34	0.00
75% LSAT	167	167	0
Median LSAT	166	166	0
25% LSAT	163	163	0

Grants and Scholarships (from prior year)

	Total #	Total %	Full-Time #	Full-Time %	Part-Time #	Part-Time %
Total # of students	801		799		2	
Total # receiving grants	408	50.9	408	51.1	0	0.0
Less than 1/2 tuition	235	29.3	235	29.4	0	0.0
Half to full tuition	173	21.6	173	21.7	0	0.0
Full tuition	0	0.0	0	0.0	0	0.0
More than full tuition	0	0.0	0	0.0	0	0.0
Median grant amount			$16,678		$0	

Informational and Library Resources

Total amount spent on library materials	$1,468,814
Study seating capacity inside the library	673
# of full-time equivalent professional librarians	10.0
Hours per week library is open	105
# of open, wired connections available to students	1,014
# of networked computers available for use by students	143
Has wireless network?	Y
Require computer?	N

JD Attrition (from prior year)

	Academic #	Other #	Total #	Total %
1st year	0	17	17	5.7
2nd year	0	1	1	0.4
3rd year	0	0	0	0.0
4th year	0	0	0	0.0

Employment (9 months after graduation)

	Total	Percentage
Employment status known	274	100.0
Employment status unknown	0	0.0
Employed	264	96.4
Pursuing graduate degrees	0	0.0
Unemployed (seeking, not seeking, or studying for the bar)	7	2.6
Type of Employment		
# employed in law firms	179	67.8
# employed in business and industry	12	4.5
# employed in government	19	7.2
# employed in public interest	8	3.0
# employed as judicial clerks	36	13.6
# employed in academia	10	3.8
Geographic Location		
# employed in state	132	50.0
# employed in foreign countries	3	1.1
# of states where employed	24	

Bar Passage Rates

First-time takers	274	Reporting %	91.61
Average school %	94.02	Average state %	91.09
Average pass difference	2.93		

Jurisdiction	Takers	Passers	Pass %	State %	Diff %
Massachusetts	158	149	94.30	92.33	1.97
New York	93	87	93.55	88.98	4.57

Boston College Law School

Office of Admissions, 885 Centre Street
Newton, MA 02459
Phone: 617.552.4351; Fax: 617.552.2917
E-mail: bclawadm@bc.edu; Website: www.bc.edu/law

■ Introduction

Since its founding in 1929, Boston College Law School has earned a national reputation for educational excellence and the highest standards of professionalism while fostering a unique spirit of community among its students, faculty, and staff. The diverse curriculum is designed to help students develop the skills and knowledge needed to adapt successfully to changes in society and the legal profession. Boston College Law School is located on an attractive 40-acre campus in Newton, Massachusetts, just minutes from downtown Boston. It is fully accredited and has a chapter of the Order of the Coif, the prestigious national law school honorary society.

■ Library and Physical Facilities

Stretched over 40 acres of rolling hills and gently sloping lawns, the BC Law campus is an intriguing mix of old-style elegance and new-world innovation—a testament to the power of technology, engineering, and design. Students can connect to the network anywhere. Data ports are available from every library carrel, as well as every classroom seat in the East Wing; wireless technology is also available anywhere in the library and in every classroom. The library encourages individual or group study, with its desk and lounge areas, computer centers, audiovisual resource rooms, and private study rooms. Each computer center is fully equipped for searching LexisNexis and Westlaw databases; legal periodical literature; official publications of Massachusetts, the United States, and the United Nations; and other legal indices. With its soaring atrium entry and light-filled spaces, the East Wing includes seven classrooms, twenty-seven faculty offices, administrative offices for a Career Services Center and a Career Resources Library, two conference rooms, and the John J. and Mary Daly Curtin Public Interest Center (a suite of offices for student groups working on public service projects). The East Wing's brick exterior complements the law library and the Stuart House administration building, as well as the Barat House alumni and development building. The three buildings form an attractive interior courtyard for outdoor use by the law school community.

All academic, administrative, library and service facilities are accessible to physically challenged persons.

■ Curriculum

The faculty of Boston College Law School strongly believes in the importance of a general legal education designed to enable graduates to adapt to the changing demands of law practice. Areas of particular focus include international law, constitutional law, business law, dispute resolution, immigration law, environmental law, criminal law, family law, tax law, intellectual property law, and clinical programs.

In the first year, all students take traditional courses, including Civil Procedure, Constitutional Law, Contracts, Property Law, Criminal Law, and Torts. In addition, an intensive, two-semester Legal Reasoning, Research, and Writing course is required. In the spring semester, students are allowed to take one three-credit elective. More than 100 courses offered in the second and third years are elective.

■ Externships

The **Semester in Practice** program offers individually designed placement with judges, government agencies, public interest organizations, and law firms in the greater Boston area. The **Attorney General Program** provides an intensive full-year clinical experience in the Government Bureau of the Massachusetts Office of the Attorney General. The **Judicial Process** course includes placement with a specific Superior Court justice. The **International Criminal Tribunals** (ICT) offer a unique opportunity to work on-site at the criminal tribunal established by the UN Security Council in The Hague, the Netherlands, and in Sarajevo. The **London Program** has both academic and experiential components. The program provides students with a critical insight into comparative legal institutions with special emphasis on international regulatory process, whether in environmental or securities regulation, antitrust, intellectual property, or human rights.

■ Clinical Programs

The Law School is committed to making clinical experiences available to all students who desire them. At the **Boston College Legal Assistance Bureau** (LAB), students assume responsibility for representation of indigent clients through the **Civil Litigation**, **Housing**, **Women and the Law**, and **Community Enterprise** clinics.

Students in the **Criminal Justice Clinic** prosecute or defend criminal cases in state court. The **Judge and Community Courts** class examines the interaction between the local court and the community it serves. In **Juvenile Rights Advocacy**, students advocate for troubled youth and work toward juvenile justice policy reform. In the **Immigration Law Clinic**, students advise clients and work on administrative and appellate litigation under the supervision of practicing attorneys.

■ Extracurricular and Cocurricular Activities

Selected students may participate in the following writing programs: *Boston College Law Review, Boston College Environmental Affairs Law Review, Boston College International and Comparative Law Review, Boston College Third World Law Journal,* and the *Uniform Commercial Code Reporter-Digest.*

Boston College Law School supports several competitions, including negotiation, client counseling, moot court, and mock trial. In addition, selected students may compete in several national moot court competitions. These competitions allow students to enhance negotiation, counseling, and oral advocacy skills. Over the years, Boston College has performed extremely well in regional and national competitions, which are judged by faculty, state and federal judges, and practicing attorneys.

■ Admission

The Law School has no minimum cutoff either for GPA or LSAT. Academic achievement and LSAT scores are extremely significant, but work and professional experience, college extracurricular activities, the quality of recommendations,

and the personal statement also play an important role in decision making.

In evaluating the undergraduate record, class rank as well as courses taken are considered. If the LSAT has been taken more than once, all scores are considered in the review process. Boston College Law School strongly encourages applications from qualified minority, disabled, or other students who have been socially, economically, or culturally disadvantaged. Each applicant is evaluated in an effort to ensure that all relevant credentials are favorably considered. The Law School has been very successful both in admitting minority and special students and in retaining them to graduation.

■ Expenses and Financial Aid

The Financial Aid Office administers the Law School's scholarship and grant programs, federal and private loan programs, and the Federal Work-Study Program. Scholarship funds are awarded on the basis of both need and merit. Approximately 85 percent of the students currently enrolled are awarded financial aid and 46 percent of these students receive scholarship and grant assistance as part of their financial aid awards.

Each year, three entering students are awarded full–tuition Public Service Scholarships because of their demonstrated commitment to public service law. The Law School also offers a Loan Repayment Assistance Program for graduates who pursue careers in legal services, government, and not-for-profit corporations.

■ Housing

In addition, The Boston College Off-Campus Housing Office provides information about neighborhoods, lists of local rental agencies, maps of local areas, and public transportation information. The office also maintains housing listings that include house rentals and renting rooms in private homes and apartments. In addition, a graduate housing fair is held in June to assist students in their housing search. For more information, please visit the Office of Residential Life website at *www.bc.edu/reslife*.

■ Career Services

The Office of Career Services is dedicated to helping students make the transition from law student to employed professional. The range of opportunities for graduates spans virtually the entire spectrum of legal practice. Each year more than 1,000 prospective employers solicit applications from Boston College law students. During the 2008–2009 recruitment season, approximately 400 law firms, government agencies, corporations, and public interest organizations from 31 states interviewed Boston College students as part of on- and off-campus recruiting programs. More than 12,000 alumni are presently practicing in 50 states and 19 foreign countries.

Applicant Profile

Boston College Law School
This grid includes only applicants who earned 120–180 LSAT scores under standard administrations.

LSAT Score	GPA 3.75 +		3.50–3.74		3.25–3.49		3.00–3.24		2.75–2.99		Below 2.75		No GPA		Total	
	Apps	Adm	Apps	Adm	Apps	Adm	Apps	Adm	Apps	Adm	Apps	Adm	Apps	Adm	Apps	Adm
175–180	8	7	16	11	9	7	4	4	2	0	4	0	0	0	43	29
170–174	61	50	57	48	73	44	34	11	10	2	8	2	1	1	244	158
165–169	318	246	428	299	274	156	148	55	55	10	32	0	15	6	1270	772
160–164	586	123	770	136	540	68	289	21	85	6	45	0	55	3	2370	357
150–159	431	28	805	53	621	20	377	3	150	0	123	0	58	0	2565	104
140–149	42	0	98	2	144	0	108	0	69	0	72	0	20	0	553	2
Below 140	3	0	10	1	16	0	23	0	25	0	40	0	10	0	127	1
Total	1449	454	2184	550	1677	295	983	94	396	18	324	2	159	10	7172	1423

Apps = Number of Applicants
Adm = Number Admitted
Reflects 99% of the total applicant pool; average LSAT data reported.

Boston University School of Law

765 Commonwealth Avenue
Boston, MA 02215
Phone: 617.353.3100
E-mail: bulawadm@bu.edu; Website: www.bu.edu/law

ABA Approved Since 1925

The Basics

Type of school	Private
Term	Semester
Application deadline	3/1
Application fee	$75
Financial aid deadline	3/1
Can first year start other than fall?	No
Student to faculty ratio	12.2 to 1
# of housing spaces available restricted to law students	
graduate housing for which law students are eligible	810

Faculty and Administrators

	Total		Men		Women		Minorities	
	Spr	Fall	Spr	Fall	Spr	Fall	Spr	Fall
Full-time	56	56	36	32	20	24	5	4
Other full-time	7	9	7	7	0	2	1	1
Deans, librarians, & others who teach	9	8	6	5	3	3	1	1
Part-time	80	79	56	50	23	29	7	12
Total	152	152	105	94	46	58	14	18

Curriculum

	Full-Time	Part-Time
Typical first-year section size	90	0
Is there typically a "small section" of the first-year class, other than Legal Writing, taught by full-time faculty	Yes	No
If yes, typical size offered last year	46	

# of classroom course titles beyond first-year curriculum		195
# of upper division courses, excluding seminars, with an enrollment:	Under 25	105
	25–49	39
	50–74	16
	75–99	6
	100+	3
# of seminars		73
# of seminar positions available		1,372
# of seminar positions filled	1,131	0
# of positions available in simulation courses		479
# of simulation positions filled	415	0
# of positions available in faculty supervised clinical courses		178
# of faculty supervised clinical positions filled	123	0
# involved in field placements	35	0
# involved in law journals	329	0
# involved in moot court or trial competitions	38	0
# of credit hours required to graduate		84

JD Enrollment and Ethnicity

	Men		Women		Full-Time		Part-Time		1st-Year		Total		JD Degs. Awd.
	#	%	#	%	#	%	#	%	#	%	#	%	
African Amer.	16	3.8	28	6.8	44	5.3	0	0.0	20	7.4	44	5.3	10
Amer. Indian	1	0.2	1	0.2	2	0.2	0	0.0	0	0.0	2	0.2	2
Asian Amer.	41	9.8	55	13.3	96	11.6	0	0.0	32	11.8	96	11.6	29
Mex. Amer.	7	1.7	3	0.7	10	1.2	0	0.0	4	1.5	10	1.2	4
Puerto Rican	5	1.2	4	1.0	9	1.1	0	0.0	2	0.7	9	1.1	1
Hispanic	14	3.4	14	3.4	28	3.4	0	0.0	6	2.2	28	3.4	6
Total Minority	84	20.1	105	25.4	189	22.9	0	0.0	64	23.6	189	22.8	52
For. Nation.	11	2.6	19	4.6	30	3.6	0	0.0	10	3.7	30	3.6	7
Caucasian	282	67.6	264	63.9	543	65.7	3	100.0	170	62.7	546	65.8	203
Unknown	40	9.6	25	6.1	65	7.9	0	0.0	27	10.0	65	7.8	7
Total	417	50.2	413	49.8	827	99.6	3	0.4	271	32.7	830		269

Transfers

Transfers in	15
Transfers out	13

Tuition and Fees

	Resident	Nonresident
Full-time	$39,658	
Part-time		
Tuition Guarantee Program	N	

Living Expenses

Estimated living expenses for singles

Living on campus	Living off campus	Living at home
$17,576	$17,576	$12,830

Boston University School of Law

ABA
Approved
Since
1925

GPA and LSAT Scores

	Total	Full-Time	Part-Time
# of apps	7,659	7,659	0
# of offers	1,801	1,801	0
# of matrics	271	271	0
75% GPA	3.83	3.83	0.00
Median GPA	3.70	3.70	0.00
25% GPA	3.50	3.50	0.00
75% LSAT	167	167	0
Median LSAT	166	166	0
25% LSAT	164	164	0

Grants and Scholarships (from prior year)

	Total		Full-Time		Part-Time	
	#	%	#	%	#	%
Total # of students	832		822		10	
Total # receiving grants	494	59.4	494	60.1	0	0.0
Less than 1/2 tuition	260	31.3	260	31.6	0	0.0
Half to full tuition	218	26.2	218	26.5	0	0.0
Full tuition	0	0.0	0	0.0	0	0.0
More than full tuition	16	1.9	16	1.9	0	0.0
Median grant amount			$15,000		$0	

Informational and Library Resources

Total amount spent on library materials	$1,622,711
Study seating capacity inside the library	600
# of full-time equivalent professional librarians	11.0
Hours per week library is open	102
# of open, wired connections available to students	22
# of networked computers available for use by students	85
Has wireless network?	Y
Require computer?	N

JD Attrition (from prior year)

	Academic	Other	Total	
	#	#	#	%
1st year	0	19	19	6.7
2nd year	0	3	3	1.1
3rd year	0	0	0	0.0
4th year	0	0	0	0.0

Employment (9 months after graduation)

	Total	Percentage
Employment status known	276	99.3
Employment status unknown	2	0.7
Employed	267	96.7
Pursuing graduate degrees	8	2.9
Unemployed (seeking, not seeking, or studying for the bar)	1	0.4
Type of Employment		
# employed in law firms	183	68.5
# employed in business and industry	14	5.2
# employed in government	14	5.2
# employed in public interest	16	6.0
# employed as judicial clerks	15	5.6
# employed in academia	19	7.1
Geographic Location		
# employed in state	122	45.7
# employed in foreign countries	4	1.5
# of states where employed	24	

Bar Passage Rates

First-time takers	265	Reporting %	89.43
Average school %	95.78	Average state %	90.84
Average pass difference	4.94		

Jurisdiction	Takers	Passers	Pass %	State %	Diff %
Massachusetts	132	129	97.73	92.33	5.40
New York	105	98	93.33	88.98	4.35

Boston University School of Law

765 Commonwealth Avenue
Boston, MA 02215
Phone: 617.353.3100
E-mail: bulawadm@bu.edu; Website: www.bu.edu/law

■ Introduction

Boston University School of Law offers one of the finest legal educations in the nation, attracting students from all over the country and abroad. A pioneer in American legal education, the school was founded in 1872 on the principles that legal education should be open to all men and women of ability without regard to background or beliefs, and that it should balance theory and analysis with practical training. Today, the school's innovative curriculum combines theoretical courses, clinical training, and specialized offerings—including concentrations, dual degrees, and semesters abroad. The faculty of distinguished scholars and teachers ranks among the most productive of the nation's law schools and are known for their superb teaching. The students represent a range of educational backgrounds, ethnicities, races, age groups, and employment histories.

Boston is a great place to study the law and launch a career. BU Law's location offers students enormous opportunities. They gain invaluable experience while in school through myriad job and internship opportunities that flow from Boston's status as a major business, financial, and legal center. Boston is home to many high-tech, start-up companies and is a leading center in health care. Boston, as the state capital, is an active government center at both the federal and state levels, making it a laboratory for clinics, pro bono volunteering, and externships.

■ Faculty

At BU Law, our faculty members make the difference—to our students, as teachers; to the law, as scholars; and to the local and global community, as advocates. They are among the nation's leading scholars, lecturers, and teachers. BU Law faculty members come from a range of backgrounds—including six US Supreme Court clerks and numerous federal court of appeals clerks—and from several schools of legal thought, such as law and economics and feminist legal theory. They have authored texts in key fields, such as securitization, labor and employment, federal courts, contracts, and administrative law, among others. They are not only the leading scholars in their fields, but they excel inside the classroom as well. Impassioned advocates who frequently lend their expertise to pro bono causes—locally, nationally, and internationally—they bring these experiences back to the school, to share inside and outside the classroom.

■ Curriculum

BU Law offers one of the widest ranges of academic opportunities available at any American law school. In addition to the traditional curriculum, first-year students take a course in legislation and a formal moot court program, with the option to pursue advanced moot court opportunities in the second and third years. BU students can explore virtually any area of law through the school's 150 classes and seminars. They can concentrate and focus their studies, if they choose, in any of five fields—international law, health law, intellectual property law, business organizations and finance law, or litigation and dispute resolution—or design their own upper-class curriculum to suit their interest and career goals. BU Law also supports six nationally recognized student-run law journals.

■ Dual-Degree Programs

Students can pursue any of 10 dual-degree programs, combining law study with graduate course work in a program that leads to a JD and a master's degree. Dual degrees include a JD/MA-International Relations, JD/MS-Mass Communication, JD/MBA-Management, JD/MBA-Health Sector Management, JD/MA-Preservation Studies, JD/MA-Philosophy, and JD/MPH-Public Health. Students interested in tax or banking can earn an accelerated, combined JD/Master of Laws (LLM) degree in these fields. BU Law recently launched a three-year, international dual-degree program leading to a JD from Boston University and an LLM in European Law from the European College of Paris, a unit of the Université Panthéon-Assas (Paris II).

■ Study Abroad

Students at BU Law can immerse themselves in a foreign legal culture for a semester, studying international and comparative law in one of BU Law's 13 semester-long, study-abroad programs. Programs offered in 2009–2010 are at Oxford University (United Kingdom); Université Panthéon-Assas Paris II (France); Université Jean Moulin Lyon 3 (France); Universidad Pontificia Comillas de Madrid (Spain); Leiden University (the Netherlands); Bucerius Law School (Germany); the University of Florence (Italy); the University of Hong Kong (China); the University of Buenos Aires (Argentina); Tel Aviv University (Israel); Tsinghua Law School (China); the National University of Singapore (Singapore); or the Graduate Institute of International and Development Studies (Switzerland).

■ Clinical Programs

BU Law has long been recognized for having some of the finest clinical offerings in the country. The clinical faculty is among the most experienced in American legal clinical education. Students gain valuable experience through the Criminal Law Clinic (as prosecutors and as adult or juvenile defenders); the Civil Litigation Program (Housing, Employment, Family, and Disability Clinic; the Asylum and Human Rights Clinic; and the Employment Rights Clinic); the Semester-in-Practice Program (Government Lawyering Externship in Washington, DC; Death Penalty Externship at the Southern Center for Human Rights in Atlanta, Georgia; and the Human Rights Externship in Geneva, Switzerland); the Community Courts Program; the Health Law Externship Program; and the Legal Externship Program (Judicial, Litigation, Government Agencies, and Public Interest). BU Law's Legislative Clinic includes the Legislative Policy and Drafting Clinic, the Legislative Counsel Clinic, the Africa i-Parliaments Clinic, and the Legislative Internship Program.

■ Public Interest Programs

BU Law has a long tradition of training public service leaders. Students may explore the world of public interest, gain experience during law school, apply for public interest positions, and learn about pro bono options that can supplement traditional legal practice. The Pro Bono Program

allows students to dedicate their developing legal skills to unmet legal needs in the Boston area and abroad. Students may participate in Pro Bono Service Trips to New Orleans, where students address post-Hurricane Katrina legal issues; to Texas, to work on the South Texas Pro Bono Asylum Representation Project (ProBAR); and on our newest trip to Thailand, to work with a nongovernmental organization (NGO) dedicated to fighting human trafficking. The Public Interest Project (PIP) provides grants through fundraising efforts to support students working in summer public interest jobs.

■ Student Life

Students are encouraged to engage in student organizations, extracurricular activities, and community service. The Student Government Association (SGA), and more than 30 active student organizations, support and foster the academic and social community. Student organizations plan numerous lectures and discussion panels as well as social and professional activities throughout the year. SGA hosts social events including a Halloween party and ski trip. If a particular interest is not currently being served, SGA and the Dean of Students assist in forming new organizations; for example, recent years have seen the formation of the Education Law Society and National Security Law Society. The Dean of Students also sponsors the Live Well, Learn Well program, which helps students maintain healthy lifestyles; the Academic Enhancement Program, which features workshops on work/family balance, exam-taking strategies and time and stress management; and a comprehensive Diversity Month which includes panel discussions on diversity and law.

■ Career Development

The BU Law Career Development Office (CDO) is committed to helping each law student see all the possibilities that a BU Law degree affords them. The CDO offers a comprehensive program of services to students and alumni—from personal advising and instructional workshops and events, to print and online resources and tools. Students benefit from the expertise of a diverse range of attorney career advisers and participate in numerous workshops to hone job search skills and learn about substantive areas of law. Alumni assist students in the First-Year Mentoring Program and the Mock Interview Program as well as panel discussions, receptions, and individual advising sessions. BU Law offers an extensive on- and off-campus recruiting program. Hundreds of employers from every practice type and setting recruit BU Law students. Our graduates pursue careers, throughout the United States and around the world, in large, mid-size, and small law firms; federal, state, and local government; nonprofit organizations; business; and academia. Entry-level salaries of our graduates vary based on practice setting and geographic location; however, BU Law graduates command competitive salaries wherever they work. The median salary for 2008 graduates who were offered private sector employment was $160,000. BU Law prepares all of its graduates with the substantive knowledge, practical legal skills, networking opportunities, and job-search strategies to meet the challenges in the legal employment market.

■ Financial Aid

Boston University School of Law is committed to making a legal education affordable. Through scholarship awards as well as federal and private loans, the School of Law provides funding for over 85 percent of its enrolled JD students. BU Law assists approximately 60 percent of JD students with scholarship aid awarded primarily on academic merit and financial need, supplemented by our merit-only scholarship programs. With the exception of our merit-only scholarships, students must apply for scholarship aid. Our Public Interest Scholars Program provides substantial financial support to select students who plan to pursue a career in public service, and, for over 15 years, BU Law's Loan Repayment Assistance Program has offered financial support to alumni pursuing careers in public interest law.

Applicant Profile

Each year Boston University School of Law enrolls a class of students characterized by extraordinary academic achievements and diverse life experiences. LSAT scores and undergraduate GPAs are important components of an application, but numbers alone never determine an admissions decision. The Admissions Committee carefully evaluates each applicant's essays, transcripts, letters of recommendation, and any other information that helps us to understand the applicant's potential. BU Law's founding commitment to diversity, starting in 1872, continues to inform our admissions decisions today. We encourage each applicant to share with us how they might contribute to BU Law's vibrant learning community. The Admissions Committee is not looking for any one quality or set of experiences but seeks to enroll a class that represents the widest range of human experience and aspiration.

Brigham Young University—J. Reuben Clark Law School

340 JRCB
Provo, UT 84602-8000
Phone: 801.422.4277; Fax: 801.422.0389
E-mail: admissions@law.byu.edu; Website: www.law.byu.edu

ABA
Approved
Since
1974

AMERICAN BAR ASSOCIATION
Section of Legal Education
and Admissions to the Bar

The Basics

Type of school	Private
Term	Semester
Application deadline	3/1
Application fee	$50
Financial aid deadline	5/1
Can first year start other than fall?	No
Student to faculty ratio	17.3 to 1
# of housing spaces available restricted to law students	
graduate housing for which law students are eligible	

Faculty and Administrators

	Total		Men		Women		Minorities	
	Spr	Fall	Spr	Fall	Spr	Fall	Spr	Fall
Full-time	21	22	15	17	6	5	3	2
Other full-time	0	0	0	0	0	0	0	0
Deans, librarians, & others who teach	17	17	13	14	4	3	1	1
Part-time	38	38	26	29	12	9	4	2
Total	76	77	54	60	22	17	8	5

JD Enrollment and Ethnicity

	Men		Women		Full-Time		Part-Time		1st-Year		Total		JD Degs. Awd.
	#	%	#	%	#	%	#	%	#	%	#	%	
African Amer.	3	1.0	4	2.6	7	1.6	0	0.0	0	0.0	7	1.6	2
Amer. Indian	3	1.0	2	1.3	5	1.1	0	0.0	2	1.4	5	1.1	3
Asian Amer.	23	7.9	12	7.7	35	7.8	0	0.0	12	8.4	35	7.8	12
Mex. Amer.	1	0.3	1	0.6	2	0.4	0	0.0	1	0.7	2	0.4	1
Puerto Rican	0	0.0	0	0.0	0	0.0	0	0.0	0	0.0	0	0.0	1
Hispanic	16	5.5	5	3.2	21	4.7	0	0.0	6	4.2	21	4.7	9
Total Minority	46	15.8	24	15.5	70	15.7	0	0.0	21	14.7	70	15.7	28
For. Nation.	0	0.0	4	2.6	4	0.9	0	0.0	2	1.4	4	0.9	0
Caucasian	239	81.8	126	81.3	365	81.7	0	0.0	120	83.9	365	81.7	122
Unknown	7	2.4	1	0.6	8	1.8	0	0.0	0	0.0	8	1.8	0
Total	292	65.3	155	34.7	447	100.0	0	0.0	143	32.0	447		150

Curriculum

	Full-Time	Part-Time
Typical first-year section size	100	0
Is there typically a "small section" of the first-year class, other than Legal Writing, taught by full-time faculty	Yes	No
If yes, typical size offered last year	49	
# of classroom course titles beyond first-year curriculum	109	
# of upper division courses, excluding seminars, with an enrollment: Under 25	51	
25–49	15	
50–74	12	
75–99	5	
100+	0	
# of seminars	32	
# of seminar positions available	940	
# of seminar positions filled	622	0
# of positions available in simulation courses	735	
# of simulation positions filled	654	0
# of positions available in faculty supervised clinical courses	26	
# of faculty supervised clinical positions filled	26	0
# involved in field placements	195	0
# involved in law journals	180	0
# involved in moot court or trial competitions	116	0
# of credit hours required to graduate	90	

Transfers

Transfers in	8
Transfers out	1

Tuition and Fees

	Resident	Nonresident
Full-time	$9,980	$19,960
Part-time		
Tuition Guarantee Program	N	

Living Expenses

Estimated living expenses for singles

Living on campus	Living off campus	Living at home
$12,600	$12,600	$5,450

Brigham Young University—J. Reuben Clark Law School

ABA
Approved
Since
1974

GPA and LSAT Scores

	Total	Full-Time	Part-Time
# of apps	733	733	0
# of offers	218	218	0
# of matrics	147	147	0
75% GPA	3.85	3.85	0.00
Median GPA	3.74	3.74	0.00
25% GPA	3.52	3.52	0.00
75% LSAT	165	165	0
Median LSAT	163	163	0
25% LSAT	160	160	0

Grants and Scholarships (from prior year)

	Total		Full-Time		Part-Time	
	#	%	#	%	#	%
Total # of students	458		458		0	
Total # receiving grants	142	31.0	142	31.0	0	0.0
Less than 1/2 tuition	65	14.2	65	14.2	0	0.0
Half to full tuition	34	7.4	34	7.4	0	0.0
Full tuition	41	9.0	41	9.0	0	0.0
More than full tuition	2	0.4	2	0.4	0	0.0
Median grant amount			$4,620		$0	

Informational and Library Resources

Total amount spent on library materials	$1,305,732
Study seating capacity inside the library	906
# of full-time equivalent professional librarians	11
Hours per week library is open	105
# of open, wired connections available to students	533
# of networked computers available for use by students	27
Has wireless network?	Y
Require computer?	Y

JD Attrition (from prior year)

	Academic	Other	Total	
	#	#	#	%
1st year	0	0	0	0.0
2nd year	0	3	3	2.0
3rd year	0	0	0	0.0
4th year	0	0	0	0.0

Employment (9 months after graduation)

	Total	Percentage
Employment status known	154	98.7
Employment status unknown	2	1.3
Employed	152	98.7
Pursuing graduate degrees	1	0.6
Unemployed (seeking, not seeking, or studying for the bar)	0	0.0
Type of Employment		
# employed in law firms	86	56.6
# employed in business and industry	19	12.5
# employed in government	19	12.5
# employed in public interest	1	0.7
# employed as judicial clerks	24	15.8
# employed in academia	2	1.3
Geographic Location		
# employed in state	61	40.1
# employed in foreign countries	4	2.6
# of states where employed	27	

Bar Passage Rates

First-time takers	146	Reporting %	77.40
Average school %	91.15	Average state %	85.58
Average pass difference	5.57		

Jurisdiction	Takers	Passers	Pass %	State %	Diff %
Utah	92	85	92.39	87.29	5.10
California	21	18	85.71	78.07	7.64

Brigham Young University—J. Reuben Clark Law School

340 JRCB
Provo, UT 84602-8000
Phone: 801.422.4277; Fax: 801.422.0389
E-mail: admissions@law.byu.edu; Website: www.law.byu.edu

■ Introduction

Since its founding just over 30 years ago, the J. Reuben Clark Law School at Brigham Young University has been distinguished by the strength of its program and the accomplishments of its graduates. The Law School has produced 13 US Supreme Court clerkships and has an enviable placement record throughout the United States in all branches of the legal profession. The Law School's relatively small entering class of 150 lends itself to individualized instruction, while the university, with its 30,000 students, provides all the athletic, cultural, and social opportunities that a student may expect from a larger school. The Law School is fully accredited by the American Bar Association, is a member of the Association of American Law Schools, and has a chapter of the Order of the Coif.

■ Library and Physical Facilities

The Howard W. Hunter Law Library is one of the most technologically advanced law libraries in the world. It houses 475 individual study carrels with full Internet and LAN computer connectivity (hardwired and wireless). Thus, each student in his or her private study space has access to electronic resources that include Westlaw, LexisNexis, and the growing Hunter Law Library Electronic Reserve, including archives of past examinations. In convenient locations, printers, copy machines, and scanners are available for students on all library floors. The law library also contains 18 group-study rooms (4 of which are family-support rooms to assist parents who need to view closed-circuit broadcasts of classes) and spacious casual seating in open areas. Office and research space along with a conference room for the Law School's four scholarly journals, two advocacy groups, and the Student Bar Association are also conveniently located in the library. Specialized rooms are dedicated to video viewing, interactive video, microforms, and television hookups. The Rex E. Lee Reading Room and the fourth floor Quiet Reading Room provide ample space for special seminars and receptions. The library houses a collection of over 500,000 volumes or volume equivalents. Via interlibrary loan, students have access to many more titles found in the catalogs and collections of over 9,100 other worldwide institutions that, like the Hunter Library, subscribe to the Online Computer Library Center.

■ Faculty and Curriculum

The combination of the small entering class size and our internationally renowned faculty creates unique opportunities for learning. Together, our faculty seek to meet the challenge of making a difference worldwide as they engage in joint research, publishing, and advocacy. The objective of the Law School's curriculum is to maximize the students' mastery of legal reasoning and legal methods while teaching a core of the basic substantive rules of the law. Over 60 courses and 40 seminars are offered each year by a faculty of 32 full-time members and 61 adjunct faculty members. In addition, the Law School provides opportunities for students to develop practical skills through international and US externships with private law firms, corporations, and agencies, as well as public defenders, legal services, city and county attorneys,

judges, attorneys general, and guardians ad litem. Students receive one credit for every 50 hours of work.

■ The Rex E. Lee Advocacy Program

In addition to knowing the law, lawyers must synthesize complex information, analyze and formulate strategy, predict outcomes, and present information persuasively. The Rex E. Lee Advocacy Program administers a two-semester required course for first-year law students in the essential skills of legal writing, research, analysis, and oral advocacy. Students receive individualized attention during one-on-one conferences with instructors and teaching assistants and in small classes. The Legal Writing Center provides additional instruction and assistance to students through individual writing conferences and online resources. In the Advocacy Program, students learn and practice the critical skills that bring success in both law school and the profession.

■ International Center for Law and Religion Studies

The BYU International Center for Law and Religion Studies promotes freedom of religion by studying and disseminating information on the laws, principles, and institutions affecting the interaction of state and religion throughout the world. The center works with scholars, government leaders, nongovernment groups, and religious organizations from a variety of countries and faith traditions, playing an important role in promoting religious liberty and the accompanying relationships between governments and religious organizations.

■ The Externship Program

The Law School offers an academic externship program as a capstone experience to students following their first year of law school. This program allows students to work with judges, law firms, corporations, public interest groups and government organizations throughout the world. During the summer of 2009, 171 students externed with 216 employers, earning an average of four units of law school credit. Forty-nine of those placements were international in twenty-three countries.

■ The Academic Success Program

The Academic Success Program (ASP) is designed to help students adjust to and meet the rigorous demands of a legal education. The ASP offers legal skills workshops with personal feedback, weekly tutorial sessions in each first-year course, individual tutoring, and one-on-one legal writing instruction to all students upon request and by dean's referral.

■ Cocurricular Programs

The objective of the cocurricular program at the Law School is to make a law review-quality experience available to larger numbers of students. Comparable standards of excellence in research, writing, and editing are offered in six programs: the *Brigham Young University Law Review*, the Board of

Advocates Moot Court, Trial Advocacy, the *BYU Journal of Public Law*, the *Brigham Young University Education and Law Journal*, and *International Law and Management Review*.

■ Career Services

The Career Services Office (CSO) is available to all students and graduates seeking employment. The CSO offers two legal career-planning courses featuring skills training and presentations by practicing attorneys who participate as guest lecturers. It also publishes a *Professional Development Handbook, Job Hunt Book, Public Service Handbook*, and *Judicial Clerkship Handbook* and maintains a webpage with links for both students and employers. About 98 percent of the graduates who are seeking work accept employment within nine months after graduation, and graduates are placed in all 50 states and a number of foreign countries. The CSO brings firms to campus every year for on-campus interviews and has interviewing events and job fairs in DC, New York, Southern California, and Nevada.

Applicant Profile

Brigham Young University—J. Reuben Clark Law School
This grid includes only applicants who earned 120–180 LSAT scores under standard administrations.

LSAT Score	3.75 +		3.50–3.74		3.25–3.49		3.00–3.24		2.75–2.99		2.50–2.74		2.25–2.49		2.00–2.24		Below 2.00		No GPA		Total	
	Apps	Adm	Apps	Adm	Apps	Adm	Apps	Adm	Apps	Adm	Apps	Adm	Apps	Adm	Apps	Adm	Apps	Adm	Apps	Adm	Apps	Adm
175–180	2	1	0	0	1	1	2	2	0	0	0	0	0	0	0	0	0	0	0	0	5	4
170–174	9	6	8	6	3	2	2	2	2	1	0	0	1	0	0	0	0	0	0	0	25	17
165–169	32	27	21	18	11	11	6	3	2	0	2	1	2	0	0	0	0	0	1	0	77	60
160–164	53	45	43	20	25	9	19	3	7	1	5	1	0	0	1	0	0	0	4	0	157	79
155–159	30	14	55	9	40	5	26	1	8	1	6	1	2	0	0	0	0	0	1	0	168	31
150–154	25	4	36	8	33	1	23	1	10	0	10	0	1	1	0	0	0	0	3	0	141	15
145–149	9	4	15	1	17	2	24	0	9	0	7	0	2	0	1	0	0	0	4	0	88	7
140–144	4	1	3	0	9	0	9	0	7	2	1	0	4	0	1	0	0	0	3	0	41	3
135–139	0	0	3	0	4	0	4	0	3	0	4	0	0	0	0	0	0	0	2	0	20	0
130–134	0	0	1	0	0	0	1	0	2	0	0	0	2	0	0	0	0	0	3	0	9	0
125–129	0	0	0	0	1	0	0	0	0	0	0	0	0	0	0	0	0	0	0	0	1	0
120–124	0	0	0	0	0	0	0	0	0	0	0	0	0	0	0	0	0	0	0	0	0	0
Total	164	102	185	62	144	31	116	12	50	5	35	3	14	1	3	0	0	0	21	0	732	216

Apps = Number of Applicants
Adm = Number Admitted
Reflects 98% of the total applicant pool; average LSAT data reported.

Brooklyn Law School

250 Joralemon Street
Brooklyn, NY 11201-9846
Phone: 718.780.7906; Fax: 718.780.0395
E-mail: admitq@brooklaw.edu; Website: www.brooklaw.edu

ABA
Approved
Since
1937

The Basics

Type of school	Private
Term	Semester
Application deadline	
Application fee	$0
Financial aid deadline	
Can first year start other than fall?	No
Student to faculty ratio	18.4 to 1
# of housing spaces available restricted to law students	558
graduate housing for which law students are eligible	

Faculty and Administrators

	Total		Men		Women		Minorities	
	Spr	Fall	Spr	Fall	Spr	Fall	Spr	Fall
Full-time	63	64	35	35	28	29	6	5
Other full-time	2	4	2	3	0	1	0	2
Deans, librarians, & others who teach	7	8	3	3	4	5	1	1
Part-time	98	77	73	59	25	18	6	7
Total	170	153	113	100	57	53	13	15

Curriculum

		Full-Time	Part-Time
Typical first-year section size		45	31
Is there typically a "small section" of the first-year class, other than Legal Writing, taught by full-time faculty		Yes	No
If yes, typical size offered last year		39	
# of classroom course titles beyond first-year curriculum		189	
# of upper division courses, excluding seminars, with an enrollment:	Under 25	163	
	25–49	52	
	50–74	21	
	75–99	17	
	100+	18	
# of seminars		91	
# of seminar positions available		1,440	
# of seminar positions filled		1,187	52
# of positions available in simulation courses		1,197	
# of simulation positions filled		934	98
# of positions available in faculty supervised clinical courses		360	
# of faculty supervised clinical positions filled		323	12
# involved in field placements		574	13
# involved in law journals		266	15
# involved in moot court or trial competitions		130	6
# of credit hours required to graduate		86	

JD Enrollment and Ethnicity

	Men		Women		Full-Time		Part-Time		1st-Year		Total		JD Degs. Awd.
	#	%	#	%	#	%	#	%	#	%	#	%	
African Amer.	25	3.3	45	6.3	50	3.9	20	11.1	14	2.8	70	4.8	32
Amer. Indian	1	0.1	1	0.1	2	0.2	0	0.0	0	0.0	2	0.1	1
Asian Amer.	85	11.4	141	19.9	203	15.9	23	12.8	77	15.5	226	15.5	70
Mex. Amer.	4	0.5	3	0.4	7	0.5	0	0.0	2	0.4	7	0.5	5
Puerto Rican	10	1.3	6	0.8	13	1.0	3	1.7	2	0.4	16	1.1	7
Hispanic	30	4.0	32	4.5	56	4.4	6	3.3	26	5.2	62	4.3	22
Total Minority	155	20.7	228	32.1	331	25.9	52	28.9	121	24.4	383	26.3	137
For. Nation.	3	0.4	6	0.8	9	0.7	0	0.0	3	0.6	9	0.6	2
Caucasian	560	74.9	455	64.1	893	69.9	122	67.8	335	67.5	1015	69.6	297
Unknown	30	4.0	21	3.0	45	3.5	6	3.3	37	7.5	51	3.5	63
Total	748	51.3	710	48.7	1278	87.7	180	12.3	496	34.0	1458		499

Transfers

Transfers in	22
Transfers out	21

Tuition and Fees

	Resident	Nonresident
Full-time	$44,015	$44,015
Part-time	$33,099	$33,099
Tuition Guarantee Program		N

Living Expenses

Estimated living expenses for singles

Living on campus	Living off campus	Living at home
$22,345	$22,345	$8,665

Brooklyn Law School

ABA
Approved
Since
1937

GPA and LSAT Scores

	Total	Full-Time	Part-Time
# of apps	5,886	4,909	977
# of offers	1,652	1,470	182
# of matrics	496	406	90
75% GPA	3.63	3.64	3.55
Median GPA	3.46	3.47	3.41
25% GPA	3.26	3.26	3.28
75% LSAT	164	164	160
Median LSAT	162	163	158
25% LSAT	159	160	157

Grants and Scholarships (from prior year)

	Total		Full-Time		Part-Time	
	#	%	#	%	#	%
Total # of students	1,490		1,211		279	
Total # receiving grants	1007	67.6	955	78.9	52	18.6
Less than 1/2 tuition	575	38.6	546	45.1	29	10.4
Half to full tuition	342	23.0	319	26.3	23	8.2
Full tuition	3	0.2	3	0.2	0	0.0
More than full tuition	87	5.8	87	7.2	0	0.0
Median grant amount			$17,164		$13,400	

Informational and Library Resources

Total amount spent on library materials	$1,372,354
Study seating capacity inside the library	665
# of full-time equivalent professional librarians	9.0
Hours per week library is open	108
# of open, wired connections available to students	1,984
# of networked computers available for use by students	142
Has wireless network?	Y
Require computer?	N

JD Attrition (from prior year)

	Academic	Other	Total	
	#	#	#	%
1st year	5	30	35	7.1
2nd year	0	0	0	0.0
3rd year	0	0	0	0.0
4th year	0	0	0	0.0

Employment (9 months after graduation)

	Total	Percentage
Employment status known	461	98.1
Employment status unknown	9	1.9
Employed	401	87.0
Pursuing graduate degrees	4	0.9
Unemployed (seeking, not seeking, or studying for the bar)	27	5.9
Type of Employment		
# employed in law firms	230	57.4
# employed in business and industry	47	11.7
# employed in government	72	18.0
# employed in public interest	22	5.5
# employed as judicial clerks	25	6.2
# employed in academia	4	1.0
Geographic Location		
# employed in state	345	86.0
# employed in foreign countries	6	1.5
# of states where employed	21	

Bar Passage Rates

First-time takers	461	Reporting %	95.44
Average school %	89.09	Average state %	88.98
Average pass difference	0.11		

Jurisdiction	Takers	Passers	Pass %	State %	Diff %
New York	440	392	89.09	88.98	0.11

Brooklyn Law School

250 Joralemon Street
Brooklyn, NY 11201-9846
Phone: 718.780.7906; Fax: 718.780.0395
E-mail: admitq@brooklaw.edu; Website: www.brooklaw.edu

■ The Law Campus

Situated at the junction of the Brooklyn Heights Historic District, the Brooklyn Civic Center, and downtown Brooklyn, our school boasts a location unrivaled for its legal, cultural, and historical character. Students share their environs with federal and state judges, government officials, and lawyers in private practice, many of them alumni. Within a few-block radius are the US District Court; US Bankruptcy Court; US Attorney's Office; the New York State Supreme Court, Appellate Division; Family Court; the Brooklyn District Attorney; the Kings County Surrogate's Court; the New York City Civil and Criminal Courts; the Legal Aid Society; and numerous law firms. These are our laboratories, a backdrop for learning few schools can replicate.

■ Renaissance Brooklyn

Multibillion-dollar construction projects have recast Brooklyn as the new center of New York City's energy. Overlooking New York Harbor and lower Manhattan lies Brooklyn's most charming neighborhood, Brooklyn Heights, where you will find much of our campus. The first New York City neighborhood to be designated as a historic district, many Heights original townhouses, brownstone mansions, carriage houses, churches, and public buildings survive, recalling old-world urban elegance. Many of our students and faculty live here in residence halls or in private apartments and homes located on graceful, tree-lined streets. Nearby neighborhoods—Carroll Gardens, Cobble Hill, Park Slope, Williamsburg, and DUMBO (Down Under the Manhattan Bridge Overpass)—also offer trendy, affordable housing and a profusion of bistros, boutiques, galleries, and clubs, all contributing to Brooklyn's growing reputation as the hippest part of New York City.

■ Manhattan at Our Doorstep

Minutes away is the financial, legal, business, and cultural crossroads of the world: Manhattan. Proximity to Wall Street gives students easy access to school-year externships and summer jobs with major law firms and financial institutions. Students enjoy a great campus in a dynamic urban environment, softened by a small-neighborhood feel. This is New York City on a human scale—Manhattan without the hassle.

■ Building for Your Future

In recent years, BLS has undertaken $134 million in capital improvements to serve its needs well into the twenty-first century. Ten residences—including our largest, the 21-story high-rise, Feil Hall—allow us to **guarantee housing** to all first-year students, engendering a strong sense of campus community. The library offers more than 570,000 multiformat volumes, periodicals and databases accessible on and off campus. As one of the largest and most modern in the city, the 578,000-square-foot facility boasts 26 group-study rooms, seating for nearly 700, and five PC/Mac labs hosting nearly 100 workstations; we offer over 2,400 other student-accessible network connections throughout our academic and residential buildings, as well as over 2,000 Wi-Fi connections.

■ Our Faculty: Diverse, Brilliant, and User-Friendly

Our 72 full-time faculty members, joined by some 125 adjuncts (including many distinguished judges, practitioners, corporate counsel, and eight visiting professors), comprise one of the largest faculties in New York. They are extraordinarily talented and, above all, superb teachers. Shaping public policy and making law in the community at large, they are also prolific authors. They are recognized nationally and globally for their scholarship in such areas as Commercial and Bankruptcy Law, Corporate and Securities Law, Evidence, Health Law, Information Privacy and Internet Law, Intellectual Property, International Business Law, Human Rights, and Women's Rights. BLS offers a congenial community. Its learning environment, while rigorous and challenging, remains supportive and nurturing. A desirable student-faculty ratio of 18.4:1 facilitates this dynamic. Faculty members are accessible to students in a way that few faculties are. There is a strong correlation between the priority we assign to teaching and mentoring and student success on the bar examination. Our 2008 graduates who took the New York State Bar Examination for the first time had a 92 percent passing rate, well ahead of the 83.2 percent statewide rate for first-time takers.

■ Our Alumni: Accomplished and Accessible

One of our great strengths is the size, stature, and loyalty of our more than 18,000 graduates in 49 states and Washington, DC; 3 US territories; and 29 foreign countries—among the largest alumni families of any law school.

■ Our Students: The Best and the Brightest

The 2009 entering class included students from 30 states and Washington, DC; Puerto Rico; and 3 foreign countries. Nearly two-thirds of the class are graduates of many of the nation's most prestigious colleges and universities. Seventy-five percent completed undergraduate work at least one year before enrolling here. Forty-four percent had LSAT scores of 163 or higher. Minorities represented 27.8 percent of the class; about half of the students were women.

■ The Career Center

Our Career Center is staffed by seven attorney-counselors and two attorneys dedicated to job development/employer relations in the public and private sectors. Job listings are readily available to students and graduates via the Internet. An average of over 97 percent of students in the 2004–2008 graduating classes were employed nine months after graduation, placing us among the top law schools nationwide. For current salary information, visit the school's website to review the Statistics and Profile section at *www.brooklaw.edu/Admissions.aspx*.

■ First-Year Program of Study

Day students take one core course in a seminar section of about 40 students, allowing for significant individualized skills training. Our goal is to help students cultivate the ability to think clearly, analyze problems thoroughly and carefully, and recognize that no legal issue exists in a social, philosophical, economic, or political vacuum. Students participate in a Legal Writing Program structured to fully develop their writing abilities. An Academic Success Program, combining an early-start summer course with a series of support workshops, helps students reach their potential. This contributes to our exceptionally high retention rate between the first and second year.

■ Upperclass Program of Study: The Art and Craft of Lawyering

Our **upperclass curriculum** bridges the gap between law school and law practice, making law school something students enjoy, not merely endure. Students create individualized programs, choosing from over 200 electives in 17 concentrations and areas of interest. Five **Certificate Programs** (in Business, Criminal, Intellectual Property, International, and Real Estate Law) recognize a student's depth of study and proficiency in these practice areas. Nearly 60 percent of all students and over 71 percent of our full-time students participate in one or more of our **26 clinics**, including nearly 350 enrolled this year in one of our in-house clinics and almost 700 students participating in externships in legal departments and judicial chambers, experiencing the law in real time. Simulation courses enrolled over 1,000 students this past year.

■ Beyond the Core Curriculum

Consistently recognized as among the country's top law schools in supporting public interest law, Brooklyn's **Edward V. Sparer Public Interest Law Fellowship Program** has placed nearly 450 students in a wide array of summer internships at leading public interest organizations nationwide and abroad. **Public Service Grants** award up to $5,000 per student to support public service employment. The **Dennis J. Block International Business Law Fellowship Program** is a rewarding educational experience for those pursuing careers in that field. An **International Human Rights Fellowship Program**, which includes $5,000 stipends for summer work, was launched last year. We sponsor four student-edited journals: the *Brooklyn Law Review*, the *Journal of Law and Policy*, the *Brooklyn Journal of International Law*, and the *Brooklyn Journal of Corporate, Financial, and Commercial Law*. **Barry L. Zaretsky Fellowships** are awarded to students based on demonstrated academic achievement and commitment to bankruptcy and/or commercial law. Over the past decade, our **Moot Court** teams have garnered 20 national championships and 37 other first prizes. Our **Center for the Study of Law, Language, and Cognition** explores how developments in the cognitive sciences—including neuroscience, psychology, and linguistics—have dramatic implications for the theory and practice of law. A **Center for Health, Science, and Public Policy** engages students in the legal issues and public policy concerns confronting health care organizations. **Joint-degree** options allow students to earn master's degrees in business administration, city and regional planning, urban planning, political science, or library and information science. Finally, we offer **study-abroad** and **exchange programs** in China, England, Germany, Italy, and South Africa.

Applicant Profile

Admission to Brooklyn Law School is based on an appraisal of each applicant's character, academic achievements, aptitude for the study of law, life experience, and other indications of professional promise. BLS does not offer an LSAT/GPA admission profile, for numbers alone cannot provide a comprehensive assessment of a candidate's potential for law school success. While matrices may be helpful to some, too often they needlessly discourage those with profiles slightly below our published numerical benchmarks who may still be competitive for admission. Moreover, such profiles tend to reduce the selection process to a two-dimensional matrix, one which fails to portray accurately our admission practices. To be sure, candidates with high test scores and commensurate grades are more likely to gain admission than those with lower grades and scores. Nevertheless, no combination of grades and scores guarantees admission. Nonquantifiable factors also significantly influence our decisions. A partial list includes the quality of schools attended, the strength of the program of study, grade trends, the content of faculty letters of evaluation, the cogency of the candidate's writing, campus leadership, significant service to the community, the nature and quality of any work experience or foreign study/travel, awards and honors, and military service. We have a century-long tradition of offering opportunities to members of underrepresented groups. For more, see *www.brooklaw.edu*.

University at Buffalo Law School, The State University of New York (SUNY)

309 John Lord O'Brian Hall
Buffalo, NY 14260
Phone: 716.645.2907; Fax: 716.645.6676
E-mail: law-admissions@buffalo.edu; Website: www.law.buffalo.edu

ABA
Approved
Since
1936

The Basics

Type of school	Public
Term	Semester
Application deadline	3/15
Application fee	$50
Financial aid deadline	3/1
Can first year start other than fall?	No
Student to faculty ratio	15.3 to 1
# of housing spaces available restricted to law students	124
graduate housing for which law students are eligible	674

Faculty and Administrators

	Total		Men		Women		Minorities	
	Spr	Fall	Spr	Fall	Spr	Fall	Spr	Fall
Full-time	38	41	27	29	11	12	5	6
Other full-time	10	10	0	3	10	7	0	0
Deans, librarians, & others who teach	12	13	5	5	6	7	1	1
Part-time	87	47	56	33	30	14	9	5
Total	147	111	88	70	57	40	15	12

Curriculum

	Full-Time	Part-Time
Typical first-year section size	65	0
Is there typically a "small section" of the first-year class, other than Legal Writing, taught by full-time faculty	No	No
If yes, typical size offered last year		

	Full-Time	Part-Time
# of classroom course titles beyond first-year curriculum	220	
# of upper division courses, excluding seminars, with an enrollment: Under 25	182	
25–49	52	
50–74	11	
75–99	10	
100+	1	
# of seminars	41	
# of seminar positions available	722	
# of seminar positions filled	408	0
# of positions available in simulation courses	1,011	
# of simulation positions filled	848	0
# of positions available in faculty supervised clinical courses	225	
# of faculty supervised clinical positions filled	153	0
# involved in field placements	76	0
# involved in law journals	339	0
# involved in moot court or trial competitions	77	0
# of credit hours required to graduate	90	

JD Enrollment and Ethnicity

	Men		Women		Full-Time		Part-Time		1st-Year		Total		JD Degs. Awd.
	#	%	#	%	#	%	#	%	#	%	#	%	
African Amer.	11	2.8	23	6.9	33	4.6	1	12.5	18	8.7	34	4.7	14
Amer. Indian	1	0.3	3	0.9	4	0.6	0	0.0	2	1.0	4	0.6	0
Asian Amer.	19	4.8	22	6.6	41	5.7	0	0.0	10	4.8	41	5.6	15
Mex. Amer.	1	0.3	2	0.6	3	0.4	0	0.0	0	0.0	3	0.4	0
Puerto Rican	6	1.5	3	0.9	9	1.3	0	0.0	0	0.0	9	1.2	2
Hispanic	5	1.3	12	3.6	17	2.4	0	0.0	7	3.4	17	2.3	11
Total Minority	43	10.9	65	19.6	107	14.9	1	12.5	37	17.8	108	14.9	42
For. Nation.	0	0.0	0	0.0	0	0.0	0	0.0	0	0.0	0	0.0	0
Caucasian	297	75.2	231	69.8	521	72.6	7	87.5	152	73.1	528	72.7	176
Unknown	55	13.9	35	10.6	90	12.5	0	0.0	19	9.1	90	12.4	28
Total	395	54.4	331	45.6	718	98.9	8	1.1	208	28.7	726		246

Transfers

Transfers in	41
Transfers out	13

Tuition and Fees

	Resident	Nonresident
Full-time	$17,577	$25,827
Part-time		
Tuition Guarantee Program	N	

Living Expenses

Estimated living expenses for singles

Living on campus	Living off campus	Living at home
$15,988	$15,988	$15,988

University at Buffalo Law School, The State University of New York (SUNY)

ABA
Approved
Since
1936

GPA and LSAT Scores

	Total	Full-Time	Part-Time
# of apps	2,104	2,104	0
# of offers	678	678	0
# of matrics	208	208	0
75% GPA	3.73	3.73	0.00
Median GPA	3.52	3.52	0.00
25% GPA	3.19	3.19	0.00
75% LSAT	159	159	0
Median LSAT	157	157	0
25% LSAT	153	153	0

Grants and Scholarships (from prior year)

	Total		Full-Time		Part-Time	
	#	%	#	%	#	%
Total # of students	745		739		6	
Total # receiving grants	560	75.2	560	75.8	0	0.0
Less than 1/2 tuition	437	58.7	437	59.1	0	0.0
Half to full tuition	0	0.0	0	0.0	0	0.0
Full tuition	119	16.0	119	16.1	0	0.0
More than full tuition	4	0.5	4	0.5	0	0.0
Median grant amount			$550		$0	

Informational and Library Resources

Total amount spent on library materials	$1,553,200
Study seating capacity inside the library	590
# of full-time equivalent professional librarians	13
Hours per week library is open	105
# of open, wired connections available to students	44
# of networked computers available for use by students	41
Has wireless network?	Y
Require computer?	N

JD Attrition (from prior year)

	Academic	Other	Total	
	#	#	#	%
1st year	0	5	5	2.2
2nd year	0	14	14	5.2
3rd year	0	1	1	0.4
4th year	0	0	0	0.0

Employment (9 months after graduation)

	Total	Percentage
Employment status known	218	93.6
Employment status unknown	15	6.4
Employed	198	90.8
Pursuing graduate degrees	8	3.7
Unemployed (seeking, not seeking, or studying for the bar)	9	4.1
Type of Employment		
# employed in law firms	121	61.1
# employed in business and industry	22	11.1
# employed in government	21	10.6
# employed in public interest	14	7.1
# employed as judicial clerks	9	4.5
# employed in academia	8	4.0
Geographic Location		
# employed in state	162	81.8
# employed in foreign countries	1	0.5
# of states where employed	20	

Bar Passage Rates

First-time takers	224	Reporting %	95.09
Average school %	81.22	Average state %	88.98

Average pass difference −7.76

Jurisdiction	Takers	Passers	Pass %	State %	Diff %
New York	213	173	81.22	88.98	−7.76

University at Buffalo Law School, The State University of New York (SUNY)

309 John Lord O'Brian Hall
Buffalo, NY 14260
Phone: 716.645.2907; Fax: 716.645.6676
E-mail: law-admissions@buffalo.edu; Website: www.law.buffalo.edu

■ Introduction

Long recognized as one of the leading public law schools in the Northeast, the University at Buffalo Law School, New York State's only public law school, continues to provide students with cutting-edge legal tools to formulate their legal education. This education allows students to gain the practical skills necessary in today's ever-changing legal marketplace.

Located in Amherst, New York—a suburb of Buffalo—the Law School has a small-school feel with all the advantages of a large university, including access to other professional and graduate departments, Division I sports, a fine arts center, a concert hall, and numerous other academic, social, and cultural opportunities. The city of Buffalo offers great skiing, great sailing, major-league sports, a first-rate orchestra, many professional theaters, a lively club scene, and access to Canada, all within minutes of the Law School. You can live comfortably, not to mention affordably, in Buffalo, the second largest city in New York.

■ Library and Physical Facilities

The Law School is housed in John Lord O'Brian Hall, a seven-story building including a state-of-the-art courtroom that provides students with an opportunity to watch judges and lawyers in action. Other new facilities include classrooms, apartments, and an elegant student lounge. The library is the core of the Law School, occupying six of the seven floors.

Like the Law School, the law library is committed to providing students with exceptional research and writing skills by assigning librarians to each research and writing instructor. This enables first-year law students to gain one-on-one instruction in various research methods.

■ Curriculum

The Law School provides a flexible curriculum that affords students a broad range of curricular options, practical coursework, and special programs. The Buffalo curriculum emphasizes the study of law in its social context, and a large number of interdisciplinary courses and programs support this emphasis. A strong clinical education program is closely tied to the core curriculum and enhances the optional concentrations. Current concentration subjects include Family Law, Finance Transactions, Affordable Housing and Community Development Law, Environmental Law, Civil Litigation, Criminal Law, Health Law, International Law, and Technology and Intellectual Property.

Instruction is offered in two semesters from early September to May, including a January bridge term, and a summer session from mid-May to mid-July. Six full-time semesters or five full-time semesters plus two summer sessions are required for graduation.

In addition to standard first-year subjects—contracts, torts, civil procedure, criminal law, property, constitution law, and research and writing—the first year includes instruction in legal profession and ethics. These courses afford an introduction to the social and economic context of the legal system and to legal institutions and processes.

Beyond the first year, students are required to complete 60 semester credit hours, including at least one seminar. The upper-division program is wholly elective. Second- and third-year students may choose from a full spectrum of survey and advanced courses covering the main fields of public and private law, a very rich selection of seminars and small group courses in special or emerging areas of law study and research, and clinics and simulations devoted to professional skills training.

The Law School also offers an LLM degree in Criminal Law and a General LLM for international and domestic students. For international students, there are special courses designed to introduce them to American law and to prepare them for the New York State bar exam. All students benefit from our small group personalized approach that allows them to design their own curriculum.

■ Special Programs

Clinical Programs—Skills training in the clinical program is coordinated with substantive law courses to give students theoretical understanding of practical issues. Students serve clients and conduct research and fieldwork in areas such as economic development, affordable housing, mediation, family violence, elder law, and environmental and development law.

Research Centers—The Law School's research centers provide multiple perspectives on the law. The Baldy Center for Law and Social Policy serves as a focal point for interdisciplinary research and teaching. The Buffalo Human Rights Center maintains cooperative links worldwide with human rights organizations, think tanks, and governmental agencies. The Edwin F. Jaeckle Center for State and Local Democracy supports a balanced academic program of theoretical study of democratic processes and the education of lawyers for public service. The Center for the Study of Business Transactions, a joint venture of the Law School and the UB School of Management, sponsors a variety of courses, research opportunities, and distinguished speakers. Because of the Buffalo Criminal Law Center, UB Law is a national leader in criminal law scholarship. Finally, the UB Law Program for Excellence in Family Law integrates teaching, research, policy, and practice to provide students with the skills and experience needed to practice family law.

Dual-Degree Programs—The school also has an extensive dual-degree program, which permits students to earn credit toward a master's or PhD degree jointly with the JD. In recent years, the most active dual-degree programs have been with political science, management, philosophy, public health, legal information management and analysis, social work, sociology, and economics. Two additional programs were added recently, allowing students to pursue pharmacy and urban planning dual degrees. Special programs can also be arranged with other departments.

Bridge Term—Second- and third-year students can enroll in up to three one-credit bridge courses taught by experienced lawyers and judges, giving students a window into current issues in practice.

New York City Program in Finance and Law—Provides University at Buffalo law students with an introduction to New York City's financial markets and a gateway to its highly competitive financial-sector job market. Each year,

University at Buffalo Law School, The State University of New York (SUNY)

approximately 25 students are selected to participate in this unique program, which is located in New York City.

■ Admission

The Law School admits first-year students only in the fall semester; transfer and visiting students in both fall and spring. Application priority deadline: March 1. LSAT and LSAC Credential Assembly Service are required.

Because quantitative factors—GPA and LSAT—may not accurately reflect a student's potential for law school success, the Admissions Committee pays close attention to the qualitative factors presented in an application. These factors include, but are not limited to, academic achievement, personal statements, character traits, writing ability, recommendations, and work experience. If an application reveals that the applicant has been educationally, socially, economically, or otherwise disadvantaged, the Admissions Committee will review the application for signs of achievement that should lead to success in law school.

■ Student Activities

There are ample extracurricular activities for student involvement. The Student Bar Association, an elected representative body, oversees all law school student organizations. The Moot Court Board sponsors mock appellate practice competitions, the *Opinion* is the student newspaper, the *Buffalo Law Review* is a professional journal edited by students, and there are specialty journals in environmental law, affordable housing and community development law, intellectual property, criminal law, human rights law, and social policy concerning women.

■ Expenses and Financial Aid

UB is able to offer a state-subsidized tuition to New York residents and a reasonable out-of-state tuition charge. In-state tuition—$16,010; out-of-state—$24,260. Estimated additional expenses—$16,000. (Tuition and living expenses subject to change without notice.)

This results in overall educational expenses that are less than half the cost of many law schools. Dean's tuition waivers and limited scholarships are available to students demonstrating high academic achievement, and state aid is offered on a need basis to qualified students. Additional alumni-sponsored scholarships are offered to second- and third-year students.

■ Career Services

The Law School's Career Services Office (CSO) should become every law student's first point of reference as he or she begins a job search. In addition to providing job search and résumé services for third-year and LLM students, the CSO also aids first- and second-year students in conducting their summer job searches.

Over the last several years, the placement rate of eligible graduates who have been employed in legal work or enrolled in an advanced-degree program has been above 95 percent. While Buffalo and New York City continue to employ the greatest number of our graduates, several northeastern states, including Washington, DC; southern states (Florida, Georgia, North Carolina); western states (California, Arizona); and midwestern states are presenting an increase in opportunities for our graduates. One-third to one-half of all our graduates begin their careers outside of western New York. For more information about career services, contact the office: telephone: 716.645.2056; fax: 716.645.7336; e-mail: *law-careers@buffalo.edu.*

Applicant Profile

University at Buffalo Law School, The State University of New York (SUNY)
This grid includes only applicants who earned 120–180 LSAT scores under standard administrations.

LSAT Score	3.75 +		3.50–3.74		3.25–3.49		3.00–3.24		2.75–2.99		2.50–2.74		2.25–2.49		2.00–2.24		Below 2.00		No GPA		Total	
	Apps	Adm	Apps	Adm	Apps	Adm	Apps	Adm	Apps	Adm	Apps	Adm	Apps	Adm	Apps	Adm	Apps	Adm	Apps	Adm	Apps	Adm
175–180	2	2	0	0	0	0	0	0	0	0	0	0	0	0	0	0	0	0	0	0	2	2
170–174	2	2	1	1	1	1	4	4	0	0	0	0	1	0	0	0	0	0	0	0	9	8
165–169	10	10	13	13	19	18	6	5	8	7	1	1	2	1	1	0	0	0	0	0	60	55
160–164	32	30	49	48	57	55	34	31	29	16	19	11	8	2	3	3	3	0	2	2	236	198
155–159	77	64	101	72	119	67	73	38	50	20	25	8	12	3	2	0	0	0	9	6	468	278
150–154	58	25	138	34	162	28	121	10	63	6	44	2	15	1	8	0	1	0	14	3	624	109
145–149	24	9	65	8	85	6	73	4	63	0	37	0	17	0	6	0	2	0	9	0	381	27
140–144	9	0	24	0	32	0	32	0	39	0	21	0	16	0	4	0	1	0	2	0	180	0
135–139	2	0	4	0	12	0	12	0	14	0	8	0	11	0	4	0	1	0	2	0	70	0
130–134	0	0	4	0	1	0	1	0	7	0	8	0	3	0	4	0	0	0	2	0	30	0
125–129	0	0	0	0	1	0	0	0	2	0	4	0	0	0	1	0	0	0	0	0	8	0
120–124	0	0	0	0	0	0	0	0	0	0	0	0	0	0	0	0	0	0	0	0	0	0
No LSAT	1	0	0	0	1	0	0	0	0	0	0	0	0	0	0	0	0	0	34	0	36	0
Total	217	142	399	176	490	175	356	92	275	49	167	22	85	7	33	3	8	0	74	11	2104	677

Apps = Number of Applicants   Adm = Number Admitted

University of California, Berkeley, School of Law

2850 Telegraph Avenue, Suite 500
Berkeley, CA 94705-7220
Phone: 510.642.2274; Fax: 510.643.6222
E-mail: admissions@law.berkeley.edu; Website: www.law.berkeley.edu

ABA Approved Since 1923

The Basics

Type of school	Public
Term	Semester
Application deadline	2/1
Application fee	$75
Financial aid deadline	3/2
Can first year start other than fall?	No
Student to faculty ratio	11.3 to 1
# of housing spaces available restricted to law students	
graduate housing for which law students are eligible	1,300

Faculty and Administrators

	Total		Men		Women		Minorities	
	Spr	Fall	Spr	Fall	Spr	Fall	Spr	Fall
Full-time	66	64	43	40	23	24	6	7
Other full-time	24	24	10	10	14	14	1	1
Deans, librarians, & others who teach	15	15	8	8	7	7	2	2
Part-time	80	52	60	38	20	14	2	3
Total	185	155	121	96	64	59	11	13

JD Enrollment and Ethnicity

	Men		Women		Full-Time		Part-Time		1st-Year		Total		JD Degs. Awd.
	#	%	#	%	#	%	#	%	#	%	#	%	
African Amer.	20	4.6	23	5.0	43	4.8	0	0.0	16	5.5	43	4.8	15
Amer. Indian	5	1.2	10	2.2	15	1.7	0	0.0	5	1.7	15	1.7	2
Asian Amer.	70	16.2	86	18.7	156	17.5	0	0.0	54	18.6	156	17.5	61
Mex. Amer.	23	5.3	24	5.2	47	5.3	0	0.0	16	5.5	47	5.3	8
Puerto Rican	0	0.0	0	0.0	0	0.0	0	0.0	0	0.0	0	0.0	0
Hispanic	17	3.9	31	6.7	48	5.4	0	0.0	22	7.6	48	5.4	13
Total Minority	135	31.3	174	37.8	309	34.6	0	0.0	113	39.0	309	34.6	99
For. Nation.	0	0.0	0	0.0	0	0.0	0	0.0	0	0.0	0	0.0	0
Caucasian	217	50.2	196	42.6	413	46.3	0	0.0	128	44.1	413	46.3	146
Unknown	80	18.5	90	19.6	170	19.1	0	0.0	49	16.9	170	19.1	31
Total	432	48.4	460	51.6	892	100.0	0	0.0	290	32.5	892		276

Curriculum

	Full-Time	Part-Time
Typical first-year section size	90	0
Is there typically a "small section" of the first-year class, other than Legal Writing, taught by full-time faculty	Yes	No
If yes, typical size offered last year	30	
# of classroom course titles beyond first-year curriculum	252	
# of upper division courses, excluding seminars, with an enrollment: Under 25	59	
25–49	80	
50–74	17	
75–99	3	
100+	31	
# of seminars	38	
# of seminar positions available	913	
# of seminar positions filled	538	0
# of positions available in simulation courses	455	
# of simulation positions filled	361	0
# of positions available in faculty supervised clinical courses	177	
# of faculty supervised clinical positions filled	142	0
# involved in field placements	127	0
# involved in law journals	295	0
# involved in moot court or trial competitions	114	0
# of credit hours required to graduate	85	

Transfers

Transfers in	45
Transfers out	0

Tuition and Fees

	Resident	Nonresident
Full-time	$35,907	$48,152
Part-time		
Tuition Guarantee Program	N	

Living Expenses

Estimated living expenses for singles

Living on campus	Living off campus	Living at home
$21,183	$21,183	$21,183

University of California, Berkeley, School of Law

ABA
Approved
Since
1923

GPA and LSAT Scores

	Total	Full-Time	Part-Time
# of apps	7,960	7,960	0
# of offers	803	803	0
# of matrics	292	292	0
75% GPA	3.95	3.95	0.00
Median GPA	3.83	3.83	0.00
25% GPA	3.68	3.68	0.00
75% LSAT	170	170	0
Median LSAT	168	168	0
25% LSAT	165	165	0

Grants and Scholarships (from prior year)

	Total		Full-Time		Part-Time	
	#	%	#	%	#	%
Total # of students	865		865		0	
Total # receiving grants	412	47.6	412	47.6	0	0.0
Less than 1/2 tuition	216	25.0	216	25.0	0	0.0
Half to full tuition	162	18.7	162	18.7	0	0.0
Full tuition	6	0.7	6	0.7	0	0.0
More than full tuition	28	3.2	28	3.2	0	0.0
Median grant amount			$14,349		$0	

Informational and Library Resources

Total amount spent on library materials	$3,181,372
Study seating capacity inside the library	307
# of full-time equivalent professional librarians	16.0
Hours per week library is open	100
# of open, wired connections available to students	213
# of networked computers available for use by students	115
Has wireless network?	Y
Require computer?	N

JD Attrition (from prior year)

	Academic	Other	Total	
	#	#	#	%
1st year	0	7	7	2.6
2nd year	0	0	0	0.0
3rd year	0	0	0	0.0
4th year	0	0	0	0.0

Employment (9 months after graduation)

	Total	Percentage
Employment status known	292	100.0
Employment status unknown	0	0.0
Employed	281	96.2
Pursuing graduate degrees	7	2.4
Unemployed (seeking, not seeking, or studying for the bar)	4	1.4
Type of Employment		
# employed in law firms	203	72.2
# employed in business and industry	11	3.9
# employed in government	14	5.0
# employed in public interest	28	10.0
# employed as judicial clerks	25	8.9
# employed in academia	0	0.0
Geographic Location		
# employed in state	194	69.0
# employed in foreign countries	6	2.1
# of states where employed	23	

Bar Passage Rates

First-time takers	270	Reporting %	84.44
Average school %	87.72	Average state %	78.07
Average pass difference	9.65		

Jurisdiction	Takers	Passers	Pass %	State %	Diff %
California	228	200	87.72	78.07	9.65

University of California, Berkeley, School of Law

2850 Telegraph Avenue, Suite 500
Berkeley, CA 94705-7220
Phone: 510.642.2274; Fax: 510.643.6222
E-mail: admissions@law.berkeley.edu; Website: www.law.berkeley.edu

■ Introduction

Learning law at Berkeley School of Law means joining a stimulating intellectual community that is part of a tradition of academic excellence, professional leadership, and public service. Berkeley's location in the San Francisco Bay Area, with influences from Silicon Valley and the Pacific Rim, provides an unparalleled opportunity to study at one of the world's leading institutions of legal education and research. Its academic program includes specialized study in business, law, and economics; environmental law; law and technology; international and comparative legal studies; and social justice and public interest. The curriculum is complemented by research centers and clinical programs that provide real client work. Berkeley law school offers a broad three-year curriculum leading to the JD degree and postgraduate programs leading to LLM and JSD degrees. The interdisciplinary Jurisprudence and Social Policy (JSP) program leads to MA and PhD degrees. The school is a member of AALS and is ABA approved.

■ Location

UC Berkeley occupies a beautiful 1,232-acre campus bordered by wooded rolling hills. Berkeley is known for its intellectual, social, and political engagement. With its multinational population, rich diversity of arts, and sense of political adventure, Berkeley reflects and affects the rest of the country. Yet, it is an intimate city of friendly neighborhoods, renowned restaurants, coffeehouses, bookstores, parks, and open spaces. Across the bay lies San Francisco, home to internationally recognized museums, the opera, ballet, symphony, and restaurants. The mild climate makes outdoor activities possible year-round.

■ Students

Berkeley Law seeks a student body with a broad set of interests, life experiences, and perspectives. The intellectual excellence, varied interests, and backgrounds of the students are among its great strengths. Students received undergraduate degrees from more than 100 universities, about half at schools outside California.

■ Faculty

Berkeley's faculty members are internationally recognized experts in fields ranging from law and technology, to youth violence and juvenile justice, to environmental law. They include recipients of Fulbright and Guggenheim fellowships and a MacArthur "genius" grant, as well as authors of casebooks used worldwide. Lecturers are drawn from prominent law firms and institutions.

■ Library and Physical Facilities

The law library is one of the finest law collections in the world. Its extensive holdings include the Robbins Religious and Civil Law Collection of titles in ecclesiastical, civil, comparative, and international law, and extensive collections of foreign, comparative, human rights, and environmental law. The law library is also a depository for United States, United Nations, and European Union documents and is linked to the university system's holdings of more than seven million volumes.

The law library provides online databases, three computer labs with Internet access, four spacious reading rooms, and a photocopying service. Multimedia capabilities are available. Wireless access is available throughout the law school complex and much of the Berkeley campus.

The school is composed of three adjoining buildings (and two courtyards) with classrooms, seminar rooms, auditoriums, the law library, a lounge, a reception room, a café, dining and study areas, and offices.

■ Housing

The campus Housing Office offers apartments, rental listings, residence halls, and student family apartments. International House accommodates students from the United States and abroad.

■ Admission

Requirements: bachelor's degree, LSAT, and registration with LSAC's Credential Assembly Service; application fee: $75; deadline: February 1 (early application strongly preferred).

Applicants' LSAT scores and undergraduate grade-point averages (GPAs) are important criteria for evaluating academic ability. Applicants may use the mean LSAT percentile and undergraduate GPAs of the previous year's admitted applicant pool as a guide for assessing their chances of admission. Because Berkeley takes other factors into account in making admission decisions, higher or lower scores and grades neither ensure nor preclude admission.

■ Student Activities

Students edit and publish 13 legal periodicals: *Asian American Law Journal*; *Berkeley Business Law Journal*; *Berkeley Journal of African American Law and Policy*; *Berkeley Journal of Criminal Law*; *Berkeley Journal of Employment and Labor Law*; *Berkeley Journal of Gender, Law and Justice*; *Berkeley Journal of International Law*; *Berkeley La Raza Law Journal*; *Berkeley Journal of Middle Eastern and Islamic Law*; *Berkeley Technology Law Journal*; *California Law Review*; *Ecology Law Quarterly*; and *Impact: A Multidisciplinary Journal Addressing the Issues of Urban Youth*.

More than 50 student groups focus on a variety of interests, including animal law, disability law, sports and entertainment law, and workers' rights.

■ JD Curriculum

Berkeley Law's broad and innovative curriculum is one of the most dynamic among law schools. Opportunities for study in specific areas of the law connect students to our renowned faculty members. The first-year curriculum includes Civil Procedure, Contracts, Criminal Law, Legal Research and Writing, Property, Torts, Written and Oral Advocacy, and two elective courses. The flexible second- and third-year

curriculums offer a variety of legal topics and course styles, including seminars, individual and group research projects, clinical work, and judicial externships. Students may work on clinical projects providing direct legal services to clients or work with lawyers on large cases or legal matters. The Center for Clinical Education, Berkeley Law's in-house clinical facility, offers the Death Penalty Clinic; the International Human Rights Law Clinic; and the Samuelson Law, Technology, and Public Policy Clinic. The East Bay Community Law Center is the community-based component of the program. Other clinical opportunities include the Domestic Violence Practicum and field placements.

Centers and Institutes

Berkeley Law's centers and institutes act as incubators for cutting-edge legal research, where students collaborate with leading scholars and practitioners working on complex issues. Projects are often centered on specific cases or legislation, and can have broad influence on law and policy in such areas as business, philosophy, public policy, sociology, and technology. The centers also sponsor conferences, roundtables, and other presentations on pertinent issues. They push the frontiers of legal scholarship and make Berkeley one of the most exciting places in the world to study law. They include:
- Berkeley Center for Criminal Justice
- Berkeley Center for Law, Business, and the Economy
- Berkeley Center on Health, Economic, and Family Security
- Berkeley Center for Law and Technology
- Center for Law, Energy, and the Environment
- Center for the Study of Law and Society
- Chief Justice Earl Warren Institute on Race, Ethnicity, and Diversity
- Institute for Legal Research

- The Miller Institute for Global Challenges and Law
- Kadish Center for Morality, Law, and Public Affairs
- Robert D. Burch Center for Tax Policy and Public Finance
- Thelton E. Henderson Center for Social Justice

Financial Aid

Requirements: FAFSA need analysis form; Need Access Application; the deadline for priority consideration is March 2. The law school seeks to provide need-based financial aid sufficient to permit any admitted student to attend. A majority of the students receive some form of financial aid.

The financial aid awarded by UC Berkeley's Financial Aid Office is need-based and includes mostly federal student loans. The financial aid awarded by Berkeley law school includes federal student loans and other campus-based awards such as work study. Additionally, the law school administers a variety of grants and scholarships based on financial need and/or need and academic merit.

Career Development

The Office of Career Development is a resource for students, alumni, and prospective employers. It operates one of the largest on-campus recruitment programs in the country, provides opportunities for legal employment, and maintains an online job database of positions available throughout the nation. The staff conducts career counseling, résumé workshops, and programs on traditional and nontraditional law careers in the private and public sectors.

Applicant Profile Not Available

University of California, Davis School of Law (King Hall)

Admission Office, 400 Mrak Hall Drive
Davis, CA 95616-5201
Phone: 530.752.6477
E-mail: admissions@law.ucdavis.edu; Website: www.law.ucdavis.edu

ABA
Approved
Since
1968

The Basics

Type of school	Public
Term	Semester
Application deadline	2/1
Application fee	$75
Financial aid deadline	3/2
Can first year start other than fall?	No
Student to faculty ratio	11.6 to 1
# of housing spaces available restricted to law students	
graduate housing for which law students are eligible	844

Faculty and Administrators

	Total		Men		Women		Minorities	
	Spr	Fall	Spr	Fall	Spr	Fall	Spr	Fall
Full-time	39	47	23	26	16	21	10	17
Other full-time	0	1	0	0	0	1	0	0
Deans, librarians, & others who teach	9	9	2	2	7	7	4	4
Part-time	22	14	14	7	6	7	2	6
Total	70	71	39	35	29	36	16	27

Curriculum

		Full-Time	Part-Time
Typical first-year section size		72	0
Is there typically a "small section" of the first-year class, other than Legal Writing, taught by full-time faculty		Yes	No
If yes, typical size offered last year		36	
# of classroom course titles beyond first-year curriculum		75	
# of upper division courses, excluding seminars, with an enrollment:	Under 25	51	
	25–49	25	
	50–74	8	
	75–99	11	
	100+	4	
# of seminars		14	
# of seminar positions available		239	
# of seminar positions filled		223	0
# of positions available in simulation courses		538	
# of simulation positions filled		482	0
# of positions available in faculty supervised clinical courses		124	
# of faculty supervised clinical positions filled		121	0
# involved in field placements		116	0
# involved in law journals		270	0
# involved in moot court or trial competitions		165	0
# of credit hours required to graduate		88	

JD Enrollment and Ethnicity

	Men		Women		Full-Time		Part-Time		1st-Year		Total		JD Degs. Awd.
	#	%	#	%	#	%	#	%	#	%	#	%	
African Amer.	6	2.1	4	1.2	10	1.7	0	0.0	4	1.9	10	1.7	5
Amer. Indian	1	0.4	1	0.3	2	0.3	0	0.0	0	0.0	2	0.3	1
Asian Amer.	70	24.7	92	28.5	162	26.7	0	0.0	54	25.2	162	26.7	41
Mex. Amer.	15	5.3	16	5.0	31	5.1	0	0.0	7	3.3	31	5.1	8
Puerto Rican	1	0.4	0	0.0	1	0.2	0	0.0	0	0.0	1	0.2	0
Hispanic	2	0.7	9	2.8	11	1.8	0	0.0	3	1.4	11	1.8	3
Total Minority	95	33.6	122	37.8	217	35.8	0	0.0	68	31.8	217	35.8	58
For. Nation.	6	2.1	4	1.2	10	1.7	0	0.0	0	0.0	10	1.7	4
Caucasian	146	51.6	145	44.9	291	48.0	0	0.0	108	50.5	291	48.0	96
Unknown	36	12.7	52	16.1	88	14.5	0	0.0	38	17.8	88	14.5	33
Total	283	46.7	323	53.3	606	100.0	0	0.0	214	35.3	606		191

Transfers

Transfers in	11
Transfers out	12

Tuition and Fees

	Resident	Nonresident
Full-time	$33,949	$44,895
Part-time		
Tuition Guarantee Program	N	

Living Expenses

Estimated living expenses for singles

Living on campus	Living off campus	Living at home
N/A	$16,332	N/A

University of California, Davis School of Law (King Hall)

ABA
Approved
Since
1968

GPA and LSAT Scores

	Total	Full-Time	Part-Time
# of apps	3,189	3,189	0
# of offers	1,026	1,026	0
# of matrics	213	213	0
75% GPA	3.72	3.72	0.00
Median GPA	3.51	3.51	0.00
25% GPA	3.23	3.23	0.00
75% LSAT	165	165	0
Median LSAT	163	163	0
25% LSAT	160	160	0

Grants and Scholarships (from prior year)

	Total		Full-Time		Part-Time	
	#	%	#	%	#	%
Total # of students	578		578		0	
Total # receiving grants	363	62.8	363	62.8	0	0.0
Less than 1/2 tuition	208	36.0	208	36.0	0	0.0
Half to full tuition	149	25.8	149	25.8	0	0.0
Full tuition	0	0.0	0	0.0	0	0.0
More than full tuition	6	1.0	6	1.0	0	0.0
Median grant amount			$11,991		$0	

Informational and Library Resources

Total amount spent on library materials	$1,117,073
Study seating capacity inside the library	311
# of full-time equivalent professional librarians	8.0
Hours per week library is open	78
# of open, wired connections available to students	0
# of networked computers available for use by students	84
Has wireless network?	Y
Require computer?	N

JD Attrition (from prior year)

	Academic	Other	Total	
	#	#	#	%
1st year	1	15	16	8.0
2nd year	0	1	1	0.5
3rd year	0	4	4	2.2
4th year	0	0	0	0.0

Employment (9 months after graduation)

	Total	Percentage
Employment status known	187	98.9
Employment status unknown	2	1.1
Employed	178	95.2
Pursuing graduate degrees	5	2.7
Unemployed (seeking, not seeking, or studying for the bar)	2	1.1
Type of Employment		
# employed in law firms	94	52.8
# employed in business and industry	13	7.3
# employed in government	19	10.7
# employed in public interest	21	11.8
# employed as judicial clerks	13	7.3
# employed in academia	6	3.4
Geographic Location		
# employed in state	155	87.1
# employed in foreign countries	0	0.0
# of states where employed	12	

Bar Passage Rates

First-time takers	199	Reporting %	89.95
Average school %	79.89	Average state %	78.07
Average pass difference	1.82		

Jurisdiction	Takers	Passers	Pass %	State %	Diff %
California	179	143	79.89	78.07	1.82

University of California, Davis School of Law (King Hall)

Admission Office, 400 Mrak Hall Drive
Davis, CA 95616-5201
Phone: 530.752.6477
E-mail: admissions@law.ucdavis.edu; Website: www.law.ucdavis.edu

■ Introduction

The School of Law at the University of California, Davis, is a national center of legal learning characterized by the scholarly excellence and ambition of its faculty and student body, as well as an abiding commitment to being a diverse community dedicated to the welfare of its constituents and the world around it. It is fully accredited by the American Bar Association and is a member of the Association of American Law Schools. The school is housed in a newly expanded state-of-the-art building, King Hall, named for Dr. Martin Luther King Jr. in honor of his efforts to bring social and political justice to disadvantaged peoples.

The Davis campus, a major research university consistently among the country's top 20 in research funding, is an hour from the San Francisco Bay Area, and 15 minutes from Sacramento, within easy reach of major recreational areas such as Napa, Carmel, and Lake Tahoe. The campus occupies 3,600 acres within the bike-friendly and charming college town of Davis.

The law school's idyllic surroundings and close proximity to the Bay Area and the state capital create abundant opportunities for a well-rounded educational experience. The campus offers a full range of excellent graduate and professional programs.

■ Library and Physical Facilities

Faculty offices, classrooms, and the Mabie Law Library are housed in King Hall, which has just undergone a major expansion and renovation that makes it one of the most beautiful and functional facilities in the country. It has two moot courtrooms, a pretrial-skills laboratory, a large computer lab, study carrels, student journal offices, lounges, an infant care co-op, and offices for student organizations, all easily accessible to disabled students. Each law student receives a key to the building to permit 24-hour access.

Study carrels are assigned to first-year students, and librarians assist students with legal research needs. Students enjoy access to numerous legal print and online resources via the library and California Digital Library.

Classrooms have the latest in audiovisual and multimedia technology. Wireless Internet access is available throughout the building.

■ Curriculum

The law school offers a three-year, full-time program in law leading to the Juris Doctor degree, and a postgraduate program leading to an LLM. At King Hall, a faculty with a national reputation for cutting-edge scholarship and devoted teaching is combined with an outstanding and diverse student body. The faculty includes worldwide leaders in many fields, including Constitutional Law; Intellectual Property; Environmental Law; Civil Rights; Critical Race Theory; Trusts, Wills, and Estates; Property; Contracts; Corporate Law and Securities; Evidence; Criminal Law and Procedure; Civil Procedure; Complex Litigation; Latinos and the Law; and Immigration Law and Policy. Each first-year section typically has fewer than 70 students, and each student is taught at least one of the required first-year courses in a small group of

30–35 students. One distinctive feature of the school is a weeklong introductory course that precedes the formal first-year curriculum. Upper-division courses may be selected within broad areas of concentration such as criminal justice, business and taxation, civil litigation, estate planning and taxation, labor and employment law, environmental law, human rights and social justice law, immigration law, intellectual property, international law, and constitutional and other public law. Students may also combine JD studies with another graduate or professional program such as an MBA.

■ Special Programs

The school is known for its superb clinical programs in which students work under the supervision of practicing lawyers in many different substantive areas. Students also participate in externships in trial and appellate courts as well as in federal, state, and local government offices and nonprofit organizations in California and Washington, DC.

The law school has four in-house clinics: Immigration, Civil Rights, Prison Law, and Family Protection. The Immigration Law Clinic, in which students work under one of the best immigration faculties in the United States, allows students to assist immigrants facing deportation.

Students participating in the Civil Rights Clinic appear in federal court in constitutional litigation, representing people who might otherwise have no counsel.

The Family Protection Clinic represents many low-income people who are not native English speakers and who need family law and domestic violence assistance.

First-year students perform an oral argument as a part of the required legal research and writing program, and can later participate if they choose in the formal Moot Court Program, which emphasizes appellate advocacy. Skills courses cover the major elements of both litigation and nonlitigation practice. These include pretrial skills (interviewing, counseling, and document drafting); negotiation, mediation, and alternative dispute resolution; business planning; and trial practice. The school has enjoyed excellent success in state, national, and international competitions in moot court and negotiations.

Students in the Public Interest Law Program receive a certificate based on required coursework, practical experience, and community service. This program culminates each year in a public service graduation ceremony, at which a graduating student is presented with the Martin Luther King Jr. Community Service Award. Students in the Environmental Law Program receive a certificate for completion of an environmental curriculum. King Hall students can also participate in a Pro Bono Program designed to both help address the unmet legal service needs of disadvantaged persons and nonprofit organizations and impress upon students the professional responsibility of lawyers to perform public service.

■ Admission

While the admission process is highly selective, it is by no means mechanical. The Admission Committee seeks excellent students of diverse backgrounds and interests. Each application is carefully reviewed with consideration given to many factors, including undergraduate grades and trends,

LSAT score, economic and other disadvantages, advanced studies, work experience, extracurricular and community activities, maturity, and commitment to the study of law. Residency is not a factor in the admission process. Open houses and information sessions for prospective applicants occur throughout the year. Guided tours can be arranged.

■ Student Life

King Hall is unusual among the nation's leading law schools for its wonderful sense of community. The student body is small compared to that of most schools, which lessens competition among a highly qualified student cohort. Students work extraordinarily well with each other, faculty, administrators, and staff. Faculty and administrators have an open-door policy for students. Cooperation and collegiality are the hallmarks of intellectual life at King Hall, and alumni look back fondly on their law school years.

An academic support program, including a bar preparation component during the third year, is available to all students. Students run five journals: the UC Davis Law Review and specialized journals in international law, environmental law, juvenile justice law, and business law.

Students sit on the student/faculty Educational Policy, Faculty Appointments, and Admission Committees. There are about 30 active student organizations encompassing a wide variety of interests. The La Raza Law Students Association's Lorenzo Patiño banquet honoring an alumnus and the King Hall Legal Foundation auction to raise funds for public interest are two of many student-sponsored events that highlight each academic year. The extremely positive attitude of King Hall students was noted and commented upon in our most recent ABA inspection report.

■ Expenses and Financial Aid

The School of Law Financial Aid office is available for the exclusive use of law students who desire counseling and advice. All financial aid services, from entrance through graduation, are administered at the law school. The school participates in all nationally recognized aid programs, such as Federal Perkins Loans and Federal Work-Study, and participates as well in the Federal Direct Loan Program. Over 63 percent of King Hall students receive need-based grants as part of their financial aid awards. Each year, two entering students are selected to receive the prestigious Martin Luther King Jr. Scholarships based on demonstrated commitment to public interest. University student loan and grant funds are available for child care. FAFSA and Need Access forms are required for aid consideration.

■ Housing

A wide variety of reasonably priced housing is available in the local community. The university maintains on-campus apartments for students and student families.

■ Career Services

The Career Services office successfully and enthusiastically assists students in securing rewarding summer and post-JD positions. Approximately 150 employers visit the school to interview students, and many others advertise using the department's online database. Career Services presents speakers and training workshops geared to student needs and to the hiring cycles of various segments of the legal and law-related job markets. Students also have access to many professional opportunities through job fairs, online nationwide listings, and other sources. Almost all students are employed at graduation.

Applicant Profile

University of California, Davis School of Law (King Hall)
This grid includes only applicants who earned 120–180 LSAT scores under standard administrations.

LSAT Score	3.75 +		3.50–3.74		3.25–3.49		3.00–3.24		2.75–2.99		2.50–2.74		2.25–2.49		2.00–2.24		Below 2.00		No GPA		Total	
	Apps	Adm	Apps	Adm	Apps	Adm	Apps	Adm	Apps	Adm	Apps	Adm	Apps	Adm	Apps	Adm	Apps	Adm	Apps	Adm	Apps	Adm
175–180	2	2	5	5	2	1	3	3	0	0	1	0	1	0	0	0	0	0	0	0	14	11
170–174	19	18	14	12	20	19	8	4	4	2	4	2	1	0	1	0	0	0	0	0	71	57
165–169	75	70	90	82	77	65	50	39	33	19	11	2	6	1	0	0	0	0	3	2	345	280
160–164	197	175	270	184	225	111	119	34	50	15	30	3	10	1	4	0	1	0	16	7	922	530
155–159	138	51	285	54	227	19	141	4	66	1	26	2	8	0	6	0	1	0	28	1	926	132
150–154	57	4	144	8	135	1	131	0	65	0	23	0	10	0	3	0	1	0	20	0	589	13
145–149	18	0	47	0	52	0	61	0	34	0	21	0	10	0	4	0	0	0	8	0	255	0
140–144	6	0	16	0	31	0	25	0	28	0	5	0	9	0	2	0	0	0	4	0	126	0
135–139	1	0	4	0	9	0	9	0	4	0	7	0	2	0	0	0	1	0	3	0	40	0
130–134	0	0	2	0	1	0	2	0	3	0	2	0	2	0	0	0	0	0	1	0	13	0
125–129	0	0	0	0	1	0	0	0	0	0	0	0	0	0	0	0	0	0	0	0	1	0
120–124	0	0	0	0	0	0	0	0	0	0	0	0	0	0	0	0	0	0	0	0	0	0
Total	513	320	877	345	780	216	549	84	287	37	130	9	59	2	20	0	4	0	83	10	3302	1023

Apps = Number of Applicants   Adm = Number Admitted   Reflects 99% of the total applicant pool; average LSAT data reported.

University of California, Hastings College of the Law

200 McAllister Street
San Francisco, CA 94102
Phone: 415.565.4623; Fax: 415.581.8946
E-mail: admiss@uchastings.edu; Website: www.uchastings.edu

The Basics

Type of school	Public
Term	Semester
Application deadline	3/1
Application fee	$75
Financial aid deadline	3/1
Can first year start other than fall?	No
Student to faculty ratio	16.5 to 1
# of housing spaces available	
restricted to law students	280
graduate housing for which law students are eligible	280

Faculty and Administrators

	Total		Men		Women		Minorities	
	Spr	Fall	Spr	Fall	Spr	Fall	Spr	Fall
Full-time	63	66	36	40	27	26	12	14
Other full-time	1	1	0	0	1	1	0	0
Deans, librarians, & others who teach	8	9	5	5	3	4	5	5
Part-time	116	106	67	61	49	45	28	29
Total	188	182	108	106	80	76	45	48

Curriculum

		Full-Time	Part-Time
Typical first-year section size		95	0
Is there typically a "small section" of the first-year class, other than Legal Writing, taught by full-time faculty		No	No
If yes, typical size offered last year			
# of classroom course titles beyond first-year curriculum		161	
# of upper division courses, excluding seminars, with an enrollment:	Under 25	133	
	25–49	43	
	50–74	22	
	75–99	17	
	100+	3	
# of seminars		68	
# of seminar positions available		1,312	
# of seminar positions filled		858	0
# of positions available in simulation courses		1,563	
# of simulation positions filled		1,143	0
# of positions available in faculty supervised clinical courses		216	
# of faculty supervised clinical positions filled		169	0
# involved in field placements		137	0
# involved in law journals		406	0
# involved in moot court or trial competitions		204	0
# of credit hours required to graduate		86	

JD Enrollment and Ethnicity

	Men		Women		Full-Time		Part-Time		1st-Year		Total		JD Degs. Awd.
	#	%	#	%	#	%	#	%	#	%	#	%	
African Amer.	16	2.5	19	2.9	34	2.6	1	14.3	13	2.8	35	2.7	13
Amer. Indian	8	1.3	4	0.6	12	0.9	0	0.0	6	1.3	12	0.9	1
Asian Amer.	104	16.4	163	24.5	265	20.5	2	28.6	90	19.1	267	20.6	100
Mex. Amer.	23	3.6	37	5.6	60	4.6	0	0.0	25	5.3	60	4.6	7
Puerto Rican	1	0.2	3	0.5	4	0.3	0	0.0	1	0.2	4	0.3	0
Hispanic	28	4.4	15	2.3	42	3.3	1	14.3	15	3.2	43	3.3	16
Total Minority	180	28.3	241	36.3	417	32.3	4	57.1	150	31.9	421	32.4	137
For. Nation.	6	0.9	17	2.6	23	1.8	0	0.0	9	1.9	23	1.8	7
Caucasian	338	53.2	302	45.5	638	49.4	2	28.6	238	50.6	640	49.3	175
Unknown	111	17.5	104	15.7	214	16.6	1	14.3	73	15.5	215	16.6	97
Total	635	48.9	664	51.1	1292	99.5	7	0.5	470	36.2	1299		416

Transfers

Transfers in	24
Transfers out	24

Tuition and Fees

	Resident	Nonresident
Full-time	$32,468	$43,693
Part-time		
Tuition Guarantee Program	N	

Living Expenses

Estimated living expenses for singles

Living on campus	Living off campus	Living at home
$19,898	$19,898	$19,898

University of California, Hastings College of the Law

ABA Approved Since 1939

GPA and LSAT Scores

	Total	Full-Time	Part-Time
# of apps	6,150	6,150	0
# of offers	1,454	1,454	0
# of matrics	469	469	0
75% GPA	3.71	3.71	0.00
Median GPA	3.58	3.58	0.00
25% GPA	3.39	3.39	0.00
75% LSAT	165	165	0
Median LSAT	164	164	0
25% LSAT	161	161	0

Grants and Scholarships (from prior year)

	Total #	Total %	Full-Time #	Full-Time %	Part-Time #	Part-Time %
Total # of students	1,251		1,244		7	
Total # receiving grants	931	74.4	931	74.8	0	0.0
Less than 1/2 tuition	891	71.2	891	71.6	0	0.0
Half to full tuition	40	3.2	40	3.2	0	0.0
Full tuition	0	0.0	0	0.0	0	0.0
More than full tuition	0	0.0	0	0.0	0	0.0
Median grant amount			$7,500		$0	

Informational and Library Resources

Total amount spent on library materials	$1,468,397
Study seating capacity inside the library	796
# of full-time equivalent professional librarians	11.0
Hours per week library is open	102
# of open, wired connections available to students	490
# of networked computers available for use by students	140
Has wireless network?	Y
Require computer?	N

JD Attrition (from prior year)

	Academic #	Other #	Total #	Total %
1st year	4	5	9	2.1
2nd year	1	28	29	6.8
3rd year	0	2	2	0.5
4th year	0	0	0	0.0

Employment (9 months after graduation)

	Total	Percentage
Employment status known	396	99.7
Employment status unknown	1	0.3
Employed	333	84.1
Pursuing graduate degrees	5	1.3
Unemployed (seeking, not seeking, or studying for the bar)	26	6.6
Type of Employment		
# employed in law firms	210	63.1
# employed in business and industry	28	8.4
# employed in government	29	8.7
# employed in public interest	20	6.0
# employed as judicial clerks	20	6.0
# employed in academia	26	7.8
Geographic Location		
# employed in state	290	87.1
# employed in foreign countries	1	0.3
# of states where employed	19	

Bar Passage Rates

First-time takers	390	Reporting %	88.21
Average school %	81.10	Average state %	78.07
Average pass difference	3.03		

Jurisdiction	Takers	Passers	Pass %	State %	Diff %
California	344	279	81.10	78.07	3.03

University of California, Hastings College of the Law

200 McAllister Street
San Francisco, CA 94102
Phone: 415.565.4623; Fax: 415.581.8946
E-mail: admiss@uchastings.edu; Website: www.uchastings.edu

■ Introduction

UC Hastings College of the Law offers a superb legal education in San Francisco, one of the world's great cities. Hastings was the first public law school in California, founded in 1878 as the law department of the University of California. The faculty at Hastings is composed of exceptional teachers who are also nationally known scholars. They are accessible to students and encourage a collaborative learning environment. Hastings has produced more judges than any other law school in the state, and its graduates can be found practicing law throughout California and the nation, in every kind of setting. Hastings graduates also have a significant presence in business and government.

The law school is situated in the heart of the city, near City Hall, state and federal courts, the arts district, the financial district, and the downtown shopping area. This central location provides access for students to pursue internships and externships with judges, city and state agencies, and nearby nonprofit research and advocacy groups. The location also provides unparalleled opportunities for recreation: theater, music, restaurants, professional and amateur sports, and a world-class transportation system.

■ Library, Technology, and Housing

Hastings is an urban campus with three buildings, all having wireless Internet access. The classroom building was renovated in 2000, and renovation of the library/administration building was completed in the fall of 2007. The new library is designed to be both comfortable and functional, with small-group study rooms, both open areas and individual carrels, and access to traditional and online research tools. McAllister Tower is a splendid, remodeled art deco building with 250 apartments, many with stunning views of the city. The building also features a comfortable lounge and a gym, including a basketball court often frequented by local attorneys and judges as well as Hastings students.

■ Curriculum

The UC Hastings curriculum offers a broad spectrum of basic and specialized courses. The law school's curricular strengths mirror the strengths of San Francisco. Students can focus on international human rights and business law, public interest law, intellectual property law, business and tax law, or litigation and its alternatives. San Francisco is a global city that draws on experts from Silicon Valley and the greater Bay Area to enrich course offerings.

■ Special Programs

- **Concentrations:** Students may earn a certificate of concentration in any of the following areas: Civil Litigation, Criminal Law, Law and Health Sciences, Intellectual Property, International Law, Public Interest Law, or Tax Law.
- **Clinics and Judicial Externships:** Hastings provides an exciting and diverse array of opportunities for students to gain practical experience. Under clinical faculty supervision, students represent real clients in in-house and out-placement clinics specializing in community development, environmental law, labor and employment, housing and disability rights, law reform, international human rights, immigrants' rights, and legislation. In these clinics, students learn a variety of lawyering techniques, including counseling and planning, litigation, alternative dispute resolution, and legislation. Simulation courses teach trial and appellate advocacy, negotiation, mediation, contract drafting, problem solving, and professional ethics. More than 100 students a year spend a semester serving as externs in the state and federal courts, including the Supreme Court of California.
- **International Programs:** Hastings offers an exceptionally strong curriculum focusing on international human rights, as well as international business and trade law. In addition, students may participate in the work of the Center for Gender and Refugee Studies, the Immigrants' Rights Clinic, and the Hastings-to-Haiti Partnership. Hastings also offers a dozen study-abroad programs in Argentina, Australia, China, Denmark, England, France, Germany, Hungary, Italy, and the Netherlands and supports students who wish to study abroad in other locations.
- **Joint-Degree Programs:** Hastings students may participate in a joint-degree program with any accredited graduate program. Hastings students have simultaneously earned degrees in public policy, public health, and business administration, among others.
- **Legal Education Opportunity Program (LEOP):** LEOP recognizes that the traditional academic criteria used to determine admission might not be the best indicators of academic potential for students from nontraditional backgrounds. LEOP admits students who have had to overcome significant obstacles and assists them to excel academically.
- **Centers and Institutes:** Students have opportunities to work in the law school's highly acclaimed research and advocacy centers: the Center for Gender and Refugee Studies, the Center for Negotiation and Dispute Resolution, the Center for State and Local Government Law, the Center for WorkLife Law, and the Public Law Research Institute.
- **LLM Program:** Graduates of non-US law schools may earn a master of laws degree in US Legal Studies.

■ Cocurricular and Student Activities

The strength and diversity of the Hastings student body are reflected in more than 60 student organizations that sponsor intellectual, social, and political events. Hastings publishes nine student-edited law reviews. The *Hastings Law Journal* is a general-interest publication. In addition, eight specialty law reviews focus on a variety of issues, including business law, constitutional law, communication and entertainment law, international and comparative law, environmental law, science and technology, and the law relating to race or gender. Students may also join the college's award-winning moot court, negotiation, client counseling, and trial practice teams, which compete in state, national, and international competitions. Students also engage in a variety of legal and

University of California, Hastings College of the Law

nonlegal community service activities in and around the Hastings neighborhood.

■ Financial Aid

The majority of UC Hastings students receive need-based and merit-based financial assistance from college-administered sources. Scholarships and grants recognize and encourage the achievement, service, and professional promise of students. Students who pursue qualifying public interest and government sector employment may receive loan repayment assistance after graduation through the Public Interest Career Assistance Program (PICAP).

■ Career Services

UC Hastings offers one of the most comprehensive law career services offices in the West. The office assists students and alumni in clarifying their goals, acquiring job search strategies, and honing interviewing techniques. It provides access to full-time, part-time, and summer job listings. Every year, more than 200 employers visit the campus to interview students for both summer associate positions and permanent postgraduation employment. Several hundred additional employers from throughout the nation participate in the recruit-by-mail program.

Applicant Profile

University of California, Hastings College of the Law
This grid includes only applicants who earned 120–180 LSAT scores under standard administrations.

LSAT Score	3.75 +		3.50–3.74		3.25–3.49		3.00–3.24		2.75–2.99		2.50–2.74		2.25–2.49		2.00–2.24		Below 2.00		No GPA		Total	
	Apps	Adm	Apps	Adm	Apps	Adm	Apps	Adm	Apps	Adm	Apps	Adm	Apps	Adm	Apps	Adm	Apps	Adm	Apps	Adm	Apps	Adm
175–180	7	0	9	0	3	1	2	0	2	0	2	0	1	0	0	0	0	0	0	0	26	1
170–174	29	1	43	1	35	11	26	11	11	1	10	3	3	0	1	0	1	0	1	1	160	29
165–169	153	94	243	176	178	130	128	56	63	5	21	1	10	0	2	0	0	0	10	7	808	469
160–164	332	238	532	292	447	150	236	33	101	4	43	1	21	0	7	0	1	0	44	14	1764	732
155–159	246	57	478	62	408	21	245	11	107	1	55	0	15	0	9	0	0	0	46	1	1609	153
150–154	114	9	203	23	260	10	228	3	117	0	54	1	27	0	3	0	2	0	34	0	1042	46
145–149	42	5	74	5	107	3	96	1	71	0	30	0	24	0	5	0	3	0	18	1	470	15
140–144	12	1	29	0	45	0	64	0	44	0	25	0	19	0	3	0	0	0	14	0	255	1
135–139	1	0	9	0	13	0	16	0	11	0	8	0	7	0	5	0	4	0	8	0	82	0
130–134	0	0	4	0	1	0	3	0	3	0	6	0	3	0	1	0	0	0	2	0	23	0
125–129	0	0	0	0	1	0	1	0	1	0	3	0	0	0	0	0	0	0	0	0	6	0
120–124	0	0	0	0	0	0	0	0	0	0	0	0	0	0	0	0	0	0	1	0	1	0
Total	936	405	1624	559	1498	326	1045	115	531	11	257	6	130	0	36	0	11	0	178	24	6246	1446

Apps = Number of Applicants
Adm = Number Admitted
Reflects 99% of the total applicant pool; average LSAT data reported.

University of California at Los Angeles (UCLA) School of Law

Law Admissions Office, 71 Dodd Hall, Box 951445
Los Angeles, CA 90095-1445
Phone: 310.825.2080
E-mail: admissions@law.ucla.edu; Website: www.law.ucla.edu

ABA
Approved
Since
1950

The Basics

Type of school	Public
Term	Semester
Application deadline	2/1
Application fee	$75
Financial aid deadline	3/2
Can first year start other than fall?	No
Student to faculty ratio	11.3 to 1
# of housing spaces available restricted to law students	
graduate housing for which law students are eligible	121

Faculty and Administrators

	Total		Men		Women		Minorities	
	Spr	Fall	Spr	Fall	Spr	Fall	Spr	Fall
Full-time	77	71	55	49	22	22	10	10
Other full-time	17	14	9	5	8	9	2	2
Deans, librarians, & others who teach	14	12	7	8	7	4	1	2
Part-time	30	19	24	16	6	3	2	1
Total	138	116	95	78	43	38	15	15

Curriculum

		Full-Time	Part-Time
Typical first-year section size		80	0
Is there typically a "small section" of the first-year class, other than Legal Writing, taught by full-time faculty		Yes	No
If yes, typical size offered last year		32	
# of classroom course titles beyond first-year curriculum		188	
# of upper division courses, excluding seminars, with an enrollment:	Under 25	70	
	25–49	37	
	50–74	15	
	75–99	12	
	100+	8	
# of seminars		51	
# of seminar positions available		810	
# of seminar positions filled		790	0
# of positions available in simulation courses		152	
# of simulation positions filled		147	0
# of positions available in faculty supervised clinical courses		207	
# of faculty supervised clinical positions filled		182	0
# involved in field placements		88	0
# involved in law journals		546	0
# involved in moot court or trial competitions		17	0
# of credit hours required to graduate		87	

JD Enrollment and Ethnicity

	Men		Women		Full-Time		Part-Time		1st-Year		Total		JD Degs. Awd.
	#	%	#	%	#	%	#	%	#	%	#	%	
African Amer.	24	4.6	22	4.5	46	4.6	0	0.0	17	5.3	46	4.6	11
Amer. Indian	8	1.5	4	0.8	12	1.2	0	0.0	4	1.3	12	1.2	8
Asian Amer.	77	14.8	105	21.4	182	18.0	0	0.0	53	16.6	182	18.0	74
Mex. Amer.	25	4.8	32	6.5	57	5.6	0	0.0	16	5.0	57	5.6	20
Puerto Rican	2	0.4	0	0.0	2	0.2	0	0.0	0	0.0	2	0.2	2
Hispanic	13	2.5	17	3.5	30	3.0	0	0.0	11	3.4	30	3.0	13
Total Minority	149	28.6	180	36.7	329	32.5	0	0.0	101	31.7	329	32.5	128
For. Nation.	10	1.9	10	2.0	20	2.0	0	0.0	7	2.2	20	2.0	5
Caucasian	252	48.4	186	38.0	438	43.3	0	0.0	138	43.3	438	43.3	146
Unknown	110	21.1	114	23.3	224	22.2	0	0.0	74	23.2	224	22.2	84
Total	521	51.5	490	48.5	1011	100.0	0	0.0	319	31.6	1011		363

Transfers

Transfers in	46
Transfers out	9

Tuition and Fees

	Resident	Nonresident
Full-time	$35,327	$45,967
Part-time		
Tuition Guarantee Program		N

Living Expenses

Estimated living expenses for singles

Living on campus	Living off campus	Living at home
N/A	$21,069	$12,777

University of California at Los Angeles (UCLA) School of Law

ABA
Approved
Since
1950

GPA and LSAT Scores

	Total	Full-Time	Part-Time
# of apps	8,255	8,255	0
# of offers	1,383	1,383	0
# of matrics	320	320	0
75% GPA	3.88	3.88	0.00
Median GPA	3.75	3.75	0.00
25% GPA	3.57	3.57	0.00
75% LSAT	169	169	0
Median LSAT	168	168	0
25% LSAT	164	164	0

Grants and Scholarships (from prior year)

	Total #	Total %	Full-Time #	Full-Time %	Part-Time #	Part-Time %
Total # of students	1,012		1,012		0	
Total # receiving grants	615	60.8	615	60.8	0	0.0
Less than 1/2 tuition	466	46.0	466	46.0	0	0.0
Half to full tuition	93	9.2	93	9.2	0	0.0
Full tuition	0	0.0	0	0.0	0	0.0
More than full tuition	56	5.5	56	5.5	0	0.0
Median grant amount			$9,557		$0	

Informational and Library Resources

Total amount spent on library materials	$2,058,000
Study seating capacity inside the library	774
# of full-time equivalent professional librarians	22.0
Hours per week library is open	97
# of open, wired connections available to students	1,820
# of networked computers available for use by students	638
Has wireless network?	Y
Require computer?	N

JD Attrition (from prior year)

	Academic #	Other #	Total #	Total %
1st year	0	14	14	4.6
2nd year	0	3	3	0.9
3rd year	0	3	3	0.8
4th year	0	0	0	0.0

Employment (9 months after graduation)

	Total	Percentage
Employment status known	337	100.0
Employment status unknown	0	0.0
Employed	323	95.8
Pursuing graduate degrees	5	1.5
Unemployed (seeking, not seeking, or studying for the bar)	3	0.9
Type of Employment		
# employed in law firms	206	63.8
# employed in business and industry	22	6.8
# employed in government	25	7.7
# employed in public interest	28	8.7
# employed as judicial clerks	34	10.5
# employed in academia	6	1.9
Geographic Location		
# employed in state	281	87.0
# employed in foreign countries	1	0.3
# of states where employed	16	

Bar Passage Rates

First-time takers	311	Reporting %	92.28
Average school %	88.50	Average state %	78.07
Average pass difference	10.43		

Jurisdiction	Takers	Passers	Pass %	State %	Diff %
California	287	254	88.50	78.07	10.43

University of California at Los Angeles (UCLA) School of Law

Law Admissions Office, 71 Dodd Hall, Box 951445
Los Angeles, CA 90095-1445
Phone: 310.825.2080
E-mail: admissions@law.ucla.edu; Website: www.law.ucla.edu

■ Introduction

Located in the heart of Southern California, and nestled in a beautiful and safe residential neighborhood, UCLA School of Law is less than seven miles from the Pacific Ocean, and is housed on the UCLA campus. The law school has established a world-class learning environment that brings together talented, prolific legal scholars and enthusiastic, exceptional students. UCLA Law acquired and maintains its strong standing by creating pioneering academic programs, cultivating top legal scholars, and educating students who go on to be leaders in our society.

Los Angeles, with its rich social and cultural scene, offers unparalleled access to numerous recreational opportunities and activities, such as sporting events, theaters, museums, and live performances. UCLA Law is close enough to the thriving metropolis of Los Angeles for students to partake in the vibrant social and cultural scene, yet secluded enough for students to focus on their legal studies. The incredible weather, the international reach of the city, and the intellectually stimulating environment all contribute to a student's law school experience.

■ Curriculum

The law school offers a three-year, full-time course of study leading to a Juris Doctor degree. Evening, summer, or part-time programs are not offered. UCLA differs from many other institutions in that it invests major resources in its first-year Lawyering Skills Program. This program combines the beginning of skills training, such as client interviewing and counseling, with traditional legal research and writing. As a requirement for graduation, each student must complete a course in Professional Responsibility and a Substantial Analytic Writing (SAW) project during the second or third year of law school.

■ Faculty

The UCLA School of Law faculty is a treasured asset. Faculty members are leaders in their respective fields and are the mainstay of UCLA Law's high-quality legal education programs. They are some of the finest teachers in the academy, expanding the frontiers of interdisciplinary legal scholarship. Each year, UCLA Law faculty members demonstrate the caliber of their intellectual abilities by publishing groundbreaking scholarship in leading academic journals and law reviews. Their work is widely referenced, as evidenced by various citation studies.

■ Special Programs

Academic Specializations: UCLA School of Law is unique in that it offers students an opportunity to specialize in five specific areas of the law: Business Law and Policy, Critical Race Studies, Entertainment and Media Law and Policy, Law and Philosophy, and the David J. Epstein Program in Public Interest Law and Policy.

Centers: UCLA School of Law has always emphasized progressive research on relevant topics. We have consistently generated groundbreaking scholarship by providing our faculty access to the tools and resources they need to conduct thoughtful, interdisciplinary research. Centers include:

- Center for Law and Economics
- Emmett Center on Climate Change and the Environment
- Empirical Research Group
- Globalization and Labor Standards
- Native Nations Law and Policy Center
- Richard S. Ziman Center for Real Estate
- UCLA-RAND Center of Law and Public Policy
- Williams Institute on Sexual Orientation Law and Public Policy

Study-Abroad and Externship Programs: Law students may spend one semester abroad through student exchange agreements with universities in Argentina, France, Israel, Japan, Norway, Spain, and Switzerland. Some students also obtain approval for an individualized study-abroad program. UCLA Law has an extensive national and international student externship program. The law school has developed a core group of judicial and agency externships which include externships with federal judges, government agencies, public interest law firms, and nonprofit organizations. In addition, the UCDC Program is a uniquely collaborative externship program in Washington, DC. All externships are full-time, semester-long programs. Students can also propose new agency externships tailored to their academic goals.

Clinical Law Program: Since pioneering clinical legal education in the early 1970s, UCLA Law's Clinical Law Program has blazed a path of innovation and excellence. Typically, there are more than 30 clinical offerings each year with more than 300 clinical spots available for students. Some examples include the Criminal Defense Clinic, Environmental Law Clinic, Immigration Clinic, Intellectual Property Clinic, International Justice Clinic, Mediation Clinic, and Sports and the Law Clinic.

■ Joint Degrees

A number of students find it advantageous to pursue formal training in another field of study concurrently with their legal training. Typically, such concurrent-degree programs lead, after four years of study, to the simultaneous award of a Juris Doctor and an advanced degree from another school or department. Formal joint-degree programs are offered in the following areas: JD/MA (Afro-American Studies), JD/MA (American Indian Studies), JD/MBA (Anderson School of Management), JD/PhD (Philosophy), JD/MPH (Public Health), JD/MPP (Public Policy), JD/MSW (Social Welfare), and JD/MA (Urban Planning).

■ Student Life and Student Activities

A collegial environment at UCLA Law affords students many opportunities for participation and leadership in numerous student organizations and student-edited journals. UCLA School of Law has 12 student journals managed and edited by students on a wide range of topics.

Diverse student interests are represented in nearly 50 student organizations. The Moot Court Honors Program is open to all second- and third-year students and offers a large and effective program of mock appellate advocacy. The program also hosts a first-year competition, as well as the prestigious Roscoe Pound competition.

University of California at Los Angeles (UCLA) School of Law

Housing

Many housing options are open to UCLA School of Law students. There are university-owned apartments for single graduate students, single students who are parents, and married students with or without children. In addition, UCLA Law hosts a Web-based service to help students with their roommate searches.

Admission and Financial Aid

All applicants must have a baccalaureate degree from an accredited university or college of approved standing and must take the LSAT no later than the February administration. Students are admitted for the fall semester only. Admission is based primarily on proven outstanding academic and intellectual ability measured largely by the LSAT and the quality of undergraduate education as determined by not only the GPA, but also by such factors as the breadth, depth, and rigor of the undergraduate educational program. The Admissions Committee may also consider whether economic, physical, or other hardships and challenges have been overcome. Distinctive programmatic contributions, community or public service, letters of recommendation, work experience, career achievement, language ability, and career goals (with particular attention paid to the likelihood of the applicant representing underrepresented communities) are also factors taken into consideration.

Both need- and merit-based aid are available. All admitted students are automatically considered for merit scholarships. To apply for need-based aid, the FAFSA (*www.fafsa.ed.gov*) and the Need Access application (*www.needaccess.org*) should be filed no later than March 2. Applicants admitted to the law school as nonresident students (for tuition purposes) are eligible to be considered for resident classification if certain eligibility requirements are met. Most nonresident law students are able to achieve residency status during the second year of law school.

Career Services

The Office of Career Services provides students and alumni with professional career services and acts as a liaison between students and employers. Each first-year student is assigned to a counselor who will assist him/her through all the phases of career preparation, from the first-year summer job to postgraduate employment. The office is also dedicated to advising and assisting students interested in pursuing postgraduate judicial clerkships—highly sought-after positions secured by about 11 percent of the Class of 2008.

The office coordinates on-campus interviews and off-campus career fairs with close to 400 interviewers from law firms, corporations, government agencies, and public interest organizations visiting the school annually. The office also hosts numerous panels, programs, and events, including an annual Small/Mid-Sized Law Firm Reception, an annual Government Reception and Information Fair, and an Alumni Mentor Program.

UCLA Law graduates are in high demand among employers from all major sectors of the country, with California, New York, and Washington, DC, representing the largest employment markets for our students.

Students and graduates seeking to pursue public interest employment can take advantage of the opportunities offered by our Office of Public Interest Programs. There is a loan repayment assistance program to increase the ability of JD graduates to pursue public service legal careers.

Applicant Profile

University of California at Los Angeles (UCLA) School of Law
This grid includes only applicants who earned 120–180 LSAT scores under standard administrations.

LSAT Score	3.75 +		3.50–3.74		3.25–3.49		3.00–3.24		2.75–2.99		2.50–2.74		2.25–2.49		2.00–2.24		Below 2.00		No GPA		Total	
	Apps	Adm	Apps	Adm	Apps	Adm	Apps	Adm	Apps	Adm	Apps	Adm	Apps	Adm	Apps	Adm	Apps	Adm	Apps	Adm	Apps	Adm
175–180	76	48	56	23	32	7	20	3	7	1	2	0	0	0	0	0	0	0	1	0	194	82
170–174	293	211	255	152	167	33	82	7	19	4	12	1	2	0	0	0	0	0	7	3	837	411
165–169	761	440	695	169	367	46	177	12	49	1	22	1	10	0	1	0	0	0	31	3	2113	672
160–164	602	131	734	53	470	25	209	6	68	2	34	0	12	0	5	0	1	0	65	1	2200	218
155–159	270	23	452	22	317	14	196	2	79	2	41	0	10	0	4	0	0	0	46	3	1415	66
150–154	104	5	204	0	208	3	175	0	89	0	44	0	11	0	7	0	1	0	38	1	881	9
145–149	44	0	83	0	100	0	83	0	56	0	30	0	16	0	7	0	1	0	22	0	442	0
140–144	12	0	26	0	46	0	54	0	40	0	22	0	15	0	5	0	0	0	12	0	232	0
135–139	1	0	13	0	12	0	21	0	18	0	11	0	6	0	6	0	1	0	7	0	96	0
130–134	0	0	1	0	3	0	5	0	3	0	3	0	6	0	5	0	0	0	3	0	29	0
125–129	0	0	0	0	1	0	0	0	0	0	2	0	0	0	0	0	0	0	1	0	4	0
120–124	0	0	0	0	0	0	0	0	0	0	0	0	0	0	0	0	0	0	2	0	2	0
Total	2163	858	2519	419	1723	128	1022	30	428	10	223	2	88	0	40	0	4	0	235	11	8445	1458

Apps = Number of Applicants   Adm = Number Admitted   Reflects 99% of the total applicant pool; average LSAT data reported.

California Western School of Law

225 Cedar Street
San Diego, CA 92101
Phone: 800.255.4252 ext. 1401 or 619.525.1401
E-mail: admissions@cwsl.edu; Website: www.CaliforniaWestern.edu

ABA
Approved
Since
1962

The Basics

Type of school	Private	
Term	Semester	
Application deadline	4/1	11/1
Application fee	$55	
Financial aid deadline	4/1	10/15
Can first year start other than fall?	Yes	
Student to faculty ratio	18.3 to 1	
# of housing spaces available restricted to law students		
graduate housing for which law students are eligible		

Faculty and Administrators

	Total		Men		Women		Minorities	
	Spr	Fall	Spr	Fall	Spr	Fall	Spr	Fall
Full-time	39	40	26	25	13	15	6	5
Other full-time	1	1	1	1	0	0	1	1
Deans, librarians, & others who teach	12	12	4	4	8	8	3	3
Part-time	35	39	19	23	15	16	3	4
Total	87	92	50	53	36	39	13	13

Curriculum

		Full-Time	Part-Time
Typical first-year section size		87	0
Is there typically a "small section" of the first-year class, other than Legal Writing, taught by full-time faculty		No	No
If yes, typical size offered last year			
# of classroom course titles beyond first-year curriculum		114	
# of upper division courses, excluding seminars, with an enrollment:	Under 25	125	
	25–49	24	
	50–74	9	
	75–99	13	
	100+	9	
# of seminars		31	
# of seminar positions available		749	
# of seminar positions filled		576	57
# of positions available in simulation courses		1,593	
# of simulation positions filled		1,172	92
# of positions available in faculty supervised clinical courses		72	
# of faculty supervised clinical positions filled		58	6
# involved in field placements		164	16
# involved in law journals		63	9
# involved in moot court or trial competitions		35	0
# of credit hours required to graduate		89	

JD Enrollment and Ethnicity

	Men		Women		Full-Time		Part-Time		1st-Year		Total		JD Degs. Awd.
	#	%	#	%	#	%	#	%	#	%	#	%	
African Amer.	9	2.2	20	4.1	24	3.0	5	5.0	9	2.9	29	3.3	3
Amer. Indian	4	1.0	3	0.6	7	0.9	0	0.0	4	1.3	7	0.8	2
Asian Amer.	51	12.7	77	15.7	117	14.8	11	10.9	43	13.7	128	14.3	32
Mex. Amer.	29	7.2	38	7.7	59	7.5	8	7.9	27	8.6	67	7.5	16
Puerto Rican	0	0.0	2	0.4	2	0.3	0	0.0	0	0.0	2	0.2	1
Hispanic	6	1.5	10	2.0	12	1.5	4	4.0	5	1.6	16	1.8	8
Total Minority	99	24.7	150	30.5	221	27.9	28	27.7	88	28.1	249	27.9	62
For. Nation.	5	1.2	3	0.6	8	1.0	0	0.0	1	0.3	8	0.9	2
Caucasian	255	63.6	292	59.5	485	61.3	62	61.4	197	62.9	547	61.3	141
Unknown	42	10.5	46	9.4	77	9.7	11	10.9	27	8.6	88	9.9	40
Total	401	45.0	491	55.0	791	88.7	101	11.3	313	35.1	892		245

Transfers

Transfers in	3
Transfers out	17

Tuition and Fees

	Resident	Nonresident
Full-time	$38,500	$38,500
Part-time	$27,100	$27,100
Tuition Guarantee Program	Y	

Living Expenses

Estimated living expenses for singles

Living on campus	Living off campus	Living at home
N/A	$21,998	$14,398

California Western School of Law

ABA
Approved
Since
1962

GPA and LSAT Scores

	Total	Full-Time	Part-Time
# of apps	2,922	2,683	239
# of offers	1,348	1,276	72
# of matrics	340	322	18
75% GPA	3.50	3.50	3.56
Median GPA	3.28	3.28	3.33
25% GPA	3.04	3.05	2.93
75% LSAT	155	155	154
Median LSAT	153	153	151
25% LSAT	150	150	148

Grants and Scholarships (from prior year)

	Total		Full-Time		Part-Time	
	#	%	#	%	#	%
Total # of students	887		793		94	
Total # receiving grants	348	39.2	323	40.7	25	26.6
Less than 1/2 tuition	163	18.4	152	19.2	11	11.7
Half to full tuition	111	12.5	105	13.2	6	6.4
Full tuition	43	4.8	38	4.8	5	5.3
More than full tuition	31	3.5	28	3.5	3	3.2
Median grant amount			$18,120		$11,667	

Informational and Library Resources

Total amount spent on library materials	$1,233,458
Study seating capacity inside the library	438
# of full-time equivalent professional librarians	9
Hours per week library is open	110
# of open, wired connections available to students	540
# of networked computers available for use by students	80
Has wireless network?	Y
Require computer?	N

JD Attrition (from prior year)

	Academic	Other	Total	
	#	#	#	%
1st year	35	31	66	18.8
2nd year	0	5	5	1.7
3rd year	2	0	2	0.9
4th year	0	0	0	0.0

Employment (9 months after graduation)

	Total	Percentage
Employment status known	230	90.2
Employment status unknown	25	9.8
Employed	189	82.2
Pursuing graduate degrees	8	3.5
Unemployed (seeking, not seeking, or studying for the bar)	20	8.7
Type of Employment		
# employed in law firms	114	60.3
# employed in business and industry	24	12.7
# employed in government	27	14.3
# employed in public interest	13	6.9
# employed as judicial clerks	9	4.8
# employed in academia	2	1.1
Geographic Location		
# employed in state	144	76.2
# employed in foreign countries	1	0.5
# of states where employed		15

Bar Passage Rates

First-time takers	247	Reporting %	74.09
Average school %	84.15	Average state %	78.07
Average pass difference	6.08		

Jurisdiction	Takers	Passers	Pass %	State %	Diff %
California	183	154	84.15	78.07	6.08

California Western School of Law

225 Cedar Street
San Diego, CA 92101
Phone: 800.255.4252 ext. 1401 or 619.525.1401
E-mail: admissions@cwsl.edu; Website: www.CaliforniaWestern.edu

■ Introduction

California Western School of Law is the independent San Diego law school that educates lawyers as creative problem solvers and principled advocates—lawyers who frame the practice of law as a helping, collaborative profession. The law school's centers and institutes offer students many opportunities to explore the full scope of the law in real-life situations. California Western, accredited by the ABA (1962) and AALS (1967), emphasizes both theory and practice—rigorous academics and renowned real-world clinical programs—and invites students to explore the wide expanse of the law while preparing for practice.

■ Library and Physical Facilities

The award winning, four-story, 50,000-square-foot law library was dedicated in 2000 by US Supreme Court Justice Anthony Kennedy. The library holds more than 333,000 volumes, approximately 3,905 serial subscriptions, microforms currently equivalent to 154,000 volumes, audio- and videotapes, computer software, and interactive videos. The library also offers an excellent computer lab. The law library is wired with high-speed digital lines for fast network communications. There are 250 data ports for laptop computers in the building.

Renovations to the historic classroom building at California Western have provided several large lecture halls, office space for 30 on-campus student organizations, an 1,840-square-foot student lounge, individual study rooms, and a computer lab. Students enjoy additional access to the student network and Internet via campus-wide wireless technology.

■ Curriculum

The California Western curriculum offers a broad and diverse selection of courses. The law school provides a rigorous, traditional legal education with an emphasis on developing problem solving, communication, writing, and analytical skills. Areas of concentration are also offered in seven fields of study: international law; labor and employment law; child, family, and elder law; criminal law; creative problem solving; intellectual property, telecommunications, and technology-regulations law; and health law and policy. Numerous academic programs, including clinical placements and skills-based learning, supplement the course curriculum.

In addition to the traditional three-year curriculum, California Western offers a trimester academic calendar that allows students to study law year-round to complete their legal education in two years. California Western also offers a part-time day program.

■ Interdisciplinary Programs

California Western offers several dual-degree programs, allowing students to study two disciplines concurrently. The dual-degree program with the University of California, San Diego, offers degrees in political science (JD/PhD) and history (JD/PhD). California Western and the University of California, San Diego, also offer a joint degree in health law studies (MAS). In addition, California Western offers a dual-degree program with San Diego State University in both business (JD/MBA) and social work (JD/MSW).

■ University of California, San Diego Affiliation

California Western and the University of California, San Diego, have an Agreement of Association that provides broad interdisciplinary opportunities for the faculty and students of both institutions. These opportunities include joint academic degrees, joint research efforts, a vibrant speaker series, sharing of facilities, and community outreach programs.

■ Study-Abroad Programs

Students have the opportunity to study in academic programs throughout the world, including in Chile, England, Ireland, Malta, and the Czech Republic. Additionally, semester-abroad opportunities are available at Victoria University of Wellington in New Zealand, the University of Aarhus in Denmark, the University of Paris X-Nanterre in France, and at Leiden University School of Law in the Netherlands.

■ Special Programs

The Center for Creative Problem Solving investigates collaborative approaches to communication, conflict resolution, and problem solving. The Center develops curriculum, research, and projects to educate students and lawyers on methods for preventing problems and creatively solving those problems that already exist. It also houses *Proyecto ACCESO*, a Latin American center for training lawyers, judges, law students, government officials, and community leaders in the skills of oral advocacy, problem solving, and other forms of conflict resolution.

Through the California Innocence Project, law students work alongside practicing criminal defense lawyers to seek the release of wrongfully convicted prisoners. Law students assist in the investigation, write briefs, and advocate for the release of clients.

The Institute of Health Law Studies is a health law center that focuses on "improving health care today for all our tomorrows." It performs research, participates in advocacy activities, engages in community service, and provides education to advance its mission.

The law school offers the LLM in Trial Advocacy specializing in Federal Criminal Law. International lawyers who are interested in studying comparative law or the US legal system may pursue the Master of Laws in Comparative Law (LLM) and the Master of Comparative Law (MCL).

■ Clinical Internship Program

California Western's Clinical Internship Program provides opportunities for students to gain practical lawyering experience in law offices, corporations, government agencies, and courts. Nearly 70 percent of California Western students participate in this popular program. Students have the opportunity to intern in almost any area of law. Out-of-town internships are available for students interested in developing these skills outside of San Diego. Our students have worked in many countries, including Argentina, Brazil, Chile, China, England, the Philippines, Poland, Singapore, Spain, Sweden, and Switzerland. Students have arranged internships at the United Nations, the Asian Development Bank, the International Criminal Tribunal for

Rwanda, Paramount Studios, the Federal Communications Commission, and the US Department of State.

■ Student Activities

The *Law Review* and the *International Law Journal* publish articles by academic scholars and practitioners as well as by California Western students. Students edit and manage these publications under supervision from faculty advisors and a professional staff.

The Moot Court Honors Board allows students interested in trial and appellate advocacy skills to practice and compete against other students. Under the supervision and guidance of faculty coaches, students also participate in advocacy competitions around the country. California Western advocacy teams are nationally recognized, and our students have won many regional and national awards in these competitions.

California Western has a vibrant student government. Nearly 30 student organizations reflect a broad range of interests and diversity.

■ Career Services

Career Services offers individualized, professional advice to students about their personal career goals and tailors strategies to assist students in reaching those goals. The department coordinates the on-campus recruitment program, practice-area panel discussions, a national alumni mentor network, the Pro Bono Honors Program, and access to technological resources for career development. Prospective employers regularly visit the campus to meet with interested students.

■ Alumni

California Western's nearly 8,000 alumni work in large firms, domestic and foreign governments, large corporations, private practice, the judiciary, and academia. The law school's Alumni Admissions Recruiter program matches alumni with prospective students in the areas in which they reside. The Admissions Office can provide prospective students with a list of alumni in their area who are available to talk with them about employment opportunities and career advice.

■ Diversity

California Western's belief is that a richly diversified student body enhances the academic and interpersonal experiences of the law school. Half of the student body is female and approximately one-third is of an ethnic minority. California Western does not discriminate on the basis of race, color, creed, religion, sex, national origin, disability, sexual orientation, or veteran status.

■ Admission

Admission decisions are made on a rolling basis. Applicants are admitted based on an evaluation of the LSAT score, undergraduate academic record, personal statement, letters of recommendation, and other criteria, including work experience, campus and community activities, life/personal experiences, and evidence of leadership promise. Students are admitted to California Western to begin in August and January. Bachelor's degree and registration with LSAC's Credential Assembly Service are required. Application deadlines: fall—April 1; spring—November 1.

■ Financial Aid and Scholarships

More than 85 percent of California Western's students receive some form of financial assistance to fund their legal education. Need-based financial aid includes loans and work study. Numerous scholarships are awarded based on academic criteria and LSAT scores. Scholarships include the prestigious Kennedy Scholarship, which, among other benefits, provides full tuition for three years. Other merit-based full and partial scholarships are awarded to incoming students, including diversity, career transition, and creative problem-solving scholarships. Academic achievement scholarships are available to continuing students. Scholarships are awarded by the Admissions Office after reviewing student admission applications.

Applicant Profile

California Western School of Law
This grid includes only applicants who earned 120–180 LSAT scores under standard administrations.

LSAT Score	3.75 +		3.50–3.74		3.25–3.49		3.00–3.24		2.75–2.99		2.50–2.74		Below 2.50		No GPA		Total	
	Apps	Adm	Apps	Adm	Apps	Adm	Apps	Adm	Apps	Adm	Apps	Adm	Apps	Adm	Apps	Adm	Apps	Adm
170–180	1	1	0	0	0	0	2	2	0	0	1	0	1	1	0	0	5	4
165–169	3	3	2	2	5	5	3	2	3	3	3	2	2	2	0	0	21	19
160–164	9	9	14	13	20	19	26	26	23	22	15	11	9	6	4	2	120	108
155–159	28	28	56	55	84	81	73	66	58	47	34	21	39	14	4	1	376	313
150–154	39	37	113	104	201	173	212	144	160	68	85	23	58	2	12	8	880	559
145–149	42	30	96	55	183	73	172	38	158	14	83	3	68	2	10	2	812	217
140–144	13	1	33	2	61	3	96	2	73	0	50	0	53	0	11	0	390	8
Below 140	2	0	11	0	19	0	28	0	30	0	20	0	36	0	10	1	156	1
Total	137	109	325	231	573	354	612	280	505	154	291	60	266	27	51	14	2760	1229

Apps = Number of Applicants   Adm = Number Admitted   Reflects 99% of the total applicant pool; average LSAT data reported.

Miscellaneous applicants with no LSAT (i.e., MCL/LLM program) and nonstandard administration not in grid

Campbell University, Norman Adrian Wiggins School of Law

225 Hillsborough Street
Raleigh, NC 27603
Phone: 919.865.5988; Fax: 919.865.5992
E-mail: admissions@law.campbell.edu; Website: www.law.campbell.edu

ABA Approved Since 1979

The Basics

Type of school	Private
Term	Semester
Application deadline	4/1
Application fee	$50
Financial aid deadline	6/15
Can first year start other than fall?	No
Student to faculty ratio	18.0 to 1
# of housing spaces available restricted to law students	
graduate housing for which law students are eligible	

Faculty and Administrators

	Total		Men		Women		Minorities	
	Spr	Fall	Spr	Fall	Spr	Fall	Spr	Fall
Full-time	15	20	13	15	2	5	2	2
Other full-time	1	2	1	2	0	0	0	0
Deans, librarians, & others who teach	4	5	2	2	2	3	0	0
Part-time	19	19	13	15	6	4	0	0
Total	39	46	29	34	10	12	2	2

Curriculum

		Full-Time	Part-Time
Typical first-year section size		40	0
Is there typically a "small section" of the first-year class, other than Legal Writing, taught by full-time faculty		Yes	No
If yes, typical size offered last year		40	
# of classroom course titles beyond first-year curriculum		90	
# of upper division courses, excluding seminars, with an enrollment:	Under 25	9	
	25–49	16	
	50–74	13	
	75–99	3	
	100+	1	
# of seminars		22	
# of seminar positions available		386	
# of seminar positions filled	287		0
# of positions available in simulation courses		275	
# of simulation positions filled	259		0
# of positions available in faculty supervised clinical courses		60	
# of faculty supervised clinical positions filled	56		0
# involved in field placements	83		0
# involved in law journals	61		0
# involved in moot court or trial competitions	112		0
# of credit hours required to graduate		90	

JD Enrollment and Ethnicity

	Men		Women		Full-Time		Part-Time		1st-Year		Total		JD Degs. Awd.
	#	%	#	%	#	%	#	%	#	%	#	%	
African Amer.	6	2.9	9	4.5	15	3.7	0	0.0	4	2.5	15	3.7	0
Amer. Indian	0	0.0	1	0.5	1	0.2	0	0.0	0	0.0	1	0.2	0
Asian Amer.	2	1.0	7	3.5	9	2.2	0	0.0	4	2.5	9	2.2	0
Mex. Amer.	3	1.5	5	2.5	8	2.0	0	0.0	3	1.9	8	2.0	1
Puerto Rican	0	0.0	0	0.0	0	0.0	0	0.0	0	0.0	0	0.0	0
Hispanic	4	2.0	6	3.0	10	2.5	0	0.0	5	3.1	10	2.5	2
Total Minority	15	7.4	28	13.9	43	10.6	0	0.0	16	10.1	43	10.6	3
For. Nation.	1	0.5	1	0.5	2	0.5	0	0.0	1	0.6	2	0.5	0
Caucasian	188	92.2	172	85.6	360	88.9	0	0.0	142	89.3	360	88.9	94
Unknown	0	0.0	0	0.0	0	0.0	0	0.0	0	0.0	0	0.0	0
Total	204	50.4	201	49.6	405	100.0	0	0.0	159	39.3	405		97

Transfers

Transfers in	2
Transfers out	3

Tuition and Fees

	Resident	Nonresident
Full-time	$30,850	$30,850
Part-time		
Tuition Guarantee Program		N

Living Expenses

Estimated living expenses for singles

Living on campus	Living off campus	Living at home
N/A	$19,270	N/A

Campbell University, Norman Adrian Wiggins School of Law

ABA
Approved
Since
1979

GPA and LSAT Scores

	Total	Full-Time	Part-Time
# of apps	1,514	1,514	0
# of offers	460	460	0
# of matrics	159	159	0
75% GPA	3.59	3.59	0.00
Median GPA	3.37	3.37	0.00
25% GPA	3.12	3.12	0.00
75% LSAT	159	159	0
Median LSAT	156	156	0
25% LSAT	154	154	0

Grants and Scholarships (from prior year)

	Total #	Total %	Full-Time #	Full-Time %	Part-Time #	Part-Time %
Total # of students	361		361		0	
Total # receiving grants	96	26.6	96	26.6	0	0.0
Less than 1/2 tuition	79	21.9	79	21.9	0	0.0
Half to full tuition	17	4.7	17	4.7	0	0.0
Full tuition	0	0.0	0	0.0	0	0.0
More than full tuition	0	0.0	0	0.0	0	0.0
Median grant amount			$14,250		$0	

Informational and Library Resources

Total amount spent on library materials	$1,030,895
Study seating capacity inside the library	395
# of full-time equivalent professional librarians	4.0
Hours per week library is open	99
# of open, wired connections available to students	59
# of networked computers available for use by students	66
Has wireless network?	Y
Require computer?	N

JD Attrition (from prior year)

	Academic #	Other #	Total #	Total %
1st year	2	15	17	11.3
2nd year	2	1	3	2.7
3rd year	1	0	1	1.0
4th year	0	0	0	0.0

Employment (9 months after graduation)

	Total	Percentage
Employment status known	104	95.4
Employment status unknown	5	4.6
Employed	98	94.2
Pursuing graduate degrees	3	2.9
Unemployed (seeking, not seeking, or studying for the bar)	3	2.9

Type of Employment

# employed in law firms	65	66.3
# employed in business and industry	5	5.1
# employed in government	22	22.4
# employed in public interest	1	1.0
# employed as judicial clerks	3	3.1
# employed in academia	1	1.0

Geographic Location

# employed in state	89	90.8
# employed in foreign countries	1	1.0
# of states where employed	6	

Bar Passage Rates

First-time takers	114	Reporting %	93.86
Average school %	95.33	Average state %	82.61
Average pass difference	12.72		

Jurisdiction	Takers	Passers	Pass %	State %	Diff %
North Carolina	107	102	95.33	82.61	12.72

Campbell University, Norman Adrian Wiggins School of Law

225 Hillsborough Street
Raleigh, NC 27603
Phone: 919.865.5988; Fax: 919.865.5992
E-mail: admissions@law.campbell.edu; Website: www.law.campbell.edu

■ Introduction

The Norman Adrian Wiggins School of Law at Campbell University is a highly demanding, purposely small, and intensely personal community of faculty and students. Campbell Law's aim, guided by transcendent values, is to develop lawyers who possess moral conviction, social compassion, and professional competence; who view the law as a calling to serve others and to create a more just society.

Campbell Law School is a private law school that is fully accredited by the American Bar Association, boasting more than three decades of excellence in legal education. Located within walking distance of the North Carolina state legislature, federal and state courts, federal, state, and local government agencies, and the region's top law firms, corporations, and nonprofits, Campbell Law provides a living legal laboratory to its students.

Campbell Law School encourages students to examine the relationship between spiritual and legal issues, to explore the theological foundations for law, to think differently about justice and the legal system, and to consider how they can help achieve a more just and merciful society. While embracing an intellectual perspective rooted in Christian tradition, Campbell Law School is committed to free and open discussion of ideas. Students are under no obligation to embrace any particular way of thinking.

For the past 21 years, Campbell Law's record of success on the North Carolina bar exam is unsurpassed by any other North Carolina law school.

Ranked No. 1 by *Forbes* as the "Best Place for Business and Careers" in 2008 and 2009, Raleigh offers a rich cultural history in a progressive setting. Raleigh is located just a few hours from legendary beaches in one direction and the scenic Blue Ridge Mountains in the other.

■ Enrollment

Campbell Law School is one of the smallest ABA-accredited private law schools in the country. With a limited first-year enrollment, students enjoy the many advantages of a law school that remains purposely small. Our community of students and faculty is intensely personal—students build a network of relationships that supports them during their legal studies and extends far beyond graduation.

Currently, our student body is comprised of 410 students from 24 different states, holding degrees from 109 colleges and universities, with 57 different majors represented. Campbell Law School is committed to enrolling a diverse student body and has an overall minority enrollment of 10 percent.

■ Faculty

Campbell Law School's faculty is a community of scholars who make teaching their priority. They are readily accessible and serve students as mentors, coaches, and professional role models. All faculty have open-door office policies and are available to consult regularly with students on an individual basis. Our professors are deeply committed to the search for knowledge through meaningful legal scholarship, but never at the expense of their devotion to the academic success and professional development of each student.

■ Facilities and Technology

Campbell Law School is located in the heart of downtown Raleigh. Each of the Law School's classrooms and courtrooms have video cameras to record lectures which most professors post via Blackboard for student review and use. In addition, the entire Law School is wireless including student access to printers.

■ Curriculum

Campbell Law School holds students to the highest standards of thinking, speaking, and writing logically. To accomplish this goal, the course of instruction is exceptionally rigorous.

In a national survey, Campbell Law School's Trial Advocacy Program has been called one of the most rigorous in the nation. Every second-year student is required to plan and participate in a mock trial. Because of this, our graduates are exceptionally well prepared to advocate for their clients, whether in the boardroom or the courtroom.

Campbell Law School offers a joint Juris Doctor/Master of Business Administration degree, and has pioneered a joint Juris Doctor/Master of Trust and Wealth Management degree, which is the only program of its kind in the country. Both of these programs can be completed within three years.

■ Special Programs

The Juvenile Justice Project is a collaboration between Campbell Law School and the North Carolina Governor's Crime Commission. Students are trained in the application of mediation and other alternative dispute-resolution processes and have the opportunity to assist in the mediation of juvenile law disputes.

Prisoner Assistance and Legal Services (PALS) provides our students an opportunity to serve older prisoners by addressing the unique problems of aging in prison.

Externship programs provide students with a meaningful education experience in a public service environment. Students receive up to two hours of academic credit for uncompensated, substantive legal work through externship placements.

The Senior Law Clinic serves the legal needs of low-income senior citizens in the greater Raleigh region.

■ Student Publications and Organizations

One of the primary motivations for keeping enrollment limited at Campbell Law School is to offer all students outstanding opportunities to gain valuable experiences in activities and organizations.

Campbell Law Review is a student publication of scholarly writings on current legal topics. It is a valued research tool for judges, attorneys, legislatures, educators, and students. Writers and editors for the *Campbell Law Review* are students who demonstrate the highest degree of academic excellence. Participation is by invitation only.

Campbell Law Observer is a monthly student publication that features reports on recent state and federal court opinions, scholarly articles on current legal topics, and subjects of general interest to members of the legal community.

Campbell University, Norman Adrian Wiggins School of Law

Campbell Law School is also the official international headquarters for the Delta Theta Phi Law Fraternity, one of the leading professional law fraternities in the world.

■ Admission

Campbell Law School's Admissions Committee takes seriously its responsibility for admitting qualified applicants. Campbell Law believes each applicant we accept has the potential to succeed in our program and pursue a legal education and professional career consistent with Campbell Law School's vision and tradition of excellence. The Admissions Committee bases its selection on the applicant's academic credentials, including LSAT score, undergraduate grade-point average (UGPA), level of writing skills, breadth of studies, and other criteria including, but not limited to, the work, life, and leadership experience, depth of particular interest, and any other aspect of an applicant's background suggesting suitability for the study and practice of law.

■ Summer Performance-Based Admission Program

Select students who are not offered regular admission in the fall class may be invited to participate in the Summer Performance-Based Admission Program. Between 35 and 50 applicants are admitted to this program and attend a seven-week session each summer. Admission to the fall class is offered to those students who perform satisfactorily in both courses. Historically, 25–33 percent of the PBAP class gain admission to the fall class.

■ Expenses and Financial Aid

Campbell Law School recognizes the high cost of a quality education. Every effort is made to ensure that no qualified applicant is denied the opportunity to study law for financial reasons. Assistance may be provided in the form of institutional scholarships, endowed scholarships, loans, and work-study programs. Approximately 35 percent of students receive scholarship assistance. Approximately 95 percent of students receive financial aid.

■ In and Around Raleigh

The Raleigh area offers students many housing options in a mix of urban, suburban, and rural areas. The Raleigh community combines the charm of small town roots with easy access to urban amenities. The region offers housing for every taste and budget.

The city offers a variety of museums, performance centers, and other cultural scenes. The area also offers a full schedule of collegiate and professional spectator sports including Atlantic Coast Conference (ACC) basketball and football, and is home to the Carolina Hurricanes (NHL).

■ Career Services

The Career and Professional Development Center helps students chart a course toward securing summer and permanent employment from their first semester at Campbell Law School.

Employers of Campbell Law School graduates include small and large firms, courts, all branches of the military, judges, government agencies and offices, public service organizations, and corporations. Our 2008 graduates enjoyed an employment rate that exceeded 93 percent within nine months of graduation.

While 80 percent of Campbell Law graduates remain in North Carolina to practice law, 20 percent choose to practice across the nation and around the world. Currently, Campbell Law alumni live and practice in 40 states and six countries.

Applicant Profile

Campbell University, Norman Adrian Wiggins School of Law
This grid includes only applicants who earned 120–180 LSAT scores under standard administrations.

LSAT Score	3.75 +		3.50–3.74		3.25–3.49		3.00–3.24		2.75–2.99		2.50–2.74		2.25–2.49		2.00–2.24		Below 2.00		No GPA		Total	
	Apps	Adm	Apps	Adm	Apps	Adm	Apps	Adm	Apps	Adm	Apps	Adm	Apps	Adm	Apps	Adm	Apps	Adm	Apps	Adm	Apps	Adm
175–180	0	0	0	0	0	0	0	0	0	0	0	0	1	1	0	0	0	0	0	0	1	1
170–174	0	0	1	1	0	0	0	0	0	0	0	0	0	0	0	0	0	0	0	0	1	1
165–169	1	1	3	3	3	3	2	1	2	2	2	2	3	3	0	0	0	0	0	0	16	15
160–164	11	11	23	22	18	18	20	18	8	5	3	3	2	0	3	1	0	0	1	1	89	79
155–159	37	34	52	48	79	77	52	38	30	16	17	2	15	3	6	2	2	0	1	0	291	220
150–154	51	30	83	42	98	40	81	19	58	9	20	1	21	2	8	2	2	0	2	0	424	145
145–149	34	3	40	2	62	2	95	2	62	2	26	0	13	0	8	0	4	0	4	1	348	12
140–144	6	0	33	0	25	0	33	0	32	0	35	0	16	0	7	0	1	0	4	0	192	0
135–139	1	0	5	0	15	0	17	0	19	0	14	0	9	0	4	0	0	0	2	0	86	0
130–134	0	0	1	0	7	0	8	0	3	0	5	0	1	0	1	0	0	0	2	0	28	0
125–129	0	0	0	0	1	0	1	0	1	0	1	0	0	0	1	0	0	0	0	0	5	0
120–124	0	0	0	0	0	0	0	0	0	0	0	0	0	0	0	0	0	0	0	0	0	0
Total	141	79	241	118	308	140	309	78	215	34	123	8	81	9	38	5	9	0	16	2	1481	473

Apps = Number of Applicants   Adm = Number Admitted   Reflects 98% of the fall applicant pool; average LSAT data reported.
Note: The admissions in the grid above include individuals who gain admission through the summer PBAP program.

Capital University Law School

303 E. Broad Street
Columbus, OH 43215-3200
Phone: 614.236.6310; Fax: 614.236.6972
E-mail: admissions@law.capital.edu; Website: www.law.capital.edu

ABA Approved Since 1950

The Basics

Type of school	Private
Term	Semester
Application deadline	5/1
Application fee	$40
Financial aid deadline	4/15
Can first year start other than fall?	No
Student to faculty ratio	15.8 to 1
# of housing spaces available restricted to law students	
graduate housing for which law students are eligible	

Faculty and Administrators

	Total		Men		Women		Minorities	
	Spr	Fall	Spr	Fall	Spr	Fall	Spr	Fall
Full-time	31	29	20	19	11	10	3	3
Other full-time	2	2	1	1	1	1	0	0
Deans, librarians, & others who teach	6	6	2	3	4	3	1	1
Part-time	31	27	25	20	6	7	2	3
Total	70	64	48	43	22	21	6	7

Curriculum

		Full-Time	Part-Time
Typical first-year section size		85	70
Is there typically a "small section" of the first-year class, other than Legal Writing, taught by full-time faculty		Yes	Yes
If yes, typical size offered last year		43	35
# of classroom course titles beyond first-year curriculum		184	
# of upper division courses, excluding seminars, with an enrollment:	Under 25	122	
	25–49	37	
	50–74	11	
	75–99	11	
	100+	0	
# of seminars		8	
# of seminar positions available		136	
# of seminar positions filled		60	29
# of positions available in simulation courses		1,457	
# of simulation positions filled		606	199
# of positions available in faculty supervised clinical courses		69	
# of faculty supervised clinical positions filled		61	9
# involved in field placements		138	24
# involved in law journals		35	12
# involved in moot court or trial competitions		24	5
# of credit hours required to graduate		89	

JD Enrollment and Ethnicity

	Men		Women		Full-Time		Part-Time		1st-Year		Total		JD Degs. Awd.
	#	%	#	%	#	%	#	%	#	%	#	%	
African Amer.	23	6.5	29	9.8	33	7.2	19	10.2	28	11.3	52	8.0	11
Amer. Indian	0	0.0	1	0.3	1	0.2	0	0.0	1	0.4	1	0.2	0
Asian Amer.	6	1.7	9	3.1	9	2.0	6	3.2	4	1.6	15	2.3	4
Mex. Amer.	0	0.0	0	0.0	0	0.0	0	0.0	0	0.0	0	0.0	0
Puerto Rican	0	0.0	0	0.0	0	0.0	0	0.0	0	0.0	0	0.0	0
Hispanic	3	0.8	5	1.7	5	1.1	3	1.6	4	1.6	8	1.2	3
Total Minority	32	9.1	44	14.9	48	10.4	28	15.0	37	15.0	76	11.7	18
For. Nation.	0	0.0	0	0.0	0	0.0	0	0.0	0	0.0	0	0.0	0
Caucasian	282	79.9	227	76.9	371	80.5	138	73.8	189	76.5	509	78.5	155
Unknown	39	11.0	24	8.1	42	9.1	21	11.2	21	8.5	63	9.7	21
Total	353	54.5	295	45.5	461	71.1	187	28.9	247	38.1	648		194

Transfers

Transfers in	5
Transfers out	12

Tuition and Fees

	Resident	Nonresident
Full-time	$31,146	$31,146
Part-time	$20,406	$20,406
Tuition Guarantee Program	N	

Living Expenses

Estimated living expenses for singles

Living on campus	Living off campus	Living at home
N/A	$15,286	$15,286

Capital University Law School

ABA
Approved
Since
1950

GPA and LSAT Scores

	Total	Full-Time	Part-Time
# of apps	1,434	1,174	260
# of offers	813	693	120
# of matrics	248	182	66
75% GPA	3.50	3.51	3.47
Median GPA	3.23	3.23	3.16
25% GPA	2.96	2.96	2.86
75% LSAT	156	156	155
Median LSAT	153	153	152
25% LSAT	150	151	150

Grants and Scholarships (from prior year)

	Total		Full-Time		Part-Time	
	#	%	#	%	#	%
Total # of students	651		446		205	
Total # receiving grants	331	50.8	263	59.0	68	33.2
Less than 1/2 tuition	272	41.8	215	48.2	57	27.8
Half to full tuition	59	9.1	48	10.8	11	5.4
Full tuition	0	0.0	0	0.0	0	0.0
More than full tuition	0	0.0	0	0.0	0	0.0
Median grant amount			$10,000		$5,000	

Informational and Library Resources

Total amount spent on library materials	$1,110,239
Study seating capacity inside the library	460
# of full-time equivalent professional librarians	5.0
Hours per week library is open	92
# of open, wired connections available to students	113
# of networked computers available for use by students	26
Has wireless network?	Y
Require computer?	N

JD Attrition (from prior year)

	Academic	Other	Total	
	#	#	#	%
1st year	21	27	48	20.4
2nd year	7	3	10	5.4
3rd year	1	0	1	0.6
4th year	0	2	2	3.9

Employment (9 months after graduation)

	Total	Percentage
Employment status known	146	81.6
Employment status unknown	33	18.4
Employed	127	87.0
Pursuing graduate degrees	1	0.7
Unemployed (seeking, not seeking, or studying for the bar)	17	11.6
Type of Employment		
# employed in law firms	72	56.7
# employed in business and industry	21	16.5
# employed in government	25	19.7
# employed in public interest	5	3.9
# employed as judicial clerks	1	0.8
# employed in academia	3	2.4
Geographic Location		
# employed in state	111	87.4
# employed in foreign countries	0	0.0
# of states where employed	12	

Bar Passage Rates

First-time takers	170	Reporting %	90.59
Average school %	94.81	Average state %	88.09
Average pass difference	6.72		

Jurisdiction	Takers	Passers	Pass %	State %	Diff %
Ohio	154	146	94.81	88.09	6.72

Capital University Law School

303 E. Broad Street
Columbus, OH 43215-3200
Phone: 614.236.6310; Fax: 614.236.6972
E-mail: admissions@law.capital.edu; Website: www.law.capital.edu

■ Introduction

Capital University Law School, located in downtown Columbus, is at the epicenter of Ohio's legal community. Our location provides students with an ideal environment to study law and a wealth of opportunities to gain practical legal experience and establish a network of contacts within the legal arena. The Law School is within walking distance of the Ohio Supreme Court, the Ohio Court of Appeals, the Ohio Attorney General's Office, the state legislature, major law firms, numerous state agencies, and Fortune 500 corporations.

Innovation and leadership are intrinsic traits of our heritage. For more than a century, Capital Law School has produced some of the region's finest judges, partners and associates of respected law firms, officials at all levels of government, business professionals, and influential community leaders. We invite you to closely examine all of the factors that distinguish this law school:

- Outstanding faculty
- Superior bar passage and employment rates
- Innovative curriculum
- Unrivaled externship opportunities
- Remarkable alumni
- Reasonable tuition (Capital Law voted a "Best Value Law School" by the *National Jurist* magazine. *http://www.nxtbook.com/nxtbooks/cypress/nationaljurist0909/#/30*)

■ Curriculum

Capital University Law School is committed to providing our full-time and part-time students with a first-rate education. The Law School's comprehensive curriculum brings an unparalleled balance between theoretical knowledge and practical applications of the law. Courses are both intellectually challenging and cutting edge; as an end result, students are equipped with essential lawyering skills that are necessary for effective, creative, and ethical legal counseling and advocacy. At graduation, our alumni have made the transition from law student to legal practitioner—prepared to meet the challenges and demands of the evolving practice of law.

Teaching is a core value at Capital University Law School. Capital Law students describe the faculty as knowledgeable, accessible, collegial, cooperative, and true mentors. Outside of the classroom, they are accomplished scholars who distinguish themselves through their research, scholarship, and authorship of books and journal publications. In a recent study, Capital's faculty ranked sixth among the faculty at peer institutions for scholarly productivity.

To learn more about Capital's incomparable curriculum and distinguished faculty, visit our website at *www.law.capital.edu.*

■ Multicultural Affairs

Capital University Law School takes pride in its history of providing a legal education for groups who historically have been excluded from or underrepresented in law schools. Capital University Law School is committed to racial and cultural diversity and beyond. The Law School supports and embraces diversity in all of its varying forms. The Law School actively recruits students who are African American, Asian, Hispanic, Native American, and students who identify as gay, lesbian, bisexual, or transgender.

Students come to Capital with diverse educational, cultural, social, and professional backgrounds. Capital University Law School embraces and values the varied perspectives that our students bring to the school.

Capital has many programs and benefits that support students of color—the presence of minority faculty, a director of multicultural affairs, availability of financial aid, academic as well as nonacademic support, and participation in the Columbus Bar Association Minority Clerkship Program are some of the things available to our students. In addition to the services at the Law School, the Columbus community also presents a diverse and supportive community for our law students to explore.

■ Special Programs

Diversity of opportunity is a trademark of Capital University Law School. Capital Law students have the unique opportunity to create their own academic path and pursue their personal passion through our specialized and innovative academic programs.

Concentrations

The Law School's concentration certificates allow students to focus their electives in specific areas of the law by combining theoretical and practical classroom experience with faculty expertise. Capital offers concentrations in eight specialty areas:

- Children and Family Law
- Civil Litigation
- Criminal Litigation
- Dispute Resolution
- Environmental Law
- Governmental Affairs
- Labor and Employment Law
- Small Business Entities and Publicly Held Companies

Joint-Degree Programs

The Law School's joint-degree programs allow students to advance their education without delaying their career plans. These accelerated programs enable students to complete two degrees with a substantial reduction in total credit hours and in less time than it would take to obtain them separately. Capital offers a Juris Doctor with one of the following degrees:

- Master of Business Administration
- Master of Sports Administration
- Master of Science in Nursing
- Master of Theology
- Master of Laws in Business
- Master of Laws in Business and Taxation
- Master of Laws in Taxation

Centers and Legal Clinics

Our commitment to immersing you in the real-world environment of law is best exemplified by our extensive externship program along with our centers and legal clinics. Students enrich their academic environment by working closely with clinical attorneys and experiencing the challenges and rewards of practicing law and giving back to the community-at-large. The Law School's centers and clinics include

- The Center for Dispute Resolution
- The National Center for Adoption Law and Policy

- The General Litigation Clinic
- The Mediation Clinic
- The Family Advocacy Clinic
- The Small Business Clinic

■ Admission

Capital University Law School seeks to attract a diverse pool of applicants who are motivated, committed, and possess the requisite skills and abilities to study law. Admission to the Law School is based on a thorough review of each individual's application file in its entirety. Rarely does any single factor, either LSAT score or undergraduate grade-point average, determine a candidate's status.

The Law School's Admission Committee carefully evaluates the competitiveness and difficulty of the candidate's undergraduate and graduate coursework, personal statement, letters of recommendation, employment history, writing ability, leadership experience, extracurricular activities, general background, and any additional information the candidate feels is important to the admission decision. All of these factors, along with the LSAT score and grade-point average, act to increase or decrease the probability of admission.

■ Student Activities

Extra and cocurricular activities range from over 20 student groups and at least 10 competition teams to the *Capital University Law Review*. Clubs are educational, professional, and social while encouraging the legal community's collaboration and engagement. Student organizations at Capital University Law School offer many opportunities for leadership development, networking, and interaction with professionals in various specialties.

The Law School supports associations for students with common values and backgrounds, as well as groups focused on specific areas of law such as sports and entertainment, environmental, and intellectual property. You will find many organizations and activities to help you round out your education.

The *Capital University Law Review* provides the legal community with scholarly analysis of contemporary legal issues. Students may expand their writing and editing skills through membership on the *Law Review*. Those wishing to hone their skills and test them in competition will want to investigate Capital's highly successful moot court teams. Students may participate in national competitions, such as the Philip C. Jessup International Law and the Frederick Douglass Moot Court competitions. Teams are also selected in the areas of environmental law, sports law, labor law, and tax.

■ Professional Development

The Capital University Office of Professional Development provides individual career counseling for students and alumni and a wide variety of career-related programs, including Continuing Legal Education Programs for alumni. The office provides an online job posting board, coordinates employer recruiting programs, and maintains an extensive library of books and other relevant resources. It also houses the Law School's Public Interest Center and administers the Pro Bono Recognition Program. See our website for additional information: *http://www.law.capital.edu/ProfessionalDevelopment/*.

Capital graduates pursue a variety of legal and nonlegal employment opportunities. For the class of 2008, 87 percent of those graduates seeking employment were employed within nine months of graduation. Private practice is the largest of these areas, with approximately 57 percent of the graduating class entering this field. Many Capital graduates enter public service (24 percent), which includes government, public interest, and judicial clerkship positions, while others find employment in corporations and academia.

Applicant Profile

Capital University Law School

LSAT Score	GPA								
	3.75 +	3.50–3.74	3.25–3.49	3.00–3.24	2.75–2.99	2.50–2.74	2.25–2.49	2.00–2.24	Below 2.00
175–180									
170–174									
165–169									
160–164									
155–159									
150–154									
145–149									
140–144									
135–139									
130–134									
125–129									
120–124									

■ Very Likely   □ Possible   ▨ Unlikely

Benjamin N. Cardozo School of Law, Yeshiva University

55 Fifth Avenue
New York, NY 10003
Phone: 212.790.0274; Fax: 212.790.0482
E-mail: lawinfo@yu.edu; Website: www.cardozo.yu.edu

ABA Approved Since 1978

The Basics

Type of school	Private
Term	Semester
Application deadline	4/1
Application fee	$70
Financial aid deadline	4/15
Can first year start other than fall?	Yes
Student to faculty ratio	15.6 to 1
# of housing spaces available restricted to law students	120
graduate housing for which law students are eligible	

Faculty and Administrators

	Total		Men		Women		Minorities	
	Spr	Fall	Spr	Fall	Spr	Fall	Spr	Fall
Full-time	57	57	38	37	19	20	6	6
Other full-time	2	2	1	1	1	1	0	0
Deans, librarians, & others who teach	7	7	5	5	2	2	1	1
Part-time	78	77	52	52	26	25	6	5
Total	144	143	96	95	48	48	13	12

JD Enrollment and Ethnicity

	Men		Women		Full-Time		Part-Time		1st-Year		Total		JD Degs. Awd.
	#	%	#	%	#	%	#	%	#	%	#	%	
African Amer.	25	4.5	27	4.8	47	4.6	5	5.0	20	5.8	52	4.6	9
Amer. Indian	2	0.4	1	0.2	3	0.3	0	0.0	0	0.0	3	0.3	1
Asian Amer.	35	6.3	68	12.1	93	9.1	10	9.9	31	9.0	103	9.2	27
Mex. Amer.	1	0.2	8	1.4	9	0.9	0	0.0	3	0.9	9	0.8	0
Puerto Rican	7	1.3	7	1.2	13	1.3	1	1.0	5	1.4	14	1.2	3
Hispanic	23	4.1	26	4.6	44	4.3	5	5.0	16	4.6	49	4.4	9
Total Minority	93	16.6	137	24.4	209	20.5	21	20.8	75	21.7	230	20.5	49
For. Nation.	9	1.6	20	3.6	28	2.7	1	1.0	11	3.2	29	2.6	18
Caucasian	270	48.3	213	37.9	428	42.0	55	54.5	185	53.5	483	43.1	111
Unknown	187	33.5	192	34.2	355	34.8	24	23.8	75	21.7	379	33.8	176
Total	559	49.9	562	50.1	1020	91.0	101	9.0	346	30.9	1121		354

Curriculum

	Full-Time	Part-Time
Typical first-year section size	49	49
Is there typically a "small section" of the first-year class, other than Legal Writing, taught by full-time faculty	No	No
If yes, typical size offered last year		
# of classroom course titles beyond first-year curriculum		156

# of upper division courses, excluding seminars, with an enrollment:		
	Under 25	70
	25–49	38
	50–74	14
	75–99	15
	100+	16

# of seminars		42
# of seminar positions available		898
# of seminar positions filled	543	0
# of positions available in simulation courses		588
# of simulation positions filled	462	0
# of positions available in faculty supervised clinical courses		136
# of faculty supervised clinical positions filled	137	0
# involved in field placements	199	0
# involved in law journals	288	0
# involved in moot court or trial competitions	81	0
# of credit hours required to graduate		84

Transfers

Transfers in	30
Transfers out	10

Tuition and Fees

	Resident	Nonresident
Full-time	$45,170	$45,170
Part-time	$45,170	$45,170
Tuition Guarantee Program		N

Living Expenses

Estimated living expenses for singles

Living on campus	Living off campus	Living at home
$24,371	$24,371	N/A

Benjamin N. Cardozo School of Law, Yeshiva University

ABA
Approved
Since
1978

GPA and LSAT Scores

	Total	Full-Time	Part-Time
# of apps	5,156	4,645	625
# of offers	1,370	1,204	166
# of matrics	370	268	102
75% GPA	3.73	3.75	3.71
Median GPA	3.59	3.60	3.56
25% GPA	3.37	3.39	3.28
75% LSAT	165	166	161
Median LSAT	162	164	160
25% LSAT	160	161	158

Grants and Scholarships (from prior year)

	Total #	Total %	Full-Time #	Full-Time %	Part-Time #	Part-Time %
Total # of students	1,102		975		127	
Total # receiving grants	614	55.7	595	61.0	19	15.0
Less than 1/2 tuition	339	30.8	323	33.1	16	12.6
Half to full tuition	196	17.8	193	19.8	3	2.4
Full tuition	73	6.6	73	7.5	0	0.0
More than full tuition	6	0.5	6	0.6	0	0.0
Median grant amount			$20,000		$6,000	

Informational and Library Resources

Total amount spent on library materials	$1,933,587
Study seating capacity inside the library	483
# of full-time equivalent professional librarians	8.0
Hours per week library is open	88
# of open, wired connections available to students	39
# of networked computers available for use by students	198
Has wireless network?	Y
Require computer?	N

JD Attrition (from prior year)

	Academic #	Other #	Total #	Total %
1st year	0	12	12	3.4
2nd year	1	3	4	1.0
3rd year	0	0	0	0.0
4th year	0	0	0	0.0

Employment (9 months after graduation)

	Total	Percentage
Employment status known	355	97.8
Employment status unknown	8	2.2
Employed	327	92.1
Pursuing graduate degrees	4	1.1
Unemployed (seeking, not seeking, or studying for the bar)	14	3.9
Type of Employment		
# employed in law firms	189	57.8
# employed in business and industry	63	19.3
# employed in government	26	8.0
# employed in public interest	34	10.4
# employed as judicial clerks	15	4.6
# employed in academia	0	0.0
Geographic Location		
# employed in state	266	81.3
# employed in foreign countries	5	1.5
# of states where employed	16	

Bar Passage Rates

First-time takers	375	Reporting %	89.60
Average school %	91.96	Average state %	88.98
Average pass difference	2.98		

Jurisdiction	Takers	Passers	Pass %	State %	Diff %
New York	336	309	91.96	88.98	2.98

Benjamin N. Cardozo School of Law, Yeshiva University

55 Fifth Avenue
New York, NY 10003
Phone: 212.790.0274; Fax: 212.790.0482
E-mail: lawinfo@yu.edu; Website: www.cardozo.yu.edu

■ Introduction

Benjamin N. Cardozo School of Law offers students a stimulating and challenging educational experience. Its curriculum combines the scholarly explanation of the philosophical and theoretical elements of the law with the professional and ethical emphasis necessary for successful practice. Courses provide depth and breadth in many specialized areas of legal study, including intellectual property law, criminal law, corporate law, and alternative dispute resolution, as well as international and human rights law, public interest law, and legal theory. Extensive clinical and externship opportunities allow students to gain practical lawyering experience while performing important community service. A Cardozo education emphasizes ethics and the pursuit of intellectual excellence.

■ Faculty

Professors at Cardozo are vibrant, intellectually curious, accessible to students, and committed to the twin goals of teaching and scholarship. They are an interdisciplinary faculty, curious and serious about how the law relates to other expressions of the human spirit such as philosophy, literature, economics, politics, and history. More than half hold advanced degrees in addition to a law degree; about a dozen hold PhDs as well. The faculty is prolific, writing on both visionary and practical subjects; many of their publications are required reading in law schools across the nation.

■ A Campus in New York City

Cardozo is located in a vibrant neighborhood in Greenwich Village, just blocks from Union Square. It is easily accessible to all points in New York City, including the courts, Wall Street, Midtown, and the art and music centers on the East and West Sides of Manhattan. The law school's state-of-the-art facility includes a moot courtroom, additional library space, a center for student life, student and faculty offices, and fully wired classrooms and seminar rooms.

The Cardozo residence hall is located on a residential, tree-lined street just one block south of the main building. Studio, one-bedroom apartments, and two-bedroom apartments—all of which are air-conditioned, fully furnished, and equipped with kitchens—are available for incoming students.

■ Students/Student Activities

The student body at Cardozo is a diverse and impressive group. A typical entering class includes graduates from more than 130 colleges, and from 34 states and 10 foreign countries. Roughly 22 percent of the class are members of minority groups and 51 percent have been out of college between 1 and 4 years. Approximately 11 percent hold at least one graduate degree.

More than half of the second- and third-year students participate on one of six student-edited journals or in the Moot Court Honor Society. Scholarly journals include the *Cardozo Law Review*, *Cardozo Arts and Entertainment Law Journal*, *Cardozo Journal of International and Comparative Law*, *Cardozo Journal of Law and Gender*, *Cardozo Journal of Conflict Resolution*, and *Cardozo Public Law, Policy, and Ethics Journal*.

■ Career Services

Cardozo students benefit from a large network of working alumni and a career services office staffed by six professional counselors, all of whom have JD degrees. Students are offered individual assistance with interviewing techniques, résumé writing, and job-search strategies, as well as workshops and opportunities for learning about a variety of legal careers from attorneys in the field.

Nearly 95 percent of those reporting from the class of 2008 were employed within several months of graduation. Approximately 60 percent of these graduates went into private practice at a median starting salary of $160,000. Nearly a quarter of the class entered the public sector in a broad range of positions, including jobs in judges' chambers, governmental agencies, and public interest organizations.

■ Clinical Opportunities/Special Programs

Cardozo has a commitment to a particular style of education that seeks to blend theory and practice—to expose students to the abstractions, intellectual and ethical conundrums, and overarching theories of the American legal system, and to the concrete skills and values they need to be first-rate attorneys. A wealth of clinical programs combine professional work experience with academic supervision, yielding students uniquely qualified to apply what they have studied. Nearly 400 students each year take advantage of one of these opportunities to represent real clients (under the supervision of expert attorneys), gaining invaluable skills while performing important community service representing the poor, the elderly, and the indigent.

In the **Innocence Project**, students represent prisoners whose innocence may be proved through DNA testing; in the **Prosecutor Practicum**, students work in the Manhattan District Attorney's Office; the **Bet Tzedek Legal Services Clinic** provides legal assistance to the elderly and disabled; the **Mediation Clinic** provides training and certification in alternative dispute resolution; the **Human Rights and Genocide Clinic** provides students with the opportunity to design and implement creative solutions to improve the lives of victims of human rights abuses throughout the world; Cardozo's simulation-based **Intensive Trial Advocacy Program** sharpens students' trial skills; and students in the **Criminal Defense Clinic** represent defendants in Manhattan Criminal Court. Other clinics include the **Family Court Clinic**, **Tax Clinic**, **Criminal Appeals Clinic**, **Immigration Law Clinic**, **Labor and Employment Clinic**, and **Securities Arbitration Clinic**.

Externships offer students the opportunity to work in a legal position, thereby developing important skills and gaining significant real-world experience. Through externships and internships, students can obtain credit for substantive legal work under the direct supervision of an attorney or judge at the work site. The **Intellectual Property Law Program** combines a specialized curriculum with related externships in this burgeoning area of practice; the

Alexander Judicial Fellows Program places outstanding third-year students in clerkships with prominent federal judges; the **Entertainment Law Experience** enables students to complete legal internships during the school year or the summer with entertainment law employers; the **Heyman/ACCA In-house Counsel Internship** introduces second- and third-year students to the practice of law in a corporate law department; in the **Holocaust Claims Restitution Practicum**, students pursue claims made by Holocaust survivors and their heirs; the **Immigration Law Externship** places students in law offices and agencies handling immigration matters; and the **Corporation Counsel's Appellate Externship** places students in the Appeals Division of the New York City Law Department (Corporation Counsel).

Cardozo's Center for Public Service Law emphasizes the school's commitment to serving the greater public good and helping students find meaningful ways to engage in public service. In the summer of 2009, more than 200 first- and second-year students received summer funding to allow them to work in the public sector—at legal services providers, public interest organizations, government agencies, district attorneys' offices, the US Attorney's Office, and federal and state judicial chambers. The Public Service Scholars Program awards scholarships to students who demonstrate a deep commitment to public service through their application for admission. The Post-graduate Public Service Fellowship provides new graduates with funding to work in the public sector prior to entering full-time employment. The Laurie M. Tisch Loan Repayment Assistance Program (LRAP) benefits graduates who choose to pursue careers in public interest/public service law by assisting with some of the burden of large educational debts.

Intellectual life at Cardozo extends beyond the classroom. The school sponsors numerous conferences, panels, and symposia that provoke dialogue and critical thought on wide-ranging topics in constitutional law, communications law and policy, human rights, corporate governance, and legal ethics.

■ Curriculum

Cardozo offers a rich curriculum that has been especially recognized for its offerings in intellectual property law (students may receive both the JD and master of laws (LLM) degrees in seven semesters), alternative dispute resolution, criminal law, corporate law, and international law. Upper-level courses are elective except for a course in professional responsibility, completion of advanced legal research, an upper-level writing requirement, and fulfillment of minimal distribution requirements.

Cardozo offers LLM degrees in intellectual property law, comparative legal thought, and in general studies. A joint-degree program between Cardozo and the Wurzweiler School of Social Work allows students to earn both the JD and MSW degrees in four years of study.

■ Admission/Alternative Entry/Financial Aid

Students may enter Cardozo in the fall, in January, or in May. Those entering in January complete six semesters of law school in two-and-a-half years. Those entering in May complete the first-year curriculum in three part-time semesters, while the second and third years are completed on a full-time basis (students will graduate in three years). These alternative entry programs can be particularly appealing to midyear graduates and returning students.

Both need- and merit-based scholarships are available. Approximately 83 percent of the students receive some financial aid. Instructions on applying for aid can be found at *www.cardozo.yu.edu/FinancialAid.*

Applicant Profile

Benjamin N. Cardozo School of Law, Yeshiva University
This grid includes only applicants who earned 120–180 LSAT scores under standard administrations.

LSAT Score	3.75 +		3.50–3.74		3.25–3.49		3.00–3.24		2.75–2.99		2.50–2.74		Below 2.50		No GPA		Total	
	Apps	Adm	Apps	Adm	Apps	Adm	Apps	Adm	Apps	Adm	Apps	Adm	Apps	Adm	Apps	Adm	Apps	Adm
170–180	56	37	43	26	36	21	20	9	8	1	12	3	5	0	3	0	183	97
165–169	163	124	205	159	137	83	93	45	42	7	11	2	13	2	10	7	674	429
160–164	308	166	397	203	340	100	186	42	80	10	36	2	31	2	39	6	1417	531
155–159	168	47	322	89	281	33	171	22	91	10	39	3	39	0	34	5	1145	209
150–154	78	15	139	18	186	11	162	5	74	6	36	2	34	0	18	3	727	60
Below 150	39	0	87	3	138	3	144	1	104	1	58	0	66	0	33	0	669	8
Total	812	389	1193	498	1118	251	776	124	399	35	192	12	188	4	137	21	4815	1334

Apps = Number of Applicants
Adm = Number Admitted
Reflects 99% of the total applicant pool; average LSAT data reported.

Case Western Reserve University School of Law

11075 East Boulevard
Cleveland, OH 44106
Phone: 216.368.3600, 800.756.0036; Fax: 216.368.1042
E-mail: lawadmissions@case.edu, lawmoney@case.edu; Website: www.law.case.edu

ABA
Approved
Since
1923

Section of Legal Education
and Admissions to the Bar

The Basics

Type of school	Private
Term	Semester
Application deadline	11/15 2/1 4/1
Application fee	$40
Financial aid deadline	5/1
Can first year start other than fall?	No
Student to faculty ratio	12.2 to 1
# of housing spaces available restricted to law students	
graduate housing for which law students are eligible	

Faculty and Administrators

	Total		Men		Women		Minorities	
	Spr	Fall	Spr	Fall	Spr	Fall	Spr	Fall
Full-time	45	41	28	27	17	14	2	2
Other full-time	7	7	3	4	3	2	1	0
Deans, librarians, & others who teach	2	2	0	0	2	2	0	0
Part-time	62	30	42	21	20	9	1	1
Total	116	80	73	52	42	27	4	3

JD Enrollment and Ethnicity

	Men		Women		Full-Time		Part-Time		1st-Year		Total		JD Degs. Awd.
	#	%	#	%	#	%	#	%	#	%	#	%	
African Amer.	8	2.2	14	5.2	20	3.2	2	9.1	7	3.3	22	3.4	13
Amer. Indian	3	0.8	3	1.1	6	1.0	0	0.0	3	1.4	6	0.9	0
Asian Amer.	19	5.1	26	9.6	44	7.1	1	4.5	16	7.6	45	7.0	21
Mex. Amer.	0	0.0	0	0.0	0	0.0	0	0.0	0	0.0	0	0.0	0
Puerto Rican	0	0.0	0	0.0	0	0.0	0	0.0	0	0.0	0	0.0	0
Hispanic	6	1.6	2	0.7	8	1.3	0	0.0	0	0.0	8	1.3	0
Total Minority	36	9.8	45	16.6	78	12.6	3	13.6	26	12.3	81	12.7	34
For. Nation.	17	4.6	8	3.0	25	4.0	0	0.0	14	6.6	25	3.9	7
Caucasian	284	77.0	195	72.0	460	74.4	19	86.4	158	74.9	479	74.8	150
Unknown	32	8.7	23	8.5	55	8.9	0	0.0	13	6.2	55	8.6	18
Total	369	57.7	271	42.3	618	96.6	22	3.4	211	33.0	640		209

Curriculum

	Full-Time	Part-Time
Typical first-year section size	70	0
Is there typically a "small section" of the first-year class, other than Legal Writing, taught by full-time faculty	No	No
If yes, typical size offered last year		

# of classroom course titles beyond first-year curriculum		162
# of upper division courses, excluding seminars, with an enrollment:	Under 25	90
	25–49	32
	50–74	11
	75–99	4
	100+	0
# of seminars		16
# of seminar positions available		182
# of seminar positions filled	133	0
# of positions available in simulation courses	223	
# of simulation positions filled	201	0
# of positions available in faculty supervised clinical courses		56
# of faculty supervised clinical positions filled	56	0
# involved in field placements	77	0
# involved in law journals	156	0
# involved in moot court or trial competitions	44	0
# of credit hours required to graduate		88

Transfers

Transfers in	16
Transfers out	12

Tuition and Fees

	Resident	Nonresident
Full-time	$38,679	$38,679
Part-time		
Tuition Guarantee Program		N

Living Expenses

Estimated living expenses for singles

Living on campus	Living off campus	Living at home
$17,725	$17,725	$17,725

Case Western Reserve University School of Law

ABA Approved Since 1923

GPA and LSAT Scores

	Total	Full-Time	Part-Time
# of apps	2,753	2,667	275
# of offers	1,164	1,126	38
# of matrics	210	195	15
75% GPA	3.63	3.64	3.57
Median GPA	3.46	3.47	3.31
25% GPA	3.20	3.21	3.20
75% LSAT	160	161	157
Median LSAT	158	159	154
25% LSAT	156	157	150

Grants and Scholarships (from prior year)

	Total #	Total %	Full-Time #	Full-Time %	Part-Time #	Part-Time %
Total # of students	658		624		34	
Total # receiving grants	364	55.3	364	58.3	0	0.0
Less than 1/2 tuition	307	46.7	307	49.2	0	0.0
Half to full tuition	56	8.5	56	9.0	0	0.0
Full tuition	1	0.2	1	0.2	0	0.0
More than full tuition	0	0.0	0	0.0	0	0.0
Median grant amount			$10,179		$0	

Informational and Library Resources

Total amount spent on library materials	$1,401,127
Study seating capacity inside the library	354
# of full-time equivalent professional librarians	10.0
Hours per week library is open	104
# of open, wired connections available to students	100
# of networked computers available for use by students	95
Has wireless network?	Y
Require computer?	N

JD Attrition (from prior year)

	Academic #	Other #	Total #	Total %
1st year	1	16	17	8.3
2nd year	3	0	3	1.2
3rd year	0	1	1	0.5
4th year	0	0	0	0.0

Employment (9 months after graduation)

	Total	Percentage
Employment status known	206	96.3
Employment status unknown	8	3.7
Employed	194	94.2
Pursuing graduate degrees	3	1.5
Unemployed (seeking, not seeking, or studying for the bar)	4	1.9
Type of Employment		
# employed in law firms	92	47.4
# employed in business and industry	33	17.0
# employed in government	33	17.0
# employed in public interest	22	11.3
# employed as judicial clerks	9	4.6
# employed in academia	4	2.1
Geographic Location		
# employed in state	88	45.4
# employed in foreign countries	6	3.1
# of states where employed	28	

Bar Passage Rates

First-time takers	206	Reporting %	70.87
Average school %	89.04	Average state %	88.01
Average pass difference	1.03		

Jurisdiction	Takers	Passers	Pass %	State %	Diff %
Ohio	92	81	88.04	88.09	−0.05
New York	32	30	93.75	88.98	4.77
Illinois	14	12	85.71	90.94	−5.23
California	8	7	87.50	78.07	9.43

Case Western Reserve University School of Law

11075 East Boulevard
Cleveland, OH 44106
Phone: 216.368.3600, 800.756.0036; Fax: 216.368.1042
E-mail: lawadmissions@case.edu, lawmoney@case.edu; Website: www.law.case.edu

■ Welcome

Case Western Reserve University School of Law has responded to the growing complexities of the ever-changing legal, social, and economic environments by implementing major curricular reforms. The result is an innovative program that provides our students with an enhanced classical legal education, an extensive array of hands-on learning opportunities for in-depth study in key fields, extensive coursework in emerging and leading-edge areas of the law (over 150 upper-level courses, more than half of which have fewer than 25 students), an understanding of the context in which legal matters and disputes take place, knowledge of other disciplines that can be used to solve legal problems, and unique methods of instruction.

■ The Curriculum and Concentrations

Shape the Law; Serve the World: We serve as our students' partners and counselors to guide them to become lawyers who help clients achieve their strategic goals, take leadership roles in their communities, and address key societal issues. The centerpiece of our curriculum is the four-semester CaseArc program, which coordinates experientially based instruction in fundamental lawyering skills with traditional classroom methods for teaching legal analysis.

Capstone Service Opportunities: We offer a capstone service opportunity for every student. Our seven labs, four clinics, and twelve externship programs offer students the opportunity not only to study the law in practice, but also to contribute to its development. Just a few examples: submit a memorandum for prosecutors in one of several international criminal tribunals through our **International War Crimes Research Lab**; do research for the International Monetary Fund and the World Bank in our **Global Corporate Governance Lab**; assist US attorneys in prosecuting civil and criminal matters through our **US Attorney Externships**; gain in-house experience through our **General Counsel** or **Hospital Law Externships**; conduct research and write memos for death penalty cases in our **Death Penalty Labs**; or conduct an examination of a medical expert in a Social Security disability claim in the **Health Law Clinic**.

Optional Concentration Program: Our Concentration Program offers in-depth learning in an area of interest and of value to employers seeking increased contributions from new lawyers. Options: Law and Technology, Law and the Arts, Criminal Law, Business Organizations, Litigation, Health Law, International Law, Individual Rights and Social Reform, and Public and Regulatory Institutions.

Dual-Degree Programs: Law, Management, Bioethics, Social Work, Biochemistry, Medicine, Nonprofit Management, Public Health, Legal History, and Political Science.

■ Centers of Excellence

The Academic Centers of Excellence provide rich opportunities that stimulate learning, networking, and career development, and include first-year electives, special seminars and symposia, clinical opportunities, internships, and work-abroad opportunities.

- Center for Business Law and Regulation
- Center for the Interdisciplinary Study of Conflict and Dispute Resolution
- Center for Law, Technology, and the Arts
- Center for Professional Ethics
- Center for Social Justice
- Frederick K. Cox International Law Center
- Law-Medicine Center
- Milton A. Kramer Law Clinic Center

■ Work and Study Abroad

Our students have far-ranging opportunities to work abroad and to receive generous stipends that support their international internships. Each year, we fund approximately 20 international law-related summer internships and postgraduate fellowships for work abroad or in the United States with an international organization, a governmental agency, or nonprofit agency. Just a sampling of recent placements:
- International Justice Mission, Nairobi, Kenya
- International Trade Centre, Geneva, Switzerland
- Special Court for Sierra Leone, Prosecutor's Office, Sierra Leone
- Supreme Court of India, New Delhi, India
- Department of Justice Immigration Court, Cleveland, OH
- Extraordinary Chambers in the Courts of Cambodia, Phnom Penh, Cambodia
- US Embassy, Sarajevo, Bosnia and Herzegovina
- Summit Law Firm, Shanghai, China
- International Criminal Tribunal for Rwanda, Arusha, Tanzania
- AIDS and Rights Alliance for Southern Africa

The law school also offers a number of stipends for summer internships in environmental and health law, as well as for public interest and social justice internships.

■ Commitment to Career Success

The Career Services Office (CSO) has implemented an ambitious program that delivers to our students real job opportunities with leading employers coast to coast. Our aggressive approach to employer development and outreach has resulted in great job success for our graduates: a 95.6 percent employment rate for our class of 2008 (national average: 92.3 percent); a median salary of $79,360 for our class of 2008 (national median: $72,000); 52 percent of our students employed through a CSO-sponsored program (national figure: 42 percent); and 54 percent of our graduates working out of state (national figure: 35 percent placement outside of the law school's state). More than 325 employers participate in our fall recruitment programs, which include on-campus interviews as well as interview programs in New York, Chicago, Los Angeles, Boston, and Washington, DC.

■ The University and Cleveland

Case Western Reserve University stands among the nation's foremost independent research institutions. It is 13th among private universities in federal research and development awards and has an endowment of well over $1 billion. The law

school is located on the university's campus in the heart of University Circle—a collection of nearly 40 cultural, medical, educational, religious, and social service institutions in a park-like setting on over 500 acres of land.

Cleveland is a world corporate center for leading national and multinational companies that specialize in transportation, insurance, retail, commercial banking, and finance. It is the headquarters for several of the nation's largest law firms and home to a number of foreign consulates. It is also a city of medicine with dozens of Cleveland hospitals and medical centers, including University Hospitals of Cleveland, the Cleveland Clinic, MetroHealth Medical Center, and other facilities with international reputations for outstanding patient care and contributions to medical research.

Unique neighborhoods are within walking distance of campus and offer students and young professionals modern and safe places to live, shop, dine, network, and socialize. Housing is also very affordable. A recent student survey indicated that the average per person monthly rent for a single was $700, $450 for shared accommodations, and $900 for family accommodations.

■ Student Activities and Leadership

There are over 30 student organizations reflecting the wide range of our students' interests, including the Black Law Students Association, Asian Pacific American Law Students Association, Federalist Society, American Constitution Society, Lambda Law Students Association, and Students for Work/Life Balance. Our students contribute to the community through such organizations as Cultivating Connections, Street Law, and Big Buddies, in cooperation with Big Brothers/Big Sisters. Our student organizations not only allow students the opportunity to explore legal interests with peers, but also provide a valuable proving ground for leadership skill development. Our student organization leaders have also taken leadership roles in their groups' national and regional

organizations, and have the opportunity to represent Case Western at national and regional conferences. Our scholarly journals are the *Case Western Reserve Law Review*, the *Journal of International Law*, *Health Matrix: Journal of Law-Medicine*, and the *Journal of Law, Technology, and the Internet*. There is also ample opportunity for participation in moot court and mock trial competitions.

■ Admission and Financial Aid

The Admission Process—Our admission process is selective. Each applicant receives full-file review. The Early Decision program application deadline is November 15; applicants are notified by December 15. The regular admission process begins in December and concludes by May 15, at which time a summer waiting list is established. The application fee for candidates who apply electronically is waived.

Financial Aid and Scholarships—Each year, we offer Academic Scholarships ranging from $5,000 to full tuition; Leadership Grants, awarded to students with unique backgrounds whose records demonstrate leadership qualities and who will enrich the diversity of the student body; interest area scholarships; and up to two Law-Medicine Fellowships, which provide a combination of scholarship aid and summer research fellowship.

Loan Repayment Assistance Program—We provide financial assistance for selected graduates who use their legal training to provide services that are in the public interest.

■ Visiting Case Western Reserve University School of Law

We offer many opportunities for prospective students to visit the law school. Just check our website to take our Virtual Tour, check the schedule for the annual Open House, or schedule an individual visit (or all three of the above).

Applicant Profile

Case Western Reserve University School of Law
This grid includes only applicants who earned 120–180 LSAT scores.

LSAT Score	GPA						
	3.75 +	3.50–3.74	3.25–3.49	3.00–3.24	2.75–2.99	2.50–2.74	Below 2.50
165–180							
163–164							
161–162							
159–160							
157–158							
154–156							
150–153							
Below 150							

■ Good Possibility　　■ Possibility　　□ Slight Possibility

The Catholic University of America, Columbus School of Law

Cardinal Station
Washington, DC 20064
Phone: 202.319.5151; Fax: 202.319.6285
E-mail: admissions@law.edu; Website: www.law.edu

ABA
Approved
Since
1925

The Basics

Type of school	Private
Term	Semester
Application deadline	3/12
Application fee	
Financial aid deadline	5/1 6/15 8/1
Can first year start other than fall?	No
Student to faculty ratio	12.8 to 1
# of housing spaces available restricted to law students	
graduate housing for which law students are eligible	

Faculty and Administrators

	Total		Men		Women		Minorities	
	Spr	Fall	Spr	Fall	Spr	Fall	Spr	Fall
Full-time	49	53	25	26	24	27	6	6
Other full-time	3	3	2	2	1	1	0	0
Deans, librarians, & others who teach	3	3	1	2	2	1	1	1
Part-time	63	48	48	31	15	17	4	4
Total	118	107	76	61	42	46	11	11

JD Enrollment and Ethnicity

	Men		Women		Full-Time		Part-Time		1st-Year		Total		JD Degs. Awd.
	#	%	#	%	#	%	#	%	#	%	#	%	
African Amer.	16	3.7	25	5.5	17	3.0	24	7.6	13	4.9	41	4.6	9
Amer. Indian	3	0.7	1	0.2	2	0.3	2	0.6	1	0.4	4	0.4	3
Asian Amer.	35	8.1	59	12.9	55	9.6	39	12.3	32	12.2	94	10.6	12
Mex. Amer.	1	0.2	0	0.0	1	0.2	0	0.0	0	0.0	1	0.1	1
Puerto Rican	0	0.0	1	0.2	1	0.2	0	0.0	0	0.0	1	0.1	2
Hispanic	13	3.0	13	2.8	20	3.5	6	1.9	4	1.5	26	2.9	13
Total Minority	68	15.7	99	21.7	96	16.7	71	22.5	50	19.0	167	18.8	40
For. Nation.	16	3.7	17	3.7	19	3.3	14	4.4	11	4.2	33	3.7	6
Caucasian	257	59.4	253	55.4	340	59.2	170	53.8	139	52.9	510	57.3	148
Unknown	92	21.2	88	19.3	119	20.7	61	19.3	63	24.0	180	20.2	51
Total	433	48.7	457	51.3	574	64.5	316	35.5	263	29.6	890		245

Curriculum

	Full-Time	Part-Time
Typical first-year section size	60	45
Is there typically a "small section" of the first-year class, other than Legal Writing, taught by full-time faculty	Yes	Yes
If yes, typical size offered last year	30	30
# of classroom course titles beyond first-year curriculum	120	

# of upper division courses, excluding seminars, with an enrollment:		
Under 25	105	
25–49	38	
50–74	20	
75–99	1	
100+	0	

# of seminars	38	
# of seminar positions available	644	
# of seminar positions filled	325	150
# of positions available in simulation courses	304	
# of simulation positions filled	169	58
# of positions available in faculty supervised clinical courses	117	
# of faculty supervised clinical positions filled	82	18
# involved in field placements	152	24
# involved in law journals	179	22
# involved in moot court or trial competitions	22	4
# of credit hours required to graduate	84	

Transfers

Transfers in	5
Transfers out	30

Tuition and Fees

	Resident	Nonresident
Full-time	$37,985	$37,985
Part-time	$29,005	$29,005
Tuition Guarantee Program	N	

Living Expenses

Estimated living expenses for singles

Living on campus	Living off campus	Living at home
$23,750	$23,750	$23,750

The Catholic University of America, Columbus School of Law

ABA
Approved
Since
1925

GPA and LSAT Scores

	Total	Full-Time	Part-Time
# of apps	3,299	2,517	782
# of offers	1,078	845	233
# of matrics	268	178	90
75% GPA	3.55	3.55	3.48
Median GPA	3.33	3.38	3.23
25% GPA	3.13	3.17	3.03
75% LSAT	160	160	158
Median LSAT	158	158	156
25% LSAT	156	157	154

Grants and Scholarships (from prior year)

	Total		Full-Time		Part-Time	
	#	%	#	%	#	%
Total # of students	920		592		328	
Total # receiving grants	226	24.6	167	28.2	59	18.0
Less than 1/2 tuition	201	21.8	143	24.2	58	17.7
Half to full tuition	24	2.6	23	3.9	1	0.3
Full tuition	1	0.1	1	0.2	0	0.0
More than full tuition	0	0.0	0	0.0	0	0.0
Median grant amount			$10,000		$7,000	

Informational and Library Resources

Total amount spent on library materials	$1,466,837
Study seating capacity inside the library	502
# of full-time equivalent professional librarians	11.0
Hours per week library is open	115
# of open, wired connections available to students	294
# of networked computers available for use by students	107
Has wireless network?	Y
Require computer?	N

JD Attrition (from prior year)

	Academic	Other	Total	
	#	#	#	%
1st year	2	31	33	10.5
2nd year	0	3	3	1.1
3rd year	0	1	1	0.4
4th year	0	0	0	0.0

Employment (9 months after graduation)

	Total	Percentage
Employment status known	269	98.5
Employment status unknown	4	1.5
Employed	245	91.1
Pursuing graduate degrees	4	1.5
Unemployed (seeking, not seeking, or studying for the bar)	19	7.1
Type of Employment		
# employed in law firms	103	42.0
# employed in business and industry	32	13.1
# employed in government	65	26.5
# employed in public interest	6	2.4
# employed as judicial clerks	30	12.2
# employed in academia	6	2.4
Geographic Location		
# employed in state	112	45.7
# employed in foreign countries	1	0.4
# of states where employed	23	

Bar Passage Rates

First-time takers	276	Reporting %	77.54
Average school %	84.11	Average state %	85.31
Average pass difference	−1.20		

Jurisdiction	Takers	Passers	Pass %	State %	Diff %
Maryland	125	110	88.00	85.51	2.49
Virginia	56	42	75.00	82.70	−7.70
New York	33	28	84.85	88.98	−4.13

The Catholic University of America, Columbus School of Law

Cardinal Station
Washington, DC 20064
Phone: 202.319.5151; Fax: 202.319.6285
E-mail: admissions@law.edu; Website: www.law.edu

■ Introduction

Founded in 1897, The Catholic University of America, Columbus School of Law is located on the 193-acre campus of the university. Students and faculty have easy access to nearly limitless legal resources: the Supreme Court, Congress, the United States and District of Columbia courts, and other federal, executive, and administrative agencies and branches of government. For a campus so close to a center of world power, it is peaceful, pleasant, and scenic, offering a sense of neighborhood and community. Classes are small and personal.

The law school is proud of its vibrant intellectual tradition and extends it to exploring new intersections of issues of law and morality. Students are trained and encouraged to use their hearts and minds, in concert with their skills, to practice effectively in the complex world of the twenty-first century. The school welcomes students of all religious, racial, and ethnic backgrounds to a program that is renowned for its consistently high number of graduates entering public and community service. The Columbus School of Law has been a member of the AALS since 1921 and approved by the ABA since 1925.

■ Enrollment/Student Body

Total enrollment is typically more than 900 students, making the School of Law the 33rd largest law school in the United States. Law students come from nearly every state and a dozen foreign countries. More than 25 percent of the school's enrollment is part time, making its evening program one of the most flexible and accommodating available anywhere. First-year classes typically have 32–70 students. Upper-class courses range from 10 to 70 students. Faculty members keep posted office hours and are accessible for informal sessions, making for a more personal education.

■ Faculty

The 64-member full-time faculty bring a wealth of experience and expertise to the classroom. The majority have practiced in the private sector. Adjunct faculty members are primarily active legal practitioners and complement the "real-world" flavor of course offerings. Classroom instruction is supplemented by many distinguished guest speakers, such as federal appellate judges, justices of the US Supreme Court, and leading academicians and theologians from around the world.

■ Library and Physical Facilities

The Library of Congress and specialized law collections throughout the city complement the law school's legal collections of over 425,000 volumes and numerous research databases. The law school facility, completed in 1994, houses all components of the law school. Law students have full access to other campus facilities, including a 40-acre athletic complex.

■ Curriculum

The prescribed first-year curriculum and method of teaching are designed to develop the analytical skills that characterize the able lawyer and to give the student familiarity with the major substantive areas of law. It is also designed as an introduction to jurisprudence and the Catholic intellectual tradition as it relates to the larger questions of social justice. While lawyers traditionally have been heavily involved with the commercial interests of private or corporate clients, law is becoming increasingly responsive to problems that affect the public interest. The CUA law school curriculum is designed to provide students with the basic knowledge to become effective lawyers in a changing legal environment.

■ Special Programs

CUA Law's institutes and special programs offer certification of a student's developed expertise in his or her chosen legal specialty. Each program provides invaluable externship opportunities, offering for-credit placements available nowhere else but in Washington, DC.

The Institute for Communications Law Studies offers unique specialized training in communications law, ranging from First Amendment law to FCC practices and procedures. Students are trained to think critically about the broader impact that mass media has upon society and human behavior.

The Comparative and International Law Institute provides superb background training to students who intend to specialize in international law. The institute offers a six-week summer-abroad program at the Jagiellonian University in Cracow, Poland.

The Law and Public Policy Program is designed for students who desire to make a difference through legislative change. The program combines classroom study in legislative and administrative processes with externships in government agencies and advocacy organizations that affect national public policy.

The Securities Law Program integrates a broad concentration of securities and corporate law courses with a required externship program. Adjunct instructors and program faculty bring vast knowledge to the classroom, as many have practiced with the Securities and Exchange Commission (SEC), the National Association of Securities Dealers (NASD), and private firms.

The Interdisciplinary Program on Law and Religion was created to provide a forum for study, research, and public discussion of the questions that arise from the nexus of law and religion. These include many of society's most challenging issues, such as bioethics, international human rights, and marriage law.

Program of Studies in Jurisprudence exists to promote inquiry into the role of law in relation to culture and culture's orientation to the human good. The scope of its inquiry is both theoretical and practical. In its theoretical aspect, the Center aims to contribute to the academic fields of jurisprudence, the philosophy of law, and Christian political and social ethics. In its practical dimension, it seeks to foster the renewal and transformation of culture, under contemporary circumstances, through law and law reform.

■ Clinical Programs

Columbus Community Legal Services recently observed its 35th year of assisting the underserved population of the

The Catholic University of America, Columbus School of Law

nation's capital. The law school offers eight clinical programs, including five that emphasize client representation, case planning, and trial and administrative advocacy. Nine simulation courses are also offered that closely approximate real-life lawyering through simulated courtroom, mediation, and arbitration exercises. The two other clinical offerings are the SEC Observer Program and the Legal Externship Program.

■ Admission

While considerable weight is given to an applicant's grade-point average and LSAT score, admission decisions are also influenced by such factors as leadership potential, class rank, substantial involvement in volunteer community service activities, potential for contributing to diversity, and relevant work experience. Close attention is also paid to a candidate's personal statement and reasons for wanting to study at CUA.

■ Student Activities

The *Catholic University Law Review*, the *Journal of Contemporary Health Law and Policy*, and *CommLaw Conspectus: Journal of Communications Law and Policy* are scholarly law journals staffed and published by outstanding students. The Moot Court Board, in addition to facilitating at least eight intraschool competitions each year, also hosts two major contests at CUA: the National Telecommunications Competition and the Sutherland Cup. There are over 40 voluntary student organizations at the Columbus School of Law, encompassing a broad range of professional interests, ethnic and racial affiliations, political and religious perspectives, and recreational activities.

■ Financial Aid

Following the offer of admission, all prospective students are automatically evaluated for merit-based scholarships. Approximately 25–30 percent of each year's entering class has been awarded a scholarship. Given the significant financial investment of a law degree, the Office of Financial Aid is committed to providing all students with timely information and guidance.

■ Career Services

The Office of Career and Professional Development actively supports students and graduates in their search for employment by providing counseling as well as workshops, panel discussions, and access to a national alumni network. A comprehensive on-campus interviewing program is conducted annually. The school's small size makes it possible for all students to secure guidance with individualized career strategy and planning.

■ Housing

The Washington, DC, metropolitan area boasts many off-campus housing opportunities for prospective law students. Each summer, the Office of Admissions assists incoming students with the housing search by coordinating a roommate name exchange, a housing workshop, and an online housing forum. Graduate Housing is available on campus. The law school is convenient to public transportation, including Washington's Metrorail system.

Applicant Profile

The Catholic University of America, Columbus School of Law
This grid includes only applicants who earned 120–180 LSAT scores under standard administrations.

LSAT Score	3.75 +		3.50–3.74		3.25–3.49		3.00–3.24		2.75–2.99		2.50–2.74		2.25–2.49		2.00–2.24		Below 2.00		No GPA		Total	
	Apps	Adm	Apps	Adm	Apps	Adm	Apps	Adm	Apps	Adm	Apps	Adm	Apps	Adm	Apps	Adm	Apps	Adm	Apps	Adm	Apps	Adm
175–180	1	1	0	0	0	0	0	0	0	0	0	0	0	0	0	0	0	0	0	0	1	1
170–174	0	0	1	1	0	0	1	1	2	1	3	1	1	0	0	0	0	0	0	0	8	4
165–169	18	17	22	19	12	10	18	16	7	5	8	3	5	0	0	0	0	0	0	0	90	70
160–164	47	45	83	75	86	79	84	73	46	22	31	14	6	1	5	0	0	0	8	5	396	314
155–159	82	71	201	157	256	157	188	76	91	23	60	11	27	1	9	0	1	0	11	9	926	505
150–154	85	28	194	39	228	35	207	30	122	9	58	0	33	0	9	0	1	0	16	5	953	146
145–149	28	0	79	4	102	5	104	7	83	5	57	2	35	0	8	0	1	0	12	0	509	23
140–144	10	0	31	0	44	0	58	0	50	0	27	0	18	0	8	0	6	0	11	0	263	0
135–139	2	0	12	0	9	0	15	0	15	0	18	0	12	0	9	0	0	0	2	0	94	0
130–134	0	0	1	0	3	0	3	0	4	0	8	0	3	0	1	0	2	0	4	0	29	0
125–129	0	0	0	0	2	0	0	0	1	0	0	0	0	0	0	0	0	0	1	0	4	0
120–124	0	0	0	0	0	0	0	0	0	0	0	0	0	0	0	0	0	0	0	0	0	0
Total	273	162	624	295	742	286	678	203	421	65	270	31	140	2	49	0	11	0	65	19	3273	1063

Apps = Number of Applicants
Adm = Number Admitted
Reflects 99% of the total applicant pool; average LSAT data reported.

This grid should be used only as a general guide, as many nonnumerical factors are considered in admission decisions.

Chapman University School of Law

One University Drive
Orange, CA 92866
Phone: 877.CHAPLAW or 714.628.2500; Fax: 714.628.2501
E-mail: lawadm@chapman.edu; Website: www.chapman.edu/law

ABA
Approved
Since
1998

The Basics

Type of school	Private
Term	Semester
Application deadline	4/15
Application fee	$65
Financial aid deadline	3/1
Can first year start other than fall?	No
Student to faculty ratio	8.9 to 1
# of housing spaces available restricted to law students	
graduate housing for which law students are eligible	20

Faculty and Administrators

	Total		Men		Women		Minorities	
	Spr	Fall	Spr	Fall	Spr	Fall	Spr	Fall
Full-time	47	52	29	35	18	17	19	25
Other full-time	1	1	1	1	0	0	1	1
Deans, librarians, & others who teach	6	6	3	3	3	3	2	2
Part-time	45	34	39	28	6	6	24	11
Total	99	93	72	67	27	26	46	39

Curriculum

		Full-Time	Part-Time
Typical first-year section size		60	60
Is there typically a "small section" of the first-year class, other than Legal Writing, taught by full-time faculty		Yes	No
If yes, typical size offered last year		45	
# of classroom course titles beyond first-year curriculum		152	
# of upper division courses, excluding seminars, with an enrollment:	Under 25	106	
	25–49	24	
	50–74	17	
	75–99	1	
	100+	0	
# of seminars		12	
# of seminar positions available		193	
# of seminar positions filled		100	0
# of positions available in simulation courses		342	
# of simulation positions filled		255	29
# of positions available in faculty supervised clinical courses		118	
# of faculty supervised clinical positions filled	77		2
# involved in field placements	153		7
# involved in law journals	221		6
# involved in moot court or trial competitions	50		6
# of credit hours required to graduate		88	

JD Enrollment and Ethnicity

	Men		Women		Full-Time		Part-Time		1st-Year		Total		JD Degs. Awd.
	#	%	#	%	#	%	#	%	#	%	#	%	
African Amer.	4	1.4	2	0.8	4	0.8	2	5.4	1	0.6	6	1.1	2
Amer. Indian	1	0.4	2	0.8	3	0.6	0	0.0	2	1.1	3	0.5	0
Asian Amer.	34	12.1	42	15.8	66	12.9	10	27.0	19	10.5	76	13.9	22
Mex. Amer.	5	1.8	11	4.2	12	2.4	4	10.8	5	2.8	16	2.9	6
Puerto Rican	0	0.0	0	0.0	0	0.0	0	0.0	0	0.0	0	0.0	0
Hispanic	13	4.6	9	3.4	22	4.3	0	0.0	13	7.2	22	4.0	2
Total Minority	57	20.2	66	24.9	107	21.0	16	43.2	40	22.1	123	22.5	32
For. Nation.	3	1.1	0	0.0	3	0.6	0	0.0	0	0.0	3	0.5	2
Caucasian	164	58.2	133	50.2	284	55.7	13	35.1	94	51.9	297	54.3	82
Unknown	58	20.6	66	24.9	116	22.7	8	21.6	47	26.0	124	22.7	43
Total	282	51.6	265	48.4	510	93.2	37	6.8	181	33.1	547		159

Transfers

Transfers in	3
Transfers out	3

Tuition and Fees

	Resident	Nonresident
Full-time	$38,046	$38,046
Part-time	$30,336	$30,336
Tuition Guarantee Program		N

Living Expenses

Estimated living expenses for singles

Living on campus	Living off campus	Living at home
$24,942	$24,942	$16,591

Chapman University School of Law

ABA
Approved
Since
1998

GPA and LSAT Scores

	Total	Full-Time	Part-Time
# of apps	2,883	2,615	268
# of offers	891	839	52
# of matrics	181	178	3
75% GPA	3.56	3.56	3.82
Median GPA	3.43	3.41	3.46
25% GPA	3.11	3.11	2.85
75% LSAT	159	159	160
Median LSAT	158	158	158
25% LSAT	156	156	151

Grants and Scholarships (from prior year)

	Total		Full-Time		Part-Time	
	#	%	#	%	#	%
Total # of students	543		507		36	
Total # receiving grants	224	41.3	224	44.2	0	0.0
Less than 1/2 tuition	100	18.4	100	19.7	0	0.0
Half to full tuition	54	9.9	54	10.7	0	0.0
Full tuition	46	8.5	46	9.1	0	0.0
More than full tuition	24	4.4	24	4.7	0	0.0
Median grant amount			$28,760		$0	

Informational and Library Resources

Total amount spent on library materials	$1,287,500
Study seating capacity inside the library	286
# of full-time equivalent professional librarians	7
Hours per week library is open	104
# of open, wired connections available to students	587
# of networked computers available for use by students	59
Has wireless network?	Y
Require computer?	N

JD Attrition (from prior year)

	Academic	Other	Total	
	#	#	#	%
1st year	14	9	23	11.6
2nd year	2	6	8	4.8
3rd year	0	0	0	0.0
4th year	0	0	0	0.0

Employment (9 months after graduation)

	Total	Percentage
Employment status known	182	99.5
Employment status unknown	1	0.5
Employed	153	84.1
Pursuing graduate degrees	7	3.8
Unemployed (seeking, not seeking, or studying for the bar)	5	2.7
Type of Employment		
# employed in law firms	87	56.9
# employed in business and industry	14	9.2
# employed in government	16	10.5
# employed in public interest	1	0.7
# employed as judicial clerks	4	2.6
# employed in academia	30	19.6
Geographic Location		
# employed in state	137	89.5
# employed in foreign countries	0	0.0
# of states where employed	12	

Bar Passage Rates

First-time takers	175	Reporting %	100.00
Average school %	76.57	Average state %	78.27
Average pass difference	−1.70		

Jurisdiction	Takers	Passers	Pass %	State %	Diff %
California	167	126	75.45	78.07	−2.62
Arizona	4	4	100.00	84.03	15.97
Utah	2	2	100.00	87.29	12.71
Washington	2	2	100.00	74.40	25.60

Chapman University School of Law

One University Drive
Orange, CA 92866
Phone: 877.CHAPLAW or 714.628.2500; Fax: 714.628.2501
E-mail: lawadm@chapman.edu; Website: www.chapman.edu/law

■ Introduction

Chapman University School of Law is located in the historic Old Towne district of Orange, California. We are part of the university that is 144 years old. The law school, established in 1995, received full approval by the ABA in 2002 and AALS accreditation in January 2006.

The law school has gained a national reputation for its high-quality faculty, students, and facilities. The law school has focus areas in entertainment law, international law, taxation, environmental/real estate/land use, and advocacy and dispute resolution; joint JD/MBA degrees and joint JD/MFA degrees in film producing; and LLM degrees in taxation and prosecutorial science. We also offer clinical opportunities in the areas of family violence, immigration law, elder law, constitutional law, and appellate practice. Our students have obtained rewarding externship and internship opportunities. The law school's successes have been aided by its location in vibrant and dynamic Orange County.

Affiliation with a well-established university allows for cross-disciplinary engagement, joint degrees, and a lively and engaging intellectual environment beyond the classroom. Chapman University offers an impressive selection of artistic and cultural opportunities for its students.

■ Enrollment/Student Body

Chapman Law has committed itself to building a small, talented, and diverse student body. Total student enrollment in 2009–2010 was approximately 575 law students.

The 2009 entering class consisted of 181 law students. The students were divided into three first-year sections. The Legal Research and Writing course has a maximum of 20 students in each of nine sections. Currently, about 10 percent of the entering class comes from outside California; that number is expected to increase over the next few years as Chapman's reputation reaches a more national audience. The minority enrollment is 23 percent.

Competition for seats is keen. Approximately 31 percent of applicants in the 2009 applicant pool were admitted.

■ Faculty

Chapman has assembled an impressive law faculty (including five former US Supreme Court clerks) who are excellent teachers, accomplished scholars, and outstanding mentors. Chapman Law's environment is conducive to learning. Students have access to the faculty and frequent opportunities to engage them in both formal and informal settings. Our student-to-faculty ratio remains 8.89 to 1.

■ Library and Physical Facilities

The beautiful Donald P. Kennedy Hall opened in 1999, with state-of-the-art learning facilities in its classrooms, law library, and trial and appellate courtrooms.

Library holdings now exceed 348,000 volumes and volume equivalents. The collection is fully accessible to students both in hard copy and through the computer network.

Library carrels and desktops are generous in number, and many are wired for Internet access. Several group study rooms are available for student use and extended research.

Two state-of-the-art courtrooms provide computers, cameras, and electronic blackboards for trial advocacy exercises, competitions, and formal hearings by visiting courts.

■ Special Programs/Clinics/Externships

The law school offers the JD/MBA and JD/MFA programs, affording students the opportunity to earn the equivalent of two accredited professional degrees in four years instead of the typical five. Chapman's George L. Argyros School of Business and Economics is AACSB accredited. Our Dodge College of Film and Media Arts is housed in a new building with the latest digital technology.

About 10 percent of the students choose to focus their electives in one of five certificate areas: entertainment law, international law, tax law, environmental/real estate/land use, or advocacy and dispute resolution. The Tax-Law Emphasis Program affords students the opportunity to represent claimants against the IRS in the US Tax Court Clinic. The Center for Land Resources allows students to network with practicing professionals. In the Externship Program, students receive placements in the offices of appellate judges, trial judges, district attorneys, and public defenders, where they gain hands-on experience and academic credit.

Clinic offerings include family violence/immigration law, elder law, entertainment, constitutional litigation, mediation, tax law, and appellate practice. Nearly all clinics allow students additional opportunities to represent actual clients in an array of legal settings.

The law school's Academic Achievement Program assists students in the mastery of the skills necessary to become successful law students and productive attorneys. The program includes individualized counseling and instruction, as well as group workshops and peer tutoring.

■ Admission

The School of Law seeks to admit stellar students who are passionately interested in a legal education that will challenge them to grow intellectually, ethically, and professionally. The law school seeks a diverse student body that will make a meaningful contribution to the legal profession. Many variables enter into the decision-making process. The applicant's entire file is considered, and each application is individually reviewed. The Admission Committee reviews the traditional numbers—your academic record and LSAT—but also considers additional indicators of potential success in law school. Such indicators include the nature and rigor of the undergraduate discipline, an upward trend in academic performance, coursework, writing ability, employment history, graduate-level courses taken and degrees earned, scholarly achievement, community and volunteer service, research projects, demonstrated leadership ability, fluency in foreign languages, personal background (including a history of overcoming adversity), and unusual contributions or other maturing experiences.

Electronic applications are required. Two letters of recommendation are required; these should be submitted directly

to LSAC. A personal statement and résumé are also required, and they should be submitted with your application. Applying early is encouraged as the entering class is filled on a rolling basis, and scholarship funds (merit and need) may be exhausted early in the admission cycle. Please follow the application instructions closely. Transfer and visitor applicants should visit our website.

There is a priority consideration deadline of April 1, 2010, for merit-based scholarships. The application deadline for the fall 2010 entering class is April 15, 2010.

■ Student Curricular and Cocurricular Activities

The law school offers many activities that enrich the academic program and provide important training in leadership. Three journals offer valuable experience in research, writing, and editing. The Student Bar Association administers a full range of programs. Other organizations include, but are not limited to, the Minority Law Students Association, the Asian Pacific American Law Students Association, the Public Interest Law Foundation, the Federalist Society, and the student-run Honor Council.

Externships allow students to earn academic credit while working in a variety of government agencies, judges' chambers, and public interest organizations, developing the practical skills and confidence they will need after graduation.

Chapman offers a range of advocacy experiences, including participation in mock trial, moot court, client counseling, international law, and negotiation competitions. Chapman teams have won regional competitions and have performed competitively in national and international tournaments. The Moot Court Board and the Mock Trial Board administer their programs and provide excellent practical training.

■ Scholarships and Financial Aid

Chapman Law offers a generous merit- and need-based scholarship program. For the 2009 entering class, more than 53 percent of new students received scholarships. After the first year, law students are eligible to renew their merit scholarships provided they maintain a GPA of 3.0 or above in their classes after the first-year grades are posted. For 2009, over $5.3 million in scholarship funds were distributed among a student body of approximately 575. This included merit- and need-based scholarships.

Chapman also offers a full range of loan programs to complement students' financial needs, including Stafford loans, Graduate PLUS loans, Perkins loans, and private loans. All students receiving scholarship funds and/or loans should plan to file the FAFSA. International students are eligible for merit scholarships.

■ Career Services

Chapman Law provides students and alumni with comprehensive career services and resources that aid law students in selecting their career direction and reaching their goals. The office is composed of a director, two assistant directors, and a recruitment coordinator. The Career Services office staff facilitates interviews for our students with legal employers during our On-Campus Interviewing Program in both the fall and spring. The office also provides students the opportunity to meet with prominent members of the legal community through frequent panels, a highly successful Attorney Mentor Program, and an extensive Mock Interview Program.

Career Services helps to match students' educational and experiential skills with both traditional and nontraditional employment opportunities. In keeping with the Chapman mission of personalized education, the Career Services Office staff meets with individual students to review résumés and cover letters; to aid in self-assessment and goal orientation; to discuss specific opportunities unique to the student's needs; and to provide training, support, and feedback in all aspects of exploring career options. The office receives regular input from the Career Services Student Advisory Board.

Applicant Profile

Chapman University School of Law

LSAT Score	GPA								
	3.75 +	3.50–3.74	3.25–3.49	3.00–3.24	2.75–2.99	2.50–2.74	2.25–2.49	2.00–2.24	Below 2.00
175–180									
170–174									
165–169									
160–164									
155–159									
150–154									
145–149									
140–144									
135–139									
130–134									
125–129									
120–124									

Very Likely   Likely   Possible   Unlikely

Charleston School of Law

81 Mary Street, PO Box 535
Charleston, SC 29402
Phone: 843.377.2143; Fax: 843.329.0491
E-mail: info@charlestonlaw.edu; Website: www.charlestonlaw.edu

*Provisional   ABA
Approved
Since
2006*

The Basics

Type of school	Private
Term	Semester
Application deadline	3/31
Application fee	$50
Financial aid deadline	4/15 5/15
Can first year start other than fall?	No
Student to faculty ratio	18.2 to 1
# of housing spaces available restricted to law students	
graduate housing for which law students are eligible	

Faculty and Administrators

	Total		Men		Women		Minorities	
	Spr	Fall	Spr	Fall	Spr	Fall	Spr	Fall
Full-time	25	26	14	15	11	11	3	4
Other full-time	3	5	2	4	1	1	0	0
Deans, librarians, & others who teach	12	12	7	7	5	5	1	1
Part-time	30	30	20	20	10	10	3	3
Total	70	73	43	46	27	27	7	8

JD Enrollment and Ethnicity

	Men		Women		Full-Time		Part-Time		1st-Year		Total		JD Degs. Awd.
	#	%	#	%	#	%	#	%	#	%	#	%	
African Amer.	15	4.1	27	9.2	25	5.4	17	8.5	14	5.9	42	6.4	5
Amer. Indian	0	0.0	1	0.3	0	0.0	1	0.5	0	0.0	1	0.2	1
Asian Amer.	3	0.8	3	1.0	4	0.9	2	1.0	1	0.4	6	0.9	0
Mex. Amer.	0	0.0	0	0.0	0	0.0	0	0.0	0	0.0	0	0.0	0
Puerto Rican	0	0.0	0	0.0	0	0.0	0	0.0	0	0.0	0	0.0	0
Hispanic	4	1.1	2	0.7	4	0.9	2	1.0	3	1.3	6	0.9	0
Total Minority	22	6.0	33	11.3	33	7.2	22	11.0	18	7.5	55	8.3	6
For. Nation.	0	0.0	0	0.0	0	0.0	0	0.0	0	0.0	0	0.0	0
Caucasian	327	89.3	244	83.3	403	87.8	168	84.0	211	88.3	571	86.6	146
Unknown	17	4.6	16	5.5	23	5.0	10	5.0	10	4.2	33	5.0	8
Total	366	55.5	293	44.5	459	69.7	200	30.3	239	36.3	659		160

Curriculum

	Full-Time	Part-Time
Typical first-year section size	62	53
Is there typically a "small section" of the first-year class, other than Legal Writing, taught by full-time faculty	No	No
If yes, typical size offered last year		
# of classroom course titles beyond first-year curriculum		77

# of upper division courses, excluding seminars, with an enrollment:	Under 25	79
	25–49	21
	50–74	15
	75–99	7
	100+	0

# of seminars		0
# of seminar positions available		305
# of seminar positions filled	176	47
# of positions available in simulation courses		786
# of simulation positions filled	271	143
# of positions available in faculty supervised clinical courses		0
# of faculty supervised clinical positions filled	0	0
# involved in field placements	71	31
# involved in law journals	71	14
# involved in moot court or trial competitions	7	2
# of credit hours required to graduate		88

Transfers

Transfers in	0
Transfers out	0

Tuition and Fees

	Resident	Nonresident
Full-time	$34,618	$34,618
Part-time	$27,824	$27,824
Tuition Guarantee Program		N

Living Expenses

Estimated living expenses for singles

Living on campus	Living off campus	Living at home
N/A	$17,450	$17,450

Charleston School of Law

ABA
Approved
Since
2006

GPA and LSAT Scores

	Total	Full-Time	Part-Time
# of apps	1,942	1,710	352
# of offers	895	785	110
# of matrics	241	189	52
75% GPA	3.40	3.43	3.30
Median GPA	3.14	3.20	2.92
25% GPA	2.87	2.95	2.51
75% LSAT	156	156	152
Median LSAT	153	154	151
25% LSAT	151	151	147

Grants and Scholarships (from prior year)

	Total		Full-Time		Part-Time	
	#	%	#	%	#	%
Total # of students	611		428		183	
Total # receiving grants	226	37.0	202	47.2	24	13.1
Less than 1/2 tuition	223	36.5	199	46.5	24	13.1
Half to full tuition	3	0.5	3	0.7	0	0.0
Full tuition	0	0.0	0	0.0	0	0.0
More than full tuition	0	0.0	0	0.0	0	0.0
Median grant amount			$7,500		$5,000	

Informational and Library Resources

Total amount spent on library materials	$805,848
Study seating capacity inside the library	354
# of full-time equivalent professional librarians	5.0
Hours per week library is open	104
# of open, wired connections available to students	0
# of networked computers available for use by students	6
Has wireless network?	Y
Require computer?	Y

JD Attrition (from prior year)

	Academic	Other	Total	
	#	#	#	%
1st year	3	5	8	3.5
2nd year	5	1	6	3.1
3rd year	0	0	0	0.0
4th year	0	1	1	4.3

Employment (9 months after graduation)

	Total	Percentage
Employment status known	152	93.3
Employment status unknown	11	6.7
Employed	103	67.8
Pursuing graduate degrees	7	4.6
Unemployed (seeking, not seeking, or studying for the bar)	36	23.7
Type of Employment		
# employed in law firms	44	42.7
# employed in business and industry	7	6.8
# employed in government	14	13.6
# employed in public interest	4	3.9
# employed as judicial clerks	32	31.1
# employed in academia	2	1.9
Geographic Location		
# employed in state	92	89.3
# employed in foreign countries	0	0.0
# of states where employed	9	

Bar Passage Rates

First-time takers	184	Reporting %	79.89
Average school %	73.47	Average state %	81.83
Average pass difference	−8.36		

Jurisdiction	Takers	Passers	Pass %	State %	Diff %
South Carolina	147	108	73.47	81.83	−8.36

Charleston School of Law

81 Mary Street, PO Box 535
Charleston, SC 29402
Phone: 843.377.2143; Fax: 843.329.0491
E-mail: info@charlestonlaw.edu; Website: www.charlestonlaw.edu

■ Introduction

The Charleston School of Law (CSOL) offers students the unique opportunity to study the time-honored practice of law amid the beauty and grace of one of the South's oldest and most prestigious cities, Charleston, South Carolina. Founded in 2003, CSOL is a freestanding school. The School of Law received provisional approval from the ABA in December 2006, and graduates are qualified to seek admission to the bar in all 50 states and the District of Columbia.

Located in beautiful downtown Charleston, South Carolina, the school is conveniently situated near the historic "four corners of the law" as well as the thriving legal community and the federal and county courthouses. The open intellectual environment at CSOL complements the progressive nature of the city of Charleston. With its diverse economy, rich cultural heritage, thriving tourist industry, and natural amenities, the city—home to one of the nation's busiest ports—is a hub of activity. Charleston is attractive, fun, and consistently named one of the best places in the country to live, work, and learn. The city is home to other institutions of higher education, including the Medical University of South Carolina, the Citadel, and the College of Charleston. The 580,000-person metropolitan area is served by a strong program of cultural activities. Spoleto Festival USA, an internationally renowned arts festival of opera, dance, music, and theater, draws more than 85,000 people to the city each summer. Visitors and residents delight in Charleston's nationally recognized restaurants, vibrant nightlife, walks along the historic Battery, tours of historic homes, boating, sailing, golf, and beachcombing on nearby Sullivan's Island, Isle of Palms, Folly Beach, or Kiawah Island.

■ Library

The Sol Blatt Jr. Law Library, located in a historic 1857 railroad building, provides the feel of Charleston while housing a state-of-the-art wireless network that provides access to the ever-growing digital collection of the library. In just three years, the library has built a digital collection that includes over 260,000 electronic titles.

Students have access on campus or through the Internet from anywhere in the world to full-text materials such as e-books, e-journals, and legal research databases on law and other law-related and interdisciplinary subjects. In addition to the basic legal research databases, Lexis and Westlaw, the library offers digital collections of books and journals from Thomson Gale, NetLibrary, ebrary, Greenwood Press, LexisNexis Matthew Bender, Law Library Microform Consortium, HeinOnline, and JSTOR. Through the library's online catalog students gain access to services such as BNA, RIA, LexisNexis Congressional, and several indices. The print collection provides students with access to materials that support classroom studies.

The library is working to offer seamless searching of all electronic resources while providing students with group-study space. The purchase and implementation of a self-checkout system provides a nonmediated circulation system to both students and faculty.

■ Expenses and Financial Aid

Tuition for the 2009–2010 academic year was as follows: full time—$34,568, part time—$27,774; estimated living expenses—$14,000. The school offers both need-based and academic merit-based scholarships. Applicants wanting to be considered for merit scholarships must have a complete file on or before February 1. Merit-based scholarship decisions are made in early March. Need-based scholarship applications must be postmarked no later than May 15. Students are eligible for federal student loans and are encouraged to complete the FAFSA no later than April 1.

■ Admission

CSOL requires applicants to have earned a bachelor's degree from an accredited institution prior to enrolling in the school. CSOL offers both a full- and part-time program of study leading to the Juris Doctor degree. Beginning students are accepted for the fall semester only. All applicants are required to take the LSAT and register with LSAC's Credential Assembly Service. Applicants should submit a completed application, a personal statement, and two letters of recommendation, plus pay a $50 application fee. Applicants who are accepted will be required to submit a dean's certification form from all colleges or universities attended for 12 or more credit hours. A résumé may also be submitted. The deadline for applying for full time is applications postmarked on or before March 1; the deadline for those applying to the part-time program is April 1.

Consideration is given to many factors; however, the two most important factors in reviewing an application are the cumulative undergraduate GPA and the LSAT. If an applicant has multiple LSAT scores, the highest score will be considered. A score is valid for three years. Other factors taken into consideration are graduate work, military or significant work experience, letters of recommendation, the personal statement, and community service.

■ Curriculum

Students at CSOL study law as a profession with an emphasis on excellence in the classroom. The low faculty-to-student ratio is a testament to the student-centered focus. Small class size promotes individual inquiry in a collegial learning atmosphere. The goals of CSOL include teaching the practice of law as a profession with the chief aim of providing public service, and instituting and coordinating legal outreach programs to the South Carolina and American Bars; local, state, and federal governments; and the general population.

Courses in torts, property, contracts, civil procedure, and legal writing and research comprise the first-year curriculum. Required upper-level courses include business associations, commercial law, constitutional law, criminal law, criminal procedure, domestic relations, equity, evidence, insurance, trust and estates, and professional responsibility, as well as an advanced writing requirement and a skills course.

All students are required to perform a minimum of 30 hours of public service prior to graduation and to participate in a professionalism program during each of the three years of law school.

Special Programs

The school offers a dynamic externship program that provides students the opportunity to gain practical work experience in legal business environments while earning course credit. Students have the opportunity to work under the direct supervision of members of the judiciary and attorneys in private practice, as well as in the public sector or in public interest jobs. In 2008, more than 110 organizations, including county public defenders' offices, state agencies, state and federal courts, and nonprofit agencies in South Carolina and beyond, offered more than 120 externship opportunities to students.

Courses in admiralty and maritime law are available to students enrolled in the school. The Charleston Maritime Law Institute was founded by students and publishes the *Maritime Law Bulletin* (MALABU).

Housing

The school does not offer on-campus housing. Charleston offers many options for off-campus living. Whether a student opts to live in the downtown historic district, at one of the nearby beaches, or in one of the many convenient neighborhoods and communities, carriage houses, apartments, or rental houses are available. The office of admission works with incoming and continuing students to find housing in the Charleston area.

Student Activities

Students have the opportunity to work on the publication of two law reviews. A student board publishes the *Charleston Law Review* on a quarterly basis. Students may also work with federal magistrate judges to publish the printed edition of the *Federal Courts Law Review*.

Moot court opportunities are also available to students enrolled in the school. In its first-ever national competition in 2006, a team of students from CSOL won the grand prize in the National Constitutional Law Moot Court Competition.

The school has more than 30 student organizations, including, but not limited to, the Student Bar Association, the Black Law Student Association, the International Law Society, the Environmental Law Society, the Real Estate Society, the Student Trial Lawyers Association, and Women in Law.

Career Services

The Career Services Office provides a wide range of career development services for CSOL students and creates opportunities to connect students with employers in an efficient and supportive manner. The office serves as a liaison between students and legal employers. The staff provides individual career counseling, programming on career-related issues, and individualized résumé-writing assistance. They also coordinate the on-campus interview program and résumé-forwarding service, as well as the school's participation in national and regional career fairs. In addition, the staff is responsible for the maintenance of a dynamic database of employers and an online career resource center.

The office is available to assist students in finding part-time employment while enrolled in law school, summer employment, and full-time permanent employment upon graduation. The Charleston area provides myriad opportunities for part-time employment while students are enrolled in their second and third years of law school.

CSOL prepares students for careers in all areas of legal practice. Regardless of a student's path after graduation, CSOL strives to instill in students the value of public service. All students must complete 30 hours of pro bono legal service under the supervision of an attorney licensed in South Carolina before they graduate. The Career Services Office develops and supports pro bono opportunities in the legal community and provides guidance to students in their selection of pro bono work.

Applicant Profile

Charleston School of Law

LSAT Score	GPA								
	3.75 +	3.50–3.74	3.25–3.49	3.00–3.24	2.75–2.99	2.50–2.74	2.25–2.49	2.00–2.24	Below 2.00
175–180									
170–174									
165–169									
160–164									
155–159									
150–154									
145–149									
140–144									
135–139									
130–134									
125–129									
120–124									

Good Possibility   Possible   Unlikely

Charlotte School of Law

2145 Suttle Avenue
Charlotte , NC 28208
Phone: 704.971.8500
E-mail: admissions@charlottelaw.edu; Website: www.charlottelaw.edu

*Provisional   ABA
Approved
Since
2008*

The Basics

Type of school	Private
Term	Semester
Application deadline	7/31 12/1
Application fee	$50
Financial aid deadline	
Can first year start other than fall?	Yes
Student to faculty ratio	18.0 to 1
# of housing spaces available	
restricted to law students	
graduate housing for which law students are eligible	

Faculty and Administrators

	Total		Men		Women		Minorities	
	Spr	Fall	Spr	Fall	Spr	Fall	Spr	Fall
Full-time	15	19	8	9	7	10	4	8
Other full-time	3	2	1	1	2	1	2	1
Deans, librarians, & others who teach	8	8	2	3	6	5	4	3
Part-time	8	16	3	9	5	7	2	6
Total	34	45	14	22	20	23	12	18

JD Enrollment and Ethnicity

	Men		Women		Full-Time		Part-Time		1st-Year		Total		JD Degs. Awd.
	#	%	#	%	#	%	#	%	#	%	#	%	
African Amer.	13	5.4	28	11.7	27	7.1	14	13.9	30	10.9	41	8.5	7
Amer. Indian	3	1.2	3	1.3	4	1.1	2	2.0	3	1.1	6	1.2	0
Asian Amer.	3	1.2	3	1.3	5	1.3	1	1.0	1	0.4	6	1.2	1
Mex. Amer.	2	0.8	7	2.9	8	2.1	1	1.0	7	2.5	9	1.9	0
Puerto Rican	1	0.4	2	0.8	2	0.5	1	1.0	2	0.7	3	0.6	0
Hispanic	9	3.7	9	3.8	12	3.2	6	5.9	11	4.0	18	3.7	1
Total Minority	31	12.9	52	21.7	58	15.3	25	24.8	54	19.6	83	17.3	9
For. Nation.	0	0.0	0	0.0	0	0.0	0	0.0	0	0.0	0	0.0	0
Caucasian	205	85.1	179	74.6	312	82.1	72	71.3	218	79.0	384	79.8	53
Unknown	5	2.1	9	3.8	10	2.6	4	4.0	4	1.4	14	2.9	2
Total	241	50.1	240	49.9	380	79.0	101	21.0	276	57.4	481		64

Curriculum

	Full-Time	Part-Time
Typical first-year section size	75	40
Is there typically a "small section" of the first-year class, other than Legal Writing, taught by full-time faculty	No	No
If yes, typical size offered last year		
# of classroom course titles beyond first-year curriculum	43	

# of upper division courses, excluding seminars, with an enrollment:		
Under 25	32	
25–49	15	
50–74	8	
75–99	2	
100+	0	

# of seminars		9
# of seminar positions available		155
# of seminar positions filled	120	18
# of positions available in simulation courses	110	
# of simulation positions filled	84	20
# of positions available in faculty supervised clinical courses		36
# of faculty supervised clinical positions filled	20	14
# involved in field placements	49	8
# involved in law journals	27	2
# involved in moot court or trial competitions	22	9
# of credit hours required to graduate		90

Transfers

Transfers in	6
Transfers out	8

Tuition and Fees

	Resident	Nonresident
Full-time	$33,166	$33,166
Part-time	$26,816	$26,816
Tuition Guarantee Program	N	

Living Expenses

Estimated living expenses for singles

Living on campus	Living off campus	Living at home
N/A	$23,177	N/A

Charlotte School of Law

ABA
Approved
Since
2008

GPA and LSAT Scores

	Total	Full-Time	Part-Time
# of apps	2,263	2,025	257
# of offers	1,209	1,118	91
# of matrics	276	234	42
75% GPA	3.40	3.40	3.40
Median GPA	3.11	3.11	3.15
25% GPA	2.76	2.76	2.73
75% LSAT	153	153	153
Median LSAT	151	151	150
25% LSAT	148	149	147

Grants and Scholarships (from prior year)

	Total		Full-Time		Part-Time	
	#	%	#	%	#	%
Total # of students	290		227		63	
Total # receiving grants	81	27.9	63	27.8	18	28.6
Less than 1/2 tuition	68	23.4	50	22.0	18	28.6
Half to full tuition	12	4.1	12	5.3	0	0.0
Full tuition	1	0.3	1	0.4	0	0.0
More than full tuition	0	0.0	0	0.0	0	0.0
Median grant amount			$10,000		$4,000	

Informational and Library Resources

Total amount spent on library materials	$883,503
Study seating capacity inside the library	370
# of full-time equivalent professional librarians	8.0
Hours per week library is open	107
# of open, wired connections available to students	0
# of networked computers available for use by students	56
Has wireless network?	Y
Require computer?	Y

JD Attrition (from prior year)

	Academic	Other	Total	
	#	#	#	%
1st year	6	18	24	17.4
2nd year	0	4	4	5.3
3rd year	0	0	0	0.0
4th year	0	0	0	0.0

Employment (9 months after graduation)

	Total	Percentage
Employment status known	0	0.0
Employment status unknown	0	0.0
Employed	0	0.0
Pursuing graduate degrees	0	0.0
Unemployed (seeking, not seeking, or studying for the bar)	0	0.0
Type of Employment		
# employed in law firms	0	0.0
# employed in business and industry	0	0.0
# employed in government	0	0.0
# employed in public interest	0	0.0
# employed as judicial clerks	0	0.0
# employed in academia	0	0.0
Geographic Location		
# employed in state	0	0.0
# employed in foreign countries	0	0.0
# of states where employed	0	

Bar Passage Rates

First-time takers	1	Reporting %	NA
Average school %	NA	Average state %	NA
Average pass difference	NA		

Jurisdiction	Takers	Passers	Pass %	State %	Diff %

Charlotte School of Law

2145 Suttle Avenue
Charlotte , NC 28208
Phone: 704.971.8500
E-mail: admissions@charlottelaw.edu; Website: www.charlottelaw.edu

■ Introduction

Welcome to Charlotte School of Law! The law is one of the oldest, most noble, and rewarding of all callings. It is also a profession that is undergoing rapid change as the Internet, knowledge management, internationalization, and other forces converge to challenge and redefine what we mean by legal practice. We are also seeing an expansion of the group to whom we provide legal services, and greatly amplify uses to which one may apply a legal education.

At Charlotte Law we have an educational model that is designed to meet the needs of a twenty-first-century lawyer. This includes a focus on you, the student. Our goal is to provide an intense engagement with faculty and staff, a personalized experience, and a rigorous yet innovative program of study that will maximize your chances of law school success, passage on the bar exam, and career opportunities.

Charlotte Law will also make you "practice-ready" by providing a program of comprehensive professional development that includes not only legal theory, but also exposure to legal practice and the inculcation of important personal, generic, and legal skills required of a rapidly changing legal profession.

Charlotte Law focuses on servant leadership. Tomorrow's lawyers cannot work in isolation, but must be engaged in, and contribute to, their communities. Such involvement will provide you with a lifelong career that is both professionally and personally rewarding, and represents the highest form of professional education.

An important part of the Charlotte Law "magic" has to do with our location in Charlotte, North Carolina. Charlotte is a dynamic, rapidly growing, international city which offers a rich array of family, educational, sports/recreational, cultural, and other opportunities. Our pleasant weather and close proximity to the sea and mountains provide a wonderful venue in which to study and pursue a career afterward. Indeed, North and South Carolina have one of the lowest proportions of lawyers in the United States and collectively is one of the fastest growing regions in the country.

Finally, knowing that seeing is believing, we invite you to visit Charlotte Law to see and feel the difference. When you do, we are confident that you will find in Team Charlotte one of the most exciting, vibrant, and enriching learning communities, dedicated to helping you achieve your full potential both personally and professionally.

■ Mission

Our entire academic mission is structured around three core concepts that we strongly believe make the Charlotte Law experience a unique and powerful one. These three ideals drive decision making as well as our academic approach; together they form a keen vision for the school.

- Practical preparation is critical. A rigorous curriculum has been created to ensure that our students are equipped with practical skills that will allow them to thrive in a professional setting. Students are taught not only the traditions and theory of law, but also how to apply this learning through critical thinking and analytical skill sets. We address what using a law degree in real life can mean to an individual both personally and professionally.
- Our students are our focus. Our faculty is driven by a desire to motivate and energize the student community in every aspect of the Charlotte School of Law experience. Professors are accessible mentors who take an active role in the development of students and help them to embrace their legal education and capitalize on the opportunities within the school's and community's network of resources. Student success is of the utmost importance to everyone at the institution, on every level.
- It is essential to reflect our community. The Charlotte School of Law believes strongly that tomorrow's leaders must reflect and interact effectively with an eclectic collective of people and cultures. Consequently, our inclusive environment fosters a demanding, yet supportive, educational setting for a richly diverse community.

■ Faculty and Administration

The Charlotte School of Law faculty and administration have come together from various backgrounds and achievements to design a practice-ready curriculum and a supportive environment where students are inspired to learn, prepared to serve, and qualified to lead with excellence. Our faculty includes outstanding legal scholars, former trial attorneys, corporate leaders, and government officials who interact with students on a daily basis. Every member of our team is deeply committed to making sure our students have the skills to bridge each area of legal practice and are better equipped for professional life no matter what path they choose for themselves upon graduation.

■ Program Options

The need for legal literacy has become a reality of complex contemporary business and government. A law degree adds value to almost any career one can imagine, and an increasing number of professionals are finding in the JD degree an experience that equips them well with the analytical, writing, counseling, and advocacy skills that are invaluable, no matter what one's calling.

Charlotte School of Law offers a full-time day program and a part-time program. In order to accommodate the varied needs of our students, the part-time program can be completed during the day or in the evening. We have both a fall and a spring start option. Both programs require the completion of 90 credit hours for graduation.

■ Admission

The Charlotte School of Law attracts applicants from not only North and South Carolina, but also from all over the United States. The process to gain admission is competitive; however, those who have scored well on the Law School Admission Test (LSAT) and have a good undergraduate grade-point average (in addition to other indicators of success) are good candidates to study law in our student-centered program.

Charlotte Law offers a full-time program (completed in three years) and a flexible part-time program (completed in four years, summers included). Applications are accepted and reviewed throughout the academic year for entrance into either our fall or spring class. We do not have an application deadline; however, in order to have the best chance of being selected to join the Charlotte Law family, you are encouraged to get your application in early and to complete the application process early (have all required materials on file). Early applicants with competitive numbers have the **best** chance of receiving a merit-based scholarship award.

The Charlotte Law admission office staff will attempt to notify an applicant if a required item is missing from the application file. However, the applicant remains ultimately responsible for ensuring that the application file is completed in a timely fashion. Applicants are strongly encouraged to retain copies of all application information submitted.

File Review Process: Fall semester applications are reviewed after October 1 of each year. The file review process continues until the class-size goal is met.

January semester applications are reviewed after September 15 of each year. The file review process continues until the class-size goal is met.

Deferred Admission: Charlotte School of Law does not defer admission from one year to the following year.

However, an applicant may be granted a deferral within the same academic year, that is, from fall matriculation to spring matriculation. Otherwise, applicants who are offered admission but do not enroll must reapply.

Transfer/Visiting Students: Applications to transfer to Charlotte School of Law or to attend as a visiting student are evaluated by the Admissions Committee and the Academic Dean on a case-by-case basis. **Transfer or visiting status is granted only to applicants who are currently in law school (i.e., no breaks in education).** If such an applicant is accepted, further details, instructions, and forms will be sent to the accepted applicant. Contact the admission office with questions: 704.971.8542 or *admissions@charlottelaw.edu*.

■ Financial Aid

At first blush, the cost to attend law school may make your dream seem out of reach. Before you move to plan B, stop and think about the cost associated with anything worth doing. Law school is an investment in you and an investment in your future.

Contact our financial aid office today to discuss your financing options before you decide to give up on your dream: 704.971.8543 or *financialaid@charlottelaw.edu*.

Applicant Profile

Charlotte School of Law has elected not to publish an admission profile based on LSAT score and UGPA. While both numerical indicators are very important in understanding an applicant's potential for success in law school, those two factors are not the only ones taken into consideration.

Charlotte Law currently uses no form of indexing system in reaching its admission decisions. Each completed application file is thoroughly reviewed in its entirety by a team of faculty and admission professionals.

The University of Chicago Law School

Admissions Office, 1111 E. 60th Street
Chicago, IL 60637
Phone: 773.702.9494; Fax: 773.834.0942
E-mail: admissions@law.uchicago.edu; Website: www.law.uchicago.edu

ABA
Approved
Since
1923

The Basics

Type of school	Private
Term	Quarter
Application deadline	2/1
Application fee	$75
Financial aid deadline	2/1 5/15
Can first year start other than fall?	No
Student to faculty ratio	9.5 to 1
# of housing spaces available restricted to law students	
graduate housing for which law students are eligible 659	

Faculty and Administrators

	Total		Men		Women		Minorities	
	Spr	Fall	Spr	Fall	Spr	Fall	Spr	Fall
Full-time	52	52	36	35	16	17	4	7
Other full-time	20	17	15	14	5	3	5	3
Deans, librarians, & others who teach	3	3	2	2	1	1	0	0
Part-time	65	31	53	24	12	7	7	3
Total	140	103	106	75	34	28	16	13

Curriculum

		Full-Time	Part-Time
Typical first-year section size		93	0
Is there typically a "small section" of the first-year class, other than Legal Writing, taught by full-time faculty		No	No
If yes, typical size offered last year			
# of classroom course titles beyond first-year curriculum		193	
# of upper division courses, excluding seminars, with an enrollment:	Under 25	48	
	25–49	42	
	50–74	14	
	75–99	9	
	100+	3	
# of seminars		116	
# of seminar positions available		1,882	
# of seminar positions filled		1,286	0
# of positions available in simulation courses		180	
# of simulation positions filled		180	0
# of positions available in faculty supervised clinical courses		195	
# of faculty supervised clinical positions filled		195	0
# involved in field placements		8	0
# involved in law journals		129	0
# involved in moot court or trial competitions		5	0
# of credit hours required to graduate		105	

JD Enrollment and Ethnicity

	Men		Women		Full-Time		Part-Time		1st-Year		Total		JD Degs. Awd.
	#	%	#	%	#	%	#	%	#	%	#	%	
African Amer.	17	5.2	20	7.6	37	6.3	0	0.0	9	4.7	37	6.3	10
Amer. Indian	2	0.6	0	0.0	2	0.3	0	0.0	2	1.0	2	0.3	1
Asian Amer.	24	7.4	44	16.7	68	11.5	0	0.0	23	12.0	68	11.5	23
Mex. Amer.	10	3.1	11	4.2	21	3.6	0	0.0	7	3.7	21	3.6	6
Puerto Rican	3	0.9	3	1.1	6	1.0	0	0.0	2	1.0	6	1.0	1
Hispanic	13	4.0	20	7.6	33	5.6	0	0.0	9	4.7	33	5.6	11
Total Minority	69	21.2	98	37.1	167	28.3	0	0.0	52	27.2	167	28.3	52
For. Nation.	8	2.5	6	2.3	14	2.4	0	0.0	5	2.6	14	2.4	3
Caucasian	208	63.8	138	52.3	346	58.6	0	0.0	118	61.8	346	58.6	125
Unknown	41	12.6	22	8.3	63	10.7	0	0.0	16	8.4	63	10.7	23
Total	326	55.3	264	44.7	590	100.0	0	0.0	191	32.4	590		203

Transfers

Transfers in	24
Transfers out	6

Tuition and Fees

	Resident	Nonresident
Full-time	$44,757	
Part-time		
Tuition Guarantee Program		N

Living Expenses

Estimated living expenses for singles

Living on campus	Living off campus	Living at home
$21,585	$21,585	$21,585

The University of Chicago Law School

ABA
Approved
Since
1923

GPA and LSAT Scores

	Total	Full-Time	Part-Time
# of apps	5,403	5,403	0
# of offers	982	982	0
# of matrics	191	191	0
75% GPA	3.84	3.84	0.00
Median GPA	3.76	3.76	0.00
25% GPA	3.63	3.63	0.00
75% LSAT	173	173	0
Median LSAT	171	171	0
25% LSAT	169	169	0

Grants and Scholarships (from prior year)

	Total		Full-Time		Part-Time	
	#	%	#	%	#	%
Total # of students	593		593		0	
Total # receiving grants	333	56.2	333	56.2	0	0.0
Less than 1/2 tuition	289	48.7	289	48.7	0	0.0
Half to full tuition	39	6.6	39	6.6	0	0.0
Full tuition	5	0.8	5	0.8	0	0.0
More than full tuition	0	0.0	0	0.0	0	0.0
Median grant amount		$10,800			$0	

Informational and Library Resources

Total amount spent on library materials	$2,217,402
Study seating capacity inside the library	483
# of full-time equivalent professional librarians	10.0
Hours per week library is open	90
# of open, wired connections available to students	1,115
# of networked computers available for use by students	26
Has wireless network?	Y
Require computer?	Y

JD Attrition (from prior year)

	Academic	Other	Total	
	#	#	#	%
1st year	0	1	1	0.5
2nd year	0	8	8	3.9
3rd year	0	2	2	1.0
4th year	0	0	0	0.0

Employment (9 months after graduation)

	Total	Percentage
Employment status known	211	100.0
Employment status unknown	0	0.0
Employed	203	96.2
Pursuing graduate degrees	3	1.4
Unemployed (seeking, not seeking, or studying for the bar)	2	0.9
Type of Employment		
# employed in law firms	165	81.3
# employed in business and industry	6	3.0
# employed in government	4	2.0
# employed in public interest	1	0.5
# employed as judicial clerks	26	12.8
# employed in academia	0	0.0
Geographic Location		
# employed in state	70	34.5
# employed in foreign countries	1	0.5
# of states where employed	22	

Bar Passage Rates

First-time takers	195	Reporting %	84.62
Average school %	95.15	Average state %	87.56
Average pass difference	7.59		

Jurisdiction	Takers	Passers	Pass %	State %	Diff %
Illinois	81	77	95.06	90.94	4.12
New York	48	45	93.75	88.98	4.77
California	36	35	97.22	78.07	19.15

The University of Chicago Law School

Admissions Office, 1111 E. 60th Street
Chicago, IL 60637
Phone: 773.702.9494; Fax: 773.834.0942
E-mail: admissions@law.uchicago.edu; Website: www.law.uchicago.edu

■ Introduction

Chicago graduates lead and innovate in government, public causes, academia, and business, as well as law. For this reason, Chicago aims not to certify lawyers, but to train well-rounded, critical, and socially conscious thinkers and doers. Three cornerstones provide the foundation for Chicago's educational mission: the marketplace of ideas, participatory learning, and interdisciplinary inquiry.

■ Enrollment/Student Body

Our students' chief passions are ideas. They have shown this passion through their academic success, and they exhibit signs of great professional promise. Over 5,000 applicants seek approximately 190 seats in each incoming class. Chicago students come from more than 100 undergraduate institutions with degrees in nearly every discipline, and one in ten have graduate degrees. Many of our students have also had interesting and successful careers before law school.

■ Faculty

What distinguishes Chicago faculty is their devotion to both teaching and scholarship. This might seem a contradiction at first, but at Chicago, teaching and scholarship complement each other. Chicago professors blaze trails in legal thought, and their revolutionary ideas infuse classroom discussion with immediacy and excitement. Our professors write the books, draft the statutes, and decide the cases that students read at law schools across America. During the 2010–2011 academic year, our faculty will teach more than 170 courses and seminars at the Law School.

■ Curriculum

As a first-year student, you will take a core sequence covering five principal areas of the law: contracts, torts, property, criminal law, and civil procedure; a required interdisciplinary course called Elements of the Law; an elective; and a year-long course on research and writing. This curriculum familiarizes you with the basic principles of Anglo-American law, cultivates legal reasoning, develops writing ability, and introduces students to interdisciplinary approaches to the law.

In the second and third years, you can choose courses from the full range of Chicago's more than 170 classes. Generally, classes are small; more than 60 percent have fewer than 25 students in them. Additionally, in an average year, about one-third of the second- and third-year students take classes in other divisions of the university. We do not ask our students to choose a concentration but rather let them put together an interdisciplinary education based on their individual interests.

■ Special Programs

The Law School encourages interdisciplinary work. All students may take 12 hours of coursework anywhere in the university. Students may also apply for three formal joint-degree programs either at the same time they apply to the Law School or in their first year. They may also work with Law School and university staff to arrange concurrent degrees. Formal joint-degree programs are with the Booth School of Business (MBA, PhD), the Harris School of Public Policy (MPP), and the Committee on International Relations (MA).

The Law School is home to a wide variety of research programs. These programs provide excellent outlets for both the theoretical and empirical work of both faculty and students. In addition, these programs host conferences, publish working papers, and support journals. Centers currently at the Law School include the Center for Civil Justice, the Center for Comparative Constitutionalism, the Center for Studies in Criminal Justice, the John M. Olin Program in Law and Economics, and the Center for Law, Philosophy and Human Values.

The Law School is committed to making big contributions to topics of national interest—health care, animal rights, and immigration policy just to name a few. The Chicago Policy Initiatives encourage faculty members and students to work together, think hard about important social problems, and propose solutions. Current projects include the Chicago Policy Initiative on Animal Law, Chicago Foster Care Project, and Climate Change Online.

■ Clinical Opportunities

Housed in the Arthur Kane Center, our clinics involve more than 120 students each year in representing clients with real-world problems. The Mandel Legal Aid Clinic handles matters involving appellate advocacy, criminal and juvenile justice, employment discrimination, civil rights, housing, immigration, and mental health. The Institute for Justice Clinic on Entrepreneurship assists aspiring entry-level entrepreneurs from low- and moderate-income neighborhoods. We also have the Immigrant Children's Advocacy Project, which provides a unique opportunity for our students to draw on immigration law, international law, family, and children's rights law. Recently added is the Exoneration Project, which provides representation to clients who are asserting their actual innocence in state and federal court. The Law School also partners with outside agencies to provide additional clinical opportunities to our students.

■ Student Activities

About 40 percent of upper-class students serve on one of the three student-edited journals, which include the *Chicago Law Review*, the *Chicago Legal Forum*, and the *Chicago Journal of International Law*. The Hinton Moot Court Board conducts a program in appellate advocacy for upper-class students, and first-year students participate in a moot court as part of the Bigelow Legal Research and Writing Program. More than 50 student organizations provide opportunities for the exploration of legal specialties, affiliation with like-minded students, or networking within identity groups.

■ Career Services

Our career services office assists students with permanent and summer employment. Six professional career advisors counsel students in one-on-one planning sessions. Programs

on types of practices and nontraditional careers are organized throughout the year for students. The office focuses on individualized counseling and coaching based on each student's career and life goals. The top five destinations our graduates choose for employment are Chicago, Los Angeles, New York, San Francisco, and Washington, DC.

■ Location

Hyde Park provides Chicago students with the best of all possible worlds—a campus with a college-town atmosphere just a few miles from the downtown area of a vibrant city. Hyde Park is a dynamic community with parks, museums, and multiple bookstores. The Law School is located at the southern end of campus, facing an expansive "front lawn" known as the Midway Plaisance. Surrounding the Law School is a tree-lined, diverse residential neighborhood, a sandy Lake Michigan beach, and two sprawling parks. The campus itself is a Gothic masterpiece where limestone buildings built around tree-shaded quadrangles sport gargoyles, ivy, and turrets. The Law School's modern building promotes interaction among faculty and students, while the recently remodeled library and classroom wing enhance the learning experience.

■ Housing

A graduate residence hall, located two blocks from the Law School, is available to law students. Most rooms are singles with private baths. In addition, the university has plenty of single- and married-student neighborhood housing available. Many students choose to rent housing from private landlords.

Housing in Chicago is very affordable compared to most major cities. Buses run frequently throughout the surrounding neighborhood, providing transportation to and from residences and the Law School. Public transportation is easily accessible to other neighborhoods in Chicago.

■ Admission

Each year we seek to create a community from among the best and brightest law school applicants. We want students who are intellectually curious, lively, and collegial in their academic approach. We want students who will take their legal education seriously, but not take themselves too seriously. And because we are preparing students to enter a multifaceted profession, we want multidimensional students with a wide range of talents, backgrounds, experiences, and accomplishments. We do not use indices, formulas, or cutoffs.

■ Financial Aid

Your Chicago legal education is an investment in your future. Because many students will not have sufficient personal resources to make this investment, Chicago provides generous financial aid. Approximately 50 percent of the students receive scholarships. The Law School also provides funding for students who work in public interest positions during their summers. After graduation, the Law School provides financial assistance to graduates who enter careers in public interest legal work through our generous Hormel Public Interest Program. Graduates earning $72,000 or less in a government, nonprofit, or public interest job can receive benefits.

Applicant Profile

We seek to create a community from among the best, the brightest, and the most interesting law school applicants. We do not believe that the LSAT and GPA alone provide us with sufficient information to evaluate an applicant's likely contributions to our community; therefore, we do not use any formulas, indices, or numerical cutoffs. We do not provide an applicant profile here because it would be based solely on the LSAT and GPA.

Chicago-Kent College of Law, Illinois Institute of Technology

Office of Admissions, 565 West Adams Street
Chicago, IL 60661
Phone: 312.906.5020; Fax: 312.906.5274
E-mail: admissions@kentlaw.edu; Website: www.kentlaw.edu

ABA
Approved
Since
1936

The Basics

Type of school	Private
Term	Semester
Application deadline	3/1
Application fee	$60
Financial aid deadline	4/1
Can first year start other than fall?	No
Student to faculty ratio	11.0 to 1
# of housing spaces available restricted to law students	
graduate housing for which law students are eligible	5

Faculty and Administrators

	Total Spr	Total Fall	Men Spr	Men Fall	Women Spr	Women Fall	Minorities Spr	Minorities Fall
Full-time	66	65	43	40	23	25	8	9
Other full-time	2	2	2	2	0	0	0	0
Deans, librarians, & others who teach	4	4	2	2	2	2	1	1
Part-time	97	87	75	69	22	18	4	6
Total	169	158	122	113	47	45	13	16

Curriculum

	Full-Time	Part-Time
Typical first-year section size	54	54
Is there typically a "small section" of the first-year class, other than Legal Writing, taught by full-time faculty	No	No
If yes, typical size offered last year		
# of classroom course titles beyond first-year curriculum	145	
# of upper division courses, excluding seminars, with an enrollment: Under 25	209	
25–49	53	
50–74	12	
75–99	5	
100+	3	
# of seminars	42	
# of seminar positions available	580	
# of seminar positions filled	255	71
# of positions available in simulation courses	623	
# of simulation positions filled	279	204
# of positions available in faculty supervised clinical courses	214	
# of faculty supervised clinical positions filled	202	8
# involved in field placements	154	8
# involved in law journals	58	7
# involved in moot court or trial competitions	67	3
# of credit hours required to graduate	87	

JD Enrollment and Ethnicity

	Men #	Men %	Women #	Women %	Full-Time #	Full-Time %	Part-Time #	Part-Time %	1st-Year #	1st-Year %	Total #	Total %	JD Degs. Awd.
African Amer.	16	3.1	33	7.6	38	4.9	11	6.1	19	6.3	49	5.2	15
Amer. Indian	1	0.2	2	0.5	3	0.4	0	0.0	0	0.0	3	0.3	0
Asian Amer.	38	7.4	50	11.5	67	8.7	21	11.7	26	8.6	88	9.3	16
Mex. Amer.	4	0.8	5	1.1	7	0.9	2	1.1	7	2.3	9	0.9	7
Puerto Rican	2	0.4	3	0.7	4	0.5	1	0.6	0	0.0	5	0.5	1
Hispanic	11	2.1	17	3.9	24	3.1	4	2.2	13	4.3	28	3.0	8
Total Minority	72	14.1	110	25.2	143	18.6	39	21.8	65	21.4	182	19.2	47
For. Nation.	14	2.7	10	2.3	18	2.3	6	3.4	6	2.0	24	2.5	2
Caucasian	379	74.0	275	63.1	539	70.1	115	64.2	202	66.4	654	69.0	210
Unknown	47	9.2	41	9.4	69	9.0	19	10.6	31	10.2	88	9.3	28
Total	512	54.0	436	46.0	769	81.1	179	18.9	304	32.1	948		287

Transfers

Transfers in	36
Transfers out	12

Tuition and Fees

	Resident	Nonresident
Full-time	$38,152	$38,152
Part-time	$27,910	$27,910
Tuition Guarantee Program	N	

Living Expenses

Estimated living expenses for singles

Living on campus	Living off campus	Living at home
$16,137	$21,562	$11,860

Chicago-Kent College of Law, Illinois Institute of Technology

ABA
Approved
Since
1936

GPA and LSAT Scores

	Total	Full-Time	Part-Time
# of apps	3,489	3,141	348
# of offers	1,516	1,383	133
# of matrics	298	246	52
75% GPA	3.67	3.69	3.59
Median GPA	3.50	3.53	3.25
25% GPA	3.11	3.21	2.96
75% LSAT	163	163	160
Median LSAT	161	161	158
25% LSAT	156	157	155

Grants and Scholarships (from prior year)

	Total		Full-Time		Part-Time	
	#	%	#	%	#	%
Total # of students	957		705		252	
Total # receiving grants	565	59.0	461	65.4	104	41.3
Less than 1/2 tuition	298	31.1	213	30.2	85	33.7
Half to full tuition	189	19.7	176	25.0	13	5.2
Full tuition	55	5.7	50	7.1	5	2.0
More than full tuition	23	2.4	22	3.1	1	0.4
Median grant amount			$20,000		$5,000	

Informational and Library Resources

Total amount spent on library materials	$830,422
Study seating capacity inside the library	459
# of full-time equivalent professional librarians	12
Hours per week library is open	96
# of open, wired connections available to students	1,800
# of networked computers available for use by students	0
Has wireless network?	Y
Require computer?	Y

JD Attrition (from prior year)

	Academic	Other	Total	
	#	#	#	%
1st year	9	24	33	9.6
2nd year	6	1	7	2.4
3rd year	0	0	0	0.0
4th year	0	0	0	0.0

Employment (9 months after graduation)

	Total	Percentage
Employment status known	290	91.2
Employment status unknown	28	8.8
Employed	262	90.3
Pursuing graduate degrees	11	3.8
Unemployed (seeking, not seeking, or studying for the bar)	12	4.1
Type of Employment		
# employed in law firms	143	54.6
# employed in business and industry	45	17.2
# employed in government	34	13.0
# employed in public interest	21	8.0
# employed as judicial clerks	13	5.0
# employed in academia	6	2.3
Geographic Location		
# employed in state	210	80.2
# employed in foreign countries	0	0.0
# of states where employed	23	

Bar Passage Rates

First-time takers	307	Reporting %	87.95
Average school %	96.30	Average state %	90.94
Average pass difference	5.36		

Jurisdiction	Takers	Passers	Pass %	State %	Diff %
Illinois	270	260	96.30	90.94	5.36

Chicago-Kent College of Law, Illinois Institute of Technology

Office of Admissions, 565 West Adams Street
Chicago, IL 60661
Phone: 312.906.5020; Fax: 312.906.5274
E-mail: admissions@kentlaw.edu; Website: www.kentlaw.edu

■ Introduction

Chicago-Kent College of Law, Illinois Institute of Technology, is a national leader in legal education, recognized for the strength of its faculty and for its innovative approaches to traditional legal education. The second oldest law school in Illinois, Chicago-Kent was founded in 1888 by two judges who believed that legal education should be available to working men and women. The law school's first female student graduated in 1891, and the first African American woman admitted to the bar in Illinois (and the second admitted to practice law in the United States) was a graduate of the class of 1894. Today, Chicago-Kent students come from 35 states and 15 countries. Forty-six percent of the students are women, and 19 percent are students of color. The law school is also proud to count among its students and graduates the 2007 and the 2008 National Trial Competition champions as well as the 2008 and 2009 National Moot Court Competition champions.

Drawing on its distinctive affiliation with Illinois Institute of Technology, Chicago-Kent is at the vanguard of exploring new frontiers in the law raised by biotechnology, cyberspace, environmental regulation, intellectual property, international business transactions and trade, and much more. Chicago-Kent is located in downtown Chicago, the heart of the city's commercial and legal communities. The law school is accredited by the American Bar Association and is a member of the Association of American Law Schools and the Order of the Coif.

■ Faculty

The foundation for academic excellence at Chicago-Kent is derived from its faculty, who engage in broad-ranging legal scholarship and research. As advisors frequently approached for their expertise, faculty members help shape policy and thinking on a variety of issues, and make it a point to involve students in their particular areas of influence.

■ Library and Facilities

Chicago-Kent's modern, ten-story building features a three-story atrium, five-level library, technologically advanced courtroom, auditorium, computer labs, student lounges, and cafeteria. Chicago-Kent's library is one of the largest law school libraries in the country. The collection includes the Library of International Relations and a wealth of material on environmental and energy law, intellectual property law, international trade law, and labor law.

The law school houses a comprehensive computer network with more than 1,900 network connections located throughout the building and library, and at each seat in the majority of classrooms. Wireless service is also available throughout the building.

Affordable housing is available in nearby urban and suburban neighborhoods. Furnished apartments are available for Chicago-Kent students at Tailor Lofts, a new loft-style development located within walking distance of the law school in student-friendly Greektown. Dormitory housing is available on the university's main campus, approximately five miles south of the law school. A free shuttle runs between the two campuses. The law school is close to all public transportation downtown.

■ Curriculum

Both full-time and part-time programs are available. Full-time students usually complete the JD degree in three years. Part-time students usually finish in four years. Students may apply to transfer between divisions after completing the first year. First-year class sizes typically range from 30 to 90 students.

Degrees available include JD, JD/MBA, JD/MPA, JD/MPH, JD/LLM in Taxation, JD/LLM in Financial Services Law, JD/LLM in Family Law, JD/MS in Finance, JD/MS in Environmental Management and Sustainability, LLM in Taxation, LLM in Financial Services Law, LLM in Family Law, LLM in International Intellectual Property Law, and LLM in International and Comparative Law.

■ Practical Skills Training

Legal Research and Writing—Chicago-Kent's acclaimed legal research and writing program is one of the most comprehensive in the nation. The three-year, five-course curriculum teaches students to research, analyze, and communicate effectively about a wide range of legal problems.

Clinical Education—The Law Offices of Chicago-Kent, one of the largest in-house clinical education programs in the country, offers 10 in-house clinical practice areas and a broad range of externships with government agencies, not-for-profit organizations, and federal and state court judges.

Trial Advocacy—The law school offers a two-semester sequence in trial advocacy and an intensive course taught by veteran judges and experienced practitioners.

■ Certificate Programs

Criminal Litigation—The program emphasizes both theory and practical skills development to provide comprehensive and balanced preparation for a career in criminal prosecution or defense.

Environmental and Energy Law—The program's interdisciplinary approach to the problems of environmental regulation and natural resources allocation prepares students for practice through a series of courses in law, economic and public policy analysis, and the scientific aspects of environmental problems.

Intellectual Property Law—The program focuses on issues relating to patent, trademark, copyright, trade secrets, and unfair competition, both in the United States and abroad.

International and Comparative Law—The program encompasses study in international business and trade, international and comparative law, and international human rights.

Labor and Employment Law—The program provides students with theoretical and practical training in the law governing the workplace.

Litigation and Alternative Dispute Resolution—The program stresses the connection between legal doctrine, skills and values, and the art of lawyering. It is designed to educate students to become reflective practitioners with a

lawyering identity that incorporates high standards of competence, ethics, and social responsibility.

Public Interest Law—The program provides students with a background in public interest law and policy, in addition to individualized curriculum and career planning. The law school also supports a number of public interest resources and activities, including the Center for Access to Justice and Technology, which aims to make justice more accessible to the public through the use of the Internet.

■ Institutes and Centers

Chicago-Kent is home to six institutes and centers with missions that range from conducting scholarly and practical research on legal and social issues to providing topical programming to developing public interest services. Through these initiatives, many of which involve cross-disciplinary projects, students learn to appreciate and adapt to major social and global influences that can change the legal profession and its practice. These six institutes and centers include
- Center for Access to Justice and Technology
- Global Law and Policy Initiative
- IIT Center for Diabetes Research and Policy
- Institute for Law and the Humanities
- Institute for Law and the Workplace
- Institute for Science, Law, and Technology

■ Admission

Admission is highly selective. Each application is individually reviewed and decisions are based on a range of factors, including quantitative and qualitative criteria. Although the GPA and LSAT are important criteria, consideration also is given to nonnumerical factors such as the nature and rigor of the undergraduate curriculum, writing ability, graduate work and

professional experience, extracurricular activities, diversity, and the personal statement. The admission requirements for the full- and part-time divisions are the same. The law school is committed to attracting and retaining students from a variety of racial, ethnic, economic, geographic, and educational backgrounds.

■ Student Activities

Student editors and staff, in association with a faculty editor, publish the *Chicago-Kent Law Review* in symposium format. Moot Court and Trial Advocacy teams successfully compete in local, regional, and national competitions each year, providing numerous opportunities to develop litigation expertise. Diverse student interests are represented in a wide variety of social, political, and professional student groups.

■ Scholarship Support

Substantial scholarship assistance is offered to entering and continuing students based on factors that include merit, financial need, and contribution to the law school community. The Honors Scholars Program provides renewable scholarships of full tuition and living expenses, research assistantships, and special seminars to a select group of students who demonstrate exceptional academic and leadership ability.

■ Career Services

The Office of Career Services, with six full-time staff, offers individual counseling on résumé writing, interview techniques, and job-search strategies and sponsors both on- and off-campus interview programs. Typically, 90 percent of graduates who seek employment find professional positions within nine months of graduation.

Applicant Profile

Chicago-Kent College of Law, Illinois Institute of Technology

LSAT Score	GPA																					
	3.75 +		3.50–3.74		3.25–3.49		3.00–3.24		2.75–2.99		2.50–2.74		2.25–2.49		2.00–2.24		Below 2.00		No GPA		Total	
	Apps	Adm	Apps	Adm	Apps	Adm	Apps	Adm	Apps	Adm	Apps	Adm	Apps	Adm	Apps	Adm	Apps	Adm	Apps	Adm	Apps	Adm
170–180	15	8	14	8	16	14	8	8	7	7	4	4	2	2	0	0	0	0	0	0	66	51
165–169	63	48	79	60	55	52	38	37	25	24	13	13	6	5	1	1	0	0	1	1	281	241
160–164	89	85	163	154	177	146	123	108	54	50	32	25	13	7	6	6	1	1	15	12	673	594
155–159	106	96	250	175	251	56	181	50	88	19	44	13	18	3	1	1	2	0	25	7	966	420
150–154	95	56	164	73	201	31	179	15	87	6	46	3	25	1	9	0	2	0	20	1	828	186
Below 150	38	6	104	4	130	5	143	2	116	2	82	0	56	0	24	0	6	0	29	0	728	19
Total	406	299	774	474	830	304	672	220	377	108	221	58	120	18	41	8	11	1	90	21	3542	1511

Apps = Number of Applicants
Adm = Number Admitted
Reflects 99% of the total applicant pool; average LSAT data reported.

This grid represents admission data for applicants to both the full- and part-time programs. The information in this grid is to be used only as an approximate gauge of the likelihood of admission and not as a guarantee. Individual accomplishments and other nonnumerical factors are also of importance to the Admissions Committee.

University of Cincinnati College of Law

PO Box 210040, Office of Admission and Financial Aid
Cincinnati, OH 45221-0040
Phone: 513.556.0078; Fax: 513.556.2391
E-mail: admissions@law.uc.edu; Website: www.law.uc.edu

ABA
Approved
Since
1923

The Basics

Type of school	Public
Term	Semester
Application deadline	12/1 3/1
Application fee	$35
Financial aid deadline	3/1
Can first year start other than fall?	No
Student to faculty ratio	9.9 to 1
# of housing spaces available restricted to law students	
graduate housing for which law students are eligible	391

Faculty and Administrators

	Total		Men		Women		Minorities	
	Spr	Fall	Spr	Fall	Spr	Fall	Spr	Fall
Full-time	32	31	16	15	16	16	4	5
Other full-time	0	0	0	0	0	0	0	0
Deans, librarians, & others who teach	5	5	4	4	1	1	0	0
Part-time	35	34	24	24	11	10	4	2
Total	72	70	44	43	28	27	8	7

JD Enrollment and Ethnicity

	Men		Women		Full-Time		Part-Time		1st-Year		Total		JD Degs. Awd.
	#	%	#	%	#	%	#	%	#	%	#	%	
African Amer.	7	3.1	16	9.7	23	5.9	0	0.0	8	5.8	23	5.9	8
Amer. Indian	1	0.4	0	0.0	1	0.3	0	0.0	1	0.7	1	0.3	0
Asian Amer.	17	7.5	13	7.9	30	7.7	0	0.0	10	7.2	30	7.7	8
Mex. Amer.	0	0.0	0	0.0	0	0.0	0	0.0	0	0.0	0	0.0	0
Puerto Rican	0	0.0	0	0.0	0	0.0	0	0.0	0	0.0	0	0.0	0
Hispanic	5	2.2	4	2.4	9	2.3	0	0.0	5	3.6	9	2.3	5
Total Minority	30	13.3	33	20.0	63	16.1	0	0.0	24	17.4	63	16.1	21
For. Nation.	0	0.0	0	0.0	0	0.0	0	0.0	0	0.0	0	0.0	0
Caucasian	196	86.7	132	80.0	328	83.9	0	0.0	114	82.6	328	83.9	87
Unknown	0	0.0	0	0.0	0	0.0	0	0.0	0	0.0	0	0.0	0
Total	226	57.8	165	42.2	391	100.0	0	0.0	138	35.3	391		108

Curriculum

	Full-Time	Part-Time
Typical first-year section size	54	0
Is there typically a "small section" of the first-year class, other than Legal Writing, taught by full-time faculty	Yes	No
If yes, typical size offered last year	21	
# of classroom course titles beyond first-year curriculum	103	

# of upper division courses, excluding seminars, with an enrollment:		
	Under 25	39
	25–49	20
	50–74	8
	75–99	1
	100+	1

# of seminars	24	
# of seminar positions available	348	
# of seminar positions filled	236	0
# of positions available in simulation courses	228	
# of simulation positions filled	228	0
# of positions available in faculty supervised clinical courses	49	
# of faculty supervised clinical positions filled	49	0
# involved in field placements	135	0
# involved in law journals	132	0
# involved in moot court or trial competitions	43	0
# of credit hours required to graduate	90	

Transfers

Transfers in	7
Transfers out	4

Tuition and Fees

	Resident	Nonresident
Full-time	$19,942	$34,776
Part-time		
Tuition Guarantee Program	N	

Living Expenses

Estimated living expenses for singles

Living on campus	Living off campus	Living at home
$16,446	$16,446	$16,446

University of Cincinnati College of Law

ABA
Approved
Since
1923

GPA and LSAT Scores

	Total	Full-Time	Part-Time
# of apps	1,322	1,322	0
# of offers	666	666	0
# of matrics	138	138	0
75% GPA	3.79	3.79	0.00
Median GPA	3.60	3.60	0.00
25% GPA	3.29	3.29	0.00
75% LSAT	161	161	0
Median LSAT	160	160	0
25% LSAT	156	156	0

Grants and Scholarships (from prior year)

	Total #	Total %	Full-Time #	Full-Time %	Part-Time #	Part-Time %
Total # of students	361		361		0	
Total # receiving grants	257	71.2	257	71.2	0	0.0
Less than 1/2 tuition	161	44.6	161	44.6	0	0.0
Half to full tuition	88	24.4	88	24.4	0	0.0
Full tuition	7	1.9	7	1.9	0	0.0
More than full tuition	1	0.3	1	0.3	0	0.0
Median grant amount			$7,000		$0	

Informational and Library Resources

Total amount spent on library materials	$813,374
Study seating capacity inside the library	336
# of full-time equivalent professional librarians	6.0
Hours per week library is open	95
# of open, wired connections available to students	6
# of networked computers available for use by students	62
Has wireless network?	Y
Require computer?	N

JD Attrition (from prior year)

	Academic #	Other #	Total #	Total %
1st year	0	12	12	9.8
2nd year	0	1	1	0.8
3rd year	0	0	0	0.0
4th year	0	0	0	0.0

Employment (9 months after graduation)

	Total	Percentage
Employment status known	122	100.0
Employment status unknown	0	0.0
Employed	111	91.0
Pursuing graduate degrees	3	2.5
Unemployed (seeking, not seeking, or studying for the bar)	5	4.1
Type of Employment		
# employed in law firms	56	50.5
# employed in business and industry	14	12.6
# employed in government	13	11.7
# employed in public interest	14	12.6
# employed as judicial clerks	7	6.3
# employed in academia	6	5.4
Geographic Location		
# employed in state	76	68.5
# employed in foreign countries	0	0.0
# of states where employed	17	

Bar Passage Rates

First-time takers	122	Reporting %	71.31
Average school %	83.91	Average state %	88.04

Average pass difference −4.13

Jurisdiction	Takers	Passers	Pass %	State %	Diff %
Ohio	79	65	82.28	88.09	−5.81
New York	6	6	100.00	88.98	11.02
Colorado	2	2	100.00	83.29	16.71

University of Cincinnati College of Law

PO Box 210040, Office of Admission and Financial Aid
Cincinnati, OH 45221-0040
Phone: 513.556.0078; Fax: 513.556.2391
E-mail: admissions@law.uc.edu; Website: www.law.uc.edu

■ Introduction

The College of Law has a rich heritage and proud traditions. Throughout its 177-year history, graduates have been leaders of the bench and bar, served in senior governmental positions, been active in the public service community, and succeeded in business, academia, and countless other fields. As the premier small, urban, public law school in America, the college is focused on being nationally recognized for its excellence, relevance, and impact. The size of the school allows for small classes and a high degree of personal interaction with faculty and other students. The law school is located on UC's recently renovated main campus in Clifton, approximately 10 minutes north of the city's central business district. This provides easy access to state, county, and federal courts, including the US Court of Appeals for the Sixth Circuit. A charter member of the AALS, UC was one of the first law schools to have a chapter of the Order of the Coif and to be approved by the ABA.

■ Student Body

The 392 students in the College of Law, approximately 135 per class, come from an amazingly wide variety of backgrounds, experiences, and perspectives. The student body is also talented academically, as the 75th/25th LSAT and UGPA percentiles for fall 2009 are 161/156 and 3.79/3.29. The applicant pool, offers of admission, and matriculants were almost evenly divided between resident and nonresident applicants. The College of Law is committed to enrolling a diverse class, as 17 percent of our students are from minority backgrounds, about 40 percent are female, and 39 percent enroll from states other than Ohio. The average age of the entering class is 25; however, 18 percent of the class are 27 or older.

■ Faculty

The college employs a full-time faculty of 32 who pride themselves on their teaching, scholarship, and accessibility to students. As the core of the academic program, faculty members bring areas of expertise into the classroom that add depth, perspective, and professionalism to the law students' studies. The student-to-faculty ratio of 9.7:1 provides ample opportunities for individual discussions with faculty or in-depth research in areas of interest.

■ Library and Physical Facilities

The Robert S. Marx Law Library has a seasoned staff that is able to assist students with research and technical questions. Two computer labs and a wireless network throughout the law building enable students to maximize online research capabilities, and our skilled IT staff members are readily available to assist law students. The law library, which can seat the entire law student body at one time, manages collections carefully to support faculty and student research and the college curriculum.

■ Curriculum

First-year students are divided into six individual sections, creating an unusual advantage of very small first-year sections (typically no larger than 25). The small-section modules allow for further inquiry beyond the typical first-year curriculum. First-year students take two courses in small sections with opportunities to study with all members of their class over the entire year. The upper level is well balanced between theory and skills-related courses. Institutes and research centers exist in the areas of international human rights, law and justice/Ohio Innocence Project, corporate law, law and psychiatry, and the center for practice. In addition, the college offers joint programs with women's studies, business, political science, community planning, and social work. The law school also offers clinical opportunities with the appellate law clinic (Sixth Circuit Court of Appeals) as well as a domestic relations clinic housed downtown at the Cincinnati Legal Aid offices.

■ Special Programs

The College of Law recognizes that a lawyer needs both a firm grasp on subject matter and expertise in professional skills. The college, therefore, has developed an extensive legal research and writing program that not only encompasses first-year courses, but upper-level courses as well. The Center for Professional Development provides students with extern experiences, which are opportunities to work with practicing attorneys and public clinics. The Rosenthal Institute for Justice has been endowed to ensure that popular programs like the Ohio Innocence Project are available to students now and in the future. Each institute and research center offers a fellowship program, research opportunities, and in-depth study in their respective areas. The college was the first to offer a joint degree in law and women's studies, and has the oldest endowed international human rights program at an American law school, the Urban Morgan Institute for Human Rights.

■ Admission Standards

Admission to the college is based upon a selective review of each applicant's file by the Admissions Committee. Although the Admissions Committee relies on the grade-point average and LSAT score to determine the applicant's academic potential, other nonquantitative factors believed to be relevant to success in law school are considered; that is, the quality of the applicant's education, participation in community service, employment experience, graduate work, and letters of recommendation. The educational philosophy of the college reflects a belief that a quality legal education is enhanced through having a heterogeneous student body. The committee, therefore, also considers race, cultural background, unusual personal circumstances, and age. Admission decisions are made on a rolling basis. The College of Law has also instituted a binding Early Decision Program. Students interested in applying through the Early Decision Program must have a completed application on file by December 1. The college is committed to enrolling a diverse and engaging class each year.

Student Activities

The College of Law offers numerous opportunities for students to sharpen their legal writing, advocacy, and leadership skills. The *University of Cincinnati Law Review* was founded in 1927 and was the first law review published by an Ohio law school. The Urban Morgan Institute for Human Rights edits the *Human Rights Quarterly*, the leading international human rights journal in the world. The *Immigration and Nationality Law Review* is an annual publication of papers on the subjects of immigration and citizenship. The *Freedom Center Journal*, a collaboration between the law school and the National Underground Railroad Freedom Center, offers opportunities to publish scholarly works about cutting-edge issues of today, informed by the legacy of historic struggles for freedom. The College of Law also offers a well-respected Moot Court Program with teams participating in many national competitions. The college hosts the Rendigs National Products Liability Moot Court Competition each spring.

Expenses and Financial Aid

For the 2009–2010 academic year, resident and nonresident tuition and fees are $19,942 and $34,776, respectively. Residents of northern Kentucky pay a special annual rate of $20,182. Nonresidents can reclassify as state residents by becoming independent and self-sustaining for their first year in law school. Cincinnati is a cosmopolitan yet affordable Midwestern city with living expenses estimated at $16,446 for the nine-month academic year. Cincinnati was recently ranked the fifth least expensive city in the nation in which to live. Scholarships are awarded to approximately 65 percent of the student body in order to attract an academically talented and diverse student body. The FAFSA should be filed by March 1 as a priority deadline in order to qualify for student loan packages by spring. A large percentage of second- and third-year students work with law firms, companies, and agencies in the Greater Cincinnati area to offset living expenses or student loan debt.

Placement

The College of Law maintains an active Center for Professional Development with a staff of three attorneys, creating one of the best staff-to-law student ratios in the country. The 2009 Ohio bar passage rate among UC students was 91 percent for first-time takers. Each year, we promote hundreds of full-time, summer, and part-time job opportunities for our students' consideration. For our class of 2008, 95 percent of those in the job market were either employed or enrolled in a full-time degree program within nine months of graduation. For those entering private practice, the average starting salary was $94,750 with a maximum of $160,000. Graduates of the class of 2008 were employed in 33 cities, 17 states, and the District of Columbia.

Applicant Profile

University of Cincinnati College of Law
This grid includes only applicants who earned 120–180 LSAT scores under standard administrations.

LSAT Score	3.75 +		3.50–3.74		3.25–3.49		3.00–3.24		2.75–2.99		2.50–2.74		2.25–2.49		2.00–2.24		Below 2.00		No GPA		Total	
	Apps	Adm	Apps	Adm	Apps	Adm	Apps	Adm	Apps	Adm	Apps	Adm	Apps	Adm	Apps	Adm	Apps	Adm	Apps	Adm	Apps	Adm
175–180	2	1	0	0	0	0	0	0	0	0	0	0	0	0	0	0	0	0	0	0	2	1
170–174	6	5	4	4	4	4	3	3	4	4	1	1	1	0	1	0	0	0	0	0	24	21
165–169	27	27	24	22	15	15	16	16	14	11	4	4	3	2	3	0	0	0	0	0	106	97
160–164	89	87	91	86	67	63	36	32	12	6	12	3	5	2	2	0	0	0	3	3	317	282
155–159	91	87	100	59	74	18	55	14	25	5	11	2	2	0	3	0	1	0	9	6	371	191
150–154	47	31	67	13	70	10	46	7	17	2	5	0	7	0	2	0	1	0	6	0	268	63
145–149	16	5	22	0	30	3	22	1	12	0	9	1	8	0	1	0	1	0	0	0	121	10
140–144	3	1	5	0	11	0	15	0	19	0	9	0	3	0	3	0	0	0	4	0	72	1
135–139	1	0	0	0	4	0	4	0	5	0	5	0	1	0	2	0	1	0	3	0	26	0
130–134	1	0	1	0	2	0	0	0	3	0	2	0	0	0	1	0	0	0	1	0	11	0
125–129	0	0	0	0	0	0	0	0	0	0	0	0	0	0	0	0	0	0	0	0	0	0
120–124	0	0	0	0	0	0	0	0	0	0	0	0	0	0	0	0	0	0	0	0	0	0
Total	283	244	314	184	277	113	197	73	111	28	58	11	30	4	18	0	4	0	26	9	1318	666

Apps = Number of Applicants
Adm = Number Admitted
Reflects 99% of the total applicant pool; average LSAT data reported.

City University of New York School of Law

65-21 Main Street
Flushing, NY 11367
Phone: 718.340.4210; Fax: 718.340.4435
E-mail: admissions@mail.law.cuny.edu; Website: www.law.cuny.edu

ABA
Approved
Since
1985

The Basics

Type of school	Public
Term	Semester
Application deadline	3/15
Application fee	$50
Financial aid deadline	5/3
Can first year start other than fall?	No
Student to faculty ratio	10.4 to 1
# of housing spaces available restricted to law students	
graduate housing for which law students are eligible	506

Faculty and Administrators

	Total		Men		Women		Minorities	
	Spr	Fall	Spr	Fall	Spr	Fall	Spr	Fall
Full-time	30	32	13	14	17	18	9	10
Other full-time	5	6	1	1	4	5	2	3
Deans, librarians, & others who teach	8	8	2	2	6	6	4	4
Part-time	12	10	6	4	6	6	3	4
Total	55	56	22	21	33	35	18	21

Curriculum

		Full-Time	Part-Time
Typical first-year section size		80	0
Is there typically a "small section" of the first-year class, other than Legal Writing, taught by full-time faculty		Yes	No
If yes, typical size offered last year		20	
# of classroom course titles beyond first-year curriculum		55	
# of upper division courses, excluding seminars, with an enrollment:	Under 25	34	
	25–49	16	
	50–74	5	
	75–99	1	
	100+	2	
# of seminars		27	
# of seminar positions available		557	
# of seminar positions filled		500	0
# of positions available in simulation courses		704	
# of simulation positions filled		641	0
# of positions available in faculty supervised clinical courses		204	
# of faculty supervised clinical positions filled		139	0
# involved in field placements		37	0
# involved in law journals		44	0
# involved in moot court or trial competitions		46	0
# of credit hours required to graduate		91	

JD Enrollment and Ethnicity

	Men		Women		Full-Time		Part-Time		1st-Year		Total		JD Degs. Awd.
	#	%	#	%	#	%	#	%	#	%	#	%	
African Amer.	12	7.9	21	8.3	33	8.1	0	0.0	16	9.7	33	8.1	8
Amer. Indian	0	0.0	0	0.0	0	0.0	0	0.0	0	0.0	0	0.0	0
Asian Amer.	16	10.5	27	10.6	43	10.6	0	0.0	14	8.5	43	10.6	23
Mex. Amer.	2	1.3	1	0.4	3	0.7	0	0.0	1	0.6	3	0.7	1
Puerto Rican	4	2.6	5	2.0	9	2.2	0	0.0	5	3.0	9	2.2	0
Hispanic	16	10.5	21	8.3	37	9.1	0	0.0	17	10.3	37	9.1	6
Total Minority	50	32.9	75	29.5	125	30.8	0	0.0	53	32.1	125	30.8	38
For. Nation.	0	0.0	4	1.6	4	1.0	0	0.0	0	0.0	4	1.0	3
Caucasian	89	58.6	161	63.4	250	61.6	0	0.0	101	61.2	250	61.6	74
Unknown	13	8.6	14	5.5	27	6.7	0	0.0	11	6.7	27	6.7	6
Total	152	37.4	254	62.6	406	100.0	0	0.0	165	40.6	406		121

Transfers

Transfers in	2
Transfers out	4

Tuition and Fees

	Resident	Nonresident
Full-time	$10,612	$16,512
Part-time	$370	$620
Tuition Guarantee Program	N	

Living Expenses

Estimated living expenses for singles

Living on campus	Living off campus	Living at home
N/A	$15,743	$6,072

City University of New York School of Law

ABA
Approved
Since
1985

GPA and LSAT Scores

	Total	Full-Time	Part-Time
# of apps	2,165	2,165	0
# of offers	575	575	0
# of matrics	158	158	0
75% GPA	3.54	3.54	0.00
Median GPA	3.31	3.31	0.00
25% GPA	3.10	3.10	0.00
75% LSAT	156	156	0
Median LSAT	153	153	0
25% LSAT	151	151	0

Grants and Scholarships (from prior year)

	Total #	Total %	Full-Time #	Full-Time %	Part-Time #	Part-Time %
Total # of students	387		385		2	
Total # receiving grants	114	29.5	114	29.6	0	0.0
Less than 1/2 tuition	63	16.3	63	16.4	0	0.0
Half to full tuition	0	0.0	0	0.0	0	0.0
Full tuition	51	13.2	51	13.2	0	0.0
More than full tuition	0	0.0	0	0.0	0	0.0
Median grant amount			$2,362		$0	

Informational and Library Resources

Total amount spent on library materials	$700,290
Study seating capacity inside the library	223
# of full-time equivalent professional librarians	7.0
Hours per week library is open	61
# of open, wired connections available to students	62
# of networked computers available for use by students	113
Has wireless network?	Y
Require computer?	N

JD Attrition (from prior year)

	Academic #	Other #	Total #	Total %
1st year	10	6	16	11.8
2nd year	0	8	8	6.3
3rd year	0	0	0	0.0
4th year	0	0	0	0.0

Employment (9 months after graduation)

	Total	Percentage
Employment status known	119	90.2
Employment status unknown	13	9.8
Employed	101	84.9
Pursuing graduate degrees	2	1.7
Unemployed (seeking, not seeking, or studying for the bar)	14	11.8
Type of Employment		
# employed in law firms	22	21.8
# employed in business and industry	7	6.9
# employed in government	17	16.8
# employed in public interest	35	34.7
# employed as judicial clerks	18	17.8
# employed in academia	2	2.0
Geographic Location		
# employed in state	64	63.4
# employed in foreign countries	0	0.0
# of states where employed	15	

Bar Passage Rates

First-time takers	129	Reporting %	82.95
Average school %	84.11	Average state %	88.98
Average pass difference	−4.87		

Jurisdiction	Takers	Passers	Pass %	State %	Diff %
New York	107	90	84.11	88.98	−4.87

City University of New York School of Law

65-21 Main Street
Flushing, NY 11367
Phone: 718.340.4210; Fax: 718.340.4435
E-mail: admissions@mail.law.cuny.edu; Website: www.law.cuny.edu

■ Mission

Following its motto of "Law in the Service of Human Needs," the mission of the City University of New York (CUNY) School of Law is to train excellent public interest lawyers through a curriculum that integrates doctrine, legal theory, clinical education, and professional responsibility.

■ Academic Program

CUNY Law's unique and integrated curriculum has made it a national leader in progressive legal education heralded by the Carnegie Foundation for the Advancement of Teaching. The curriculum engages students in a thoughtful combination of rigorous coursework in traditional substantive areas and a lawyering program that teaches the skills recognized by the American Bar Association as necessary for competent practice (problem solving, legal analysis and reasoning, legal research, factual investigation, and communication—including legal writing and oral argument, counseling, negotiation, litigation and alternative dispute resolution procedures, organization and management of legal work, and recognition and resolution of ethical dilemmas). All first-year students take a required two-semester Lawyering Seminar where they focus on the fundamental skills of legal analysis and legal writing and engage in simulations requiring a wide range of lawyering tasks: they draft documents, interview and counsel clients, engage in negotiations, and make arguments before trial and appellate courts. Faculty guidance, supervision, and feedback permeate the process. In the second year, each student elects a four-credit Lawyering Seminar focused on developing more advanced lawyering skills in a subject matter area of his or her choice, including trial practice, mediation, labor, and appellate advocacy. Nineteen CUNY law students were offered Revson Fellowships in the summer 2009. Excellent and comprehensive academic support is provided by the Irene Diamond Professional Skills Center.

■ Clinical Programs

Clinical Programs include Community Economic Development, Criminal Defense, Elder Law, Equality, Health Law, Immigrant and Refugee Rights, International Women's Human Rights, and Mediation. Following Lawyering Seminars in the first two years, all students have opportunities to participate in 12- to 16-credit clinical courses in their third year. Students engage in individual representation of clients and work on projects in collaboration with community groups, organizers, and international organizations to address issues of social justice. Recent work includes legal victories in low-wage labor campaigns, amicus briefs to International Tribunals, community education projects throughout New York, and interdisciplinary representation of clients who have suffered trauma from torture and domestic abuse.

■ Diversity

The diversity of New York City is reflected in our dynamic student body and faculty. Women constitute 63 percent of the student body; minorities, 31 percent. Faculty percentages are similar: 65 percent are women and 37 percent are people of color. The concern for diversity is also threaded through the curriculum; for example, a required course for all first-year students is Liberty, Equality, and Due Process, which examines issues of racial and gender equality and sexual orientation in the context of legal and historical analysis.

■ Student Life

Despite the relatively small size of the law school, numerous student organizations thrive on campus. Students also have a major role in the law school's governance, recognizing and preparing them for their future as professionals and community leaders. One exemplary student program is the Mississippi Project that, since 1992, has sent a delegation of law students to Mississippi over midyear break to work with lawyers in civil rights organizations across the state. CUNY students work and learn together in an exceptionally collaborative, noncompetitive atmosphere and interact on a first-name basis with the faculty. The student experience is further enriched by New York City's cultural offerings and by the exceptional resources of the third-largest university system in the country, CUNY.

■ Faculty

Most of the faculty have themselves been public interest practitioners, with experience in a wide area of issues, including employment discrimination, immigration, racial justice, environmental law, women's rights, labor, and international law. They have worked in China, Haiti, South Africa, Mongolia, Costa Rica, the Middle East, Russia, Papua New Guinea, Australia, Central America, the Philippines, and many other countries. Their prestigious awards include Fulbright, Ford, MacArthur, Revson, Rockefeller, and National Endowment for the Humanities fellowships. Their scholarship reflects their interest in, among other areas, international human rights and access to justice for underserved communities.

■ Career Opportunities

CUNY law graduates are employed in the full range of public interest jobs—legal services and public defender organizations, government agencies, international human rights organizations, not-for-profits, and the judiciary. Approximately 85 percent of alumni/ae secure positions within eight months of graduation. Historically, 60–65 percent of graduates enter the public interest/public service profession each year, while 25–30 percent are employed at private firms from large to small and solo community-based practices. CUNY law graduates are consistently awarded judicial clerkships and prestigious public interest postgraduate fellowships that include the Equal Justice Works, Skadden, Soros, Echoing Green, Independence Foundation, and the Georgetown University Law Center fellowships. Although the vast majority are employed in the mid-Atlantic states, CUNY graduates can be found throughout the United States and abroad where they are engaged in international human rights work.

City University of New York School of Law

Child Care

The law school offers an on-site Children's Center, which provides high-quality, reasonably priced all-day care for children (three months through five years) of students, faculty, and staff. The Center provides an age-appropriate curriculum based on the National Association for the Education of Young Children (NAEYC) standards. The Center enables parents to pursue their education and further their career while fulfilling their responsibility to their children.

Special Opportunities

The law school offers a number of unique programs and initiatives that enrich the experience of students and provide continuing support for graduates. The Haywood Burns Chair in Civil Rights is a visiting faculty position, which allows distinguished faculty, practitioners, and jurists—for 2009–2010, Professor Dean Spade from Seattle University School of Law—to share their experience and knowledge of civil and human rights. The Community Legal Resource Network provides resources and supports graduates working in solo or small-firm practices in underserved communities.

Students in CUNY Immigrant Initiatives expand their knowledge of issues facing immigrant communities and provide direct service in a variety of areas. A new curricular initiative, the Worker Employment Labor Program, is designed to develop legal skills in representing workers in diverse settings. Finally, the law school is part of a rich university, the City University of New York, and law students may take some interdisciplinary graduate courses with the approval of the Academic Dean.

Nontraditional Students

The law school's student profile includes many individuals returning to school after careers, and many who possess advanced degrees. The average age of the student body is 27; some students enter directly from undergraduate school while others are older, making the law school a comfortable environment.

Affordable Tuition

CUNY offers an excellent legal education at substantially less than half the cost of most private law schools.

Applicant Profile

City University of New York School of Law
This grid includes only applicants who earned 120–180 LSAT scores under standard administrations.

LSAT Score	3.75 +		3.50–3.74		3.25–3.49		3.00–3.24		2.75–2.99		2.50–2.74		2.25–2.49		2.00–2.24		Below 2.00		No GPA		Total	
	Apps	Adm	Apps	Adm	Apps	Adm	Apps	Adm	Apps	Adm	Apps	Adm	Apps	Adm	Apps	Adm	Apps	Adm	Apps	Adm	Apps	Adm
175–180	0	0	0	0	0	0	0	0	0	0	1	1	0	0	0	0	0	0	0	0	1	1
170–174	2	2	1	1	2	2	0	0	0	0	1	0	0	0	0	0	0	0	0	0	6	5
165–169	3	2	10	9	3	1	7	7	2	2	1	0	0	0	0	0	0	0	2	2	28	23
160–164	20	17	20	15	26	16	14	6	18	9	6	3	9	1	2	1	0	0	3	1	118	69
155–159	26	22	46	37	53	37	64	32	44	17	22	3	16	4	6	0	2	0	5	1	284	153
150–154	46	30	83	52	137	78	130	62	75	15	41	6	32	2	14	0	2	0	15	3	575	248
145–149	27	3	78	12	117	23	125	16	101	5	66	2	28	0	11	0	2	1	28	1	583	63
140–144	10	0	49	2	66	0	76	4	83	0	53	1	45	0	12	0	4	0	23	0	421	7
135–139	5	0	16	0	28	0	19	0	27	0	29	0	21	0	14	0	4	0	5	0	168	0
130–134	0	0	1	0	7	0	6	0	7	0	6	0	9	0	4	0	2	0	4	0	46	0
125–129	0	0	1	0	1	0	2	0	2	0	0	0	0	0	0	0	0	0	0	0	6	0
120–124	0	0	0	0	0	0	0	0	0	0	0	0	0	0	0	0	0	0	0	0	0	0
Total	139	76	305	128	440	157	443	127	359	48	226	16	160	7	63	1	16	1	85	8	2236	569

Apps = Number of Applicants
Adm = Number Admitted
Reflects 99% of the total applicant pool; average LSAT data reported.

Cleveland State University—Cleveland-Marshall College of Law

Office of Law Admissions, 1801 Euclid Avenue, LB 138
Cleveland, OH 44115-2214
Phone: 216.687.2304, toll-free 866.687.2304; Fax: 216.687.6881
E-mail: admissions@law.csuohio.edu; Website: www.law.csuohio.edu

ABA
Approved
Since
1957

The Basics

Type of school	Public
Term	Semester
Application deadline	5/1
Application fee	$0
Financial aid deadline	5/1
Can first year start other than fall?	No
Student to faculty ratio	13.2 to 1
# of housing spaces available restricted to law students	
graduate housing for which law students are eligible	25

Faculty and Administrators

	Total		Men		Women		Minorities	
	Spr	Fall	Spr	Fall	Spr	Fall	Spr	Fall
Full-time	37	37	20	20	17	17	6	6
Other full-time	0	0	0	0	0	0	0	0
Deans, librarians, & others who teach	6	6	2	2	4	4	1	1
Part-time	37	34	27	24	10	10	2	4
Total	80	77	49	46	31	31	9	11

Curriculum

		Full-Time	Part-Time
Typical first-year section size		52	38
Is there typically a "small section" of the first-year class, other than Legal Writing, taught by full-time faculty		No	No
If yes, typical size offered last year			
# of classroom course titles beyond first-year curriculum		95	
# of upper division courses, excluding seminars, with an enrollment:	Under 25	87	
	25–49	36	
	50–74	11	
	75–99	1	
	100+	0	
# of seminars		13	
# of seminar positions available		195	
# of seminar positions filled		73	44
# of positions available in simulation courses		150	
# of simulation positions filled		99	49
# of positions available in faculty supervised clinical courses		90	
# of faculty supervised clinical positions filled		60	15
# involved in field placements		44	7
# involved in law journals		62	11
# involved in moot court or trial competitions		24	9
# of credit hours required to graduate		90	

JD Enrollment and Ethnicity

	Men		Women		Full-Time		Part-Time		1st-Year		Total		JD Degs. Awd.
	#	%	#	%	#	%	#	%	#	%	#	%	
African Amer.	26	7.0	30	11.3	33	6.8	23	14.6	25	12.4	56	8.8	12
Amer. Indian	1	0.3	1	0.4	2	0.4	0	0.0	1	0.5	2	0.3	1
Asian Amer.	7	1.9	11	4.2	12	2.5	6	3.8	2	1.0	18	2.8	6
Mex. Amer.	0	0.0	0	0.0	0	0.0	0	0.0	0	0.0	0	0.0	0
Puerto Rican	0	0.0	2	0.8	2	0.4	0	0.0	2	1.0	2	0.3	0
Hispanic	6	1.6	9	3.4	11	2.3	4	2.5	3	1.5	15	2.3	3
Total Minority	40	10.7	53	20.0	60	12.4	33	21.0	33	16.4	93	14.6	22
For. Nation.	4	1.1	2	0.8	6	1.2	0	0.0	0	0.0	6	0.9	2
Caucasian	327	87.4	209	78.9	413	85.7	123	78.3	168	83.6	536	83.9	176
Unknown	3	0.8	1	0.4	3	0.6	1	0.6	0	0.0	4	0.6	1
Total	374	58.5	265	41.5	482	75.4	157	24.6	201	31.5	639		201

Transfers

Transfers in	5
Transfers out	5

Tuition and Fees

	Resident	Nonresident
Full-time	$16,764	$22,996
Part-time	$12,895	$17,689
Tuition Guarantee Program	N	

Living Expenses

Estimated living expenses for singles

Living on campus	Living off campus	Living at home
$18,800	$18,800	$18,800

Cleveland State University—Cleveland-Marshall College of Law

ABA
Approved
Since
1957

GPA and LSAT Scores

	Total	Full-Time	Part-Time
# of apps	0	1,513	309
# of offers	622	543	79
# of matrics	203	158	45
75% GPA	3.64	3.68	3.59
Median GPA	3.44	3.46	3.44
25% GPA	3.19	3.19	3.25
75% LSAT	158	158	158
Median LSAT	156	156	155
25% LSAT	153	153	151

Grants and Scholarships (from prior year)

	Total		Full-Time		Part-Time	
	#	%	#	%	#	%
Total # of students	666		481		185	
Total # receiving grants	249	37.4	219	45.5	30	16.2
Less than 1/2 tuition	148	22.2	132	27.4	16	8.6
Half to full tuition	59	8.9	50	10.4	9	4.9
Full tuition	42	6.3	37	7.7	5	2.7
More than full tuition	0	0.0	0	0.0	0	0.0
Median grant amount			$4,070		$1,805	

Informational and Library Resources

Total amount spent on library materials	$902,622
Study seating capacity inside the library	493
# of full-time equivalent professional librarians	8.0
Hours per week library is open	95
# of open, wired connections available to students	183
# of networked computers available for use by students	121
Has wireless network?	Y
Require computer?	N

JD Attrition (from prior year)

	Academic	Other	Total	
	#	#	#	%
1st year	18	18	36	17.3
2nd year	0	1	1	0.5
3rd year	1	0	1	0.5
4th year	0	0	0	0.0

Employment (9 months after graduation)

	Total	Percentage
Employment status known	200	97.6
Employment status unknown	5	2.4
Employed	179	89.5
Pursuing graduate degrees	2	1.0
Unemployed (seeking, not seeking, or studying for the bar)	14	7.0
Type of Employment		
# employed in law firms	95	53.1
# employed in business and industry	42	23.5
# employed in government	22	12.3
# employed in public interest	5	2.8
# employed as judicial clerks	9	5.0
# employed in academia	6	3.4
Geographic Location		
# employed in state	159	88.8
# employed in foreign countries	1	0.6
# of states where employed	15	

Bar Passage Rates

First-time takers	187	Reporting %	88.24
Average school %	90.30	Average state %	88.09
Average pass difference	2.21		

Jurisdiction	Takers	Passers	Pass %	State %	Diff %
Ohio	165	149	90.30	88.09	2.21

Cleveland State University—Cleveland-Marshall College of Law

Office of Law Admissions, 1801 Euclid Avenue, LB 138
Cleveland, OH 44115-2214
Phone: 216.687.2304, toll-free 866.687.2304; Fax: 216.687.6881
E-mail: admissions@law.csuohio.edu; Website: www.law.csuohio.edu

■ Introduction

Founded in 1897, Cleveland-Marshall College of Law was the first law school in Ohio to admit women and one of the first to admit minorities. Becoming part of Cleveland State University in 1969, the law school has maintained its long-standing reputation for educating some of the region's outstanding leaders of the bench and bar, heads of law firms and corporations, and distinguished public servants. C|M|Law continues to enhance its national reputation and influence with its law lecture series and visiting scholars program, through outreach efforts with its National Advisory Council, and through the law school's recruiting activities. The college receives applications from prospective students from over 450 different colleges and universities. Tuition for Ohio residents is among the lowest in the state and tuition for non-Ohio residents is the lowest in the state.

C|M|Law offers full-time and part-time (day and evening) programs. After completing the program selected for the first year of law school, a student may switch programs according to his or her scheduling needs. The student body is diverse in many ways. Approximately half of the students are female, roughly 15–20 percent of each entering class is likely to be over the age of 30, and many students have had careers in other fields or earned advanced degrees before beginning the study of law. The college's pro bono, extracurricular, and cocurricular activities help to round out the richness of experience gained by studying law at C|M|Law.

■ Location

C|M|Law is located on the university's urban campus in downtown Cleveland. In early 2008, the law school was newly renovated with an updated Moot Court Room, a new three-tiered glass entrance, and new spaces for our clinics, student organizations, and faculty conferences. Students at C|M|Law enjoy all that the city has to offer, including the Cleveland Museums of Art and Contemporary Art, the world-renowned Cleveland Orchestra, the Botanical Garden, Playhouse Square, the House of Blues, and professional sports teams. On the North Coast Harbor sit the Great Lakes Science Center, and the Rock and Roll Hall of Fame and Museum. The law school is in close proximity to the federal, state, and county courthouses. Cleveland is also the headquarters for many large corporations and law firms.

■ The Curriculum

The urban setting of the college brings challenging legal experiences to students. Clinical programs include the law and public policy, employment law, urban development law, fair housing, environmental law, and community health advocacy law clinics that offer students academic credit for serving clients in a variety of areas. Externship programs include the Judicial Externship Program in which students work with state appellate and federal court judges; the Public Interest Externship Program designed to offer experiences in office settings such as the county prosecutor and public defender, the bankruptcy trustee, the Office of Immigration and Customs Enforcement, and the US Attorney (civil and criminal); and the

Independent Externship Program where students may propose a placement in a public service office. By completing core and elective courses in their chosen areas, students may undertake a concentration in five areas: business law, civil litigation and dispute resolution, criminal law, employment and labor law, and international and comparative law. C|M|Law has a newly established Center for Health Law and Policy.

■ Joint-Degree Programs and Graduate Program

Five joint-degree programs are offered: the *JD/MPA* (Master of Public Administration); the *JD/MUPDD* (Master of Urban Planning, Design, and Development); the *JD/MBA* (Master of Business Administration); the *JD/MAES* (Master of Arts in Environmental Studies); and the *JD/MSES* (Master of Science in Environmental Science). The law school also offers a graduate *LLM* degree.

■ Pro Bono Program

The Pro Bono Program at C|M|Law offers a variety of community service opportunities. Popular placements include teaching practical law in public high schools, assisting with the legal needs of women recently released from incarceration, or addressing the concerns of the poor by delivering legal assistance in cooperation with local attorneys and community agencies.

■ Admission

While admission to Cleveland-Marshall is competitive, it need not be intimidating. The admissions committee reviews all applications with care and sensitivity, taking into consideration academic performance, LSAT scores, work and life experience, and readiness for the rigors of legal education. We are committed to enrolling academically talented and diverse students. In doing so, we recognize and embrace that academic talent and diversity can be identified in many interesting and exciting ways. Undergraduate grades and LSAT results are the most significant factors in our admission decision; however, an applicant's personal statement, letters of recommendation, and overall strength of the file are factors also strongly considered in the admission process. Criteria for admission are identical for full- and part-time applicants.

■ The Legal Career Opportunities Program

The Legal Career Opportunities Program (LCOP) invites applications from individuals who demonstrate the ability to succeed in law school but have encountered life circumstances or other adversities that have affected their traditional academic indicators, such as LSAT scores and/or undergraduate grades. In most cases, applicants to the LCOP program have academic indicators that are a bit lower than those of regularly admitted applicants; however, LCOP applicants demonstrate through their career and professional accomplishments, personal statements, letters of recommendation, graduate work, and/or significantly improved academic performance over a period of time, their likelihood for success in law school. LCOP is not a provisional program. Being admitted through the program is acceptance to law school. Students admitted through LCOP

are required to enroll in a course during the summer prior to the beginning of their first year.

■ Scholarships, Financial Aid, and Loan Repayment Assistance

Applicants are considered for scholarships when their files are reviewed. There is no separate application process. Scholarships range from $2,000 a year to full in-state tuition. Our financial aid program utilizes combinations of scholarships, fellowships, work-study employment, and loans. C|M|Law has a loan repayment assistance program (LRAP) to help support students choosing to work in public service jobs upon graduation.

■ Library and Technology

The C|M|Law library is one of the 15 largest academic law libraries in the country, with 85,000 net square feet housing more than 500,000 volumes. At C|M|Law, students have access to online research services, a computer lab, group study rooms, a bibliographic instruction room, and a media center. Students study in the four-story, light-filled atrium where there are over 200 student carrels with built-in power and network ports for portable computers. Cutting-edge technology is used in classrooms and our moot courtroom, and a state-of-the-art wireless network allows use of personal computers throughout the campus. C|M|Law has been recognized for its use and support of technology by the *National Jurist* magazine and the American Association of Law Libraries.

■ Career Services

Cleveland, the largest legal market between New York City and Chicago, is home to more than 300 law firms. The location of the college enables students to access these firms for law clerk positions easily. Likewise, the federal and state courts nearby provide an external classroom for judicial externships.

The Office of Career Planning (OCP) invites many practicing attorneys to participate in programs and presentations. Many times these attorneys are alumni in the area, but often they are from firms desiring to help students professionally. The OCP staff offers over 20 programs per year providing a base of knowledge about legal and professional careers. The programs range from interview techniques and judicial clerkship seminars to practice-specific areas such as intellectual property, employment law, and health care law. The OCP posts over 1,500 permanent and law clerk jobs per year. Counseling and career guidance is provided by experienced staff members with JDs and counseling experience.

Programs and materials are easily accessible for both full- and part-time students. Handbooks and pamphlets are available to students in hard copy and many are also on the Web.

■ Housing and Student Life

C|M|Law students live in convenient and affordable housing throughout the city and surrounding suburbs. In addition, the University offers on-campus housing and meal plans. On-campus housing information is available from the Cleveland State University Department of Residence Life at 216.687.5196 or online at *www.csuohio.edu/reslife/*. The law school's Office of Admissions maintains a roommate referral list and is available to assist students in locating off-campus housing.

The university's brand-new $29 million recreation center connects to the Physical Education Building, which houses Woodling Gym and Busbey Natatorium—providing direct access to the university's Olympic-size swimming pool. The state-of-the-art facility has basketball, racquetball, and squash courts; weight training and fitness areas; an indoor jogging track; locker rooms; multipurpose rooms; and a parking facility.

Applicant Profile

Cleveland State University—Cleveland-Marshall College of Law

LSAT Score	GPA																
	3.75 +		3.50–3.74		3.25–3.49		3.00–3.24		2.75–2.99		2.50–2.74		Below 2.50		No GPA		Total
	Apps	Adm	Apps	Adm	Apps	Adm	Apps	Adm	Apps	Adm	Apps	Adm	Apps	Adm	Apps	Adm	Apps	Adm
170–180	0	0	4	4	0	0	1	1	1	1	0	0	1	0	0	0	7	6
165–169	5	4	5	3	8	7	5	5	2	2	1	0	1	1	1	0	28	22
160–164	19	16	25	20	17	13	11	8	15	10	7	4	13	5	5	2	112	78
155–159	39	32	65	60	54	39	50	41	27	16	20	10	16	2	5	1	276	201
150–154	52	38	88	65	111	65	106	43	65	18	36	10	44	4	13	2	515	245
145–149	36	7	71	11	80	10	105	9	65	1	51	3	43	1	9	1	460	43
140–144	5	1	37	5	64	7	55	3	54	5	43	1	36	3	16	1	310	26
Below 140	5	0	16	1	27	2	41	0	45	1	43	1	45	0	15	0	237	5
Total	161	98	311	169	361	143	374	110	274	54	201	29	199	16	64	7	1945	626

Apps = Number of Applicants
Adm = Number Admitted
Reflects 99% of the total applicant pool; average LSAT data reported.

University of Colorado Law School

Office of Admissions, UCB 403 - Wolf Law Building
Boulder, CO 80309-0403
Phone: 303.492.7203; Fax: 303.492.2542
E-mail: lawadmin@colorado.edu; Website: www.colorado.edu/law

ABA
Approved
Since
1923

The Basics

Type of school	Public
Term	Semester
Application deadline	11/15 3/15
Application fee	$65
Financial aid deadline	4/1
Can first year start other than fall?	No
Student to faculty ratio	11.5 to 1
# of housing spaces available restricted to law students graduate housing for which law students are eligible	547

Faculty and Administrators

	Total		Men		Women		Minorities	
	Spr	Fall	Spr	Fall	Spr	Fall	Spr	Fall
Full-time	35	41	21	24	14	17	4	9
Other full-time	2	2	1	1	1	1	0	0
Deans, librarians, & others who teach	6	6	4	3	2	3	2	2
Part-time	34	21	22	17	11	4	6	1
Total	77	70	48	45	28	25	12	12

Curriculum

	Full-Time	Part-Time
Typical first-year section size	84	0
Is there typically a "small section" of the first-year class, other than Legal Writing, taught by full-time faculty	Yes	No
If yes, typical size offered last year	39	
# of classroom course titles beyond first-year curriculum	105	

# of upper division courses, excluding seminars, with an enrollment:		
Under 25	85	
25–49	31	
50–74	13	
75–99	7	
100+	0	

# of seminars	19	
# of seminar positions available	243	
# of seminar positions filled	195	0
# of positions available in simulation courses	451	
# of simulation positions filled	348	0
# of positions available in faculty supervised clinical courses	126	
# of faculty supervised clinical positions filled	103	0
# involved in field placements	182	0
# involved in law journals	144	0
# involved in moot court or trial competitions	59	0
# of credit hours required to graduate	89	

JD Enrollment and Ethnicity

	Men		Women		Full-Time		Part-Time		1st-Year		Total		JD Degs. Awd.
	#	%	#	%	#	%	#	%	#	%	#	%	
African Amer.	8	2.9	7	2.6	15	2.7	0	0.0	7	4.2	15	2.7	10
Amer. Indian	11	4.0	6	2.2	17	3.1	0	0.0	5	3.0	17	3.1	3
Asian Amer.	9	3.3	30	11.0	39	7.1	0	0.0	14	8.5	39	7.1	13
Mex. Amer.	4	1.5	6	2.2	10	1.8	0	0.0	6	3.6	10	1.8	5
Puerto Rican	4	1.5	1	0.4	5	0.9	0	0.0	4	2.4	5	0.9	0
Hispanic	11	4.0	14	5.1	25	4.6	0	0.0	11	6.7	25	4.6	9
Total Minority	47	17.2	64	23.4	111	20.3	0	0.0	47	28.5	111	20.3	40
For. Nation.	1	0.4	2	0.7	3	0.5	0	0.0	1	0.6	3	0.5	0
Caucasian	226	82.5	207	75.8	433	79.2	0	0.0	117	70.9	433	79.2	126
Unknown	0	0.0	0	0.0	0	0.0	0	0.0	0	0.0	0	0.0	0
Total	274	50.1	273	49.9	547	100.0	0	0.0	165	30.2	547		166

Transfers

Transfers in	16
Transfers out	1

Tuition and Fees

	Resident	Nonresident
Full-time	$25,399	$33,463
Part-time		
Tuition Guarantee Program		Y

Living Expenses

Estimated living expenses for singles

Living on campus	Living off campus	Living at home
$17,047	$14,925	$10,461

University of Colorado Law School

ABA Approved Since 1923

GPA and LSAT Scores

	Total	Full-Time	Part-Time
# of apps	3,059	3,059	0
# of offers	709	709	0
# of matrics	166	166	0
75% GPA	3.78	3.78	0.00
Median GPA	3.68	3.68	0.00
25% GPA	3.42	3.42	0.00
75% LSAT	165	165	0
Median LSAT	163	163	0
25% LSAT	160	160	0

Grants and Scholarships (from prior year)

	Total #	Total %	Full-Time #	Full-Time %	Part-Time #	Part-Time %
Total # of students	520		520		0	
Total # receiving grants	261	50.2	261	50.2	0	0.0
Less than 1/2 tuition	114	21.9	114	21.9	0	0.0
Half to full tuition	36	6.9	36	6.9	0	0.0
Full tuition	85	16.3	85	16.3	0	0.0
More than full tuition	26	5.0	26	5.0	0	0.0
Median grant amount			$9,838		$0	

Informational and Library Resources

Total amount spent on library materials	$1,411,712
Study seating capacity inside the library	444
# of full-time equivalent professional librarians	8.0
Hours per week library is open	104
# of open, wired connections available to students	81
# of networked computers available for use by students	78
Has wireless network?	Y
Require computer?	N

JD Attrition (from prior year)

	Academic #	Other #	Total #	Total %
1st year	0	0	0	0.0
2nd year	0	1	1	0.6
3rd year	0	0	0	0.0
4th year	0	0	0	0.0

Employment (9 months after graduation)

	Total	Percentage
Employment status known	165	96.5
Employment status unknown	6	3.5
Employed	153	92.7
Pursuing graduate degrees	1	0.6
Unemployed (seeking, not seeking, or studying for the bar)	2	1.2
Type of Employment		
# employed in law firms	60	39.2
# employed in business and industry	7	4.6
# employed in government	20	13.1
# employed in public interest	13	8.5
# employed as judicial clerks	36	23.5
# employed in academia	5	3.3
Geographic Location		
# employed in state	113	73.9
# employed in foreign countries	3	2.0
# of states where employed	8	

Bar Passage Rates

First-time takers	155	Reporting %	86.45
Average school %	93.28	Average state %	83.29
Average pass difference	9.99		

Jurisdiction	Takers	Passers	Pass %	State %	Diff %
Colorado	134	125	93.28	83.29	9.99

University of Colorado Law School

Office of Admissions, UCB 403 - Wolf Law Building
Boulder, CO 80309-0403
Phone: 303.492.7203; Fax: 303.492.2542
E-mail: lawadmin@colorado.edu; Website: www.colorado.edu/law

■ Introduction

Colorado Law, established in 1892, is located on the Boulder campus of the University of Colorado and lies at the foot of the Rocky Mountains. High admission standards, a relatively small student body, and a favorable faculty-to-student ratio assure a stimulating and challenging academic environment that encourages class participation and interaction with faculty. The school is a charter member of the AALS and is ABA approved.

■ Faculty

Faculty members have a demonstrated record of excellence in teaching, research, and public service. They include some of the nation's leading scholars on constitutional law, criminal law, dispute resolution, environmental law, evidence, family law, health law, international law, labor and employment, natural resources, securities, tax, and telecommunications law.

■ Physical Facilities and Library

The law school is housed in the 180,000-square-foot Wolf Law Building, located on the edge of the CU Boulder campus. The Wolf Law Building features state-of-the-art classrooms, two high-tech courtrooms, and the largest resource collection and most technologically advanced law library in the 12-state Rocky Mountain region. The Wolf Law Building is the first Gold-certified public law school building in the country under the standards of the US Green Building Council's Leadership in Energy and Environmental Design certification program.

The William A. Wise Law Library, the largest law library in the state, serves the students, staff, and faculty of Colorado Law, as well as the bench and bar. The library holds over half a million volumes and provides access to thousands of electronic journals and databases. Law students also have access to the resources of other university and college libraries in Colorado through a statewide delivery system. Students can connect laptops to the school's wireless network or use one of the 65 computers available in the library to perform online legal research.

■ Special Programs

In the Criminal Defense Clinic, students are taught basic criminal practice skills and represent clients in actual cases, from beginning to end, in municipal and county courts in Boulder County.

In the Civil Practice Clinic, students represent low-income clients in a variety of civil law settings, including family court and in front of administrative law judges. Students take the lead in all hearings and trials.

The Appellate Advocacy Clinic alternates annually between attorneys from the public defender's office and the attorney general's office. Each student, under direct supervision of an instructor, is responsible for completing an appellate brief and attending the oral argument in the Colorado Supreme Court or the Colorado Court of Appeals.

The Juvenile and Family Law Program (JFLP) provides students with opportunities to acquire specialized knowledge in the field; fosters collaboration between students, academics, and practitioners; and engages in interdisciplinary study and practice.

The American Indian Law Clinic provides students with faculty-supervised experience giving legal assistance in matters including tribal sovereignty, child welfare, preservation of tribal identity, employment discrimination, public benefits, preservation of Native lands, and more.

In the Entrepreneurial Law Clinic, students work with local entrepreneurs, providing transactional legal services for the formation and development of small businesses in Colorado.

The Technology Law and Policy Clinic gives students the opportunity to advocate in the public interest concerning technology issues in front of regulatory entities, courts, legislatures, and standard-setting bodies.

The Natural Resources Law Center has three major areas of activity: research and publication, legal education, and the distinguished visitors and fellows program. The Natural Resources Litigation Clinic involves students in representing public interest clients in environmental litigation related to federal public land protection.

The Byron R. White Center for the Study of American Constitutional Law furthers the study, teaching, and publication of constitutional law. The White Center hosts the annual Ira C. Rothgerber Constitutional Law Conference, which exposes students to analysis and debate of contemporary constitutional issues and supports research in constitutional law.

The Silicon Flatirons Center for Law, Technology, and Entrepreneurship's mission is to create an environment for analyzing the dynamic changes in the telecommunications marketplace and regulatory environment.

The Center for Energy and Environmental Security is an interdisciplinary research and policy center. It is designed to facilitate progress toward a global, sustainable energy future through the innovative use of laws, policies, quality information, and technology solutions.

The University of Colorado Law School has a partnership with the University of San Diego (USD) School of Law to give our students access to an extensive Summer Law Study Abroad program. They offer courses in seven locations: Barcelona, Dublin, Florence, London, Oxford, Paris, and Russia (Moscow/St. Petersburg).

■ Curriculum

Colorado Law offers a wide variety of coursework. With a limited number of additional hours, students can earn a certificate in tax, American Indian law, intellectual property and technology law, juvenile and family law, or environmental law.

The first-year curriculum is required of all students. During the second and third years, students may emphasize such areas of the law as natural resources, environmental law, criminal law, business, constitutional law, tax, public interest, American Indian law, litigation, intellectual property law, and jurisprudence. Established joint-degree programs are the JD/MBA, JD/MD, JD/MPA, JD/MST, JD/MURP, and a JD/MS or PhD in Environmental Science.

Students can broaden their international perspectives and understanding of law and law practice by participating in the JD/LLB dual-degree program with the University of Alberta

Faculty of Law. This dual-degree program enhances the ability of both law schools to prepare lawyers to practice in a global community.

■ Admission

Admission to Colorado Law is quite competitive. At a minimum, a bachelor's degree from an institution that is accredited by an agency recognized by the US Department of Education is required. The binding Early Decision application deadline is November 15; the regular application deadline is March 15. The LSAT and registration with LSAC's Credential Assembly Service are also required. Offers of admission are based on GPA and LSAT score, but these scores are considered in the context of the entire application. Substantial weight is accorded to special qualities such as leadership, character, diversity, and commitment to service. The school seeks to increase the ethnic, cultural, and other diversity of its student body. The earliest admission letters go out in December, and the class is filled on a rolling basis. Admission is possible from a waiting list. Colorado Law accepts a small number of transfer students in the fall semester only. Law students may seek visiting status in the fall or spring semester. Transfer/visitor admission criteria includes law school performance.

■ Financial Aid

Scholarships for incoming students are based on merit and financial need. Nonresident students qualify for lower resident tuition rates by maintaining domicile in Colorado for 12 consecutive months. Students may not be employed during their first year, but limited outside employment is compatible with second- and third-year schedules. Current students may apply for additional scholarships and awards for their second and third years. Students applying for financial aid should file the FAFSA as soon as possible after January 1 and before the priority deadline of April 1.

■ Student Activities

Over 35 student organizations invite participation in projects, programs, and social activities. The *University of Colorado Law Review*, *Journal on Telecommunications and High Technology Law*, and *Colorado Journal of International Environmental Law and Policy* are professional journals edited entirely by students. Students also participate in a number of moot court competitions and have won regional, national, and international recognition in these events.

■ Housing

For information about the university's family housing, call 303.492.6384. Most students live in apartments and houses in the surrounding community.

■ Career Development

Colorado Law students find satisfying careers after law school with the assistance of an energetic and dedicated staff in the Office of Career Development. The professional counselors advise students and alumni on decisions about career direction, professionalism, legal employers, and alternatives to traditional legal careers. Specifically, the office directly assists students in finding internships, externships, clerkships, and other job opportunities during and after law school. The office solicits employers nationwide to interview on campus and to hire students through off-campus programs. The office helped develop the Colorado Pledge to Diversity 1L Summer Clerkship Program.

Applicant Profile

University of Colorado Law School
This grid includes only applicants who earned 120–180 LSAT scores under standard administrations.

LSAT Score	GPA 3.75 +		3.50–3.74		3.25–3.49		3.00–3.24		2.75–2.99		2.50–2.74		2.25–2.49		2.00–2.24		Below 2.00		No GPA		Total	
	Apps	Adm	Apps	Adm	Apps	Adm	Apps	Adm	Apps	Adm	Apps	Adm	Apps	Adm	Apps	Adm	Apps	Adm	Apps	Adm	Apps	Adm
175–180	6	6	3	3	1	1	1	0	2	1	1	0	0	0	1	0	0	0	0	0	15	11
170–174	22	21	14	12	13	7	4	1	2	2	4	1	1	0	0	0	0	0	0	0	60	44
165–169	76	66	101	57	75	25	43	16	15	1	12	0	3	0	1	0	0	0	2	1	328	166
160–164	217	137	275	120	198	55	112	20	39	5	24	0	8	0	3	0	2	0	8	4	886	341
155–159	145	37	254	36	204	13	123	9	50	1	25	0	10	0	2	0	1	0	5	0	819	96
150–154	61	11	118	10	128	8	114	5	62	1	25	0	11	0	2	0	1	0	7	0	529	35
145–149	25	2	36	2	51	3	53	0	35	0	16	0	13	0	3	0	1	0	0	0	233	7
140–144	6	0	17	0	27	0	29	0	23	0	14	1	5	0	2	0	0	0	2	0	125	1
135–139	0	0	2	0	5	0	6	0	3	0	4	0	1	0	3	0	1	0	3	0	28	0
130–134	0	0	0	0	1	0	0	0	1	0	3	0	5	0	1	0	0	0	1	0	12	0
125–129	0	0	0	0	0	0	0	0	0	0	1	0	0	0	1	0	0	0	0	0	2	0
120–124	0	0	0	0	0	0	0	0	0	0	0	0	0	0	0	0	0	0	0	0	0	0
Total	558	280	820	240	703	112	485	51	232	11	129	2	57	0	19	0	6	0	28	5	3037	701

Apps = Number of Applicants   Adm = Number Admitted   Reflects 99% of the total applicant pool; average LSAT data reported.

Columbia University School of Law

435 West 116th Street
New York, NY 10027
Phone: 212.854.2670; Fax: 212.854.1109
E-mail: admissions@law.columbia.edu; Website: www.law.columbia.edu/admissions

ABA
Approved
Since
1923

The Basics

Type of school	Private
Term	Semester
Application deadline	11/15 2/15
Application fee	$75
Financial aid deadline	3/1
Can first year start other than fall?	No
Student to faculty ratio	10.1 to 1
# of housing spaces available restricted to law students	489
graduate housing for which law students are eligible	631

Faculty and Administrators

	Total		Men		Women		Minorities	
	Spr	Fall	Spr	Fall	Spr	Fall	Spr	Fall
Full-time	103	105	72	73	31	32	13	12
Other full-time	8	7	7	6	1	1	1	2
Deans, librarians, & others who teach	16	17	4	5	12	12	1	1
Part-time	134	92	100	63	34	28	15	6
Total	261	221	183	147	78	73	30	21

Curriculum

	Full-Time	Part-Time
Typical first-year section size	95	0
Is there typically a "small section" of the first-year class, other than Legal Writing, taught by full-time faculty	Yes	No
If yes, typical size offered last year	32	
# of classroom course titles beyond first-year curriculum	237	
# of upper division courses, excluding seminars, with an enrollment: Under 25	92	
25–49	37	
50–74	19	
75–99	15	
100+	17	
# of seminars	131	
# of seminar positions available	2,460	
# of seminar positions filled	1,845	0
# of positions available in simulation courses	429	
# of simulation positions filled	397	0
# of positions available in faculty supervised clinical courses	161	
# of faculty supervised clinical positions filled	161	0
# involved in field placements	160	0
# involved in law journals	641	0
# involved in moot court or trial competitions	79	0
# of credit hours required to graduate	83	

JD Enrollment and Ethnicity

	Men		Women		Full-Time		Part-Time		1st-Year		Total		JD Degs. Awd.
	#	%	#	%	#	%	#	%	#	%	#	%	
African Amer.	30	4.4	75	11.8	105	8.0	0	0.0	36	9.0	105	8.0	32
Amer. Indian	1	0.1	1	0.2	2	0.2	0	0.0	1	0.3	2	0.2	3
Asian Amer.	87	12.9	111	17.5	198	15.1	0	0.0	67	16.8	198	15.1	62
Mex. Amer.	19	2.8	18	2.8	37	2.8	0	0.0	17	4.3	37	2.8	14
Puerto Rican	8	1.2	11	1.7	19	1.5	0	0.0	3	0.8	19	1.5	8
Hispanic	8	1.2	7	1.1	15	1.1	0	0.0	4	1.0	15	1.1	10
Total Minority	153	22.7	223	35.1	376	28.7	0	0.0	128	32.2	376	28.7	129
For. Nation.	59	8.7	57	9.0	116	8.9	0	0.0	24	6.0	116	8.9	37
Caucasian	442	65.5	334	52.6	775	59.2	1	100.0	227	57.0	776	59.2	279
Unknown	21	3.1	21	3.3	42	3.2	0	0.0	19	4.8	42	3.2	8
Total	675	51.5	635	48.5	1309	99.9	1	0.1	398	30.4	1310		453

Transfers

Transfers in	79
Transfers out	7

Tuition and Fees

	Resident	Nonresident
Full-time	$48,004	$48,004
Part-time		
Tuition Guarantee Program		N

Living Expenses

Estimated living expenses for singles

Living on campus	Living off campus	Living at home
$21,265	$21,265	$5,580

Columbia University School of Law

ABA
Approved
Since
1923

GPA and LSAT Scores

	Total	Full-Time	Part-Time
# of apps	8,505	8,505	0
# of offers	1,235	1,235	0
# of matrics	400	400	0
75% GPA	3.81	3.81	0.00
Median GPA	3.72	3.72	0.00
25% GPA	3.60	3.60	0.00
75% LSAT	175	175	0
Median LSAT	172	172	0
25% LSAT	170	170	0

Grants and Scholarships (from prior year)

	Total		Full-Time		Part-Time	
	#	%	#	%	#	%
Total # of students	1,267		1,266		1	
Total # receiving grants	691	54.5	691	54.6	0	0.0
Less than 1/2 tuition	518	40.9	518	40.9	0	0.0
Half to full tuition	115	9.1	115	9.1	0	0.0
Full tuition	31	2.4	31	2.4	0	0.0
More than full tuition	27	2.1	27	2.1	0	0.0
Median grant amount			$10,250		$0	

Informational and Library Resources

Total amount spent on library materials	$2,414,258
Study seating capacity inside the library	369
# of full-time equivalent professional librarians	19
Hours per week library is open	102
# of open, wired connections available to students	3,028
# of networked computers available for use by students	135
Has wireless network?	Y
Require computer?	N

JD Attrition (from prior year)

	Academic	Other	Total	
	#	#	#	%
1st year	0	1	1	0.3
2nd year	0	6	6	1.4
3rd year	0	0	0	0.0
4th year	0	0	0	0.0

Employment (9 months after graduation)

	Total	Percentage
Employment status known	408	100.0
Employment status unknown	0	0.0
Employed	405	99.3
Pursuing graduate degrees	1	0.2
Unemployed (seeking, not seeking, or studying for the bar)	2	0.5
Type of Employment		
# employed in law firms	331	81.7
# employed in business and industry	8	2.0
# employed in government	7	1.7
# employed in public interest	12	3.0
# employed as judicial clerks	44	10.9
# employed in academia	4	1.0
Geographic Location		
# employed in state	268	66.2
# employed in foreign countries	14	3.5
# of states where employed	23	

Bar Passage Rates

First-time takers	355	Reporting %	92.96
Average school %	96.67	Average state %	88.98
Average pass difference	7.69		

Jurisdiction	Takers	Passers	Pass %	State %	Diff %
New York	330	319	96.67	88.98	7.69

Columbia University School of Law

435 West 116th Street
New York, NY 10027
Phone: 212.854.2670; Fax: 212.854.1109
E-mail: admissions@law.columbia.edu; Website: www.law.columbia.edu/admissions

■ Introduction

Columbia Law School is distinguished, perhaps uniquely among leading US law schools, as an international center of legal education that stimulates its students to consider the full dimensions of the possibility of the law—as an intellectual pursuit, as a career, and as an instrument of human progress. The character of academic and social life at Columbia is fiercely democratic, dynamic, creative, and innovative. The Law School is especially committed to educating students of differing perspectives, from diverse backgrounds, and with varied life experiences.

Professional prospects for Columbia Law School graduates are quite extraordinary. Our graduates proceed to productive careers in every conceivable arena of practice, business, and advocacy. While Columbia-trained attorneys are especially well-regarded for their work in corporate law and finance, an unusually high number also serve as state and federal judges, prosecutors, civil rights and human rights advocates, legal scholars, public defenders, entrepreneurs, business executives, elected government officials, and national and international leaders. Many alumni contribute significantly to the shaping of US culture at large. Currently, our graduates serve in leadership roles across the fields of government, art, music, film, publishing, science, professional athletics, philanthropy, and higher education.

With an exceptionally talented student body and faculty and a strong tradition of encouraging students with specialized interests to develop those interests in depth, Columbia Law School provides a legal education that gives our students a singular capacity for imagination, originality, and high responsibility in their professional lives.

■ JD Student Body Profile

Columbia continues to place among the handful of the most highly selective JD programs in our nation—as evaluated by the principal criteria used to measure admission selectivity (application volume, acceptance rates, LSAT scores, and academic performance). Indeed, in recent years, the demand for a Columbia legal education has never been greater, and the academic credentials of our entering classes are stronger than ever. Columbia's JD student body is further distinguished by standing as one of the most culturally diverse among America's leading law schools. Men and women choosing to study law at Columbia hail from the small towns, farms, and suburbs of the West, Midwest, and South; the industrial corridors and ivy halls of the Northeast; the inner cities of every major US metropolis; and the international centers of Europe, Asia, Africa, and Latin America.

Each entering class reflects the broad range of economic, ethnic, and cultural backgrounds found in the United States. And from around the world, we welcome students who will enrich learning at Columbia and thereafter advance the developing legal cultures of their homelands.

With one of the largest percentages of international students in its JD program of any leading law school; with one of the very highest percentages of students of color; with its students hailing from 48 states, roughly 32 foreign countries, and more than 200 different colleges and

universities; and with 15 percent of its JD students having earned at least one graduate or professional degree before studying law, Columbia's student body abounds with a diversity of life experiences, cultural backgrounds, and intellectual perspectives.

■ The Law School Campus

Columbia Law School's main building, Jerome Greene Hall, has undergone significant expansion and improvements devoted primarily to our students, including library renovations and the creation of a student commons that includes a student lounge and café. New seminar rooms and state-of-the-art multimedia classrooms have also been designed to provide students with full Internet and other legal research access. Across the street from Greene Hall is William C. Warren Hall, home to the *Columbia Law Review*, Morningside Heights Legal Services (a law school clinic serving our community), and the Center for Public Interest Law.

William and June Warren Hall includes amphitheater-style classrooms equipped with modern teaching resources, a center for the law school's international programs, and conference facilities. It is also home to the offices of Admissions, Financial Aid, Registration Services, Student Services, Graduate Legal Studies, and International Programs.

The expansion of the law school's facilities have greatly enhanced the quality of life and learning at Columbia. Students have a superb learning environment that is conducive to community building and social and intellectual engagement, and reflects the changing nature of legal education in the twenty-first century.

■ Library Resources and Research Facilities

Columbia's library is one of the largest and most comprehensive law collections in the world. It is especially rich in US law and legal history, international law, comparative law, Roman law, and the legal literature of the major European countries, China, and Japan. Access to the Internet and electronic documents provide additional resources, with materials from Germany, South Africa, and a wide range of international organizations. In addition, the many libraries of the university, containing more than seven million volumes, are available to law students.

The law library's online catalog provides complete access to the library's collection, acts as an index to the major legal serials, and provides access to the online catalogs of other major law school libraries. Columbia provides its law students with some of the most sophisticated technologies of any law school in the nation.

■ Curriculum

The foundation of the JD program consists of Legal Methods (an intensive three-week introductory course), Legal Practice Workshop (a two-semester course that provides training in legal research, writing, and analysis), Contracts, Torts, Constitutional Law, Civil Procedure, Property, Criminal Law, Foundation Year Moot Court, and one elective focusing on the law's engagement with public policy, the intellectual and

historical foundations of the rule of law, or the law's transnational and comparative expression. Recent elective offerings have included Art of Legal Persuasion; Critical Legal Thought; Foundations of the Regulatory State; Law and Contemporary Society; Law and Economics; Law and Social Science; Lawyering Across Multiple Legal Orders; Legislation; Principles of Intellectual Property; Regulation: Decentralization and Globalization; the Regulatory and Administrative State; the Rule of Law: Perspectives and Philosophy; and Terror and Consent.

Columbia has a special commitment to clinical education, which places the student in the role of a lawyer doing a lawyer's actual work under intensive faculty supervision. Some examples of clinical opportunities are Lawyering in the Digital Age, Nonprofit Organizations/Small Business, Child Advocacy, Mediation, Environmental Law, Human Rights, and a clinic in Sexuality and Gender Law, the first clinic of its type in the nation. Unique to Columbia is a summer program which places more than 150 students in civil and human rights internships in law firms and organizations throughout this country and around the world. Especially distinguished are Columbia's offerings in international, foreign, and comparative law; constitutional law and theory; corporate and securities law; intellectual property; critical race theory; human rights; and public interest law.

■ Research Centers and Special Programs

Research centers and special programs include the Kernochan Center for Law, Media, and the Arts; Julius Silver Program in Law, Science, and Technology; Center for Climate Change Law; Center for Law and Philosophy; Center for Law and Economic Studies; Center for the Study of Law and Culture; Center for Public Interest Law; Program on Careers in Law and Teaching; Human Rights Institute; Parker School of Foreign and Comparative Law; Center for Chinese Legal Studies; Center for Japanese Legal Studies; Center for Korean Legal Studies; European Legal Studies Center; Center for Contract and Economic Organization; Center on Corporate Governance; Center on Crime, Community, and the Law; Center on Global Legal Problems; Center for Institutional and Social Change; Vale Columbia Center on Sustainable International Investment; Social Justice Initiatives; and the Charles Evans Gerber Transactional Studies Program.

■ Admission

All first-year students enter in mid-August. Candidates applying for regular admission should apply after September 1 of the year preceding their desired matriculation, but before February 15, the application deadline. Early Decision candidates must complete their applications by November 15 and are notified in December. All other applications are generally reviewed in the order in which they are completed, and decisions are made and sent out on a rolling basis.

Applicant Profile Not Available

University of Connecticut School of Law

45 Elizabeth Street
Hartford, CT 06105
Phone: 860.570.5100; Fax: 860.570.5153
E-mail: admissions@law.uconn.edu; Website: www.law.uconn.edu

*ABA
Approved
Since
1933*

The Basics

Type of school	Public
Term	Semester
Application deadline	3/1
Application fee	$60
Financial aid deadline	3/1
Can first year start other than fall?	No
Student to faculty ratio	11.4 to 1
# of housing spaces available restricted to law students	
graduate housing for which law students are eligible	

Faculty and Administrators

	Total		Men		Women		Minorities	
	Spr	Fall	Spr	Fall	Spr	Fall	Spr	Fall
Full-time	40	44	28	29	12	15	5	7
Other full-time	8	7	3	2	5	5	0	0
Deans, librarians, & others who teach	5	6	2	2	3	4	1	1
Part-time	71	44	62	36	9	8	4	4
Total	124	101	95	69	29	32	10	12

Curriculum

	Full-Time	Part-Time
Typical first-year section size	62	69
Is there typically a "small section" of the first-year class, other than Legal Writing, taught by full-time faculty	Yes	Yes
If yes, typical size offered last year	22	35
# of classroom course titles beyond first-year curriculum	147	
# of upper division courses, excluding seminars, with an enrollment: Under 25	90	
25–49	27	
50–74	15	
75–99	0	
100+	0	
# of seminars	53	
# of seminar positions available	1,040	
# of seminar positions filled	629	175
# of positions available in simulation courses	659	
# of simulation positions filled	505	144
# of positions available in faculty supervised clinical courses	240	
# of faculty supervised clinical positions filled	165	35
# involved in field placements	118	59
# involved in law journals	183	18
# involved in moot court or trial competitions	29	6
# of credit hours required to graduate	86	

JD Enrollment and Ethnicity

	Men		Women		Full-Time		Part-Time		1st-Year		Total		JD Degs. Awd.
	#	%	#	%	#	%	#	%	#	%	#	%	
African Amer.	17	4.9	20	6.9	27	6.0	10	5.2	8	4.4	37	5.8	12
Amer. Indian	3	0.9	1	0.3	2	0.4	2	1.0	2	1.1	4	0.6	1
Asian Amer.	22	6.3	29	10.0	39	8.7	12	6.3	14	7.7	51	8.0	8
Mex. Amer.	0	0.0	3	1.0	2	0.4	1	0.5	0	0.0	3	0.5	0
Puerto Rican	2	0.6	4	1.4	3	0.7	3	1.6	0	0.0	6	0.9	5
Hispanic	15	4.3	16	5.5	18	4.0	13	6.8	12	6.6	31	4.8	6
Total Minority	59	16.9	73	25.1	91	20.2	41	21.5	36	19.8	132	20.6	32
For. Nation.	3	0.9	5	1.7	6	1.3	2	1.0	2	1.1	8	1.2	0
Caucasian	260	74.3	185	63.6	313	69.6	132	69.1	131	72.0	445	69.4	141
Unknown	28	8.0	28	9.6	40	8.9	16	8.4	13	7.1	56	8.7	35
Total	350	54.6	291	45.4	450	70.2	191	29.8	182	28.4	641		208

Transfers

Transfers in	18
Transfers out	9

Tuition and Fees

	Resident	Nonresident
Full-time	$20,374	$42,094
Part-time	$14,246	$29,406
Tuition Guarantee Program	N	

Living Expenses

Estimated living expenses for singles

Living on campus	Living off campus	Living at home
N/A	$18,740	$9,490

University of Connecticut School of Law

ABA
Approved
Since
1933

GPA and LSAT Scores

	Total	Full-Time	Part-Time
# of apps	2,409	2,268	992
# of offers	837	582	255
# of matrics	182	120	62
75% GPA	3.59	3.59	3.59
Median GPA	3.38	3.43	3.29
25% GPA	3.20	3.22	3.06
75% LSAT	162	163	160
Median LSAT	161	162	158
25% LSAT	158	160	156

Grants and Scholarships (from prior year)

	Total		Full-Time		Part-Time	
	#	%	#	%	#	%
Total # of students	667		479		188	
Total # receiving grants	380	57.0	335	69.9	45	23.9
Less than 1/2 tuition	159	23.8	126	26.3	33	17.6
Half to full tuition	181	27.1	170	35.5	11	5.9
Full tuition	13	1.9	13	2.7	0	0.0
More than full tuition	27	4.0	26	5.4	1	0.5
Median grant amount			$10,000		$5,000	

Informational and Library Resources

Total amount spent on library materials	$1,502,500
Study seating capacity inside the library	810
# of full-time equivalent professional librarians	8.0
Hours per week library is open	89
# of open, wired connections available to students	778
# of networked computers available for use by students	125
Has wireless network?	Y
Require computer?	N

JD Attrition (from prior year)

	Academic	Other	Total	
	#	#	#	%
1st year	0	10	10	5.2
2nd year	0	1	1	0.5
3rd year	0	4	4	1.9
4th year	0	0	0	0.0

Employment (9 months after graduation)

	Total	Percentage
Employment status known	179	96.8
Employment status unknown	6	3.2
Employed	165	92.2
Pursuing graduate degrees	3	1.7
Unemployed (seeking, not seeking, or studying for the bar)	6	3.4
Type of Employment		
# employed in law firms	96	58.2
# employed in business and industry	23	13.9
# employed in government	17	10.3
# employed in public interest	4	2.4
# employed as judicial clerks	21	12.7
# employed in academia	4	2.4
Geographic Location		
# employed in state	109	66.1
# employed in foreign countries	1	0.6
# of states where employed	13	

Bar Passage Rates

First-time takers	216	Reporting %	66.20
Average school %	92.31	Average state %	88.28
Average pass difference	4.03		

Jurisdiction	Takers	Passers	Pass %	State %	Diff %
Connecticut	143	132	92.31	88.28	4.03

University of Connecticut School of Law

45 Elizabeth Street
Hartford, CT 06105
Phone: 860.570.5100; Fax: 860.570.5153
E-mail: admissions@law.uconn.edu; Website: www.law.uconn.edu

■ Introduction

As a result of several decades of sustained intellectual and foundational growth, the University of Connecticut School of Law has emerged as one of the leading public law schools in the United States. Because of Connecticut's extraordinary ratio of full-time students to full-time faculty, 75 percent of the advanced courses have 25 or fewer students. An outstanding and accessible faculty, an intensive first-year skills program, a rich and varied curriculum, including more than a dozen legal clinics, four student-edited journals, student organizations active across the spectrum of legal and social concerns, a regular flow of visiting lecturers, and a committed body of graduates throughout the country combine to make the University of Connecticut a law school of exceptional strength.

■ Library and Physical Facilities

The campus, listed on the National Register of Historic Places, is arguably the most beautiful in the United States. The library, completed in 1996, is one of the largest legal research and technology centers in the world, with more than 500,000 volumes housed in the 120,000-square-foot facility.

With its immediate neighbors—the Hartford Seminary, the University of Hartford, the Connecticut Historical Society, and the Connecticut Attorney General's Office—the school is part of an academic enclave in a turn-of-the-century residential neighborhood.

■ Dual-Degree Programs

The law school offers several interdisciplinary programs: JD/LLM in Insurance Law, JD/Master of Business Administration, JD/Master of Library Science, JD/Master of Public Administration, JD/Master of Public Health, and JD/Master of Social Work.

■ International Study Programs

The economic and political realities of globalization place new demands on the graduates of the law school. International law occupies an increasingly prominent place in the curriculum, reinforced by the student-edited *Connecticut Journal of International Law*. The law school has formal and informal study-abroad programs with universities in Aix-en-Provence, Berlin, Dublin, Exeter, Haifa, Leiden, London, Mannheim, San Juan, Siena, and Tilburg. These relationships bring a wealth of international visitors to the school. Legal scholars have visited and lectured from Argentina, Bosnia, China, the Czech Republic, France, Germany, Great Britain, Hungary, Israel, Japan, Korea, the Netherlands, Poland, Russia, South Africa, Taiwan, and Ukraine.

The LLM in United States Legal Studies for graduates of foreign law schools provides further opportunity for our students to learn from and study with peers trained in different legal systems.

■ Student Activities

Selected students may participate in one of four student-edited journals: the *Connecticut Law Review*, the *Connecticut Journal of International Law*, the *Connecticut Insurance Law Journal*, and the *Connecticut Public Interest Law Journal*.

The Connecticut Moot Court Board and the Mock Trial Association provide students with the opportunity to practice oral advocacy in intramural and interscholastic competitions. Participants have placed extremely well in regional, national, and international competitions.

The Student Bar Association is the representative student government of the school. It manages an annual budget consisting of funds derived from the student activities fee and university tuition to support the various student organizations and to generally enhance the quality of student life. Under the governance of the Student Bar, a large number of student-run organizations, reflecting the diversity of our students, have active chapters on campus.

■ Special Programs

Connecticut was a pioneer in clinical legal education, and our clinics continue to be a distinguishing strength of the school. If you are interested in the way law intersects with other disciplines or with such varied topics as human rights, intellectual property, or health care, you will find courses and specialists to meet your needs. Offerings in environmental law are supplemented by a semester exchange program with Vermont Law School.

The **Center for Children's Advocacy, Inc.**, a nonprofit corporation affiliated with the law school, works on behalf of the legal rights of underprivileged children. The **Connecticut Urban Legal Initiative, Inc.**, another nonprofit corporation housed at the law school, identifies neighborhood problems that typify urban blight and devises strategies to address them. The **Insurance Law Center** offers a specialized insurance curriculum with its LLM program, innovative research initiatives on the role of insurance in law and society, conferences and workshops, and the student-edited *Connecticut Insurance Law Journal*.

The **Intellectual Property Certificate Program** exposes participants to a broad curriculum of courses, from classes on patent, trademark, and copyright law to specialized seminars, including those in art law, cyberlaw, and European Union IP law. In addition, our Intellectual Property and Entrepreneurship clinic was selected by the US PTO to participate in a special clinical program. The **Tax Studies Certificate Program** affords an opportunity to participate in a supervised writing project, externship, or clinic in the area of tax law. Participants in the certificate program may begin their tax studies in Federal Income Tax in their first year and continue the study of taxation in a variety of courses during the last four semesters of law school. A **Human Rights Certificate Program** offers students the opportunity to work with world-renowned experts at the law school and the College of Liberal Arts and Sciences in a demanding and varied interdisciplinary study of global affairs and social justice. The law school has also created a **Law and Public Policy Certificate Program**, a flexible program in which students may enroll in a diverse collection of courses with

faculty at the law school and within the University of Connecticut's Department of Public Policy.

The **Semester in Washington, DC**, places selected students in selected federal agencies, legislative offices, or nonprofit groups for one semester of service.

■ Career Planning

Connecticut operates a comprehensive career planning office for the benefit of students and alumni/ae. The school offers a geographically diverse on-campus interviewing program, extensive individual and group counseling, a resource library, job listings, employment information sessions, and newsletters.

The school holds three off-campus interview programs each fall in Washington, DC; Boston; and New York City and schedules on-campus interviews through the year. In addition, the school participates in several off-site job fairs.

Within six months of graduation, 92.2 percent of the Class of 2008 were employed, including 12.7 percent in judicial clerkships.

■ Services for Students With Disabilities

The director of student services, Dr. Jane Thierfeld Brown, works with students with disabilities in the development and implementation of reasonable accommodations to allow access to the school's physical facilities as well as its educational and extracurricular programs.

Students with disabilities who are considering applying or who have been admitted to the School of Law are invited to tour the campus. Students may contact the dean's office for discussion of accommodations.

Applicant Profile

University of Connecticut School of Law
This grid includes only full-time applicants with LSAT scores earned under standard administrations.

LSAT Score	3.75 +		3.50–3.74		3.25–3.49		3.00–3.24		2.75–2.99		2.50–2.74		2.25–2.49		2.00–2.24		Below 2.00		No GPA		Total	
	Apps	Adm	Apps	Adm	Apps	Adm	Apps	Adm	Apps	Adm	Apps	Adm	Apps	Adm	Apps	Adm	Apps	Adm	Apps	Adm	Apps	Adm
175–180	0	0	0	0	0	0	2	1	0	0	1	0	1	1	0	0	0	0	0	0	4	2
170–174	10	5	3	3	9	8	5	5	4	2	1	0	2	0	1	0	0	0	0	0	35	23
165–169	24	19	40	31	41	28	26	11	9	5	5	0	3	0	1	0	0	0	1	0	150	94
160–164	101	79	144	100	145	89	81	38	36	15	19	6	8	2	2	0	1	0	8	4	545	333
155–159	110	35	177	53	183	57	123	30	61	10	31	2	12	1	1	0	0	0	15	0	713	188
150–154	61	8	104	20	145	14	96	8	61	4	32	0	12	0	6	0	2	0	19	1	538	55
145–149	23	1	48	4	62	4	60	5	34	1	25	2	8	0	4	0	3	0	3	0	270	17
140–144	6	0	18	1	23	0	33	1	17	0	13	0	5	0	6	0	0	0	6	0	127	2
135–139	1	0	6	0	9	0	16	0	13	0	9	0	7	0	3	0	2	0	1	0	67	0
130–134	0	0	3	0	2	0	5	0	4	0	1	0	0	0	3	0	1	0	2	0	21	0
125–129	0	0	0	0	0	0	0	0	1	0	2	0	3	0	2	0	0	0	1	0	9	0
120–124	0	0	0	0	0	0	0	0	0	0	0	0	0	0	0	0	0	0	0	0	0	0
Total	336	147	543	212	619	200	447	99	240	37	139	10	61	4	29	0	9	0	56	5	2479	714

Apps = Number of Applicants
Adm = Number Admitted
Reflects 99% of total applicant pool; average LSAT data reported.

Cornell Law School

Myron Taylor Hall
Ithaca, NY 14853-4901
Phone: 607.255.5141
E-mail: lawadmit@lawschool.cornell.edu; Website: www.lawschool.cornell.edu

ABA
Approved
Since
1923

The Basics

Type of school	Private
Term	Semester
Application deadline	2/1
Application fee	$80
Financial aid deadline	3/15
Can first year start other than fall?	No
Student to faculty ratio	10.0 to 1
# of housing spaces available	
restricted to law students	48
graduate housing for which law students are eligible	150

Faculty and Administrators

	Total		Men		Women		Minorities	
	Spr	Fall	Spr	Fall	Spr	Fall	Spr	Fall
Full-time	51	46	35	31	16	15	5	6
Other full-time	0	0	0	0	0	0	0	0
Deans, librarians, & others who teach	11	10	5	4	6	6	1	1
Part-time	26	29	21	22	5	7	1	0
Total	88	85	61	57	27	28	7	7

JD Enrollment and Ethnicity

	Men		Women		Full-Time		Part-Time		1st-Year		Total		JD Degs. Awd.
	#	%	#	%	#	%	#	%	#	%	#	%	
African Amer.	11	3.7	27	8.4	38	6.1	0	0.0	17	8.3	38	6.1	9
Amer. Indian	3	1.0	5	1.6	8	1.3	0	0.0	4	2.0	8	1.3	3
Asian Amer.	24	8.0	61	18.9	85	13.7	0	0.0	29	14.1	85	13.7	17
Mex. Amer.	10	3.3	11	3.4	21	3.4	0	0.0	9	4.4	21	3.4	2
Puerto Rican	5	1.7	5	1.6	10	1.6	0	0.0	6	2.9	10	1.6	4
Hispanic	13	4.3	14	4.3	27	4.3	0	0.0	14	6.8	27	4.3	3
Total Minority	66	22.0	123	38.2	189	30.4	0	0.0	79	38.5	189	30.4	38
For. Nation.	30	10.0	27	8.4	57	9.2	0	0.0	14	6.8	57	9.2	10
Caucasian	204	68.0	172	53.4	376	60.5	0	0.0	112	54.6	376	60.5	140
Unknown	0	0.0	0	0.0	0	0.0	0	0.0	0	0.0	0	0.0	0
Total	300	48.2	322	51.8	622	100.0	0	0.0	205	33.0	622		188

Curriculum

	Full-Time	Part-Time
Typical first-year section size	99	0
Is there typically a "small section" of the first-year class, other than Legal Writing, taught by full-time faculty	Yes	No
If yes, typical size offered last year	33	
# of classroom course titles beyond first-year curriculum	137	

# of upper division courses, excluding seminars, with an enrollment:	Under 25	37
	25–49	18
	50–74	8
	75–99	7
	100+	3

# of seminars	52	
# of seminar positions available	810	
# of seminar positions filled	594	0
# of positions available in simulation courses	332	
# of simulation positions filled	283	0
# of positions available in faculty supervised clinical courses	151	
# of faculty supervised clinical positions filled	141	0
# involved in field placements	52	0
# involved in law journals	277	0
# involved in moot court or trial competitions	201	0
# of credit hours required to graduate	84	

Transfers

Transfers in	10
Transfers out	4

Tuition and Fees

	Resident	Nonresident
Full-time	$49,020	$49,020
Part-time		
Tuition Guarantee Program		N

Living Expenses

Estimated living expenses for singles

Living on campus	Living off campus	Living at home
$18,300	$18,300	$18,300

Cornell Law School

ABA Approved Since 1923

GPA and LSAT Scores

	Total	Full-Time	Part-Time
# of apps	4,207	4,207	0
# of offers	900	900	0
# of matrics	205	205	0
75% GPA	3.80	3.80	0.00
Median GPA	3.63	3.63	0.00
25% GPA	3.48	3.48	0.00
75% LSAT	168	168	0
Median LSAT	167	167	0
25% LSAT	165	165	0

Grants and Scholarships (from prior year)

	Total #	Total %	Full-Time #	Full-Time %	Part-Time #	Part-Time %
Total # of students	591		591		0	
Total # receiving grants	218	36.9	218	36.9	0	0.0
Less than 1/2 tuition	158	26.7	158	26.7	0	0.0
Half to full tuition	60	10.2	60	10.2	0	0.0
Full tuition	0	0.0	0	0.0	0	0.0
More than full tuition	0	0.0	0	0.0	0	0.0
Median grant amount			$18,000		$0	

Informational and Library Resources

Total amount spent on library materials	$1,519,799
Study seating capacity inside the library	419
# of full-time equivalent professional librarians	9.0
Hours per week library is open	168
# of open, wired connections available to students	32
# of networked computers available for use by students	63
Has wireless network?	Y
Require computer?	N

JD Attrition (from prior year)

	Academic #	Other #	Total #	Total %
1st year	0	4	4	2.0
2nd year	0	0	0	0.0
3rd year	0	0	0	0.0
4th year	0	0	0	0.0

Employment (9 months after graduation)

	Total	Percentage
Employment status known	186	100.0
Employment status unknown	0	0.0
Employed	182	97.8
Pursuing graduate degrees	1	0.5
Unemployed (seeking, not seeking, or studying for the bar)	3	1.6
Type of Employment		
# employed in law firms	156	85.7
# employed in business and industry	0	0.0
# employed in government	3	1.6
# employed in public interest	6	3.3
# employed as judicial clerks	16	8.8
# employed in academia	1	0.5
Geographic Location		
# employed in state	109	59.9
# employed in foreign countries	4	2.2
# of states where employed	21	

Bar Passage Rates

First-time takers	187	Reporting %	70.59
Average school %	99.24	Average state %	88.98
Average pass difference	10.26		

Jurisdiction	Takers	Passers	Pass %	State %	Diff %
New York	132	131	99.24	88.98	10.26

Cornell Law School

Myron Taylor Hall
Ithaca, NY 14853-4901
Phone: 607.255.5141
E-mail: lawadmit@lawschool.cornell.edu; Website: www.lawschool.cornell.edu

■ Lawyers in the Best Sense

When Cornell University's founding president, Andrew Dickson White, began to lay plans for a law department at Cornell University, he wrote that he wanted to educate "not swarms of hastily prepared pettifoggers, but a fair number of well-trained, large-minded, morally based *lawyers in the best sense . . ."* He hoped graduates of the school would become "a blessing to the country, at the bar, on the bench, and in various public bodies." More than a century since President White's vision, this ideal still holds true. A small, top-tier law school located in beautiful surroundings, Cornell draws on, and contributes to, the resources of a great university, consistently producing well-rounded lawyers and accomplished practitioners cut from a different cloth. Cornell is a national center of learning located in Ithaca, New York, the heart of the Finger Lakes region of New York State. The law school's small classes, broad curriculum, and distinguished faculty, combined with the advantages of being part of one of the world's leading research universities, make it ideal for those who value both depth and breadth in their legal studies. Students find Ithaca to be a safe and nonstressful, yet culturally rich, environment in which to pursue legal studies.

■ Enrollment/Student Body

Seventy percent of Cornell's entering students have taken one or more years between completion of their undergraduate degree and enrollment in law school. Selective admission standards, combined with an emphasis on applicants' unique records and achievements, ensure that the student body is made up of people with wide-ranging interests, skills, concerns, and backgrounds.

■ Library, Physical Facilities, and Computing

The law school is located in the renovated and expanded Myron Taylor Hall, at the heart of the scenic 740-acre Cornell University campus. Hughes Hall, the law school dormitory, is adjacent to the main law school building and contains single rooms for about 45 students and a dining facility.

Cornell is one of the nation's leaders in the development and support of electronic legal research. It combines outstanding collections with professional expertise and access to worldwide electronic information sources for Anglo-American, as well as foreign and international law. Students have access to the full array of Internet services. The law school's multiple-node network, wireless network, and computer terminals are available to students for word processing, legal research, statistical analysis, and database management. Students also have access to the many satellite computer clusters and mainframe facilities located on the university campus.

■ Faculty

Cornell's faculty are known not only as prolific scholars but also as great teachers. Tenured and tenure-track faculty teach and produce scholarship in their area of law; clinical faculty run client-focused and simulation courses centered around legal aid and several specialty clinics; and a large number of

visitors, associated faculty from other university divisions, and adjunct faculty teach at the school each year. Many of the latter group are legal scholars and professors from other countries who teach in the Law School's significant international program.

■ Curriculum/Clinical Studies

Cornell offers a national law curriculum leading to the JD degree. First-year students take a group of required courses and an intensive lawyering course stressing a variety of legal research, writing, and advocacy techniques. After the first year, students may choose from a wide range of elective courses, including many seminars and problem courses.

The Cornell Legal Aid Clinic, offering legal services to individuals financially unable to employ an attorney, provides students with the chance to engage in the supervised practice of law under the direction of experienced attorneys. Clinical faculty also conduct a variety of other specialized clinics and skills courses within the regular curriculum. Students can select from a bevy of clinical courses, such as the Public Interest Clinic (three different levels); the Immigration Appellate Law and Advocacy Clinic; Capital Appellate Clinic; Capital Trial Clinic; Child Advocacy Clinic; Capital Punishment: Post Conviction Litigation Clinic; Criminal Defense Trial Clinic; Indigent Representation; International Human Rights Clinic; Labor Law Clinic; Land Use, Development, and Natural Resources Protection Clinic; Prosecution Trial Clinic; Securities Law Clinic; Water Law Clinic; and US Attorney's Office Clinic.

■ Joint Degrees

Being part of a world-renowned university, and the interdisciplinary environment it provides, is of great benefit. Cornell Law School and Cornell University offer many opportunities for combined-degree programs, including both three- and four-year programs for the JD/MBA (Business degree from the Johnson School of Graduate Management); JD/MPA (Public Affairs degree from the Cornell Institute of Public Affairs); JD/MILR (Labor Relations degree from the School of Industrial and Labor Relations); JD/MRP (Regional Planning degree from the College of Architecture, Art, and Planning); and a JD/MA or PhD in a variety of fields (Master's or PhD degree from the Graduate School). Law students can also take as many as 12 credits outside of the law school for law school credit.

■ International Legal Studies

The Berger International Legal Studies Program is one of the country's oldest and most distinguished programs in international legal education. The Clarke Program in East Asian Law and Culture brings an exciting interdisciplinary and humanistic focus to the study of law in East Asia. Cornell's comprehensive program features a unique JD specialization opportunity; a three-year JD/LLM degree in International and Comparative Law; a four-year JD/Master en Droit (French law degree) program; a three-year JD/MLLP (German law degree) program; a three-year JD/Master in Global Business Law; a Paris summer institute with the

Université Paris 1 (Panthéon-Sorbonne); a comprehensive speaker series; Mori, Hamada, and Matsumoto (Tokyo law firm) Faculty Exchange; Conseil Constitutional Clerkship (French Supreme Court Clerkship); a large number of visiting foreign professors and scholars; a weekly luncheon discussion series; international moot court competitions; law clinics; internships; and a leading journal of international and comparative law edited by students. Students have the option to spend one semester abroad at a partner law school (we have agreements with 15 partner schools in 11 different countries), or to design an individual "term away" at a foreign law facility with which Cornell is not partnered.

In addition, the Clarke Initiative for Law and Development in the Middle East sponsors seminars, colloquia, and lectures and supports student and faculty exchanges with institutions in the region.

■ Programs and Projects

Cornell Law School is the home for several unique programs and projects of interest to students. These programs and projects include the following: Avon Global Center for Women and Justice (improve access to justice in an effort to eliminate violence against women and girls); Cornell Death Penalty Project (clinics and symposia related to capital punishment); e-Rulemaking Initiative (technology and practice of e-rulemaking); Clarke Scholars Program (visiting scholars); Journal of Empirical Legal Studies (only legal journal dedicated exclusively to empirical legal scholarship); Legal Information Institute (world's leading investigator of new ways to perform electronic legal research); Clarke Business Law Institute (classes, more faculty, seminars, conferences, and other programming); BR Legal (represent start-up companies); and Empirical Studies Project (empirical study of court cases).

■ Student Activities

Student-edited law journals include the *Cornell Law Review* (published continuously since 1916), the *Cornell International Law Journal* (established in 1967), and the *Cornell Journal of Law and Public Policy*. Student organizations and activities include American Constitution Society, Asian Pacific American Law Students Association, Black Law Students Association, Briggs Society of International Law, Business Law Society, Christian Legal Society, Cornell Advocates for Human Rights, Cornell Animal Legal Defense Fund, Cornell Sports and Entertainment Law Consortium, Cornell Law Student Association, Cornell Law Yearbook Club, Cornell Law Democrats, Cornell Law Republicans, Environmental Law Society, Federalist Society, J. Reuben Clark Law Society, Jewish Law Student Association, LAMBDA, Latino American Law Students Association, LLM Association, MS JD Board, Moot Court Board, National Lawyers Guild, Native American Law Students Association, Phi Alpha Delta, Phi Delta Phi, Public Interest Law Union, South Asian Law Students Association, Students for Marriage Equality, Transfer Network Association, and the Women's Law Coalition.

■ Expenses and Financial Aid

Cornell offers an institutional-based financial aid program. About 40 percent of students receive scholarship aid (awards averaging more than $19,000 per year), with a higher percentage receiving government-backed loans.

Our Public Interest Low Income Protection Plan, one of the most generous of such programs, assists those choosing qualifying public interest law jobs through the use of a moderated loan repayment plan and loan forgiveness.

■ Career Services

Cornell's students continue to be among the most recruited in the country. Every fall, hundreds of employers from across the country recruit Cornell students on campus and at job fairs in Boston, Chicago, Dallas, Los Angeles, New York, San Francisco, Miami, Atlanta, and Washington, DC. A professionally staffed Career Services Office provides employment counseling to students and serves as a liaison to legal employers. In addition, Cornell has two full-time professional staff members (Assistant Dean and Director for Public Service) dedicated to public interest job opportunities and counseling.

Applicant Profile

Admission to Cornell Law is very competitive. Members of the most recent entering class had an aggregate 3.61 undergraduate grade-point average and median LSAT scores that placed them in the 96th percentile nationwide (167). But Cornell Law does not evaluate candidates by the numbers alone. The admission committee carefully considers such nonquantifiable factors as extracurricular and community activities, life experience and work background, and recommendations. Cornell Law subscribes to the university's 130-year tradition of affirmative action, and members of traditionally underrepresented minority groups are encouraged to mention their status where they think it is relevant. The decision to offer admission ultimately rests on whether the committee is convinced that the applicant will be an energetic, productive, and successful member of the Cornell Law community and eventually, the legal profession.

Creighton University School of Law

2500 California Plaza
Omaha, NE 68178
Phone: 402.280.2586; Fax: 402.280.3161
E-mail: lawadmit@creighton.edu; Website: http://www.creighton.edu/law

The Basics

Type of school	Private
Term	Semester
Application deadline	5/1
Application fee	$50
Financial aid deadline	7/1
Can first year start other than fall?	No
Student to faculty ratio	17.6 to 1
# of housing spaces available restricted to law students	
graduate housing for which law students are eligible	

Faculty and Administrators

	Total		Men		Women		Minorities	
	Spr	Fall	Spr	Fall	Spr	Fall	Spr	Fall
Full-time	22	22	17	16	5	6	3	3
Other full-time	4	3	2	2	2	1	1	1
Deans, librarians, & others who teach	9	10	6	7	3	3	0	0
Part-time	24	19	16	10	8	9	0	0
Total	59	54	41	35	18	19	4	4

JD Enrollment and Ethnicity

	Men		Women		Full-Time		Part-Time		1st-Year		Total		JD Degs. Awd.
	#	%	#	%	#	%	#	%	#	%	#	%	
African Amer.	4	1.4	7	3.4	9	1.9	2	15.4	6	3.3	11	2.3	2
Amer. Indian	0	0.0	1	0.5	1	0.2	0	0.0	0	0.0	1	0.2	0
Asian Amer.	8	2.9	11	5.4	19	4.0	0	0.0	7	3.8	19	3.9	3
Mex. Amer.	2	0.7	3	1.5	5	1.1	0	0.0	2	1.1	5	1.0	1
Puerto Rican	1	0.4	0	0.0	1	0.2	0	0.0	1	0.5	1	0.2	0
Hispanic	7	2.5	5	2.4	11	2.3	1	7.7	4	2.2	12	2.5	0
Total Minority	22	7.9	27	13.2	46	9.8	3	23.1	20	10.9	49	10.1	6
For. Nation.	1	0.4	0	0.0	1	0.2	0	0.0	1	0.5	1	0.2	1
Caucasian	256	91.8	176	85.9	423	89.8	9	69.2	161	88.0	432	89.3	139
Unknown	0	0.0	2	1.0	1	0.2	1	7.7	1	0.5	2	0.4	0
Total	279	57.6	205	42.4	471	97.3	13	2.7	183	37.8	484		146

Curriculum

	Full-Time	Part-Time
Typical first-year section size	83	0
Is there typically a "small section" of the first-year class, other than Legal Writing, taught by full-time faculty	No	No
If yes, typical size offered last year		

# of classroom course titles beyond first-year curriculum		84
# of upper division courses, excluding seminars, with an enrollment:	Under 25	119
	25–49	31
	50–74	8
	75–99	2
	100+	0
# of seminars		12
# of seminar positions available		235
# of seminar positions filled	211	0
# of positions available in simulation courses		496
# of simulation positions filled	442	0
# of positions available in faculty supervised clinical courses		36
# of faculty supervised clinical positions filled	20	0
# involved in field placements	51	0
# involved in law journals	30	0
# involved in moot court or trial competitions	50	0
# of credit hours required to graduate		94

Transfers

Transfers in	5
Transfers out	10

Tuition and Fees

	Resident	Nonresident
Full-time	$30,294	$30,294
Part-time	$17,670	$17,670
Tuition Guarantee Program		N

Living Expenses

Estimated living expenses for singles

Living on campus	Living off campus	Living at home
$20,655	$20,655	$7,155

Creighton University School of Law

ABA
Approved
Since
1924

GPA and LSAT Scores

	Total	Full-Time	Part-Time
# of apps	1,366	1,314	52
# of offers	771	753	18
# of matrics	177	173	4
75% GPA	3.64	3.64	3.10
Median GPA	3.43	3.43	2.92
25% GPA	3.13	3.15	2.79
75% LSAT	156	156	152
Median LSAT	153	153	149
25% LSAT	151	151	147

Grants and Scholarships (from prior year)

	Total		Full-Time		Part-Time	
	#	%	#	%	#	%
Total # of students	463		446		17	
Total # receiving grants	225	48.6	225	50.4	0	0.0
Less than 1/2 tuition	155	33.5	155	34.8	0	0.0
Half to full tuition	53	11.4	53	11.9	0	0.0
Full tuition	16	3.5	16	3.6	0	0.0
More than full tuition	1	0.2	1	0.2	0	0.0
Median grant amount			$9,796		$0	

Informational and Library Resources

Total amount spent on library materials	$1,431,356
Study seating capacity inside the library	371
# of full-time equivalent professional librarians	6.0
Hours per week library is open	106
# of open, wired connections available to students	174
# of networked computers available for use by students	44
Has wireless network?	Y
Require computer?	N

JD Attrition (from prior year)

	Academic #	Other #	Total #	Total %
1st year	4	15	19	10.7
2nd year	0	1	1	0.7
3rd year	0	0	0	0.0
4th year	0	0	0	0.0

Employment (9 months after graduation)

	Total	Percentage
Employment status known	146	100.0
Employment status unknown	0	0.0
Employed	130	89.0
Pursuing graduate degrees	4	2.7
Unemployed (seeking, not seeking, or studying for the bar)	11	7.5
Type of Employment		
# employed in law firms	63	48.5
# employed in business and industry	27	20.8
# employed in government	30	23.1
# employed in public interest	2	1.5
# employed as judicial clerks	7	5.4
# employed in academia	0	0.0
Geographic Location		
# employed in state	63	48.5
# employed in foreign countries	0	0.0
# of states where employed	27	

Bar Passage Rates

First-time takers	143	Reporting %	100.00
Average school %	89.53	Average state %	87.49
Average pass difference	2.04		

Jurisdiction	Takers	Passers	Pass %	State %	Diff %
Nebraska	43	38	88.37	89.15	−0.78
Iowa	24	23	95.83	90.11	5.72
Arizona	11	11	100.00	84.03	15.97
Colorado	9	8	88.89	83.29	5.60
Others (22)	56	48	85.71		

Creighton University School of Law

2500 California Plaza
Omaha, NE 68178
Phone: 402.280.2586; Fax: 402.280.3161
E-mail: lawadmit@creighton.edu; Website: http://www.creighton.edu/law

■ The School of Law

The School of Law, established in 1904, has been a member of the Association of American Law Schools (AALS) since 1907 and approved by the American Bar Association (ABA) since 1924. Alumni from the law school are practicing in all 50 states and in several foreign countries. The law school's current enrollment is 485. Students come from 41 states and 157 undergraduate institutions.

■ Introduction

Creighton University, a privately endowed and supported Jesuit university, was founded in 1878. Creighton is the most diverse educational institution of its size in the nation. In addition to the School of Law, Creighton has a School of Medicine, School of Dentistry, School of Pharmacy and Health Professions, School of Nursing, College of Business Administration, College of Arts and Sciences, and a Graduate School, making it the center of professional education in the Midwest. The university is located just blocks from downtown Omaha, a metropolitan area with a population of approximately 800,000. Known as the River City, Omaha is the heart of the Midlands and the largest metroplex between Chicago and Denver.

■ Faculty

The faculty is composed of 27 full-time professors and a group of part-time specialists chosen from the bench and bar. Creighton's full-time faculty members have earned reputations as outstanding classroom teachers. In addition, faculty scholarship brings to the classroom insights gained through the publication of leading texts and thought-provoking articles. A distinguished adjunct faculty of judges and practicing attorneys teach courses in specialty areas. Faculty offices surround the Law School Commons making them easily accessible to students. Faculty members maintain an open-door policy that encourages students to drop in to discuss the latest case, current events, or the newest restaurant in town.

■ Library and Physical Facilities

The School of Law is entirely contained in the Ahmanson Law Center. The attractive Klutznick Law Library/McGrath North Mullin and Kratz Legal Research Center encompasses 46,741 assignable square feet and is located on both levels of the Ahmanson Law Center. Wireless network coverage is campus-wide. Many tables and carrels are also wired with both power and data connections. A variety of comfortable individual, group study, reading room, and computer-use seating options are available in a pleasant, service-oriented setting. In addition to other legal information specialists, the Law Library employs four lawyer-librarians (JD/MLS librarians) who each deliver reference service and teach.

The Law Library provides access to one of the finest legal collections in the region. It houses a large, carefully selected array of print and electronic Anglo-American, comparative, and international law resources. Other features of the library include three computer labs, two reading rooms, and an inspiring rare book collection comprised primarily of British legal texts and treatises from the sixteenth to the nineteenth centuries.

■ Areas of Concentration

Students may earn a certificate indicating that they focused their studies in a particular area of concentration. Areas of concentration are (a) Business Law, (b) Criminal Law and Procedure, (c) International and Comparative Law, and (d) Litigation. The curriculum prepares students for the practice of law in any state.

■ Combined-Degree Programs

Creighton's School of Law, College of Business Administration, and Graduate School offer a JD/MBA, a JD/MS in Information Technology Management, a JD/MS in Negotiation and Dispute Resolution, and a JD/MA in International Relations.

■ Clinics and Internships

The Milton R. Abrahams Legal Clinic provides third-year students with the opportunity to learn the lawyering process in a way that is not provided in most law school courses. Clinic students represent low-income clients on a variety of civil matters that vary in complexity. Students conduct interviews, prepare pleadings, conduct legal research and writing, and appear in court for hearings and trials. Clinic Students are certified to practice law under the supervision of Clinic faculty and licensed attorneys.

The Community Economic Development (CED) Law Clinic provides students with an opportunity to work on a broad range of transactional and business law issues affecting community development. Students in the CED Clinic represent a client base of small business owners and nonprofit and community-based organizations that serve low-income communities across the state of Nebraska and Western Iowa.

Students may also participate in a broad variety of internships with city, county, and federal legal offices in the Omaha area.

■ Werner Institute for Negotiation and Dispute Resolution

The Werner Institute, the most richly endowed program of its kind in the country, is an emerging national leader in the field of conflict resolution with an interdisciplinary curriculum leading to graduate certificates and master's degrees in the field. The institute places a strong emphasis on a systems approach to conflict resolution and focuses on the preparation of leaders in the field with specialized applications in areas of greatest need, such as conflict within and among organizations, businesses, health care, and communities.

■ Student Activities

The Student Bar Association (SBA) is the student government of the law school. The purpose of the organization is to make

law students aware of the obligations and opportunities existing for lawyers through SBA activities, promote a consciousness of professional responsibility, and provide a forum for student activities. The *Creighton Law Review*, edited and managed by students, is a scholarly legal journal that is circulated nationally and internationally. The school has over 20 different active student organizations.

Financial Aid and Scholarships

Creighton University School of Law offers two types of financial aid: merit-based scholarships and federal government loans. Students seeking financial aid and scholarships must complete the Free Application for Federal Student Aid (FAFSA). Creighton University participates in the US Department of Education's Direct Loan Program. All first-year scholarships have merit requirements, including, but not limited to, LSAT score and undergraduate grade-point average. Admitted applicants with an LSAT score and undergraduate grade-point average above Creighton's medians for the previous year will receive strong consideration for scholarship assistance. Applicants who qualify for a scholarship will be notified at the time of acceptance.

Frances M. Ryan Diversity Scholarship Program

The School of Law actively recruits minority students and has a substantial diversity scholarship program. Applicants who wish to be considered for a Ryan Diversity Scholarship must make note of it on their admission application.

Career Development Office

The Career Development Office provides a full array of services to Creighton Law students, including individual career counseling, a law alumni network stretching from coast to coast, on-campus and off-campus interview programs, alumni networking events in a variety of cities nationwide, and a dynamic website that allows students to explore career opportunities throughout the world. Creighton's 2008 graduating class had a 92 percent employment rate nine months after graduation. Graduates of 2008 are working in the areas of business, government, private practice, public interest, and as judicial clerks in 26 states and the District of Columbia.

Applicant Profile

Creighton University School of Law
This grid includes only applicants who earned 120–180 LSAT scores under standard administration.

LSAT Score	3.75 +		3.50–3.74		3.25–3.49		3.00–3.24		2.75–2.99		2.50–2.74		2.25–2.49		2.00–2.24		Below 2.00		No GPA		Total	
	Apps	Adm	Apps	Adm	Apps	Adm	Apps	Adm	Apps	Adm	Apps	Adm	Apps	Adm	Apps	Adm	Apps	Adm	Apps	Adm	Apps	Adm
175–180	0	0	0	0	0	0	0	0	0	0	0	0	0	0	0	0	0	0	0	0	0	0
170–174	1	1	1	1	1	1	0	0	0	0	0	0	0	0	0	0	0	0	0	0	3	3
165–169	3	3	4	4	4	4	1	1	0	0	3	2	1	1	0	0	0	0	0	0	16	15
160–164	20	20	23	23	15	14	6	5	4	4	4	2	3	3	2	2	0	0	0	0	77	73
155–159	51	51	47	46	50	48	46	43	26	23	20	13	8	5	1	0	2	1	3	2	254	232
150–154	63	61	85	81	100	91	86	60	67	32	26	4	14	4	4	0	3	0	6	4	454	337
145–149	32	19	60	31	89	32	62	10	51	6	28	3	17	1	3	0	1	0	3	0	346	102
140–144	7	1	18	3	34	0	30	0	26	0	14	1	11	0	6	0	1	0	3	0	150	5
135–139	1	0	7	0	6	0	9	0	8	0	13	0	9	0	3	0	1	0	1	0	58	0
130–134	0	0	1	0	0	0	0	0	1	0	1	0	0	0	0	0	0	0	3	0	6	0
125–129	0	0	0	0	0	0	0	0	1	0	1	0	3	0	0	0	0	0	0	0	5	0
120–124	0	0	0	0	0	0	0	0	0	0	0	0	0	0	0	0	0	0	0	0	0	0
Total	178	156	246	189	299	190	240	119	184	65	110	25	66	14	19	2	8	1	19	6	1369	767

Apps = Number of Applicants
Adm = Number Admitted
Reflects 99% of the total applicant pool; average LSAT data reported.

University of Dayton School of Law

300 College Park, 112 Keller Hall
Dayton, OH 45469-2760
Phone: 937.229.3555; Fax: 937.229.4194
E-mail: lawinfo@notes.udayton.edu; Website: http://law.udayton.edu

ABA
Approved
Since
1975

The Basics

Type of school	Private
Term	Semester
Application deadline	3/1 5/1
Application fee	$50
Financial aid deadline	4/1 7/1
Can first year start other than fall?	Yes
Student to faculty ratio	16.2 to 1
# of housing spaces available	
restricted to law students	24
graduate housing for which law students are eligible	52

Faculty and Administrators

	Total		Men		Women		Minorities	
	Spr	Fall	Spr	Fall	Spr	Fall	Spr	Fall
Full-time	24	25	13	15	11	10	4	5
Other full-time	2	2	0	0	2	2	0	0
Deans, librarians, & others who teach	7	7	3	3	4	4	1	1
Part-time	31	23	22	16	9	7	1	2
Total	64	57	38	34	26	23	6	8

Curriculum

	Full-Time	Part-Time
Typical first-year section size	90	0
Is there typically a "small section" of the first-year class, other than Legal Writing, taught by full-time faculty	No	No
If yes, typical size offered last year		
# of classroom course titles beyond first-year curriculum	70	
# of upper division courses, excluding seminars, with an enrollment: Under 25	57	
25–49	20	
50–74	14	
75–99	6	
100+	1	
# of seminars	12	
# of seminar positions available	180	
# of seminar positions filled	147	0
# of positions available in simulation courses	457	
# of simulation positions filled	419	0
# of positions available in faculty supervised clinical courses	20	
# of faculty supervised clinical positions filled	22	0
# involved in field placements	156	0
# involved in law journals	32	0
# involved in moot court or trial competitions	28	0
# of credit hours required to graduate	90	

JD Enrollment and Ethnicity

	Men		Women		Full-Time		Part-Time		1st-Year		Total		JD Degs. Awd.
	#	%	#	%	#	%	#	%	#	%	#	%	
African Amer.	18	6.2	19	9.0	37	7.4	0	0.0	17	8.3	37	7.4	6
Amer. Indian	1	0.3	2	1.0	3	0.6	0	0.0	2	1.0	3	0.6	2
Asian Amer.	6	2.1	7	3.3	13	2.6	0	0.0	6	2.9	13	2.6	3
Mex. Amer.	1	0.3	2	1.0	3	0.6	0	0.0	1	0.5	3	0.6	4
Puerto Rican	0	0.0	2	1.0	2	0.4	0	0.0	1	0.5	2	0.4	2
Hispanic	6	2.1	6	2.9	12	2.4	0	0.0	3	1.5	12	2.4	2
Total Minority	32	11.0	38	18.1	70	14.0	0	0.0	30	14.7	70	14.0	19
For. Nation.	3	1.0	2	1.0	5	1.0	0	0.0	2	1.0	5	1.0	0
Caucasian	255	87.9	170	81.0	425	85.0	0	0.0	172	84.3	425	85.0	131
Unknown	0	0.0	0	0.0	0	0.0	0	0.0	0	0.0	0	0.0	0
Total	290	58.0	210	42.0	500	100.0	0	0.0	204	40.8	500		150

Transfers

Transfers in	7
Transfers out	22

Tuition and Fees

	Resident	Nonresident
Full-time	$32,684	$32,684
Part-time		
Tuition Guarantee Program	N	

Living Expenses

Estimated living expenses for singles

Living on campus	Living off campus	Living at home
$14,500	$14,500	$14,500

University of Dayton School of Law

ABA Approved Since 1975

GPA and LSAT Scores

	Total	Full-Time	Part-Time
# of apps	2,097	2,097	0
# of offers	1,214	1,214	0
# of matrics	202	202	0
75% GPA	3.40	3.40	0.00
Median GPA	3.16	3.16	0.00
25% GPA	2.87	2.87	0.00
75% LSAT	153	153	0
Median LSAT	151	151	0
25% LSAT	148	148	0

Grants and Scholarships (from prior year)

	Total		Full-Time		Part-Time	
	#	%	#	%	#	%
Total # of students	479		479		0	
Total # receiving grants	225	47.0	225	47.0	0	0.0
Less than 1/2 tuition	197	41.1	197	41.1	0	0.0
Half to full tuition	26	5.4	26	5.4	0	0.0
Full tuition	0	0.0	0	0.0	0	0.0
More than full tuition	2	0.4	2	0.4	0	0.0
Median grant amount			$10,000		$0	

Informational and Library Resources

Total amount spent on library materials	$793,521
Study seating capacity inside the library	489
# of full-time equivalent professional librarians	5
Hours per week library is open	102
# of open, wired connections available to students	38
# of networked computers available for use by students	15
Has wireless network?	Y
Require computer?	N

JD Attrition (from prior year)

	Academic	Other	Total	
	#	#	#	%
1st year	6	31	37	17.5
2nd year	3	4	7	6.0
3rd year	0	0	0	0.0
4th year	0	0	0	0.0

Employment (9 months after graduation)

	Total	Percentage
Employment status known	122	96.8
Employment status unknown	4	3.2
Employed	114	93.4
Pursuing graduate degrees	1	0.8
Unemployed (seeking, not seeking, or studying for the bar)	7	5.7
Type of Employment		
# employed in law firms	66	57.9
# employed in business and industry	15	13.2
# employed in government	15	13.2
# employed in public interest	5	4.4
# employed as judicial clerks	10	8.8
# employed in academia	3	2.6
Geographic Location		
# employed in state	71	62.3
# employed in foreign countries	0	0.0
# of states where employed	26	

Bar Passage Rates

First-time takers	116	Reporting %	71.55
Average school %	91.57	Average state %	88.29
Average pass difference	3.28		

Jurisdiction	Takers	Passers	Pass %	State %	Diff %
Ohio	77	72	93.51	88.09	5.42
Illinois	6	4	66.67	90.94	−24.27

University of Dayton School of Law

300 College Park, 112 Keller Hall
Dayton, OH 45469-2760
Phone: 937.229.3555; Fax: 937.229.4194
E-mail: lawinfo@notes.udayton.edu; Website: http://law.udayton.edu

■ Introduction and Mission

The mission of the School of Law is to enroll a diverse group of intellectually curious, self-disciplined, and well-motivated men and women, and to educate them in the substantive and procedural principles of public and private law. We seek to graduate highly qualified attorneys who will uphold the highest professional standards and recognize that service to others is the chief measure of professional competence.

We are a full-time JD program, providing a distinguished tradition of concern for the individual student in a supportive and professional environment. Our curriculum gives students a foundation in traditional courses but also helps them develop their skills with innovative programs such as our legal skills courses and our curricular concentrations in Advocacy and Dispute Resolution; Personal and Transactional Law; and Intellectual Property, Cyberlaw and Creativity. Our diverse student body of 450 promotes ample opportunity for one-on-one interaction with faculty, staff, and fellow students, creating an atmosphere of collegiality and active involvement in a myriad of law school organizations. We also have LLM and MSL programs in Intellectual Property and Technology. The University of Dayton School of Law is accredited by the ABA and is a member of the AALS.

■ Keller Hall and the University of Dayton

Joseph E. Keller Hall is a 122,500-square-foot complex featuring a dramatic atrium, a variety of classroom space, and a spacious law library with technology integrated throughout the building. Ready access is provided via our wireless network from virtually any location in the law building. Every seat in the 325,000-volume **Zimmerman Law Library** has access to a power outlet. The school's wireless network is also accessible from every seat in the library. The library also contains a computer training center where students learn to conduct online and computer-based research. Group study rooms allow students to meet in groups of up to 20.

Founded in 1850, the **University of Dayton** enrolls more than 10,000 undergraduate and graduate students in a campus setting. Located minutes from the city's center, the campus contains a fitness center and provides student services, on-campus housing, child care, meal plans, and banking. On-campus housing is available for half of the entering law students within three blocks of the law school.

■ The Dayton Community

With a population of approximately 850,000, the Dayton Metro Area offers the many amenities of larger urban areas while retaining its scenic, lush, and green open spaces. As the birthplace of the Wright Brothers, the city offers a variety of flight-related museums and events, as well as a variety of other cultural and recreational activities. Housing is varied and affordable, as are shopping, restaurants, and entertainment districts. Many state and local parks are available for biking, swimming, hiking, and boating. If students want to explore beyond Dayton, they can reach Cincinnati or Columbus in a 50–75 minute drive, or the quaint towns of Yellow Springs, Waynesville, or Lebanon within a 30-minute drive from campus.

■ Curriculum and Programs

Summer or Fall Start—Entering students may choose between a May or an August start to begin their full load of first-year courses.

Two-, Two-and-a-half, or Three-Year Law Degree—Students may complete their studies in either five semesters (accelerated) or six semesters (traditional). The summer-start combined with the five-semester accelerated study option allows a student to earn a JD in two calendar years.

Curriculum—UDSL offers a traditional education that blends theory and practice with a focus on attaining essential lawyering and problem-solving skills. The emphasis on acquiring legal skills through real-world practical experience, capstone and clinic courses, and a required externship prepares students for a successful legal career. Students may choose from various curricular concentrations focused on particular areas of the law, and are awarded a certificate in their chosen area upon graduation and successful completion of required concentration courses.

Externships—An externship is a semester-long legal apprenticeship in a legal setting, such as a governmental agency, law firm, corporation, court, or legal aid office. An externship provides students the opportunity to practice their craft, to observe highly respected attorneys and judges at work, and to network with the legal community.

Capstone Courses—Upper-level courses that are designed as a synthesis and completion of previously studied material. In these courses, students demonstrate their ability to apply to real and simulated legal problems the substantive knowledge and practical skills acquired during their education.

■ Graduate Programs

Master of Laws (LLM) in Intellectual Property and Technology Law—This program is for students who already possess a JD and desire to further their legal expertise in the area of intellectual property.

Master of Study of Law (MSL) in Intellectual Property and Technology Law—This program is for students who do not possess a JD but desire to gain an in-depth understanding of intellectual property.

■ Faculty

With backgrounds that span a spectrum of legal endeavors, many of our faculty members are known nationally for their expertise and scholarship. As prominent scholars and leaders, our professors transfer their expertise to students both inside and outside of the classroom. Students consistently praise our faculty, not only for their outstanding teaching skills, but also for their constant involvement in, concern for, and support of students' lives.

■ Student Life

Collegiality, support, and a positive atmosphere distinguish our student body, which benefits from the diversity of classmates in race, age, gender, and background. Students may participate in organizations that help develop writing, research, and oral

advocacy skills; those that speak to their mutual professional interests; or those that provide support of a student's personal and biographical background and interests. Our Student Bar Association is made up of officers and representatives from each class who oversee all student organizations and is the voice of student governance at the law school.

Career Services and Bar Passage

Our Career Services Office Assistant Dean and his staff are committed to providing comprehensive career planning and placement services to assist students with identifying and securing positions commensurate with each individual's interests and career goals. Over half of our students are employed in private practice and about one-third find positions in business, industry, the government, or the military. Our graduates are employed in most states and several countries. They take an active interest in the life of the law school, participating in panel discussions, mentor programs, and alumni events, as well as contributing their time and resources to various scholarship and fundraising activities.

Our graduates have been consistently successful in bar passage and attribute this success to our curriculum as well as to our excellent **Road to Bar Passage Program**. This program involves students from their first year of law school right through to the exam. A series of workshops informs students about bar examinations and how to prepare for them. Thanks to our curriculum and Road to Bar Passage Program, our graduates have been highly successful in passing the Ohio and other states' bar examinations.

Admission

The Admissions Committee looks for a well-rounded and diverse group of students. Undergraduate GPA and LSAT score are highly considered, but commitment, motivation, leadership, and a breadth and depth of experiences are also a large part of the applicant review. Decisions are made on a rolling basis, beginning November 1 and continuing through late spring.

Financial Aid

One third to one half of the entering class receive scholarships. The majority of our scholarships are merit based, with the goal of diversifying the class also taken into consideration. Renewal of merit scholarships is dependent upon academic performance at the end of the preceding two semesters.

Federal loans up to $20,500 are also available to our students. Alternative loans may also be used to cover the cost of a legal education, should scholarships and federal loans not do so. Federal and alternative loans are available pending a student's citizenship status and credit rating.

Prospective Students

Prospective students are encouraged to contact the Office of Admissions to schedule informational visits or obtain assistance with questions or concerns. Office hours are 8:30 AM to 4:30 PM, Monday through Friday.

Applicant Profile

University of Dayton School of Law
This grid includes all full-time applicants who earned LSAT scores on the 120–180 scale under standard test administrations and whose submission files were complete and reviewed by the faculty admission committee.

LSAT Score	3.75 +		3.50–3.74		3.25–3.49		3.00–3.24		2.75–2.99		2.50–2.74		2.25–2.49		2.00–2.24		Below 2.00		No GPA		Total	
	Apps	Adm	Apps	Adm	Apps	Adm	Apps	Adm	Apps	Adm	Apps	Adm	Apps	Adm	Apps	Adm	Apps	Adm	Apps	Adm	Apps	Adm
175–180	0	0	0	0	0	0	0	0	0	0	0	0	0	0	0	0	0	0	0	0	0	0
170–174	1	1	0	0	0	0	1	1	0	0	0	0	0	0	0	0	0	0	0	0	2	2
165–169	4	4	2	2	2	2	2	1	3	3	1	1	1	1	1	0	0	0	0	0	16	14
160–164	10	10	15	13	11	11	14	14	8	8	5	3	3	1	2	1	1	0	0	0	69	61
155–159	36	36	56	55	45	45	39	37	23	20	10	8	13	2	4	0	1	0	2	1	229	204
150–154	53	51	116	110	136	131	110	104	86	77	30	19	21	6	8	3	1	0	4	2	565	503
145–149	42	31	93	45	120	67	134	72	92	40	49	9	31	3	6	1	2	0	5	1	574	269
140–144	7	2	36	9	68	20	65	10	62	10	37	3	15	0	8	0	1	0	6	1	305	55
135–139	2	0	8	0	17	3	18	0	21	1	16	0	9	0	5	1	1	0	2	0	99	6
130–134	4	0	4	0	2	0	4	0	2	0	2	0	5	0	6	0	0	0	3	0	32	0
125–129	0	0	1	0	1	0	1	0	1	0	1	0	2	0	0	0	0	0	0	0	7	0
120–124	0	0	0	0	0	0	0	0	1	0	0	0	0	0	0	0	0	0	0	0	1	0
Total	159	135	331	235	402	279	388	239	299	159	151	43	100	13	40	6	7	0	22	5	1899	1114

Apps = Number of Applicants   Adm = Number Admitted   Reflects 99% of the total applicant pool; average LSAT data reported.

The information on this grid should be used as a general guide only. The University of Dayton School of Law Admissions Committee reviews all aspects of the application, including the undergraduate record, letters of recommendation, personal statement and optional diversity statement, work and extracurricular activities, and the breadth and depth of an applicant's personal background and experiences. All of these factors are fully considered before a final decision is made.

University of Denver Sturm College of Law

2255 E. Evans Avenue, Suite 115
Denver, CO 80208
Phone: 303.871.6135; Fax: 303.871.6992
E-mail: admissions@law.du.edu; Website: www.law.du.edu

ABA
Approved
Since
1923

The Basics

Type of school	Private
Term	Semester
Application deadline	
Application fee	$60
Financial aid deadline	3/1
Can first year start other than fall?	No
Student to faculty ratio	15.5 to 1
# of housing spaces available restricted to law students	
graduate housing for which law students are eligible	21

Faculty and Administrators

	Total		Men		Women		Minorities	
	Spr	Fall	Spr	Fall	Spr	Fall	Spr	Fall
Full-time	51	58	29	30	22	28	9	10
Other full-time	8	7	5	5	3	2	2	1
Deans, librarians, & others who teach	14	12	9	8	5	4	5	4
Part-time	47	56	38	45	9	11	4	0
Total	120	133	81	88	39	45	20	15

Curriculum

		Full-Time	Part-Time
Typical first-year section size		80	60
Is there typically a "small section" of the first-year class, other than Legal Writing, taught by full-time faculty		Yes	Yes
If yes, typical size offered last year		40	40
# of classroom course titles beyond first-year curriculum		171	
# of upper division courses, excluding seminars, with an enrollment:	Under 25	188	
	25–49	63	
	50–74	24	
	75–99	10	
	100+	1	
# of seminars		33	
# of seminar positions available		438	
# of seminar positions filled		384	54
# of positions available in simulation courses		420	
# of simulation positions filled		344	76
# of positions available in faculty supervised clinical courses		93	
# of faculty supervised clinical positions filled	88		5
# involved in field placements		365	32
# involved in law journals		350	11
# involved in moot court or trial competitions	48		5
# of credit hours required to graduate		90	

JD Enrollment and Ethnicity

	Men		Women		Full-Time		Part-Time		1st-Year		Total		JD Degs. Awd.
	#	%	#	%	#	%	#	%	#	%	#	%	
African Amer.	9	1.7	18	3.7	16	2.0	11	4.7	9	3.0	27	2.7	13
Amer. Indian	12	2.2	8	1.7	13	1.7	7	3.0	4	1.4	20	2.0	10
Asian Amer.	28	5.2	30	6.2	48	6.1	10	4.3	14	4.7	58	5.7	14
Mex. Amer.	0	0.0	0	0.0	0	0.0	0	0.0	0	0.0	0	0.0	0
Puerto Rican	0	0.0	0	0.0	0	0.0	0	0.0	0	0.0	0	0.0	0
Hispanic	30	5.6	45	9.4	57	7.3	18	7.8	14	4.7	75	7.4	15
Total Minority	79	14.7	101	21.0	134	17.0	46	19.8	41	13.9	180	17.7	52
For. Nation.	0	0.0	0	0.0	0	0.0	0	0.0	0	0.0	0	0.0	0
Caucasian	425	79.1	361	75.1	610	77.6	176	75.9	251	84.8	786	77.2	276
Unknown	33	6.1	19	4.0	42	5.3	10	4.3	4	1.4	52	5.1	24
Total	537	52.8	481	47.2	786	77.2	232	22.8	296	29.1	1018		352

Transfers

Transfers in	10
Transfers out	7

Tuition and Fees

	Resident	Nonresident
Full-time	$35,700	$35,700
Part-time	$26,244	$26,244
Tuition Guarantee Program		N

Living Expenses

Estimated living expenses for singles

Living on campus	Living off campus	Living at home
$16,537	$16,537	$16,537

University of Denver Sturm College of Law

ABA
Approved
Since
1923

GPA and LSAT Scores

	Total	Full-Time	Part-Time
# of apps	2,925	2,587	338
# of offers	961	862	99
# of matrics	300	237	63
75% GPA	3.69	3.69	3.67
Median GPA	3.51	3.52	3.43
25% GPA	3.23	3.27	3.15
75% LSAT	160	161	158
Median LSAT	159	159	156
25% LSAT	155	156	154

Grants and Scholarships (from prior year)

	Total		Full-Time		Part-Time	
	#	%	#	%	#	%
Total # of students	1,092		839		253	
Total # receiving grants	335	30.7	294	35.0	41	16.2
Less than 1/2 tuition	167	15.3	143	17.0	24	9.5
Half to full tuition	126	11.5	113	13.5	13	5.1
Full tuition	42	3.8	38	4.5	4	1.6
More than full tuition	0	0.0	0	0.0	0	0.0
Median grant amount			$17,600		$10,630	

Informational and Library Resources

Total amount spent on library materials	$2,026,583
Study seating capacity inside the library	333
# of full-time equivalent professional librarians	8
Hours per week library is open	108
# of open, wired connections available to students	1,535
# of networked computers available for use by students	28
Has wireless network?	Y
Require computer?	Y

JD Attrition (from prior year)

	Academic	Other	Total	
	#	#	#	%
1st year	9	10	19	6.5
2nd year	8	2	10	2.5
3rd year	0	1	1	0.3
4th year	0	0	0	0.0

Employment (9 months after graduation)

	Total	Percentage
Employment status known	313	99.7
Employment status unknown	1	0.3
Employed	274	87.5
Pursuing graduate degrees	12	3.8
Unemployed (seeking, not seeking, or studying for the bar)	17	5.4
Type of Employment		
# employed in law firms	143	52.2
# employed in business and industry	47	17.2
# employed in government	38	13.9
# employed in public interest	10	3.6
# employed as judicial clerks	27	9.9
# employed in academia	2	0.7
Geographic Location		
# employed in state	212	77.4
# employed in foreign countries	2	0.7
# of states where employed	22	

Bar Passage Rates

First-time takers	352	Reporting %	76.70
Average school %	80.37	Average state %	83.29
Average pass difference –2.92			

Jurisdiction	Takers	Passers	Pass %	State %	Diff %
Colorado	270	217	80.37	83.29	–2.92

University of Denver Sturm College of Law

2255 E. Evans Avenue, Suite 115
Denver, CO 80208
Phone: 303.871.6135; Fax: 303.871.6992
E-mail: admissions@law.du.edu; Website: www.law.du.edu

■ Introduction

The University of Denver Sturm College of Law opened its doors in 1892, and has been breaking ground in legal education ever since. Our faculty pride themselves in training students for successful careers as legal practitioners by offering a variety of challenging and exciting courses in addition to experiential learning opportunities through our Student Law Office, internships with law firms, and clerkships with judges. Our new building, with over 181,000 square feet spanning four stories, is the first law building to be awarded the Gold Leadership in Energy and Environmental Design (LEED) certification by the US Green Building Council. Downtown Denver—where the state legislature, courthouses, regional federal agencies, state agencies, and law firms are found—is 15 minutes away on the Light Rail, and the Rocky Mountains are just a short drive to the west.

■ Curriculum/Special Programs

The Sturm College of Law provides a solid foundation of core classes on which to build your career in law. In addition, we offer a wide range of specialized classes that permit our faculty to bring their scholarship into the classroom.

Lawyering Process Course—The first year curriculum includes an innovative Lawyering Process course, which provides first-year students an introduction to the law and the legal system, and teaches students how to research legal questions and write about them in several formats.

Environmental and Natural Resources Law—Drawing upon its location in one of the nation's natural resource and energy capitals, the University of Denver Sturm College of Law offers a rich program in environmental and natural resources law. Extensive course offerings are supplemented with abundant opportunities for internships at local natural resource companies, environmental advocacy and protection groups, and government enforcement agencies. Students may also participate in our Environmental Law Clinic, student organizations, the *Water Law Review*, writing competitions, and natural resources moot court competitions.

International Legal Studies—The International Legal Studies program is designed for students interested in international comparative law, international organizations, or transnational business. Students in the program may work on the *Denver Journal of International Law and Policy* as staff members and editors. The International Law Society and Ved Nanda Center for International Law sponsor a rich schedule of outside speakers and an annual conference focused on a current issue in international law.

Business Law—As one of the nation's biggest tourism magnets, Denver provides a practical back drop for students interested in business and commercial law. In addition to foundation courses and specialized seminars, corporate internships and highly prized one-semester assignments with large local corporations are available for interested students to pursue.

Lawyering in Spanish—This program celebrates the globalization of Spanish culture by providing an opportunity to learn the specialized vocabulary and counseling techniques required to represent Spanish-speaking clients in the US and abroad.

Clinics—In 1904 the University of Denver launched the first Student Law Office (SLO) in the United States. The SLO offers the following clinics: Civil Litigation, Civil Rights, Community Law, Criminal Representation, Environmental, and Mediation/Arbitration. Students represent indigent clients at all levels of the dispute resolution process. If the case reaches the litigation phase, the student handles all aspects of pretrial, trial preparation, and the trial itself under faculty supervision.

■ Student Activities

Trial Advocacy—The University of Denver Sturm College of Law Moot Court Board is dedicated to providing students the highest quality legal scenarios presented under the most realistic conditions possible. The board manages and produces six legal competitions per academic year and provides logistical support to DU Law's traveling teams. Based upon their performance in national trial competition and the Association of Trial Lawyers of America National Student Trial Advocacy Competition, DU's trial advocacy team has been among 16 law school teams invited to participate in the National Institute for Trial Advocacy Tournament of Champions.

Journals—Five scholarly journals are edited at the Sturm College of Law, allowing students to participate in research in varied fields. Academic credit is awarded for work on the *Denver University Law Review, Denver Journal of International Law and Policy, Sports and Entertainment Law Journal, Transportation Law Journal*, and the *University of Denver Water Law Review*.

Student Organizations—A wide range of student organizations contribute to the vibrant environment of the Sturm College of Law. Among those groups are the Animal Legal Defense Fund, Asian Pacific American Law Students' Association, Black Law Students' Association, Business Law Society, Christian Legal Society, Federalist Society, International Law Society, Intellectual Property Law Society, Natural Resources and Environmental Law Society, Jewish Law Students Association, Latino Law Students Association, Native American Law Students Association, Phi Alpha Delta, Public Interest Law Group, and Sports and Entertainment Law Society.

■ Admission

All applications should be submitted online and reach the Sturm College of Law between September and February to receive maximum consideration for admission for the following August. Students may only begin law study in the fall semester. Applicants must take the LSAT and register with LSAC's Credential Assembly Service. LSAT scores and records of academic performance are individually evaluated in the admission process. The applicant's personal statement, résumé, and letters of recommendation are thoroughly reviewed, as well as, work experience, significant personal accomplishments, leadership roles, a commitment to community service, and other activities that show initiative, growth, and maturity.

■ Expenses and Financial Aid

All admitted students are considered for scholarships. No additional application is required, except for the Chancellor Scholarship. Scholarships offered to entering first-year students may be renewed each year based on satisfactory academic performance.

The Chancellor Scholar program is offered to students with a demonstrated history of excellence in scholarship and public service. The program awards full-tuition scholarships to a limited number of qualified students committed to public interest issues. The scholarships are available to entering first-year day-division and evening-division students.

Additional one-year scholarships may be offered to continuing students based on law school performance. Students may also apply for federal loans, up to the cost of attendance.

■ Career Services

The Career Development Center (CDC) assists students and alumni in the formulation of career plans and connects potential employers with qualified applicants. Their services include educating students and alumni in developing necessary skills to locate and obtain satisfying and meaningful employment, connecting students and alumni to the world of work, and facilitating employers' connections with students and alumni.

■ Housing

On-campus graduate housing is available at the University of Denver. However, the majority of law students choose to live off campus.

Applicant Profile

University of Denver Sturm College of Law
This grid includes only applicants who earned 120–180 LSAT scores under standard administrations.

LSAT Score	GPA 3.75 +		3.50–3.74		3.25–3.49		3.00–3.24		2.75–2.99		2.50–2.74		2.25–2.49		2.00–2.24		Below 2.00		No GPA		Total	
	Apps	Adm	Apps	Adm	Apps	Adm	Apps	Adm	Apps	Adm	Apps	Adm	Apps	Adm	Apps	Adm	Apps	Adm	Apps	Adm	Apps	Adm
175–180	0	0	0	0	0	0	0	0	0	0	0	0	0	0	0	0	0	0	0	0	0	0
170–174	6	6	3	3	2	2	1	1	1	1	1	1	1	0	1	1	0	0	0	0	16	15
165–169	18	17	16	15	18	16	20	17	5	5	6	4	4	0	1	0	0	0	0	0	88	74
160–164	59	57	82	80	94	92	68	64	44	34	26	12	10	0	3	1	1	0	1	1	388	341
155–159	102	74	211	130	203	72	171	53	80	29	35	5	23	2	13	1	4	0	7	1	849	367
150–154	100	44	165	52	237	19	208	14	124	12	50	3	31	1	7	0	1	0	13	4	936	149
145–149	42	10	85	10	106	4	103	3	59	2	35	0	17	0	5	0	0	0	4	0	456	29
140–144	10	0	25	0	35	0	43	0	35	0	24	0	14	0	6	0	1	0	3	0	196	0
135–139	1	0	3	0	8	0	13	0	8	0	12	0	3	0	3	0	1	0	3	0	55	0
130–134	0	0	0	0	0	0	3	0	4	0	1	0	2	0	1	0	0	0	2	1	13	1
125–129	0	0	0	0	0	0	1	0	0	0	2	0	0	0	0	0	0	0	2	1	5	1
120–124	0	0	0	0	0	0	0	0	0	0	0	0	1	0	0	0	0	0	0	0	1	0
Total	338	208	590	290	703	205	631	152	360	83	192	25	106	3	40	3	8	0	35	8	3003	977

Apps = Number of Applicants
Adm = Number Admitted
Reflects 99% of the total applicant pool; average LSAT data reported.

DePaul University College of Law

25 East Jackson Boulevard
Chicago, IL 60604-2219
Phone: 312.362.6831 or 800.428.7453; Fax: 312.362.5280
E-mail: lawinfo@depaul.edu; Website: www.law.depaul.edu

ABA
Approved
Since
1925

The Basics

Type of school	Private
Term	Semester
Application deadline	3/1
Application fee	$60
Financial aid deadline	4/1
Can first year start other than fall?	No
Student to faculty ratio	13.4 to 1
# of housing spaces available restricted to law students	
graduate housing for which law students are eligible	254

Faculty and Administrators

	Total		Men		Women		Minorities	
	Spr	Fall	Spr	Fall	Spr	Fall	Spr	Fall
Full-time	55	60	31	34	24	26	10	8
Other full-time	2	2	2	2	0	0	0	0
Deans, librarians, & others who teach	4	3	3	2	1	1	1	1
Part-time	66	61	39	43	27	18	6	6
Total	127	126	75	81	52	45	17	15

Curriculum

		Full-Time	Part-Time
Typical first-year section size		90	97
Is there typically a "small section" of the first-year class, other than Legal Writing, taught by full-time faculty		No	No
If yes, typical size offered last year			
# of classroom course titles beyond first-year curriculum		156	
# of upper division courses, excluding seminars, with an enrollment:	Under 25	108	
	25–49	28	
	50–74	13	
	75–99	8	
	100+	1	
# of seminars		19	
# of seminar positions available		380	
# of seminar positions filled		190	56
# of positions available in simulation courses		876	
# of simulation positions filled		170	498
# of positions available in faculty supervised clinical courses		200	
# of faculty supervised clinical positions filled		139	7
# involved in field placements		134	0
# involved in law journals		91	0
# involved in moot court or trial competitions		45	0
# of credit hours required to graduate		86	

JD Enrollment and Ethnicity

	Men		Women		Full-Time		Part-Time		1st-Year		Total		JD Degs. Awd.
	#	%	#	%	#	%	#	%	#	%	#	%	
African Amer.	21	4.2	51	9.8	54	7.0	18	7.1	34	9.3	72	7.0	27
Amer. Indian	1	0.2	2	0.4	2	0.3	1	0.4	1	0.3	3	0.3	0
Asian Amer.	23	4.6	40	7.7	44	5.7	19	7.5	26	7.1	63	6.1	14
Mex. Amer.	3	0.6	7	1.3	9	1.2	1	0.4	4	1.1	10	1.0	0
Puerto Rican	1	0.2	1	0.2	2	0.3	0	0.0	1	0.3	2	0.2	0
Hispanic	29	5.7	69	13.2	72	9.3	26	10.2	38	10.4	98	9.5	34
Total Minority	78	15.4	170	32.6	183	23.7	65	25.5	104	28.6	248	24.1	75
For. Nation.	6	1.2	10	1.9	12	1.6	4	1.6	6	1.6	16	1.6	7
Caucasian	403	79.8	332	63.6	557	72.2	178	69.8	227	62.4	735	71.6	206
Unknown	18	3.6	10	1.9	20	2.6	8	3.1	27	7.4	28	2.7	32
Total	505	49.2	522	50.8	772	75.2	255	24.8	364	35.4	1027		320

Transfers

Transfers in	12
Transfers out	13

Tuition and Fees

	Resident	Nonresident
Full-time	$37,975	$37,975
Part-time	$24,830	$24,830
Tuition Guarantee Program		Y

Living Expenses

Estimated living expenses for singles

Living on campus	Living off campus	Living at home
$22,407	$22,407	$22,407

DePaul University College of Law

ABA Approved Since 1925

AMERICAN BAR ASSOCIATION
Section of Legal Education
and Admissions to the Bar

GPA and LSAT Scores

	Total	Full-Time	Part-Time
# of apps	5,068	4,366	702
# of offers	1,988	1,658	330
# of matrics	364	252	112
75% GPA	3.53	3.57	3.41
Median GPA	3.35	3.40	3.26
25% GPA	3.09	3.11	3.04
75% LSAT	161	162	157
Median LSAT	158	159	156
25% LSAT	154	158	154

Grants and Scholarships (from prior year)

	Total		Full-Time		Part-Time	
	#	%	#	%	#	%
Total # of students	1,184		909		275	
Total # receiving grants	631	53.3	528	58.1	103	37.5
Less than 1/2 tuition	467	39.4	377	41.5	90	32.7
Half to full tuition	152	12.8	148	16.3	4	1.5
Full tuition	0	0.0	0	0.0	0	0.0
More than full tuition	12	1.0	3	0.3	9	3.3
Median grant amount			$13,000		$4,000	

Informational and Library Resources

Total amount spent on library materials	$1,210,176
Study seating capacity inside the library	446
# of full-time equivalent professional librarians	8
Hours per week library is open	95
# of open, wired connections available to students	70
# of networked computers available for use by students	190
Has wireless network?	Y
Require computer?	N

JD Attrition (from prior year)

	Academic	Other	Total	
	#	#	#	%
1st year	12	21	33	9.0
2nd year	0	7	7	1.5
3rd year	1	1	2	0.7
4th year	1	0	1	1.7

Employment (9 months after graduation)

	Total	Percentage
Employment status known	306	99.7
Employment status unknown	1	0.3
Employed	274	89.5
Pursuing graduate degrees	2	0.7
Unemployed (seeking, not seeking, or studying for the bar)	17	5.6
Type of Employment		
# employed in law firms	151	55.1
# employed in business and industry	55	20.1
# employed in government	36	13.1
# employed in public interest	9	3.3
# employed as judicial clerks	4	1.5
# employed in academia	15	5.5
Geographic Location		
# employed in state	223	81.4
# employed in foreign countries	1	0.4
# of states where employed	21	

Bar Passage Rates

First-time takers	300	Reporting %	89.00
Average school %	89.14	Average state %	90.94
Average pass difference	−1.80		

Jurisdiction	Takers	Passers	Pass %	State %	Diff %
Illinois	267	238	89.14	90.94	−1.80

DePaul University College of Law

25 East Jackson Boulevard
Chicago, IL 60604-2219
Phone: 312.362.6831 or 800.428.7453; Fax: 312.362.5280
E-mail: lawinfo@depaul.edu; Website: www.law.depaul.edu

■ Introduction

DePaul University is the largest private university in Illinois and enjoys the advantages of its vibrant urban setting. Its strong reputation for academic excellence is distinguished by its dedicated faculty, unrivaled professional skills training, and its genuine sense of community.

Located in the heart of Chicago's business and legal communities, the College of Law affords extensive contact with Chicago's legal community. It is within walking distance of the state and federal courts, government offices, and many law firms. DePaul law alumni include the mayor of Chicago, numerous state and federal judges, and managing partners of Chicago law firms. The college offers full-time, part-time, and summer programs. DePaul is fully accredited by the ABA, and is a member of AALS and the Order of the Coif.

■ Students

Founded in 1898 by Vincentian Fathers as a school for children of immigrants, DePaul University students represent a rich diversity in age, ethnicity, education, and career experiences. Because of the broad diversity of backgrounds and experiences of its law students, there is a connectedness within the institution that creates a genuine sense of community. Fifty percent of full-time students in the entering class of 2009 were women, while 32 percent were minorities. More than half of the students in the 2009 entering full-time class were from out of state. The average age of full-time students is 24, while the average age of part-time students is 26.

■ Faculty

DePaul faculty members, including many who have earned advanced degrees, are recognized scholars who represent a variety of professional backgrounds and interests. Consistent with the university's Vincentian mission of service to the community, faculty members work tirelessly in service to the legal profession and to the community, and they have achieved national recognition in teaching, research, scholarly activities, and professional service. The faculty is extremely accessible, approachable, and deeply committed to its students.

■ Library, Research Centers, and Institutes

The three-story law library offers extensive resources for study and research. Its staff includes 7 professional librarians and 12 full-time support staff.

The College of Law also maintains 15 research centers and institutes:
- Health Law Institute
- International Aviation Law Institute
- International Human Rights Law Institute
- International Weapons Control Center
- Asian Legal Studies Institute
- Schiller, DuCanto, and Fleck Family Law Center
- Center for Intellectual Property Law and Information Technology
- Center for Justice in Capital Cases
- Center for Animal Law

- Center for Public Interest Law
- Center for Dispute Resolution
- Center for Law and Science
- Center for Art, Museum, and Cultural Heritage Law
- Center for Jewish Law and Judaic Studies
- Center for Church-State Studies

■ Special Programs

Academic Support Program: DePaul is committed to ensuring that all students have the tools they need to attain academic success. Toward that end, DePaul has one of the premier academic support programs in the nation.

Legal Clinic: Students gain valuable hands-on experience in nine clinical concentrations: Advanced Immigrant Detainee, Asylum/Immigration, Civil Rights Law, Criminal Appeals, Death Penalty, Family Law, Misdemeanor, Special Education Advocacy, and Technology/Intellectual Property.

Field Placement Program: Providing students with academic credit through supervised field work, externships are offered by federal and state judges, various municipal agencies, and a number of nonprofit and for-profit organizations.

Mediation Program: Students learn essential client counseling skills by working with mediators on cases referred by the County Domestic Relations Courts.

Skills Competitions: As a leader in the field of professional skills, DePaul has enjoyed considerable success in skills competitions. DePaul student teams regularly place among the top in both regional and national moot court competitions.

Certificate Programs: DePaul offers eleven comprehensive certificate programs, including Business Law, Child and Family Law, Criminal Law, Health Law, International and Comparative Law, Public Interest Law, Taxation, and four in Intellectual Property Law (General, Arts and Museum, Information Technology, and Patents).

Asian Legal Studies Institute: Students receive academic credit for summer courses taken at Beijing Foreign Studies University in China. Students focus on legal principles and planning related to international transactions in the Asia-Pacific region. Lectures are presented by professors from DePaul and major Chinese law schools.

Chiapas Human Rights Practicum: Conducted entirely in Spanish, the practicum places student workers in human rights offices in the state of Chiapas, Mexico, where basic human rights violations are an everyday reality.

European Legal Studies Program: This program offers students the option to study in Madrid, Spain, or Prague, the Czech Republic. The programs include a number of tours of legal, business, and political institutions in each country.

Human Rights Law in the Americas: Located in San Jose, Costa Rica, this program introduces students to the basic principles of international law with an overview of the Inter-American Human Rights System.

Legal Dimensions of Doing Business in Latin America: Taking place in Buenos Aires, Argentina, students study the legal principles and practices that shape business law in Latin America.

University College Dublin (UCD) Student Exchange Program: DePaul and UCD have a student exchange program

in which second-year students undertake legal studies abroad during their spring semester.

Joint-Degree and Master of Laws (LLM) Programs: DePaul offers five joint-degree and four master of laws programs:

- JD/MBA in coordination with DePaul's nationally recognized Kellstadt Graduate School of Business.
- JD/MS in Public Service Management promotes effective management of government and nonprofit organizations.
- JD/MA in International Studies offers concentrations in International Political Economy and Global Culture and complements DePaul's strong international law offerings.
- JD/MA and JD/MS in Computer Science explore the intersections of law, computer science, telecommunications, and information systems.
- DePaul's master of laws (LLM) programs include Health Law, Intellectual Property Law, International Law, and Taxation.

Special First-Year Legal Writing Sections: Students may apply for a seat in one of four special sections of Legal Analysis, Research, and Communication, focusing on child and family law, health law, intellectual property law, and public interest law.

■ Housing

Located in Chicago's Loop just two blocks south of the law school, the University Center of Chicago (UCC) is a recently developed residence hall offering furnished apartments and suites. Amenities include a rooftop garden, multimedia rooms, a fitness center, food court, laundry facilities, shops on the lower level, 24-hour security, and keycard access to the building and elevators.

■ Admission

DePaul adheres to a policy of nondiscrimination and encourages applications from traditionally underrepresented groups. Admission decisions are based on a variety of factors, and each file is reviewed thoroughly. Undergraduate GPA and LSAT scores are significant admission criteria. For the 2009–2010 academic year, 4,401 candidates applied for admission to the full-time program, while 708 applied to the part-time program. Admitted students are automatically considered for available merit-based scholarships.

■ Career Services

Alumni, faculty, and students contribute to an active and aggressive career services network. The teaching and publishing reputations of the faculty, as well as the largest alumni bench and bar network in the Chicago area, complement three full-time DePaul law career services officers.

Applicant Profile

DePaul University College of Law
This grid includes only applicants who earned 120–180 LSAT scores under standard administrations.

LSAT Score	3.75 +		3.50–3.74		3.25–3.49		3.00–3.24		2.75–2.99		2.50–2.74		2.25–2.49		2.00–2.24		Below 2.00		No GPA		Total	
	Apps	Adm	Apps	Adm	Apps	Adm	Apps	Adm	Apps	Adm	Apps	Adm	Apps	Adm	Apps	Adm	Apps	Adm	Apps	Adm	Apps	Adm
175–180	1	1	0	0	0	0	0	0	0	0	0	0	0	0	0	0	0	0	0	0	1	1
170–174	3	3	6	6	10	10	3	3	4	4	1	1	2	0	0	0	0	0	0	0	29	27
165–169	42	41	54	54	42	42	31	28	27	25	18	14	11	8	1	0	0	0	2	2	228	214
160–164	144	134	207	194	213	181	156	119	79	56	51	40	23	10	11	4	2	0	11	7	897	745
155–159	166	140	337	242	356	211	263	125	133	55	73	28	25	5	12	0	5	0	22	12	1392	818
150–154	114	49	224	78	329	93	264	52	173	32	96	12	40	1	10	0	2	0	13	1	1265	318
145–149	46	13	121	27	167	38	166	22	118	20	82	5	47	1	12	0	5	0	16	1	780	127
120–144	15	2	44	1	75	8	105	5	81	2	76	1	44	0	20	0	5	0	17	0	482	19
Total	531	383	993	602	1192	583	988	354	615	194	397	101	192	25	66	4	19	0	81	23	5074	2269

Apps = Number of Applicants
Adm = Number Admitted
Reflects 99% of the total applicant pool; average LSAT data reported.

University of Detroit Mercy School of Law

Admissions Office, 651 East Jefferson Avenue
Detroit, MI 48226
Phone: 313.596.0264
E-mail: udmlawao@udmercy.edu; Website: www.law.udmercy.edu

ABA
Approved
Since
1933

AMERICAN BAR ASSOCIATION
Section of Legal Education
and Admissions to the Bar

The Basics

Type of school	Private
Term	Semester
Application deadline	4/15
Application fee	$50
Financial aid deadline	4/1
Can first year start other than fall?	No
Student to faculty ratio	14.1 to 1
# of housing spaces available restricted to law students	
graduate housing for which law students are eligible	

Faculty and Administrators

	Total		Men		Women		Minorities	
	Spr	Fall	Spr	Fall	Spr	Fall	Spr	Fall
Full-time	40	39	22	21	18	18	3	3
Other full-time	0	0	0	0	0	0	0	0
Deans, librarians, & others who teach	13	13	6	6	7	7	2	2
Part-time	33	35	20	25	13	10	4	1
Total	86	87	48	52	38	35	9	6

Curriculum

	Full-Time	Part-Time
Typical first-year section size	58	32
Is there typically a "small section" of the first-year class, other than Legal Writing, taught by full-time faculty	No	No
If yes, typical size offered last year		
# of classroom course titles beyond first-year curriculum		96
# of upper division courses, excluding seminars, with an enrollment: Under 25		104
25–49		41
50–74		15
75–99		0
100+		0
# of seminars		11
# of seminar positions available		176
# of seminar positions filled	110	19
# of positions available in simulation courses	554	
# of simulation positions filled	391	66
# of positions available in faculty supervised clinical courses		210
# of faculty supervised clinical positions filled	145	16
# involved in field placements	111	5
# involved in law journals	52	7
# involved in moot court or trial competitions	56	5
# of credit hours required to graduate		90

JD Enrollment and Ethnicity

	Men		Women		Full-Time		Part-Time		1st-Year		Total		JD Degs. Awd.
	#	%	#	%	#	%	#	%	#	%	#	%	
African Amer.	30	7.6	48	14.3	38	6.5	40	27.8	25	8.9	78	10.7	15
Amer. Indian	2	0.5	2	0.6	4	0.7	0	0.0	2	0.7	4	0.5	0
Asian Amer.	16	4.1	13	3.9	26	4.4	3	2.1	10	3.6	29	4.0	4
Mex. Amer.	0	0.0	0	0.0	0	0.0	0	0.0	0	0.0	0	0.0	0
Puerto Rican	0	0.0	0	0.0	0	0.0	0	0.0	0	0.0	0	0.0	0
Hispanic	7	1.8	11	3.3	12	2.0	6	4.2	5	1.8	18	2.5	3
Total Minority	55	13.9	74	22.1	80	13.7	49	34.0	42	14.9	129	17.7	22
For. Nation.	71	18.0	77	23.0	145	24.7	3	2.1	60	21.4	148	20.3	31
Caucasian	269	68.1	184	54.9	361	61.6	92	63.9	179	63.7	453	62.1	162
Unknown	0	0.0	0	0.0	0	0.0	0	0.0	0	0.0	0	0.0	0
Total	395	54.1	335	45.9	586	80.3	144	19.7	281	38.5	730		215

Transfers

Transfers in	1
Transfers out	33

Tuition and Fees

	Resident	Nonresident
Full-time	$16,085	$16,085
Part-time	$12,884	$12,884
Tuition Guarantee Program		N

Living Expenses

Estimated living expenses for singles

Living on campus	Living off campus	Living at home
N/A	$20,836	$13,259

University of Detroit Mercy School of Law

ABA
Approved
Since
1933

GPA and LSAT Scores

	Total	Full-Time	Part-Time
# of apps	1,926	1,707	219
# of offers	859	772	87
# of matrics	282	243	39
75% GPA	3.38	3.38	3.31
Median GPA	3.16	3.15	3.17
25% GPA	2.93	2.93	2.91
75% LSAT	153	154	149
Median LSAT	150	150	147
25% LSAT	146	147	144

Grants and Scholarships (from prior year)

	Total		Full-Time		Part-Time	
	#	%	#	%	#	%
Total # of students	736		589		147	
Total # receiving grants	174	23.6	148	25.1	26	17.7
Less than 1/2 tuition	154	20.9	130	22.1	24	16.3
Half to full tuition	18	2.4	16	2.7	2	1.4
Full tuition	2	0.3	2	0.3	0	0.0
More than full tuition	0	0.0	0	0.0	0	0.0
Median grant amount			$5,500		$3,011	

Informational and Library Resources

Total amount spent on library materials	$1,196,691
Study seating capacity inside the library	323
# of full-time equivalent professional librarians	6
Hours per week library is open	92
# of open, wired connections available to students	0
# of networked computers available for use by students	52
Has wireless network?	Y
Require computer?	N

JD Attrition (from prior year)

	Academic	Other	Total	
	#	#	#	%
1st year	21	47	68	26.2
2nd year	0	0	0	0.0
3rd year	0	2	2	0.9
4th year	0	1	1	3.6

Employment (9 months after graduation)

	Total	Percentage
Employment status known	207	98.1
Employment status unknown	4	1.9
Employed	154	74.4
Pursuing graduate degrees	1	0.5
Unemployed (seeking, not seeking, or studying for the bar)	40	19.3
Type of Employment		
# employed in law firms	88	57.1
# employed in business and industry	34	22.1
# employed in government	8	5.2
# employed in public interest	7	4.5
# employed as judicial clerks	9	5.8
# employed in academia	8	5.2
Geographic Location		
# employed in state	89	57.8
# employed in foreign countries	26	16.9
# of states where employed	19	

Bar Passage Rates

First-time takers	226	Reporting %	58.85
Average school %	71.43	Average state %	82.13
Average pass difference–10.70			

Jurisdiction	Takers	Passers	Pass %	State %	Diff %
Michigan	133	95	71.43	82.13	–10.70

University of Detroit Mercy School of Law

Admissions Office, 651 East Jefferson Avenue
Detroit, MI 48226
Phone: 313.596.0264
E-mail: udmlawao@udmercy.edu; Website: www.law.udmercy.edu

■ Introduction

Founded in 1912, the University of Detroit Mercy (UDM) School of Law is a private law school in downtown Detroit sponsored by the Society of Jesus (Jesuits) and the Sisters of Mercy of the Americas. Located opposite the General Motors headquarters in the Renaissance Center, the School of Law is within walking distance of federal and state courts, downtown law firms, and Detroit's municipal center. Windsor, Ontario, Canada, is a five-minute drive by tunnel or bridge across the Detroit River. Metropolitan Detroit not only offers renowned cultural institutions like the Detroit Institute of Art, the Detroit Symphony, and the Detroit Opera House, but also provides a distinctive setting for the study of contemporary legal issues such as energy and the environment, immigration, global transactions, and complex corporate transactions.

The School of Law offers a comprehensive legal education through day and evening programs that incorporate a broad array of required and elective courses. The school is approved by the ABA and is a member of the AALS.

■ Law School Campus

The School of Law campus includes faculty offices, classrooms, and common areas with wireless access, administrative and student services offices, a bookstore, a cafeteria, and student organization offices, all located within the law school complex. The school's Kresge Law Library contains comfortable individual and group study, reading, and computer areas. The library houses more than 340,000 volumes and serves as a federal depository.

■ Curriculum

The School of Law offers a three-year, full-time program; four-year, part-time day and evening programs; and a five-year, part-time evening program, all leading to the JD degree. Required courses include Core Concepts, Contracts, Property, Torts, Civil Procedure, Applied Legal Theory and Analysis, Criminal Law, Constitutional Law, Evidence, Professional Responsibility, Taxation, two Law Firm Program department courses, an international or comparative law elective, a clinic, and a seminar.

The school's first-year Core Concepts course not only introduces students to statutory analysis and interpretation, but requires them to solve legal problems that cut across torts, contracts, property, and civil procedure. In UDM's Law Firm Program, students in their last year of law school work on complex transactions. As in a law firm, they work with their fellow students in different capacities to resolve the various issues that make up the core transaction. Throughout the required Law Firm Program courses, students draft documents, complete due diligence, counsel clients and receive instruction, litigate, and more.

The School of Law's legal education program offers numerous clinical opportunities: the Urban Law Clinic, the Immigration Law Clinic, mediation training and the Mediation Clinic, the Veterans Clinic, an Environmental Law Clinic, an Appellate Advocacy Clinic through the State Appellate Defender Office, a Criminal Law Clinic, a Consumer Debt Clinic, and a wide array of externships. UDM's Mobile Law Offices have taken the clinic's immigration, veterans, and other services beyond the campus and into the community. The Veterans Clinic travels not only in Michigan but across the country assisting low-income veterans with federal benefits.

■ Special Programs

- **JD/LED**—The University of Detroit Mercy School of Law (UDM) and the Instituto Tecnológico y de Estudios Superiores de Monterrey (ITESM), Mexico's leading private law school, have partnered to offer the Degree of the Americas program, a multiple-degree program that allows students bilingual in Spanish and English to earn law degrees in three countries: the United States, Mexico, and Canada. Students enrolled in this program can earn two (JD/LED) or three (JD/LLB/LED) degrees in significantly less time than would be required for each degree pursued independently. UDM School of Law is the only US ABA-approved law school to provide students bilingual in Spanish and English an opportunity to take so many courses in Mexican law. As part of this program, UDM offers 14 courses in Mexican law taught in Spanish by professors from ITESM. All UDM students may take these courses as electives and have them count toward their degree.

- **Joint JD/MBA**—The School of Law and the College of Business Administration collaborate to offer an integrated degree program leading to the JD and MBA degrees. Students enrolled in the joint-degree program can earn both degrees in significantly less time than would be required for degrees pursued independently. Students are first admitted to and attend law school. At the end of the first year of law school, students apply to the joint-degree program.

- **JD/LLB**—The School of Law and the University of Windsor Faculty of Law offer a unique JD/LLB program designed to educate students to understand the legal doctrines and cultures of the United States and Canada. A student completes 60 credit hours of coursework at UDM and 44 credit hours of coursework at the University of Windsor. Most required courses taken at both law schools cover US and Canadian law relevant to the subject areas. The program enables the successful student to obtain an American Bar Association-approved Juris Doctor (JD) from the University of Detroit Mercy and the Bachelor of Laws (LLB) degree from the University of Windsor.

- **Intellectual Property Law Institute**—Through a consortium with other law schools, the School of Law offers a wide variety of courses in intellectual property such as Copyright Law, Patent Law, Computer Law, Entertainment Law, and others.

- **French Scholar Program**—The School of Law participates in a professional exchange program with the University of Clermont-Ferrand. French scholars visiting the law school each spring teach a comparative law course in English while UDM scholars teach at Clermont-Ferrand.

- **Special Summer Program (SSP)**—The School of Law offers this program for applicants who do not meet the minimum standards for admission, but who show potential for the study of law. This seven-week program, beginning in late May, requires students to demonstrate ability in the study of

substantive law and in legal writing and research in order to gain admission as a regular student in the fall semester.

■ Student Organizations and Activities

The School of Law's students edit and publish the *Law Review*, a quarterly publication of scholarly articles.

A student **Moot Court Board of Advocacy** administers the School of Law's Gallagher and Professional Responsibility competitions; participates in state, regional, and national competitions in first amendment law, ethics, and other areas; and helps to administer the G. Mennen Williams mandatory moot court competition for first-year students. Last year, Moot Court members at UDM participated in several distinctive national competitions, including the Niagra Cup (national championship), the McGee National Civil Rights competition (best oralist), and Immigration Law (best brief). This year, members will argue in more than 13 national competitions and already have won the first national invitational moot court competition.

The **Student Bar Association (SBA)**, affiliated with the Law Student Division of the American Bar Association, plays a significant role in student affairs. As the student government of the school, the SBA authorizes other student organizations, including the Black Law Student Alliance, the Environmental Law Society, Phi Alpha Delta, St. Thomas More Society, the Women's Law Caucus, the Arab and Chaldean Law Student Society, the Sports and Entertainment Law Society, and many others. Students also regularly publish a student newsletter, *In Brief*.

In 2006, UDM School of Law received the Judy M. Weightman Memorial Public Interest Award from the American Bar Association (ABA) Student Law Division. This award recognizes outstanding community service projects,

public interest programming, and strong commitment to helping others in need. UDM's Student Bar Association nominated UDM for this award.

■ Career Services

The school's Career Services Office provides students with a wide range of opportunities through which they may explore career paths in law. The office sponsors a Preparing to Practice series for upper-class students that introduces them to a variety of practice areas and issues. The Career Services staff provide career counseling services, including résumé and cover letter review. The office administers the school's annual on-campus interview programs, maintains a job information hotline and newsletter, sponsors a mock interview program for first-year students, and hosts special events to acquaint students with practitioners.

■ Admission

The School of Law encourages applicants to submit an application for admission by April 15. The Admission Committee considers all elements of an application, including undergraduate grade-point average, Law School Admission Test scores, writing skills, leadership and maturity as evidenced by work and service experiences, graduate work, letters of recommendation, and the personal statement. The committee reviews applications as they become complete on a continuous basis and communicates decisions as early as possible. An applicant may accept an offer of admission by submitting the required nonrefundable deposits, which are credited toward tuition. The University of Detroit Mercy and the School of Law adhere to nondiscrimination policies.

Applicant Profile

University of Detroit Mercy School of Law
This grid includes only applicants who earned 120–180 LSAT scores under standard administrations.

LSAT Score	3.75 +		3.50–3.74		3.25–3.49		3.00–3.24		2.75–2.99		2.50–2.74		2.25–2.49		2.00–2.24		Below 2.00		No GPA		Total	
	Apps	Adm	Apps	Adm	Apps	Adm	Apps	Adm	Apps	Adm	Apps	Adm	Apps	Adm	Apps	Adm	Apps	Adm	Apps	Adm	Apps	Adm
175–180	0	0	0	0	0	0	0	0	0	0	0	0	0	0	0	0	0	0	0	0	0	0
170–174	0	0	1	1	1	0	0	0	1	1	0	0	0	0	0	0	0	0	0	0	3	2
165–169	3	2	0	0	0	0	0	0	2	1	0	0	0	0	2	1	0	0	1	1	8	5
160–164	12	9	7	5	3	2	10	7	8	5	1	0	0	0	0	0	2	0	24	19	67	47
155–159	11	8	14	10	17	16	23	18	24	18	11	7	9	6	2	1	2	0	68	57	181	141
150–154	22	17	46	42	43	37	75	54	44	31	29	22	14	9	7	3	3	0	78	33	361	248
145–149	15	15	51	44	79	53	91	64	73	52	48	16	27	6	8	4	1	0	66	8	459	262
140–144	9	8	38	30	77	47	84	38	82	16	59	7	34	1	21	0	4	0	42	0	450	147
135–139	7	0	12	2	22	1	34	2	36	0	31	0	25	0	15	0	5	0	17	0	204	5
130–134	2	0	5	0	6	0	8	0	17	0	12	0	7	0	7	0	3	0	8	0	75	0
125–129	0	0	1	0	0	0	1	0	2	0	1	0	4	0	2	0	4	0	1	0	16	0
120–124	0	0	0	0	0	0	0	0	1	0	1	0	0	0	0	0	0	0	1	0	3	0
Total	81	59	175	134	248	156	326	183	290	124	193	52	120	22	64	9	24	0	306	118	1827	857

Apps = Number of Applicants
Adm = Number Admitted
Reflects 99% of the total applicant pool; average LSAT data reported.

University of the District of Columbia—David A. Clarke School of Law

4200 Connecticut Avenue NW
Washington, DC 20008
Phone: 202.274.7341; Fax: 202.274.5583
E-mail: lawadmission@udc.edu; Website: www.law.udc.edu

ABA Approved Since 1991

The Basics

Type of school	Public
Term	Semester
Application deadline	3/15
Application fee	$35
Financial aid deadline	3/2
Can first year start other than fall?	No
Student to faculty ratio	12.2 to 1
# of housing spaces available restricted to law students	
graduate housing for which law students are eligible	

Faculty and Administrators

	Total		Men		Women		Minorities	
	Spr	Fall	Spr	Fall	Spr	Fall	Spr	Fall
Full-time	16	20	9	12	7	8	8	9
Other full-time	4	5	0	0	4	5	2	2
Deans, librarians, & others who teach	3	3	1	1	2	2	1	1
Part-time	15	17	9	8	6	9	9	11
Total	38	45	19	21	19	24	20	23

Curriculum

		Full-Time	Part-Time
Typical first-year section size		96	27
Is there typically a "small section" of the first-year class, other than Legal Writing, taught by full-time faculty		Yes	No
If yes, typical size offered last year		40	
# of classroom course titles beyond first-year curriculum			44
# of upper division courses, excluding seminars, with an enrollment:	Under 25		30
	25–49		13
	50–74		4
	75–99		3
	100+		0
# of seminars			10
# of seminar positions available			155
# of seminar positions filled		142	0
# of positions available in simulation courses			40
# of simulation positions filled		30	0
# of positions available in faculty supervised clinical courses			155
# of faculty supervised clinical positions filled		155	0
# involved in field placements		17	0
# involved in law journals		39	0
# involved in moot court or trial competitions		12	0
# of credit hours required to graduate			90

JD Enrollment and Ethnicity

	Men		Women		Full-Time		Part-Time		1st-Year		Total		JD Degs. Awd.
	#	%	#	%	#	%	#	%	#	%	#	%	
African Amer.	35	28.2	51	30.2	75	28.2	11	40.7	37	30.3	86	29.4	20
Amer. Indian	1	0.8	2	1.2	3	1.1	0	0.0	0	0.0	3	1.0	0
Asian Amer.	7	5.6	16	9.5	20	7.5	3	11.1	11	9.0	23	7.8	3
Mex. Amer.	4	3.2	2	1.2	6	2.3	0	0.0	1	0.8	6	2.0	0
Puerto Rican	2	1.6	5	3.0	7	2.6	0	0.0	4	3.3	7	2.4	0
Hispanic	13	10.5	7	4.1	20	7.5	0	0.0	8	6.6	20	6.8	3
Total Minority	62	50.0	83	49.1	131	49.2	14	51.9	61	50.0	145	49.5	26
For. Nation.	0	0.0	0	0.0	0	0.0	0	0.0	0	0.0	0	0.0	0
Caucasian	60	48.4	79	46.7	126	47.4	13	48.1	56	45.9	139	47.4	43
Unknown	2	1.6	7	4.1	9	3.4	0	0.0	5	4.1	9	3.1	0
Total	124	42.3	169	57.7	266	90.8	27	9.2	122	41.6	293		69

Transfers

Transfers in	2
Transfers out	2

Tuition and Fees

	Resident	Nonresident
Full-time	$7,980	$15,330
Part-time	$6,130	$11,630
Tuition Guarantee Program		N

Living Expenses

Estimated living expenses for singles

Living on campus	Living off campus	Living at home
N/A	$30,440	$15,140

University of the District of Columbia—David A. Clarke School of Law

ABA Approved Since 1991

GPA and LSAT Scores

	Total	Full-Time	Part-Time
# of apps	1,601	1,601	0
# of offers	336	336	0
# of matrics	123	96	27
75% GPA	3.26	3.28	3.21
Median GPA	3.05	3.06	3.01
25% GPA	2.80	2.83	2.60
75% LSAT	153	153	154
Median LSAT	151	151	151
25% LSAT	149	149	149

Grants and Scholarships (from prior year)

	Total #	Total %	Full-Time #	Full-Time %	Part-Time #	Part-Time %
Total # of students	251		251		0	
Total # receiving grants	150	59.8	150	59.8	0	0.0
Less than 1/2 tuition	57	22.7	57	22.7	0	0.0
Half to full tuition	56	22.3	56	22.3	0	0.0
Full tuition	37	14.7	37	14.7	0	0.0
More than full tuition	0	0.0	0	0.0	0	0.0
Median grant amount			$3,800		$0	

Informational and Library Resources

Total amount spent on library materials	$706,384
Study seating capacity inside the library	230
# of full-time equivalent professional librarians	8
Hours per week library is open	101
# of open, wired connections available to students	6
# of networked computers available for use by students	15
Has wireless network?	Y
Require computer?	Y

JD Attrition (from prior year)

	Academic #	Other #	Total #	Total %
1st year	3	8	11	12.5
2nd year	1	1	2	2.2
3rd year	0	0	0	0.0
4th year	0	0	0	0.0

Employment (9 months after graduation)

	Total	Percentage
Employment status known	57	83.8
Employment status unknown	11	16.2
Employed	43	75.4
Pursuing graduate degrees	6	10.5
Unemployed (seeking, not seeking, or studying for the bar)	5	8.8
Type of Employment		
# employed in law firms	12	27.9
# employed in business and industry	7	16.3
# employed in government	8	18.6
# employed in public interest	8	18.6
# employed as judicial clerks	5	11.6
# employed in academia	2	4.7
Geographic Location		
# employed in state	23	53.5
# employed in foreign countries	0	0.0
# of states where employed	11	

Bar Passage Rates

First-time takers	73	Reporting %	75.34
Average school %	80.00	Average state %	82.06

Average pass difference −2.06

Jurisdiction	Takers	Passers	Pass %	State %	Diff %
Maryland	26	24	92.31	85.51	6.80
District of Columbia	11	9	81.82	72.37	9.45
Florida	5	4	80.00	80.76	−0.76
Virginia	5	2	40.00	82.70	−42.70
Others (2)	8	5	62.50		

University of the District of Columbia—David A. Clarke School of Law

4200 Connecticut Avenue NW
Washington, DC 20008
Phone: 202.274.7341; Fax: 202.274.5583
E-mail: lawadmission@udc.edu; Website: www.law.udc.edu

■ Introduction

In 1986, the District of Columbia Council authorized the establishment of the District of Columbia School of Law. The council created a dual mission for the School of Law and charged its Board of Governors with a mandate to recruit and enroll, to the degree feasible, students from ethnic, racial, or other population groups that in the past had been underrepresented among persons admitted to the bar. It also charged the board with representing the legal needs of low-income persons, particularly those who reside in the District of Columbia.

The DC School of Law, the only publicly funded law school in Washington, DC, merged with the University of the District of Columbia (UDC) in 1996 and became the University of the District of Columbia School of Law. In April 1998, the UDC School of Law was named the UDC David A. Clarke School of Law (UDC-DCSL). The law school operates full-time day and part-time evening programs.

■ Library and Physical Facilities

The School of Law is located on the University of the District of Columbia's Van Ness campus in the upper northwest section of Washington, DC, a neighborhood known for its harmonious blend of residences, businesses, embassies, and the Rock Creek Park.

The law library is a teaching-, research-, and practice-oriented library. It contains more than 257,000 volumes and volume equivalents. The law library expands its collection on an ongoing basis, with an emphasis on reference and scholarly materials that support legal education and the clinical programs. The library's online catalog is available at *http://catalog.law.udc.edu/search*.

The Charles N. and Hilda H. M. Mason Law Library is a beautiful and modern facility that provides the traditional and high-tech resources required for today's study of the law. In addition, the Internet and law library resources are accessible via the law library's wireless LAN throughout the law library and the School of Law.

The university and law school campus are conveniently located on the Metro's Red Line at the UDC/Van Ness subway stop.

■ Curriculum

Consistent with UDC School of Law's mission, the basic program is designed to provide a well-rounded theoretical and practical legal education that will enable students to be effective and ethical advocates, and to represent the legal needs of low-income residents through the school's legal clinics.

Full-time and part-time first-year students participate in Orientation, which introduces them to the study of law and to the School of Law community. During Orientation, students take Law and Justice, a course which introduces legal, political, social, and philosophical aspects of poverty and inequality in American society. They also take Lawyering Process I. Students participate in the Dean's Reception and in other events planned by the Dean of Students and student organizations.

In the first year, students must complete 40 hours of community service and take a prescribed program consisting of required courses and one elective course. After the first year, students must also take courses in Evidence, Constitutional Law I and II, Professional Responsibility, and Moot Court. Each UDC-DCSL student is required to produce significant pieces of writing each of the three years of study. The School of Law offers summer courses and clinics, including an internship program; it does not allow early graduation.

While the emphasis of the school is on public interest law, the overall curriculum—clinic and classroom—provides the skills necessary to pursue any field of law.

■ Clinical Program

Students must complete two, seven-credit clinics during their second and third years. The clinics offered in the 2009–2010 academic year were Housing and Consumer, HIV/AIDS, Juvenile and Special Education, Legislation, Government Accountability Project, Community Development and Small Business, Low Income Taxpayer, and the new Immigration Law Clinic (Fall 2010).

■ Academic Support and Summer Program

UDC-DCSL considers academic support to be an integral part of its course of study. Students in academic difficulty at the end of their first semester may apply to the enhanced program, which may involve adjusting course loads, taking a legal reasoning course, counseling, and group and individual tutoring. In addition, faculty members hold extra review sessions during the semester in required courses and provide sample examination questions with model answers.

The School of Law offers the Mason Enhancement Program for Academic Success, a four-week conditional-admission summer program, to selected entering students.

■ Internship Program

Students in the second and third year may elect to do a four- or ten-credit internship, where they may work in federal or local government agencies; judicial, legislative, or congressional offices; or in public interest legal organizations. Students are required to attend a weekly internship seminar at the school. The School of Law emphasizes the importance of supervision, educational merit, and public service in each internship.

■ Admission

Admission is based upon academic and nonacademic achievements and professional promise. UDC-DCSL considers the applicant's LSAT score and GPA in tandem with other criteria that it believes may provide a more accurate measure of a candidate's determination, commitment, and potential for success in the study of law. The Admission Committee also considers other submitted application materials, such as the personal statement and essays, recommendations, community service, and employment experience. Applicants are encouraged to contact the Admission Office or to visit *www.law.udc.edu* for information about visiting the School of Law, sitting in on a class, and attending one of the Law Day-Open House programs.

University of the District of Columbia—David A. Clarke School of Law

■ Financial Assistance and Scholarships

The financial aid policy provides students with financial assistance to support full-time and part-time study. This is usually accomplished through a combination of scholarships, grants, and loans. These include merit- and need-based scholarships, the Federal Stafford and GradPLUS loan programs, and federal and other work-study employment. About 63 percent of UDC-DCSL students receive scholarship assistance, and 96 percent receive some form of financial aid. Detailed information about financial aid application policies and procedures is available on the School of Law's website.

■ Student Activities

The first issue of the annual *District of Columbia Law Review* was published in 1992. Active student organizations include the Student Bar Association, Black Law Students Association, International Law Students Association, Voces Juridicas,

OutLaw, Women's Law Society, Sports and Entertainment Student Lawyers Association, Phi Alpha Delta, Innocence Project, and the National Lawyers Guild.

■ Career Services

The Career Services Office provides employment information, individual career counseling, and résumé assistance to the School of Law's student body and graduates. The office maintains listings of permanent job openings, fellowships, summer clerkships, and part-time opportunities. The office also coordinates potential internship sites and invites employers to conduct on-campus interviews. The office provides resources for career planning, counseling sessions to assist students in developing their career goals, résumé workshops, and other relevant seminars.

Applicant Profile

The David A. Clarke School of Law prides itself on its admission philosophy, comprehensive and competitive admission process, and student diversity. While the applicant profile grids can be helpful to students, they may also discourage some students whose numerical profiles are slightly below the school's LSAT and GPA medians, but whose life experiences, for example, may be compelling. Numbers do not always provide an accurate picture of an applicant's potential for law study or motivation to succeed. The School of Law, therefore, does not provide an applicant profile grid, but rather a brief description of its student body. The student body is a diverse and accomplished group. The age range of students is 20 to 62 years. The average age is 28

years. People of color comprise about half of the student body. Women comprise more than half of the students. More than 30 states and over 115 undergraduate schools are represented in the student body. About 125 students are admitted each year. Smaller class sizes provide students with an ideal student-to-faculty ratio and a rich theoretical and practical learning environment. The LSAT mean for the fall 2009 entering class was 152, and the 25th and 75th LSAT percentiles were 149 and 153, respectively. The GPA median and mean were both about 3.00. The student body represents strong competency and contribution potential for the study of law.

Drake University Law School

2507 University Avenue
Des Moines, IA 50311-4505
Phone: 800.44.DRAKE, ext. 2782 or 515.271.2782; Fax: 515.271.1990
E-mail: lawadmit@drake.edu; Website: www.law.drake.edu

ABA
Approved
Since
1923

The Basics

Type of school	Private
Term	Semester
Application deadline	4/1
Application fee	$50
Financial aid deadline	3/1
Can first year start other than fall?	Yes
Student to faculty ratio	14.5 to 1
# of housing spaces available restricted to law students	
graduate housing for which law students are eligible	82

Faculty and Administrators

	Total		Men		Women		Minorities	
	Spr	Fall	Spr	Fall	Spr	Fall	Spr	Fall
Full-time	24	27	15	17	9	10	3	3
Other full-time	1	2	1	2	0	0	1	1
Deans, librarians, & others who teach	9	9	5	5	4	4	0	0
Part-time	19	19	14	14	5	5	2	0
Total	53	57	35	38	18	19	6	4

Curriculum

		Full-Time	Part-Time
Typical first-year section size		81	0
Is there typically a "small section" of the first-year class, other than Legal Writing, taught by full-time faculty		No	No
If yes, typical size offered last year			
# of classroom course titles beyond first-year curriculum		98	
# of upper division courses, excluding seminars, with an enrollment:	Under 25	68	
	25–49	21	
	50–74	8	
	75–99	1	
	100+	0	
# of seminars		15	
# of seminar positions available		298	
# of seminar positions filled		172	0
# of positions available in simulation courses		885	
# of simulation positions filled		464	0
# of positions available in faculty supervised clinical courses		107	
# of faculty supervised clinical positions filled		108	0
# involved in field placements		76	0
# involved in law journals		162	0
# involved in moot court or trial competitions		69	0
# of credit hours required to graduate		90	

JD Enrollment and Ethnicity

	Men		Women		Full-Time		Part-Time		1st-Year		Total		JD Degs. Awd.
	#	%	#	%	#	%	#	%	#	%	#	%	
African Amer.	11	4.2	19	9.1	30	6.7	0	0.0	9	5.4	30	6.4	6
Amer. Indian	1	0.4	0	0.0	1	0.2	0	0.0	1	0.6	1	0.2	0
Asian Amer.	4	1.5	3	1.4	7	1.6	0	0.0	2	1.2	7	1.5	2
Mex. Amer.	4	1.5	1	0.5	5	1.1	0	0.0	3	1.8	5	1.1	0
Puerto Rican	0	0.0	1	0.5	1	0.2	0	0.0	0	0.0	1	0.2	2
Hispanic	4	1.5	0	0.0	4	0.9	0	0.0	2	1.2	4	0.9	4
Total Minority	24	9.3	24	11.5	48	10.6	0	0.0	17	10.2	48	10.3	14
For. Nation.	1	0.4	6	2.9	4	0.9	3	18.8	7	4.2	7	1.5	0
Caucasian	193	74.5	152	73.1	332	73.6	13	81.2	114	68.7	345	73.9	108
Unknown	41	15.8	26	12.5	67	14.9	0	0.0	29	17.5	67	14.3	13
Total	259	55.5	208	44.5	451	96.6	16	3.4	167	35.5	467		135

Transfers

Transfers in	3
Transfers out	2

Tuition and Fees

	Resident	Nonresident
Full-time	$31,186	$31,186
Part-time		
Tuition Guarantee Program		N

Living Expenses

Estimated living expenses for singles

Living on campus	Living off campus	Living at home
N/A	$16,700	$5,320

Drake University Law School

ABA
Approved
Since
1923

GPA and LSAT Scores

	Total	Full-Time	Part-Time
# of apps	1,078	1,069	36
# of offers	584	575	9
# of matrics	156	150	6
75% GPA	3.64	3.64	3.93
Median GPA	3.42	3.42	3.41
25% GPA	3.10	3.12	3.10
75% LSAT	158	158	159
Median LSAT	155	155	156
25% LSAT	153	153	155

Grants and Scholarships (from prior year)

	Total		Full-Time		Part-Time	
	#	%	#	%	#	%
Total # of students	445		437		8	
Total # receiving grants	267	60.0	267	61.1	0	0.0
Less than 1/2 tuition	135	30.3	135	30.9	0	0.0
Half to full tuition	97	21.8	97	22.2	0	0.0
Full tuition	20	4.5	20	4.6	0	0.0
More than full tuition	15	3.4	15	3.4	0	0.0
Median grant amount			$14,035		$0	

Informational and Library Resources

Total amount spent on library materials	$858,817
Study seating capacity inside the library	705
# of full-time equivalent professional librarians	6
Hours per week library is open	109
# of open, wired connections available to students	180
# of networked computers available for use by students	133
Has wireless network?	Y
Require computer?	N

JD Attrition (from prior year)

	Academic	Other	Total	
	#	#	#	%
1st year	2	2	4	2.4
2nd year	0	0	0	0.0
3rd year	0	0	0	0.0
4th year	0	0	0	0.0

Employment (9 months after graduation)

	Total	Percentage
Employment status known	130	100.0
Employment status unknown	0	0.0
Employed	118	90.8
Pursuing graduate degrees	4	3.1
Unemployed (seeking, not seeking, or studying for the bar)	4	3.1
Type of Employment		
# employed in law firms	60	50.8
# employed in business and industry	24	20.3
# employed in government	14	11.9
# employed in public interest	7	5.9
# employed as judicial clerks	11	9.3
# employed in academia	2	1.7
Geographic Location		
# employed in state	74	62.7
# employed in foreign countries	0	0.0
# of states where employed		21

Bar Passage Rates

First-time takers	139	Reporting %	74.10
Average school %	90.29	Average state %	90.37

Average pass difference –0.08

Jurisdiction	Takers	Passers	Pass %	State %	Diff %
Iowa	81	73	90.12	90.11	0.01
Wisconsin	11	11	100.00	91.79	8.21
Illinois	11	9	81.82	90.94	–9.12

Drake University Law School

2507 University Avenue
Des Moines, IA 50311-4505
Phone: 800.44.DRAKE, ext. 2782 or 515.271.2782; Fax: 515.271.1990
E-mail: lawadmit@drake.edu; Website: www.law.drake.edu

■ Introduction

Drake University Law School can trace its history back to 1865, making it one of the nation's 25 oldest law schools. Accredited by the ABA, the Law School provides a personal education with a low (14:1) student-to-faculty ratio. Our commitment to an education that balances theory and practice has earned the Law School a reputation for training proven practitioners.

Drake Law School's location in Des Moines—the capital's only law school—provides students the opportunity to get hands-on experience with the executive, judicial, and legislative branches of state government; the federal courts; federal and state administrative agencies; and a wide array of law firms and businesses.

■ Legal Clinic

The Drake Legal Clinic, housed in the Neal and Bea Smith Law Center, is one of the best training facilities in the country. The Center operates much like a real law firm providing incomparable hands-on experience to students who participate. This state-of-the-art facility includes a technologically enhanced courtroom, office space for students, a library, and seminar rooms.

■ First-Year Trial Practicum

The only program of its kind in the country, the Trial Practicum adds an important experiential learning dimension to the first-year curriculum. During the spring semester, students observe an actual state court trial—from jury selection to verdict—in the courtroom of the Neal and Bea Smith Law Center. Break-out discussion groups and posttrial debriefings of the attorneys, judges, and jurors poignantly illustrate how law on the books becomes law in action.

■ Centers of Excellence and Certificate Programs

Agricultural Law Center—Our internationally recognized agricultural law program addresses the important issues in American and international law and policy regarding food production. Students conduct research, publish an agricultural law journal, and write articles on a wide range of topics. The center frequently hosts international agricultural law scholars who teach courses on international issues and topics such as farmland preservation, legal issues in biotechnology, and tax planning for agricultural businesses. The center also offers a series of one-week courses for students and attorneys in the Summer Agricultural Law Institute. The center offers a **Food and Agricultural Law Certificate** program, the first of its kind at an American law school.

Constitutional Law Center—Drake is one of only four schools selected to receive a congressional endowment for the establishment of a Constitutional Law Resource Center. The center sponsors a lecture series and annual symposia featuring nationally recognized constitutional scholars. The nationally renowned Dwight D. Opperman Lecture in Constitutional Law has been delivered by ten current and former justices of the United States Supreme Court. The center also offers a **Constitutional Law and Civil Rights Certificate** program and conducts the Summer Institute in Constitutional Law, a program designed for first-year students interested in getting their law school careers off to an early start. Students beginning in the Summer Institute who elect to take additional summer courses may accelerate their studies and graduate in December of their third year.

Health Law and Policy Center—In fall 2008, Drake Law School launched the Health Law and Policy Center to promote an interdisciplinary understanding of local, national, and international issues in health law and policy. The mission of the center is to advance the understanding and development of health law, bioethics, and the medical humanities, and to prepare students for professional success and personal satisfaction through leadership and service in the health care and health law communities. The center also offers a **Health Law Certificate** program.

Intellectual Property Law Center—Our dynamic center offers an innovative curriculum, providing students with a solid foundation in both the theoretical and practical aspects of intellectual property law. The center features an annual summer institute that brings together judges, policymakers, industry leaders, attorneys, academics, and students to explore cutting-edge issues at the intersection of intellectual property, biotechnology, and agricultural sciences. In addition, the center serves as an international research hub, fostering partnerships with leading research institutions from around the world. Every year, the center sponsors groundbreaking symposia and distinguished lectures, hosts eminent speakers and internationally recognized experts, publishes books and an occasional paper series, and develops international research and outreach programs.

Center for Legislative Practice—Drake is one of only a few schools in the country that offers a **Legislative Practice Certificate**. Classroom study and a wide range of internships expose students to the underpinnings of legislative and rule-making processes. Students who complete the program are uniquely prepared to work for administrative or government agencies, to research and draft legislation, to represent businesses and organizations with government interests, or to work in a variety of other public-policy-making positions. Drake's close proximity to the state capital and other state and federal offices, trade associations, union headquarters, and public interest group agencies provides students with numerous opportunities to learn firsthand how these institutions operate.

The **Middleton Center for Children's Rights** pursues a broad agenda, advancing children's rights through the legal process, training, public information, and public policy formation. Drake Law students learn the interdisciplinary process essential to addressing the complex issues involved in child welfare and children's rights.

The **International and Comparative Law and Human Rights Certificate** program combines coursework in Drake's international and comparative law and related course offerings with a required study abroad experience.

Litigation and Dispute Resolution Certification—Drake Law School has achieved a well-deserved reputation for its education and training of future litigators, mediators, negotiators, and judges. Our alumni are well represented among the nation's leading trial and appellate lawyers and on both the federal and

state courts. The Litigation and Dispute Resolution Certificate program capitalizes on the school's traditional strengths in advocacy and dispute resolution.

■ Summer in France

Add an international element to your legal education by participating in our summer program at the University of Nantes Law School in France. Classes in comparative and international law and on-site visits to European legal institutions allow you to absorb and experience another country's legal system and be better prepared to practice law in a global society.

■ Joint-Degree Programs

Students may combine their Juris Doctor degree with the Master of Business Administration, Master of Public Administration or Doctor of Pharmacy degree from Drake University. Students may also combine the JD degree with a Master of Arts in Political Science or Master of Science in Agricultural Economics (in cooperation with Iowa State University); a Master of Social Work (in cooperation with the University of Iowa); a Master of Health Care Administration or Master of Public Health (in cooperation with Des Moines University).

■ Student Activities

Law students participate in many student organizations and cocurricular activities. Drake students publish two journals, the *Drake Law Review* and the *Journal of Agricultural Law*. *Drake Law Review* was named among the nation's 30 most-cited legal periodicals by the courts from 1997–2008. Drake moot court teams consistently win regional competitions and finish strongly in national competitions. The award-winning Student Bar Association and honorary societies provide students with leadership, public service, and learning opportunities. Drake students have also formed more than thirty organizations around their special interests, including Drake Law Women, Black Law Students Association, Asian Pacific Law Student Association, Hispanic Law Student Association, International Law Society, Christian Legal Society, Environmental Law Society, Federalist Society, American Constitution Society, National Lawyers Guild, Intellectual Property Law Society, Agricultural Law Society, Alternative Dispute Resolution Society, and an organization for students with alternative sexual orientation.

■ Networking

Drake Law School alumni practice in all 50 states and several foreign countries. The Career Development Office has a comprehensive, national alumni network set up to assist students with their career plans no matter where they want to go. Attorneys who participate in the alumni career network help students learn about the job market in their state and help ensure a smooth transition for students from law school to practice. Many area alumni also participate in our Partner's Program, which pairs first-year law students with practicing attorneys.

■ Career Development

The Career Development Office offers career planning and counseling services, assistance with résumés and cover letter preparation, salary and geographical employment statistics, nationwide job postings, and state bar examination information. The office also arranges interviews—both on and off campus—and exchanges job listings with 90 other law schools around the country.

Applicant Profile

Drake University Law School
This grid includes only applicants who earned 120–180 LSAT scores under standard administrations.

LSAT Score	3.75 +		3.50–3.74		3.25–3.49		3.00–3.24		2.75–2.99		2.50–2.74		2.25–2.49		2.00–2.24		Below 2.00		No GPA		Total	
	Apps	Adm	Apps	Adm	Apps	Adm	Apps	Adm	Apps	Adm	Apps	Adm	Apps	Adm	Apps	Adm	Apps	Adm	Apps	Adm	Apps	Adm
175–180	0	0	0	0	0	0	1	1	0	0	0	0	0	0	0	0	0	0	0	0	1	1
170–174	0	0	0	0	0	0	0	0	0	0	0	0	0	0	0	0	0	0	0	0	0	0
165–169	9	9	4	4	2	2	3	3	1	1	2	2	0	0	2	2	0	0	0	0	23	23
160–164	30	29	18	18	9	9	10	10	2	2	3	3	5	5	0	0	1	1	0	0	78	77
155–159	49	48	43	41	50	50	47	47	27	24	17	12	11	8	5	3	0	0	3	1	252	234
150–154	33	28	58	50	81	57	52	29	45	13	18	2	14	2	3	0	1	0	1	1	306	182
145–149	23	9	46	18	48	10	48	7	36	4	30	3	11	0	2	0	1	0	4	2	249	53
140–144	11	0	11	1	21	1	31	0	15	0	9	0	12	0	2	0	0	0	4	0	116	2
135–139	3	0	2	0	7	0	7	0	10	0	5	0	5	0	3	0	0	0	0	0	42	0
130–134	0	0	0	0	1	0	1	0	2	0	1	0	0	0	2	0	0	0	1	0	8	0
125–129	0	0	0	0	0	0	1	0	1	0	1	0	1	0	0	0	0	0	0	0	5	0
120–124	0	0	0	0	0	0	0	0	1	0	0	0	0	0	0	0	0	0	0	0	1	0
Total	158	123	182	132	219	129	201	97	140	44	86	22	59	15	20	5	3	1	13	4	1081	572

Apps = Number of Applicants   Adm = Number Admitted   Reflects 99% of the total applicant pool; average LSAT data reported.

Duke University School of Law

Science Drive & Towerview Road, Box 90393
Durham, NC 27708-0393
Phone: 919.613.7020; Fax: 919.613.7257
E-mail: admissions@law.duke.edu; Website: http://admissions.law.duke.edu

ABA
Approved
Since
1931

The Basics

Type of school	Private
Term	Semester
Application deadline	2/15
Application fee	$70
Financial aid deadline	3/15
Can first year start other than fall?	Yes
Student to faculty ratio	9.7 to 1
# of housing spaces available restricted to law students	
graduate housing for which law students are eligible	

Faculty and Administrators

	Total		Men		Women		Minorities	
	Spr	Fall	Spr	Fall	Spr	Fall	Spr	Fall
Full-time	56	54	43	40	13	14	6	6
Other full-time	9	8	4	3	5	5	1	1
Deans, librarians, & others who teach	11	11	5	5	6	6	1	1
Part-time	55	28	38	18	17	10	4	2
Total	131	101	90	66	41	35	12	10

JD Enrollment and Ethnicity

	Men		Women		Full-Time		Part-Time		1st-Year		Total		JD Degs. Awd.
	#	%	#	%	#	%	#	%	#	%	#	%	
African Amer.	26	6.9	31	10.9	55	8.8	2	5.7	17	7.4	57	8.6	18
Amer. Indian	1	0.3	0	0.0	1	0.2	0	0.0	0	0.0	1	0.2	0
Asian Amer.	25	6.6	30	10.6	52	8.3	3	8.6	17	7.4	55	8.3	18
Mex. Amer.	3	0.8	2	0.7	5	0.8	0	0.0	3	1.3	5	0.8	3
Puerto Rican	2	0.5	1	0.4	3	0.5	0	0.0	1	0.4	3	0.5	1
Hispanic	9	2.4	18	6.3	26	4.2	1	2.9	8	3.5	27	4.1	8
Total Minority	66	17.5	82	28.9	142	22.7	6	17.1	46	20.1	148	22.4	48
For. Nation.	4	1.1	6	2.1	9	1.4	1	2.9	3	1.3	10	1.5	0
Caucasian	249	66.0	166	58.5	391	62.5	24	68.6	149	65.1	415	62.8	142
Unknown	58	15.4	30	10.6	84	13.4	4	11.4	31	13.5	88	13.3	29
Total	377	57.0	284	43.0	626	94.7	35	5.3	229	34.6	661		219

Curriculum

	Full-Time	Part-Time
Typical first-year section size	68	0
Is there typically a "small section" of the first-year class, other than Legal Writing, taught by full-time faculty	Yes	No
If yes, typical size offered last year	38	
# of classroom course titles beyond first-year curriculum	184	

# of upper division courses, excluding seminars, with an enrollment:		
	Under 25	109
	25–49	36
	50–74	11
	75–99	3
	100+	5

# of seminars	96	
# of seminar positions available	1,276	
# of seminar positions filled	938	0
# of positions available in simulation courses	432	
# of simulation positions filled	356	0
# of positions available in faculty supervised clinical courses	167	
# of faculty supervised clinical positions filled	145	0
# involved in field placements	33	0
# involved in law journals	298	0
# involved in moot court or trial competitions	122	0
# of credit hours required to graduate	84	

Transfers

Transfers in	13
Transfers out	10

Tuition and Fees

	Resident	Nonresident
Full-time	$45,271	$45,271
Part-time		
Tuition Guarantee Program		N

Living Expenses

Estimated living expenses for singles

Living on campus	Living off campus	Living at home
$16,692	$16,692	$16,692

Duke University School of Law

ABA
Approved
Since
1931

GPA and LSAT Scores

	Total	Full-Time	Part-Time
# of apps	6,334	6,334	0
# of offers	1,161	1,161	0
# of matrics	228	228	0
75% GPA	3.84	3.84	0.00
Median GPA	3.76	3.76	0.00
25% GPA	3.60	3.60	0.00
75% LSAT	171	171	0
Median LSAT	169	169	0
25% LSAT	167	167	0

Grants and Scholarships (from prior year)

	Total #	Total %	Full-Time #	Full-Time %	Part-Time #	Part-Time %
Total # of students	640		611		29	
Total # receiving grants	433	67.7	433	70.9	0	0.0
Less than 1/2 tuition	393	61.4	393	64.3	0	0.0
Half to full tuition	32	5.0	32	5.2	0	0.0
Full tuition	8	1.3	8	1.3	0	0.0
More than full tuition	0	0.0	0	0.0	0	0.0
Median grant amount			$14,000		$0	

Informational and Library Resources

Total amount spent on library materials	$1,895,982
Study seating capacity inside the library	585
# of full-time equivalent professional librarians	9
Hours per week library is open	104
# of open, wired connections available to students	894
# of networked computers available for use by students	100
Has wireless network?	Y
Require computer?	N

JD Attrition (from prior year)

	Academic #	Other #	Total #	Total %
1st year	0	0	0	0.0
2nd year	0	10	10	4.6
3rd year	0	0	0	0.0
4th year	0	0	0	0.0

Employment (9 months after graduation)

	Total	Percentage
Employment status known	207	100.0
Employment status unknown	0	0.0
Employed	203	98.1
Pursuing graduate degrees	1	0.5
Unemployed (seeking, not seeking, or studying for the bar)	0	0.0
Type of Employment		
# employed in law firms	153	75.4
# employed in business and industry	6	3.0
# employed in government	3	1.5
# employed in public interest	6	3.0
# employed as judicial clerks	33	16.3
# employed in academia	2	1.0
Geographic Location		
# employed in state	19	9.4
# employed in foreign countries	0	0.0
# of states where employed	30	

Bar Passage Rates

First-time takers	207	Reporting %	82.13
Average school %	92.95	Average state %	85.76
Average pass difference	7.19		

Jurisdiction	Takers	Passers	Pass %	State %	Diff %
New York	50	48	96.00	88.98	7.02
California	30	25	83.33	78.07	5.26
North Carolina	22	21	95.45	82.61	12.84
Georgia	19	18	94.74	89.27	5.47
Others (7)	49	46	93.88		

Duke University School of Law

Science Drive & Towerview Road, Box 90393
Durham, NC 27708-0393
Phone: 919.613.7020; Fax: 919.613.7257
E-mail: admissions@law.duke.edu; Website: http://admissions.law.duke.edu

■ Introduction

Duke Law School is one of the nation's leading law schools, known for its emphasis on leadership, ethics, scholarly research, and programs that serve the profession and the community. Students come to Duke Law from every state and, as alumni, work in top law firms and companies around the country and world.

One of the reasons students choose Duke Law is its collaborative environment, where growth is encouraged not only through rigorous scholarship, but also through cooperation and support. Because the school is small, students enjoy uniquely close interactions with faculty and fellow students. Duke Law's faculty members are among the nation's most respected experts in fields ranging from constitutional law and national security to intellectual property and international business. In addition, professors are deeply dedicated to teaching and are accessible and responsive to students. Their open-door policy encourages students to ask questions, continue discussions, and seek advice on specialized interests. Faculty-student interaction extends beyond the classroom to committee work, research, pro bono opportunities, career counseling, and mentoring. Ultimately, students experience a supportive environment where the focus is on training and developing the whole person in an atmosphere that values different perspectives, backgrounds, and orientations.

■ Enrollment/Student Body

Duke Law admits a select group of students with diverse backgrounds who have in common a record of academic excellence. In 2009, JD students came to Duke from 43 states and 4 foreign countries. These students represented 112 different undergraduate institutions and had a wealth of different experiences. Approximately 34 percent of the students entering Duke Law in 2009 came directly from college, while the other 66 percent entered law school after gaining experience for a year or more in another profession or graduate school.

■ Faculty

Central to Duke Law's success is its faculty. Well respected in the legal field, Duke Law professors are known for groundbreaking legal scholarship that impacts public policy and the legal profession. A large number of faculty are also practitioners in both the public and private sectors in the United States and abroad. Their backgrounds are as varied as they are distinguished: they are former Fulbright Scholars, Rhodes Scholars, and Marshall Scholars. A number of faculty members have served as Supreme Court clerks, and one was the chief judge for the US Court of Military Appeals. Faculty members hold joint appointments in departments throughout the university and have obtained PhDs in a wide variety of disciplines. Several visiting professors from abroad teach at Duke Law each year, and many full-time faculty members have extensive international connections.

■ Dual Degrees

Duke Law faculty believe that society is best served by lawyers with diverse education and training. The law school jointly sponsors numerous academic and professional programs in conjunction with other schools or departments at Duke University. In addition, students may pursue a three-year JD/DESS (Diplôme d'études supérieures spécialisées) in global business law in partnership with Université Paris I and Sciences Po in Paris.

The law school and the graduate school jointly sponsor programs of study in law and several other disciplines, including (at the master's level) Art History, Biomedical Engineering, Classical Studies, Cultural Anthropology, East Asian Studies, Economics, Electrical and Computer Engineering, English, Environmental Science and Policy, History, Humanities, International Development Policy, Literature, Mechanical Engineering, Philosophy, Political Science, Psychology, Religion, Romance Studies, and Sociology. The only additional time necessary to obtain both degrees is the summer prior to the first year of school. At the doctoral level, dual programs in Philosophy and Political Science are available.

The law school offers dual-professional degrees with the Fuqua School of Business, the Divinity School, the Nicholas School of the Environment, the School of Medicine, and the Sanford School of Public Policy. A special option is available to complete the JD/MBA in seven semesters.

Duke Law students may also earn graduate certificates in Slavic, Eurasian, and East European Legal Studies; Health Care Policy; Health System Management; or Women's Studies.

■ Special Programs

- **JD/LLM in International and Comparative Law**—Duke Law has pioneered a unique joint-degree program that makes it possible for students to earn a JD and a Master of Laws in International and Comparative Law concurrently in three years. The only additional time needed is the summer prior to the first year of law school and the first half of the following summer, during which students attend one of Duke's Institutes in Transnational Law, either in Switzerland or Hong Kong.
- **International Study Abroad and Externships**—Duke Law has arrangements with 21 top foreign universities, which give all interested Duke students an opportunity to study abroad. Duke Law also offers international externship opportunities at public sector institutions that engage in international work. Duke has preapproved externships, but students are also encouraged to submit their own proposals.
- **Legal Clinics**—Duke Law School's clinical program has grown exponentially and houses a variety of clinics that offer a wide range of hands-on opportunities. A newly constructed clinical office suite brings a number of the programs together, allowing them to function as a public interest law firm. Clinical opportunities include: AIDS Legal Project, Animal Law Clinic, Appellate Litigation Clinic, Children's Law Clinic, Community Enterprise Clinic, Environmental Law and Policy Clinic, Guantanamo Defense Clinic, and Wrongful Convictions Clinic.

- **Centers**—Interdisciplinary collaboration at Duke is fostered by a number of centers and programs, including the Arts Project; Center for Criminal Justice and Professional Responsibility; Center for Genome Ethics, Law, and Policy; Center for the Study of the Public Domain; Center on Law, Ethics, and National Security; Global Capital Markets Center; Nicholas Institute for Environmental Policy Solutions; and Program in Public Law. The school also is establishing two new centers: the Center for Sports and the Law and the Center on Race and Politics.
- **Duke in DC**—Duke Law offers students with an interest in public policy at the federal level the opportunity to spend a semester in Washington, DC. They will pursue an externship that may include positions on Capitol Hill, on the personal staff of house members and senators, with congressional committees, with NGOs and lobbying groups, and in the executive branch.

■ Admission and Financial Aid

Admission to Duke Law School is highly competitive. In addition to the academic criteria, other factors may help to distinguish some applicants. These include capacity for leadership, dedication to community service, excellence in a particular field, motivation, graduate study, work experience, extracurricular activities, and character.

Duke Law tries to achieve broad diversity in terms of general background, geography, and undergraduate institutions represented. Students are chosen not only for their potential for academic success, but also because of qualities that will enhance the overall character of the class.

Admitted applicants are eligible for consideration for merit- and need-based scholarship awards. A select group of outstanding entering students are chosen each year as Mordecai Scholars and receive a full-tuition scholarship. Mordecai Scholars possess a record of extraordinary leadership and scholarly achievement prior to law school, and the personal qualities that are likely to result in community involvement and leadership.

■ Cocurricular Activities

Scholarship in the classroom is reinforced through a variety of opportunities for hands-on leadership training and professional experience. Through pro bono work, legal clinics, public interest projects, moot court, and opportunities for scholarly writing and editing on eight different legal journals, Duke prepares students for the real-world practice of law.

■ Professional Development

The award-winning Duke Blueprint provides structure to students' legal education and professional development by challenging them to engage intellectually, embody integrity, build relationships, serve the community, and become effective leaders.

Duke Law graduates find employment in all sectors of the legal profession and in all parts of the United States and the world. Many begin their careers in law firms. Top law firms from across the country interview on campus each year, and the number of interviews available and offers made far exceeds the number of students interviewing. Others pursue judicial clerkships—15 percent of the graduating class of 2008—or work for government agencies or business enterprises. Historically, 100 percent of each class finds employment and average salaries are among the highest in the country.

Duke places special emphasis on support for students interested in a career in public service. Staff from both the Career Center and the Office of Pro Bono and Public Interest help students find opportunities both during and after law school. The law school provides financial support for these goals with grants to subsidize summer employment and a Loan Repayment Assistance Program for graduates who enter a life of public service.

Applicant Profile

Duke University School of Law
This grid includes only applicants who earned 120–180 LSAT scores under standard administrations.

LSAT Score	3.75 +		3.50–3.74		3.25–3.49		3.00–3.24		2.75–2.99		2.50–2.74		Below 2.50		No GPA		Total	
	Apps	Adm	Apps	Adm	Apps	Adm	Apps	Adm	Apps	Adm	Apps	Adm	Apps	Adm	Apps	Adm	Apps	Adm
170–180	664	297	484	249	157	16	60	1	24	0	8	0	3	0	7	1	1407	564
165–169	1102	298	648	144	223	9	98	2	29	0	10	0	8	0	38	3	2156	456
160–164	445	52	417	35	217	10	113	4	26	0	10	0	9	0	42	1	1279	102
155–159	173	7	219	15	157	6	88	2	48	0	16	0	8	0	27	0	736	30
150–154	50	0	79	0	77	0	69	0	37	0	18	0	9	0	14	0	353	0
145–149	17	0	25	0	60	0	38	0	18	0	13	0	8	0	8	0	187	0
140–144	5	0	19	0	23	0	21	0	12	0	8	0	7	0	6	0	101	0
Below 140	2	0	8	0	12	0	18	0	19	0	10	0	15	0	3	0	87	0
Total	2458	654	1899	443	926	41	505	9	213	0	93	0	67	0	145	5	6306	1152

Apps = Number of Applicants   Adm = Number Admitted   Reflects 99% of the total applicant pool; average LSAT data reported.

Duquesne University School of Law

201 Edward J. Hanley Hall, 900 Locust Street
Pittsburgh, PA 15282-0700
Phone: 412.396.6296; Fax: 412.396.1073
E-mail: campion@duq.edu; Website: www.duq.edu/law

ABA
Approved
Since
1960

The Basics

Type of school	Private
Term	Semester
Application deadline	4/1 5/1 6/1
Application fee	$60
Financial aid deadline	5/31
Can first year start other than fall?	No
Student to faculty ratio	19.5 to 1
# of housing spaces available restricted to law students	
graduate housing for which law students are eligible	

Faculty and Administrators

	Total		Men		Women		Minorities	
	Spr	Fall	Spr	Fall	Spr	Fall	Spr	Fall
Full-time	27	26	20	18	7	8	4	4
Other full-time	1	1	0	0	1	1	0	0
Deans, librarians, & others who teach	8	8	4	4	4	4	2	2
Part-time	41	34	29	22	12	12	2	1
Total	77	69	53	44	24	25	8	7

Curriculum

	Full-Time	Part-Time
Typical first-year section size	83	60
Is there typically a "small section" of the first-year class, other than Legal Writing, taught by full-time faculty	Yes	No
If yes, typical size offered last year	57	
# of classroom course titles beyond first-year curriculum		85
# of upper division courses, excluding seminars, with an enrollment: Under 25		48
25–49		16
50–74		14
75–99		15
100+		0
# of seminars		19
# of seminar positions available		464
# of seminar positions filled	204	92
# of positions available in simulation courses		117
# of simulation positions filled	107	9
# of positions available in faculty supervised clinical courses		76
# of faculty supervised clinical positions filled	56	9
# involved in field placements	60	12
# involved in law journals	123	35
# involved in moot court or trial competitions	28	5
# of credit hours required to graduate		86

JD Enrollment and Ethnicity

	Men		Women		Full-Time		Part-Time		1st-Year		Total		JD Degs. Awd.
	#	%	#	%	#	%	#	%	#	%	#	%	
African Amer.	5	1.5	16	4.4	14	3.1	7	2.7	1	0.4	21	3.0	11
Amer. Indian	1	0.3	0	0.0	0	0.0	1	0.4	0	0.0	1	0.1	1
Asian Amer.	10	2.9	5	1.4	8	1.8	7	2.7	9	3.8	15	2.1	4
Mex. Amer.	0	0.0	0	0.0	0	0.0	0	0.0	0	0.0	0	0.0	0
Puerto Rican	0	0.0	0	0.0	0	0.0	0	0.0	0	0.0	0	0.0	0
Hispanic	4	1.2	4	1.1	6	1.3	2	0.8	4	1.7	8	1.1	3
Total Minority	20	5.8	25	6.9	28	6.3	17	6.6	14	6.0	45	6.4	19
For. Nation.	1	0.3	2	0.6	1	0.2	2	0.8	2	0.9	3	0.4	0
Caucasian	313	91.5	317	87.6	397	89.0	233	90.3	212	90.2	630	89.5	188
Unknown	8	2.3	18	5.0	20	4.5	6	2.3	7	3.0	26	3.7	0
Total	342	48.6	362	51.4	446	63.4	258	36.6	235	33.4	704		207

Transfers

Transfers in	0
Transfers out	9

Tuition and Fees

	Resident	Nonresident
Full-time	$30,866	$30,866
Part-time	$23,874	$23,874
Tuition Guarantee Program		N

Living Expenses

Estimated living expenses for singles

Living on campus	Living off campus	Living at home
$12,008	$12,008	$3,650

Duquesne University School of Law

ABA
Approved
Since
1960

GPA and LSAT Scores

	Total	Full-Time	Part-Time
# of apps	1,064	852	212
# of offers	496	397	99
# of matrics	224	161	63
75% GPA	3.63	3.67	3.59
Median GPA	3.42	3.43	3.42
25% GPA	3.19	3.25	3.13
75% LSAT	154	155	154
Median LSAT	151	153	150
25% LSAT	150	152	149

Grants and Scholarships (from prior year)

	Total #	Total %	Full-Time #	Full-Time %	Part-Time #	Part-Time %
Total # of students	703		476		227	
Total # receiving grants	169	24.0	153	32.1	16	7.0
Less than 1/2 tuition	91	12.9	81	17.0	10	4.4
Half to full tuition	21	3.0	16	3.4	5	2.2
Full tuition	47	6.7	46	9.7	1	0.4
More than full tuition	10	1.4	10	2.1	0	0.0
Median grant amount			$14,813		$8,147	

Informational and Library Resources

Total amount spent on library materials	$749,012
Study seating capacity inside the library	411
# of full-time equivalent professional librarians	8
Hours per week library is open	102
# of open, wired connections available to students	26
# of networked computers available for use by students	68
Has wireless network?	Y
Require computer?	N

JD Attrition (from prior year)

	Academic #	Other #	Total #	Total %
1st year	16	1	17	7.9
2nd year	3	8	11	4.9
3rd year	0	0	0	0.0
4th year	0	0	0	0.0

Employment (9 months after graduation)

	Total	Percentage
Employment status known	139	90.3
Employment status unknown	15	9.7
Employed	121	87.1
Pursuing graduate degrees	3	2.2
Unemployed (seeking, not seeking, or studying for the bar)	11	7.9

Type of Employment

# employed in law firms	69	57.0
# employed in business and industry	21	17.4
# employed in government	13	10.7
# employed in public interest	1	0.8
# employed as judicial clerks	15	12.4
# employed in academia	2	1.7

Geographic Location

# employed in state	87	71.9
# employed in foreign countries	0	0.0
# of states where employed	18	

Bar Passage Rates

First-time takers	154	Reporting %	91.56
Average school %	95.74	Average state %	86.69
Average pass difference	9.05		

Jurisdiction	Takers	Passers	Pass %	State %	Diff %
Pennsylvania	141	135	95.74	86.69	9.05

Duquesne University School of Law

201 Edward J. Hanley Hall, 900 Locust Street
Pittsburgh, PA 15282-0700
Phone: 412.396.6296; Fax: 412.396.1073
E-mail: campion@duq.edu; Website: www.duq.edu/law

■ Introduction

The Duquesne University School of Law is a Catholic law
school that has been in existence since 1911 and is the
only multiple-division law school in western Pennsylvania.
Admission requirements, instruction, and the nature and
scope of the work required of students are identical for both
the full-time day division and the part-time evening and
part-time day divisions. The School of Law is approved by
the ABA and is a member of the AALS.

Situated on the attractive 43-acre Duquesne University
campus, the law school is within walking distance to the
vibrant Pittsburgh downtown legal, corporate, and
government communities.

Recognized as one of the best cities in which to practice
law and a center for corporate and legal headquarters,
Pittsburgh is a leading metropolis for high technology
ventures and a thriving arts and cultural community, with
major-league sports entertainment.

■ Library and Physical Facilities

Duquesne's proximity to the Pittsburgh region's legal center
makes the law school library a major source for legal research
and information services. The Duquesne law library has
assumed management responsibility of the Allegheny County
Law Library, resulting in one of the largest collections of legal
materials in Pennsylvania.

The law school recently completed a $12 million renovation
and expansion, adding 33,000 square feet to Hanley Hall. The
four new floors of space include a state-of-the-art moot
courtroom (giving us three), three new technology-aided
classrooms with ports and power sources at every seat, an
upgraded lounge area with a cafeteria, new faculty and
administrative offices, student locker areas, a conference
room, and a wireless computer lab.

■ Curriculum

The course of study offered at the School of Law is sufficiently
broad to prepare students for practice in all states. Three years
are required for completion of the course of study in the day
division, four years in the evening division and the part-time
day division. Eighty-six credits are required for graduation.

While emphasis is placed upon skills such as legal research
and writing and trial advocacy, the required courses are
sufficiently broad to provide all students with the requisite
skills to become competent lawyers in any field of practice.
A wide selection of elective courses, seminars, and student
in-house and internal clinics allows students to focus on
specialized legal fields and explore the contemporary
problems of law and society.

■ Admission

*Bachelor's degree required; Application deadlines: day, April 1;
evening, May 1; part-time day, June 1; rolling admission; LSAT
and registration with LSAC's Credential Assembly Service
(CAS) required.*

All candidates for admission must take the LSAT, register for
the Credential Assembly Service (CAS), and be graduates of an
accredited college or university before enrolling in the law
school. Personal interviews are not granted, but applicants are
encouraged to schedule an appointment to visit the school for
an information session or a tour of the facilities.

The admission process is selective. Most applicants apply
well in advance of the deadlines. Students are admitted only
for the fall semester.

In evaluating applications, the complete academic record is
reviewed with consideration given to the competitiveness of
the undergraduate institution, the college major, rank in class,
and the overall academic performance. The LSAT is
considered an important factor. Graduate study,
extracurricular activities, and recommendations also
contribute to the committee's assessment. Work experience
is considered when an applicant has been employed full time
for a significant length of time.

■ Joint-Degree Programs

The School of Law offers the following joint-degree
programs: JD/MBA, JD/MS-Environmental Science and
Management, JD/MA-Healthcare Ethics, and JD/MDiv.

■ Clinical Opportunities

The School of Law operates five in-house live client clinics.

The **Economic and Community Development Law Clinic** is
a unique, nationally recognized clinic. Students represent
nonprofit organizations that provide a vast array of greatly
needed services to the community. Through the **Civil and
Family Justice Law Clinic**, students represent indigent
individuals who would not otherwise find assistance through
the civil justice system. The **Criminal Advocacy Clinic** is
operated in cooperation with the Allegheny County District
Attorney's and Public Defender's offices. Through the
Federal Low Income Tax Practicum, students learn litigation
skills as they represent clients in appeals conferences,
settlement negotiations, and before the US Tax Court. The
Securities Arbitration Practicum, created with the support of
the Securities and Exchange Commission, is designed to
enable law students to represent small investors through the
NASD Dispute Resolution process.

■ International Programs

The law school has established a summer program and faculty
exchange with the Chinese University of Political Science and
Law (CUPL). Located in Beijing, CUPL, with official ties to
China's Ministry of Justice, is the most prestigious center for
legal study in all of China. Duquesne has an outstanding
ABA-approved summer program of study on Comparative
Law and the European Union at the American College,
Dublin. The Duquesne law school has recently established an
ABA-approved program for law students in Vatican City,
focusing on subjects relating to Canon Law and Roman Law.
Duquesne is the only law school offering a program for law
students within Vatican City.

■ Student Activities

The Student Bar Association maintains a liaison between students and faculty and sponsors social and professional activities for the student body.

Membership in the *Duquesne Law Review* is based on the demonstrated academic ability of the student as well as his or her interest in becoming active in this publication. *Juris*, the law school news magazine, is an ABA award-winning publication containing articles of current interest to the entire legal community. Students also publish the *Duquesne Business Law Journal*.

■ Financial Aid

Duquesne consistently strives to ensure that the outstanding private legal education provided by the law school is within the reach of all qualified students. Merit scholarships are awarded to outstanding day-division applicants, grants-in-aid are awarded primarily on the basis of need, and state and federal government-sponsored loans are available.

■ Housing

Law students have access to an array of housing options throughout the neighborhoods of Pittsburgh and the surrounding communities. The Office of Commuter Affairs will assist law students in their search for housing by providing a list of available locations. For further information, please write to the Office of Commuter Affairs, Duquesne University, Pittsburgh, PA 15282 or call 412.396.6660.

■ Career Services

The Career Services Office staff offers assistance to students and alumni who are interested in obtaining full-time, part-time, and summer employment. The office offers a fall and spring on-campus interview program in which law firms, government agencies, corporations, and accounting firms conduct individual interviews.

The School of Law is a member of the National Association for Law Placement, the National Association for Public Interest Law Publication Network, and the Allegheny County Bar Association Minority Job Fair.

Graduates have consistently been placed at a rate at or above 90 percent within six months of graduation. The law school has nearly 5,000 alumni throughout the United States and in several foreign countries.

Applicant Profile

The law school recognizes the different strengths presented by our day division, evening division, and part-time day students and acknowledges that the diversity in the groups cannot be accurately or completely represented in a single grid of average undergraduate GPA and LSAT scores. Graduate degrees, personal and professional accomplishments, and extensive employment experience predominate in the evening, part-time, and day divisions.

These factors are considered crucial to an individual assessment of admissibility. Applications are reviewed individually, and factors such as leadership experience, community service, and other nonacademic experiences are considered. Applicants should contact the Admissions Office for specific information on the current year's class; phone: 412.396.6296. Applicants are encouraged to visit the law school.

Earle Mack School of Law, Drexel University

3320 Market Street, Suite 100
Philadelphia, PA 19104
Phone: 215.895.1529
E-mail: LawAdmissions@drexel.edu; Website: www.earlemacklaw.drexel.edu/admissions-home.asp

Provisional   *ABA*
Approved
Since
2008

The Basics

Type of school	Private
Term	Quarter
Application deadline	8/10
Application fee	$0
Financial aid deadline	
Can first year start other than fall?	No
Student to faculty ratio	16.4 to 1
# of housing spaces available restricted to law students	
graduate housing for which law students are eligible	

Faculty and Administrators

	Total		Men		Women		Minorities	
	Spr	Fall	Spr	Fall	Spr	Fall	Spr	Fall
Full-time	20	22	12	12	8	10	5	5
Other full-time	4	5	0	0	4	5	1	1
Deans, librarians, & others who teach	5	5	2	3	3	2	1	0
Part-time	47	27	30	15	17	12	4	1
Total	76	59	44	30	32	29	11	7

JD Enrollment and Ethnicity

	Men		Women		Full-Time		Part-Time		1st-Year		Total		JD Degs. Awd.
	#	%	#	%	#	%	#	%	#	%	#	%	
African Amer.	6	2.8	21	10.8	27	6.6	0	0.0	6	3.8	27	6.6	11
Amer. Indian	3	1.4	1	0.5	4	1.0	0	0.0	3	1.9	4	1.0	1
Asian Amer.	6	2.8	9	4.6	15	3.7	0	0.0	5	3.2	15	3.7	11
Mex. Amer.	4	1.9	1	0.5	5	1.2	0	0.0	2	1.3	5	1.2	0
Puerto Rican	1	0.5	4	2.1	5	1.2	0	0.0	3	1.9	5	1.2	1
Hispanic	9	4.2	8	4.1	17	4.1	0	0.0	9	5.8	17	4.1	3
Total Minority	29	13.5	44	22.6	73	17.8	0	0.0	28	17.9	73	17.8	27
For. Nation.	4	1.9	6	3.1	10	2.4	0	0.0	4	2.6	10	2.4	6
Caucasian	159	74.0	133	68.2	292	71.2	0	0.0	104	66.7	292	71.2	122
Unknown	23	10.7	12	6.2	35	8.5	0	0.0	20	12.8	35	8.5	6
Total	215	52.4	195	47.6	410	100.0	0	0.0	156	38.0	410		161

Curriculum

	Full-Time	Part-Time
Typical first-year section size	78	0
Is there typically a "small section" of the first-year class, other than Legal Writing, taught by full-time faculty	No	No
If yes, typical size offered last year		
# of classroom course titles beyond first-year curriculum	84	
# of upper division courses, excluding seminars, with an enrollment: Under 25	60	
25–49	36	
50–74	7	
75–99	2	
100+	0	
# of seminars	11	
# of seminar positions available	199	
# of seminar positions filled	168	0
# of positions available in simulation courses	804	
# of simulation positions filled	630	0
# of positions available in faculty supervised clinical courses	0	
# of faculty supervised clinical positions filled	0	0
# involved in field placements	124	0
# involved in law journals	47	0
# involved in moot court or trial competitions	38	0
# of credit hours required to graduate	130	

Transfers

Transfers in	7
Transfers out	1

Tuition and Fees

	Resident	Nonresident
Full-time	$32,921	$32,921
Part-time		
Tuition Guarantee Program	N	

Living Expenses

Estimated living expenses for singles

Living on campus	Living off campus	Living at home
$21,435	$21,435	$7,485

Earle Mack School of Law, Drexel University

ABA
Approved
Since
2008

GPA and LSAT Scores

	Total	Full-Time	Part-Time
# of apps	2,862	2,862	0
# of offers	937	937	0
# of matrics	156	156	0
75% GPA	3.70	3.70	0.00
Median GPA	3.42	3.42	0.00
25% GPA	3.09	3.09	0.00
75% LSAT	163	163	0
Median LSAT	160	160	0
25% LSAT	156	156	0

Grants and Scholarships (from prior year)

	Total		Full-Time		Part-Time	
	#	%	#	%	#	%
Total # of students	422		422		0	
Total # receiving grants	374	88.6	374	88.6	0	0.0
Less than 1/2 tuition	133	31.5	133	31.5	0	0.0
Half to full tuition	194	46.0	194	46.0	0	0.0
Full tuition	47	11.1	47	11.1	0	0.0
More than full tuition	0	0.0	0	0.0	0	0.0
Median grant amount			$24,347		$0	

Informational and Library Resources

Total amount spent on library materials	$992,642
Study seating capacity inside the library	283
# of full-time equivalent professional librarians	6
Hours per week library is open	93
# of open, wired connections available to students	731
# of networked computers available for use by students	16
Has wireless network?	Y
Require computer?	Y

JD Attrition (from prior year)

	Academic	Other	Total	
	#	#	#	%
1st year	4	6	10	7.0
2nd year	2	0	2	1.7
3rd year	0	0	0	0.0
4th year	0	0	0	0.0

Employment (9 months after graduation)

	Total	Percentage
Employment status known	0	0.0
Employment status unknown	0	0.0
Employed	0	0.0
Pursuing graduate degrees	0	0.0
Unemployed (seeking, not seeking, or studying for the bar)	0	0.0
Type of Employment		
# employed in law firms	0	0.0
# employed in business and industry	0	0.0
# employed in government	0	0.0
# employed in public interest	0	0.0
# employed as judicial clerks	0	0.0
# employed in academia	0	0.0
Geographic Location		
# employed in state	0	0.0
# employed in foreign countries	0	0.0
# of states where employed	0	

Bar Passage Rates

First-time takers	0	Reporting %	NA
Average school %	NA	Average state %	NA
Average pass difference	NA		

Jurisdiction	Takers	Passers	Pass %	State %	Diff %

Earle Mack School of Law, Drexel University

3320 Market Street, Suite 100
Philadelphia, PA 19104
Phone: 215.895.1529
E-mail: LawAdmissions@drexel.edu; Website: www.earlemacklaw.drexel.edu/admissions-home.asp

■ Introduction

Drexel University has long believed in the value of experiential education and promoted learning opportunities for students outside of the classroom. This deeply rooted educational philosophy led the Earle Mack School of Law at Drexel University to develop imaginative approaches to legal education that produce outstanding lawyers who share a commitment to serving the public good.

Our approach integrates theory and practice so that students master both legal principles and the real-world skills needed to apply them. By adapting Drexel University's signature emphasis on hands-on learning to the law school setting, we are forging connections between legal educators, practitioners, and the public we aim to serve, thereby fostering a new civic professionalism.

We give students a multitude of opportunities for hands-on learning. The Co-op Program allows opportunities to gain experience in a variety of legal settings. The Clinical Program allows students to represent clients in criminal and civil matters though our in-house Appellate Litigation Clinic and Field Clinics with three of Philadelphia's premiere public interest organizations. Our top-notch Trial Advocacy Program prepares students to argue before trial and appellate courts. Our Pro Bono Program provides yet another avenue for gaining practical experience.

The law school has demonstrated its strong support for the Co-op Program in many ways: by allotting a significant number of credits for the program, by hiring faculty with extensive practice experience to teach the classroom component and to work closely with the supervising attorneys in the field, and by maintaining a low faculty-to-student ratio. Well over 100 co-op partners and other supervising attorneys have joined us to help realize this new vision of professional legal education for the twenty-first century.

■ Location

Located in the University City neighborhood just adjacent to downtown Philadelphia, the law school is mere blocks from the heart of one of the nation's largest and most dynamic legal communities. University City is so named because of the 40,000 students from Drexel University and the University of Pennsylvania who combine to create an exciting, vibrant community. Thanks to our location, affordable student housing is located a short walk or trolley ride away, and students are able to meet after class at many of the nearby restaurants, trendy shops, and bars.

■ Faculty and Curriculum

Our faculty of nationally recognized scholars and experienced practitioners share a commitment to innovative teaching and the integration of theory and practice.

Professors at the Earle Mack School of Law have distinguished backgrounds in scholarship and legal practice. The faculty includes pioneers who helped establish disciplines like health law and who are engaged in path-breaking approaches to legal education.

In the first year, we offer strong introductory classes that emphasize professionalism. The first-year curriculum also features a rigorous introduction to legal methods, which starts during orientation. First-year students also receive an introduction to the skills of interviewing, negotiation, and counseling, and gain critical legal writing and oral advocacy skills.

Upper-level students choose from elective courses in areas as diverse as e-commerce law, criminal law, employment law, family law, international law, animal rights, bioethics, sports law, and securities law. Courses from Trial Advocacy to Transactional Lawyering feature simulations that allow students to put their skills to practice while they're still in class.

For students seeking an in-depth introduction to a single area of practice, the law school offers three concentrations in the fields of intellectual property, health law, and business and entrepreneurship law. In partnership with Drexel University's respected Psychology Department, we offer a joint JD-PhD in psychology. We plan to launch the following joint-degree programs: JD-MBA, JD-MPH, and JD-MSPP.

With varied concentration options, an intensive emphasis on skills, and professors who bring practice into the classroom, the curriculum prepares students to enter professional practice with confidence and savvy.

■ Admission

When considering applicants, the Earle Mack School of Law does not employ cutoffs or numerical formulas. Rather, we look at an applicant's entire application and take into consideration both objective factors like the LSAT and GPA, as well as subjective factors like leadership skills, work experience, and commitment to service.

We utilize rolling admissions, which means it is never too late to apply. Nevertheless, we encourage students to apply as early in the year as possible, since scholarship and admission decisions are weighted favorably towards early applicants.

■ Co-op Program

Our Co-op Program provides a unique opportunity for law students to synthesize the legal theory learned in the classroom with the critical knowledge and professional skills learned in the field under the close supervision of experienced practitioners. Our commitment to integrating the Co-op Program into the curriculum and the singular focus students give to their placements distinguish it from experiential programs offered by other law schools.

The Co-op Program is a semester-long field placement during the second or third year of study that allows a student to work in a law firm, corporation, judicial office, public interest organization, or government agency. Each placement is chosen for the quality experience that it can provide law students as part of their overall academic experience. Students learn the law relevant to the practice area and the skills needed to succeed there. They also get acquainted with the host institution and the industries to which it belongs while building professional networks with the practitioners who work there.

Clinical Program

Students gain firsthand experience representing clients while earning academic credit through our year-long Clinical Program.

The Civil Litigation Field Clinic, which operates in tandem with the AIDS Law Project of Pennsylvania, allows students to represent clients in Landlord-Tenant Court, in guardianship cases, and in administrative-law hearings to determine eligibility for disability benefits.

The Criminal Litigation Field Clinic, which operates in partnership with the Defender Association of Philadelphia, allows students to represent clients in preliminary hearings on felonies and to argue legal motions and try misdemeanor cases in Philadelphia's municipal court.

The Public Health and Environmental Law Field Clinic, developed in concert with the Public Interest Law Center of Philadelphia, enables students to help community leaders and neighborhood organizations explore and pursue legal strategies to address environmental and public health concerns.

Our in-house Appellate Litigation Clinic offers students the unique opportunity to practice law before state and federal appellate courts. Students provide valuable legal services to needy individuals who otherwise would not be able obtain representation to appeal matters involving constitutional law, criminal law, immigration law, and the rights of the indigent and the incarcerated.

Trial Advocacy Program

The law school's innovative Trial Advocacy Program trains students in the essential practical skills of litigation.

In Pretrial Advocacy, students learn how to interview a client, plan pretrial investigation, identify and retain experts, and draft pleadings and motions. During the trial preparation phase, students also learn how to develop the cornerstone of any successful litigation strategy: a theory of the case. They also learn deposition strategies and techniques, as well as other discovery techniques.

In Trial Advocacy, experienced trial lawyers and judges teach effective trial techniques by providing live demonstrations relating to jury selection, opening and closing statements, and direct- and cross-examination of lay and expert witnesses. Students also learn how computer technology is used to create and introduce state-of-the-art trial exhibits that will enhance the presentation of evidence at trial. Trial Advocacy ends with a capstone experience in which each student litigates a mock trial in a real courtroom before real judges and veteran attorneys.

Pro Bono Service

Providing pro bono service to individuals or groups traditionally underserved by the private bar is the goal of our mandatory 50-hour Pro Bono Service Requirement. Students will make an immediate impact in the world by helping those most in need. In addition, the program strives to educate students about their ethical responsibility to provide assistance and improve access to legal services throughout their legal careers. Finally, the program highlights public service opportunities that students may want to pursue as a career path.

Working with supervising attorneys, students develop their legal skills and gain practical, hands-on experience in a real legal setting. The Pro Bono Service Requirement is a vital part of our curriculum that demonstrates the commitment of faculty and administrators to developing our students' professionalism.

Applicant Profile

Earle Mack School of Law, Drexel University

LSAT Score	GPA								
	3.75 +	3.50–3.74	3.25–3.49	3.00–3.24	2.75–2.99	2.50–2.74	2.25–2.49	2.00–2.24	Below 2.00
175–180									
170–174									
165–169									
160–164									
155–159									
150–154									
145–149									
140–144									
120–139									

Good Possibility   Possible   Unlikely

Elon University School of Law

201 North Greene Street
Greensboro, NC 27401
Phone: 336.279.9200; Fax: 336.279.8199
E-mail: law@elon.edu; Website: www.law.elon.edu

Provisional ABA Approved Since 2008

The Basics

Type of school	Private
Term	Semester
Application deadline	7/31
Application fee	$50
Financial aid deadline	
Can first year start other than fall?	No
Student to faculty ratio	17.3 to 1
# of housing spaces available restricted to law students	
graduate housing for which law students are eligible	

Faculty and Administrators

	Total		Men		Women		Minorities	
	Spr	Fall	Spr	Fall	Spr	Fall	Spr	Fall
Full-time	16	14	11	9	5	5	1	2
Other full-time	2	3	1	2	1	1	0	0
Deans, librarians, & others who teach	5	6	3	3	2	3	1	1
Part-time	33	14	21	9	12	5	1	0
Total	56	37	36	23	20	14	3	3

Curriculum

		Full-Time	Part-Time
Typical first-year section size		30	0
Is there typically a "small section" of the first-year class, other than Legal Writing, taught by full-time faculty		Yes	No
If yes, typical size offered last year		30	
# of classroom course titles beyond first-year curriculum		54	
# of upper division courses, excluding seminars, with an enrollment:	Under 25	10	
	25–49	7	
	50–74	12	
	75–99	3	
	100+	3	
# of seminars		20	
# of seminar positions available		541	
# of seminar positions filled		447	0
# of positions available in simulation courses		181	
# of simulation positions filled		180	0
# of positions available in faculty supervised clinical courses		8	
# of faculty supervised clinical positions filled		8	0
# involved in field placements		52	0
# involved in law journals		20	0
# involved in moot court or trial competitions		25	0
# of credit hours required to graduate		90	

Transfers

Transfers in	1
Transfers out	2

Tuition and Fees

	Resident	Nonresident
Full-time	$30,750	$30,750
Part-time		
Tuition Guarantee Program	N	

Living Expenses

Estimated living expenses for singles

Living on campus	Living off campus	Living at home
N/A	$22,000	$22,000

JD Enrollment and Ethnicity

	Men		Women		Full-Time		Part-Time		1st-Year		Total		JD Degs. Awd.
	#	%	#	%	#	%	#	%	#	%	#	%	
African Amer.	5	2.9	13	9.2	18	5.7	0	0.0	9	7.5	18	5.7	5
Amer. Indian	0	0.0	1	0.7	1	0.3	0	0.0	0	0.0	1	0.3	0
Asian Amer.	6	3.5	4	2.8	10	3.2	0	0.0	2	1.7	10	3.2	2
Mex. Amer.	0	0.0	0	0.0	0	0.0	0	0.0	0	0.0	0	0.0	0
Puerto Rican	0	0.0	0	0.0	0	0.0	0	0.0	0	0.0	0	0.0	0
Hispanic	4	2.3	2	1.4	6	1.9	0	0.0	5	4.2	6	1.9	0
Total Minority	15	8.7	20	14.1	35	11.1	0	0.0	16	13.3	35	11.1	7
For. Nation.	0	0.0	0	0.0	0	0.0	0	0.0	0	0.0	0	0.0	0
Caucasian	149	86.1	118	83.1	267	84.8	0	0.0	104	86.7	267	84.8	100
Unknown	9	5.2	4	2.8	13	4.1	0	0.0	0	0.0	13	4.1	0
Total	173	54.9	142	45.1	315	100.0	0	0.0	120	38.1	315		107

Elon University School of Law

ABA
Approved
Since
2008

GPA and LSAT Scores

	Total	Full-Time	Part-Time
# of apps	761	761	0
# of offers	316	316	0
# of matrics	121	121	0
75% GPA	3.49	3.49	0.00
Median GPA	3.21	3.21	0.00
25% GPA	2.99	2.99	0.00
75% LSAT	156	156	0
Median LSAT	154	154	0
25% LSAT	152	152	0

Grants and Scholarships (from prior year)

	Total		Full-Time		Part-Time	
	#	%	#	%	#	%
Total # of students	311		311		0	
Total # receiving grants	216	69.5	216	69.5	0	0.0
Less than 1/2 tuition	177	56.9	177	56.9	0	0.0
Half to full tuition	35	11.3	35	11.3	0	0.0
Full tuition	4	1.3	4	1.3	0	0.0
More than full tuition	0	0.0	0	0.0	0	0.0
Median grant amount			$6,000		$0	

Informational and Library Resources

Total amount spent on library materials	$677,054
Study seating capacity inside the library	333
# of full-time equivalent professional librarians	4
Hours per week library is open	102
# of open, wired connections available to students	102
# of networked computers available for use by students	32
Has wireless network?	Y
Require computer?	N

JD Attrition (from prior year)

	Academic	Other	Total	
	#	#	#	%
1st year	1	6	7	6.7
2nd year	0	1	1	1.0
3rd year	0	0	0	0.0
4th year	0	0	0	0.0

Employment (9 months after graduation)

	Total	Percentage
Employment status known	0	0.0
Employment status unknown	0	0.0
Employed	0	0.0
Pursuing graduate degrees	0	0.0
Unemployed (seeking, not seeking, or studying for the bar)	0	0.0
Type of Employment		
# employed in law firms	0	0.0
# employed in business and industry	0	0.0
# employed in government	0	0.0
# employed in public interest	0	0.0
# employed as judicial clerks	0	0.0
# employed in academia	0	0.0
Geographic Location		
# employed in state	0	0.0
# employed in foreign countries	0	0.0
# of states where employed	0	

Bar Passage Rates

First-time takers		Reporting %	NA
Average school %	NA	Average state %	NA
Average pass difference	NA		

Jurisdiction	Takers	Passers	Pass %	State %	Diff %

Elon University School of Law

201 North Greene Street
Greensboro, NC 27401
Phone: 336.279.9200; Fax: 336.279.8199
E-mail: law@elon.edu; Website: www.law.elon.edu

■ Introduction

Founded in 2006, Elon University School of Law is building on Elon's reputation as the nation's top-ranked university for engaged learning and leadership education. The law school received provisional approval from the American Bar Association in June 2008, and its graduates are qualified to seek admission to the bar in all 50 states and the District of Columbia.

■ Location

Elon University School of Law is located in downtown Greensboro, North Carolina, the third largest city in North Carolina, with a regional population of about 1.5 million. The law school is located at the center of the area's legal community, including major law firms, government offices, and district and federal courts. The downtown area also provides a rich cultural environment, with restaurants, music venues, museums and theaters, a new minor league baseball stadium, and recreational facilities. All law students are provided free memberships to a new YMCA just a few blocks from the law school.

■ Advisory Board

The law school's advisory board includes prominent judges, attorneys, and business leaders who advise the university in shaping the vision for the school and its future development. The board is chaired by David Gergen, who held positions in the administrations of Presidents Nixon, Ford, Reagan, and Clinton. The board also includes two former North Carolina governors, three former North Carolina Supreme Court chief justices, a former president of the American Bar Association, and a former US ambassador.

■ Curriculum

The law school operates on a three-term model, with fall and spring semesters of 13 weeks and a winter term offering courses and practical experiences in leadership and the law. While at Elon, students take a wide array of required courses and electives, and each student selects at least one of four concentrations in their second year: Business, Litigation, Public Interest, and General Practice.

■ Leadership Emphasis

Over the course of the three-year program, Elon Law incorporates the best of leadership education through courses, community activities, and capstone experiences. Elon lawyers will begin their careers as knowledgeable, self-aware, skillful, and innovative professionals. The Joseph M. Bryan Distinguished Leadership Lecture Series brings accomplished leaders from a variety of disciplines to Elon to share their experiences and perspectives.

■ Preceptor Program

More than 50 volunteer attorneys serve annually as preceptors to Elon's first-year law students. As professional advisers, they observe and provide feedback to students about their classroom performances and invite students to accompany them to observe trials or initial client interviews, depositions, and mediations. Through these experiences, students are mentored and guided in their professional development and entry to the legal profession.

■ Clinics

Two clinical programs at Elon Law put legal theory into practice, providing students with essential lawyering skills through casework management, research, writing, client interaction, and courtroom advocacy, while also helping individuals in need. Current clinical offerings include the Juvenile Justice Intervention and Mediation Clinic and a Wills Clinic. The Legal Aid Housing and Domestic Relations field placement program and externships in governmental, judicial, and public interest law offices provide students with additional opportunities to gain practical legal experience.

■ Engaged Learning and CELL

In addition to offering students extensive field-based experiences with practicing attorneys, judges, and business leaders, Elon law professors employ various methods of instruction, including Socratic, group presentations, projects, and problem method, actively engaging students in their studies. To facilitate the faculty's development as excellent teachers and their ability to tap students' potential for learning, the law school has established the Center for Engaged Learning in the Law (CELL).

■ Law Library

The depth and breadth of the Elon Law library collection compares favorably with more established law schools and is considerably larger than typical academic law libraries at their earliest stage of development. Students may access a wide variety of digital and online databases from both on- and off-campus locations. The collection is designed specifically to support the four practice-area concentrations with additional emphasis in the areas of leadership and professional ethics. The library, like the rest of the law school building, is served by a wireless network with full, high-speed Internet access.

■ Facilities

The School of Law is located in the four-floor, 84,000-square-foot H. Michael Weaver Building, specially designed to support Elon's engaged approach to legal education. Elon Law is one of only a few schools in the nation to house a working court. The North Carolina Business Court uses the school's high-tech courtroom, and the court's offices are also located within the building, giving students the opportunity to observe and interact with judges and attorneys. The law school's facilities also include a clinical law center, tiered classrooms with extensive multimedia capabilities, a spacious and comfortable library, full wireless network access, and a coffee bar and welcoming common area for students.

Career Services

The Career Services Office serves as a liaison with legal employers and students in North Carolina and beyond and provides a wide array of services. The office provides career programming and skills workshops for students and coordinates on-campus interviewing sessions, résumé requests, and job fair participation on national and state levels. Students have had significant success in securing employment after graduation and in internship placements with judges, law firms, and other legal employers during the summer and academic year.

Admissions

Each year, the law school seeks to enroll a talented and diverse class of approximately 120 students. Early-decision applicants receive decisions by December 31. Regular-decision applications are accepted throughout the admission cycle and decisions on these applications are made on a rolling basis throughout this period, with most decisions made by the middle of April. Prospective students are encouraged to visit the school to speak with an admissions professional, tour the law school with a student ambassador, and visit a class.

Financial Planning

Financial aid is available to law students in the form of scholarships and loans. A large percentage of students, approximately 75 percent of each entering class, receive scholarship awards. Merit scholarships are awarded based on applicants' potential for outstanding contributions to the law school, the legal profession, and society. Financial need will also be considered and can be explained in a letter to the law school's scholarship committee requesting consideration for an award. Many law students participate in federal loan programs such as subsidized Federal Stafford Loans, unsubsidized Federal Stafford Loans, and GradPlus Loans.

Applicant Profile

Elon University School of Law

LSAT Score	GPA								
	3.75 +	3.50–3.74	3.25–3.49	3.00–3.24	2.75–2.99	2.50–2.74	2.25–2.49	2.00–2.24	Below 2.00
175–180									
170–174									
165–169									
160–164									
155–159									
150–154									
145–149									
140–144									
135–139									
130–134									
125–129									
120–124									

■ Good Possibility □ Possible ▨ Unlikely

Emory University School of Law

Gambrell Hall, 1301 Clifton Road
Atlanta, GA 30322-2770
Phone: 404.727.6802; Fax: 404.727.2477
E-mail: lawinfo@law.emory.edu; Website: www.law.emory.edu

ABA
Approved
Since
1923

The Basics

Type of school	Private
Term	Semester
Application deadline	3/1
Application fee	$70
Financial aid deadline	3/1
Can first year start other than fall?	No
Student to faculty ratio	10.5 to 1
# of housing spaces available restricted to law students graduate housing for which law students are eligible	500

Faculty and Administrators

	Total		Men		Women		Minorities	
	Spr	Fall	Spr	Fall	Spr	Fall	Spr	Fall
Full-time	54	57	31	32	23	25	7	7
Other full-time	3	3	1	1	2	2	0	0
Deans, librarians, & others who teach	5	5	3	3	2	2	1	1
Part-time	35	42	30	31	5	11	3	8
Total	97	107	65	67	32	40	11	16

Curriculum

	Full-Time	Part-Time
Typical first-year section size	75	0
Is there typically a "small section" of the first-year class, other than Legal Writing, taught by full-time faculty	Yes	No
If yes, typical size offered last year	38	
# of classroom course titles beyond first-year curriculum	165	
# of upper division courses, excluding seminars, with an enrollment: Under 25	95	
25–49	27	
50–74	9	
75–99	12	
100+	2	
# of seminars	20	
# of seminar positions available	294	
# of seminar positions filled	225	0
# of positions available in simulation courses	1,018	
# of simulation positions filled	892	0
# of positions available in faculty supervised clinical courses	80	
# of faculty supervised clinical positions filled	62	0
# involved in field placements	188	0
# involved in law journals	172	0
# involved in moot court or trial competitions	83	0
# of credit hours required to graduate	90	

JD Enrollment and Ethnicity

	Men		Women		Full-Time		Part-Time		1st-Year		Total		JD Degs. Awd.
	#	%	#	%	#	%	#	%	#	%	#	%	
African Amer.	17	4.6	48	14.0	65	9.1	0	0.0	14	5.6	65	9.1	21
Amer. Indian	2	0.5	6	1.8	8	1.1	0	0.0	5	2.0	8	1.1	0
Asian Amer.	33	8.8	39	11.4	72	10.1	0	0.0	26	10.5	72	10.1	15
Mex. Amer.	0	0.0	0	0.0	0	0.0	0	0.0	0	0.0	0	0.0	0
Puerto Rican	0	0.0	0	0.0	0	0.0	0	0.0	0	0.0	0	0.0	0
Hispanic	42	11.3	32	9.4	74	10.3	0	0.0	26	10.5	74	10.3	8
Total Minority	94	25.2	125	36.5	219	30.6	0	0.0	71	28.6	219	30.6	44
For. Nation.	14	3.8	16	4.7	30	4.2	0	0.0	10	4.0	30	4.2	9
Caucasian	228	61.1	174	50.9	402	56.2	0	0.0	154	62.1	402	56.2	134
Unknown	37	9.9	27	7.9	64	9.0	0	0.0	13	5.2	64	9.0	30
Total	373	52.2	342	47.8	715	100.0	0	0.0	248	34.7	715		217

Transfers

Transfers in	22
Transfers out	7

Tuition and Fees

	Resident	Nonresident
Full-time	$41,376	$41,376
Part-time		
Tuition Guarantee Program	N	

Living Expenses

Estimated living expenses for singles

Living on campus	Living off campus	Living at home
$24,462	$24,462	$24,462

Emory University School of Law

ABA
Approved
Since
1923

GPA and LSAT Scores

	Total	Full-Time	Part-Time
# of apps	4,558	4,562	0
# of offers	1,149	1,149	0
# of matrics	248	248	0
75% GPA	3.68	3.68	0.00
Median GPA	3.57	3.57	0.00
25% GPA	3.37	3.37	0.00
75% LSAT	167	167	0
Median LSAT	166	166	0
25% LSAT	165	165	0

Grants and Scholarships (from prior year)

	Total		Full-Time		Part-Time	
	#	%	#	%	#	%
Total # of students	697		697		0	
Total # receiving grants	483	69.3	483	69.3	0	0.0
Less than 1/2 tuition	279	40.0	279	40.0	0	0.0
Half to full tuition	186	26.7	186	26.7	0	0.0
Full tuition	4	0.6	4	0.6	0	0.0
More than full tuition	14	2.0	14	2.0	0	0.0
Median grant amount				$18,000		$0

Informational and Library Resources

Total amount spent on library materials	$1,150,075
Study seating capacity inside the library	516
# of full-time equivalent professional librarians	9
Hours per week library is open	109
# of open, wired connections available to students	64
# of networked computers available for use by students	73
Has wireless network?	Y
Require computer?	N

JD Attrition (from prior year)

	Academic	Other	Total	
	#	#	#	%
1st year	0	4	4	1.8
2nd year	0	10	10	3.9
3rd year	0	0	0	0.0
4th year	0	0	0	0.0

Employment (9 months after graduation)

	Total	Percentage
Employment status known	238	97.1
Employment status unknown	7	2.9
Employed	222	93.3
Pursuing graduate degrees	2	0.8
Unemployed (seeking, not seeking, or studying for the bar)	6	2.5
Type of Employment		
# employed in law firms	150	67.6
# employed in business and industry	21	9.5
# employed in government	11	5.0
# employed in public interest	5	2.3
# employed as judicial clerks	18	8.1
# employed in academia	0	0.0
Geographic Location		
# employed in state	89	40.1
# employed in foreign countries	2	0.9
# of states where employed		29

Bar Passage Rates

First-time takers	140	Reporting %	77.14
Average school %	93.52	Average state %	89.27
Average pass difference	4.25		

Jurisdiction	Takers	Passers	Pass %	State %	Diff %
Georgia	108	101	93.52	89.27	4.25

Emory University School of Law

Gambrell Hall, 1301 Clifton Road
Atlanta, GA 30322-2770
Phone: 404.727.6802; Fax: 404.727.2477
E-mail: lawinfo@law.emory.edu; Website: www.law.emory.edu

■ Introduction

Emory's location in Atlanta, a national business and legal center, gives law students the opportunity to take advanced classes from, and work with, some of the leading judges and lawyers in the United States. Atlanta also is one of America's most beautiful and culturally diverse cities.

The law school also benefits from being located on the campus of Emory University, which was founded in 1836. Emory University School of Law is accredited by the American Bar Association, is a member of the Association of American Law Schools, and has a chapter of the Order of the Coif.

■ Curriculum

The basic program of study involves three years of full-time study leading to the JD degree. The fall semester runs from late August to mid-December; the spring semester begins in early January and ends in mid-May.

The program of courses for the first year is generally prescribed, though beginning with the spring 2011 semester, first-year students may choose one elective. The program of courses for the second and third years primarily is elective. Students can sample a broad spectrum of courses or concentrate on a particular area of law.

All first-year courses and the basic second- and third-year courses are taught by full-time faculty members. A distinguished group of judges and practicing attorneys offer specialized courses.

■ Library and Physical Facilities

Emory School of Law is located in Gambrell Hall, part of Emory's 630-acre campus in Druid Hills, six miles southeast of downtown Atlanta.

Gambrell Hall contains classrooms, faculty offices, administrative offices, student-organization offices, and a 325-seat auditorium. The school provides wireless Internet access throughout its facilities. Gambrell Hall also houses a state-of-the-art courtroom with computer connections for judge, counsel, and jury; a document camera; a DVD player; videoconferencing; and a four-camera operation with feeds to remote locations.

The Hugh F. MacMillan Law Library sits adjacent to Gambrell Hall and is designed for easy student access. Students are trained on LexisNexis and Westlaw terminals and learn both the techniques of computer-assisted legal research and traditional research methods. Students also may use the library's computer labs that offer Apple and PC computers.

■ Special Programs

Emory Law combines a practical and disciplined approach toward the study of law with a commitment to providing students experiential learning opportunities that engage them in the many roles the law plays in our society. Our students engage the law through learning opportunities that create graduates who are ready to apply their knowledge to make an impact in real and significant ways, as lawyers and as citizens of the world. We teach the practice of law through our outstanding programs in trial techniques, intellectual property, child advocacy, and environmental law, as well as through expanded emphasis on transactional skills. Our centers of excellence in law and religion, world law, feminism and legal theory, and transactional law are interdisciplinary, integrative, and international in approach.

Emory's Trial Techniques Program affords our students exposure to the challenges of conducting direct and cross-examination, developing a case theory and approach, and conducting opening and closing arguments. More than half of the students participate in Emory's field placement program, where students may earn academic credit clerking for a federal judge, researching intellectual property issues for major corporations such as the Coca-Cola Company, and representing clients on behalf of Atlanta Legal Aid.

Emory Law's Center for Transactional Law and Practice is at the forefront of educating students and professionals on topics related to business transactions. Students participate through Emory's Transactional Law Certificate Program, while the center offers a number of workshops and seminars designed specifically for practicing attorneys. The center also regularly hosts a conference for educators in the area of teaching transactional skills.

Students also may gain practical experience in intellectual property and corporate/commercial law by participating in TI:GER (Technological Innovation: Generating Economic Results), a program of technology and business law cosponsored by Emory's School of Law and Economics Department and Georgia Institute of Technology's Dupree School of Management. Students may participate in one of Emory's own clinics: the Barton Child Law and Policy Clinic, working to promote and protect the well-being of neglected and abused children; the Barton Juvenile Defender Clinic, representing children charged with delinquent acts; the Turner Environmental Law Clinic, offering a practical clinical education to the aspiring environmental attorney; or the International Humanitarian Law Clinic, focusing on upholding the rule of law on behalf of detainees and on educating and training officials in war-torn countries on humanitarian law.

Emory offers a comprehensive international law program and is home to the World Law Institute. Emory Law capitalizes on the presence of other strong campus programs by combining coursework and programs to create unique and synergistic programs of study. The law school offers joint-degree programs with Emory's Goizueta School of Business, Candler School of Theology, School of Public Health, and the Graduate School of Arts and Sciences.

■ Admission

The law school accepts beginning students for the fall term only. Prior to enrollment, a student must have earned a bachelor's degree from an approved institution. Applications for admission must be received by Emory no later than March 1. Early applications are encouraged. Many factors are considered in making admission decisions. Of particular importance are academic accomplishments and LSAT scores. Extracurricular activities, work experience, level of quality and difficulty of undergraduate courses, performance in graduate school, and letters of recommendation are also considered.

We encourage applications from members of underrepresented groups, and such applicants should provide the Dean of Admission with specific information about their background or accomplishments that would be of particular interest. Applicants are encouraged to visit the law school. Upon acceptance, applicants are required to submit a nonrefundable $750 tuition deposit to reserve a space in the entering class.

Student Activities

A wide variety of organizations and activities are available to students. There are three law reviews at Emory—*Emory Law Journal*, *Emory Bankruptcy Developments Journal*, and *Emory International Law Review*—and more than 30 percent of the second- and third-year students are involved in law review research, writing, and editing.

Students also participate in moot court and mock trial. Each first-year student prepares a brief and presents an oral argument. In addition, many second- and third-year students compete in intramural and national moot court competitions.

There are approximately 40 student organizations reflecting a broad range of special interest and social groups as well as a very active Student Bar Association.

Career Services

A full-time career services office assists students in obtaining permanent, summer, and part-time employment. It arranges interviews with employers from many parts of the country and maintains extensive files on a wide variety of professional opportunities across the United States. Many Emory graduates join private law firms after graduation. Others work as judicial clerks, enter government service, or work for banks, corporations, or legal aid agencies.

The majority of Emory's students stay in the Southeast. Approximately 25 percent work in the Northeast and Mid-Atlantic. Smaller percentages work in the Midwest, Southwest, and West.

The career services office provides extensive training on résumé writing, interview skills, and job-search techniques, as well as numerous opportunities to network with attorneys in a variety of practice areas and settings.

Applicant Profile

Emory University School of Law

LSAT Score	GPA									
	3.75 +	3.50–3.74	3.25–3.49	3.00–3.24	2.75–2.99	2.50–2.74	2.25–2.49	2.00–2.24	Below 2.00
175–180									
170–174									
165–169									
160–164									
155–159									
150–154									
145–149									
140–144									
135–139									
130–134									
125–129									
120–124									

Good Possibility   Possible   Unlikely

Note: This graph reflects admission decisions as of 6/1/09 and is to be used as a general guide to determining chances for admittance. It does not reflect actual decisions but should serve as a guideline.

Average LSAT data reported.

Faulkner University, Thomas Goode Jones School of Law

5345 Atlanta Highway
Montgomery, AL 36109
Phone: 334.386.7210
E-mail: law@faulkner.edu; Website: www.faulkner.edu/law

The Basics

Type of school	Private
Term	Semester
Application deadline	6/15
Application fee	$30
Financial aid deadline	
Can first year start other than fall?	No
Student to faculty ratio	12.8 to 1
# of housing spaces available restricted to law students	
graduate housing for which law students are eligible	

Faculty and Administrators

	Total		Men		Women		Minorities	
	Spr	Fall	Spr	Fall	Spr	Fall	Spr	Fall
Full-time	19	20	15	15	4	5	3	3
Other full-time	2	1	0	0	2	1	0	0
Deans, librarians, & others who teach	9	9	4	4	5	5	0	0
Part-time	1	4	0	2	1	2	0	1
Total	31	34	19	21	12	13	3	4

Curriculum

		Full-Time	Part-Time
Typical first-year section size		60	0
Is there typically a "small section" of the first-year class, other than Legal Writing, taught by full-time faculty		No	No
If yes, typical size offered last year			
# of classroom course titles beyond first-year curriculum		43	
# of upper division courses, excluding seminars, with an enrollment:	Under 25	34	
	25–49	13	
	50–74	7	
	75–99	0	
	100+	0	
# of seminars		9	
# of seminar positions available		108	
# of seminar positions filled		56	6
# of positions available in simulation courses		210	
# of simulation positions filled		136	28
# of positions available in faculty supervised clinical courses		90	
# of faculty supervised clinical positions filled		60	4
# involved in field placements		48	8
# involved in law journals		25	4
# involved in moot court or trial competitions		29	1
# of credit hours required to graduate		90	

JD Enrollment and Ethnicity

	Men		Women		Full-Time		Part-Time		1st-Year		Total		JD Degs. Awd.
	#	%	#	%	#	%	#	%	#	%	#	%	
African Amer.	12	5.7	12	9.3	24	7.4	0	0.0	13	8.7	24	7.0	2
Amer. Indian	4	1.9	1	0.8	5	1.5	0	0.0	1	0.7	5	1.5	0
Asian Amer.	2	0.9	3	2.3	4	1.2	1	5.6	2	1.3	5	1.5	0
Mex. Amer.	0	0.0	0	0.0	0	0.0	0	0.0	0	0.0	0	0.0	0
Puerto Rican	0	0.0	0	0.0	0	0.0	0	0.0	0	0.0	0	0.0	0
Hispanic	1	0.5	4	3.1	5	1.5	0	0.0	1	0.7	5	1.5	1
Total Minority	19	9.0	20	15.5	38	11.8	1	5.6	17	11.3	39	11.4	3
For. Nation.	0	0.0	0	0.0	0	0.0	0	0.0	0	0.0	0	0.0	0
Caucasian	191	90.1	108	83.7	282	87.3	17	94.4	133	88.7	299	87.7	69
Unknown	2	0.9	1	0.8	3	0.9	0	0.0	0	0.0	3	0.9	0
Total	212	62.2	129	37.8	323	94.7	18	5.3	150	44.0	341		72

Transfers

Transfers in	1
Transfers out	5

Tuition and Fees

	Resident	Nonresident
Full-time	$30,870	
Part-time		
Tuition Guarantee Program		N

Living Expenses

Estimated living expenses for singles

Living on campus	Living off campus	Living at home
$19,200	$19,200	$19,200

Faulkner University, Thomas Goode Jones School of Law

ABA Approved Since 2006

GPA and LSAT Scores

	Total	Full-Time	Part-Time
# of apps	747	747	0
# of offers	405	405	0
# of matrics	150	150	0
75% GPA	3.33	3.33	0.00
Median GPA	3.07	3.07	0.00
25% GPA	2.76	2.76	0.00
75% LSAT	152	152	0
Median LSAT	149	149	0
25% LSAT	147	147	0

Grants and Scholarships (from prior year)

	Total		Full-Time		Part-Time	
	#	%	#	%	#	%
Total # of students	304		263		41	
Total # receiving grants	89	29.3	80	30.4	9	22.0
Less than 1/2 tuition	28	9.2	26	9.9	2	4.9
Half to full tuition	46	15.1	40	15.2	6	14.6
Full tuition	15	4.9	14	5.3	1	2.4
More than full tuition	0	0.0	0	0.0	0	0.0
Median grant amount			$14,000		$5,695	

Informational and Library Resources

Total amount spent on library materials	$680,861
Study seating capacity inside the library	218
# of full-time equivalent professional librarians	5
Hours per week library is open	98
# of open, wired connections available to students	205
# of networked computers available for use by students	42
Has wireless network?	Y
Require computer?	N

JD Attrition (from prior year)

	Academic	Other	Total	
	#	#	#	%
1st year	16	22	38	30.2
2nd year	2	2	4	4.1
3rd year	0	0	0	0.0
4th year	0	1	1	5.0

Employment (9 months after graduation)

	Total	Percentage
Employment status known	60	100.0
Employment status unknown	0	0.0
Employed	54	90.0
Pursuing graduate degrees	2	3.3
Unemployed (seeking, not seeking, or studying for the bar)	3	5.0
Type of Employment		
# employed in law firms	37	68.5
# employed in business and industry	4	7.4
# employed in government	6	11.1
# employed in public interest	2	3.7
# employed as judicial clerks	4	7.4
# employed in academia	1	1.9
Geographic Location		
# employed in state	49	90.7
# employed in foreign countries	0	0.0
# of states where employed	2	

Bar Passage Rates

First-time takers	62	Reporting %	98.39
Average school %	93.44	Average state %	89.03
Average pass difference	4.41		

Jurisdiction	Takers	Passers	Pass %	State %	Diff %
Alabama	58	54	93.10	89.02	4.08
Georgia	3	3	100.00	89.27	10.73

The information on these pages was provided by the law school.

Faulkner University, Thomas Goode Jones School of Law

5345 Atlanta Highway
Montgomery, AL 36109
Phone: 334.386.7210
E-mail: law@faulkner.edu; Website: www.faulkner.edu/law

■ Introduction

Faulkner University's Thomas Goode Jones School of Law has a long and rich tradition of educating students for the practice of law in Alabama. The school was founded in 1928 by Circuit Judge Walter B. Jones and named in honor of his father, a former soldier, lawyer, and governor. In 1901, at the urging of Booker T. Washington, Thomas Goode Jones was appointed by President Theodore Roosevelt to be United States District Judge for the Northern and Middle Districts of Alabama. He authored the Alabama Code of Ethics, a document that was the first state code of ethics and the model for the American Bar Association's 1908 Canons of Professional Ethics.

The School of Law is committed to the education of outstanding lawyers. In keeping with its distinctive Christian mission, the school embraces academic excellence and emphasizes a strong commitment to integrity within a caring Christian environment that sustains and nurtures faith. Students are encouraged to dedicate their lives to the service of others.

The School of Law became part of Faulkner University in 1983. Since its inception, the school has produced over 2,000 alumni who have become practicing attorneys, judges, and other contributors to the legal profession. The American Bar Association granted provisional approval of the School of Law in June 2006.

■ Montgomery and the River Region

The School of Law is located in the capital of Alabama. Montgomery is widely known as the birthplace of the Confederacy and the civil rights movement. It is regarded as one of the nation's most historically significant cities. One can visit the First White House of the Confederacy and the steps of the state capitol building where Jefferson Davis was sworn in as president of the Confederate States of America. On these same steps, Dr. Martin Luther King Jr. completed the freedom march from Selma to Montgomery. Here Dr. King asked for equality for all people, regardless of race. Other historic sites include the Dexter Avenue King Memorial Baptist Church, the Civil Rights Memorial designed by Maya Lin, and the Rosa L. Parks Library and Museum.

Along with its rich history, Montgomery is known for its contribution to the arts. Its most notable contribution is the Wynton M. Blount Cultural Park, which includes the Montgomery Museum of Fine Arts, the internationally acclaimed Alabama Shakespeare Festival, and the beautiful Shakespeare Gardens.

Montgomery offers a small-town atmosphere with big-city amenities that add to the quality of life enjoyed by all who reside in the capital city. It is also an excellent place to study law with the Supreme Court of Alabama, the Alabama legislature, and over 200 law firms and other organizations that employ lawyers within a short driving distance of campus.

■ Library and Physical Facilities

The George H. Jones Jr. Law Library supports the School of Law's curriculum and the legal research requirements of its students and faculty. It provides access to legal and academic materials offered by the latest technology. Computers on both floors of the library enable free access to the Internet, word processing packages, and legal databases. A spacious computer lab facilitates computer-assisted legal instruction and research. Data ports are available throughout the library, and every study room and study carrel is electronically wired and ready for laptop computers.

The School of Law is housed in a beautiful, neo-Federal-style building that accommodates the George H. Jones Jr. Law Library, the Judge Walter B. Jones Moot Court Room, and the Institute for Dispute Resolution. It includes state-of-the-art research and lecture facilities with seven classrooms and two large conference rooms. All classrooms are outfitted for laptop computers and wireless Internet is available throughout the building and library. Students have access to the student lounge for congregation and conference rooms for student organization meetings.

■ Institute for Dispute Resolution

The Alternative Dispute Resolution (ADR) Program enables law students to integrate their knowledge of conflict management principles and dispute resolution processes with professional skills. This program allows students to receive training normally available only through on-the-job experience after graduation.

Students can earn a certificate in ADR, which is not a supplemental degree but an opportunity for Juris Doctor candidates to enrich their skills training while still in law school. The certificate in ADR requires completion of the following courses: Arbitration, Dispute Resolution Processes, Interviewing/Counseling and Negotiation, Mediation Clinic, and an elective skills course. All of the certificate courses contain both an academic component and a skills component.

■ Clinical Opportunities and Externships

The School of Law operates three clinical programs: the Mediation Clinic, the Family Violence Clinic, and the Elder Law Clinic. The Mediation Clinic allows students to mediate cases set for trial at Montgomery County District Court. The Family Violence Clinic provides pro bono services for clients unable to pay for representation and works in conjunction with the Legal Services Corporation of Alabama and the Family Sunshine Center. Students with limited-practice authority cards interview clients, provide advice, prepare pleadings, and represent clients in court proceedings. Students without limited-practice authority cards assist in case preparation and research. The School of Law and Legal Services Corporation of Alabama are the recipients of the Family Sunshine Center's President's Special Service Award in recognition of outstanding service and support through the Family Violence Clinic.

The School of Law established the Elder Law Clinic after receiving a grant from the federal government through the Commerce, Justice, and Science spending bill. This clinic provides pro bono services in matters of estate planning, Medicare, nursing home issues, Social Security, long-term care insurance, and disability planning to name a few.

Faulkner University, Thomas Goode Jones School of Law

The School of Law's Externship Program affords students the opportunity to supplement their classroom experience by working in a variety of legal settings. Externships include a classroom component that covers topics relating to the legal system, judicial process, and professionalism. Students develop their lawyering skills and gain real-world experience in the legal community, as they work side by side with judges and practicing attorneys, under the supervision of the director of clinical programs and externships.

■ Public Interest Program

As part of a Christian university, the School of Law seeks not only to provide legal knowledge and practical skills necessary to produce competent and ethical members of the legal community, but also to instill in students an attitude of service. This commitment to serve those who otherwise could not afford such assistance complements the legal profession's rich tradition of service.

The Public Interest Program provides opportunities for students to begin their career of service while utilizing the practical skills obtained in their legal education. This program is voluntary and provides students with opportunities to work for nonprofit organizations, government agencies, and private attorneys or firms conducting pro bono legal work. Students are challenged to perform at least 50 hours of voluntary service during their law school career. Students providing public interest service qualify for recognition, including notation of service on transcripts, a certificate of accomplishment, special recognition in the graduation program, and eligibility for the Public Interest Service Award.

■ Student Organizations

The Student Bar Association (SBA) serves the student body and every student is a member. The SBA fosters relationships with members of the legal community and sponsors social functions and fundraising events. Other student organizations at the law school include American Association for Justice, American Constitution Society, Animal Law Society, Black Law Students Association, Board of Advocates, Christian Legal Society, Federalist Society, Honor Court, Jones Law Republicans, Phi Alpha Delta, and Women Students Association.

The *Faulkner Law Review* is a scholarly legal journal published by student editors and members. Members write comments and notes on legal developments and landmark cases. They also select and edit articles submitted for publication by lawyers, judges, professors, and other scholars. Membership is considered an honor and provides students an opportunity to hone their research and writing skills.

■ Scholarships, Tuition, and Fees

The School of Law offers merit-based scholarships to qualified entering students. Admitted applicants are automatically under scholarship consideration. Awards range from 10 percent tuition forgiveness to 100 percent tuition forgiveness. Scholarships are also available to upper-level students who perform well academically in law school.

Please consult the law school's website for current tuition rates. Students pay a Student Activities Fee of $350, which is charged only once at the outset of a student's law school career and an Emergency Notification Fee of $10, which is charged per semester.

Applicant Profile

Faulkner University, Thomas Goode Jones School of Law

LSAT Score	GPA								
	3.75 +	3.50–3.74	3.25–3.49	3.00–3.24	2.75–2.99	2.50–2.74	2.25–2.49	2.00–2.24	Below 2.00
175–180									
170–174									
165–169									
160–164									
155–159									
150–154									
145–149									
140–144									
Below 140									

■ Good Possibility   ■ Possible   □ Unlikely

Average LSAT data reported.

Florida A&M University College of Law

201 Beggs Avenue
Orlando, FL 32801
Phone: 407.254.3268; Fax: 407.254.3213
E-mail: famulaw.admissions@famu.edu; Website: www.law.famu.edu

ABA
Approved
Since
2004

The Basics

Type of school	Public
Term	Semester
Application deadline	4/1
Application fee	$30
Financial aid deadline	3/1
Can first year start other than fall?	No
Student to faculty ratio	19.4 to 1
# of housing spaces available restricted to law students	
graduate housing for which law students are eligible	

Faculty and Administrators

	Total		Men		Women		Minorities	
	Spr	Fall	Spr	Fall	Spr	Fall	Spr	Fall
Full-time	20	24	7	11	13	13	14	16
Other full-time	14	17	7	9	6	7	9	11
Deans, librarians, & others who teach	7	11	3	4	4	7	6	9
Part-time	13	7	10	6	3	1	8	4
Total	54	59	27	30	26	28	37	40

Curriculum

		Full-Time	Part-Time
Typical first-year section size		60	60
Is there typically a "small section" of the first-year class, other than Legal Writing, taught by full-time faculty		No	No
If yes, typical size offered last year			
# of classroom course titles beyond first-year curriculum		134	
# of upper division courses, excluding seminars, with an enrollment:	Under 25	55	
	25–49	24	
	50–74	19	
	75–99	0	
	100+	0	
# of seminars		9	
# of seminar positions available		205	
# of seminar positions filled		97	8
# of positions available in simulation courses		258	
# of simulation positions filled		185	50
# of positions available in faculty supervised clinical courses		144	
# of faculty supervised clinical positions filled		79	18
# involved in field placements		19	1
# involved in law journals		37	5
# involved in moot court or trial competitions		36	1
# of credit hours required to graduate		90	

JD Enrollment and Ethnicity

	Men #	Men %	Women #	Women %	Full-Time #	Full-Time %	Part-Time #	Part-Time %	1st-Year #	1st-Year %	Total #	Total %	JD Degs. Awd.
African Amer.	85	30.6	164	49.0	174	45.2	75	32.9	80	34.3	249	40.6	87
Amer. Indian	3	1.1	2	0.6	2	0.5	3	1.3	1	0.4	5	0.8	0
Asian Amer.	11	4.0	11	3.3	16	4.2	6	2.6	16	6.9	22	3.6	7
Mex. Amer.	1	0.4	2	0.6	3	0.8	0	0.0	0	0.0	3	0.5	0
Puerto Rican	4	1.4	4	1.2	3	0.8	5	2.2	3	1.3	8	1.3	0
Hispanic	42	15.1	48	14.3	49	12.7	41	18.0	31	13.3	90	14.7	24
Total Minority	146	52.5	231	69.0	247	64.2	130	57.0	131	56.2	377	61.5	118
For. Nation.	0	0.0	0	0.0	0	0.0	0	0.0	0	0.0	0	0.0	0
Caucasian	125	45.0	98	29.3	128	33.2	95	41.7	96	41.2	223	36.4	44
Unknown	7	2.5	6	1.8	10	2.6	3	1.3	6	2.6	13	2.1	2
Total	278	45.4	335	54.6	385	62.8	228	37.2	233	38.0	613		164

Transfers

Transfers in	2
Transfers out	24

Tuition and Fees

	Resident	Nonresident
Full-time	$9,036	$28,302
Part-time	$6,627	$20,755
Tuition Guarantee Program	N	

Living Expenses

Estimated living expenses for singles

Living on campus	Living off campus	Living at home
N/A	$13,690	$7,971

Florida A&M University College of Law

ABA
Approved
Since
2004

GPA and LSAT Scores

	Total	Full-Time	Part-Time
# of apps	1,807	1,519	288
# of offers	559	452	107
# of matrics	234	165	69
75% GPA	3.32	3.36	3.25
Median GPA	3.07	3.06	3.09
25% GPA	2.75	2.78	2.67
75% LSAT	150	149	150
Median LSAT	146	146	147
25% LSAT	144	144	145

Grants and Scholarships (from prior year)

	Total		Full-Time		Part-Time	
	#	%	#	%	#	%
Total # of students	603		424		179	
Total # receiving grants	58	9.6	38	9.0	20	11.2
Less than 1/2 tuition	23	3.8	8	1.9	15	8.4
Half to full tuition	24	4.0	22	5.2	2	1.1
Full tuition	11	1.8	8	1.9	3	1.7
More than full tuition	0	0.0	0	0.0	0	0.0
Median grant amount			$5,000		$2,000	

Informational and Library Resources

Total amount spent on library materials	$726,573
Study seating capacity inside the library	416
# of full-time equivalent professional librarians	5
Hours per week library is open	100
# of open, wired connections available to students	0
# of networked computers available for use by students	37
Has wireless network?	Y
Require computer?	N

JD Attrition (from prior year)

	Academic	Other	Total	
	#	#	#	%
1st year	23	64	87	38.0
2nd year	3	9	12	6.9
3rd year	1	0	1	0.6
4th year	0	0	0	0.0

Employment (9 months after graduation)

	Total	Percentage
Employment status known	88	93.6
Employment status unknown	6	6.4
Employed	72	81.8
Pursuing graduate degrees	6	6.8
Unemployed (seeking, not seeking, or studying for the bar)	7	8.0
Type of Employment		
# employed in law firms	40	55.6
# employed in business and industry	6	8.3
# employed in government	11	15.3
# employed in public interest	6	8.3
# employed as judicial clerks	1	1.4
# employed in academia	3	4.2
Geographic Location		
# employed in state	38	52.8
# employed in foreign countries	0	0.0
# of states where employed	6	

Bar Passage Rates

First-time takers	108	Reporting %	97.22
Average school %	65.71	Average state %	80.76

Average pass difference −15.05

Jurisdiction	Takers	Passers	Pass %	State %	Diff %
Florida	105	69	65.71	80.76	−15.05

Florida A&M University College of Law

201 Beggs Avenue
Orlando, FL 32801
Phone: 407.254.3268; Fax: 407.254.3213
E-mail: famulaw.admissions@famu.edu; Website: www.law.famu.edu

■ A Unique History

The College of Law is proud to be a part of Florida A&M University (FAMU), the largest single-campus historically black university in the United States in terms of enrollment and in terms of the number of baccalaureate degrees granted. Founded in 1887, FAMU is a comprehensive, public, coeducational, and fully accredited land-grant university offering a broad range of instruction, research, and service programs at the undergraduate, graduate, and professional levels. Located on the highest of seven hills in the capital city of Tallahassee, FAMU is the third oldest of the nine institutions in Florida's State University System. The College of Law's rich tradition of excellence dates back to its original founding in 1949. Between 1949 and 1968, the College of Law graduated 57 students. In 2002, the FAMU College of Law reopened in downtown Orlando, Florida, as the only public law school in Central Florida. In 2006, the College of Law moved into its brand-new permanent building at 201 Beggs Avenue. The College of Law offers a quality legal education at an affordable price in state-of-the-art facilities and has been nationally recognized for its diverse student body and its clinical programs. The College of Law received full accreditation from the American Bar Association in July 2009.

The College of Law is located in Orlando, considered to be one of the most beautiful and dynamic cities in Florida. A racially and culturally diverse community, Orlando is considered not only one of the fastest growing metropolitan areas in Florida, but also one of the fastest major employment markets in the nation. Orlando offers affordable housing, great weather year-round, and easy access to cultural and recreational activities such as Disney World, Universal Studios, and various professional athletic teams. Located in the heart of downtown, the College of Law is within walking distance of government buildings, courthouses, and a wide variety of cultural, educational, and recreational opportunities.

■ An Active and Multicultural Student Body

Since opening in the fall of 2002, FAMU College of Law has admitted eight entering classes and has a current student enrollment exceeding 600 students. The College of Law has consistently received national recognition as one of the most diverse law schools in the nation, making for a classroom experience unduplicated elsewhere. The College of Law is committed to helping its students further develop their talents, professional skills, and goals. To that end, we offer cocurricular and extracurricular activities, including our award-winning competition teams. These cocurricular and extracurricular programs enhance not only the study of the law, but students' leadership and professional abilities and oral and written communication skills. FAMU College of Law students are very active within the law school and in the Central Florida community. As students at a recently reestablished law school, they have taken on the challenge of establishing organizations that will serve current and future students for years to come. The FAMU College of Law Student Bar Association supports and governs all student activities and organizations at the College of Law. Since 2002, students have founded the Jesse J. McCrary Jr. Chapter of the National Black Law Students Association;

the Association of Trial Lawyers of America; the Women's Law Caucus; the Entertainment, Arts, and Sports Law Society; the Hispanic Law Students; the Federalist Society; Phi Alpha Delta; and many other student organizations.

■ Programs of Study

The FAMU College of Law offers both a full-time day program and a part-time evening program of study. Full-time day program students must successfully complete six semesters or three academic years in order to fulfill their degree requirements. Enrollment in the day program represents a commitment to the full-time study of law. Part-time evening program students must successfully complete their degree requirements in four years consisting of eight semesters and three summers. Part-time evening classes typically meet Monday through Thursday beginning at 6:00 PM. The part-time evening program is designed for students who are unable to attend school on a full-time basis and want to earn a law degree while working full time. Courses in both programs demand the same standards of performance by students and are taught by full-time faculty members who are assisted by adjunct faculty.

■ Curriculum

The law school offers a rigorous traditional curriculum of required and elective courses that are complemented by extensive skills training that includes an intensive three-year writing program and a strong clinical program. The College of Law's curriculum is designed to provide students with both the intellectual and practical skills necessary to meet the demands of the modern practice of law by combining theoretical coursework with clinical and practical experiences. Through the use of elective courses and leading practitioners as adjunct faculty, students are introduced to emerging trends and developments in the law.

■ The Center for International Law and Justice

The Center for International Law and Justice was created to cultivate student interest in human rights and freedom, providing students with a substantive background in international law and foreign affiars as well as the application of policy in the developing world—specifically, Africa, Asia, the Caribbean, and Latin America. Beginning in the first year of study, students may opt into the international law track. The center offers a new certificate of study in **International Human Rights Law and Global Justice Studies**. In addition, the center annually awards an International Human Rights Fellowship, which provides scholarship and summer internship support to a student with a track record of public service and a keen interest or experience in international human rights law and international affairs.

■ A Commitment to Public Service

At the core of the College of Law mission is a commitment to public service. As such, all students are required to engage in public service by participating in and satisfactorily completing

one of several available clinical offerings or by completing at least 20 hours in a pro bono experience. The College of Law was recently ranked seventh in the nation for providing clinical opportunities by *National Jurist* magazine. The Clinical Program educates students in the practical art of lawyering, while providing quality legal representation to underserved individuals and organizations. Additionally, the Clinical Program helps students explore career potential by exposing them to a broad spectrum of legal opportunities. Via a combination of in-house clinics and externships, the Clinical Program includes the following practice areas: Guardian Ad Litem, Community Economic Development, Housing, Homelessness and Legal Advocacy, Criminal Defense, Criminal Prosecution, Death Penalty, and Volunteer Income Tax Assistance.

■ Amazing Affordability

Tuition rates at FAMU College of Law are consistently the most affordable among Florida law schools, and nationally, FAMU Law tuition rates offer a tremendous value. For the 2009–2010 academic year, tuition for Florida residents was $301.23 per credit hour, and tuition for non-Florida residents was $943.43 per credit hour. Approximately 90 percent of law students are receiving some form of financial aid, including federal loans and merit-based scholarships. Merit-based scholarships are awarded to a select number of entering full-time and part-time students who have excelled academically and who possess other outstanding qualifications for the study of law. All admitted students are automatically considered for these awards, which vary from $1,000 to full-tuition.

■ The Admission Process

Admission to the College of Law has become increasingly competitive. Accordingly, applicants are strongly encouraged to apply early in the process to maximize chances for admission. The law school seeks diligent, hardworking students with a broad array of talents and experiences who demonstrate both an exceptional aptitude for the study of law and a strong history of, or commitment to, public service. Selection for admission is based on a thorough evaluation of all factors in an applicant's file. While an applicant's academic record and LSAT performance are weighted heavily in the evaluation process, the Admissions Committee considers other factors, including writing ability, as evidenced by the LSAT writing sample and the personal statement; community and public service; academic honors and awards; work experience; leadership ability; extracurricular activities; letters of recommendation; and character and motivation.

■ Applicant Profile

While an applicant's undergraduate record and LSAT score are important, they are not the sole determinants for admission to law school. There are no combinations of grades or scores that assure admission or denial. An applicant's transcripts are analyzed for breadth and depth of coursework, trends in grades, and rank. The competitiveness of an applicant's school and major are taken into consideration as are special activities, honors, and awards received by the applicant. Other aspects of the application significantly influence the decision, such as work experience and evidence of a commitment to, or interest in, public service. In making its decision, the faculty Admissions Committee aims to enroll an entering class of students with the strongest combination of qualifications and the greatest potential to contribute to FAMU College of Law and to the legal profession.

Applicant Profile

Florida A&M University College of Law
This grid includes only applicants who earned 120–180 LSAT scores under standard administrations.

LSAT Score	GPA 3.75 +		3.50–3.74		3.25–3.49		3.00–3.24		2.75–2.99		2.50–2.74		2.25–2.49		2.00–2.24		Below 2.00		No GPA		Total	
	Apps	Adm	Apps	Adm	Apps	Adm	Apps	Adm	Apps	Adm	Apps	Adm	Apps	Adm	Apps	Adm	Apps	Adm	Apps	Adm	Apps	Adm
175–180	0	0	0	0	0	0	0	0	0	0	0	0	0	0	0	0	0	0	0	0	0	0
170–174	0	0	0	0	0	0	0	0	0	0	0	0	0	0	0	0	0	0	0	0	0	0
165–169	0	0	0	0	0	0	0	0	0	0	1	1	0	0	0	0	0	0	0	0	1	1
160–164	2	2	1	1	0	0	4	3	0	0	0	0	0	0	0	0	0	0	0	0	7	6
155–159	4	4	0	0	5	5	5	2	9	7	3	1	9	3	3	0	0	0	0	0	38	22
150–154	6	5	20	18	21	17	32	20	26	14	26	20	17	7	3	0	2	0	2	0	155	101
145–149	11	9	38	24	57	41	79	54	71	32	70	32	38	11	11	2	7	0	6	4	388	209
140–144	9	2	48	23	102	48	99	36	139	54	106	24	72	4	29	1	5	0	20	4	629	196
135–139	10	2	19	1	47	5	56	6	71	1	78	1	45	0	27	0	8	0	10	2	371	18
130–134	1	0	8	0	14	1	23	1	30	1	31	0	18	0	10	0	2	0	13	0	150	3
125–129	0	0	1	0	3	0	3	0	7	0	7	0	2	0	5	0	3	0	0	0	31	0
120–124	0	0	0	0	0	0	1	0	0	0	1	0	0	0	0	0	0	0	1	0	3	0
Total	43	24	135	67	249	117	302	122	353	109	323	79	201	25	88	3	27	0	52	10	1773	556

Apps = Number of Applicants   Adm = Number Admitted   Reflects 98% of the applicant pool; average LSAT data reported.

Florida Coastal School of Law

8787 Baypine Road
Jacksonville, FL 32256
Phone: 904.680.7710, toll-free: 877.210.2591; Fax: 904.680.7692
E-mail: admissions@fcsl.edu; Website: www.fcsl.edu

ABA
Approved
Since
2002

The Basics

Type of school	Private
Term	Semester
Application deadline	8/1
Application fee	$0
Financial aid deadline	
Can first year start other than fall?	Yes
Student to faculty ratio	21.0 to 1
# of housing spaces available restricted to law students	
graduate housing for which law students are eligible	

Faculty and Administrators

	Total		Men		Women		Minorities	
	Spr	Fall	Spr	Fall	Spr	Fall	Spr	Fall
Full-time	57	61	28	27	29	34	9	7
Other full-time	3	2	0	0	3	2	1	1
Deans, librarians, & others who teach	10	10	2	2	8	8	2	2
Part-time	55	58	37	40	18	18	4	4
Total	125	131	67	69	58	62	16	14

Curriculum

	Full-Time	Part-Time
Typical first-year section size	82	0
Is there typically a "small section" of the first-year class, other than Legal Writing, taught by full-time faculty	No	No
If yes, typical size offered last year		

# of classroom course titles beyond first-year curriculum		129
# of upper division courses, excluding seminars, with an enrollment:	Under 25	116
	25–49	75
	50–74	48
	75–99	1
	100+	1
# of seminars		21
# of seminar positions available		425

# of seminar positions filled	347	0
# of positions available in simulation courses	2,200	
# of simulation positions filled	1,881	0
# of positions available in faculty supervised clinical courses	150	
# of faculty supervised clinical positions filled	122	0
# involved in field placements	218	0
# involved in law journals	55	0
# involved in moot court or trial competitions	112	0
# of credit hours required to graduate	90	

JD Enrollment and Ethnicity

	Men		Women		Full-Time		Part-Time		1st-Year		Total		JD Degs. Awd.
	#	%	#	%	#	%	#	%	#	%	#	%	
African Amer.	47	5.6	109	14.3	149	9.7	7	10.6	75	11.3	156	9.7	34
Amer. Indian	10	1.2	10	1.3	19	1.2	1	1.5	7	1.1	20	1.2	5
Asian Amer.	44	5.2	52	6.8	95	6.2	1	1.5	36	5.4	96	6.0	24
Mex. Amer.	7	0.8	8	1.0	15	1.0	0	0.0	10	1.5	15	0.9	4
Puerto Rican	4	0.5	12	1.6	14	0.9	2	3.0	5	0.8	16	1.0	1
Hispanic	75	8.9	55	7.2	123	8.0	7	10.6	67	10.1	130	8.1	17
Total Minority	187	22.2	246	32.2	415	27.0	18	27.3	200	30.1	433	27.0	85
For. Nation.	0	0.0	0	0.0	0	0.0	0	0.0	0	0.0	0	0.0	0
Caucasian	546	64.9	456	59.7	964	62.6	38	57.6	410	61.7	1002	62.4	225
Unknown	108	12.8	62	8.1	160	10.4	10	15.2	54	8.1	170	10.6	108
Total	841	52.4	764	47.6	1539	95.9	66	4.1	664	41.4	1605		418

Transfers

Transfers in	4
Transfers out	78

Tuition and Fees

	Resident	Nonresident
Full-time	$32,662	$32,662
Part-time	$26,442	$26,442
Tuition Guarantee Program	N	

Living Expenses

Estimated living expenses for singles

Living on campus	Living off campus	Living at home
N/A	$19,579	$19,579

Florida Coastal School of Law

ABA
Approved
Since
2002

GPA and LSAT Scores

	Total	Full-Time	Part-Time
# of apps	6,331	6,274	57
# of offers	4,151	4,118	33
# of matrics	722	702	20
75% GPA	3.42	3.42	3.38
Median GPA	3.20	3.21	3.00
25% GPA	2.94	2.95	2.57
75% LSAT	153	153	153
Median LSAT	150	150	148
25% LSAT	147	147	147

Grants and Scholarships (from prior year)

	Total		Full-Time		Part-Time	
	#	%	#	%	#	%
Total # of students	1,470		1,308		162	
Total # receiving grants	597	40.6	589	45.0	8	4.9
Less than 1/2 tuition	546	37.1	539	41.2	7	4.3
Half to full tuition	50	3.4	49	3.7	1	0.6
Full tuition	1	0.1	1	0.1	0	0.0
More than full tuition	0	0.0	0	0.0	0	0.0
Median grant amount			$7,000		$4,000	

Informational and Library Resources

Total amount spent on library materials	$1,244,157
Study seating capacity inside the library	516
# of full-time equivalent professional librarians	12
Hours per week library is open	105
# of open, wired connections available to students	3,780
# of networked computers available for use by students	91
Has wireless network?	Y
Require computer?	N

JD Attrition (from prior year)

	Academic	Other	Total	
	#	#	#	%
1st year	46	69	115	20.1
2nd year	15	22	37	8.3
3rd year	1	0	1	0.2
4th year	0	0	0	0.0

Employment (9 months after graduation)

	Total	Percentage
Employment status known	325	96.4
Employment status unknown	12	3.6
Employed	297	91.4
Pursuing graduate degrees	11	3.4
Unemployed (seeking, not seeking, or studying for the bar)	6	1.8
Type of Employment		
# employed in law firms	144	48.5
# employed in business and industry	39	13.1
# employed in government	46	15.5
# employed in public interest	52	17.5
# employed as judicial clerks	8	2.7
# employed in academia	7	2.4
Geographic Location		
# employed in state	219	73.7
# employed in foreign countries	1	0.3
# of states where employed		33

Bar Passage Rates

First-time takers	347	Reporting %	72.91
Average school %	83.00	Average state %	80.76
Average pass difference	2.24		

Jurisdiction	Takers	Passers	Pass %	State %	Diff %
Florida	253	210	83.00	80.76	2.24

Florida Coastal School of Law

8787 Baypine Road
Jacksonville, FL 32256
Phone: 904.680.7710, toll-free: 877.210.2591; Fax: 904.680.7692
E-mail: admissions@fcsl.edu; Website: www.fcsl.edu

■ Introduction

Fully accredited by the ABA, Florida Coastal School of Law offers the finest legal education, coupling traditional approaches with student/faculty partnerships and practical, real-world perspectives. Led by exceptional internationally accomplished faculty, Coastal Law creates an innovative educational experience that produces first-rate lawyers with uncompromised ethics and professional responsibility, as well as sharp legal skills.

■ Our Students

Coastal Law students represent more than 320 undergraduate colleges and universities from nearly every state in the US, as well as Puerto Rico, the Virgin Islands, Canada, Germany, and China. While enrolled, students work closely with faculty members who not only share their legal expertise, but also their experiences, perspectives, and expansive networks. We believe our supportive learning environment makes a difference in students' educational experiences and personal growth, ultimately giving them an edge in professional preparation.

■ Our Faculty

Coastal Law's full-time faculty members represent approximately 50 ABA-accredited law schools from across the country including Harvard University, George Washington University, Duke University, Georgetown University, Columbia University, New York University, and the University of Florida. Together, they boast international legal and academic accomplishments, from authoring dozens of case books and articles to counseling the Iraqi Constitutional Commission and advising the United Nations' war crimes tribunal in The Hague. Further, as former judges, government officials, general and in-house counsel, corporate executives, and attorneys practicing in law firms, they offer realistic legal perspectives.

■ Our City

Coastal Law is located in Jacksonville, which was named among the "Top 5 Up and Coming Areas of 2006" by *Good Morning America* and among the "Top 10 Places to Live" by *Money* magazine. Jacksonville is a metropolitan center of more than one million people, including one of the youngest populations in Florida. Boasting 68 miles of ocean coastline, 300 miles of riverfront, and one of the largest park systems in the country, it offers an outstanding array of outdoor activities of all types. Dotted with unique neighborhoods, exceptional arts, entertainment, culture, and a variety of professional sports, including the NFL, PGA Tour, LPGA, ATP Tennis, and baseball, Jacksonville provides the idyllic setting for a legal education during warm winters and beach-filled summers.

■ Curriculum and Certificate Programs

Among the many advantages that set Coastal Law apart from our comparator schools is the curriculum, which allows our students to align career choices with specialized areas of expertise. Successful completion of a certificate program not only represents significant learning, but can also exhibit to potential employers a student's dedication to the corresponding practice area. Coastal Law offers five certificate programs: **Sports Law, Family Law, International and Comparative Law, Environmental Law**, and **Advanced Legal Research, Writing, and Drafting**.

■ Live Client Clinics

Under the supervision of full-time faculty members, Coastal Law students can gain experience representing indigent clients, and play a part in each phase of legal representation including the initial client interview, case planning and development, drafting letters and pleadings, discovery and negotiation, and even representing their clinic clients in court and administrative hearings. Clinical programs include: **Family and Child Advocacy, Juvenile Law, Consumer Law, Immigrant Rights, Disability and Benefits Law**, and **Housing Rights**.

■ Joint-Degree Programs

The Davis College of Business at Jacksonville University, a first-tier program, and Florida Coastal School of Law have created a joint-degree program through which qualified students may pursue a Juris Doctor (JD) and a Masters in Business Administration (MBA) from both schools simultaneously. Graduates with a joint JD/MBA degree can develop the skills needed to pursue careers in the business and legal professions, especially where those areas overlap such as investment and commercial banking, management consulting, government regulation, and business policy analysis. In addition to concurrently participating in the academic and social life of both schools, students will be able to obtain both diplomas in four years, as compared to the five years required to earn both degrees when pursued separately.

■ Bar Preparation and Success

Coastal Law's bar passage rate for first-time takers consistently surpasses the statewide average. In 2005, the school's bar passage rate ranked number 1 among Florida law schools and, more recently, in July 2009, exceeded the state average by more than 3 points. To ensure these results, we work with students to identify personal learning styles and customize time management skills. Coastal Law students also have open access to our academic success counselors and to bar preparation classes and study groups. Coastal provides every student with the resources required to succeed academically, on the bar exam, and as they transition into practice.

■ Career Services

Coastal Law's Career Services Department (CSD) is committed to empowering students and alumni to pursue the careers of their choice. From individual counseling, résumé critiques, and job-search strategies to attorney panels and on-campus interviewing programs, the CSD offers comprehensive services and resources that can guide students along individual

career paths. In addition, the CSD offers our alumni assistance in making changes in practice, career direction, or geographic area.

■ Closing Invitation From the Dean

The basic curriculum and the traditional three-year time period required for legal education have remained very constant for more than a century. However, it is more important than ever that a law school take maximum advantage of this limited time to prepare its graduates to enter the profession well equipped. At Florida Coastal School of Law, the study of law blends acquiring a comprehensive knowledge of the law with developing the critical thinking and practical skills essential to its practice. Ensuring the careful balance of each of these components is an integral part of the educational process we deliver. To determine whether Florida Coastal School of Law is right for you, feel free to contact any member of our law school community and ask them about their experiences here. We also welcome visitors and encourage campus tours.

Applicant Profile

Florida Coastal School of Law
This grid includes only applicants who earned 120–180 LSAT scores under standard administrations.

LSAT Score	3.75 +		3.50–3.74		3.25–3.49		3.00–3.24		2.75–2.99		2.50–2.74		2.25–2.49		2.00–2.24		Below 2.00		No GPA		Total	
	Apps	Adm	Apps	Adm	Apps	Adm	Apps	Adm	Apps	Adm	Apps	Adm	Apps	Adm	Apps	Adm	Apps	Adm	Apps	Adm	Apps	Adm
175–180	0	0	0	0	0	0	0	0	0	0	0	0	0	0	0	0	0	0	0	0	0	0
170–174	1	1	0	0	1	1	1	1	0	0	0	0	0	0	0	0	0	0	0	0	3	3
165–169	2	2	1	1	0	0	1	1	0	0	2	2	1	0	2	1	0	0	0	0	9	7
160–164	5	5	7	7	9	8	13	12	9	8	8	7	4	3	3	1	1	0	1	1	60	52
155–159	106	94	169	149	185	164	140	123	130	107	74	60	28	23	10	7	1	0	4	1	847	728
150–154	184	171	361	337	446	399	352	320	295	250	177	143	65	35	25	11	5	0	14	7	1924	1673
145–149	97	87	268	241	349	295	415	310	253	118	167	64	66	5	19	1	9	0	20	8	1663	1129
140–144	27	21	107	78	191	80	262	82	193	13	138	12	75	1	34	1	9	0	19	4	1055	292
135–139	12	3	26	6	71	6	75	5	92	2	90	4	49	0	15	0	4	0	6	0	440	26
130–134	4	0	9	0	10	0	27	0	36	0	28	0	15	0	12	0	2	0	10	0	153	0
125–129	0	0	2	0	1	0	3	0	7	0	3	0	2	0	2	0	1	0	2	0	23	0
120–124	0	0	0	0	0	0	0	0	0	0	1	0	0	0	0	0	0	0	0	0	1	0
Total	438	384	950	819	1263	953	1289	854	1015	498	688	292	305	67	122	22	32	0	76	21	6178	3910

Apps = Number of Applicants
Adm = Number Admitted
Reflects 98% of the total applicant pool; average LSAT data reported.

University of Florida, Fredric G. Levin College of Law

Assistant Dean for Admissions, PO Box 117622, 141 Bruton-Geer Hall
Gainesville, FL 32611-7622
Phone: 352.273.0890, Toll-free: 877.429.1297; Fax: 352.392.4087
E-mail: admissions@law.ufl.edu; Website: www.law.ufl.edu

ABA Approved Since 1925

The Basics

Type of school	Public
Term	Semester
Application deadline	1/15
Application fee	$30
Financial aid deadline	4/7
Can first year start other than fall?	No
Student to faculty ratio	15.9 to 1
# of housing spaces available restricted to law students	
graduate housing for which law students are eligible	

Faculty and Administrators

	Total		Men		Women		Minorities	
	Spr	Fall	Spr	Fall	Spr	Fall	Spr	Fall
Full-time	62	57	28	28	34	29	10	11
Other full-time	2	3	1	2	1	1	1	1
Deans, librarians, & others who teach	19	18	11	11	8	7	3	2
Part-time	32	32	25	20	6	11	1	2
Total	115	110	65	61	49	48	15	16

Curriculum

	Full-Time	Part-Time
Typical first-year section size	105	0
Is there typically a "small section" of the first-year class, other than Legal Writing, taught by full-time faculty	No	No
If yes, typical size offered last year		
# of classroom course titles beyond first-year curriculum	166	

# of upper division courses, excluding seminars, with an enrollment:		
Under 25	85	
25–49	44	
50–74	27	
75–99	11	
100+	9	

# of seminars	36	
# of seminar positions available	553	
# of seminar positions filled	506	0
# of positions available in simulation courses	595	
# of simulation positions filled	567	0
# of positions available in faculty supervised clinical courses	221	
# of faculty supervised clinical positions filled	159	0
# involved in field placements	269	0
# involved in law journals	391	0
# involved in moot court or trial competitions	88	0
# of credit hours required to graduate	88	

JD Enrollment and Ethnicity

	Men		Women		Full-Time		Part-Time		1st-Year		Total		JD Degs. Awd.
	#	%	#	%	#	%	#	%	#	%	#	%	
African Amer.	22	3.8	47	8.9	69	6.2	0	0.0	27	8.8	69	6.2	25
Amer. Indian	2	0.3	6	1.1	8	0.7	0	0.0	3	1.0	8	0.7	1
Asian Amer.	36	6.3	39	7.3	75	6.8	0	0.0	20	6.5	75	6.8	21
Mex. Amer.	0	0.0	0	0.0	0	0.0	0	0.0	0	0.0	0	0.0	0
Puerto Rican	0	0.0	0	0.0	0	0.0	0	0.0	0	0.0	0	0.0	0
Hispanic	52	9.0	55	10.4	107	9.7	0	0.0	24	7.8	107	9.7	41
Total Minority	112	19.5	147	27.7	259	23.4	0	0.0	74	24.2	259	23.4	88
For. Nation.	11	1.9	9	1.7	20	1.8	0	0.0	4	1.3	20	1.8	6
Caucasian	438	76.2	366	68.9	804	72.7	0	0.0	223	72.9	804	72.7	327
Unknown	14	2.4	9	1.7	23	2.1	0	0.0	5	1.6	23	2.1	9
Total	575	52.0	531	48.0	1106	100.0	0	0.0	306	27.7	1106		430

Transfers

Transfers in	25
Transfers out	14

Tuition and Fees

	Resident	Nonresident
Full-time	$14,228	$33,593
Part-time		
Tuition Guarantee Program	N	

Living Expenses

Estimated living expenses for singles

Living on campus	Living off campus	Living at home
$12,960	$13,100	$6,460

University of Florida, Fredric G. Levin College of Law

ABA
Approved
Since
1925

GPA and LSAT Scores

	Total	Full-Time	Part-Time
# of apps	3,170	3,170	0
# of offers	780	780	0
# of matrics	307	307	0
75% GPA	3.85	3.85	0.00
Median GPA	3.67	3.69	0.00
25% GPA	3.42	3.42	0.00
75% LSAT	163	163	0
Median LSAT	161	161	0
25% LSAT	158	158	0

Grants and Scholarships (from prior year)

	Total		Full-Time		Part-Time	
	#	%	#	%	#	%
Total # of students	1,224		1,224		0	
Total # receiving grants	343	28.0	343	28.0	0	0.0
Less than 1/2 tuition	299	24.4	299	24.4	0	0.0
Half to full tuition	30	2.5	30	2.5	0	0.0
Full tuition	14	1.1	14	1.1	0	0.0
More than full tuition	0	0.0	0	0.0	0	0.0
Median grant amount			$3,000		$0	

Informational and Library Resources

Total amount spent on library materials	$1,312,442
Study seating capacity inside the library	765
# of full-time equivalent professional librarians	9
Hours per week library is open	96
# of open, wired connections available to students	0
# of networked computers available for use by students	46
Has wireless network?	Y
Require computer?	Y

JD Attrition (from prior year)

	Academic	Other	Total	
	#	#	#	%
1st year	1	22	23	5.8
2nd year	0	5	5	1.3
3rd year	0	3	3	0.7
4th year	0	0	0	0.0

Employment (9 months after graduation)

	Total	Percentage
Employment status known	482	100.0
Employment status unknown	0	0.0
Employed	421	87.3
Pursuing graduate degrees	40	8.3
Unemployed (seeking, not seeking, or studying for the bar)	16	3.3
Type of Employment		
# employed in law firms	273	64.8
# employed in business and industry	34	8.1
# employed in government	55	13.1
# employed in public interest	20	4.8
# employed as judicial clerks	19	4.5
# employed in academia	12	2.9
Geographic Location		
# employed in state	314	74.6
# employed in foreign countries	6	1.4
# of states where employed	23	

Bar Passage Rates

First-time takers	481	Reporting %	99.17
Average school %	88.69	Average state %	81.47
Average pass difference	7.22		

Jurisdiction	Takers	Passers	Pass %	State %	Diff %
Florida	414	368	88.89	80.76	8.13
Georgia	19	18	94.74	89.27	5.47
New York	12	11	91.67	88.98	2.69
California	10	7	70.00	78.07	−8.07
Others (10)	22	19	86.36		

University of Florida, Fredric G. Levin College of Law

Assistant Dean for Admissions, PO Box 117622, 141 Bruton-Geer Hall
Gainesville, FL 32611-7622
Phone: 352.273.0890, Toll-free: 877.429.1297; Fax: 352.392.4087
E-mail: admissions@law.ufl.edu; Website: www.law.ufl.edu

■ Introduction

The University of Florida Levin College of Law is one of the nation's most comprehensive and widely respected law schools. It was founded in 1909, has been a member of the Association of American Law Schools since 1920, and was approved by the American Bar Association in 1925. It boasts an impressive list of distinguished visitors to campus, including four Supreme Court justices in the last five years. Its beautiful campus features expansive, state-of-the-art facilities thanks to efforts such as a $25 million expansion and renovation project completed in 2005 and a trial advocacy center completed in November 2009.

The college's faculty are highly accomplished scholars, educators, and practitioners whose broad knowledge base and strong teaching skills are highly praised in student evaluations. Many are authors of treatises, casebooks, or major books used by law schools and practitioners throughout the nation, as well as hundreds of articles in law reviews and specialty journals.

The law school also is known for graduating state and national legal, political, business, government, and educational leaders, and for nurturing a strong alumni network. UF Law graduates include four—soon to be five—ABA presidents, numerous federal and state judges, partners in major national and international law firms, members of Congress and the cabinet, governors, and state legislators. Alumni support has built the endowment into one of the largest in the country for public law schools. This, combined with the state's financial assistance, allows the college to remain affordable while its academic quality rivals many of the best-known private colleges.

The University of Florida is one of the nation's largest and most comprehensive universities, is a member of the prestigious Association of American Universities, and is recognized as one of the nation's leading research universities by the Carnegie Commission on Higher Education. The campus occupies 2,000 acres, mostly within the city of Gainesville's 106,000-population area in North Central Florida. The area is consistently ranked among the best places to live in America, with extensive educational, cultural, and recreational offerings.

■ Programs and Curriculum

The Levin College of Law offers students both strong fundamentals and a diverse range of specializations and interdisciplinary options. The activities and scholarship of approximately 80 full-time faculty allow for interesting programs and curricular concentrations. More than 70 courses and 15–20 seminars are offered each semester. Students can earn a certificate in Environmental and Land Use Law, Estates and Trusts Practice, Family Law, Intellectual Property Law, or International and Comparative Law. The Levin College of Law also offers one of the most extensive joint-degree programs of any US law school, including popular joint degrees in Business, Public Health/Medicine, Education, and Engineering, among many other areas. Students can gain hands-on experience in litigation, negotiation, mediation, client relations, and government service at the highest levels

through a broad array of courses, study-abroad opportunities, externships, pro bono work, and clinical programs. The first-year curriculum is required, as is a second-year drafting course. All students must complete a major senior-year research and writing project.

The richness and diversity of the school's faculty, student body, and course offerings are strengthened by the presence of its top ranked Graduate Tax Program—leading to an LLM in Taxation, LLM in International Taxation, or SJD in Taxation. The school also offers an LLM in Environmental and Land Use Law, as well as an LLM in Comparative Law for foreign lawyers. In addition, UF is a major hub for international legal programs and has decades of experience and relationships in Latin America and Europe. The college's innovative centers and institutes include the Center for Governmental Responsibility, Center on Children and Families, Center for the Study of Race and Race Relations, Center for Estate and Elder Law Planning, and Institute for Dispute Resolution.

■ Student/Extracurricular Activities

More than 65 active extracurricular organizations at the law school help students develop valuable skills and professional contacts as well as make a positive difference in the community. Students can earn credits and polish their legal skills through cocurricular organizations such as the *Florida Law Review*, *Florida Journal of International Law*, *University of Florida Journal of Law and Public Policy*, *Journal of Technology Law and Policy*, and trophy-winning US and international moot court and trial teams.

■ Library and Facilities

Following completion in 2005 of a major expansion and renovation project, the Lawton Chiles Legal Information Center is now one of the largest academic law libraries in the Southeast and among the top 20 in the nation in terms of space. The expanded library offers comfortable study areas, reading rooms, computer training labs, multimedia workstations, and reference rooms for use by students and faculty. Two new three-story education buildings feature spacious, state-of-the-art classrooms equipped to offer the latest in teaching technology, including desktop outlets for laptop use, wireless Internet access, and "smart podia."

The most recent addition to the law school is a sophisticated, high-tech, two-and-a-half story advocacy center with a fully functional trial and appellate courtroom, audience gallery, and bench for seven judges, completed in November 2009.

■ Career Development

Professional counselors in the college's Center for Career Development offer a wide variety of services and programs to help students plan a self-directed career search and develop marketing skills that will serve them for many years to come. Staff members help students develop legal credentials; capitalize on their diverse strengths and experiences; explore legal and nontraditional career paths; and find summer internships, externships, and clerkships, as well as permanent

postgraduation employment. They also help link students with alumni, practitioners, and the community. UF Law continues to host one of the South's largest on-campus recruiting programs, which brings numerous employers to campus each year. Other resources include workshops and seminars on practical career skills, individual career and job-search counseling, on- and off-campus networking events, and a Web-based job bank with downloadable handouts, samples, and forms.

■ Admission

Through its admissions process, the Levin College of Law seeks to admit and enroll students who will excel academically, attain the highest standards of professional excellence and integrity, and bring vision, creativity and commitment to the legal profession. The LSAT, LSAC Credential Assembly Service, admissions statement, and résumé are required. Four recommendation letters are allowed. A bachelor's degree from an accredited college or university is required prior to enrollment.

The admissions staff and the faculty admissions committee base their decisions on the applicant's academic credentials, including LSAT score, UGPA, level of writing skills, and breadth of studies, as well as on other information including, but not limited to, the applicant's work and other life experience, leadership experience, depth of particular interest, and any other aspect of an applicant's background suggesting suitability for the study and practice of law.

Students may transfer in August, January, or May from ABA-approved law schools, but only applicants who have completed the required first-year, full-time curriculum before enrolling at UF and who are in the upper one-third of their class will be considered. A transfer certification form from the

dean is required and no more than 29 semester hours will be transferred.

The law school seeks to enroll approximately 300 (full-time only) students each fall. The college places great importance on obtaining a diverse class and actively recruits minority students. To arrange a meeting or tour of the law school, contact the Admissions Office.

■ Expenses and Financial Aid

The 2009–2010 semester credit-hour fees are $474.25 for Florida residents and $1,119.74 for nonresidents. Additional expenses total approximately $13,225 for books, supplies, computer (required), clothing, room, food, transportation, student orientation fee (entering students only), and personal/insurance.

Merit-based and merit/need-based scholarships and grants, and short- and long-term loans (FAFSA required) are available to qualified students. Merit awards are based on information collected in the application for admission. To be considered for merit/need-based scholarships and need-based grants, admitted students must submit a FAFSA and a UF application for need-based scholarships and grants.

Address inquiries to: Office of Admissions, University of Florida Levin College of Law, PO Box 117622, Gainesville, FL 32611-7622, or admissions@law.ufl.edu.

■ Housing

Housing is available for single students in dormitories and for families in university apartments. Plentiful off-campus housing is available. New and current UF law students may access the UF College of Law Roommate Referral System online.

Applicant Profile

University of Florida, Fredric G. Levin College of Law
This grid includes only applicants who earned 120–180 LSAT scores under standard administrations.

LSAT Score	GPA 3.75 +		3.50–3.74		3.25–3.49		3.00–3.24		2.75–2.99		2.50–2.74		2.25–2.49		2.00–2.24		Below 2.00		No GPA		Total	
	Apps	Adm	Apps	Adm	Apps	Adm	Apps	Adm	Apps	Adm	Apps	Adm	Apps	Adm	Apps	Adm	Apps	Adm	Apps	Adm	Apps	Adm
175–180	4	3	2	2	3	3	0	0	0	0	0	0	0	0	0	0	0	0	0	0	9	8
170–174	16	14	10	9	7	5	6	5	2	1	3	2	1	0	0	0	0	0	1	0	46	36
165–169	57	56	60	51	33	27	25	15	9	4	6	1	6	3	0	0	0	0	4	4	200	161
160–164	167	136	187	110	143	53	100	26	33	5	16	3	7	1	2	0	1	0	7	4	663	338
155–159	237	99	293	53	237	20	153	8	57	0	22	1	13	1	1	0	0	0	24	9	1037	191
150–154	111	7	184	12	188	4	139	6	61	2	32	0	14	0	4	0	1	0	23	3	757	34
145–149	44	1	96	6	93	1	73	2	44	0	30	0	7	0	3	0	1	0	10	1	401	11
140–144	16	2	30	2	45	0	40	1	24	0	19	0	9	0	2	0	0	0	8	0	193	5
135–139	2	0	10	0	13	0	10	0	19	0	11	0	7	0	3	0	2	0	4	0	81	0
130–134	0	0	0	0	2	0	1	0	6	0	5	0	0	0	4	0	0	0	3	0	21	0
125–129	1	0	0	0	0	0	0	0	0	0	1	0	0	0	0	0	0	0	0	0	2	0
120–124	0	0	0	0	0	0	0	0	0	0	0	0	0	0	0	0	0	0	0	0	0	0
Total	655	318	872	245	764	113	547	63	255	12	145	7	64	5	19	0	5	0	84	21	3410	784

Apps = Number of Applicants
Adm = Number Admitted
Reflects 99% of the total applicant pool; average LSAT data reported.

Florida International University College of Law

RDB 1055
Miami, FL 33186
Phone: 305.348.8006; Fax: 305.348.2965
E-mail: lawadmit@fiu.edu; Website: http://law.fiu.edu/

ABA
Approved
Since
2004

The Basics

Type of school	Public
Term	Semester
Application deadline	5/1
Application fee	$20
Financial aid deadline	3/1
Can first year start other than fall?	No
Student to faculty ratio	16.2 to 1
# of housing spaces available restricted to law students	
graduate housing for which law students are eligible	20

Faculty and Administrators

	Total		Men		Women		Minorities	
	Spr	Fall	Spr	Fall	Spr	Fall	Spr	Fall
Full-time	25	25	15	13	10	12	11	12
Other full-time	1	1	1	1	0	0	1	1
Deans, librarians, & others who teach	6	6	2	2	4	4	4	5
Part-time	23	21	19	11	4	10	8	9
Total	55	53	37	27	18	26	24	27

JD Enrollment and Ethnicity

	Men		Women		Full-Time		Part-Time		1st-Year		Total		JD Degs. Awd.
	#	%	#	%	#	%	#	%	#	%	#	%	
African Amer.	24	7.4	32	10.8	18	6.1	38	11.6	24	10.1	56	9.0	10
Amer. Indian	1	0.3	4	1.3	2	0.7	3	0.9	4	1.7	5	0.8	0
Asian Amer.	6	1.8	7	2.4	7	2.4	6	1.8	8	3.4	13	2.1	3
Mex. Amer.	0	0.0	0	0.0	0	0.0	0	0.0	0	0.0	0	0.0	0
Puerto Rican	0	0.0	0	0.0	0	0.0	0	0.0	0	0.0	0	0.0	0
Hispanic	125	38.3	148	49.8	119	40.5	154	46.8	94	39.7	273	43.8	53
Total Minority	156	47.9	191	64.3	146	49.7	201	61.1	130	54.9	347	55.7	66
For. Nation.	0	0.0	3	1.0	2	0.7	1	0.3	2	0.8	3	0.5	2
Caucasian	160	49.1	96	32.3	139	47.3	117	35.6	102	43.0	256	41.1	44
Unknown	10	3.1	7	2.4	7	2.4	10	3.0	3	1.3	17	2.7	6
Total	326	52.3	297	47.7	294	47.2	329	52.8	237	38.0	623		118

Curriculum

	Full-Time	Part-Time
Typical first-year section size	80	77
Is there typically a "small section" of the first-year class, other than Legal Writing, taught by full-time faculty	No	No
If yes, typical size offered last year		
# of classroom course titles beyond first-year curriculum	66	

# of upper division courses, excluding seminars, with an enrollment:		
	Under 25	93
	25–49	33
	50–74	12
	75–99	1
	100+	0

	Full-Time	Part-Time
# of seminars	11	
# of seminar positions available	165	
# of seminar positions filled	118	26
# of positions available in simulation courses	205	
# of simulation positions filled	149	30
# of positions available in faculty supervised clinical courses	0	
# of faculty supervised clinical positions filled	0	0
# involved in field placements	0	0
# involved in law journals	38	4
# involved in moot court or trial competitions	109	20
# of credit hours required to graduate	90	

Transfers

Transfers in	3
Transfers out	5

Tuition and Fees

	Resident	Nonresident
Full-time	$12,800	$26,584
Part-time	$9,682	$20,021
Tuition Guarantee Program		N

Living Expenses

Estimated living expenses for singles

Living on campus	Living off campus	Living at home
$17,852	$24,016	$12,156

Florida International University College of Law

*ABA
Approved
Since
2004*

GPA and LSAT Scores

	Total	Full-Time	Part-Time
# of apps	2,443	1,957	486
# of offers	632	515	117
# of matrics	250	168	82
75% GPA	3.62	3.67	3.48
Median GPA	3.40	3.45	3.24
25% GPA	3.13	3.18	2.90
75% LSAT	156	156	155
Median LSAT	154	154	153
25% LSAT	151	152	150

Grants and Scholarships (from prior year)

	Total		Full-Time		Part-Time	
	#	%	#	%	#	%
Total # of students	532		365		167	
Total # receiving grants	137	25.8	116	31.8	21	12.6
Less than 1/2 tuition	92	17.3	89	24.4	3	1.8
Half to full tuition	26	4.9	9	2.5	17	10.2
Full tuition	13	2.4	12	3.3	1	0.6
More than full tuition	6	1.1	6	1.6	0	0.0
Median grant amount			$3,165		$2,453	

Informational and Library Resources

Total amount spent on library materials	$742,561
Study seating capacity inside the library	322
# of full-time equivalent professional librarians	7
Hours per week library is open	95
# of open, wired connections available to students	35
# of networked computers available for use by students	52
Has wireless network?	Y
Require computer?	N

JD Attrition (from prior year)

	Academic	Other	Total	
	#	#	#	%
1st year	16	8	24	11.3
2nd year	0	1	1	0.6
3rd year	1	0	1	0.7
4th year	0	0	0	0.0

Employment (9 months after graduation)

	Total	Percentage
Employment status known	87	93.5
Employment status unknown	6	6.5
Employed	80	92.0
Pursuing graduate degrees	1	1.1
Unemployed (seeking, not seeking, or studying for the bar)	6	6.9
Type of Employment		
# employed in law firms	32	40.0
# employed in business and industry	11	13.7
# employed in government	6	7.5
# employed in public interest	3	3.7
# employed as judicial clerks	1	1.2
# employed in academia	0	0.0
Geographic Location		
# employed in state	78	97.5
# employed in foreign countries	0	0.0
# of states where employed	3	

Bar Passage Rates

First-time takers	93	Reporting %	89.25
Average school %	87.95	Average state %	80.76
Average pass difference	7.19		

Jurisdiction	Takers	Passers	Pass %	State %	Diff %
Florida	83	73	87.95	80.76	7.19

Florida International University College of Law

RDB 1055
Miami, FL 33186
Phone: 305.348.8006; Fax: 305.348.2965
E-mail: lawadmit@fiu.edu; Website: http://law.fiu.edu/

■ Introduction

The Florida International University College of Law was
established by an act of the Florida legislature in June 2000.
Its first class was admitted in the fall of 2002 and received
approval by the ABA in 2004.

Florida International University is a public research
university which enrolls approximately 39,000 students, most
on its beautiful University Park campus, where the College of
Law is located. This campus is the site of the new
state-of-the-art law building designed by nationally and
internationally renowned architect Robert A. M. Stern. The
campus enjoys nearby access to South Florida's beaches,
Everglades National Park, and the Florida Keys.

The College of Law reflects the diverse character and the
international perspective of the city of Miami. The curriculum
incorporates important developments in the globalization of
both public and private law. The academic program takes a
pervasive approach to both international and comparative law,
incorporating their perspectives into all domestic law classes.

■ Curriculum and Special Programs

The FIU College of Law's academic program, while devoted
to all the traditional components of an excellent American
legal education, also emphasizes international and
comparative law. To this end, the required curriculum
includes a three-hour, first-year course titled Introduction to
International and Comparative Law. Further, all domestic law
courses include an international or comparative law
dimension. This pervasive approach to international and
comparative law encourages students to analyze legal
systemic, political, economic, social, and other cultural
differences that may contribute to different legal treatment of
comparable problems in different countries. The College of
Law also offers a foreign summer program in Sevilla, Spain.

As Miami's premier public research university, FIU offers a
broad range of high quality, graduate-level degree programs.
Law students interested in interdisciplinary study may take
advantage of several joint-degree programs, including the
following: JD/Master of Business Administration, JD/Master of
International Business, JD/Master of Latin American and
Caribbean Studies, JD/Master of Public Administration, JD/MS
in Psychology, JD/Master of Social Work, JD/MS in Criminal
Justice, and JD/Master of Science in Environmental Sciences.

In addition to a strong doctrinal program, the College of
Law's Clinical Program advances the law school's goals of
educating lawyers for the ethical and effective practice of law
and of promoting community service through the
representation of real clients. Presently, there are four clinics
available—the Carlos A. Costa Immigration and Human Rights
Clinic, the Community Development Clinic, the Juvenile
Justice Clinic, and the Criminal Law Clinic—as well as
externships in Criminal Law and the Florida Judiciary. The
curriculum also emphasizes instruction in the legal skills and
values of the profession. The Legal Skills and Values Program
combines demanding traditional instruction in legal research
and writing with an introduction to other lawyering skills, like
interviewing and counseling, and issues of professionalism.

Moreover, as a public, urban law school, the College of Law
is committed to serving the community of which it is a part by
educating future lawyers who will understand the value—to
the community and to themselves personally—of helping
those in need. In recognition of this important mission,
students must satisfy a community service requirement.

■ Admission

The FIU College of Law offers both a full-time day and
part-time evening program. The review of applications is
done on a rolling basis. An LSAC Credential Assembly Service
report, three letters of recommendation, and a personal
statement are required.

While a prospective student's academic record and LSAT
performance are weighted heavily in the evaluative process,
the Admissions Committee considers other factors, including
leadership ability, commitment to public service, command of
global issues, work history, military service, any history of
criminality or academic misconduct, and evidence of
obstacles that an applicant may have overcome (for example,
English is not the applicant's native language, discrimination,
economic or family hardship, and severe medical conditions,
etc.). The Admissions Committee encourages each applicant
to answer all questions with candor, detail, and, where
appropriate, to give specific examples of relevant
background experiences.

Transfer students from other ABA-approved law schools
may apply if they are in good standing at their current
institutions. Visit our website at *http://law.fiu.edu/* for
additional information.

■ Financial Aid

The primary financial aid resources available to students are
loans and need- or merit-based scholarships. Students must
apply for financial aid (FAFSA) to be considered for any type
of loan or need-based scholarship. No separate application is
needed for merit-based scholarships. Eligible students will be
considered based on the information provided in their
admission application. Financial aid is granted on an annual
basis, and awards are subject to student eligibility and
availability of funds. Tuition is comparable to other Florida
state-supported law schools at $416 per credit for Florida
residents and $875 per credit for nonresidents. An additional
$21,228 (approximate) can be expected to cover room and
board, books, transportation, and personal expenses. Please
call 305.348.8006 for further information.

■ Library

The Law Library supports the law school curriculum and
research of its students and faculty. It contains approximately
210,000 volumes in book and microform format. The Law
Library provides law students with a full range of electronic
legal information resources, including Westlaw, LexisNexis,
HeinOnline, BNA, CCH, and other Web-based databases.
When doing cross-discipline research, law students may use
the FIU Green Library's 1.5 million volumes and extensive
electronic resources. The Law Library is staffed by six full-time

and two part-time professional librarians, four with JD degrees. In addition to a comprehensive collection of core US materials, the library is developing an extensive collection of international, comparative, and foreign law materials, with a particular focus on Latin America and the Caribbean, international trade, and the workings of international law institutions.

■ Career Planning and Placement

The Office of Career Planning and Placement is committed to providing law students with the skills and resources necessary to identify their career goals and to assisting students in tailoring strategies for reaching those goals. The office facilitates both on- and off-campus recruitment for summer and permanent legal positions as well as an active internship program. Other services include individual career counseling sessions; workshops and handbooks regarding résumé preparation, interview skills and techniques, and job searches; and mock interviews with local attorneys.

■ Student Activities

Success in law school involves more than just intellectual curiosity and a sense of purpose. It involves the refining of time management skills, handling stress proactively, and forging relationships with faculty and peers. It also involves making the best possible use of available services and opportunities. Students bring a wealth of distinctive educational and professional experiences to the College of Law. However, they all share a common interest and goal: service to the law school, the local community, and the profession. Together with the support of the faculty and the administration, students have created a number of organizations and cocurricular activities reflective of this commitment. In its brief but productive history, the College of Law has established a thriving clinical and externship program, award-winning moot court and trial advocacy programs competing locally and nationally against teams throughout the country, and 23 student organizations, including the Student Bar Association.

Applicant Profile

The Florida International University College of Law Admissions Committee seeks to enroll a diverse group of students who have demonstrated academic and personal achievement. While a prospective student's academic record and LSAT performance are weighted heavily in the evaluative process, the Admissions Committee considers other factors, including leadership ability, commitment to public service,

command of global issues, work history, military service, any history of criminality or academic misconduct, and evidence of obstacles that an applicant may have overcome (for example, English is not the applicant's native language, discrimination, economic or family hardship, severe medical condition, disability, etc.).

The Florida State University College of Law

425 West Jefferson Street
Tallahassee, FL 32306-1601
Phone: 850.644.3787; Fax: 850.644.7284
E-mail: admissions@law.fsu.edu; Website: www.law.fsu.edu

ABA
Approved
Since
1968

The Basics

Type of school	Public
Term	Semester
Application deadline	4/1
Application fee	$30
Financial aid deadline	2/1
Can first year start other than fall?	No
Student to faculty ratio	14.2 to 1
# of housing spaces available restricted to law students	
graduate housing for which law students are eligible	1,000

Faculty and Administrators

	Total		Men		Women		Minorities	
	Spr	Fall	Spr	Fall	Spr	Fall	Spr	Fall
Full-time	44	43	26	24	18	19	6	6
Other full-time	0	0	0	0	0	0	0	0
Deans, librarians, & others who teach	15	15	3	3	12	12	4	4
Part-time	29	28	19	22	10	6	5	2
Total	88	86	48	49	40	37	15	12

Curriculum

		Full-Time	Part-Time
Typical first-year section size		83	0
Is there typically a "small section" of the first-year class, other than Legal Writing, taught by full-time faculty		No	No
If yes, typical size offered last year			
# of classroom course titles beyond first-year curriculum		119	
# of upper division courses, excluding seminars, with an enrollment:	Under 25	92	
	25–49	39	
	50–74	11	
	75–99	8	
	100+	2	
# of seminars		26	
# of seminar positions available		473	
# of seminar positions filled		352	0
# of positions available in simulation courses		964	
# of simulation positions filled		708	0
# of positions available in faculty supervised clinical courses		60	
# of faculty supervised clinical positions filled		46	0
# involved in field placements		124	0
# involved in law journals		166	0
# involved in moot court or trial competitions		63	0
# of credit hours required to graduate		88	

JD Enrollment and Ethnicity

	Men		Women		Full-Time		Part-Time		1st-Year		Total		JD Degs. Awd.
	#	%	#	%	#	%	#	%	#	%	#	%	
African Amer.	26	5.8	38	12.1	64	8.4	0	0.0	16	6.5	64	8.4	17
Amer. Indian	1	0.2	2	0.6	3	0.4	0	0.0	1	0.4	3	0.4	1
Asian Amer.	5	1.1	9	2.9	14	1.8	0	0.0	7	2.9	14	1.8	8
Mex. Amer.	2	0.4	1	0.3	3	0.4	0	0.0	2	0.8	3	0.4	0
Puerto Rican	1	0.2	1	0.3	2	0.3	0	0.0	1	0.4	2	0.3	3
Hispanic	23	5.1	22	7.0	45	5.9	0	0.0	21	8.6	45	5.9	18
Total Minority	58	12.9	73	23.2	131	17.2	0	0.0	48	19.6	131	17.2	47
For. Nation.	1	0.2	0	0.0	1	0.1	0	0.0	0	0.0	1	0.1	3
Caucasian	382	85.1	234	74.5	616	80.7	0	0.0	195	79.6	616	80.7	213
Unknown	8	1.8	7	2.2	15	2.0	0	0.0	2	0.8	15	2.0	1
Total	449	58.8	314	41.2	763	100.0	0	0.0	245	32.1	763		264

Transfers

Transfers in	45
Transfers out	7

Tuition and Fees

	Resident	Nonresident
Full-time	$14,239	$31,250
Part-time		
Tuition Guarantee Program	N	

Living Expenses

Estimated living expenses for singles

Living on campus	Living off campus	Living at home
$18,300	$18,300	$18,300

The Florida State University College of Law

ABA
Approved
Since
1968

GPA and LSAT Scores

	Total	Full-Time	Part-Time
# of apps	3,316	3,316	0
# of offers	860	860	0
# of matrics	244	244	0
75% GPA	3.74	3.74	0.00
Median GPA	3.53	3.53	0.00
25% GPA	3.23	3.23	0.00
75% LSAT	162	162	0
Median LSAT	160	160	0
25% LSAT	159	159	0

Grants and Scholarships (from prior year)

	Total		Full-Time		Part-Time	
	#	%	#	%	#	%
Total # of students	771		771		0	
Total # receiving grants	276	35.8	276	35.8	0	0.0
Less than 1/2 tuition	208	27.0	208	27.0	0	0.0
Half to full tuition	45	5.8	45	5.8	0	0.0
Full tuition	14	1.8	14	1.8	0	0.0
More than full tuition	9	1.2	9	1.2	0	0.0
Median grant amount			$2,000		$0	

Informational and Library Resources

Total amount spent on library materials	$866,520
Study seating capacity inside the library	420
# of full-time equivalent professional librarians	10
Hours per week library is open	168
# of open, wired connections available to students	0
# of networked computers available for use by students	23
Has wireless network?	Y
Require computer?	Y

JD Attrition (from prior year)

	Academic	Other	Total	
	#	#	#	%
1st year	2	20	22	8.8
2nd year	0	0	0	0.0
3rd year	2	1	3	1.1
4th year	0	0	0	0.0

Employment (9 months after graduation)

	Total	Percentage
Employment status known	308	98.1
Employment status unknown	6	1.9
Employed	293	95.1
Pursuing graduate degrees	6	1.9
Unemployed (seeking, not seeking, or studying for the bar)	3	1.0
Type of Employment		
# employed in law firms	141	48.1
# employed in business and industry	28	9.6
# employed in government	74	25.3
# employed in public interest	32	10.9
# employed as judicial clerks	6	2.0
# employed in academia	12	4.1
Geographic Location		
# employed in state	228	77.8
# employed in foreign countries	1	0.3
# of states where employed	20	

Bar Passage Rates

First-time takers	291	Reporting %	89.00
Average school %	86.87	Average state %	80.76
Average pass difference	6.11		

Jurisdiction	Takers	Passers	Pass %	State %	Diff %
Florida	259	225	86.87	80.76	6.11

The Florida State University College of Law

425 West Jefferson Street
Tallahassee, FL 32306-1601
Phone: 850.644.3787; Fax: 850.644.7284
E-mail: admissions@law.fsu.edu; Website: www.law.fsu.edu

■ Introduction

Florida State University College of Law is recognized as one of the nation's top-tier law schools in terms of academic reputation. The school encourages close working relationships among students and faculty of the sort that characterize the best liberal arts colleges. Expert faculty members are accessible to students and are available to teach students outside of the classroom as well as inside the classroom.

Florida State University College of Law's liberal arts orientation means that students have a strong sense of community. Students are proud of the law school and of one another.

The liberal arts orientation also places great value on the insights of other disciplines that can be brought to bear upon the study of law. It is important to the faculty to integrate into the study of law insights from such diverse disciplines as history, philosophy, psychology, sociology, economics, and finance.

Florida State offers law students a wealth of legal employment opportunities. Located in Tallahassee, a city with more than 450 law firms and numerous government agencies, Florida State University College of Law is just steps away from the state Capitol, the Florida Supreme Court, the First District Court of Appeal, and the United States District Court for the Northern District of Florida.

■ Enrollment/Student Body

Florida State University College of Law receives 14 applications for every seat in its entering class. The school's liberal arts orientation values students from a wide variety of backgrounds. Currently, the talented and diverse student body represents 34 states, 16 countries, and 181 colleges and universities. *Hispanic Business* magazine (2009) recognizes us as the nation's third best law school for Hispanic students.

■ Curriculum

Florida State University College of Law's three-year curriculum is rich and diverse. It begins with traditional courses and expands to include the latest in theoretical and interdisciplinary analyses. The first-year curriculum is rigorous, traditional, and prescribed. It provides a foundation in history, doctrine, process, and analysis. The second- and third-year curriculum is deliberately structured to provide students with the opportunity to obtain a broad and interdisciplinary exposure to different areas of law.

The law school has four cocurricular academic organizations, including two student-edited journals, and trial and appellate advocacy teams. The journals include the *Florida State University Law Review* and the *Journal of Land Use and Environmental Law*, and all have been rated high on "impact factor" by Washington and Lee University. The law school's advocacy teams are regionally and nationally competitive.

■ Special Programs

Florida State University College of Law has especially strong programs in three areas: environmental law, international law, and business, with certificate programs in environmental law and in international law. The law school's program in environmental law is recognized as one of the best in the country. The law school's business program emphasizes economics and finance. The law school also has one of the strongest criminal law programs in the region.

Building on its highly ranked environmental law program, Florida State University College of Law offers an LLM in Environmental Law and Policy. The law school's newest degree offering gives JD holders the opportunity to concentrate in or enhance their knowledge of environmental law, land use law, natural resources law, and energy law.

The law school also offers an LLM in American Law for foreign lawyers, which provides foreign graduate students trained in law the opportunity to develop an understanding of the American legal system and the role of law in the United States.

Florida State University College of Law offers eight joint-degree programs in cooperation with other colleges, schools, and departments at Florida State. The joint degrees bring together law with business, economics, information studies, international affairs, public administration, social work, child and family sciences, and urban and regional planning.

Florida State University College of Law has one of the most extensive externship programs in the United States. The clinical externship program places students in more than 80 offices throughout Florida and elsewhere. Students may even select international externships with the International Bar Association in London, the International Criminal Tribunal for the former Yugoslavia, and the Supreme Court of Botswana.

The law school's Public Interest Law Center provides on-campus clinical legal training for second- and third-year students. Students are certified by the Florida Supreme Court to practice law as interns and, under the supervision of licensed attorneys, are responsible for all facets of cases to which they are assigned.

Florida State University College of Law also sponsors a summer program at Oxford University in England. As the oldest ongoing summer program in Oxford sponsored by a US law school, it provides students with a unique opportunity to study comparative law and the history of the common law and its institutions in their original setting.

■ Library and Physical Facilities

The physical facilities of Florida State University College of Law consist of B.K. Roberts Hall, the connected Research Center, and the Village Green, which is comprised of four restored houses. All of the law school's classrooms are either new or recently remodeled. Classrooms are equipped with technology podiums that allow professors to present multimedia lectures. A strong wireless infrastructure allows students to utilize the Internet during class.

Florida State University College of Law students have 24/7 access to the research center. The distinctive feature of the research center is that its faculty proactively trains students and other faculty members to produce highly sophisticated, cost-effective legal research. For example, we offer specialized courses in efficient research relating to economics, business and tax law, environmental law, and international law. The law school's research center was also

significantly remodeled in 2007. Highlights include an improved student seating area for studying and cosmetic improvements in the lobby and circulation desk area.

Florida State University College of Law is acquiring, as an addition, a 50,000-square-foot modern courthouse directly across the street from its present facilities. The 2007 Florida Legislature has appropriated money for the law school to plan its move into the adjacent First District Court of Appeal building. Among other things, this acquisition will give Florida State University College of Law one of the nation's finest facilities for trial and appellate advocacy.

■ Student Activities

Students have the opportunity to participate in many extracurricular organizations. More than 30 student and service organizations allow students to become leaders at the law school and active participants in the legal community. Some of the active student organizations include the American Constitution Society; Real Estate and Trust Law Society; Public Interest Law Students Association; Women's Law Symposium; Black Law Students Association; Christian Legal Society; Entertainment, Art, and Sports Law Society; Federalist Society; International Law Students Association; Dispute Resolution Society; Environmental Law Society; Lawtinos; OUTLaw; and Law Partners, a support group for spouses and significant others of law students. Both Phi Delta Phi and Phi Alpha Delta legal honoraries maintain a chapter on campus. Florida State University College of Law was granted a chapter of the Order of the Coif in 1979. The Student Bar Association serves an active student government role and coordinates many law school-sponsored social activities, community projects, and programs. In 2008 and 2009, our Student Bar Association was selected "SBA of the Year" by the Law Student Division of the American Bar Association.

■ Career Services and Bar Exam

The law school provides assistance to law students, graduates, and legal employers through its Placement Office. Our successful and enthusiastic alumni remain very engaged in our law school. Florida State University College of Law students have access to a list of more than 600 alumni who have volunteered to serve them as Placement Mentors. Students are encouraged to take advantage of the law school's on- and off-campus interviewing programs and individual career counseling services. A variety of seminars and workshops on career options, résumé writing, and interviewing skills are also available.

Ninety-eight percent of the graduating class of 2008 was placed within nine months of graduation. Graduates work in 49 states and in major markets including Atlanta, Chicago, New York, Los Angeles, and Washington, DC. Graduates are prominent in all Florida cities and have placed first in the state in five of the last eight administrations of the Florida Bar Exam. Graduates who take the exam in jurisdictions outside of Florida do equally well.

Applicant Profile

The Florida State University College of Law Fall 2009 Decisions
This grid includes only applicants who earned 120–180 LSAT scores under standard administrations.

LSAT Score	3.75 +		3.50–3.74		3.25–3.49		3.00–3.24		2.75–2.99		2.50–2.74		2.25–2.49		2.00–2.24		Below 2.00		No GPA		Total	
	Apps	Adm	Apps	Adm	Apps	Adm	Apps	Adm	Apps	Adm	Apps	Adm	Apps	Adm	Apps	Adm	Apps	Adm	Apps	Adm	Apps	Adm
175–180	2	2											0		0		0		0		2	2
170–174	5	5	4	4	4	4	5	5			2	2	0		0		0		0		20	20
165–169	25	25	23	23	21	21	14	12	9	8	9	9	5	5	3	2	1	0	1	1	111	106
160–164	114	113	140	140	116	112	105	102	52	46	16	11	3	0	1	0	1	0	2	1	550	525
155–159	204	87	268	75	211	25	148	4	60	2	25	0	9	0	3	0	1	0	13	0	942	193
150–154	121	5	173	8	194	1	158	0	82	0	27	0	17	0	9	0	1	0	11	0	793	14
145–149	50	0	95	0	100	0	96	0	58	0	47	0	16	0	5	0	2	0	11	0	480	0
140–144	22	0	36	0	45	0	53	0	34	0	30	0	15	0	6	0	1	0	4	0	246	0
135–139	3	0	11	0	19	0	26	0	19	0	20	0	8	0	4	0	3	0	2	0	115	0
130–134	3	0		0	5	0	5	0	9	0	5	0	4	0		0	1	0	2	0	34	0
125–129	1	0		0	1	0		0		0	1	0		0				0			3	0
120–124							1								1				0		2	0
Blank																					18	
Total	550	237	750	250	716	163	611	123	323	56	182	22	77	5	32	2	11	0	46	2	3316	860

Apps = Number of Applicants
Adm = Number Admitted
Reflects 99% of the total applicant pool; high LSAT data reported.

Fordham University School of Law

140 West 62nd Street
New York, NY 10023
Phone: 212.636.6810; Fax: 212.636.7984
E-mail: lawadmissions@law.fordham.edu; Website: http://law.fordham.edu

ABA
Approved
Since
1936

The Basics

Type of school	Private
Term	Semester
Application deadline	3/1
Application fee	$70
Financial aid deadline	4/1
Can first year start other than fall?	No
Student to faculty ratio	13.6 to 1
# of housing spaces available restricted to law students	130
graduate housing for which law students are eligible	69

Faculty and Administrators

	Total		Men		Women		Minorities	
	Spr	Fall	Spr	Fall	Spr	Fall	Spr	Fall
Full-time	86	80	53	47	33	33	19	14
Other full-time	1	1	0	0	1	1	0	0
Deans, librarians, & others who teach	19	19	8	8	11	11	4	4
Part-time	157	147	99	92	58	55	19	19
Total	263	247	160	147	103	100	42	37

JD Enrollment and Ethnicity

	Men		Women		Full-Time		Part-Time		1st-Year		Total		JD Degs. Awd.
	#	%	#	%	#	%	#	%	#	%	#	%	
African Amer.	33	4.4	53	7.4	70	6.0	16	5.2	20	4.2	86	5.9	19
Amer. Indian	2	0.3	2	0.3	3	0.3	1	0.3	0	0.0	4	0.3	3
Asian Amer.	44	5.8	57	8.0	74	6.4	27	8.7	30	6.3	101	6.9	38
Mex. Amer.	5	0.7	1	0.1	6	0.5	0	0.0	5	1.1	6	0.4	2
Puerto Rican	7	0.9	8	1.1	13	1.1	2	0.6	10	2.1	15	1.0	3
Hispanic	61	8.1	51	7.1	103	8.9	9	2.9	25	5.3	112	7.6	42
Total Minority	152	20.2	172	24.1	269	23.2	55	17.8	90	18.9	324	22.1	107
For. Nation.	18	2.4	12	1.7	29	2.5	1	0.3	5	1.1	30	2.0	9
Caucasian	427	56.6	374	52.3	627	54.1	174	56.3	279	58.6	801	54.5	261
Unknown	157	20.8	157	22.0	235	20.3	79	25.6	102	21.4	314	21.4	93
Total	754	51.3	715	48.7	1160	79.0	309	21.0	476	32.4	1469		470

Curriculum

	Full-Time	Part-Time
Typical first-year section size	80	80
Is there typically a "small section" of the first-year class, other than Legal Writing, taught by full-time faculty	Yes	Yes
If yes, typical size offered last year	40	40
# of classroom course titles beyond first-year curriculum	247	
# of upper division courses, excluding seminars, with an enrollment: Under 25	56	
25–49	54	
50–74	28	
75–99	30	
100+	7	
# of seminars	202	
# of seminar positions available	3,431	
# of seminar positions filled	1,914	1,076
# of positions available in simulation courses	1,640	
# of simulation positions filled	732	511
# of positions available in faculty supervised clinical courses	582	
# of faculty supervised clinical positions filled	134	24
# involved in field placements	233	44
# involved in law journals	452	22
# involved in moot court or trial competitions	198	9
# of credit hours required to graduate	83	

Transfers

Transfers in	30
Transfers out	20

Tuition and Fees

	Resident	Nonresident
Full-time	$44,996	$44,996
Part-time	$33,816	$33,816
Tuition Guarantee Program		N

Living Expenses

Estimated living expenses for singles

Living on campus	Living off campus	Living at home
$24,494	$24,494	$24,494

Fordham University School of Law

*ABA
Approved
Since
1936*

GPA and LSAT Scores

	Total	Full-Time	Part-Time
# of apps	8,843	7,294	1,549
# of offers	1,904	1,635	269
# of matrics	476	318	158
75% GPA	3.74	3.77	3.66
Median GPA	3.59	3.64	3.42
25% GPA	3.37	3.44	3.28
75% LSAT	167	167	165
Median LSAT	165	166	163
25% LSAT	162	164	161

Grants and Scholarships (from prior year)

	Total		Full-Time		Part-Time	
	#	%	#	%	#	%
Total # of students	1,536		1,229		307	
Total # receiving grants	513	33.4	459	37.3	54	17.6
Less than 1/2 tuition	476	31.0	427	34.7	49	16.0
Half to full tuition	28	1.8	28	2.3	0	0.0
Full tuition	8	0.5	3	0.2	5	1.6
More than full tuition	1	0.1	1	0.1	0	0.0
Median grant amount			$10,000		$6,600	

Informational and Library Resources

Total amount spent on library materials	$1,873,987
Study seating capacity inside the library	442
# of full-time equivalent professional librarians	14
Hours per week library is open	119
# of open, wired connections available to students	601
# of networked computers available for use by students	223
Has wireless network?	Y
Require computer?	N

JD Attrition (from prior year)

	Academic	Other	Total	
	#	#	#	%
1st year	2	4	6	1.3
2nd year	1	24	25	5.1
3rd year	0	2	2	0.4
4th year	0	0	0	0.0

Employment (9 months after graduation)

	Total	Percentage
Employment status known	468	99.2
Employment status unknown	4	0.8
Employed	435	92.9
Pursuing graduate degrees	6	1.3
Unemployed (seeking, not seeking, or studying for the bar)	20	4.3
Type of Employment		
# employed in law firms	330	75.9
# employed in business and industry	42	9.7
# employed in government	22	5.1
# employed in public interest	15	3.4
# employed as judicial clerks	19	4.4
# employed in academia	3	0.7
Geographic Location		
# employed in state	367	84.4
# employed in foreign countries	1	0.2
# of states where employed	14	

Bar Passage Rates

First-time takers	456	Reporting %	100.00
Average school %	94.08	Average state %	88.98
Average pass difference	5.10		

Jurisdiction	Takers	Passers	Pass %	State %	Diff %
New York	456	429	94.08	88.98	5.10

Fordham University School of Law

140 West 62nd Street
New York, NY 10023
Phone: 212.636.6810; Fax: 212.636.7984
E-mail: lawadmissions@law.fordham.edu; Website: http://law.fordham.edu

■ Introduction

Fordham Law has been dedicated to preparing great lawyers and great leaders for more than a century. The school's unique approach to a complete legal education places strong focus on academic excellence, the craft of lawyering, and an unwavering focus on ethics and the obligation of public service. The commitment to these values, combined with the school's New York City location, means that Fordham Law graduates have the opportunity to pursue a broad spectrum of career choices. Today, Fordham ranks seventh among schools placing the greatest number of attorneys in the nation's top 25 law firms. Beyond that, the school's signature public service and human rights programs educate lawyers who work to create significant change in the world. A faculty distinguished by its commitment both to teaching and to scholarship creates an atmosphere in which students feel appreciated and valued as they prepare to become part of the next generation of leaders.

Fordham lawyers practice in 48 states, in the District of Columbia, and in 57 nations around the world. Among our 17,000 living alumni are partners and associates of leading law firms, CEOs of major corporations, academics, and individuals engaged in public service. Fordham's central Manhattan location provides convenient access to all New York City has to offer, enabling students to begin their careers at the center of the world's legal, financial, and entertainment capital. Such proximity puts students close to a broad range of professional opportunities at some of the largest law firms in the world, the busiest federal and state courts, the US Attorney General's Offices, a myriad of state and federal agencies, and Wall Street.

The campus is just two blocks away from Central Park. Lincoln Center for the Performing Arts is right across the street.

■ Curriculum

Fordham's faculty of scholar-teachers recognize the importance of welcoming students, being accessible, and encouraging them. The large faculty enables Fordham to offer a remarkable depth of courses that reinforce its traditional strengths in contracts, commercial law, corporate law, evidence, and international law, as well as enhance its significant scholarship in the fields of constitutional law and jurisprudence, international human rights, legal ethics, legal history, intellectual property, and clinical legal education.

Fordham also promotes the art and science of legal analysis and the cultivation of a vigorous ongoing dialogue between students and professor through the following nationally renowned academic centers:

Brendan Moore Advocacy Center fosters the teaching and study of lawyers as advocates, with special emphasis on client representation at the trial level.

Center for Corporate, Securities, and Financial Law serves as the focal point for the school's business law programs and includes roundtable discussions with business leaders, corporate law practitioners, and state and federal regulators.

The Leitner Center for International Law and Justice contributes to the promotion of social justice by encouraging knowledge of, and respect for, international law and human rights standards. The center oversees an annual fact-finding mission, providing law students the opportunity to participate in human rights work overseas.

Louis Stein Center for Law and Ethics promotes the integration of ethical perspectives in legal practice, legal institutions, and the development of the law generally. The center also oversees the Stein Scholars Program, a program for students who demonstrate commitment to public service and who undertake specialized academic work in legal ethics.

The Feerick Center for Social Justice and Dispute Resolution brings together the major stakeholders responsible for solving our most difficult urban social issues. Uniquely combining the insights of a think tank, the urgency inherent in a mission to achieve social justice, the balance required of a mediation center, and the educational mission of a law school, the center works with all parties to frame concrete and achievable solutions to the endemic problems plaguing the urban poor. The center also houses a clinic, providing hands-on social justice experience to students each year.

The Center on Law and Information Policy (CLIP) will make significant contributions to the development of law and policy for the information economy and teach the next generation of leaders. CLIP focuses on five key areas of technology law and policy, regulation of information innovation and knowledge creation, privacy and security, technology and governance, and the protection of intellectual property and information.

■ Cocurricular Activities

There are six student-edited law journals at Fordham, as well as two intramural moot court competitions.

The school also participates in interschool competitions, fielding award-winning appellate moot court teams, trial advocacy teams, and alternative dispute resolution teams.

■ Worldwide Significance

Long before "globalism" was mainstream, Fordham was devoting resources to programs that, today, are internationally known, including:

- the nation's preeminent Center on European Union Law;
- the school's Stein Center for Law and Ethics (see Curriculum section);
- an International Antitrust Law and Policy Conference, now in its 37th year;
- an annual International Intellectual Property Law Conference, now in its 18th year;
- the Leitner Center for International Law and Justice (see Curriculum section);
- a Belfast/Dublin summer program, which offers two weeks of study in each city with a special emphasis on international alternative dispute resolution;
- a summer program in Seoul, Korea, at Sungkyunkwan University College of Law (SKKU) offers courses in international and comparative law as well as internships at local law firms, companies, and governmental offices;
- semester study-abroad programs offered in Italy, the Netherlands, Germany, Spain, Mexico, Canada, Korea, and the People's Republic of China; and

- four graduate degree programs—the LLM in International Business and Trade Law; the LLM in Banking, Corporate, and Finance Law; the LLM in Intellectual Property and Information Technology Law; and the LLM in International Law and Justice—that have created a network of Fordham alumni in more than 80 countries.
- a Ghana summer law program, building on our long and successful history of partnership with Ghanaian legal institutions, offers students the opportunity to study Ghanaian and international law, as well as internships in Ghana.

■ Experiential Programs

Fordham's clinical program encourages students to integrate legal analysis with lawyering theory and skills by assuming lawyering roles or performing lawyering functions in problem-solving settings. Fordham Law's clinical program—one of the largest in the nation—engages more than 300 students in live-client clinics and simulation courses in 17 practice areas, including an innovative interdisciplinary Child and Family Litigation Clinic, where students are placed on teams supervised by law, social work, and psychology faculty. Fordham also offers one of the widest ranges of externship placements in American legal education—more than 250 opportunities at nonprofit and nongovernmental organizations and in state and federal courts.

■ Career Services and Placement

Fordham's career services office assists students and alumni in planning their careers. For the past several years, between 97 and 100 percent of our graduates obtained employment within nine months of graduation. The program features:
- an on-campus interview program that brings more than 250 potential employers to campus to conduct more than 6,000 individual student interviews;
- a searchable, proprietary, online database of job listings; and
- individualized student counseling, mock videotaped interviews with optional critiques, seminars on interviewing skills and networking, and assistance with résumé preparation, including 24-hour turnaround time for edits.

■ Public Service

Fordham believes that the development of a lifelong commitment to public service is an integral part of a legal education. Last year, Fordham law students volunteered more than 100,000 hours of public service, and more than half of the graduating class devoted 50 or more hours of their time through the school's nationally recognized Public Interest Resource Center. The PIRC's 21 student-run organizations address issues concerning the environment, housing for the poor, domestic violence, unemployment, police brutality, the death penalty, immigration, and community service. Fordham also has created a Loan Forgiveness Program as well as a Loan Repayment Assistance Program (LRAP) to assist those who pursue public service careers. Today, Fordham continues to set the standard for law schools nationwide by assisting and inspiring those students who, regardless of their ultimate career choice, are committed to the spirit of *pro bono publico*—work for the public good.

■ Living at Lincoln Center

Approximately 80 spaces are set aside for entering students in McMahon Hall, the university's Lincoln Center residence. Students live in two- or three-bedroom apartments, each of which contains private bedrooms, a living room, full kitchen, and bath. Preference is given to those students who live beyond a commutable distance from the law school. Inquiries regarding housing should be directed to the law school admission office.

■ Applicant Profile

Fordham's Admissions Committee—comprised of full-time faculty members and assistant deans—evaluates each complete application received. While the best available evidence suggests that LSAT scores and undergraduate GPAs should be accorded significant weight in evaluating most applicants, the Admissions Committee believes that securing the most interesting, diverse, and exciting class involves the evaluation of other qualitative factors as well. The combination of academic excellence and experiences is considered in evaluating applicants' potential contributions to the success of their Fordham and professional experiences.

Applicant Profile

Fordham University School of Law
This grid includes only applicants who earned 120–180 LSAT scores under standard administrations.

LSAT Score	GPA												
	3.75 +		3.50–3.74		3.25–3.49		3.00–3.24		Below 3.00		No GPA		Totals	
	Apps	Adm	Apps	Adm	Apps	Adm	Apps	Adm	Apps	Adm	Apps	Adm	Apps	Adm
170–180	153	126	156	122	114	69	74	22	54	3	5	3	556	345
165–169	414	345	584	421	382	162	190	45	109	9	39	7	1718	989
160–164	561	185	800	128	650	84	325	37	189	4	80	5	2605	443
155–159	282	18	466	26	472	35	303	17	211	3	49	0	1783	99
120–154	186	6	397	5	468	7	420	5	586	5	124	0	2181	28
Total	1596	680	2403	702	2086	357	1312	126	1149	24	297	15	8843	1904

Apps = Number of Applicants   Adm = Number Admitted   Reflects 99% of the total applicant pool; average LSAT data reported.

Franklin Pierce Law Center

Two White Street
Concord, NH 03301
Phone: 603.228.9217; Fax: 603.228.1074
E-mail: admissions@piercelaw.edu; Website: www.piercelaw.edu

ABA
Approved
Since
1974

The Basics

Type of school	Private
Term	Semester
Application deadline	4/1
Application fee	$55
Financial aid deadline	
Can first year start other than fall?	No
Student to faculty ratio	14.3 to 1
# of housing spaces available restricted to law students graduate housing for which law students are eligible	3

Curriculum

	Full-Time	Part-Time
Typical first-year section size	80	0
Is there typically a "small section" of the first-year class, other than Legal Writing, taught by full-time faculty	Yes	No
If yes, typical size offered last year	15	
# of classroom course titles beyond first-year curriculum	107	

# of upper division courses, excluding seminars, with an enrollment:		
	Under 25	101
	25–49	16
	50–74	9
	75–99	8
	100+	0

# of seminars		13
# of seminar positions available		250
# of seminar positions filled	161	0
# of positions available in simulation courses		713
# of simulation positions filled	601	0
# of positions available in faculty supervised clinical courses		193
# of faculty supervised clinical positions filled	142	0
# involved in field placements	98	0
# involved in law journals	48	0
# involved in moot court or trial competitions	63	0
# of credit hours required to graduate		85

Faculty and Administrators

	Total		Men		Women		Minorities	
	Spr	Fall	Spr	Fall	Spr	Fall	Spr	Fall
Full-time	25	25	15	14	10	11	2	2
Other full-time	8	6	5	4	3	2	1	0
Deans, librarians, & others who teach	6	7	3	3	3	4	0	0
Part-time	30	21	21	14	9	7	1	0
Total	69	59	44	35	25	24	4	2

Transfers

Transfers in	3
Transfers out	9

Tuition and Fees

	Resident	Nonresident
Full-time	$36,980	$36,980
Part-time	$27,755	$27,755
Tuition Guarantee Program	N	

JD Enrollment and Ethnicity

	Men		Women		Full-Time		Part-Time		1st-Year		Total		JD Degs. Awd.
	#	%	#	%	#	%	#	%	#	%	#	%	
African Amer.	10	3.7	13	8.0	23	5.4	0	0.0	8	5.2	23	5.3	5
Amer. Indian	0	0.0	1	0.6	1	0.2	0	0.0	0	0.0	1	0.2	2
Asian Amer.	25	9.4	15	9.2	40	9.3	0	0.0	16	10.5	40	9.3	9
Mex. Amer.	3	1.1	1	0.6	4	0.9	0	0.0	3	2.0	4	0.9	3
Puerto Rican	1	0.4	0	0.0	1	0.2	0	0.0	0	0.0	1	0.2	1
Hispanic	5	1.9	5	3.1	10	2.3	0	0.0	3	2.0	10	2.3	1
Total Minority	44	16.5	35	21.5	79	18.4	0	0.0	30	19.6	79	18.4	21
For. Nation.	11	4.1	10	6.1	20	4.7	1	100.0	7	4.6	21	4.9	10
Caucasian	195	73.0	109	66.9	304	70.9	0	0.0	109	71.2	304	70.7	91
Unknown	17	6.4	9	5.5	26	6.1	0	0.0	7	4.6	26	6.0	22
Total	267	62.1	163	37.9	429	99.8	1	0.2	153	35.6	430		144

Living Expenses

Estimated living expenses for singles

Living on campus	Living off campus	Living at home
$19,664	$19,664	$19,664

Franklin Pierce Law Center

ABA
Approved
Since
1974

GPA and LSAT Scores

	Total	Full-Time	Part-Time
# of apps	1,336	1,336	0
# of offers	671	671	0
# of matrics	158	158	0
75% GPA	3.62	3.62	0.00
Median GPA	3.35	3.35	0.00
25% GPA	3.06	3.06	0.00
75% LSAT	155	155	0
Median LSAT	152	152	0
25% LSAT	149	149	0

Grants and Scholarships (from prior year)

	Total		Full-Time		Part-Time	
	#	%	#	%	#	%
Total # of students	433		433		0	
Total # receiving grants	249	57.5	249	57.5	0	0.0
Less than 1/2 tuition	217	50.1	217	50.1	0	0.0
Half to full tuition	29	6.7	29	6.7	0	0.0
Full tuition	3	0.7	3	0.7	0	0.0
More than full tuition	0	0.0	0	0.0	0	0.0
Median grant amount			$6,500		$0	

Informational and Library Resources

Total amount spent on library materials	$1,102,193
Study seating capacity inside the library	306
# of full-time equivalent professional librarians	7
Hours per week library is open	105
# of open, wired connections available to students	320
# of networked computers available for use by students	51
Has wireless network?	Y
Require computer?	N

JD Attrition (from prior year)

	Academic	Other	Total	
	#	#	#	%
1st year	1	18	19	11.9
2nd year	1	0	1	0.7
3rd year	0	0	0	0.0
4th year	0	0	0	0.0

Employment (9 months after graduation)

	Total	Percentage
Employment status known	117	99.2
Employment status unknown	1	0.8
Employed	106	90.6
Pursuing graduate degrees	1	0.9
Unemployed (seeking, not seeking, or studying for the bar)	6	5.1
Type of Employment		
# employed in law firms	63	59.4
# employed in business and industry	17	16.0
# employed in government	6	5.7
# employed in public interest	7	6.6
# employed as judicial clerks	9	8.5
# employed in academia	3	2.8
Geographic Location		
# employed in state	23	21.7
# employed in foreign countries	1	0.9
# of states where employed	24	

Bar Passage Rates

First-time takers	114	Reporting %	71.05
Average school %	90.13	Average state %	89.09
Average pass difference	1.04		

Jurisdiction	Takers	Passers	Pass %	State %	Diff %
New Hampshire	30	28	93.33	88.27	5.06
Massachusetts	22	20	90.91	92.33	–1.42
New York	22	19	86.36	88.98	–2.62
Virginia	7	6	85.71	82.70	3.01

Franklin Pierce Law Center

Two White Street
Concord, NH 03301
Phone: 603.228.9217; Fax: 603.228.1074
E-mail: admissions@piercelaw.edu; Website: www.piercelaw.edu

■ Introduction

Franklin Pierce Law Center is known throughout the world as an innovative leader in legal education, providing its students with the skills to lead and serve, and to meet the emerging needs of a global society. Pierce Law emphasizes individually tailored legal programs and a broad range of learning settings, including lectures and seminars, real-client clinics, independent study, and externships in law firms, in courts, and in private and public agencies. In addition, we promote a community spirit of caring and compassion, with a close working relationship between students and faculty. Self-reliant students who know their own strengths and objectives thrive at Pierce Law and find the focus on personal pride and responsibility more motivating than fear or competition.

Pierce Law is one of the smallest private law schools in the United States. Each entering class numbers approximately 150 students, allowing for a 13.6:1 student-to-teacher ratio. Classes are small, especially after the first year. Seventy-five of the 109 elective courses enroll 35 or fewer students.

Located in New Hampshire's capital city of Concord (45,000 population), Pierce Law is ideally situated one hour from Boston, the Atlantic seacoast, the state's Lakes Region, and the White Mountains.

■ Special Programs

- **Intellectual Property**—The internationally recognized intellectual and industrial property specialization (patents, licensing, technology transfer, trade secrets, trademarks, cyberlaw, and copyrights) is supported by 12 full-time faculty members, all intellectual property lawyers. Training includes learning to advise clients regarding intellectual property protection, infringement, and technology transfer. Students with technical backgrounds may focus on patent law, many passing the patent bar prior to graduation. Other intellectual property areas do not require a technical background.
- **Commerce and Technology Law**—The business curriculum prepares students for traditional types of practice and brings new opportunities for students choosing to confront the legal issues involving electronic commerce. The business and e-commerce curriculum also integrates well with the intellectual property curriculum, particularly for students interested in business and legal innovations associated with the Internet.
- **Social Justice Institute**—This hands-on professional training program prepares students for public interest law in private practice, governmental service, social policy advocacy, and criminal practice. Clinic students represent clients in cases involving misdemeanor and felony defense; predatory lending; bankruptcy and consumer fraud; unemployment compensation; as well as trademark, copyright, and small business transactions. In addition, students have the opportunity to assist in projects with the Institute for Health, Law, and Ethics.
- **Criminal Law**—Our criminal law curriculum offers courses, individual mentoring, clinics, and externships to prepare students for careers in prosecution or defense. Criminal

Practice Clinic students represent clients charged with misdemeanor and juvenile offenses at the district court level. In the Appellate Defender Program, students prepare briefs for the New Hampshire Supreme Court in criminal cases. Externship opportunities are available in prosecutorial positions at the local, state, and federal level, and in defense positions with law firms and governmental agencies.
- **International Criminal Law and Justice**—This program is designed to prepare the next generation of lawyers, peacekeepers, policy makers, and law enforcement professionals who will be confronting global issues of criminal law and justice. The program includes a one-week seminar in Washington, DC; explores legal responses to terrorism, counterfeiting, intellectual property crimes, human trafficking; and more.

■ International Summer Institutes in China and Ireland

- The Intellectual Property Summer Institute at Tsinghua University in Beijing offers an overview of China's patent, copyright, and trademark laws, as well as an introduction to some of the major international instruments and institutions regulating international trade and intellectual property.
- The eLaw Summer Institute at University College Cork, Ireland, focuses on law and emerging policy of the information age.

■ Academic Opportunities

The *Daniel Webster Scholar Honors Program* is a comprehensive, practice-based program focused on making law students client-ready. Admission to the program is competitive; application is made at the end of the 1L year. Second- and third-year students complete a range of courses, demonstrate their developing professional skills and judgment, and compile a portfolio of work. Students who successfully complete the program will be certified as having passed the New Hampshire bar examination, subject to passing character and fitness requirements.

The Pierce Law *Externship Program* exchanges a full-credit semester in the classroom for a real-life experience working in an active legal position. Externs work with experienced attorneys and judges while under the close supervision of a faculty member.

■ Joint-Degree Programs and LLM

Pierce Law offers three dual-degree programs: JD/Master of Laws (LLM) in Intellectual Property, JD/LLM in Commerce and Technology, and JD/LLM in International Criminal Law and Justice. Summer programs enable students to earn additional credits needed to complete joint-degree programs in three years. The three LLM degrees are designed for law graduates who wish to examine the legally sophisticated intellectual property issues that often arise in policy making and teaching.

Franklin Pierce Law Center

Student Activities

Students prepare notes and comments for *IDEA: The Intellectual Property Law Review* and *Pierce Law Review*. Students organize and participate in a wide variety of formal organizations and informal activities and events throughout the year.

Career Services

The Career Services Office works with students and alumni to find the best match to meet their skills and interests in changing legal markets. The office provides extensive individual counseling and guidance; brings attorneys to campus to provide firsthand information about the practice of law; advises students of all resources through weekly publications and job boards; coordinates the efforts of faculty, staff, and student groups to provide information about opportunities to gain experience; and conducts outreach to employers. More than 75 percent of our graduates secure positions outside New Hampshire. Over 95 percent of our graduates are employed within six months after graduation.

Clinics

- Intellectual Property and Business Transaction Clinic
- Administrative Law and Advocacy Clinic
- Pierce Law Innocence Project
- Consumer and Commercial Law Clinic
- Criminal Practice Clinic
- Appellate Defender Program
- Street Law Project
- Intellectual Property Amicus Clinic
- International Technology Transfer Institute

Admission

While LSAT scores and grade-point average are factors that must be considered in the decision-making process, neither alone determines admission. Every application receives a thorough and thoughtful review. The candidate's personal statement, letters of recommendation, and résumé are evaluated along with the numbers. Community service, employment during college, and other nonacademic accomplishments are given weight to the extent that they reflect initiative, social responsibility, focus, and maturity.

Applicant Profile

Pierce Law seeks to admit students who will make a contribution to the law school community, to the legal profession, and to society. Admission is based on a whole-person review of each application, including academic ability and aptitude, demonstration of academic success, relevant experience that addresses the school's mission or areas of excellence, leadership, diversity, moral character, community service, and other qualitative personal attributes. Pierce Law values diverse opinions, backgrounds, and perspectives; this enrichment within the classroom and community is core to the educational experience.

George Mason University School of Law

3301 Fairfax Drive MS 1G3
Arlington, VA 22201
Phone: 703.993.8010; Fax: 703.993.8088
E-mail: lawadmit@gmu.edu; Website: www.law.gmu.edu

ABA
Approved
Since
1980

The Basics

Type of school	Public
Term	Semester
Application deadline	4/1
Application fee	$35
Financial aid deadline	3/1
Can first year start other than fall?	No
Student to faculty ratio	13.2 to 1
# of housing spaces available restricted to law students	
graduate housing for which law students are eligible	

Faculty and Administrators

	Total		Men		Women		Minorities	
	Spr	Fall	Spr	Fall	Spr	Fall	Spr	Fall
Full-time	38	39	31	32	7	7	7	6
Other full-time	2	2	0	0	2	2	0	1
Deans, librarians, & others who teach	3	3	3	3	0	0	0	0
Part-time	101	68	74	52	26	16	7	4
Total	144	112	108	87	35	25	14	11

Curriculum

	Full-Time	Part-Time
Typical first-year section size	48	60
Is there typically a "small section" of the first-year class, other than Legal Writing, taught by full-time faculty	No	No
If yes, typical size offered last year		
# of classroom course titles beyond first-year curriculum		133
# of upper division courses, excluding seminars, with an enrollment: Under 25		163
25–49		41
50–74		11
75–99		5
100+		0
# of seminars		34
# of seminar positions available		510
# of seminar positions filled	222	188
# of positions available in simulation courses		330
# of simulation positions filled	161	135
# of positions available in faculty supervised clinical courses		180
# of faculty supervised clinical positions filled	65	20
# involved in field placements	88	8
# involved in law journals	184	23
# involved in moot court or trial competitions	33	13
# of credit hours required to graduate		89

JD Enrollment and Ethnicity

	Men		Women		Full-Time		Part-Time		1st-Year		Total		JD Degs. Awd.
	#	%	#	%	#	%	#	%	#	%	#	%	
African Amer.	8	2.0	10	3.4	12	2.5	6	2.8	1	0.4	18	2.6	4
Amer. Indian	2	0.5	1	0.3	2	0.4	1	0.5	3	1.2	3	0.4	0
Asian Amer.	42	10.3	31	10.7	52	10.8	21	9.7	22	8.9	73	10.5	11
Mex. Amer.	0	0.0	0	0.0	0	0.0	0	0.0	0	0.0	0	0.0	0
Puerto Rican	0	0.0	0	0.0	0	0.0	0	0.0	0	0.0	0	0.0	0
Hispanic	12	3.0	13	4.5	20	4.2	5	2.3	6	2.4	25	3.6	7
Total Minority	64	15.8	55	18.9	86	17.9	33	15.2	32	13.0	119	17.1	22
For. Nation.	5	1.2	4	1.4	8	1.7	1	0.5	4	1.6	9	1.3	4
Caucasian	302	74.4	213	73.2	340	70.8	175	80.6	159	64.4	515	73.9	204
Unknown	35	8.6	19	6.5	46	9.6	8	3.7	52	21.1	54	7.7	0
Total	406	58.2	291	41.8	480	68.9	217	31.1	247	35.4	697		230

Transfers

Transfers in	27
Transfers out	13

Tuition and Fees

	Resident	Nonresident
Full-time	$20,556	$34,220
Part-time	$16,921	$28,145
Tuition Guarantee Program	N	

Living Expenses

Estimated living expenses for singles

Living on campus	Living off campus	Living at home
$15,490	$22,720	$10,500

George Mason University School of Law

ABA
Approved
Since
1980

GPA and LSAT Scores

	Total	Full-Time	Part-Time
# of apps	5,269	4,624	1,787
# of offers	1,300	1,144	156
# of matrics	246	190	56
75% GPA	3.83	3.83	3.81
Median GPA	3.72	3.65	3.72
25% GPA	3.21	3.20	3.25
75% LSAT	165	165	163
Median LSAT	163	163	161
25% LSAT	158	158	157

Grants and Scholarships (from prior year)

	Total		Full-Time		Part-Time	
	#	%	#	%	#	%
Total # of students	672		454		218	
Total # receiving grants	82	12.2	68	15.0	14	6.4
Less than 1/2 tuition	58	8.6	51	11.2	7	3.2
Half to full tuition	21	3.1	14	3.1	7	3.2
Full tuition	0	0.0	0	0.0	0	0.0
More than full tuition	3	0.4	3	0.7	0	0.0
Median grant amount			$8,000		$8,000	

Informational and Library Resources

Total amount spent on library materials	$1,004,760
Study seating capacity inside the library	369
# of full-time equivalent professional librarians	6
Hours per week library is open	98
# of open, wired connections available to students	888
# of networked computers available for use by students	80
Has wireless network?	Y
Require computer?	N

JD Attrition (from prior year)

	Academic	Other	Total	
	#	#	#	%
1st year	2	24	26	16.3
2nd year	1	3	4	1.7
3rd year	1	1	2	1.0
4th year	0	0	0	0.0

Employment (9 months after graduation)

	Total	Percentage
Employment status known	222	99.6
Employment status unknown	1	0.4
Employed	215	96.8
Pursuing graduate degrees	0	0.0
Unemployed (seeking, not seeking, or studying for the bar)	1	0.5
Type of Employment		
# employed in law firms	101	47.0
# employed in business and industry	21	9.8
# employed in government	37	17.2
# employed in public interest	18	8.4
# employed as judicial clerks	27	12.6
# employed in academia	11	5.1
Geographic Location		
# employed in state	92	42.8
# employed in foreign countries	2	0.9
# of states where employed	18	

Bar Passage Rates

First-time takers	183	Reporting %	71.04
Average school %	88.46	Average state %	82.70

Average pass difference 5.76

Jurisdiction	Takers	Passers	Pass %	State %	Diff %
Virginia	130	115	88.46	82.70	5.76

George Mason University School of Law

3301 Fairfax Drive MS 1G3
Arlington, VA 22201
Phone: 703.993.8010; Fax: 703.993.8088
E-mail: lawadmit@gmu.edu; Website: www.law.gmu.edu

■ Introduction

George Mason University School of Law sits on the doorstep of the nation's capital. One of Virginia's public law schools, it was established by authority of the Virginia General Assembly in 1979. By virtue of its unparalleled location, George Mason is able to offer its students numerous opportunities for practical experiences during their law school career.

■ Library and Physical Facilities

In January 1999, the law school relocated to a new, state-of-the-art facility equipped with electrical and data connections at every classroom and library seat, and two ultramodern moot courtrooms.

The school is a member of the library network of the Consortium for Continuing Higher Education in Northern Virginia, affording access to general university and public library collections.

■ Enrollment/Student Body

George Mason University is an equal opportunity/affirmative action institution.

■ Curriculum

George Mason University School of Law offers both full- and part-time divisions. The full-time division operates during the day and takes three years to complete. Students who elect the part-time division study at night and take four years to complete the requirements for the Juris Doctor degree.

George Mason offers an interdisciplinary approach to legal study. A grounding in economics and basic mathematical and financial skills is important to a sophisticated legal education and to the development of a competent attorney. To ensure that George Mason graduates have this grounding, all students take a first-year course in Economic Foundations.

George Mason law students complete a three-year legal writing program, which emphasizes the use of technology and continual practice of skills in the development of actual transactions and cases.

The curriculum begins with exposure to the courses fundamental to a well-rounded legal education. Students at George Mason may also elect to enroll in one of our specialty programs, thus demonstrating depth as well as breadth in their training. All specialties are offered in both the full-time and part-time divisions.

George Mason has a number of programs offering students practical experience: Immigration Law, Public Interest Law, Domestic Relations, Law and Mental Illness, Regulatory Law, the Patent Law, and the Clinic for Legal Assistance to Service Members and the Legal Clinic. As a leader in technology and law, George Mason is the headquarters for the National Center for Technology and Law, which brings together academics, high-tech industry leaders, and policymakers to debate and formulate national policy to keep pace with technological advances. George Mason is also home to the Center for Infrastructure Protection (CIP), a program that fully integrates the disciplines of law, policy, and technology for enhancing the security of cyber networks and economic processes supporting the nation's critical infrastructure.

■ Special Programs

- **Homeland and National Security Law**—enables students interested in specializing in this field to present potential employers (both in government and in the private sector) with a credential that reflects a solid foundation in homeland and national security law.
- **Corporate and Securities Law**—prepares students to work in a variety of fields related to corporate law and financial markets. By developing a thorough understanding of both law and underlying theory, students are prepared to deal with rapidly changing business and legal environments.
- **Regulatory Law**—prepares students for practice in, and before, the numerous agencies that regulate business and other activities. Students are taught economics, the economic analysis of law, administrative law, legislation, lobbying, and negotiation, as well as several substantive areas of regulatory law.
- **International Business**—prepares students for practice in the rapidly changing global business community and provides them with a well-rounded legal education emphasizing analytical and writing skills.
- **Litigation Law**—provides an academic program for students interested in litigation and other dispute resolution processes. This is not a clinical training program. The track courses focus on the processes of dispute resolution and lawyers' roles from an analytical perspective.
- **Intellectual Property Law**—is designed for students having a degree in engineering or one of the physical or biological sciences who intend to practice within the field of intellectual property.
- **Technology Law Program**—combines coursework in the fields of technology law, intellectual property law, and business law. The program prepares students for work in law firms that serve high-technology clients, as in-house counsel for Internet start-up companies, and as attorneys for state and federal regulatory agencies with jurisdiction over technology industries.
- **LLM Programs**—for students wishing to pursue specialized study beyond the JD, George Mason offers two LLM programs: (1) the **LLM in Law and Economics**, and (2) the **LLM in Intellectual Property Law**. Detailed information about these programs is available at *www.law.gmu.edu/academics/llm.html*.
- Additionally, George Mason offers programs in Criminal Law, Legal and Economic Theory, Personal Law, and Tax Law.

■ Admission

Two of the primary factors considered in the admission process are performance on the LSAT and undergraduate grade-point average. Other factors that are considered include difficulty of undergraduate major, undergraduate institution attended, possession of advanced degrees, writing ability, recommendations, extracurricular activities, employment experience, demonstrated commitment to public and community service, leadership skills and

experience, history of overcoming personal or professional challenges, and other academic, personal, and professional achievements.

■ Student Activities

George Mason University provides many services to enhance the law school experience and enable students to take full advantage of the university's educational and personal enrichment opportunities.

Student activities include the *George Mason Law Review; Civil Rights Law Journal;* the *Journal of Law, Economics, and Policy;* the *Journal of International Law;* a prestigious Moot Court program; an active Trial Advocacy program; a newspaper; and numerous law-related organizations. Students have an unparalleled opportunity to gain experience in such varied settings as the Office of the US Attorney for both the District of Columbia and the Eastern District of Virginia, as well as federal courts and agencies, local governments, and private firms. Information about Mason's various student organizations can be found at: *http://law.gmu/students/orgs.*

Diversity Student Services, Academic Support Services, Disability Support Services, and the Office of Veterans Services provide specialized assistance, as does the Counseling Center, where a staff of professionals help students to reach personal, social, and academic goals.

■ Expenses and Financial Aid

George Mason University participates in the Direct Lending Program. There is no deadline for applying for financial aid, but applicants should complete the FAFSA as soon as possible in order to assure the timely award of aid.

In addition to loans available through the Direct Lending Program, George Mason students are eligible for a number of merit-based fellowships.

■ Career Services

The Office of Career, Academic, and Alumni Services aids students and alumni in finding permanent, part-time, and summer jobs by serving as a clearinghouse for information on available positions. It also advises on résumé and interview preparation and coordinates on-campus interviews. More than 150 firms, businesses, and government agencies recruit on campus each year. Graduates find employment in the legal profession throughout the country.

Applicant Profile

George Mason University School of Law
This grid includes only applicants who earned 120–180 LSAT scores under standard administrations.

LSAT Score	3.75 +		3.50–3.74		3.25–3.49		3.00–3.24		2.75–2.99		2.50–2.74		2.25–2.49		2.00–2.24		Below 2.00		No GPA		Total	
	Apps	Adm	Apps	Adm	Apps	Adm	Apps	Adm	Apps	Adm	Apps	Adm	Apps	Adm	Apps	Adm	Apps	Adm	Apps	Adm	Apps	Adm
175–180	3	3	1	1	0	0	3	3	3	1	2	0	0	0	0	0	0	0	0	0	12	8
170–174	13	13	14	13	22	18	13	10	9	5	8	4	6	1	0	0	0	0	0	0	85	64
165–169	93	83	109	94	94	75	74	56	53	35	29	17	11	3	3	0	0	0	4	3	470	366
160–164	251	221	348	107	347	116	243	76	103	17	43	14	17	2	5	1	1	0	34	10	1392	564
155–159	244	184	379	26	336	9	268	10	119	5	63	1	29	1	11	0	3	0	43	0	1495	236
150–154	120	34	201	3	207	0	203	0	120	0	63	0	33	0	11	0	1	0	24	0	983	37
145–149	28	1	73	0	91	0	115	0	91	0	51	0	30	0	6	0	4	0	17	0	506	1
140–144	17	0	29	0	49	0	53	0	42	0	33	0	17	0	7	0	6	0	15	0	268	0
135–139	4	0	10	0	16	0	28	0	27	0	25	0	11	0	7	0	2	0	6	0	136	0
130–134	0	0	1	0	6	0	3	0	13	0	10	0	4	0	5	0	1	0	9	0	52	0
125–129	0	0	0	0	1	0	1	0	0	0	2	0	1	0	2	0	1	0	0	0	8	0
120–124	0	0	0	0	0	0	0	0	0	0	0	0	0	0	0	0	0	0	0	0	0	0
Total	773	539	1165	244	1169	218	1004	155	580	63	329	36	159	7	57	1	19	0	152	13	5407	1276

Apps = Number of Applicants
Adm = Number Admitted
Reflects 99% of the total applicant pool; average LSAT data reported.

This chart is to be used as a general guide only. Every application is reviewed and evaluated in its entirety.

The George Washington University Law School

2000 H Street NW
Washington, DC 20052
Phone: 202.994.7230; Fax: 202.994.3597
E-mail: jdadmit@law.gwu.edu; Website: www.law.gwu.edu

ABA
Approved
Since
1923

The Basics

Type of school	Private
Term	Semester
Application deadline	12/15 3/31
Application fee	$80
Financial aid deadline	5/1
Can first year start other than fall?	No
Student to faculty ratio	14.2 to 1
# of housing spaces available restricted to law students	538
graduate housing for which law students are eligible	390

Faculty and Administrators

	Total		Men		Women		Minorities	
	Spr	Fall	Spr	Fall	Spr	Fall	Spr	Fall
Full-time	78	103	49	57	28	45	11	16
Other full-time	3	2	1	1	2	1	1	0
Deans, librarians, & others who teach	11	10	8	7	3	3	2	2
Part-time	250	177	175	122	75	53	20	22
Total	342	292	233	187	108	102	34	40

Curriculum

	Full-Time	Part-Time
Typical first-year section size	103	127
Is there typically a "small section" of the first-year class, other than Legal Writing, taught by full-time faculty	Yes	No
If yes, typical size offered last year	36	
# of classroom course titles beyond first-year curriculum	213	

# of upper division courses, excluding seminars, with an enrollment:		
Under 25	215	
25–49	74	
50–74	35	
75–99	15	
100+	14	

# of seminars	75	
# of seminar positions available	1,200	
# of seminar positions filled	618	336
# of positions available in simulation courses	1,337	
# of simulation positions filled	784	386
# of positions available in faculty supervised clinical courses	147	
# of faculty supervised clinical positions filled	139	8
# involved in field placements	331	7
# involved in law journals	395	26
# involved in moot court or trial competitions	233	39
# of credit hours required to graduate	84	

JD Enrollment and Ethnicity

	Men		Women		Full-Time		Part-Time		1st-Year		Total		JD Degs. Awd.
	#	%	#	%	#	%	#	%	#	%	#	%	
African Amer.	33	3.5	50	7.3	62	4.7	21	6.9	21	4.0	83	5.1	38
Amer. Indian	5	0.5	8	1.2	11	0.8	2	0.7	4	0.8	13	0.8	5
Asian Amer.	84	8.9	69	10.1	111	8.4	42	13.8	48	9.2	153	9.4	60
Mex. Amer.	0	0.0	0	0.0	0	0.0	0	0.0	0	0.0	0	0.0	0
Puerto Rican	0	0.0	0	0.0	0	0.0	0	0.0	0	0.0	0	0.0	0
Hispanic	54	5.7	44	6.4	85	6.4	13	4.3	27	5.2	98	6.0	33
Total Minority	176	18.6	171	24.9	269	20.3	78	25.7	100	19.2	347	21.3	136
For. Nation.	17	1.8	17	2.5	30	2.3	4	1.3	18	3.5	34	2.1	2
Caucasian	618	65.3	384	56.0	816	61.4	186	61.2	322	61.9	1002	61.4	352
Unknown	135	14.3	114	16.6	213	16.0	36	11.8	80	15.4	249	15.3	63
Total	946	58.0	686	42.0	1328	81.4	304	18.6	520	31.9	1632		553

Transfers

Transfers in	51
Transfers out	24

Tuition and Fees

	Resident	Nonresident
Full-time	$42,205	$42,205
Part-time	$32,648	$32,648
Tuition Guarantee Program	N	

Living Expenses

Estimated living expenses for singles

Living on campus	Living off campus	Living at home
$25,750	$22,700	$22,700

The George Washington University Law School

ABA
Approved
Since
1923

GPA and LSAT Scores

	Total	Full-Time	Part-Time
# of apps	9,592	8,906	686
# of offers	2,145	2,929	116
# of matrics	506	456	50
75% GPA	3.86	3.86	3.83
Median GPA	3.77	3.77	3.53
25% GPA	3.41	3.45	3.16
75% LSAT	168	168	167
Median LSAT	167	167	165
25% LSAT	163	163	162

Grants and Scholarships (from prior year)

	Total		Full-Time		Part-Time	
	#	%	#	%	#	%
Total # of students	1,683		1,398		285	
Total # receiving grants	764	45.4	716	51.2	48	16.8
Less than 1/2 tuition	511	30.4	472	33.8	39	13.7
Half to full tuition	89	5.3	80	5.7	9	3.2
Full tuition	81	4.8	81	5.8	0	0.0
More than full tuition	83	4.9	83	5.9	0	0.0
Median grant amount			$13,000		$8,968	

Informational and Library Resources

Total amount spent on library materials	$2,756,725
Study seating capacity inside the library	637
# of full-time equivalent professional librarians	22
Hours per week library is open	110
# of open, wired connections available to students	54
# of networked computers available for use by students	71
Has wireless network?	Y
Require computer?	Y

JD Attrition (from prior year)

	Academic	Other	Total	
	#	#	#	%
1st year	0	34	34	6.4
2nd year	1	1	2	0.4
3rd year	0	1	1	0.2
4th year	0	0	0	0.0

Employment (9 months after graduation)

	Total	Percentage
Employment status known	528	99.8
Employment status unknown	1	0.2
Employed	514	97.3
Pursuing graduate degrees	8	1.5
Unemployed (seeking, not seeking, or studying for the bar)	5	0.9
Type of Employment		
# employed in law firms	337	65.6
# employed in business and industry	35	6.8
# employed in government	60	11.7
# employed in public interest	21	4.1
# employed as judicial clerks	49	9.5
# employed in academia	11	2.1
Geographic Location		
# employed in state	268	52.1
# employed in foreign countries	5	1.0
# of states where employed	26	

Bar Passage Rates

First-time takers	529	Reporting %	86.01
Average school %	95.18	Average state %	85.29
Average pass difference	9.89		

Jurisdiction	Takers	Passers	Pass %	State %	Diff %
New York	142	135	95.07	88.98	6.09
Virginia	111	103	92.79	82.70	10.09
Maryland	85	81	95.29	85.51	9.78
California	61	58	95.08	78.07	17.01
Others (4)	56	56	100.00		

The George Washington University Law School

2000 H Street NW
Washington, DC 20052
Phone: 202.994.7230; Fax: 202.994.3597
E-mail: jdadmit@law.gwu.edu; Website: www.law.gwu.edu

■ Introduction

Established in 1865, the George Washington University Law School is the oldest law school in the District of Columbia. Its history of academic excellence, significant contributions to legal scholarship, and outstanding record of service to the community have earned GW a position of local, national, and international prominence. Its talented student body is one of the most diverse of any national law school, and its students graduate to become leaders in all areas of practice. While GW has long been recognized as a leader in fields including constitutional law, intellectual property law, international law, environmental law, government procurement, and clinical education, all of the law school's academic programs reflect the demands of a changing profession and the global nature of society and the law.

■ Facilities and Library

The law school complex extends along two sides of the University Yard, the largest open space on GW's urban campus. Its attractive and comfortable classrooms and three moot courtrooms incorporate technology to support a broad range of teaching methods. "Smart podiums" provide access to the Internet and local network, and support videoconferencing. Cameras and microphones allow faculty to teach online in streaming video or record classes for later viewing or listening. Power outlets for notebook computers are provided at each student station in most classrooms. The entire facility is wireless.

More than 600,000 volumes are at the core of the Jacob Burns Law Library's research collection. In addition, the library offers a variety of legal and law-related databases and automated indexes to enhance research capabilities. A staff of 40 full-time and numerous part-time employees administer and maintain the library during its liberal hours of operation and offer information, instruction, and other research support services.

Law students also have full access to the many amenities of the GW campus, including the Lerner Health and Wellness Center, a state-of-the-art complex featuring a wide range of fitness facilities and classes.

■ Curriculum

One of the law school's greatest strengths is the richness and diversity of its curriculum. With more than 250 elective courses and seminars, students have an opportunity to sample a broad array of areas of the law and to tailor their programs to their interests and career aspirations. In addition to traditionally taught classes, the curriculum includes a number of simulation courses that teach skills such as drafting, trial and appellate advocacy, negotiations, mediation, and over a dozen different clinical programs in which students learn skills while working directly with clients.

To teach this extensive curriculum, a dynamic and accessible full-time faculty is joined by distinguished members of the bar and bench who teach some of the more specialized courses on an adjunct basis. Excellence in teaching is highly prized at GW, a fact that is readily apparent from scores and comments on semester course evaluations.

■ Clinical Programs and Public Interest

GW's long-standing commitment to public service has culminated in a wide variety of opportunities for students to serve the community while gaining important practical experience. A nationally recognized clinical program gives students the opportunity to work with real clients—many of whom might otherwise be without representation—while at the same time honing their skills. Clinical programs include civil litigation, consumer mediation, domestic violence advocacy, federal and criminal appeal, environmental law, health rights law, immigration, international human rights, older prisoners, public justice advocacy, small business/community development, and vaccine injury.

A student-faculty public interest committee publicizes and encourages student participation in volunteer legal activities, provides career development programs, and administers the Pro Bono Program, which extends special commendation to students who engage in a certain number of pro bono hours while attending the law school. The law school makes public service a more feasible option for its students by providing special forms of financial assistance in the form of summer subsidies, fellowships for third-year students, and loan reimbursement assistance for recent graduates of the law school.

The law school takes full advantage of its location in the nation's capital through its extensive externship program, which lets students work on a broad range of issues in government agencies, nonprofit organizations, and courts.

■ Joint-Degree and Study-Abroad Programs

Joint degrees are offered in the areas of business, public administration, public health, public policy, international affairs, history, and women's studies.

Summer study-abroad opportunities include the GW-Oxford Program in International Human Rights Law, the GW-Munich Intellectual Property Law Program, and the GW-Augsburg (Germany) Student Exchange Program. GW is also a member of the North American Consortium on Legal Education, which allows students to study at member Canadian and Mexican law schools.

■ Student Activities

Membership is available on seven publications—the *George Washington Law Review*, the *George Washington International Law Review*, the *Environmental Law Journal*, the *Public Contract Law Journal* (cosponsored by the ABA section), the *Federal Circuit Bar Journal*, the *American Intellectual Property Law Quarterly Journal* (published by AIPLA and housed at GW), and the *International Law in Domestic Courts Journal*. Three skills boards—the Moot Court Board, Mock Trial Board, and Alternative Dispute Resolution Board—provide opportunities for participation in inter- and intrascholastic competitions. In addition, approximately 45 student groups are active at the law school, sponsoring social, educational, career, and public interest related programs. Each year, the Enrichment Program hosts a series of distinguished speakers. Recent guests have included

Supreme Court justices, legal scholars, popular authors, and leaders from government and public interest organizations.

■ Career Development

The Career Development Office provides effective career advising services to students and alumni, enabling them to engage in a meaningful job search, to compete as professionals in the employment market, and to make well-informed choices leading to long-term career satisfaction. The CDO offers a broad range of services, including individual counseling, group seminars, substantive legal practice area programs, interviewing programs, job and internship fairs, online job postings, handouts, a career resource library, an alumni career advisor network, a biweekly newsletter, and a comprehensive website.

■ Financial Assistance

The Law Financial Aid Office counsels and assists applicants and current students in applying for various sources of financial aid: federal and commercial loans at negotiated, competitive terms; need-based tuition grants; and outside scholarships. All applicants are considered for merit-based aid. An estimated 85 percent of GW law students receive some sort of financial aid.

The law school's Loan Reimbursement Assistance Program (LRAP) is designed to alleviate the financial burdens of GW law graduates who pursue public interest employment. The LRAP assists qualified graduates by providing "forgivable" loans to those whose annual income—after taking into consideration their annual law school loan payments—falls below a certain target income.

Applicant Profile

The George Washington University Law School
This grid includes only applicants who earned 120–180 LSAT scores under standard administrations.

LSAT Score	GPA 3.75 + Apps	Adm	3.50–3.74 Apps	Adm	3.25–3.49 Apps	Adm	3.00–3.24 Apps	Adm	2.75–2.99 Apps	Adm	2.50–2.74 Apps	Adm	2.25–2.49 Apps	Adm	2.00–2.24 Apps	Adm	Below 2.00 Apps	Adm	No GPA Apps	Adm	Total Apps	Adm
175–180	30	28	19	17	16	15	10	9	7	5	3	1	2	0	1	0	0	0	0	0	88	75
170–174	112	105	115	100	117	101	52	34	24	8	17	10	5	1	1	0	0	0	3	2	446	361
165–169	546	469	666	313	411	156	211	67	81	13	45	9	15	2	2	0	0	0	29	16	2006	1045
160–164	791	375	968	65	685	36	365	22	137	5	55	0	21	0	7	1	0	0	84	12	3113	516
155–159	341	65	558	14	436	10	262	6	103	1	65	0	21	0	7	0	2	0	62	2	1857	98
150–154	146	20	239	7	257	6	218	1	92	0	53	1	32	0	5	0	1	0	34	1	1077	36
145–149	49	0	92	2	117	1	109	0	44	0	46	0	22	0	7	0	2	0	19	0	507	3
140–144	10	0	34	0	40	0	34	0	35	0	23	0	15	0	6	0	3	0	14	0	214	0
135–139	3	0	13	0	19	0	28	0	20	0	19	0	8	0	7	0	0	0	10	0	127	0
130–134	0	0	6	0	2	0	5	0	6	0	7	0	7	0	4	0	1	0	7	0	45	0
125–129	0	0	0	0	0	0	0	0	1	0	6	0	0	0	3	0	0	0	0	0	10	0
120–124	0	0	0	0	0	0	0	0	0	0	0	0	0	0	0	0	1	0	0	0	1	0
Total	2028	1062	2710	518	2100	325	1294	139	550	32	339	21	148	3	50	1	10	0	262	33	9491	2134

Apps = Number of Applicants
Adm = Number Admitted
Reflects 99% of the total applicant pool; average LSAT data reported.

Georgetown University Law Center

600 New Jersey Avenue, NW, Room 589
Washington, DC 20001
Phone: 202.662.9010; Fax: 202.662.9439
E-mail: admis@law.georgetown.edu; Website: www.law.georgetown.edu

ABA
Approved
Since
1924

The Basics

Type of school	Private
Term	Semester
Application deadline	3/1
Application fee	$80
Financial aid deadline	3/1
Can first year start other than fall?	No
Student to faculty ratio	12.4 to 1
# of housing spaces available restricted to law students	291
graduate housing for which law students are eligible	

Faculty and Administrators

	Total		Men		Women		Minorities	
	Spr	Fall	Spr	Fall	Spr	Fall	Spr	Fall
Full-time	123	124	80	78	43	46	12	13
Other full-time	3	3	1	1	2	2	2	2
Deans, librarians, & others who teach	18	18	6	6	12	12	2	2
Part-time	122	122	98	99	24	23	3	6
Total	266	267	185	184	81	83	19	23

Curriculum

		Full-Time	Part-Time
Typical first-year section size		117	129
Is there typically a "small section" of the first-year class, other than Legal Writing, taught by full-time faculty		Yes	Yes
If yes, typical size offered last year		26	35
# of classroom course titles beyond first-year curriculum		407	
# of upper division courses, excluding seminars, with an enrollment:	Under 25	157	
	25–49	76	
	50–74	26	
	75–99	8	
	100+	18	
# of seminars		261	
# of seminar positions available		3,883	
# of seminar positions filled		1,898	948
# of positions available in simulation courses		1,743	
# of simulation positions filled		926	451
# of positions available in faculty supervised clinical courses		307	
# of faculty supervised clinical positions filled		286	0
# involved in field placements		121	6
# involved in law journals		700	56
# involved in moot court or trial competitions		174	3
# of credit hours required to graduate		85	

JD Enrollment and Ethnicity

	Men		Women		Full-Time		Part-Time		1st-Year		Total		JD Degs. Awd.
	#	%	#	%	#	%	#	%	#	%	#	%	
African Amer.	55	5.1	115	12.8	145	8.9	25	7.1	54	9.1	170	8.6	58
Amer. Indian	5	0.5	1	0.1	2	0.1	4	1.1	3	0.5	6	0.3	1
Asian Amer.	83	7.7	94	10.5	146	9.0	31	8.8	36	6.1	177	8.9	60
Mex. Amer.	8	0.7	3	0.3	8	0.5	3	0.8	4	0.7	11	0.6	4
Puerto Rican	1	0.1	0	0.0	0	0.0	1	0.3	1	0.2	1	0.1	4
Hispanic	40	3.7	39	4.3	66	4.1	13	3.7	19	3.2	79	4.0	26
Total Minority	192	17.7	252	28.1	367	22.5	77	21.8	117	19.7	444	22.4	153
For. Nation.	34	3.1	30	3.3	54	3.3	10	2.8	20	3.4	64	3.2	18
Caucasian	791	73.0	538	59.9	1102	67.7	227	64.1	395	66.6	1329	67.1	388
Unknown	67	6.2	78	8.7	105	6.4	40	11.3	61	10.3	145	7.3	117
Total	1084	54.7	898	45.3	1628	82.1	354	17.9	593	29.9	1982		676

Transfers

Transfers in	81
Transfers out	10

Tuition and Fees

	Resident	Nonresident
Full-time	$43,750	$43,750
Part-time	$38,280	$38,280
Tuition Guarantee Program	N	

Living Expenses

Estimated living expenses for singles

Living on campus	Living off campus	Living at home
$22,250	$22,250	$16,275

Georgetown University Law Center

ABA Approved Since 1924

GPA and LSAT Scores

	Total	Full-Time	Part-Time
# of apps	11,653	10,731	922
# of offers	2,645	2,459	186
# of matrics	590	463	127
75% GPA	3.79	3.81	3.78
Median GPA	3.65	3.68	3.62
25% GPA	3.42	3.42	3.42
75% LSAT	171	172	168
Median LSAT	169	170	166
25% LSAT	167	168	163

Grants and Scholarships (from prior year)

	Total #	Total %	Full-Time #	Full-Time %	Part-Time #	Part-Time %
Total # of students	2,005		1,631		374	
Total # receiving grants	616	30.7	610	37.4	6	1.6
Less than 1/2 tuition	413	20.6	407	25.0	6	1.6
Half to full tuition	184	9.2	184	11.3	0	0.0
Full tuition	15	0.7	15	0.9	0	0.0
More than full tuition	4	0.2	4	0.2	0	0.0
Median grant amount			$15,000		$9,730	

Informational and Library Resources

Total amount spent on library materials	$2,960,864
Study seating capacity inside the library	1,083
# of full-time equivalent professional librarians	27
Hours per week library is open	107
# of open, wired connections available to students	840
# of networked computers available for use by students	218
Has wireless network?	Y
Require computer?	Y

JD Attrition (from prior year)

	Academic #	Other #	Total #	Total %
1st year	0	10	10	1.7
2nd year	0	2	2	0.3
3rd year	0	1	1	0.1
4th year	1	1	2	2.6

Employment (9 months after graduation)

	Total	Percentage
Employment status known	637	98.8
Employment status unknown	8	1.2
Employed	612	96.1
Pursuing graduate degrees	8	1.3
Unemployed (seeking, not seeking, or studying for the bar)	13	2.0
Type of Employment		
# employed in law firms	453	74.0
# employed in business and industry	28	4.6
# employed in government	38	6.2
# employed in public interest	33	5.4
# employed as judicial clerks	48	7.8
# employed in academia	7	1.1
Geographic Location		
# employed in state	216	35.3
# employed in foreign countries	12	2.0
# of states where employed	33	

Bar Passage Rates

First-time takers	637	Reporting %	74.88
Average school %	93.72	Average state %	85.85
Average pass difference	7.87		

Jurisdiction	Takers	Passers	Pass %	State %	Diff %
New York	249	241	96.79	88.98	7.81
Maryland	97	88	90.72	85.51	5.21
California	73	65	89.04	78.07	10.97
Virginia	58	53	91.38	82.70	8.68

Georgetown University Law Center

600 New Jersey Avenue, NW, Room 589
Washington, DC 20001
Phone: 202.662.9010; Fax: 202.662.9439
E-mail: admis@law.georgetown.edu; Website: www.law.georgetown.edu

■ Introduction

Georgetown University Law Center, founded in 1870, is a dynamic and diverse intellectual community in which to study law. Its curriculum includes more courses and seminars than any other law school. Its distinguished full-time faculty is the nation's largest and is augmented by the experience and perspective of outstanding members of the bench and bar. The goal is education in its fullest sense—not only mastery of law, but a sense of the philosophical, political, and ethical dimensions of law. Preeminent in the fields of constitutional, international, and tax law, as well as clinical legal education, the Georgetown Law's faculty is also known for its expertise in civil rights, corporate law, environmental law, family law, feminist jurisprudence, health law, human rights, immigration and refugee law, intellectual property law, legal history, and securities law. The Supreme Court, the Congress of the United States, and the Library of Congress are within walking distance of the campus, forming a unique environment for creative legal thought and learning.

■ The Law Center Campus

Georgetown Law's campus is the culmination of a longtime goal to create a campus that will nurture students in mind, body, and spirit. The Hotung building brings all the major components of Georgetown Law's international programs under one roof and includes the John Wolff International and Comparative Law Library. The Sport and Fitness Center features a four-lane lap pool, basketball and racquetball courts, and a café and lounge with wireless network connectivity.

The Law Center's Edward Bennett Williams Law Library houses the fourth largest academic law library collection in the nation. The library also provides students with access to Web-based services providing the most advanced research support available.

Georgetown Law's McDonough Hall, with its lecture halls, seminar rooms, faculty offices, bookstore, student dining area, and lounges, is the academic center of the campus.

Housing for approximately 300 students is available in the Gewirz Student Center. It offers a variety of apartment styles with one, two, and three bedrooms. Apartments designed for students with disabilities are also available.

■ Curriculum

Georgetown Law offers full-time and part-time programs leading to the JD degree. Entry to both programs is in the fall. First-year students in the full-time program choose either the A or B curriculum. Curriculum A is the traditional first-year curriculum, which parallels those at all major law schools, and includes one elective course in the spring semester. Curriculum B includes courses that emphasize the sources of law in history, philosophy, political theory, and economics. It also seeks to reflect the increasingly public nature of contemporary law. A residency of six semesters is required for full-time students and eight semesters for part-time students.

The curriculum includes an innovative program for first-year students titled "Week One: Law in a Global Context." Involving an intensive week of study of complex problems of international and transnational law, the purpose is to deepen students' understanding of how legal problems increasingly transcend national boundaries and involve more than one legal system. Week One also introduces students to Georgetown Law's extensive experiential curriculum, where students may choose from problem-solving, simulation, externship and other experiential learning courses, up to and including our nationally and internationally recognized clinics.

Georgetown Law offers a large and wide-ranging upper-level curriculum. Of the more than 350 courses offered to upper-class students, more than 150 have enrollments under 25 students.

■ Joint Degrees

Georgetown Law offers 12 joint-degree programs: JD/Master of Public Policy; JD/Master of Science in Foreign Service; JD/Master of Arts in Arab Studies; JD/Master of Arts in German and European Studies; JD/Master of Arts in Latin American Studies; JD/Master of Arts in Russian and East European Studies; JD/Master of Arts in Security Studies; JD/Master of Business Administration; JD/Master of Public Health (with Johns Hopkins School of Public Health); JD/Master of Arts or Doctorate in Philosophy; JD/Doctorate in Government; and the JD/LLM in Taxation.

■ Transnational, International, and Comparative Law Programs

Georgetown Law has many highly regarded programs dealing with different aspects of cross-border law.

The Global Law Scholars Program, which combines language skills with directed legal training, provides an opportunity for a limited number of full-time JD students to prepare for a law practice involving more than one legal system.

Georgetown Law's Institute of International Economic Law awards a certificate in World Trade Organization studies to students who fulfill special course requirements. The Law Center's International Summer Internship Program offers students opportunities to work abroad in law firms, corporations, and government organizations. Students have the unique opportunity to study for a semester in London at Georgetown Law's own Center for Transnational Legal studies, a partnership of 20 leading schools from five continents. Georgetown Law also offers a summer law program in London with distinguished professors from Europe and the US, as well as the opportunity to study abroad for a semester at prestigious institutions in Europe, Asia, India, Israel, Latin America, and Australia.

■ Clinical Programs and Public Interest Law

Georgetown Law, a pioneer in clinical legal education, offers an unmatched clinical program. Our 12 clinics offer approximately 300 students per year an opportunity to enroll in clinics where (1) they represent clients in court or in administrative hearings, or (2) they work in a nontrial context in federal and local agencies, schools, and other institutions.

Georgetown Law's unparalleled public interest offerings include a loan repayment assistance program, a stand-alone

public interest career office, guaranteed summer funding for public interest and government internships, a comprehensive student pro bono program, an extensive and diverse public interest curriculum, and a public interest scholarship program. The Office of Public Interest and Community Service (OPICS) houses a public interest resource library, provides specialist career advising on government and nonprofit internships and employment, oversees student and student group volunteer activities, and serves as the student liaison to the faculty and administration.

■ Admission

Georgetown Law evaluates candidates on two scales: academic or objective criteria and personal criteria. Academic information includes undergraduate and graduate records and LSAT scores. Personal factors include extracurricular activities, recommendations, work experience, and diversity of background. Georgetown Law does not use numerical cutoffs. Early application is encouraged since Georgetown Law employs a rolling admission process.

■ Student Activities

Students edit and publish 11 scholarly journals. The *Law Weekly*, the school newspaper, is printed under student direction. The Barristers Council is responsible for the many appellate advocacy, mock trial, and alternative dispute resolution programs. Students participate in the decision processes of the Law Center through the Student Bar Association and student/faculty committees. Over 70 law student organizations support personal, social, and professional interests.

■ Financial Aid

Georgetown Law offers need-based, three-year financial aid grants to approximately one-third of the entering full-time class. Federal and commercial loans, along with on- and off-campus work-study opportunities, are available. Approximately 87 percent of Georgetown Law's JD students obtain financial aid.

Acknowledged as one of the nation's top programs by Equal Justice Works, Georgetown Law's Loan Repayment Assistance Program assists JD graduates in pursuing careers in public service.

■ Career Services

The Office of Career Services offers a wide range of career counseling and related programming. First-year students are assigned a section advisor who works individually with them throughout law school. The fall recruiting program is one of the largest in the country, and OCS sponsors a robust judicial clerkship application process.

Applicant Profile

Since the Georgetown Law Admissions Committee takes into consideration a number of factors in evaluating whether a candidate would be suitable for admission, we cannot provide an applicant profile based solely on GPA and LSAT scores. In making such determinations, the Committee focuses on various aspects of a candidate's background and experience that, in combination with academic record and LSAT scores, give insight into a candidate's suitability for admission.

University of Georgia School of Law

Harold Hirsch Hall, 225 Herty Drive
Athens, GA 30602-6012
Phone: 706.542.7060; Fax: 706.542.5556
E-mail: ugajd@uga.edu; Website: www.law.uga.edu

ABA
Approved
Since
1930

Section of Legal Education
and Admissions to the Bar

The Basics

Type of school	Public
Term	Semester
Application deadline	3/1
Application fee	$50
Financial aid deadline	3/1
Can first year start other than fall?	No
Student to faculty ratio	12.2 to 1
# of housing spaces available restricted to law students	
graduate housing for which law students are eligible	710

Faculty and Administrators

	Total		Men		Women		Minorities	
	Spr	Fall	Spr	Fall	Spr	Fall	Spr	Fall
Full-time	49	45	32	29	17	16	6	5
Other full-time	5	6	1	1	4	5	1	0
Deans, librarians, & others who teach	6	6	3	3	3	3	0	0
Part-time	20	14	15	12	5	2	1	1
Total	80	71	51	45	29	26	8	6

Curriculum

		Full-Time	Part-Time
Typical first-year section size		80	0
Is there typically a "small section" of the first-year class, other than Legal Writing, taught by full-time faculty		No	No
If yes, typical size offered last year			
# of classroom course titles beyond first-year curriculum		124	
# of upper division courses, excluding seminars, with an enrollment:	Under 25	89	
	25–49	32	
	50–74	17	
	75–99	9	
	100+	0	
# of seminars		33	
# of seminar positions available		594	
# of seminar positions filled		561	0
# of positions available in simulation courses		370	
# of simulation positions filled		355	0
# of positions available in faculty supervised clinical courses		415	
# of faculty supervised clinical positions filled		400	0
# involved in field placements		185	0
# involved in law journals		209	0
# involved in moot court or trial competitions		369	0
# of credit hours required to graduate		88	

JD Enrollment and Ethnicity

	Men		Women		Full-Time		Part-Time		1st-Year		Total		JD Degs. Awd.
	#	%	#	%	#	%	#	%	#	%	#	%	
African Amer.	24	6.6	59	17.9	83	12.0	0	0.0	28	11.6	83	12.0	28
Amer. Indian	1	0.3	0	0.0	1	0.1	0	0.0	1	0.4	1	0.1	0
Asian Amer.	17	4.7	14	4.3	31	4.5	0	0.0	9	3.7	31	4.5	10
Mex. Amer.	0	0.0	0	0.0	0	0.0	0	0.0	0	0.0	0	0.0	0
Puerto Rican	0	0.0	0	0.0	0	0.0	0	0.0	0	0.0	0	0.0	0
Hispanic	5	1.4	4	1.2	9	1.3	0	0.0	3	1.2	9	1.3	5
Total Minority	47	12.9	77	23.4	124	17.9	0	0.0	41	16.9	124	17.9	43
For. Nation.	2	0.5	0	0.0	2	0.3	0	0.0	0	0.0	2	0.3	4
Caucasian	258	70.7	205	62.3	463	66.7	0	0.0	163	67.4	463	66.7	125
Unknown	58	15.9	47	14.3	105	15.1	0	0.0	38	15.7	105	15.1	40
Total	365	52.6	329	47.4	694	100.0	0	0.0	242	34.9	694		212

Transfers

Transfers in	18
Transfers out	1

Tuition and Fees

	Resident	Nonresident
Full-time	$14,448	$30,226
Part-time		
Tuition Guarantee Program		N

Living Expenses

Estimated living expenses for singles

Living on campus	Living off campus	Living at home
$12,016	$15,320	$9,630

University of Georgia School of Law

ABA
Approved
Since
1930

GPA and LSAT Scores

	Total	Full-Time	Part-Time
# of apps	3,076	3,076	0
# of offers	857	857	0
# of matrics	241	241	0
75% GPA	3.80	3.80	0.00
Median GPA	3.70	3.70	0.00
25% GPA	3.40	3.40	0.00
75% LSAT	165	165	0
Median LSAT	164	164	0
25% LSAT	161	161	0

Grants and Scholarships (from prior year)

	Total #	Total %	Full-Time #	Full-Time %	Part-Time #	Part-Time %
Total # of students	660		660		0	
Total # receiving grants	423	64.1	423	64.1	0	0.0
Less than 1/2 tuition	251	38.0	251	38.0	0	0.0
Half to full tuition	165	25.0	165	25.0	0	0.0
Full tuition	6	0.9	6	0.9	0	0.0
More than full tuition	1	0.2	1	0.2	0	0.0
Median grant amount		$5,000		$0		

Informational and Library Resources

Total amount spent on library materials	$1,532,407
Study seating capacity inside the library	433
# of full-time equivalent professional librarians	8
Hours per week library is open	121
# of open, wired connections available to students	0
# of networked computers available for use by students	34
Has wireless network?	Y
Require computer?	N

JD Attrition (from prior year)

	Academic #	Other #	Total #	Total %
1st year	1	7	8	3.5
2nd year	0	2	2	0.9
3rd year	0	0	0	0.0
4th year	0	0	0	0.0

Employment (9 months after graduation)

	Total	Percentage
Employment status known	200	98.5
Employment status unknown	3	1.5
Employed	193	96.5
Pursuing graduate degrees	6	3.0
Unemployed (seeking, not seeking, or studying for the bar)	1	0.5
Type of Employment		
# employed in law firms	111	57.5
# employed in business and industry	14	7.3
# employed in government	22	11.4
# employed in public interest	11	5.7
# employed as judicial clerks	33	17.1
# employed in academia	2	1.0
Geographic Location		
# employed in state	148	76.7
# employed in foreign countries	1	0.5
# of states where employed	18	

Bar Passage Rates

First-time takers	174	Reporting %	100.00
Average school %	98.85	Average state %	88.83
Average pass difference	10.02		

Jurisdiction	Takers	Passers	Pass %	State %	Diff %
Georgia	163	161	98.77	89.27	9.50
North Carolina	6	6	100.00	82.61	17.39
South Carolina	5	5	100.00	81.83	18.17

University of Georgia School of Law

Harold Hirsch Hall, 225 Herty Drive
Athens, GA 30602-6012
Phone: 706.542.7060; Fax: 706.542.5556
E-mail: ugajd@uga.edu; Website: www.law.uga.edu

■ Introduction

The University of Georgia School of Law (Georgia Law), founded in 1859, is on the campus of the University of Georgia in Athens, Georgia. The university provides an excellent setting for the study of law with superb libraries and outstanding academic, cultural, recreational, and social opportunities. Athens, a town of 100,000, is the commercial and legal center for northeast Georgia and is approximately one hour from downtown Atlanta. Athens also features a cultural richness ranging from antebellum homes to the latest in the alternative music scene.

The School of Law is approved by the ABA, is a member of the AALS, and has a chapter of the Order of the Coif.

■ The Student Body

The law school student body shares a strong sense of community, and the school prides itself on the collegiality among students, faculty, and staff. The entering class usually numbers in the low 200s, and the entire student body, including LLM students, averages 650 students. The law school is also a vital part of the university community, which supports a cosmopolitan mix of over 33,000 undergraduate, graduate, and professional students. Many law students take advantage of these assets by taking courses in other schools and colleges of the university and by participating in the intellectual and social life of the campus.

■ Curriculum

The law curriculum is rich and diverse. The first year of study consists of required core courses; after its completion, students may choose from a wealth of classes, seminars, and clinical programs to suit their interests.

Clinical program opportunities, both criminal and civil, abound. Clinical education expands upon the classroom knowledge by providing essential experiential learning. Students interested in criminal law can participate in the Prosecutorial Clinic, the Criminal Defense Clinic, or the Capital Assistance Project. Students interested in environmental law, family law, public interest law, and any of a number of other areas of study will find that the Civil Externship Clinic, Family Violence Clinic, Land Use Clinic, Mediation Practicum, Public Interest Practicum, Environmental Law Practicum, and the Special Education Practicum add to their understanding and preparedness.

■ Faculty

While some law schools choose to emphasize either scholarship or teaching, the University of Georgia seeks a balance of the two, firmly believing that classroom teaching is enhanced by scholarly expertise. The college town setting fosters student-faculty interaction by increasing faculty availability and promoting a conducive atmosphere for dialogue.

The faculty includes authors of some of our country's leading legal scholarship, recipients of the university's highest honors for teaching excellence, Fulbright Scholars, and former law clerks for the US Supreme Court and appellate courts. Most bring practical experience to the classroom as well; they have been trial and corporate attorneys, and many continue to accept pro bono cases or serve as consultants.

Faculty expertise is expanded by the addition of outstanding adjuncts, attorneys from the region's most powerful firms, international attorneys, government leaders, and prominent practitioners. In addition, the law school's Dean Rusk Center—International, Comparative, and Graduate Legal Studies annually is host to several international scholars who may teach mini-courses in their areas of interest. Recent courses include international human rights, dispute settlement in the World Trade Organization, and EC competition law.

■ Educational Enrichment Programs

University of Georgia law students have several opportunities to expand their educational horizons. First, joint programs with other schools and colleges in the university enable students to complete two degrees in less time than it would take to pursue them separately. Existing joint programs include JD/MBA (business administration), JD/MPA (public administration), JD/MHP (historic preservation), JD/MSW (social work), and JD/MEd in Sports Studies.

Students may also take graduate coursework in other schools and colleges of the university and have it count as elective credit toward the 88 semester hours required for graduation. For example, students interested in tax law might take courses in the school of accounting, and students interested in public policy might take courses in the School of Public and International Affairs. Finally, those who are not interested in the joint-degree programs but want more coursework than can be satisfied by elective credit may pursue other advanced degrees at the same time they are fulfilling the requirements for the law degree.

■ Study Abroad

Nothing helps one to better understand the culture of another country than actually studying and living in a foreign land. At Georgia Law, this concept is fully embraced. Several opportunities for legal study and work experience in other parts of the world are provided on an annual basis. They include:

Georgia Law at Oxford—This exciting 15-week program runs from January through April and is one of the few semester-long study-abroad programs offered by an American law school. Selected second- and third-year law students take four courses and receive 12 semester hours of credit.

Global Internship Program—Established in 2001, this initiative provides students with six to ten weeks of study or work experience in one of more than 25 countries spanning the world. Each participant receives funding from the law school to help offset travel and living costs.

Brussels Seminar on the Law and Institutions of the European Union—For more than three decades, Georgia Law has participated in this seminar, a three-week intensive course on EU law held at the Institut d'Etudes Européennes of the Université Libre de Bruxelles. Georgia Law students received partial tuition scholarships in the summer of 2008.

Georgia Law Summer Program in China—Partnering with Tsinghua University in Beijing and Fudan University in

Shanghai, this three-week study-abroad program in China's two largest cities offers an introduction to the Chinese legal system with an emphasis on commercial and trade law. There is the potential for Georgia Law students to remain in the country at the end of the program for a four- to six-week internship in one of several law firms. Georgia Law students received partial tuition scholarships in the summer of 2008.

Equal Justice Foundation Fellowships—These awards provide grants to law students who engage in public interest legal work in positions that otherwise would not be funded. Recently, EJF fellowship recipients have used their funds to gain international experience and aid foreign causes.

■ Library and Physical Facilities

The law library's vast collection makes it among the largest in legal education. While it has extensive holdings in international law, it focuses on being a functional library serving the needs of students. The university's main library is adjacent to the law school and is one of the largest research libraries in the nation.

The law school is headquartered in Hirsch Hall on the northern edge of the campus, the most scenic and historic section of the university. Dean Rusk Hall, adjacent to Hirsch Hall, provides additional classroom and office space. The majority of clinical settings are just a short walk away in the downtown area.

■ Career Services

The law school offers a fully staffed career services office that assists law students and graduates. Placement rates are among the highest in the nation, and a very high percentage of students work as summer associates around the country prior to beginning the second and third years of study. The career services website is a comprehensive source of information.

Alumni practice in 47 states and over 50 countries. Employers from all 50 states and 25 countries have utilized the Legal Career Services Office to target Georgia Law students for summer and full-time employment.

■ Advocacy Programs

Georgia Law's accomplished Moot Court and Mock Trial programs focus on developing critical oral and written advocacy skills. Team members learn how to write persuasively and how to make convincing oral presentations that will withstand intense scrutiny by the court. Through this incredible practical learning experience, Georgia Law students become powerful advocates.

Georgia Law's Moot Court and Mock Trial programs have won 6 national titles, 15 regional crowns and 5 state trophies in the last 6 years.

■ Student Publications

Students at Georgia Law publish three highly regarded legal journals: the *Georgia Law Review*, the *Georgia Journal of International and Comparative Law*, and the *Journal of Intellectual Property Law*, a nationally recognized IP specialty journal. The journals, which are frequently cited by federal and state courts, textbooks, treatises, and other law reviews, follow the customary format, with articles from leading scholars and practitioners comprising the bulk of the content and another section consisting of student notes.

Applicant Profile

University of Georgia School of Law
This grid includes only applicants who earned 120–180 LSAT scores under standard administrations.

LSAT Score	3.75 +		3.50–3.74		3.25–3.49		3.00–3.24		2.75–2.99		2.50–2.74		2.25–2.49		2.00–2.24		Below 2.00		No GPA		Total	
	Apps	Adm	Apps	Adm	Apps	Adm	Apps	Adm	Apps	Adm	Apps	Adm	Apps	Adm	Apps	Adm	Apps	Adm	Apps	Adm	Apps	Adm
175–180	4	4	2	2	1	1	0	0	1	1	1	0	0	0	0	0	0	0	0	0	9	8
170–174	30	29	15	14	9	8	7	5	2	2	1	0	0	0	0	0	0	0	0	0	64	58
165–169	118	116	110	108	47	43	20	19	17	15	5	3	1	0	1	0	0	0	4	4	323	308
160–164	289	171	226	103	151	53	85	28	36	5	12	2	2	0	3	0	0	0	14	2	818	364
155–159	243	29	246	21	165	6	110	8	47	0	24	0	13	0	3	0	1	0	16	0	868	64
150–154	92	14	112	16	126	11	74	2	38	0	19	0	11	0	1	0	1	0	6	0	480	43
145–149	26	3	35	2	56	1	49	1	35	0	17	0	6	0	4	0	1	0	9	0	238	7
140–144	8	2	25	0	38	0	32	0	18	0	10	0	6	0	3	0	0	0	4	0	144	2
135–139	2	0	2	0	8	0	8	0	10	0	8	0	6	0	2	0	2	0	0	0	48	0
130–134	0	0	1	0	0	0	2	0	7	0	2	0	3	0	1	0	0	0	2	0	18	0
125–129	0	0	0	0	1	0	3	0	1	0	0	0	0	0	0	0	0	0	0	0	5	0
120–124	0	0	0	0	0	0	0	0	1	0	0	0	0	0	0	0	0	0	0	0	1	0
Total	812	368	774	266	602	123	390	63	213	23	99	5	48	0	18	0	5	0	55	6	3016	854

Apps = Number of Applicants   Adm = Number Admitted   Reflects 100% of the total applicant pool; average LSAT data reported.

Georgia State University College of Law

PO Box 4037
Atlanta, GA 30302-4037
Phone: 404.413.9000; Fax: 404.413.9225
E-mail: admissions@gsulaw2.gsu.edu; Website: http://law.gsu.edu

ABA Approved Since 1984

The Basics

Type of school	Public
Term	Semester
Application deadline	3/15
Application fee	$50
Financial aid deadline	4/1
Can first year start other than fall?	No
Student to faculty ratio	10.7 to 1
# of housing spaces available restricted to law students	
graduate housing for which law students are eligible	650

Faculty and Administrators

	Total		Men		Women		Minorities	
	Spr	Fall	Spr	Fall	Spr	Fall	Spr	Fall
Full-time	46	46	27	26	19	20	6	7
Other full-time	8	8	2	2	6	6	0	0
Deans, librarians, & others who teach	9	9	5	5	4	4	4	4
Part-time	35	12	25	7	10	5	3	4
Total	98	75	59	40	39	35	13	15

Curriculum

		Full-Time	Part-Time
Typical first-year section size		70	70
Is there typically a "small section" of the first-year class, other than Legal Writing, taught by full-time faculty		No	No
If yes, typical size offered last year			
# of classroom course titles beyond first-year curriculum		112	
# of upper division courses, excluding seminars, with an enrollment:	Under 25	94	
	25–49	34	
	50–74	14	
	75–99	2	
	100+	0	
# of seminars		30	
# of seminar positions available		435	
# of seminar positions filled		346	0
# of positions available in simulation courses		240	
# of simulation positions filled		238	0
# of positions available in faculty supervised clinical courses		115	
# of faculty supervised clinical positions filled		71	0
# involved in field placements		139	0
# involved in law journals		60	0
# involved in moot court or trial competitions		74	0
# of credit hours required to graduate		90	

JD Enrollment and Ethnicity

	Men		Women		Full-Time		Part-Time		1st-Year		Total		JD Degs. Awd.
	#	%	#	%	#	%	#	%	#	%	#	%	
African Amer.	28	7.9	33	10.4	37	7.7	24	12.4	20	9.4	61	9.1	26
Amer. Indian	2	0.6	2	0.6	3	0.6	1	0.5	0	0.0	4	0.6	0
Asian Amer.	21	5.9	29	9.1	39	8.1	11	5.7	17	8.0	50	7.4	6
Mex. Amer.	0	0.0	0	0.0	0	0.0	0	0.0	0	0.0	0	0.0	0
Puerto Rican	0	0.0	0	0.0	0	0.0	0	0.0	0	0.0	0	0.0	0
Hispanic	10	2.8	7	2.2	11	2.3	6	3.1	2	0.9	17	2.5	2
Total Minority	61	17.2	71	22.3	90	18.8	42	21.8	39	18.4	132	19.6	34
For. Nation.	0	0.0	0	0.0	0	0.0	0	0.0	0	0.0	0	0.0	0
Caucasian	250	70.4	221	69.5	338	70.4	133	68.9	156	73.6	471	70.0	122
Unknown	44	12.4	26	8.2	52	10.8	18	9.3	17	8.0	70	10.4	26
Total	355	52.7	318	47.3	480	71.3	193	28.7	212	31.5	673		182

Transfers

Transfers in	12
Transfers out	2

Tuition and Fees

	Resident	Nonresident
Full-time	$11,838	$32,862
Part-time	$10,980	$25,032
Tuition Guarantee Program	Y	

Living Expenses

Estimated living expenses for singles

Living on campus	Living off campus	Living at home
$15,226	$14,515	$7,810

Georgia State University College of Law

ABA
Approved
Since
1984

GPA and LSAT Scores

	Total	Full-Time	Part-Time
# of apps	0	2,493	321
# of offers	491	410	81
# of matrics	217	168	49
75% GPA	3.78	3.80	3.73
Median GPA	3.60	3.60	3.52
25% GPA	3.20	3.20	3.10
75% LSAT	162	162	161
Median LSAT	161	161	159
25% LSAT	159	159	158

Grants and Scholarships (from prior year)

	Total		Full-Time		Part-Time	
	#	%	#	%	#	%
Total # of students	665		472		193	
Total # receiving grants	142	21.4	98	20.8	44	22.8
Less than 1/2 tuition	74	11.1	48	10.2	26	13.5
Half to full tuition	4	0.6	4	0.8	0	0.0
Full tuition	64	9.6	46	9.7	18	9.3
More than full tuition	0	0.0	0	0.0	0	0.0
Median grant amount			$2,500		$2,500	

Informational and Library Resources

Total amount spent on library materials	$942,299
Study seating capacity inside the library	335
# of full-time equivalent professional librarians	15
Hours per week library is open	103
# of open, wired connections available to students	926
# of networked computers available for use by students	141
Has wireless network?	Y
Require computer?	N

JD Attrition (from prior year)

	Academic	Other	Total	
	#	#	#	%
1st year	3	13	16	7.7
2nd year	0	2	2	0.9
3rd year	0	0	0	0.0
4th year	0	0	0	0.0

Employment (9 months after graduation)

	Total	Percentage
Employment status known	182	98.9
Employment status unknown	2	1.1
Employed	177	97.3
Pursuing graduate degrees	3	1.6
Unemployed (seeking, not seeking, or studying for the bar)	1	0.5
Type of Employment		
# employed in law firms	99	55.9
# employed in business and industry	32	18.1
# employed in government	17	9.6
# employed in public interest	11	6.2
# employed as judicial clerks	6	3.4
# employed in academia	7	4.0
Geographic Location		
# employed in state	160	90.4
# employed in foreign countries	1	0.6
# of states where employed	9	

Bar Passage Rates

First-time takers	172	Reporting %	100.00
Average school %	94.19	Average state %	89.27
Average pass difference	4.92		

Jurisdiction	Takers	Passers	Pass %	State %	Diff %
Georgia	172	162	94.19	89.27	4.92

Georgia State University College of Law

PO Box 4037
Atlanta, GA 30302-4037
Phone: 404.413.9000; Fax: 404.413.9225
E-mail: admissions@gsulaw2.gsu.edu; Website: http://law.gsu.edu

■ Introduction

Georgia State University College of Law is located in downtown Atlanta, the center for legal, financial, and governmental activities in the Southeast. This location provides easy access to federal, state, and local courts and agencies; the state capital and legislature; corporations; major law firms in the metropolitan area; and the library and other facilities of Georgia State University.

The College of Law began operation in 1982. The College of Law is accredited by the ABA and is a member of the AALS.

■ Library and Physical Facilities

The College of Law library is designed and equipped to meet the demanding research needs of today's students, faculty members, staff, and members of the legal community. With a collection of more than 163,404 hard-copy volumes and more than 191,256 microform-equivalent volumes, the library provides research materials in American, British, Canadian, and international law. Students find a host of computer applications available in the law library computer lab, which is staffed by computer consultants. The college dedicates state-of-the-art computer equipment for training purposes only in our computer training room. The classrooms and study carrels accommodate laptop computers.

The College of Law is one of the leading law schools in the Southeast. Located on a 39-acre campus in the heart of downtown Atlanta, the building houses a moot courtroom equipped with state-of-the-art video technology and provides activities directed toward trial and appellate advocacy. Students have access to many other campus facilities, including the athletic complex, which offers a variety of individual fitness opportunities and team sports.

■ Curriculum

The college offers students the opportunity to study full or part time and provides a traditional yet innovative curriculum. It offers extensive coverage of the foundational areas of the law to first-year students while providing an array of elective opportunities in public and private law. Opportunities range from the study of legal philosophy and jurisprudence to vital skills training through courses in litigation, counseling, negotiation, legal drafting, and alternative dispute resolution.

The growth of technology in our lives is reflected in courses in Intellectual Property and Computers and the Law; in our innovative course, Law and the Internet; and in the increasing use of computer programs and online discussion groups. Opportunities exist for in-depth study in international and comparative law, environmental law, health law, tax law, employment law, commercial law, and bankruptcy.

■ Admission

The College of Law actively seeks to enroll a student body with diversity in educational, cultural, and racial backgrounds that will enrich the educational experience of the entire group.

Applicants are encouraged to visit. Please make arrangements through the Office of Admissions to tour the campus; talk with students, faculty, and admissions staff; or attend a class.

■ Special Programs

Joint-Degree Programs—Six joint JD and master's degree programs are available with Georgia State University's J. Mack Robinson College of Business, the Andrew Young School of Policy Studies, the Department of Philosophy in the College of Arts and Sciences, and the College of Architecture at the Georgia Institute of Technology.

International Programs—Students have the opportunity to participate in two summer-abroad programs. These are the Transnational Comparative Dispute Resolution Program in Europe and the Summer Legal and Policy Study Program in comparative and international law in Brazil.

Clinics—The Low-Income Taxpayer Clinic and the Health Law Partnership (HeLP) Clinic provide a live-client component to the college's Lawyer Skills Externship Development Program. Both clinics give students hands-on, real-life experience in client representation and handling cases. Work in the Tax Clinic teaches case management, evidence gathering, document preparation, interviewing, counseling, and effective negotiation. The Health Law Partnership Clinic offers a community service clinic that provides students with opportunities to work on cases related to children's health and welfare, including clinics on site at three Atlanta-area children's hospitals where low-income children and their families are eligible for these services aimed at eliminating socioeconomic barriers to optimum health.

Externships—Externships are designed to tie theoretical knowledge to a practical base of experience in the profession. Externships involve actual participation in rendering legal services. Students interested in the externship program should contact the Lawyer Skills Development Externship Office.

Trial Advocacy—The College of Law offers students an extensive variety of opportunities in the area of trial advocacy. Our litigation workshop, offered each spring semester, provides second-year students with an intensive skills training experience. Working in small seminar groups, students are asked to conduct drafting and simulation exercises on all phases of the pretrial and trial process, including a full jury trial. In addition to the workshop, the college offers several advanced litigation courses in which students can further enhance their advocacy skills in civil and criminal areas.

Moot Court—Each year, students compete in several of the most challenging and prestigious moot court competitions throughout the country. The Moot Court Program has achieved substantial renown and success in its 27-year history. The National Moot Court Competition, sponsored by the Association of the Bar of the City of New York, is the oldest and most recognized national competition, and the College of Law became the first law school in Georgia to place first in that competition. Teams from the college have since won numerous other competitions.

Centers—The College of Law has two centers: the Center for Law, Health, and Society and the Center for the Comparative Study of Metropolitan Growth. The Center for

Georgia State University College of Law

Law, Health, and Society promotes the integration of health law and ethics into (1) health policy and research, (2) the health sciences, (3) the provision of health services, and (4) the interdisciplinary education of law students. The Center for the Comparative Study of Metropolitan Growth produces research, teaching, and academic exchange on the range of issues relating to metropolitan growth.

■ Student Activities

The *Georgia State University Law Review* is published four times a year by students who have demonstrated outstanding writing and academic skills.

The college also boasts a nationally renowned student mock trial program in which our students compete annually in numerous mock trial competitions held at locations throughout the country. Our student teams have amassed an incredible record of success at the national, regional, and state levels. The College of Law has won four national championships, competed in five national finals, and won eight regional and several state championships.

The College of Law regards student organizations as an important part of a legal education experience and encourages participation in our wide variety of organizations, some traditionally found in law schools, some less common. The college recognizes 30 organizations, most of which are affiliated with national professional associations. We are proud of the accomplishments of these groups.

■ Career Services

The Career Services Office offers a broad range of services. Students may begin using the office in November of the first year of law school and may continue utilizing career planning services throughout their careers. Specific programs geared toward minority students are the Atlanta Bar Association Minority Clerkship Program and the Southeastern Minority Job Fair. Typically, over 95 percent of each graduating class accepts employment within six months of graduation.

Applicant Profile

Georgia State University College of Law
This grid includes only applicants who earned 120–180 LSAT scores under standard administrations.

LSAT Score	3.75 +		3.50–3.74		3.25–3.49		3.00–3.24		2.75–2.99		2.50–2.74		Below 2.50		No GPA		Total	
	Apps	Adm	Apps	Adm	Apps	Adm	Apps	Adm	Apps	Adm	Apps	Adm	Apps	Adm	Apps	Adm	Apps	Adm
170–180	0	0	0	0	4	4	1	1	2	1	1	1	3	0	0	0	11	7
165–169	6	6	7	6	11	8	7	5	10	6	4	3	3	0	1	1	49	35
160–164	56	53	67	59	66	56	57	50	32	18	13	4	6	2	3	1	300	243
155–159	84	51	141	79	158	70	126	43	58	14	36	6	23	5	8	4	634	272
150–154	59	10	126	17	162	7	137	11	88	2	35	0	27	0	9	2	643	49
145–149	34	0	69	0	98	1	107	0	71	1	53	0	33	0	12	0	477	2
140–144	7	0	42	0	80	0	70	0	62	0	54	0	44	0	13	0	372	0
Below 140	8	0	18	0	30	0	51	0	50	0	50	0	72	0	13	0	292	0
Total	254	120	470	161	609	146	556	110	373	42	246	14	211	7	59	8	2778	608

Apps = Number of Applicants
Adm = Number Admitted
Reflects 99% of the total applicant pool; average LSAT data reported.

Golden Gate University School of Law

536 Mission Street, Office of Admissions
San Francisco, CA 94105-2968
Phone: 415.442.6630 or 800.GGU.4YOU; Fax: 415.442.6631
E-mail: lawadmit@ggu.edu; Website: www.ggu.edu/law

ABA
Approved
Since
1956

The Basics

Type of school	Private
Term	Semester
Application deadline	4/1 6/1
Application fee	$60
Financial aid deadline	
Can first year start other than fall?	No
Student to faculty ratio	15.2 to 1
# of housing spaces available restricted to law students	
graduate housing for which law students are eligible	

Faculty and Administrators

	Total		Men		Women		Minorities	
	Spr	Fall	Spr	Fall	Spr	Fall	Spr	Fall
Full-time	30	34	17	20	13	14	6	7
Other full-time	2	3	0	0	2	3	0	0
Deans, librarians, & others who teach	9	8	3	2	6	6	0	0
Part-time	76	63	42	32	34	31	10	9
Total	117	108	62	54	55	54	16	16

Curriculum

	Full-Time	Part-Time
Typical first-year section size	70	46
Is there typically a "small section" of the first-year class, other than Legal Writing, taught by full-time faculty	No	No
If yes, typical size offered last year		
# of classroom course titles beyond first-year curriculum	122	
# of upper division courses, excluding seminars, with an enrollment: Under 25	172	
25–49	40	
50–74	9	
75–99	3	
100+	0	
# of seminars	18	
# of seminar positions available	325	
# of seminar positions filled	130	24
# of positions available in simulation courses	531	
# of simulation positions filled	369	47
# of positions available in faculty supervised clinical courses	135	
# of faculty supervised clinical positions filled	74	5
# involved in field placements	198	9
# involved in law journals	87	9
# involved in moot court or trial competitions	70	5
# of credit hours required to graduate	88	

JD Enrollment and Ethnicity

	Men		Women		Full-Time		Part-Time		1st-Year		Total		JD Degs. Awd.
	#	%	#	%	#	%	#	%	#	%	#	%	
African Amer.	6	2.2	11	3.1	10	1.9	7	6.5	7	2.8	17	2.7	2
Amer. Indian	4	1.4	3	0.8	7	1.3	0	0.0	4	1.6	7	1.1	2
Asian Amer.	55	19.9	74	20.6	105	19.8	24	22.2	55	22.3	129	20.3	34
Mex. Amer.	9	3.2	7	1.9	12	2.3	4	3.7	5	2.0	16	2.5	3
Puerto Rican	0	0.0	1	0.3	1	0.2	0	0.0	0	0.0	1	0.2	0
Hispanic	10	3.6	16	4.4	21	4.0	5	4.6	10	4.0	26	4.1	3
Total Minority	84	30.3	112	31.1	156	29.5	40	37.0	81	32.8	196	30.8	44
For. Nation.	4	1.4	8	2.2	11	2.1	1	0.9	3	1.2	12	1.9	1
Caucasian	156	56.3	188	52.2	286	54.1	58	53.7	127	51.4	344	54.0	111
Unknown	33	11.9	52	14.4	76	14.4	9	8.3	36	14.6	85	13.3	28
Total	277	43.5	360	56.5	529	83.0	108	17.0	247	38.8	637		184

Transfers

Transfers in	3
Transfers out	16

Tuition and Fees

	Resident	Nonresident
Full-time	$36,860	$36,860
Part-time	$25,880	$25,880
Tuition Guarantee Program	N	

Living Expenses

Estimated living expenses for singles

Living on campus	Living off campus	Living at home
N/A	$23,515	N/A

Golden Gate University School of Law

ABA
Approved
Since
1956

GPA and LSAT Scores

	Total	Full-Time	Part-Time
# of apps	2,769	2,419	350
# of offers	1,372	1,257	115
# of matrics	243	199	44
75% GPA	3.39	3.43	3.18
Median GPA	3.14	3.20	2.90
25% GPA	2.84	2.88	2.63
75% LSAT	155	155	155
Median LSAT	153	153	154
25% LSAT	151	151	151

Grants and Scholarships (from prior year)

	Total		Full-Time		Part-Time	
	#	%	#	%	#	%
Total # of students	654		515		139	
Total # receiving grants	248	37.9	220	42.7	28	20.1
Less than 1/2 tuition	198	30.3	175	34.0	23	16.5
Half to full tuition	36	5.5	32	6.2	4	2.9
Full tuition	14	2.1	13	2.5	1	0.7
More than full tuition	0	0.0	0	0.0	0	0.0
Median grant amount			$7,500		$5,000	

Informational and Library Resources

Total amount spent on library materials	$1,111,460
Study seating capacity inside the library	463
# of full-time equivalent professional librarians	7
Hours per week library is open	95
# of open, wired connections available to students	572
# of networked computers available for use by students	130
Has wireless network?	Y
Require computer?	N

JD Attrition (from prior year)

	Academic	Other	Total	
	#	#	#	%
1st year	32	26	58	22.1
2nd year	1	2	3	1.6
3rd year	1	1	2	1.2
4th year	0	0	0	0.0

Employment (9 months after graduation)

	Total	Percentage
Employment status known	192	94.6
Employment status unknown	11	5.4
Employed	163	84.9
Pursuing graduate degrees	13	6.8
Unemployed (seeking, not seeking, or studying for the bar)	11	5.7
Type of Employment		
# employed in law firms	84	51.5
# employed in business and industry	20	12.3
# employed in government	24	14.7
# employed in public interest	12	7.4
# employed as judicial clerks	7	4.3
# employed in academia	15	9.2
Geographic Location		
# employed in state	140	85.9
# employed in foreign countries	2	1.2
# of states where employed	11	

Bar Passage Rates

First-time takers	208	Reporting %	96.63
Average school %	71.64	Average state %	78.07

Average pass difference −6.43

Jurisdiction	Takers	Passers	Pass %	State %	Diff %
California	201	144	71.64	78.07	−6.43

Golden Gate University School of Law

536 Mission Street, Office of Admissions
San Francisco, CA 94105-2968
Phone: 415.442.6630 or 800.GGU.4YOU; Fax: 415.442.6631
E-mail: lawadmit@ggu.edu; Website: www.ggu.edu/law

■ Introduction

Founded in 1901, Golden Gate University School of Law is located in the heart of San Francisco's legal and financial district. The law school is noted for integrating legal theory and practical skills training. Golden Gate has a distinguished faculty who share a strong commitment to both excellence in teaching and accessibility to students. The law school is a fully ABA-accredited program and is a member in good standing of the AALS.

■ Program Options

The law school offers both a full-time day and a part-time evening program. The full-time program involves three years of study and the part-time program involves four years of study. Golden Gate Law also offers an enhanced JD program under the Honors Lawyering Program and offers two formal joint-degree programs.

■ Honors Lawyering Program

The Honors Lawyering Program (HLP) takes a unique approach to legal education, integrating the theory, skills, and values learned in the classroom with actual work in the legal community—a modern version of the traditional apprenticeship. HLP students attend a regular first-year curriculum, participate in an intensive skills-focused summer session, and work at a full-time fall apprenticeship. In the spring, students return to full-time classes with a new appreciation for the application of law to practice. During their third year, students complete a second apprenticeship and have the option to enroll in additional, practice-based courses. HLP courses meet in small sections that integrate lawyering skills training with the substantive law curriculum. By the third week, students begin representing real clients under the guidance and supervision of the professors, who are themselves practicing attorneys. Students may apprentice in private law firms, companies, courts, government agencies, and public interest organizations.

■ Public Interest Law

At Golden Gate Law, the law curriculum and programs integrate public interest law and service to the community. Students may earn a public interest law certificate of specialization by completing 14 credits of approved elective courses, a 150-hour public interest practicum, and 25 hours of work for a campus or community organization. Students with prior commitment to public and community service may be selected to participate in the Public Interest Law Scholars Program (PISP), which provides students with scholarships and a summer employment stipend.

■ Joint Degrees and Certificates of Specialization

Students may earn the following joint degrees: JD/MBA and JD/PhD in Clinical Psychology.
Golden Gate also offers JD students the opportunity to earn specialization certificates in Business Law, Criminal Law, Environmental Law, Intellectual Property Law, International Law, Labor and Employment Law, Litigation, Public Interest Law, Real Estate Law, and Taxation. Requirements for the areas of specialization vary, but students generally complete coursework and clinical practice to earn a certificate.

■ Clinical Programs

Golden Gate University has one of the most extensive clinical programs in the country, offering students opportunities to earn academic credit while working closely with practicing attorneys.
The law school has two on-site clinics. In the Women's Employment Rights Clinic, students represent low-income women with employment-related problems. Through the Environmental Law and Justice Clinic, students assist Northern California communities in protecting their environmental interests and reducing their exposure to toxins.
In field-placement clinics, students work under the supervision of faculty, judges, and attorneys in government agencies, law offices, and judges' chambers. These off-site clinics include the Civil Field Placement Clinic, Criminal Litigation Clinic, Environmental Law Clinic, Immigration and Refugee Policy Clinic, Judicial Externship Program, Landlord-Tenant Clinic, Pro Bono Tax Clinic, and Real Estate Clinic.

■ Summer Programs

Students in our study-abroad program take courses covering a number of international topics currently of interest in the legal world. The curriculum combines introductory courses on the host country's legal systems and comparative law courses. Students also benefit from learning under the guidance of faculty from Golden Gate University School of Law, from faculty and practitioners at other ABA-accredited law schools, and from faculty and practitioners in the host country. Golden Gate Law currently offers a summer-abroad program in Paris, France.

■ Graduate Programs

Golden Gate University School of Law offers five LLM programs: Environmental Law, Intellectual Property Law, International Legal Studies, Taxation, and US Legal Studies. It also offers an SJD program in International Legal Studies.

■ Law Library

The Law Library houses the largest law collection in the San Francisco financial district—more than 350,000 volumes. Its holdings include a comprehensive series of case law reporters, statutes, digests, encyclopedias, periodicals, and treatises dealing with American law; a strong tax collection; a microforms collection; and a growing body of work in environmental law, law and literature, and international law. International law holdings target selected Pacific Rim countries and English, Canadian, and other Commonwealth materials. Students in the Law Library have access to the Internet and a variety of Internet-based legal databases.

Golden Gate University School of Law

Career Services and Placement

The Law Career Services (LCS) office helps students prepare for a successful legal career by providing many services throughout law school and beyond. LCS helps students research the legal market, develop contacts, and build skills through jobs and internships. For first-year students, LCS provides an online *Job Search Guide* and workshops on writing résumés and cover letters. For upper-division students, LCS offers print and online job listings; talks by graduates about their career experiences; individual and small-group career counseling; job-search skills workshops, panels, and events highlighting the career paths of Golden Gate alumni and other attorneys; special recruitment programs; and more. Many of these services continue after graduation.

Law Reviews, Journals, and Student Organizations

Golden Gate Law publishes the *Golden Gate University Law Review*, the *Environmental Law Journal*, and the *Annual Survey of International and Comparative Law*. The *Law Review* and journals provide students with the opportunity to showcase their research, writing, and editing skills. The law school also has more than 25 student organizations ranging from groups representing minority students to groups focusing on specific areas of law. An active student government represents the law school student body on important issues facing individuals, student organizations, and the law school.

Through these groups, students have many opportunities to participate in programs and attend lectures hosted by a variety of organizations and journals. These opportunities enrich the law school learning experience, and students are strongly encouraged to participate at all levels.

Admission and Scholarships

Golden Gate University School of Law awards scholarships to both entering and continuing students. All students are reviewed for scholarships as part of the admission process. Scholarships awarded to entering students are awarded on a three- or four-year basis. Students maintain their full-tuition dean's scholarship or their partial-tuition faculty scholarship by earning a 3.0 required-course GPA. Students who do not receive a scholarship at the time they are admitted, but who achieve a 3.0 required-course GPA at the end of their first year, may be eligible for a merit scholarship as a continuing student. To maintain a merit scholarship students must continue to earn a 3.0 required-course GPA.

Golden Gate Law also offers a Public Interest Scholars Program (PISP) Scholarship and an Environmental Law Scholarship. These scholarships are awarded in the amount of $5,000 per year, on a three-year basis, and require a 2.5 required-course GPA to maintain the scholarship. Both the PISP Scholarship and the Environmental Law Scholarship require a separate statement of interest and a list of prior commitment/activities from the student to be considered.

Applicant Profile

Golden Gate University School of Law
This grid includes only applicants who earned 120–180 LSAT scores under standard administrations.

LSAT Score	GPA 3.75 +		3.50–3.74		3.25–3.49		3.00–3.24		2.75–2.99		2.50–2.74		2.25–2.49		2.00–2.24		Below 2.00		No GPA		Total	
	Apps	Adm	Apps	Adm	Apps	Adm	Apps	Adm	Apps	Adm	Apps	Adm	Apps	Adm	Apps	Adm	Apps	Adm	Apps	Adm	Apps	Adm
175–180	0	0	0	0	0	0	0	0	0	0	0	0	0	0	0	0	0	0	0	0	0	0
170–174	0	0	1	1	2	2	0	0	0	0	0	0	1	1	0	0	0	0	0	0	4	4
165–169	1	1	8	7	9	9	14	12	8	5	0	0	2	2	0	0	0	0	0	0	42	36
160–164	24	23	29	26	40	37	36	33	19	18	12	7	9	7	2	1	1	1	4	2	176	155
155–159	41	39	89	83	120	116	91	80	64	51	40	27	20	9	8	4	4	2	8	4	485	415
150–154	57	49	126	109	197	154	209	136	155	89	82	31	38	15	20	4	6	2	12	6	902	595
145–149	34	16	82	28	119	36	151	32	134	12	83	2	43	1	15	3	2	0	11	2	674	132
140–144	10	3	31	4	49	2	84	2	73	0	39	0	28	0	20	0	2	0	10	0	346	11
135–139	1	0	6	1	18	1	22	0	23	0	21	0	16	0	5	0	1	0	2	0	115	2
130–134	1	0	1	0	2	0	8	0	10	0	6	0	5	0	4	0	1	0	6	0	44	0
125–129	0	0	0	0	0	0	1	0	1	0	0	0	1	0	0	0	0	0	0	0	3	0
120–124	0	0	0	0	0	0	0	0	0	0	0	0	0	0	0	0	0	0	1	0	1	0
Total	169	131	373	259	556	357	616	295	487	175	283	67	163	35	74	12	17	5	54	14	2792	1350

Apps = Number of Applicants
Adm = Number Admitted
Reflects 99% of the total applicant pool; average LSAT data reported.

This chart is a general guide only. Nonnumerical factors are strongly considered for all applicants. "No GPA" includes applicants who received their undergraduate degrees from foreign institutions and/or US institutions in which letter grades are not utilized or calculated.

Gonzaga University School of Law

PO Box 3528
Spokane, WA 99220-3528
Phone: 800.793.1710 or 509.313.5532; Fax: 509.313.3697
E-mail: admissions@lawschool.gonzaga.edu; Website: www.law.gonzaga.edu

ABA
Approved
Since
1951

AMERICAN BAR ASSOCIATION
Section of Legal Education
and Admissions to the Bar

The Basics

Type of school	Private
Term	Semester
Application deadline	4/15
Application fee	$50
Financial aid deadline	2/1
Can first year start other than fall?	Yes
Student to faculty ratio	15.3 to 1
# of housing spaces available restricted to law students	
graduate housing for which law students are eligible	526

Faculty and Administrators

	Total		Men		Women		Minorities	
	Spr	Fall	Spr	Fall	Spr	Fall	Spr	Fall
Full-time	30	28	16	14	14	14	2	2
Other full-time	0	1	0	0	0	1	0	0
Deans, librarians, & others who teach	5	5	3	3	2	2	1	1
Part-time	31	30	21	23	10	7	1	0
Total	66	64	40	40	26	24	4	3

Curriculum

	Full-Time	Part-Time
Typical first-year section size	70	0
Is there typically a "small section" of the first-year class, other than Legal Writing, taught by full-time faculty	No	No
If yes, typical size offered last year		
# of classroom course titles beyond first-year curriculum		94
# of upper division courses, excluding seminars, with an enrollment: Under 25		40
25–49		30
50–74		21
75–99		3
100+		0
# of seminars		4
# of seminar positions available		82
# of seminar positions filled	82	0
# of positions available in simulation courses		282
# of simulation positions filled	244	0
# of positions available in faculty supervised clinical courses		104
# of faculty supervised clinical positions filled	109	0
# involved in field placements	117	0
# involved in law journals	57	0
# involved in moot court or trial competitions	29	0
# of credit hours required to graduate		90

JD Enrollment and Ethnicity

	Men		Women		Full-Time		Part-Time		1st-Year		Total		JD Degs. Awd.
	#	%	#	%	#	%	#	%	#	%	#	%	
African Amer.	0	0.0	2	1.0	2	0.4	0	0.0	1	0.5	2	0.4	0
Amer. Indian	4	1.3	2	1.0	6	1.2	0	0.0	5	2.7	6	1.1	4
Asian Amer.	9	2.8	12	5.8	20	3.9	1	10.0	11	5.9	21	4.0	6
Mex. Amer.	3	0.9	1	0.5	4	0.8	0	0.0	3	1.6	4	0.8	0
Puerto Rican	0	0.0	0	0.0	0	0.0	0	0.0	0	0.0	0	0.0	0
Hispanic	5	1.6	6	2.9	11	2.1	0	0.0	7	3.8	11	2.1	1
Total Minority	21	6.6	23	11.1	43	8.3	1	10.0	27	14.5	44	8.4	11
For. Nation.	0	0.0	0	0.0	0	0.0	0	0.0	0	0.0	0	0.0	0
Caucasian	265	83.3	165	79.3	421	81.6	9	90.0	112	60.2	430	81.7	169
Unknown	32	10.1	20	9.6	52	10.1	0	0.0	47	25.3	52	9.9	4
Total	318	60.5	208	39.5	516	98.1	10	1.9	186	35.4	526		184

Transfers

Transfers in	4
Transfers out	13

Tuition and Fees

	Resident	Nonresident
Full-time	$31,460	$31,460
Part-time		
Tuition Guarantee Program		N

Living Expenses

Estimated living expenses for singles

Living on campus	Living off campus	Living at home
$14,404	$14,404	$14,404

Gonzaga University School of Law

ABA Approved Since 1951

GPA and LSAT Scores

	Total	Full-Time	Part-Time
# of apps	1,513	1,513	0
# of offers	649	649	0
# of matrics	188	188	0
75% GPA	3.51	3.51	0.00
Median GPA	3.30	3.30	0.00
25% GPA	3.05	3.05	0.00
75% LSAT	157	157	0
Median LSAT	155	155	0
25% LSAT	153	153	0

Grants and Scholarships (from prior year)

	Total		Full-Time		Part-Time	
	#	%	#	%	#	%
Total # of students	549		545		4	
Total # receiving grants	372	67.8	372	68.3	0	0.0
Less than 1/2 tuition	326	59.4	326	59.8	0	0.0
Half to full tuition	29	5.3	29	5.3	0	0.0
Full tuition	17	3.1	17	3.1	0	0.0
More than full tuition	0	0.0	0	0.0	0	0.0
Median grant amount			$12,000		$0	

Informational and Library Resources

Total amount spent on library materials	$828,424
Study seating capacity inside the library	507
# of full-time equivalent professional librarians	5
Hours per week library is open	110
# of open, wired connections available to students	140
# of networked computers available for use by students	83
Has wireless network?	Y
Require computer?	N

JD Attrition (from prior year)

	Academic	Other	Total	
	#	#	#	%
1st year	2	31	33	18.3
2nd year	1	0	1	0.6
3rd year	0	0	0	0.0
4th year	0	0	0	0.0

Employment (9 months after graduation)

	Total	Percentage
Employment status known	158	96.9
Employment status unknown	5	3.1
Employed	135	85.4
Pursuing graduate degrees	13	8.2
Unemployed (seeking, not seeking, or studying for the bar)	6	3.8
Type of Employment		
# employed in law firms	70	51.9
# employed in business and industry	16	11.9
# employed in government	20	14.8
# employed in public interest	10	7.4
# employed as judicial clerks	11	8.1
# employed in academia	3	2.2
Geographic Location		
# employed in state	84	62.2
# employed in foreign countries	1	0.7
# of states where employed	13	

Bar Passage Rates

First-time takers	171	Reporting %	95.91
Average school %	79.89	Average state %	76.92
Average pass difference	2.97		

Jurisdiction	Takers	Passers	Pass %	State %	Diff %
Washington	104	85	81.73	74.40	7.33
California	14	6	42.86	78.07	-35.21
Oregon	12	10	83.33	78.64	4.69
Utah	9	7	77.78	87.29	-9.51
Others (5)	25	23	92.00		

Gonzaga University School of Law

PO Box 3528
Spokane, WA 99220-3528
Phone: 800.793.1710 or 509.313.5532; Fax: 509.313.3697
E-mail: admissions@lawschool.gonzaga.edu; Website: www.law.gonzaga.edu

■ Introduction

Gonzaga University School of Law belongs to a long and distinguished tradition of humanistic, Catholic, and Jesuit education. Founded in 1887, Gonzaga continues to maintain the tradition of academic excellence in education that is at the heart of the mission of the 450-year-old Jesuit order. The School of Law, established in 1912, is a member of the AALS and is approved by the ABA. Gonzaga University is committed to educating a diverse student community, including students of all backgrounds and beliefs.

The campus is located in Spokane, Washington, a four-season city with the Spokane River flowing through its center. Step outside the School of Law onto the Centennial Trail to enjoy the picturesque walk into beautiful downtown Spokane. The metropolitan area of approximately 400,000 people serves as the regional hub of the Inland Northwest, a large area running from the Cascade Mountains in the west to the Rockies in the east. Canada is a mere 100 miles to the north. For domestic and international travel, the Spokane International Airport is conveniently located 10 miles from the Gonzaga University campus.

Spokane is a cultural center for the area, with professional and amateur theater groups, a symphony, and numerous art galleries and other cultural offerings. Spokane also serves as a regional economic hub for health care, agriculture, light industry, as well as a recreational sports area abundant with lakes, mountains, and forests. In minutes you can get away from the city's robust, rapidly growing business community to the surrounding pine-covered hills.

■ Physical Facilities and Library

Rising from the banks of the beautiful Spokane River, Gonzaga University School of Law provides a stunning setting for research and learning. The law school offers a variety of classroom and library environments that support today's interactive teaching methods. Features throughout the building encourage students to greet each other and linger to talk and debate ideas in beautiful outdoor spaces, roof plazas, balconies, and comfortable lounges. Miles of state-of-the-art voice, data, and video cable provide the highway for audiovisual, computer, and telecommunications technology throughout the building. The mix of classrooms, rooms for simulations of various sizes, and clinical teaching space provide flexibility to preserve the best of traditional law teaching while introducing new methods. The Chastek Library is the largest legal research facility between Seattle and Minneapolis. With a collection of over 300,000 volumes and microform equivalents, plus an extensive array of electronic resources, the library provides access to legal materials and offers many services to support the instructional, research, and scholarly endeavors of the law school and university community. The School of Law library is equipped with a wireless network and has two computer labs. Librarians provide reference support and regularly teach sessions on legal research using both traditional and electronic resources.

■ Curriculum and Faculty

There is a deliberate and delicate balance to legal education at Gonzaga. The rigorous curriculum focuses on legal analysis, problem solving, values, and ethics. Equally as important is the emphasis on practical experience to develop real-world lawyering skills. The unique first-year program at Gonzaga that exposes students to simulated skills training in litigation and transactional work in the fall and spring semesters, respectively, evidences Gonzaga's commitment to these goals.

The term "teaching faculty" applies in a very special way to the School of Law faculty. The Jesuit tradition demands a high degree of student-professor interaction inside and outside the classroom, and this emphasis attracts exceptional faculty. Gonzaga's focus on the individual student, a favorable student-to-faculty ratio, and the promotion of positive rather than negative competition provides an atmosphere of success in which to study.

■ Special Programs

The first-year program at Gonzaga pairs two doctrinal courses each semester with a skills and professionalism lab that immediately begins the process of turning law students into lawyers. In the fall semester, Civil Procedure and Torts are paired with a lab that emphasizes the development of litigation skills. In addition, students are introduced to legal theory during the fall of first year, via a course emphasizing different perspectives on the law. In the spring, Contracts and Property are paired with a lab that exposes the students to the business law side of the profession. Both labs also include instruction and exercises that are designed to help our students begin to identify and develop the professional values and habits that will be a part of their lives as attorneys. All students are required to engage in experiential learning, either through working in a professional externship or in Gonzaga's legal clinic, during their final year of studies.

Gonzaga offers three dual-degree programs leading to the JD/MBA, the JD/MAcc, and the JD/MSW degrees. These prepare students to enter fields that require, respectively, thorough knowledge of business, accountancy, social services, and the law.

■ Admission

The School of Law endeavors to attract students with ambitious minds, professional motivation, and commitment to the highest ethics and values of the legal profession and to public service. Consideration of applicants is not restricted to impersonal statistics, but includes recognition and review of the enriching qualities of applicants reflected in their personal statement, résumé, and letters of recommendation. Gonzaga seeks to enroll an ethnically and geographically diverse student body.

■ Student Activities

Gonzaga's educational philosophy is based on the centuries-old Ignatian model of educating the whole person—mind, body, and spirit. Students, therefore, find it

easy to become involved in a broad range of activities at the School of Law. Gonzaga is a major player in national moot court competitions and fields a variety of moot court teams. The student-run *Gonzaga Law Review* is circulated throughout the country, and the *Gonzaga Journal of International Law*, the online international law journal, receives submissions from around the world. The Student Bar Association is a strong, active organization that encourages student involvement, and there is ample opportunity to participate in intraschool moot court competitions, legal fraternities, and other organizations and activities. Gonzaga's student organizations are diverse in nature and, whatever your interests or career goals, there are activities available that will enhance your knowledge and abilities, while contributing to the community.

■ Housing

The Gonzaga campus is in a residential area within close proximity to downtown Spokane. Housing is available within walking distance to the law school, and rental rates are reasonably priced compared to most large population centers. University owned on- and off-campus housing is available to law students on a space available basis. For further information please review the Gonzaga University Housing and Residence Office website: *www.gonzaga.edu/ Student-Life/Off-Campus-Living/GU-Owned.asp.*

■ Financial Aid

Law school is a career investment. For students who need financial assistance to help fund this investment, we encourage filing the FAFSA. Gonzaga also provides more than $1 million in scholarship aid each year, and your admission application will serve as your scholarship application. However, students who are interested in applying for the Thomas More Scholarship need to apply separately. Gonzaga awards up to five Thomas More Scholarships a year, covering 100 percent of tuition.

■ Career Services

The Career Services Office is committed to serving the needs of employers, students, and alumni. The office's priority is to match qualified students and alumni with employers. Recognizing that career development is a lifelong process, the office provides graduates access to career services throughout their professional lives. In addition, the office provides employers with timely and effective assistance to fill their organization's hiring needs. Employers are encouraged to utilize our recruitment services, including online job postings, job fairs, customized recruiting, and interviewing programs. Career services is focused on professional development, including up-to-date job listings, library resources, interview tools, workshops, career counseling, and presentations by attorneys discussing the practice of law. Prospective students are encouraged to meet with career counselors to learn more about legal opportunities.

Applicant Profile

Gonzaga University School of Law
This grid includes only applicants who earned 120–180 LSAT scores under standard administrations.

LSAT Score	3.75 +		3.50–3.74		3.25–3.49		3.00–3.24		2.75–2.99		2.50–2.74		2.25–2.49		2.00–2.24		Below 2.00		No GPA		Total	
	Apps	Adm	Apps	Adm	Apps	Adm	Apps	Adm	Apps	Adm	Apps	Adm	Apps	Adm	Apps	Adm	Apps	Adm	Apps	Adm	Apps	Adm
170–180	0	0	0	0	1	1	1	0	0	0	0	0	0	0	0	0	0	0	0	0	2	1
165–169	6	5	4	2	3	3	5	5	1	1	5	4	0	0	0	0	0	0	0	0	24	20
160–164	16	16	14	13	16	16	14	12	18	13	9	7	3	0	4	0	1	0	0	0	95	77
155–159	38	37	49	47	69	66	58	53	57	45	18	14	13	0	5	0	2	0	2	0	311	262
150–154	50	28	100	59	135	70	142	60	104	39	24	8	16	0	2	0	0	0	4	0	577	264
145–149	23	3	55	3	61	6	67	7	50	2	29	1	18	0	7	0	1	0	3	0	314	22
140–144	8	0	19	0	27	0	30	0	21	0	13	0	8	0	6	0	1	0	0	0	133	0
Below 140	2	0	4	0	5	0	9	0	10	0	7	0	8	0	2	0	0	0	3	0	50	0
Total	143	89	245	124	317	162	326	137	261	100	105	34	66	0	26	0	5	0	12	0	1506	646

Apps = Number of Applicants
Adm = Number Admitted
Reflects 99% of the total applicant pool; average LSAT data reported.

Hamline University School of Law

1536 Hewitt Avenue
St. Paul, MN 55104
Phone: 651.523.2461, 800.388.3688; Fax: 651.523.3064
E-mail: lawadm@hamline.edu; Website: www.hamline.edu/law

ABA
Approved
Since
1975

The Basics

Type of school	Private
Term	Semester
Application deadline	4/1
Application fee	$35
Financial aid deadline	4/1
Can first year start other than fall?	No
Student to faculty ratio	14.8 to 1
# of housing spaces available restricted to law students	
graduate housing for which law students are eligible	60

Curriculum

	Full-Time	Part-Time
Typical first-year section size	58	46
Is there typically a "small section" of the first-year class, other than Legal Writing, taught by full-time faculty	No	No
If yes, typical size offered last year		
# of classroom course titles beyond first-year curriculum		134
# of upper division courses, excluding seminars, with an enrollment: Under 25		103
25–49		60
50–74		17
75–99		2
100+		0
# of seminars		17
# of seminar positions available		291
# of seminar positions filled	147	87
# of positions available in simulation courses		1,368
# of simulation positions filled	423	506
# of positions available in faculty supervised clinical courses		121
# of faculty supervised clinical positions filled	72	31
# involved in field placements	79	44
# involved in law journals	73	19
# involved in moot court or trial competitions	57	8
# of credit hours required to graduate		88

Faculty and Administrators

	Total		Men		Women		Minorities	
	Spr	Fall	Spr	Fall	Spr	Fall	Spr	Fall
Full-time	32	35	20	20	12	15	5	6
Other full-time	1	2	1	2	0	0	0	0
Deans, librarians, & others who teach	8	9	2	1	6	8	2	2
Part-time	71	45	46	25	25	20	3	1
Total	112	91	69	48	43	43	10	9

JD Enrollment and Ethnicity

	Men		Women		Full-Time		Part-Time		1st-Year		Total		JD Degs. Awd.
	#	%	#	%	#	%	#	%	#	%	#	%	
African Amer.	5	1.7	17	4.9	17	3.6	5	2.7	5	2.4	22	3.4	5
Amer. Indian	1	0.3	4	1.1	1	0.2	4	2.2	1	0.5	5	0.8	2
Asian Amer.	9	3.0	23	6.6	25	5.3	7	3.8	7	3.4	32	4.9	10
Mex. Amer.	0	0.0	0	0.0	0	0.0	0	0.0	0	0.0	0	0.0	0
Puerto Rican	0	0.0	0	0.0	0	0.0	0	0.0	0	0.0	0	0.0	0
Hispanic	14	4.7	12	3.4	14	3.0	12	6.6	7	3.4	26	4.0	10
Total Minority	29	9.6	56	16.0	57	12.2	28	15.4	20	9.8	85	13.1	27
For. Nation.	0	0.0	7	2.0	6	1.3	1	0.5	2	1.0	7	1.1	2
Caucasian	244	81.1	250	71.6	356	76.1	138	75.8	167	81.5	494	76.0	190
Unknown	28	9.3	36	10.3	49	10.5	15	8.2	16	7.8	64	9.8	16
Total	301	46.3	349	53.7	468	72.0	182	28.0	205	31.5	650		235

Transfers

Transfers in	3
Transfers out	9

Tuition and Fees

	Resident	Nonresident
Full-time	$32,014	$32,014
Part-time	$23,078	$23,078
Tuition Guarantee Program		N

Living Expenses

Estimated living expenses for singles

Living on campus	Living off campus	Living at home
$12,226	$15,360	$15,360

Hamline University School of Law

ABA
Approved
Since
1975

GPA and LSAT Scores

	Total	Full-Time	Part-Time
# of apps	1,506	1,331	175
# of offers	744	628	116
# of matrics	207	147	60
75% GPA	3.66	3.68	3.51
Median GPA	3.42	3.47	3.23
25% GPA	3.16	3.27	2.95
75% LSAT	158	159	155
Median LSAT	154	155	150
25% LSAT	150	151	147

Grants and Scholarships (from prior year)

	Total #	Total %	Full-Time #	Full-Time %	Part-Time #	Part-Time %
Total # of students	716		509		207	
Total # receiving grants	336	46.9	275	54.0	61	29.5
Less than 1/2 tuition	122	17.0	92	18.1	30	14.5
Half to full tuition	132	18.4	105	20.6	27	13.0
Full tuition	76	10.6	73	14.3	3	1.4
More than full tuition	6	0.8	5	1.0	1	0.5
Median grant amount			$18,058		$10,834	

Informational and Library Resources

Total amount spent on library materials	$866,992
Study seating capacity inside the library	335
# of full-time equivalent professional librarians	6
Hours per week library is open	116
# of open, wired connections available to students	506
# of networked computers available for use by students	48
Has wireless network?	Y
Require computer?	Y

JD Attrition (from prior year)

	Academic #	Other #	Total #	Total %
1st year	6	18	24	10.3
2nd year	0	6	6	2.8
3rd year	0	1	1	0.4
4th year	0	0	0	0.0

Employment (9 months after graduation)

	Total	Percentage
Employment status known	187	93.0
Employment status unknown	14	7.0
Employed	165	88.2
Pursuing graduate degrees	4	2.1
Unemployed (seeking, not seeking, or studying for the bar)	8	4.3
Type of Employment		
# employed in law firms	67	40.6
# employed in business and industry	44	26.7
# employed in government	14	8.5
# employed in public interest	12	7.3
# employed as judicial clerks	25	15.2
# employed in academia	1	0.6
Geographic Location		
# employed in state	122	73.9
# employed in foreign countries	1	0.6
# of states where employed	18	

Bar Passage Rates

First-time takers	202	Reporting %	76.73
Average school %	91.62	Average state %	91.17
Average pass difference	0.45		

Jurisdiction	Takers	Passers	Pass %	State %	Diff %
Minnesota	139	129	92.81	91.09	1.72
Wisconsin	16	13	81.25	91.79	−10.54

Hamline University School of Law

1536 Hewitt Avenue
St. Paul, MN 55104
Phone: 651.523.2461, 800.388.3688; Fax: 651.523.3064
E-mail: lawadm@hamline.edu; Website: www.hamline.edu/law

■ Introduction

Hamline University School of Law is a collaborative community where students work together to best serve clients and society. Hamline offers a full-time weekday and part-time weekend program, both of which provide a challenging curriculum, excellent faculty, and diverse experiential learning opportunities. Our expert faculty challenges students to realize their full potential through innovative educational experiences—both inside and outside the classroom. Hamline students graduate ready to practice law and inspired to use their legal education to solve problems and make a difference in the world.

The school also serves as a catalyst for reframing the legal landscape through distinguished guest speakers, thought-provoking symposia, and nationally recognized centers of excellence, such as Hamline's Dispute Resolution Institute and Health Law Institute. A Business Law Institute will be added in 2010. Hamline's faculty includes nationally recognized experts in bioethics, intellectual property, international trade, corporate law, and critical race theory. Other faculty members are renowned for scholarship and academic leadership in health law, dispute resolution, corporate law, constitutional law, and many other fields.

Hamline alumni are employed in all aspects of the law, which include private practice, government agencies, public and private corporate environments, as well as in the court system as prosecutors, public defenders, and members of the judiciary at the state and federal levels. Some alumni use their legal education as a backdrop for nontraditional legal employment outside the justice system. Hamline alumni are active and involved with the School of Law by serving as moot court competition judges, adjunct faculty, practicum supervisors, program and classroom speakers, and as mentors for individual students.

■ Library and Facilities

Located within the vibrant St. Paul-Minneapolis urban setting, the Hamline University School of Law is situated in the heart of Hamline University's 55 acre campus. The Law Library staff is readily available to provide support services, along with nearly 300,000 volumes and electronic databases—giving students access to the libraries of seven other colleges and universities through a consortium agreement. Hamline's Annette K. Levine Moot Court Room provides a technologically relevant setting for moot court competitions and for observing actual court proceedings.

■ Rigorous and Supportive Learning Environment

Hamline's core curriculum provides the analytical grounding necessary for success. In addition to a rich full-time program, Hamline offers a unique part-time weekend program that is taught by the same respected faculty members who teach in the day program. The law school also offers dual-degree and course exchange options, which allow students to combine their legal education with a second disciplinary focus in the areas of business administration, public administration, nonprofit management, creative writing, and organizational leadership.

Led by the internationally heralded Dispute Resolution Institute, our curriculum in negotiations, arbitration, and mediation is second to none. In addition, the Health Law Institute offers extensive academic and experiential learning opportunities for students interested in pursuing careers in the health law arena.

Hamline's rigorous offerings reflect considerable depth, enabling students to concentrate their studies in a variety of substantive areas: alternative dispute resolution, corporate/commercial law, child advocacy, criminal law, government and regulatory affairs, health law, intellectual property, international law, labor and employment law, litigation and trial practice, property law, and public law and human rights.

At Hamline, professors move beyond traditional lectures to offer truly collaborative, student-centered classroom experiences while simultaneously conducting cutting-edge scholarship. Our accessible professors are dedicated to an "open door" policy. An emphasis on seminars allows students to learn in small classes, make presentations, and create original research on topics of personal interest, ensuring that students work closely with Hamline's dedicated faculty throughout their law school experience. The Constance Bakken Fellows program provides funding for collaborative research between faculty and students.

■ Experiential Learning: At Home and Abroad

Hamline students further expand their skills by competing in appellate advocacy and negotiation competitions throughout the country and around the world. Hamline's 11 legal clinics give students real-world experience in the practice of health law, immigration law, small business planning, criminal law, child advocacy, alternative dispute resolution, education law, and trial practice. Each clinic operates as a small law office with students handling their own caseload and representing clients under the supervision of experienced in-house or adjunct faculty members. Students who participate in these clinics not only receive credit toward their Juris Doctor, they also gain a wealth of knowledge in case management and other lawyering skills as well as valuable contacts in the professional legal community.

Likewise, Hamline's externship program enables students to work directly with mentor attorneys and judges, and places students in private law firms, corporations, judges' chambers, public agencies, legislative offices, and businesses. This training allows students to absorb real-world legal lessons and provides them with valuable professional legal contacts. In addition, all Hamline students must complete 24 pro bono service hours as a graduation requirement.

Hamline encourages international study for the development of a truly global perspective. Many students participate in an international exchange program with Hamline's European law school partners. Others compete in the Vienna International Moot Court Competition. Hamline provides conferences, classes, and training in London, Oslo, Budapest, and Jerusalem, among other foreign locations. With international lawyers from around the world in our LLM

program and our academic programs abroad, Hamline offers a truly global learning environment.

A Dynamic Student Community

Hamline attracts a dynamic and diverse student population. Students in our fall 2009 incoming class represented 30 states and 97 undergraduate institutions, and 10 percent were students of color. Hamline also offers a graduate program leading to a Master of Laws (LLM) degree for lawyers holding an LLB or equivalent degree from outside the United States. Recent LLM students have hailed from India, Cameroon, Italy, and beyond. These students contribute to the cultural richness of the Hamline learning community.

Opportunities for student involvement abound at Hamline University School of Law. The *Hamline Law Review* and the *Hamline Journal of Public Law and Policy* are entirely staffed by law students. Hamline students also provide editorial assistance for the internationally respected *Journal of Law and Religion*. Hamline students can participate on more than 15 moot court teams and, with 25 active student organizations, students easily find professional, cultural, and social connections to match their interests.

Hamline law students believe they can make a difference in their community and frequently this passion can be seen through the innovative programs and initiatives they develop on campus. In recent years, for example, members of the Hamline Latino Law Student Association (LLSA) launched an annual event, Juris Fiesta, which raises funds for the newly established Latino Law Student Scholarship and attracts national Latino legal leaders as keynote speakers. Another student organization, the Hamline Veteran's Association, has also launched a scholarship.

Career Assistance

The Career Services Office (CSO) is committed to assisting all Hamline law students in career planning and job searches. Dedicated and experienced counselors provide informational programs, mock interviews, one-on-one career counseling, résumé assistance, networking opportunities, and an online job bank. They also organize on-campus interviews with prospective employers and work extensively with employers to advance Hamline law students and to solicit postings and information. Students are strongly encouraged to participate in CSO programs at Hamline and to build professional networks with alumni and other legal professionals while earning their Juris Doctor.

Admission and Financial Aid

The School of Law maintains a selection process that emphasizes a rigorous but fair examination of each person as an individual, not merely as a set of credentials. In addition to the LSAT and undergraduate GPA, the admission committee gives significant weight to motivation, personal experiences, employment history, graduate education, maturity, letters of recommendation, and the ability to articulate one's interest in, and suitability for, the study of law. Hamline's admission policy is designed to enhance the academic rigor, professional dedication, social concern, and diversity of the student body, including cultural, economic, sexual orientation, racial, and ethnic composition. Hamline also provides a comprehensive financial aid program, which includes merit-based scholarships. At Hamline, 95 percent of law students qualify for need-based loans.

Applicant Profile

Hamline University School of Law
This grid includes only applicants with 120–180 LSAT scores earned under standard administrations.

LSAT Score	GPA 3.75 +		3.50–3.74		3.25–3.49		3.00–3.24		2.75–2.99		2.50–2.74		2.25–2.49		2.00–2.24		Below 2.00		No GPA		Totals	
	Apps	Adm	Apps	Adm	Apps	Adm	Apps	Adm	Apps	Adm	Apps	Adm	Apps	Adm	Apps	Adm	Apps	Adm	Apps	Adm	Apps	Adm
175–180	0	0	0	0	0	0	0	0	0	0	1	0	0	0	0	0	0	0	0	0	1	0
170–174	1	1	1	1	1	1	0	0	1	1	0	0	0	0	0	0	0	0	0	0	4	4
165–169	7	6	6	6	7	6	3	2	1	1	1	0	0	0	1	0	0	0	0	0	26	21
160–164	21	21	23	22	26	25	12	12	11	9	3	2	4	0	0	0	0	0	0	0	100	91
155–159	43	39	52	48	49	48	42	39	25	19	12	1	5	1	1	0	2	0	1	0	232	195
150–154	49	46	82	74	86	69	73	47	51	14	23	4	12	2	9	1	1	0	4	2	390	259
145–149	38	32	67	41	91	37	99	19	51	9	51	2	30	1	11	0	1	0	9	2	448	143
140–144	13	6	21	11	44	11	40	3	40	4	16	0	13	0	6	0	2	0	8	0	203	35
135–139	1	1	5	0	12	0	9	0	16	0	14	0	5	0	1	0	0	0	3	0	66	1
130–134	1	0	0	0	2	0	0	0	3	0	4	0	4	0	1	0	1	0	3	0	19	0
125–129	0	0	0	0	1	0	0	0	0	0	2	0	1	0	1	0	0	0	1	0	6	0
120–124	0	0	0	0	0	0	0	0	0	0	0	0	0	0	1	0	0	0	0	0	1	0
Total	174	152	257	203	319	197	278	122	199	57	127	9	74	4	32	1	7	0	29	4	1496	749

Apps = Number of Applicants
Adm = Number Admitted
Reflects 99% of the total applicant pool; average LSAT data reported.

This chart is to be used as a general guide only. Nonnumerical factors are strongly considered for all applicants.

Harvard Law School

1515 Massachusetts Avenue, Austin Hall
Cambridge, MA 02138
Phone: 617.495.3109
E-mail: jdadmiss@law.harvard.edu; Website: www.law.harvard.edu

ABA
Approved
Since
1923

The Basics

Type of school	Private
Term	Semester
Application deadline	2/1
Application fee	$85
Financial aid deadline	4/1
Can first year start other than fall?	No
Student to faculty ratio	11.0 to 1
# of housing spaces available restricted to law students	603
graduate housing for which law students are eligible	4,211

Faculty and Administrators

	Total		Men		Women		Minorities	
	Spr	Fall	Spr	Fall	Spr	Fall	Spr	Fall
Full-time	140	124	111	97	29	27	14	9
Other full-time	29	28	17	15	12	13	2	2
Deans, librarians, & others who teach	15	15	8	8	7	7	3	3
Part-time	3	5	1	5	2	0	0	0
Total	187	172	137	125	50	47	19	14

Curriculum

	Full-Time	Part-Time
Typical first-year section size	80	0
Is there typically a "small section" of the first-year class, other than Legal Writing, taught by full-time faculty	No	No
If yes, typical size offered last year		

# of classroom course titles beyond first-year curriculum		346
# of upper division courses, excluding seminars, with an enrollment:	Under 25	124
	25–49	71
	50–74	41
	75–99	11
	100+	15
# of seminars		84
# of seminar positions available		966
# of seminar positions filled	1,001	0
# of positions available in simulation courses		520
# of simulation positions filled	438	0
# of positions available in faculty supervised clinical courses		601
# of faculty supervised clinical positions filled	513	0
# involved in field placements	198	0
# involved in law journals	1,000	0
# involved in moot court or trial competitions	365	0
# of credit hours required to graduate		82

JD Enrollment and Ethnicity

	Men		Women		Full-Time		Part-Time		1st-Year		Total		JD Degs. Awd.
	#	%	#	%	#	%	#	%	#	%	#	%	
African Amer.	85	9.1	115	13.8	200	11.3	0	0.0	67	11.9	200	11.3	70
Amer. Indian	6	0.6	5	0.6	11	0.6	0	0.0	6	1.1	11	0.6	7
Asian Amer.	85	9.1	94	11.3	179	10.1	0	0.0	57	10.1	179	10.1	76
Mex. Amer.	16	1.7	12	1.4	28	1.6	0	0.0	8	1.4	28	1.6	12
Puerto Rican	4	0.4	6	0.7	10	0.6	0	0.0	2	0.4	10	0.6	5
Hispanic	41	4.4	36	4.3	77	4.4	0	0.0	27	4.8	77	4.4	26
Total Minority	237	25.5	268	32.1	505	28.6	0	0.0	167	29.6	505	28.6	196
For. Nation.	29	3.1	28	3.4	57	3.2	0	0.0	22	3.9	57	3.2	23
Caucasian	508	54.6	431	51.6	939	53.2	0	0.0	290	51.3	939	53.2	296
Unknown	156	16.8	108	12.9	264	15.0	0	0.0	80	14.2	264	15.0	52
Total	930	52.7	835	47.3	1765	100.0	0	0.0	565	32.0	1765		567

Transfers

Transfers in	39
Transfers out	0

Tuition and Fees

	Resident	Nonresident
Full-time	$45,026	
Part-time		
Tuition Guarantee Program		N

Living Expenses

Estimated living expenses for singles

Living on campus	Living off campus	Living at home
$22,874	$22,874	$22,874

Harvard Law School

ABA
Approved
Since
1923

GPA and LSAT Scores

	Total	Full-Time	Part-Time
# of apps	7,391	7,391	0
# of offers	833	833	0
# of matrics	559	559	0
75% GPA	3.96	3.96	0.00
Median GPA	3.89	3.89	0.00
25% GPA	3.76	3.76	0.00
75% LSAT	176	176	0
Median LSAT	173	173	0
25% LSAT	171	171	0

Grants and Scholarships (from prior year)

	Total		Full-Time		Part-Time	
	#	%	#	%	#	%
Total # of students	1,730		1,730		0	
Total # receiving grants	814	47.1	814	47.1	0	0.0
Less than 1/2 tuition	510	29.5	510	29.5	0	0.0
Half to full tuition	276	16.0	276	16.0	0	0.0
Full tuition	20	1.2	20	1.2	0	0.0
More than full tuition	8	0.5	8	0.5	0	0.0
Median grant amount			$15,490		$0	

Informational and Library Resources

Total amount spent on library materials	$3,572,636
Study seating capacity inside the library	802
# of full-time equivalent professional librarians	37
Hours per week library is open	121
# of open, wired connections available to students	2,750
# of networked computers available for use by students	165
Has wireless network?	Y
Require computer?	N

JD Attrition (from prior year)

	Academic	Other	Total	
	#	#	#	%
1st year	0	2	2	0.4
2nd year	0	4	4	0.7
3rd year	0	1	1	0.2
4th year	0	0	0	0.0

Employment (9 months after graduation)

	Total	Percentage
Employment status known	590	100.0
Employment status unknown	0	0.0
Employed	575	97.5
Pursuing graduate degrees	6	1.0
Unemployed (seeking, not seeking, or studying for the bar)	4	0.7
Type of Employment		
# employed in law firms	379	65.9
# employed in business and industry	25	4.3
# employed in government	21	3.7
# employed in public interest	35	6.1
# employed as judicial clerks	109	19.0
# employed in academia	6	1.0
Geographic Location		
# employed in state	63	11.0
# employed in foreign countries	23	4.0
# of states where employed	35	

Bar Passage Rates

First-time takers	588	Reporting %	62.41
Average school %	97.28	Average state %	89.74
Average pass difference	7.54		

Jurisdiction	Takers	Passers	Pass %	State %	Diff %
New York	284	274	96.48	88.98	7.50
Massachusetts	83	83	100.00	92.33	7.67

Harvard Law School

1515 Massachusetts Avenue, Austin Hall
Cambridge, MA 02138
Phone: 617.495.3109
E-mail: jdadmiss@law.harvard.edu; Website: www.law.harvard.edu

■ A Legal Metropolis

Harvard Law School combines the resources of the world's premier center for legal education and research with educational settings designed to enrich individual and interactive learning. The result is a uniquely vibrant and collaborative environment. Harvard's scope generates enormous vitality—an unparalleled breadth and depth of academic options, a wide array of research programs, a diverse student body drawn from across the nation and around the world, and a global network of distinguished alumni. Harvard Law School offers students a curriculum of unparalleled breadth: more than 350 courses, seminars, and reading groups that together reflect the remarkable range of the faculty's expertise and interests. Within this dynamic environment, law students have broad opportunities for intellectual engagement with faculty and classmates. Over 120 of these courses have fewer than 25 students enrolled, plus there are almost 85 seminars in which small groups of students work closely with faculty. First-year sections have fewer than 80 students, and opportunities to work directly with faculty members abound. For example, all first-year students may join in intimate (fewer than 15 students), faculty-led reading groups on topics ranging from cyberlaw to climate change to terrorism. Harvard's extensive resources and collaborative approach create unmatched opportunities to prepare for leadership in public service, private practice, the judiciary, academia, business, or government.

■ Public Service

HLS strongly promotes public service. The school guarantees funding for summer public interest work, and over 500 JD students received funds to work in 35 countries and 33 states plus Washington, DC, in 2009. The Office of Public Interest Advising provides comprehensive services to students pursuing public service careers. The Low Income Protection Plan allows graduates substantial financial flexibility to pursue lower-paying employment, and a variety of fellowship programs provide additional support to graduates entering public service. Reflecting its public service commitment, HLS has a 40-hour minimum pro bono work requirement, with students actually completing an average of more than 500 hours of pro bono work during law school.

■ Faculty

The centerpiece of the HLS experience is working directly with scholars who shape the landscape of American and international law. The faculty includes leading specialists in every subject area. Beyond the classroom, students provide critical support to faculty producing cutting-edge research and influencing the development of the law and of societies around the world.

■ International Scope

Harvard Law School presents students with tremendous opportunities to engage in the world. With students coming from more than 60 countries to study here and with hundreds of current students going abroad each year to work, study, engage in research, or advocate for change, HLS is truly a global crossroads. Each year, the Law School offers more than 75 courses, seminars, and reading groups taught with an international, foreign, or comparative law component. Research centers, such as the East Asian Legal Studies Program or the Program on International Financial Systems, offer students access to visiting scholars and cutting-edge ideas through colloquia, conferences, and research opportunities. Harvard's more than 3,500 alumni living outside the United States provide an unparalleled network of opportunity for potential collaboration and camaraderie for members of the community. In addition, scholars come to HLS from all over the world to make use of the incredible international collections housed in the law library.

■ Student Life

At HLS, a wide variety of extracurricular activities complement and enrich the classroom and clinical experiences. Whether exploring professional interests, serving the public, or merely socializing, students engage in an enormous range of activity on the HLS campus beyond the classroom. At present, there are more than 90 student organizations and journals at HLS. Student organizations based on social, political, service, or professional interests plan workshops, panels, concerts, networking opportunities, and conferences for almost every day of the academic year. Other activities planned by first-year social chairs, the second-year social committee, the third-year class marshals, as well as the Dean of Students Office, create a collegial and community-oriented environment on campus. Students are given a wide range of opportunities to create and implement ideas for activities and are encouraged to pursue their interests by forming new student organizations or planning one-time events.

■ Clinical Programs

The Clinical Legal Education Program is one of the most important and valued aspects of a Harvard Law School education, confirming our commitment to public service and to providing our students with the best possible educational experience. With dozens of in-house clinics and hundreds of externships, Harvard Law School has more clinical opportunities than any law school in the world. Some of the clinics include Mediation and Negotiation, Supreme Court Advocacy, Immigration, Human Rights, CyberLaw, Child Advocacy, Criminal Justice, Criminal Prosecution, Death Penalty, Disability Law, Domestic Violence, Education Law, Employment Civil Rights, Environmental Law, Estate Planning, Family Law, GLBT Law, Gender Violence, Government Lawyer, Health Law, Post-Foreclosure Eviction Defense, Predatory Lending/Consumer Protection, Sports Law, and War Crimes Prosecution.

Clinical education at HLS helps to introduce and explore the roles and responsibilities of a lawyer. Taking a clinical course may aid students in thinking about what sort of law practice or lawyering work they like most. Mentored practice, in an educational setting, also helps students begin to understand

their learning styles while getting a head start on learning the skills they will need when they begin their careers.

The Clinical Legal Education Program at Harvard Law School has three basic components:

- direct student responsibility for clients in a realistic practice setting;
- supervision and mentoring by an experienced practitioner; and
- companion classroom sessions in which clinical experience supports and contributes to further discussion and thought.

In 2008–2009, nearly 1,000 students participated in clinical work. Clinical courses get enthusiastic reviews from student participants, most of whom find them challenging and educational. Many students find that this practical lawyering produces a sense of personal accomplishment as well as professional development because, in most cases, they are truly increasing access to justice for the most marginalized members of society. HLS also offers externship placements at various government agencies, nonprofits, and small firms. Students can also design faculty-sponsored independent

clinical work projects in any area they cannot find as part of the curriculum. Finally, many students take advantage of the winter term, spending three to four weeks off campus in a clinical setting and then coming back to campus and continuing the work remotely for the following semester.

■ Employment After Graduation

More than 500 employers recruit on campus at HLS each year. Upon graduation, roughly 65 percent of HLS graduates enter private practice, about 20 percent enter judicial clerkships, and about 15 percent enter public interest or government work, business and industry, academia, or other unique pursuits. Virtually every year, the number of HLS graduates clerking for the US Supreme Court surpasses the number from any other law school. In fact, approximately one fourth of all Supreme Court clerks over the last decade graduated from HLS. After clerkships, many HLS graduates pursue careers in public interest, government, and academia.

Applicant Profile

HLS does not provide a profile chart because it would be based solely upon undergraduate GPA and LSAT scores. Admission decisions are based on many factors beyond the GPA and LSAT. Each application is read thoroughly by our team of admissions professionals and faculty admissions committee members. Although most admitted candidates graduated near the top of their college classes and present LSAT scores in the top few percentiles, a significant proportion of candidates who meet these characterizations

may not be offered admission. At the same time, some admitted candidates apply with lower GPA and LSAT credentials but offer combined academic and other achievements that impress the admission committee. Candidates with higher grades and scores tend to be admitted at higher rates than candidates with lower grades and scores, but at no point on the GPA or LSAT scales are the chances for admission to Harvard Law School zero or 100 percent.

University of Hawai'i at Mānoa | William S. Richardson School of Law

2515 Dole Street
Honolulu, HI 96822-2350
Phone: 808.956.7966; Fax: 808.956.3813
E-mail: lawadm@hawaii.edu; Website: www.law.hawaii.edu

The Basics

Type of school	Public
Term	Semester
Application deadline	3/1
Application fee	$60
Financial aid deadline	3/1
Can first year start other than fall?	No
Student to faculty ratio	7.8 to 1
# of housing spaces available restricted to law students	
graduate housing for which law students are eligible	36

Faculty and Administrators

	Total		Men		Women		Minorities	
	Spr	Fall	Spr	Fall	Spr	Fall	Spr	Fall
Full-time	31	32	14	15	17	17	12	12
Other full-time	11	10	4	4	7	6	7	7
Deans, librarians, & others who teach	12	13	2	2	10	11	7	7
Part-time	42	15	29	9	13	6	18	9
Total	96	70	49	30	47	40	44	35

JD Enrollment and Ethnicity

	Men		Women		Full-Time		Part-Time		1st-Year		Total		JD Degs. Awd.
	#	%	#	%	#	%	#	%	#	%	#	%	
African Amer.	0	0.0	6	3.2	5	1.8	1	2.4	2	1.3	6	1.8	2
Amer. Indian	2	1.4	0	0.0	2	0.7	0	0.0	1	0.7	2	0.6	1
Asian Amer.	76	55.1	109	58.0	165	57.9	20	48.8	90	59.6	185	56.7	50
Mex. Amer.	1	0.7	0	0.0	1	0.4	0	0.0	1	0.7	1	0.3	0
Puerto Rican	1	0.7	0	0.0	1	0.4	0	0.0	0	0.0	1	0.3	0
Hispanic	2	1.4	2	1.1	3	1.1	1	2.4	1	0.7	4	1.2	1
Total Minority	82	59.4	117	62.2	177	62.1	22	53.7	95	62.9	199	61.0	54
For. Nation.	3	2.2	3	1.6	6	2.1	0	0.0	3	2.0	6	1.8	2
Caucasian	28	20.3	33	17.6	51	17.9	10	24.4	23	15.2	61	18.7	17
Unknown	25	18.1	35	18.6	51	17.9	9	22.0	30	19.9	60	18.4	15
Total	138	42.3	188	57.7	285	87.4	41	12.6	151	46.3	326		88

Curriculum

	Full-Time	Part-Time
Typical first-year section size	97	24
Is there typically a "small section" of the first-year class, other than Legal Writing, taught by full-time faculty	No	No
If yes, typical size offered last year		
# of classroom course titles beyond first-year curriculum		87
# of upper division courses, excluding seminars, with an enrollment: Under 25		58
25–49		10
50–74		3
75–99		2
100+		0
# of seminars		55
# of seminar positions available		567
# of seminar positions filled	435	48
# of positions available in simulation courses	153	
# of simulation positions filled	116	0
# of positions available in faculty supervised clinical courses	134	
# of faculty supervised clinical positions filled	105	0
# involved in field placements	61	0
# involved in law journals	49	0
# involved in moot court or trial competitions	36	0
# of credit hours required to graduate		89

Transfers

Transfers in	0
Transfers out	4

Tuition and Fees

	Resident	Nonresident
Full-time	$15,581	$28,565
Part-time	$13,055	$23,869
Tuition Guarantee Program		N

Living Expenses

Estimated living expenses for singles

Living on campus	Living off campus	Living at home
$11,290	$15,599	$5,928

University of Hawai'i at Mānoa | William S. Richardson School of Law

ABA Approved Since 1974

GPA and LSAT Scores

	Total	Full-Time	Part-Time
# of apps	1,151	1,098	318
# of offers	269	224	45
# of matrics	124	87	37
75% GPA	3.68	3.68	3.61
Median GPA	3.45	3.51	3.43
25% GPA	3.18	3.21	3.02
75% LSAT	158	160	154
Median LSAT	156	157	151
25% LSAT	153	155	147

Grants and Scholarships (from prior year)

	Total #	Total %	Full-Time #	Full-Time %	Part-Time #	Part-Time %
Total # of students	300		264		36	
Total # receiving grants	95	31.7	93	35.2	2	5.6
Less than 1/2 tuition	76	25.3	74	28.0	2	5.6
Half to full tuition	18	6.0	18	6.8	0	0.0
Full tuition	1	0.3	1	0.4	0	0.0
More than full tuition	0	0.0	0	0.0	0	0.0
Median grant amount			$5,223		$5,223	

Informational and Library Resources

Total amount spent on library materials	$452,855
Study seating capacity inside the library	380
# of full-time equivalent professional librarians	5
Hours per week library is open	94
# of open, wired connections available to students	266
# of networked computers available for use by students	45
Has wireless network?	Y
Require computer?	Y

JD Attrition (from prior year)

	Academic #	Other #	Total #	Total %
1st year	0	6	6	5.1
2nd year	0	2	2	2.2
3rd year	0	0	0	0.0
4th year	0	0	0	0.0

Employment (9 months after graduation)

	Total	Percentage
Employment status known	98	100.0
Employment status unknown	0	0.0
Employed	90	91.8
Pursuing graduate degrees	3	3.1
Unemployed (seeking, not seeking, or studying for the bar)	0	0.0
Type of Employment		
# employed in law firms	33	36.7
# employed in business and industry	8	8.9
# employed in government	17	18.9
# employed in public interest	4	4.4
# employed as judicial clerks	22	24.4
# employed in academia	6	6.7
Geographic Location		
# employed in state	74	82.2
# employed in foreign countries	3	3.3
# of states where employed	8	

Bar Passage Rates

First-time takers	91	Reporting %	81.32
Average school %	86.49	Average state %	88.48
Average pass difference	−1.99		

Jurisdiction	Takers	Passers	Pass %	State %	Diff %
Hawaii	74	64	86.49	88.48	−1.99

University of Hawai'i at Mānoa | William S. Richardson School of Law

2515 Dole Street
Honolulu, HI 96822-2350
Phone: 808.956.7966; Fax: 808.956.3813
E-mail: lawadm@hawaii.edu; Website: www.law.hawaii.edu

■ Introduction

The William S. Richardson School of Law at the University of Hawai'i is located at the foot of beautiful Mānoa Valley, minutes from sandy beaches and lush rain forests, as well as from the economic and legal center of urban Honolulu. We offer an excellent academic program with professors committed to outstanding teaching, scholarship, and community service. Our school is also noted for its collegial atmosphere, accessible faculty, and extraordinary cultural and ethnic diversity.

Placement after graduation is consistently very high. Our distinguished alumni serve as leaders in Hawai'i, as well as in national and international arenas. We are recognized in particular as a center for studies in environmental law, Native Hawaiian law, and international law with an Asian and Pacific focus. The William S. Richardson School of Law is fully accredited by the American Bar Association and is a member of the American Association of Law Schools.

■ Programs of Study

We offer a three-year, full-time JD program and an evening, part-time JD program. Law students may earn certificates in Environmental Law, Pacific-Asian Legal Studies, and Native Hawaiian Law. Summer courses are available as well as specialized short courses with distinguished visiting faculty in January (J Term). We also offer a one-year LLM program for foreign lawyers studying American law.

■ Environmental Law Program

The Law School's Environmental Law Program (ELP) was established in 1988 in recognition of the special challenges our state faces in developing an environmentally sustainable economy within a unique and fragile island environment. It has grown into a comprehensive program with a regional, national, and international reputation for excellence in teaching, scholarship, and public service. The ELP has several components: (1) Certificate in Environmental Law; (2) Faculty and Student Scholarship; (3) Community Outreach and Education; (4) Moot Court; (5) Colloquia Series; (6) Off-Campus Learning; (7) Student-Led Environmental Law Society; (8) Career Counseling and Placement; and (9) Professional Service. Thanks to its dedicated faculty, alumni, and friends throughout Hawai'i and the Pacific region, ELP offers unparalleled opportunities for students interested in focusing their studies in the environmental law field.

■ Pacific-Asian Legal Studies

Enhanced by Hawai'i's location, population, culture, and economic relationships, we offer a strong program in Pacific-Asian Legal Studies (PALS). The program has the two-fold purpose of conducting research and enriching the JD curriculum. Many faculty members have expertise in Pacific/Asian scholarship, teaching, and law reform. Recent course offerings in PALS have included, for example, Chinese Business Law, Chinese Law and Society, Pacific Island Legal Systems, Korean Law, Philippine Law, Japanese Law and

Society, and US-Japan Business Transactions. The certificate in Pacific-Asian Legal Studies allows students to focus their coursework and to earn recognition of their specialization in addition to the JD.

Selected students may do a full semester externship for academic credit with the court systems in certain Pacific Island nations or, with approval, in agencies or entities in Asia or elsewhere. Students may also arrange a semester of study with law faculties in Asia.

■ Ka Huli Ao Center for Excellence in Native Hawaiian Law

Ka Huli Ao Center for Excellence in Native Hawaiian Law was established in 2005 by a federal grant administered by the US Department of Education. The Center focuses on education, research, community outreach, and the preservation of invaluable historical, legal, traditional, and customary materials. It offers new courses and supports Native Hawaiian law students as they pursue legal careers and leadership roles. Students may earn a certificate in Native Hawaiian Law.

■ Clinical Opportunities

All students are required to take at least one clinical course, and most students will take many such practice courses. We offer an extensive number of clinical and professional skills opportunities. Clinical courses teach and model excellent practical skills and stress a reflective method of looking at lawyering behavior. These courses are taught by full-time faculty as well as by some of Hawai'i's finest judges and lawyers who evaluate and mentor student efforts in presenting oral arguments, handling depositions, and negotiating for their clients in simulated sessions as well as with real clients. Skills taught in the various clinical courses include interviewing, counseling, drafting, fact investigation, negotiation, alternative dispute resolution, motion practice, trial practice, appellate practice, and legal writing. Our Clinical Program directly addresses the legal problems faced by Hawai'i's most vulnerable people.

■ Community Service and Pro Bono

Our Pro Bono Program introduces students to public interest voluntary service and encourages them to respond directly to unmet needs in the community. Each student must do at least 60 hours of law-related work in one or more agencies or projects approved by the Law School pro bono advisor. In the past, students have worked for such public service groups as the Legal Aid Society of Hawai'i, Volunteer Legal Services, Native Hawaiian Legal Corporation, and the Earthjustice Legal Defense Fund.

■ JD Admission

Admission to both our full- and part-time JD programs is determined by an applicant's academic achievement, aptitude for the study of law, and professional promise. Preference is given to residents of Hawai'i and to nonresidents with strong ties to, or special interest in,

University of Hawai'i at Mānoa | William S. Richardson School of Law

Hawai'i, the Asia/Pacific region, environmental law, or other programs in the Law School. Approximately 20 percent of the student body are nonresidents.

In addition to the LSAT and undergraduate GPA, factors considered for admission include academic work beyond the bachelor's degree, work experience, writing ability, community service, diversity, overcoming hardship, and unusual accomplishments.

Applications from students wishing to transfer, or from those wishing to visit for a semester or two, are considered for both August and January admission.

■ LLM Admission

Our Master of Laws (LLM) Program is restricted to applicants who have earned a bachelor's degree in law, or its equivalent, from an institution outside the United States. Admission decisions are based upon a candidate's transcripts of previous law study, work experience, English writing ability, letters of recommendation, and TOEFL or IELTS scores. There is no LSAT requirement.

■ Student Activities

Student editorial boards publish the *University of Hawai'i Law Review* and the online *Asian-Pacific Law and Policy Journal*. Students also organize and participate in many facets of the moot court program, including competing in several national moot court competitions. Student teams regularly have performed very well, bringing home national and international titles and awards.

Most students are active in a variety of organizations within the Law School and in the Honolulu community. A sampling includes Advocates for Public Interest Law (APIL), student divisions of the American Bar Association and American Trial Lawyers Association, American Inns of Court, Phi Delta Phi and Delta Theta Phi, Association of Women Law Students, Hawai'i Women Lawyers, and the Environmental Law Society. Student affinity groups include the Filipino Law Students Association; Black Law Students Association; Hispanic Law Students Association; LAMBDA; and the 'Ahahui O Hawai'i, an organization of Native Hawaiian law students.

■ Library and Physical Facilities

The library assigns study carrels with wired and wireless internet access. Seminar/discussion rooms are also available for study groups. The classroom building features a moot courtroom and an open courtyard for informal conversations and activities. Law students have full access to all facilities of the University, including the health, counseling, and computing centers, as well as extensive athletic facilities. The classroom building has wireless Internet throughout for students, faculty, and staff.

■ Career Services

We assist students and alumni in obtaining part-time, summer, and associate positions in both the public and private sectors through our Career Development Office. Most students choose to remain in Hawai'i and the Asia/Pacific region, so that about 85 percent of our graduates work in Hawai'i after graduation. Many firms in Honolulu, government employers, and public interest organizations participate in the fall on-campus interview season for second- and third-year students. Our students also are unusually successful in obtaining sought-after judicial clerkships upon graduation. Recent graduating classes have had an employment rate six months after graduation varying from 90–100 percent.

Applicant Profile

University of Hawai'i at Mānoa | William S. Richardson School of Law
This grid includes only applicants who earned 120–180 LSAT scores under standard administrations.

LSAT Score	GPA 3.75 + Apps	Adm	3.50–3.74 Apps	Adm	3.25–3.49 Apps	Adm	3.00–3.24 Apps	Adm	2.75–2.99 Apps	Adm	2.50–2.74 Apps	Adm	2.25–2.49 Apps	Adm	2.00–2.24 Apps	Adm	Below 2.00 Apps	Adm	No GPA Apps	Adm	Totals Apps	Adm
175–180	0	0	0	0	0	0	0	0	0	0	0	0	0	0	0	0	0	0	0	0	0	0
170–174	2	2	0	0	3	3	1	0	1	0	0	0	2	0	0	0	0	0	0	0	9	5
165–169	6	5	13	8	5	1	5	3	7	1	6	0	0	0	0	0	0	0	0	0	42	18
160–164	25	19	32	22	20	12	27	8	11	3	8	2	5	0	0	0	0	0	2	2	130	68
155–159	25	15	53	27	70	27	58	14	28	5	13	1	10	0	2	0	3	0	3	3	265	92
150–154	24	6	50	16	88	18	69	15	37	2	19	1	11	1	4	0	0	0	13	5	315	64
145–149	17	4	22	4	42	2	48	1	43	2	18	0	11	0	3	0	0	0	5	0	211	13
140–144	6	1	11	2	15	0	24	0	28	0	23	0	4	0	5	1	0	0	2	0	118	4
135–139	1	1	2	0	3	0	7	0	11	1	9	0	3	1	2	0	0	0	0	0	38	3
130–134	0	0	0	0	2	0	0	0	4	0	2	0	0	0	3	0	1	0	3	0	15	0
125–129	0	0	1	0	2	0	0	0	0	0	1	0	0	0	0	0	0	0	0	0	4	0
120–124	0	0	0	0	0	0	0	0	0	0	0	0	0	0	0	0	0	0	0	0	0	0
Total	106	53	184	79	250	63	243	41	168	14	97	4	49	2	17	1	5	0	28	10	1147	267

Apps = Number of Applicants   Adm = Number Admitted   Reflects 99% of the total applicant pool; average LSAT data reported.

Hofstra University School of Law

121 Hofstra University
Hempstead, NY 11549
Phone: 516.463.5916; Fax: 516.463.6264
E-mail: lawadmissions@hofstra.edu; Website: http://law.hofstra.edu

ABA
Approved
Since
1971

AMERICAN BAR ASSOCIATION
Section of Legal Education
and Admissions to the Bar

The Basics

Type of school	Private
Term	Semester
Application deadline	4/15
Application fee	$75
Financial aid deadline	4/1
Can first year start other than fall?	No
Student to faculty ratio	15.4 to 1
# of housing spaces available restricted to law students	
graduate housing for which law students are eligible	225

Faculty and Administrators

	Total		Men		Women		Minorities	
	Spr	Fall	Spr	Fall	Spr	Fall	Spr	Fall
Full-time	54	60	31	43	23	17	9	10
Other full-time	1	1	0	0	1	1	0	0
Deans, librarians, & others who teach	4	3	0	0	4	3	1	1
Part-time	42	39	35	35	7	4	5	7
Total	101	103	66	78	35	25	15	18

JD Enrollment and Ethnicity

	Men		Women		Full-Time		Part-Time		1st-Year		Total		JD Degs. Awd.
	#	%	#	%	#	%	#	%	#	%	#	%	
African Amer.	19	3.3	73	13.5	69	7.3	23	13.5	23	5.9	92	8.3	30
Amer. Indian	1	0.2	3	0.6	4	0.4	0	0.0	2	0.5	4	0.4	0
Asian Amer.	52	9.1	57	10.6	92	9.8	17	10.0	51	13.0	109	9.8	34
Mex. Amer.	5	0.9	3	0.6	8	0.9	0	0.0	4	1.0	8	0.7	1
Puerto Rican	2	0.4	13	2.4	11	1.2	4	2.4	5	1.3	15	1.4	3
Hispanic	30	5.3	40	7.4	57	6.1	13	7.6	23	5.9	70	6.3	14
Total Minority	109	19.2	189	35.0	241	25.7	57	33.5	108	27.5	298	26.9	82
For. Nation.	17	3.0	16	3.0	31	3.3	2	1.2	15	3.8	33	3.0	4
Caucasian	397	69.8	302	55.9	606	64.5	93	54.7	259	65.9	699	63.0	226
Unknown	46	8.1	33	6.1	61	6.5	18	10.6	11	2.8	79	7.1	50
Total	569	51.3	540	48.7	939	84.7	170	15.3	393	35.4	1109		362

Curriculum

	Full-Time	Part-Time
Typical first-year section size	97	81
Is there typically a "small section" of the first-year class, other than Legal Writing, taught by full-time faculty	Yes	Yes
If yes, typical size offered last year	32	45
# of classroom course titles beyond first-year curriculum	131	

# of upper division courses, excluding seminars, with an enrollment:		
Under 25	79	
25–49	52	
50–74	12	
75–99	19	
100+	4	

# of seminars	50	
# of seminar positions available	1,000	
# of seminar positions filled	585	126
# of positions available in simulation courses	1,059	
# of simulation positions filled	671	200
# of positions available in faculty supervised clinical courses	150	
# of faculty supervised clinical positions filled	117	17
# involved in field placements	104	16
# involved in law journals	181	7
# involved in moot court or trial competitions	42	0
# of credit hours required to graduate	87	

Transfers

Transfers in	10
Transfers out	37

Tuition and Fees

	Resident	Nonresident
Full-time	$41,780	$41,780
Part-time	$31,259	$31,259
Tuition Guarantee Program	N	

Living Expenses

Estimated living expenses for singles

Living on campus	Living off campus	Living at home
$22,352	$20,573	$9,596

Hofstra University School of Law

ABA
Approved
Since
1971

GPA and LSAT Scores

	Total	Full-Time	Part-Time
# of apps	4,893	4,573	320
# of offers	1,891	1,853	38
# of matrics	401	391	10
75% GPA	3.70	3.70	3.67
Median GPA	3.56	3.56	3.41
25% GPA	3.27	3.27	3.08
75% LSAT	159	159	158
Median LSAT	157	157	156
25% LSAT	155	155	152

Grants and Scholarships (from prior year)

	Total		Full-Time		Part-Time	
	#	%	#	%	#	%
Total # of students	1,143		847		296	
Total # receiving grants	441	38.6	397	46.9	44	14.9
Less than 1/2 tuition	241	21.1	218	25.7	23	7.8
Half to full tuition	153	13.4	137	16.2	16	5.4
Full tuition	47	4.1	42	5.0	5	1.7
More than full tuition	0	0.0	0	0.0	0	0.0
Median grant amount			$16,000		$12,000	

Informational and Library Resources

Total amount spent on library materials	$1,452,916
Study seating capacity inside the library	490
# of full-time equivalent professional librarians	12
Hours per week library is open	101
# of open, wired connections available to students	160
# of networked computers available for use by students	78
Has wireless network?	Y
Require computer?	N

JD Attrition (from prior year)

	Academic	Other	Total	
	#	#	#	%
1st year	11	47	58	15.3
2nd year	0	3	3	0.9
3rd year	0	1	1	0.3
4th year	0	0	0	0.0

Employment (9 months after graduation)

	Total	Percentage
Employment status known	342	99.7
Employment status unknown	1	0.3
Employed	320	93.6
Pursuing graduate degrees	7	2.0
Unemployed (seeking, not seeking, or studying for the bar)	12	3.5
Type of Employment		
# employed in law firms	154	48.1
# employed in business and industry	83	25.9
# employed in government	41	12.8
# employed in public interest	9	2.8
# employed as judicial clerks	18	5.6
# employed in academia	10	3.1
Geographic Location		
# employed in state	269	84.1
# employed in foreign countries	0	0.0
# of states where employed	18	

Bar Passage Rates

First-time takers	350	Reporting %	88.57
Average school %	86.45	Average state %	88.98
Average pass difference	−2.53		

Jurisdiction	Takers	Passers	Pass %	State %	Diff %
New York	310	268	86.45	88.98	−2.53

Hofstra University School of Law

121 Hofstra University
Hempstead, NY 11549
Phone: 516.463.5916; Fax: 516.463.6264
E-mail: lawadmissions@hofstra.edu; Website: http://law.hofstra.edu

■ Introduction

Hofstra Law School prepares motivated students to have an impact in the legal community and beyond. For nearly 40 years, the Law School has provided an education rich in both the theory and skills needed to produce outstanding lawyers, business executives, and community leaders. Located on the campus of Hofstra University in Hempstead, New York, the Law School is 20 miles outside New York City in suburban Long Island. Hofstra Law School offers a JD program, as well as LLM graduate degrees in American Legal Studies (for foreign law graduates) and Family Law. Joint degrees are available in conjunction with the University's Frank G. Zarb School of Business (JD/MBA) and College of Liberal Arts and Sciences (JD/MA in Applied Social Research and Policy Analysis).

■ Vibrant Campus Life

Hofstra Law School, situated on the 240-acre Hofstra University main campus, provides a vibrant community for students studying the law. Few, if any, law schools can match the combination of Hofstra Law's lush campus and its easy access to New York City, the hub of the nation's legal profession. Students living on campus in graduate housing enjoy a parklike setting that is home to one of the country's great arboretums. Yet, they can also take a free Hofstra shuttle bus to train stations that provide service to Manhattan in less than 40 minutes or drive just a few miles to world-class beaches.

■ Cutting-Edge Curriculum

As one of only a few US law schools to require Transnational Law as a first-year course, Hofstra Law School is at the forefront of the changing realities of legal practice. This innovative course allows students to put their studies into a broader context by exploring the relationship between international law, foreign legal systems, and the American legal system. With more than 200 upper-level course offerings, students can explore practically any area of law, and they can craft an individualized course of study from the Law School's 15 area-specific concentrations. Hofstra's advanced curriculum helps to develop well-trained and highly employable professionals. In fact, a recent survey of tristate law firms conducted by the Hanover Research Council revealed that compared to graduates from other law schools, Hofstra graduates received an overall higher rating in a majority of competencies, including business knowledge, communication skills, advocacy skills, and general workplace skills.

■ Internationally Renowned Faculty

Hofstra Law School's full-time faculty consists of more than 50 nationally and internationally recognized scholars who represent diverse fields. Faculty members have clerked for US Supreme Court justices, chaired major American Bar Association and law reform committees, received awards for scholarship and leadership in legal education and community affairs, and are recognized leaders in clinical and skills training. In the past five years, the Law School's full-time faculty members wrote or edited more than 20 books and

250 articles and essays. These publications reflect a wide range of interests and expertise, ongoing participation in important scholarly debates, and significant contributions to the study and teaching of law. The faculty's open-door policy creates an accessible and collegial environment and reflects its engagement with students.

■ Student Life

Hofstra students publish four journals: *Hofstra Law Review*, *Hofstra Labor & Employment Law Journal*, *Family Court Review*, and *Hofstra Journal of International Business and Law*. There are more than 40 student organizations, ranging from Hofstra Law Women and the Black Law Students Association to the Public Justice Foundation and the Corporate Law Society.

■ Professional Career Services

The Office of Career Services (OCS) provides a wide range of services to facilitate the career and professional development of Hofstra Law students, including helping students find employment in both the private and public sectors. OCS provides individual career and professional-development counseling, educational programming, mock interviews, an extensive online employer database, and comprehensive on-campus interviewing. OCS's team of experienced career counselors is available to assist students with all phases of the job search; one counselor is specifically dedicated to promoting postgraduate judicial clerkships and opportunities with government agencies and public interest organizations. In addition, OCS has developed an innovative Classroom to Career program (C2C), highlighting critical elements of professional development and soft skills not taught as part of a traditional law school curriculum. The thoughtful and professional guidance of OCS has helped Hofstra students obtain positions with private law firms, government agencies, public interest organizations, and federal and state judges.

■ Revolutionary Clinical Program

Hofstra Law is widely recognized as a pioneer in fully integrating clinical education into a traditional law school curriculum. By the late 1970s, the school had one of the largest clinical programs in the nation. Over the years, its clinics have become well-known in legal circles in the metropolitan area. As students represent individuals facing real legal challenges, they gain valuable hands-on experience: they advocate in court, counsel clients, conduct fact investigations, and mediate disputes. Hofstra's current clinical opportunities are in Asylum, Child Advocacy, Community and Economic Development, Criminal Justice, Law Reform Advocacy, Mediation, and Securities Arbitration.

■ Training for Legal Practice

Recognizing that the well-rounded graduate needs to apply classroom theory to real-world situations, the Law School offers extensive skills and simulation-based training. The Externship Program provides an opportunity to gain

substantive legal experience under the direct supervision and guidance of an experienced attorney. Other training tools include moot court competitions, conferences, workshops with accomplished attorneys, intensive pretrial and mediation courses, and a trial techniques program based on the curriculum of the National Institute for Trial Advocacy.

■ International Legal Education

The Law School offers extensive study-abroad programs, including summer sessions in Freiburg, Germany; Pisa, Italy; and Sydney, Australia as well as a winter intersession in Curaçao. These programs have featured prominent jurists, such as Supreme Court Justices Antonin Scalia and Ruth Bader Ginsburg. Hofstra Law School is also a founding member of the European-American Consortium for Legal Education, which allows students to participate in a semester-long exchange program with Belgium's Ghent University, Finland's Helsinki University, the Netherlands' Erasmus University Rotterdam, Italy's Parma University, or Poland's Warsaw University.

■ Engaging Centers and Institutes

Both nationally and internationally recognized, Hofstra Law School's centers and institutes attract thought leaders for research, debate, and the exchange of knowledge.

Center for Applied Legal Reasoning: This multidisciplinary center focuses on the study of theories of legal reasoning and the development of pedagogies to train students for the practice of law.

Center for Children, Families and the Law: An interdisciplinary organization, this center is dedicated to education, research, and public service focused on children and families involved in the legal system.

Center for Legal Advocacy: This center features innovative programs aimed at improving client representation skills and enhancing the level of advocacy in the profession.

Institute for Health Law and Policy: Designed to train attorneys in the field of health law, this institute concentrates on the study and formulation of health care policy.

Institute for the Study of Conflict Transformation: This institute promotes the understanding of conflict processes and intervention from the transformative mediation framework.

Institute for the Study of Legal Ethics: As a research center, this institute explores critical issues concerning lawyers' ethics and the legal profession.

Institute for the Study of Gender, Law and Policy: The mission of this institute is to facilitate teaching, research, and scholarship concerning gender as it relates to law and public policy.

Law, Logic and Technology Research Laboratory: This laboratory provides a unique setting for the study of how the quality of legal reasoning impacts the rule of law.

■ Rewarding Fellowships and Scholarships

Each year, the Law School awards fellowships to entering JD students based on their demonstrated commitment to advocacy in several areas. Fellowship recipients receive tuition assistance, gain valuable internship experience, and pursue a course of study that provides the knowledge and skills needed to make an impact in their chosen field. The **Child and Family Advocacy Fellowship** is awarded to individuals who plan to use their legal education to advocate for the interests of children and families. The **Health Law and Policy Fellowship** is awarded to individuals who want to represent medical providers, patients, and pharmaceutical companies and advance health law policy. The **Lesbian, Gay, Bisexual and Transgender Rights Fellowship** is awarded to individuals who plan to use their legal education to advocate for the interests of the LGBT community. The **Dwight L. Greene Memorial Scholarship** is awarded to individuals who have a commitment to advocacy on behalf of minority groups. Other endowed scholarships are available for entering and continuing law students. Information about these opportunities is available at *http://law.hofstra.edu*.

Applicant Profile

Admission to Hofstra Law School is competitive. Full-time students in the most recent entering class had a median LSAT score of 157 and a median undergraduate GPA of 3.56. The Admissions Committee reviews not only applicant's academic record and LSAT performance, but the entire application to determine whether the applicant is likely to be successful at Hofstra Law. Hofstra Law seeks a diverse student body made up of individuals who will thrive in the School's experiential-learning program that trains them to make an impact in the legal profession, the business world and society.

University of Houston Law Center

100 Law Center
Houston, TX 77204-6060
Phone: 713.743.2280; Fax: 713.743.2194
E-mail: lawadmissions@uh.edu; Website: www.law.uh.edu

ABA
Approved
Since
1950

The Basics

Type of school	Public
Term	Semester
Application deadline	11/15 2/15 5/15
Application fee	$70
Financial aid deadline	4/1
Can first year start other than fall?	No
Student to faculty ratio	11.8 to 1
# of housing spaces available restricted to law students	20
graduate housing for which law students are eligible	850

Faculty and Administrators

	Total		Men		Women		Minorities	
	Spr	Fall	Spr	Fall	Spr	Fall	Spr	Fall
Full-time	60	57	43	39	17	18	8	9
Other full-time	11	11	4	4	7	7	1	1
Deans, librarians, & others who teach	4	4	4	4	0	0	0	0
Part-time	82	69	62	47	20	22	13	13
Total	157	141	113	94	44	47	22	23

JD Enrollment and Ethnicity

	Men		Women		Full-Time		Part-Time		1st-Year		Total		JD Degs. Awd.
	#	%	#	%	#	%	#	%	#	%	#	%	
African Amer.	25	5.0	47	11.9	52	7.3	20	10.9	21	8.3	72	8.0	16
Amer. Indian	2	0.4	2	0.5	2	0.3	2	1.1	2	0.8	4	0.4	0
Asian Amer.	48	9.5	44	11.1	72	10.1	20	10.9	29	11.4	92	10.2	36
Mex. Amer.	25	5.0	23	5.8	39	5.5	9	4.9	12	4.7	48	5.3	3
Puerto Rican	0	0.0	2	0.5	1	0.1	1	0.5	2	0.8	2	0.2	0
Hispanic	16	3.2	22	5.6	33	4.6	5	2.7	5	2.0	38	4.2	25
Total Minority	116	23.1	140	35.4	199	27.8	57	31.1	71	28.0	256	28.5	80
For. Nation.	9	1.8	4	1.0	12	1.7	1	0.5	3	1.2	13	1.4	0
Caucasian	375	74.6	247	62.5	498	69.7	124	67.8	178	70.1	622	69.3	204
Unknown	3	0.6	4	1.0	6	0.8	1	0.5	2	0.8	7	0.8	2
Total	503	56.0	395	44.0	715	79.6	183	20.4	254	28.3	898		286

Curriculum

	Full-Time	Part-Time
Typical first-year section size	70	50
Is there typically a "small section" of the first-year class, other than Legal Writing, taught by full-time faculty	Yes	Yes
If yes, typical size offered last year	35	25

# of classroom course titles beyond first-year curriculum		196
# of upper division courses, excluding seminars, with an enrollment:	Under 25	125
	25–49	38
	50–74	17
	75–99	10
	100+	3
# of seminars		25
# of seminar positions available		362
# of seminar positions filled	235	52
# of positions available in simulation courses		626
# of simulation positions filled	387	77
# of positions available in faculty supervised clinical courses		180
# of faculty supervised clinical positions filled	155	11
# involved in field placements	153	7
# involved in law journals	148	22
# involved in moot court or trial competitions	88	28
# of credit hours required to graduate		90

Transfers

Transfers in	8
Transfers out	2

Tuition and Fees

	Resident	Nonresident
Full-time	$21,029	$28,439
Part-time	$15,125	$20,065
Tuition Guarantee Program		N

Living Expenses

Estimated living expenses for singles

Living on campus	Living off campus	Living at home
$12,512	$15,456	$9,410

University of Houston Law Center

ABA Approved Since 1950

GPA and LSAT Scores

	Total	Full-Time	Part-Time
# of apps	3,652	3,021	631
# of offers	903	817	86
# of matrics	256	205	51
75% GPA	3.62	3.63	3.54
Median GPA	3.34	3.37	3.28
25% GPA	3.08	3.08	3.02
75% LSAT	163	164	161
Median LSAT	161	162	160
25% LSAT	159	160	156

Grants and Scholarships (from prior year)

	Total		Full-Time		Part-Time	
	#	%	#	%	#	%
Total # of students	948		748		200	
Total # receiving grants	467	49.3	467	62.4	0	0.0
Less than 1/2 tuition	407	42.9	407	54.4	0	0.0
Half to full tuition	54	5.7	54	7.2	0	0.0
Full tuition	6	0.6	6	0.8	0	0.0
More than full tuition	0	0.0	0	0.0	0	0.0
Median grant amount			$5,000		$0	

Informational and Library Resources

Total amount spent on library materials	$1,282,530
Study seating capacity inside the library	546
# of full-time equivalent professional librarians	10
Hours per week library is open	107
# of open, wired connections available to students	12
# of networked computers available for use by students	15
Has wireless network?	Y
Require computer?	N

JD Attrition (from prior year)

	Academic	Other	Total	
	#	#	#	%
1st year	0	3	3	1.0
2nd year	1	9	10	3.4
3rd year	0	4	4	1.3
4th year	0	1	1	2.2

Employment (9 months after graduation)

	Total	Percentage
Employment status known	300	99.3
Employment status unknown	2	0.7
Employed	288	96.0
Pursuing graduate degrees	3	1.0
Unemployed (seeking, not seeking, or studying for the bar)	7	2.3
Type of Employment		
# employed in law firms	166	57.6
# employed in business and industry	61	21.2
# employed in government	29	10.1
# employed in public interest	12	4.2
# employed as judicial clerks	11	3.8
# employed in academia	6	2.1
Geographic Location		
# employed in state	261	90.6
# employed in foreign countries	2	0.7
# of states where employed	15	

Bar Passage Rates

First-time takers	287	Reporting %	96.52
Average school %	91.34	Average state %	84.54
Average pass difference	6.80		

Jurisdiction	Takers	Passers	Pass %	State %	Diff %
Texas	277	253	91.34	84.54	6.80

University of Houston Law Center

100 Law Center
Houston, TX 77204-6060
Phone: 713.743.2280; Fax: 713.743.2194
E-mail: lawadmissions@uh.edu; Website: www.law.uh.edu

■ Introduction

The University of Houston (UH) Law Center is located at the University of Houston, three miles south of downtown. The state-assisted UH Law Center, located in one of the nation's top 10 largest legal markets, is noted throughout the South and Southwest not only for its excellence, but also for its progressive and innovative approach to the teaching of law. The College of Law, the academic branch of the UH Law Center, is fully accredited by the American Bar Association and the American Association of Law Schools and has a chapter of the Order of the Coif, the national legal honorary scholastic society. The Law Center confers a Juris Doctor (JD) degree as a first degree in law and a Master of Laws (LLM) degree to students pursuing work beyond the JD degree.

■ Curriculum/Basic Program of Study

The first-year curriculum at the UH Law Center is prescribed. Students are also required to complete a course in professional responsibility and one major piece of legal research and writing before graduation. Emphasis is placed on legal theory and the varying approaches to the law.

■ Special Programs

The University of Houston Law Center emphasizes current legal and administrative problems confronting the region and nation, including intellectual property law, environmental law, energy law, tax law, health law, and international law. The UH Law Center is home to the Health Law and Policy Institute, a research and instruction center on interdisciplinary issues. The UH Law Center is also host to the Criminal Justice Institute; the Institute for Higher Education Law and Governance; the Institute for Intellectual Property and Information Law; the Center for Environment, Energy and Natural Resources Law; the Center for Children, Law, and Policy; the Blakely Advocacy Institute; and the Center for Consumer Law.

■ Clinical Programs and Trial Advocacy

The UH Law Center offers a wide variety of opportunities to gain hands-on experience. The UH Law Center houses several clinics, which gives students practice opportunities in providing legal services to indigent clients. The available clinics include the civil practice clinic, consumer law clinic, criminal practice clinic, immigration clinic, mediation clinic, and transactional clinic. Students can also choose from among different areas of concentration, such as externships focusing on health or environmental law or select an internship with a government agency or a court.

Practice skills courses coordinated through the Blakely Advocacy Institute are an integral part of the curriculum. Students can enhance their skills in trial, negotiation, pretrial, and appellate work through hands-on courses that simulate real-life situations. Several levels of courses are offered in civil and criminal advocacy. Intramural mock trial and moot court competitions are sponsored by the Advocates, an affiliated student organization. The institute also sponsors teams for criminal and civil interscholastic moot court and mock trial competitions, with UH Law Center students earning top honors in national and international competitions.

■ Activities

Extracurricular activities give voice to the diversity of the campus. Student groups represent special interests and provide important avenues to help law students succeed. Many arrange mentoring programs and match first-year students with second- or third-year students or working professionals. Others coordinate résumé-writing workshops, guest speaker forums, preregistration discussions of specific course offerings, or law-related charitable efforts that benefit the community.

The Student Bar Association (SBA) has input into every facet of student life at the UH Law Center. The SBA participates in the first-year orientation, organizes the annual charity Fun Run, aids in the selection of student representatives to sit on various faculty committees, and represents student attitudes and views both within and outside the UH Law Center.

Students are encouraged to become involved in one or more student organizations; to participate in the scholarly *Houston Law Review, Houston Journal of International Law, Houston Journal of Health Law and Policy, Houston Business and Tax Law Journal, Environmental and Energy Law and Policy Journal,* and the *Journal of Consumer and Commercial Law;* and to compete in tournaments ranging from moot court to mock trial, from mediation to negotiation.

UH Law Center students are active in a large number of student organizations including the Association of Women in Law, Black Law Students Association, Hispanic Law Students Association, Asian Law Students Association, Outlaw (GLBT student organization), Lex Judaica (Jewish students), Muslim Law Students Association, J. Reuben Clark Law Society, Christian Legal Society, Public Interest Law Organization, Health Law Organization, Intellectual Property Student Organization, Energy and Environmental Law Society, Federalist Society, International Law Society, American Constitution Society for Law and Policy, Phi Delta Phi, Phi Alpha Delta, Delta Theta Phi, and Sports and Entertainment Law Organization.

■ Career Development

The Office of Career Development strives for a creative approach in its job search partnership with students. The First Year Initiative exposes first-year students to a comprehensive career education series that surveys dozens of career opportunities. Students in small groups actively gather the information they need to make informed decisions on their career plans.

The Office of Career Development also presents a variety of panel discussions, receptions, and seminars with members of the Houston legal community to assist students in understanding law career options. Topics covered include duties and responsibilities of a law clerk, judicial clerkship opportunities, solo practice, and nontraditional uses of a law degree.

The office provides individual assistance in résumé preparation and interviewing techniques for all students and

alumni. The annual On Campus Interview Program for second- and third-year students seeking summer clerkships and permanent positions to commence upon graduation attracts approximately 100 prospective employers to the campus.

■ Admission

The UH Law Center enrolls full-time (day) students and part-time (evening) students beginning in the fall semester, which starts in August. There is no spring or summer admission.

Demonstrated academic ability and strong LSAT scores are not the only criteria for admission. Consideration is also given to background, achievements, honors, extracurricular activities, service to others, unique abilities, hardships overcome, advanced degrees, employment, and leadership. The UH Law Center is also committed to diversity, and the UH System Board of Regents recognizes and endorses the benefits of diversity in the university setting. The Admissions Committee will consider the following additional factors: cultural history, ethnic origin, and race. These and other elements may be addressed in a personal statement of up to three pages, double-spaced.

Applicant Profile

University of Houston Law Center
This grid includes only applicants who earned 120–180 LSAT scores under standard administrations.

LSAT Score	GPA 3.75 +		3.50–3.74		3.25–3.49		3.00–3.24		2.75–2.99		2.50–2.74		Below 2.50		No GPA		Total	
	Apps	Adm	Apps	Adm	Apps	Adm	Apps	Adm	Apps	Adm	Apps	Adm	Apps	Adm	Apps	Adm	Apps	Adm
170–180	7	7	6	6	6	6	7	7	3	3	0	0	2	2	1	1	32	32
165–169	40	38	39	39	34	32	34	34	19	18	8	5	3	0	2	2	179	168
160–164	125	114	134	115	117	91	104	84	55	37	32	14	11	4	12	9	590	468
155–159	136	30	230	46	197	45	145	27	88	9	42	1	29	0	16	7	883	165
150–154	106	14	185	11	190	11	184	9	122	2	66	2	34	0	15	0	902	49
145–149	53	3	79	4	104	1	116	1	89	0	55	1	37	0	18	0	551	10
140–144	14	1	34	1	68	1	71	0	52	0	42	0	43	0	20	2	344	5
Below 140	7	0	10	0	27	0	33	0	35	0	42	1	30	0	14	0	198	1
Total	488	207	717	222	743	187	694	162	463	69	287	24	189	6	98	21	3679	898

Apps = Number of Applicants
Adm = Number Admitted
Reflects 99% of the total applicant pool; average LSAT data reported.

Howard University School of Law

Office of Admissions, 2900 Van Ness Street NW
Washington, DC 20008
Phone: 202.806.8008/8009; Fax: 202.806.8162
E-mail: admissions@law.howard.edu; Website: www.law.howard.edu

ABA
Approved
Since
1931

The Basics

Type of school	Private
Term	Semester
Application deadline	3/15
Application fee	$60
Financial aid deadline	2/15
Can first year start other than fall?	No
Student to faculty ratio	16.5 to 1
# of housing spaces available restricted to law students	
graduate housing for which law students are eligible	15

Faculty and Administrators

	Total		Men		Women		Minorities	
	Spr	Fall	Spr	Fall	Spr	Fall	Spr	Fall
Full-time	24	24	15	15	9	9	19	19
Other full-time	7	7	2	2	5	5	7	7
Deans, librarians, & others who teach	9	7	3	3	6	4	8	6
Part-time	26	21	16	12	10	9	18	11
Total	66	59	36	32	30	27	52	43

Curriculum

		Full-Time	Part-Time
Typical first-year section size		50	0
Is there typically a "small section" of the first-year class, other than Legal Writing, taught by full-time faculty		No	No
If yes, typical size offered last year			
# of classroom course titles beyond first-year curriculum		120	
# of upper division courses, excluding seminars, with an enrollment:	Under 25	69	
	25–49	19	
	50–74	12	
	75–99	0	
	100+	0	
# of seminars		35	
# of seminar positions available		525	
# of seminar positions filled		263	0
# of positions available in simulation courses		325	
# of simulation positions filled		274	0
# of positions available in faculty supervised clinical courses		206	
# of faculty supervised clinical positions filled		104	0
# involved in field placements		54	0
# involved in law journals		60	0
# involved in moot court or trial competitions		47	0
# of credit hours required to graduate		88	

JD Enrollment and Ethnicity

	Men		Women		Full-Time		Part-Time		1st-Year		Total		JD Degs. Awd.
	#	%	#	%	#	%	#	%	#	%	#	%	
African Amer.	142	77.2	224	78.9	366	78.2	0	0.0	123	74.5	366	78.2	99
Amer. Indian	3	1.6	2	0.7	5	1.1	0	0.0	1	0.6	5	1.1	0
Asian Amer.	10	5.4	14	4.9	24	5.1	0	0.0	7	4.2	24	5.1	10
Mex. Amer.	2	1.1	1	0.4	3	0.6	0	0.0	0	0.0	3	0.6	0
Puerto Rican	1	0.5	3	1.1	4	0.9	0	0.0	0	0.0	4	0.9	0
Hispanic	3	1.6	3	1.1	6	1.3	0	0.0	4	2.4	6	1.3	1
Total Minority	161	87.5	247	87.0	408	87.2	0	0.0	135	81.8	408	87.2	110
For. Nation.	6	3.3	19	6.7	25	5.3	0	0.0	15	9.1	25	5.3	11
Caucasian	12	6.5	17	6.0	29	6.2	0	0.0	10	6.1	29	6.2	7
Unknown	5	2.7	1	0.4	6	1.3	0	0.0	5	3.0	6	1.3	4
Total	184	39.3	284	60.7	468	100.0	0	0.0	165	35.3	468		132

Transfers

Transfers in	0
Transfers out	4

Tuition and Fees

	Resident	Nonresident
Full-time	$24,490	$24,490
Part-time		
Tuition Guarantee Program		N

Living Expenses

Estimated living expenses for singles

Living on campus	Living off campus	Living at home
N/A	$21,981	N/A

Howard University School of Law

ABA
Approved
Since
1931

GPA and LSAT Scores

	Total	Full-Time	Part-Time
# of apps	2,000	2,000	0
# of offers	443	443	0
# of matrics	160	160	0
75% GPA	3.51	3.51	0.00
Median GPA	3.20	3.20	0.00
25% GPA	2.92	2.92	0.00
75% LSAT	156	156	0
Median LSAT	153	153	0
25% LSAT	150	150	0

Grants and Scholarships (from prior year)

	Total		Full-Time		Part-Time	
	#	%	#	%	#	%
Total # of students	454		451		3	
Total # receiving grants	251	55.3	251	55.7	0	0.0
Less than 1/2 tuition	108	23.8	108	23.9	0	0.0
Half to full tuition	119	26.2	119	26.4	0	0.0
Full tuition	5	1.1	5	1.1	0	0.0
More than full tuition	19	4.2	19	4.2	0	0.0
Median grant amount		$10,000		$0		

Informational and Library Resources

Total amount spent on library materials	$704,813
Study seating capacity inside the library	374
# of full-time equivalent professional librarians	8
Hours per week library is open	105
# of open, wired connections available to students	607
# of networked computers available for use by students	205
Has wireless network?	Y
Require computer?	Y

JD Attrition (from prior year)

	Academic	Other	Total	
	#	#	#	%
1st year	7	8	15	8.3
2nd year	3	2	5	3.6
3rd year	1	0	1	0.8
4th year	0	0	0	0.0

Employment (9 months after graduation)

	Total	Percentage
Employment status known	132	86.8
Employment status unknown	20	13.2
Employed	124	93.9
Pursuing graduate degrees	1	0.8
Unemployed (seeking, not seeking, or studying for the bar)	7	5.3
Type of Employment		
# employed in law firms	62	50.0
# employed in business and industry	12	9.7
# employed in government	20	16.1
# employed in public interest	4	3.2
# employed as judicial clerks	20	16.1
# employed in academia	0	0.0
Geographic Location		
# employed in state	43	34.7
# employed in foreign countries	0	0.0
# of states where employed		21

Bar Passage Rates

First-time takers	131	Reporting %	71.76
Average school %	63.82	Average state %	85.74
Average pass difference	−21.92		

Jurisdiction	Takers	Passers	Pass %	State %	Diff %
Maryland	39	25	64.10	85.51	−21.41
New York	36	27	75.00	88.98	−13.98
California	11	3	27.27	78.07	−50.80
Virginia	8	5	62.50	82.70	−20.20

Howard University School of Law

Office of Admissions, 2900 Van Ness Street NW
Washington, DC 20008
Phone: 202.806.8008/8009; Fax: 202.806.8162
E-mail: admissions@law.howard.edu; Website: www.law.howard.edu

■ Introduction

Howard University, a coeducational, private institution in Washington, DC, was chartered by the US Congress in 1867. Howard is historically (and continues to be) a majority African American institution that offers an educational experience of exceptional quality and value to students with high academic potential. Particular emphasis is placed on providing educational opportunities for promising African Americans and other persons of color who are underrepresented in the legal profession, as well as for nonminority persons with a strong interest in civil and human rights and public service. The main campus of Howard is located in northwest Washington, DC, on Georgia Avenue, and the law school is located on a separate 22-acre campus on Van Ness Street NW, adjacent to Connecticut Avenue, approximately three miles from the main campus.

The School of Law opened its doors in 1869. Originally, there was a great need to train lawyers with a strong commitment to helping black Americans secure and protect their newly established rights. Today, as a national law school, Howard is dedicated to protecting the rights of all Americans and understands that its place in the annals of legal history demands that it maintains and exemplifies truth, equality, and excellence in the pursuit of justice. The law school has a diverse student body and faculty. Howard University School of Law is fully accredited by the American Bar Association and the Association of American Law Schools, and certifies its graduates for bar examination in all jurisdictions of the United States.

■ Special Programs

The School of Law has a strong commitment to public service and to human and civil rights. Many programs and activities of the school reflect that fact. The school also provides an opportunity for clinical experience in civil and criminal litigation. Howard law school also offers a summer study-abroad program in comparative and international law at the University of the Western Cape in South Africa. The six-week program is approved by the ABA and offers constitutional, business, and trade law courses for credit. A student-exchange program has been established with Vermont Law School and Brigham Young University. Through the exchange program, a limited number of third-year JD students may spend a semester at one of these law schools to take advantage of curricular offerings that may be of specific interest to them.

The Institute for Intellectual Property and Social Justice (IIPSJ) is concerned with disparity of access to, and exploitation of, intellectual property as it relates to racial and economic inequities. IIPSJ's focus is on examining and utilizing intellectual property to advance social justice in this country and globally. IIPSJ sponsors numerous programs for students, attorneys, and judges; publishes papers; and supports externships for students.

■ Curriculum

The curriculum leading to the first degree in law covers three academic years of two semesters each. During the first two years, emphasis is on the fundamental analytical concepts and skills of the law and the system by which it is administered—the functions required of a lawyer within a legal system based upon the common law. The curriculum in the third year provides diversified experience and a solid foundation of whatever specialization is desired.

■ Degree Programs

The School of Law offers programs leading to the Juris Doctor (JD), Master of Laws (LLM) for foreign law graduates, and Juris Doctor/Master in Business Administration (JD/MBA) degrees.

An applicant to the JD program must have a baccalaureate degree from an accredited college or university before enrolling in the Howard University School of Law. Competitive numerical predictors for admission to Howard University include a Law School Admission Test (LSAT) score of 153 and above and an undergraduate grade-point average (UGPA) of 3.4. In addition to the LSAT score and UGPA, we consider the rigor of an applicant's undergraduate course of study, letters of recommendation (particularly from faculty members who have taught the applicant), any graduate study, employment, extracurricular activities, and other indicators of potential for success in law school and excellence in the profession.

Applicants to the JD/MBA program must apply and meet the independent admission requirements of both schools, including completion of the GMAT.

The LLM program offers foreign law graduates an opportunity to further their legal studies through advanced study and research. To be admitted as a candidate for the LLM degree, applicants must be in high academic standing; have a degree in law from an accredited foreign university or its equivalent (as determined by the faculty of law); and have some experience in the judiciary, administrative establishment, bar, or law faculty.

■ Research Facilities

Howard University School of Law has a state-of-the-art, four-story, 76,000-square-foot law library. This facility provides space for a book collection of up to 215,000 volumes; seating for over 295 students (more than 70 percent of the student population), including 90 open carrels, with all locations wired for computer use; enlarged microfilm and audiovisual facilities; and distinctive rooms of wood and brick for special collections, newspaper and periodical reading, and the rare book collection.

The law library is both a working collection for law students and lawyers and a research institution for legal scholars. The civil rights archive contains briefs, working papers, and materials of the NAACP and other civil rights organizations. The library has a collection that emphasizes civil and political rights and literature to support study of the legal problems of the poor. Its collection has been expanded to also include considerable CD-ROM resources. The law library has an online catalogue system, e-mail capabilities, and Internet access.

■ Student Activities

The *Howard Law Journal* publishes legal materials for scholarly and professional interest. The national and international moot court teams, which sponsor intramural

competition and participate in competitions nationwide, have won numerous honors. The Student Bar Association is the general student government organization. The *Barrister*, the student newspaper, publishes several issues a year. Other organizations represent students from diverse ethnic backgrounds, including African Americans, Latinos, Africans, Caribbean Islanders, and Asian Pacific Islanders.

■ Career Services

The Office of Career Services is an integral part of the law school. To assist students, the office offers workshops on job-search techniques and résumé writing, as well as seminars on career development and practice specialties. The office also maintains an extensive resource library with online employer research systems, newsletters, and updated listings of career opportunities. Each year, the Office of Career Services sponsors two on-campus interview programs, and more than 500 recruiters from law firms, government agencies, and corporations visit the law school with offers of employment for promising students and graduates. Approximately 4,500 interviews are scheduled annually. Graduates receive highly competitive and prestigious judicial clerkships and work for large and small private firms; federal, state, and local government agencies; public interest organizations; and public and private corporations throughout the United States.

Applicant Profile

Howard University School of Law
This grid includes only applicants who earned 120–180 LSAT scores under standard administrations.

LSAT Score	3.75 +		3.50–3.74		3.25–3.49		3.00–3.24		2.75–2.99		2.50–2.74		2.25–2.49		2.00–2.24		Below 2.00		No GPA		Totals	
	Apps	Adm	Apps	Adm	Apps	Adm	Apps	Adm	Apps	Adm	Apps	Adm	Apps	Adm	Apps	Adm	Apps	Adm	Apps	Adm	Apps	Adm
175–180	0	0	0	0	0	0	0	0	0	0	0	0	0	0	0	0	0	0	0	0	0	0
170–174	0	0	1	1	0	0	0	0	0	0	0	0	0	0	0	0	0	0	0	0	1	1
165–169	0	0	0	0	1	1	0	0	0	0	2	2	0	0	1	0	0	0	0	0	4	3
160–164	9	5	7	5	8	6	9	5	3	1	7	4	3	0	0	0	0	0	0	0	46	26
155–159	8	7	33	31	42	27	43	29	28	16	21	9	9	2	5	1	0	0	3	1	192	123
150–154	21	16	56	32	95	58	97	41	85	31	43	9	26	1	4	0	3	1	5	0	435	189
145–149	33	17	69	36	103	21	137	30	99	14	78	4	42	1	10	1	3	0	7	0	581	124
140–144	20	4	57	6	110	2	84	0	98	0	76	1	48	0	16	0	2	0	9	0	520	13
135–139	6	0	21	0	43	1	43	0	45	0	40	0	35	0	13	0	3	0	4	0	253	1
130–134	2	0	3	0	7	0	18	0	14	0	14	0	13	0	3	0	0	0	7	0	81	0
125–129	1	0	0	0	2	0	2	0	1	0	3	0	1	0	2	0	1	0	1	0	14	0
120–124	0	0	0	0	0	0	0	0	1	0	0	0	0	0	0	0	0	0	0	0	1	0
Total	100	49	247	111	411	116	433	105	374	62	284	29	177	4	54	2	12	1	36	1	2128	480

Apps = Number of Applicants
Adm = Number Admitted
Reflects 99% of the total applicant pool; average LSAT data reported.

University of Idaho College of Law

PO Box 442321
Moscow, ID 83844-2321
Phone: 208.885.2300; Fax: 208.885.5709
E-mail: lawadmit@uidaho.edu; Website: www.law.uidaho.edu

ABA Approved Since 1925

The Basics

Type of school	Public
Term	Semester
Application deadline	2/15
Application fee	$50
Financial aid deadline	2/15
Can first year start other than fall?	No
Student to faculty ratio	16.5 to 1
# of housing spaces available restricted to law students	
graduate housing for which law students are eligible	300

Faculty and Administrators

	Total		Men		Women		Minorities	
	Spr	Fall	Spr	Fall	Spr	Fall	Spr	Fall
Full-time	15	16	9	10	6	6	2	2
Other full-time	6	5	1	0	5	5	0	0
Deans, librarians, & others who teach	8	9	4	4	4	5	1	1
Part-time	11	5	7	3	4	2	0	0
Total	40	35	21	17	19	18	3	3

Curriculum

	Full-Time	Part-Time
Typical first-year section size	53	0
Is there typically a "small section" of the first-year class, other than Legal Writing, taught by full-time faculty	No	No
If yes, typical size offered last year		
# of classroom course titles beyond first-year curriculum		96

# of upper division courses, excluding seminars, with an enrollment:		
	Under 25	70
	25–49	15
	50–74	4
	75–99	5
	100+	1

	Full-Time	Part-Time
# of seminars	20	
# of seminar positions available	370	
# of seminar positions filled	242	0
# of positions available in simulation courses	209	
# of simulation positions filled	175	0
# of positions available in faculty supervised clinical courses	150	
# of faculty supervised clinical positions filled	104	0
# involved in field placements	70	0
# involved in law journals	35	0
# involved in moot court or trial competitions	31	0
# of credit hours required to graduate	90	

JD Enrollment and Ethnicity

	Men		Women		Full-Time		Part-Time		1st-Year		Total		JD Degs. Awd.
	#	%	#	%	#	%	#	%	#	%	#	%	
African Amer.	3	1.6	0	0.0	3	0.9	0	0.0	1	0.9	3	0.9	0
Amer. Indian	4	2.1	3	2.3	7	2.2	0	0.0	3	2.6	7	2.2	2
Asian Amer.	7	3.6	3	2.3	10	3.1	0	0.0	1	0.9	10	3.1	6
Mex. Amer.	1	0.5	0	0.0	1	0.3	0	0.0	1	0.9	1	0.3	1
Puerto Rican	0	0.0	0	0.0	0	0.0	0	0.0	0	0.0	0	0.0	0
Hispanic	9	4.7	9	7.0	18	5.6	0	0.0	8	7.0	18	5.6	3
Total Minority	24	12.4	15	11.6	39	12.2	0	0.0	14	12.3	39	12.1	12
For. Nation.	1	0.5	3	2.3	3	0.9	1	33.3	1	0.9	4	1.2	2
Caucasian	161	83.4	103	79.8	262	82.1	2	66.7	93	81.6	264	82.0	77
Unknown	7	3.6	8	6.2	15	4.7	0	0.0	6	5.3	15	4.7	2
Total	193	59.9	129	40.1	319	99.1	3	0.9	114	35.4	322		93

Transfers

Transfers in	5
Transfers out	4

Tuition and Fees

	Resident	Nonresident
Full-time	$11,776	$21,856
Part-time		
Tuition Guarantee Program	N	

Living Expenses

Estimated living expenses for singles

Living on campus	Living off campus	Living at home
$15,838	$15,838	$10,240

University of Idaho College of Law

ABA
Approved
Since
1925

GPA and LSAT Scores

	Total	Full-Time	Part-Time
# of apps	743	743	0
# of offers	355	355	0
# of matrics	114	114	0
75% GPA	3.64	3.64	0.00
Median GPA	3.35	3.35	0.00
25% GPA	3.09	3.09	0.00
75% LSAT	157	157	0
Median LSAT	155	155	0
25% LSAT	152	152	0

Grants and Scholarships (from prior year)

	Total		Full-Time		Part-Time	
	#	%	#	%	#	%
Total # of students	307		305		2	
Total # receiving grants	110	35.8	104	34.1	6	300.0
Less than 1/2 tuition	69	22.5	66	21.6	3	150.0
Half to full tuition	19	6.2	16	5.2	3	150.0
Full tuition	17	5.5	17	5.6	0	0.0
More than full tuition	5	1.6	5	1.6	0	0.0
Median grant amount			$2,271		$0	

Informational and Library Resources

Total amount spent on library materials	$922,745
Study seating capacity inside the library	330
# of full-time equivalent professional librarians	4
Hours per week library is open	86
# of open, wired connections available to students	306
# of networked computers available for use by students	52
Has wireless network?	Y
Require computer?	N

JD Attrition (from prior year)

	Academic	Other	Total	
	#	#	#	%
1st year	0	7	7	6.7
2nd year	1	0	1	1.0
3rd year	0	0	0	0.0
4th year	0	0	0	0.0

Employment (9 months after graduation)

	Total	Percentage
Employment status known	99	97.1
Employment status unknown	3	2.9
Employed	84	84.8
Pursuing graduate degrees	3	3.0
Unemployed (seeking, not seeking, or studying for the bar)	10	10.1
Type of Employment		
# employed in law firms	31	36.9
# employed in business and industry	5	6.0
# employed in government	18	21.4
# employed in public interest	7	8.3
# employed as judicial clerks	20	23.8
# employed in academia	2	2.4
Geographic Location		
# employed in state	54	64.3
# employed in foreign countries	0	0.0
# of states where employed	13	

Bar Passage Rates

First-time takers	93	Reporting %	98.92
Average school %	77.18	Average state %	80.23
Average pass difference –3.05			

Jurisdiction	Takers	Passers	Pass %	State %	Diff %
Idaho	54	44	81.48	79.75	1.73
Washington	15	7	46.67	74.40	–27.73
Utah	6	5	83.33	87.29	–3.96
Montana	4	4	100.00	92.47	7.53
Others (8)	13	11	84.62		

University of Idaho College of Law

PO Box 442321
Moscow, ID 83844-2321
Phone: 208.885.2300; Fax: 208.885.5709
E-mail: lawadmit@uidaho.edu; Website: www.law.uidaho.edu

■ Introduction

Emphasizing quality over quantity, the College of Law is founded on collegiality and a dedication to the highest ideals of a noble profession. Each student is assured individual attention. The college provides emphases in natural resources and environmental law, Native American law, business law and entrepreneurship, and advocacy coupled with mediation and dispute resolution. Students may combine study in a residential university community with an opportunity to spend a semester in Boise, Idaho, one of America's fastest growing metropolitan areas.

The College of Law, established in 1909, has been a member of the AALS since 1914 and has been accredited by the ABA since 1925. The College of Law is located on the main campus of the University of Idaho in Moscow, about 90 miles south of Spokane, Washington, and about 8 miles east of Washington State University in Pullman, Washington. Known as the "Heart of the Arts," the Moscow-Pullman community is the cultural center of a vast inland area of the Northwest covering parts of Idaho, Washington, and Oregon. In addition to cultural and entertainment events attracted by two major universities, the area is renowned for outstanding outdoor recreation.

■ Enrollment/Student Body

With an overall enrollment around 300, students at the College of Law come with a wide variety of backgrounds and experiences. Students come mostly from the West, representing almost 100 colleges and universities, 24 different states, and several foreign countries. Approximately 60 percent of our students are Idaho residents. The College of Law welcomes and actively seeks diversity, with particular attention to students of color and those who have overcome socioeconomic disadvantage. Due to our highly selective admission process and positive learning environment, including an academic support program run by a licensed attorney, academic attrition is less than 5 percent.

■ Technology, Library, and Physical Facilities

The College of Law occupies a building with full wireless Internet access and a newly renovated, state-of-the-art courtroom. The law library houses a collection of over 240,000 volumes and volume-equivalents and more than 4,800 serial titles. This is combined with two computer labs, and LexisNexis, Westlaw, Dialog, and HeinOnline services, plus the US Congressional Serial Set. Membership in the Western Library Network and the Inland Northwest Library Automation Network allows users to access holdings of libraries across the nation. Law students have access to the other libraries of the University of Idaho and those at Washington State University.

■ Curriculum

The College of Law focuses on professionalism, beginning with small-group discussions with distinguished lawyers and judges during New Student Orientation. Our distinctive Pro

Bono Program engages every student in substantial, law-related public service and provides a learning experience outside the classroom. After the first year, students may choose to focus on advocacy/dispute resolution, business law/entrepreneurship, or natural resources/environmental law, including an interdisciplinary Water of the West program (see Dual Degrees). The curriculum also provides enrichments in international law, Native American law, skills training, and ethics and civic leadership. Real-world exposure is provided through extensive clinical opportunities, a Semester in Practice program in the Boise metropolitan area, and our Externship Program. Graduates enter careers throughout the United States.

■ Practical Skills

In addition to our Pro Bono Program (mentioned above), third-year students may earn their limited license to practice law in Idaho and work in our live-client clinic. The live-client offerings include a general practice clinic, an appellate clinic in which students argue before federal and state appellate courts, an immigration law clinic in which students represent clients in federal immigration tribunals, a small business legal clinic, a tax clinic, a domestic violence clinic, and a victims' rights clinic. The college also sponsors a special trial advocacy course and is home to the Northwest Institute for Dispute Resolution.

Students may participate in the ABA National Moot Court competition, as well as a wide variety of faculty- and lawyer-supervised skills competitions in subject areas, including bankruptcy, environmental law, international human rights, evidence, mock trial, mediation, and negotiation.

Externships enable students to work with the Supreme Court and Court of Appeals of Idaho, the United States Court of Appeals for the Ninth Circuit, the United States District Court for the District of Idaho, the Attorney General of Idaho, the United States Attorney for the District of Idaho, various county offices, and selected nonprofit organizations in Idaho and elsewhere. Eligible third-year students may participate in the Semester in Practice program in Boise.

■ Dual Degrees

Dual JD/MS/PhD degrees in water resources management are offered as part of the one-of-a-kind Water of the West initiative in cooperation with the University of Idaho College of Natural Resources. There are three options for emphasis: engineering and science, science and management, and law, management, and policy.

Dual JD/MS Environmental Science degrees are available in cooperation with the University of Idaho College of Graduate Studies Environmental Science Program.

Dual JD/Master of Accounting degrees in cooperation with the University of Idaho College of Business and Economics are also available. The program is particularly valuable for students interested in practicing tax law.

Finally, a joint JD/Master of Business Administration is offered in cooperation with Washington State University, allowing students to take advantage of the resources of two of the Northwest's premier educational institutions.

Admission

Applications are accepted beginning in October preceding the year in which enrollment is desired. Our law program is full-time and located in Moscow, Idaho. Applicants must submit college transcripts and letters of recommendation through the Credential Assembly Service (CAS). The application deadline is February 15, but we recommend late-fall application. Applications submitted after February 15 will be reviewed, but timely applications will receive priority consideration. The Admission Committee looks at each applicant holistically, including but not limited to LSAT score, academic record and background, writing ability, personal statement, work and life experiences, and recommendations.

Student Activities

Students belong to more than 20 active student organizations. The Student Bar Association represents student interests, both educational and social. The *Idaho Law Review*, which covers topics ranging from state and regional problems to national and international issues, and *The Crit* (an electronic journal of critical legal studies), give students valuable writing and editing experience. The Board of

Student Advocates and the Law Students for Appropriate Dispute Resolution coordinate intramural competitions and provide opportunities for students to participate in national competitions that build professional skills. Other groups include the American Civil Liberties Union, the Federalist Society, Multicultural Law Caucus, Native American Law Students Association, the Sexual Orientation Diversity Alliance, Black Law Students Association, J. Reuben Clark Society, and the Women's Law Caucus.

Career Development

The Career Development Office, run by a licensed attorney, facilitates students' career planning and their search for summer and permanent employment. The office actively promotes job opportunities, including arranging on-campus interview and recruit-by-mail programs. Historically, over 90 percent of graduates find employment within six months of graduation or go on to advanced graduate study. The college has exceptional success placing students in federal and state judicial clerkships as the first step in their careers. A majority of students find employment in Idaho, although Utah, Washington, and Oregon are also popular. Idaho graduates are employed throughout the US and several foreign countries.

Applicant Profile

University of Idaho College of Law
This grid includes only applicants who earned 120–180 LSAT scores under standard administrations.

LSAT Score	3.75 +		3.50–3.74		3.25–3.49		3.00–3.24		2.75–2.99		2.50–2.74		2.25–2.49		2.00–2.24		Below 2.00		No GPA		Total	
	Apps	Adm	Apps	Adm	Apps	Adm	Apps	Adm	Apps	Adm	Apps	Adm	Apps	Adm	Apps	Adm	Apps	Adm	Apps	Adm	Apps	Adm
175–180	0	0	0	0	0	0	0	0	0	0	0	0	0	0	0	0	0	0	0	0	0	0
170–174	0	0	0	0	0	0	0	0	0	0	1	0	0	0	0	0	0	0	0	0	1	0
165–169	1	1	2	2	3	3	0	0	2	2	0	0	1	1	1	1	0	0	0	0	10	10
160–164	6	6	10	10	8	8	10	10	8	8	1	1	1	1	1	1	0	0	0	0	45	45
155–159	20	20	35	35	32	31	28	28	12	12	10	8	5	3	0	0	1	1	2	1	145	139
150–154	25	17	39	24	57	32	41	20	30	7	11	2	9	3	3	0	1	0	2	0	218	105
145–149	13	8	35	6	42	10	42	8	22	1	21	1	8	2	2	1	0	0	2	0	187	37
140–144	7	2	8	3	18	2	9	2	13	2	9	0	7	0	6	0	1	0	4	0	82	11
135–139	2	0	3	0	5	0	5	0	8	0	0	0	3	0	0	0	0	0	1	0	27	0
130–134	1	0	0	0	0	0	2	0	2	0	2	0	3	0	1	0	0	0	1	0	12	0
125–129	0	0	0	0	1	0	0	0	1	0	0	0	2	0	0	0	0	0	0	0	4	0
120–124	0	0	0	0	0	0	0	0	0	0	0	0	0	0	0	0	0	0	0	0	0	0
Total	75	54	132	80	166	86	137	68	98	32	55	12	39	10	14	3	3	1	12	1	731	347

Apps = Number of Applicants
Adm = Number Admitted
Reflects 99% of the total applicant pool; average LSAT data reported.

University of Illinois College of Law

504 East Pennsylvania Avenue
Champaign, IL 61820
Phone: 217.244.6415
E-mail: admissions@law.illinois.edu; Website: www.law.illinois.edu

The Basics

Type of school	Public
Term	Semester
Application deadline	3/15
Application fee	
Financial aid deadline	3/15
Can first year start other than fall?	No
Student to faculty ratio	13.1 to 1
# of housing spaces available restricted to law students	
graduate housing for which law students are eligible	1,821

Faculty and Administrators

	Total		Men		Women		Minorities	
	Spr	Fall	Spr	Fall	Spr	Fall	Spr	Fall
Full-time	38	38	27	27	11	11	6	8
Other full-time	7	7	3	3	4	4	0	0
Deans, librarians, & others who teach	12	12	6	6	6	6	0	0
Part-time	45	34	29	24	16	10	5	3
Total	102	91	65	60	37	31	11	11

Curriculum

		Full-Time	Part-Time
Typical first-year section size		63	0
Is there typically a "small section" of the first-year class, other than Legal Writing, taught by full-time faculty		Yes	No
If yes, typical size offered last year		32	
# of classroom course titles beyond first-year curriculum		128	
# of upper division courses, excluding seminars, with an enrollment:	Under 25	70	
	25–49	40	
	50–74	10	
	75–99	7	
	100+	0	
# of seminars		44	
# of seminar positions available		793	
# of seminar positions filled		459	0
# of positions available in simulation courses		778	
# of simulation positions filled		772	0
# of positions available in faculty supervised clinical courses		33	
# of faculty supervised clinical positions filled	32		0
# involved in field placements		199	0
# involved in law journals		161	0
# involved in moot court or trial competitions	60		0
# of credit hours required to graduate		90	

JD Enrollment and Ethnicity

	Men		Women		Full-Time		Part-Time		1st-Year		Total		JD Degs. Awd.
	#	%	#	%	#	%	#	%	#	%	#	%	
African Amer.	22	6.2	25	9.6	47	7.6	0	0.0	10	4.4	47	7.6	16
Amer. Indian	4	1.1	1	0.4	5	0.8	0	0.0	1	0.4	5	0.8	1
Asian Amer.	30	8.4	25	9.6	55	8.9	0	0.0	30	13.1	55	8.9	26
Mex. Amer.	0	0.0	0	0.0	0	0.0	0	0.0	0	0.0	0	0.0	0
Puerto Rican	0	0.0	0	0.0	0	0.0	0	0.0	0	0.0	0	0.0	0
Hispanic	16	4.5	16	6.2	32	5.2	0	0.0	10	4.4	32	5.2	15
Total Minority	72	20.2	67	25.8	139	22.5	0	0.0	51	22.3	139	22.5	58
For. Nation.	17	4.8	15	5.8	32	5.2	0	0.0	8	3.5	32	5.2	14
Caucasian	236	66.1	151	58.1	387	62.7	0	0.0	149	65.1	387	62.7	108
Unknown	32	9.0	27	10.4	59	9.6	0	0.0	21	9.2	59	9.6	12
Total	357	57.9	260	42.1	617	100.0	0	0.0	229	37.1	617		192

Transfers

Transfers in	9
Transfers out	7

Tuition and Fees

	Resident	Nonresident
Full-time	$36,420	$43,420
Part-time		
Tuition Guarantee Program		N

Living Expenses

Estimated living expenses for singles

Living on campus	Living off campus	Living at home
$15,474	$15,474	$15,474

University of Illinois College of Law

ABA
Approved
Since
1923

GPA and LSAT Scores

	Total	Full-Time	Part-Time
# of apps	3,516	3,516	0
# of offers	1,031	1,031	0
# of matrics	232	232	0
75% GPA	3.90	3.90	0.00
Median GPA	3.80	3.80	0.00
25% GPA	3.20	3.20	0.00
75% LSAT	167	167	0
Median LSAT	166	166	0
25% LSAT	160	160	0

Grants and Scholarships (from prior year)

	Total		Full-Time		Part-Time	
	#	%	#	%	#	%
Total # of students	587		587		0	
Total # receiving grants	523	89.1	523	89.1	0	0.0
Less than 1/2 tuition	313	53.3	313	53.3	0	0.0
Half to full tuition	157	26.7	157	26.7	0	0.0
Full tuition	53	9.0	53	9.0	0	0.0
More than full tuition	0	0.0	0	0.0	0	0.0
Median grant amount			$11,500		$0	

Informational and Library Resources

Total amount spent on library materials	$1,475,522
Study seating capacity inside the library	313
# of full-time equivalent professional librarians	9
Hours per week library is open	102
# of open, wired connections available to students	802
# of networked computers available for use by students	55
Has wireless network?	Y
Require computer?	Y

JD Attrition (from prior year)

	Academic	Other	Total	
	#	#	#	%
1st year	0	10	10	5.3
2nd year	0	2	2	1.0
3rd year	0	0	0	0.0
4th year	0	0	0	0.0

Employment (9 months after graduation)

	Total	Percentage
Employment status known	210	99.1
Employment status unknown	2	0.9
Employed	188	89.5
Pursuing graduate degrees	8	3.8
Unemployed (seeking, not seeking, or studying for the bar)	5	2.4
Type of Employment		
# employed in law firms	113	60.1
# employed in business and industry	26	13.8
# employed in government	26	13.8
# employed in public interest	5	2.7
# employed as judicial clerks	13	6.9
# employed in academia	5	2.7
Geographic Location		
# employed in state	121	64.4
# employed in foreign countries	2	1.1
# of states where employed	22	

Bar Passage Rates

First-time takers	203	Reporting %	89.66
Average school %	91.21	Average state %	90.81
Average pass difference	0.40		

Jurisdiction	Takers	Passers	Pass %	State %	Diff %
Illinois	170	155	91.18	90.94	0.24
New York	12	11	91.67	88.98	2.69

University of Illinois College of Law

504 East Pennsylvania Avenue
Champaign, IL 61820
Phone: 217.244.6415
E-mail: admissions@law.illinois.edu; Website: www.law.illinois.edu

■ Introduction

Established over a century ago, the University of Illinois College of Law fosters excellence in legal education through a close community of faculty members and students, where teaching goes hand in hand with scholarship. The resources—intellectual, cultural, and recreational—of one of the world's largest and best universities are readily available to our law students, as is the appealing ambience of a university community. The college's comparatively low tuition makes the program an outstanding value.

■ Library and Physical Facilities

A hallmark of a great university and a great law school is its library. The University Library in Urbana-Champaign is the largest public university library in the country. The Jenner Law Library holds 750,000 volumes and provides access to an equally wide array of electronic resources. In addition to US legal materials, the Jenner Law Library has extensive holdings in foreign and international law and houses a world-class collection of rare legal materials. Equally significant is Jenner's professional staff. Ten of its 11 law librarians have JDs in addition to master's degrees in library science. Law librarians teach legal research and work closely with students to support research and learning.

Directly across the street from the law school is one of the country's largest physical education buildings, with indoor and outdoor swimming pools, tennis courts, four gyms, weight and exercise equipment, archery, and ball courts of all kinds. The facility is free for students.

■ Joint-Degree Programs

The College of Law administers 12 formal joint JD and master's or doctoral degree programs. The combined degrees available are JD-MBA, JD-MCS, JD-MEd, JD-EdM, JD-PhD, JD-MHRIR, JD-MA in Journalism, JD-MD, JD-MS in Chemistry, JD-MS in Natural Resources, JD-MUP, and JD-DVM.

■ Special Programs

Environmental Law—The college has an active program of environmental and planning studies. Beyond the first-year course in property, the college offers courses in environmental law, natural resources, and land-use planning.

Intellectual Property (IP)—The College of Law boasts a strong intellectual property curriculum and offers a rich array of courses taught by nationally known faculty and experienced practitioners. Students choose from a variety of offerings ranging from core patent, copyright, and trademark courses to cutting-edge classes like Law and Regulation of Cyberspace, Internet and Web Law, International Copyright Principles, and International IP Transfers. Beyond its own curriculum, the College of Law's intellectual property faculty capitalizes upon the university's highly regarded academic programs in science and engineering, as well as its National Center for Supercomputing Applications, recognized as the world's leader in computer design applications. The College of Law is currently collaborating with these premier university departments to develop joint-degree programs in the rapidly changing intellectual property arena.

Interdisciplinary Study—While the College of Law course offerings are so varied that it would take a student 12 years to sample all of them, students interested in related subjects outside the law school may receive up to 12 hours of credit for study in another discipline. This flexibility allows students to complement their legal education with advanced coursework in a highly regarded university.

International Legal Studies—Students pursuing international legal studies can choose from 15 international and comparative law courses. Faculty members have long-standing international connections, and some collaborate with international scholars and legal experts to teach these courses.

Public Interest Law and Public Policy—As one of the premier public law schools, the College of Law plays a special role in educating students to both serve the public interest and formulate public policy. The college's commitment to public interest law is demonstrated by the pro bono notation placed on diplomas of graduates who have performed at least 60 hours of unpaid legal work. In addition, students may choose from a variety of timely courses addressing public interest and policy issues.

Skills Training—The college offers four live-client clinics: Civil Litigation Clinic, International Human Rights Clinic, Transactions and Community Economic Development Clinic, and Employee Justice Clinic, as well as classes in legal drafting, business planning, advanced bankruptcy, environmental management, estate planning, and tax practice. All challenge students to solve concrete problems and draft legal documents in a variety of fields. Courses on computer applications in the law and quantitative methods in legal decision-making familiarize students with sophisticated techniques necessary in today's law practice; these include computerized methods of document preparation and information retrieval, statistical analysis, the use of computer simulations in litigation, and the calculation of damage awards.

Taxation—Illinois offers one of the strongest tax curricula in the country, with core courses that address all aspects of tax practice and advanced offerings that integrate tax problems with other fields of law.

Trial Advocacy Program—The college's Trial Advocacy Program is especially popular, enrolling about three-quarters of the third-year class. The year-long program teaches the art of courtroom litigation and concludes with students conducting a day-long mock trial.

■ Housing

College of Law students live both off campus and in graduate- or married-student campus housing. For information concerning campus housing, contact the Graduate and Family Housing Department at 217.333.5656.

In addition, the Urbana-Champaign area has ample private rental opportunities available at relatively low cost. Most current College of Law students choose to live in private, off-campus housing due to its low cost and easy access to the award-winning Urbana-Champaign mass transit system, which is free for all University of Illinois students.

Student Activities

The small size and tight-knit community of the College of Law allow students to directly participate in an extensive variety of activities. Students run and write for the *University of Illinois Law Review*, the *Elder Law Journal*, the *University of Illinois Journal of Law, Technology, and Policy*, and the "Illinois Law Update" during their second and third years. In addition, second- and third-year students may participate in seven different moot court competitions that feature internal, external, and national contests, and several live-client legal clinics. First-year students also have many opportunities to get involved at the College of Law through the negotiation and client counseling competitions and several faculty-student committees. Finally, most students participate in at least one of the almost 35 student organizations. These organizations plan countless lectures, debates, charitable activities, sporting events, law firm visits, and social receptions, including the always anticipated annual formal ball.

Scholarships

The College of Law offers a number of scholarships, ranging from $1,000 to full tuition, awarded to students who show the greatest promise in the study of law. Previous academic success is a primary consideration; the committee also considers other relevant factors.

Applicant Profile

Our admission process takes into consideration many factors beyond the undergraduate GPA and the LSAT score. A statistical grid, as is typically provided here, only takes into consideration these two factors. Admission decisions at the University of Illinois College of Law are based on the Admission Committee's experienced judgment applied to individual cases. Consequently, we have chosen not to provide applicants with a grid that does not accurately portray our admission process.

Indiana University Maurer School of Law—Bloomington

211 S. Indiana Avenue
Bloomington, IN 47405-7001
Phone: 812.855.4765; Fax: 812.855.1967
E-mail: lawadmis@indiana.edu; Website: www.law.indiana.edu

ABA
Approved
Since
1937

The Basics

Type of school	Public
Term	Semester
Application deadline	3/1
Application fee	$50
Financial aid deadline	3/1
Can first year start other than fall?	No
Student to faculty ratio	9.5 to 1
# of housing spaces available restricted to law students	
graduate housing for which law students are eligible	800

Faculty and Administrators

	Total		Men		Women		Minorities	
	Spr	Fall	Spr	Fall	Spr	Fall	Spr	Fall
Full-time	53	55	33	39	20	16	8	8
Other full-time	2	3	1	2	1	1	0	0
Deans, librarians, & others who teach	19	17	11	10	8	7	0	0
Part-time	20	14	14	13	5	1	0	0
Total	94	89	59	64	34	25	8	8

Curriculum

	Full-Time	Part-Time
Typical first-year section size	72	0
Is there typically a "small section" of the first-year class, other than Legal Writing, taught by full-time faculty	No	No
If yes, typical size offered last year		
# of classroom course titles beyond first-year curriculum	138	
# of upper division courses, excluding seminars, with an enrollment: Under 25	105	
25–49	27	
50–74	12	
75–99	7	
100+	3	
# of seminars	36	
# of seminar positions available	511	
# of seminar positions filled	306	0
# of positions available in simulation courses	309	
# of simulation positions filled	246	0
# of positions available in faculty supervised clinical courses	126	
# of faculty supervised clinical positions filled	126	0
# involved in field placements	217	0
# involved in law journals	73	0
# involved in moot court or trial competitions	321	0
# of credit hours required to graduate	88	

JD Enrollment and Ethnicity

	Men		Women		Full-Time		Part-Time		1st-Year		Total		JD Degs. Awd.
	#	%	#	%	#	%	#	%	#	%	#	%	
African Amer.	16	4.4	30	11.6	46	7.4	0	0.0	12	5.5	46	7.4	16
Amer. Indian	0	0.0	0	0.0	0	0.0	0	0.0	0	0.0	0	0.0	2
Asian Amer.	19	5.2	18	6.9	37	6.0	0	0.0	13	6.0	37	5.9	8
Mex. Amer.	15	4.1	14	5.4	29	4.7	0	0.0	9	4.1	29	4.7	8
Puerto Rican	0	0.0	0	0.0	0	0.0	0	0.0	0	0.0	0	0.0	0
Hispanic	0	0.0	0	0.0	0	0.0	0	0.0	0	0.0	0	0.0	0
Total Minority	50	13.8	62	23.9	112	18.1	0	0.0	34	15.6	112	18.0	34
For. Nation.	0	0.0	0	0.0	0	0.0	0	0.0	0	0.0	0	0.0	0
Caucasian	310	85.4	196	75.7	504	81.3	2	100.0	182	83.5	506	81.4	159
Unknown	3	0.8	1	0.4	4	0.6	0	0.0	2	0.9	4	0.6	4
Total	363	58.4	259	41.6	620	99.7	2	0.3	218	35.0	622		197

Transfers

Transfers in	6
Transfers out	11

Tuition and Fees

	Resident	Nonresident
Full-time	$24,891	$40,691
Part-time		
Tuition Guarantee Program	N	

Living Expenses

Estimated living expenses for singles

Living on campus	Living off campus	Living at home
$13,730	$13,730	$13,730

Indiana University Maurer School of Law—Bloomington

*ABA
Approved
Since
1937*

GPA and LSAT Scores

	Total	Full-Time	Part-Time
# of apps	2,524	2,524	0
# of offers	805	805	0
# of matrics	220	220	0
75% GPA	3.83	3.83	0.00
Median GPA	3.70	3.70	0.00
25% GPA	3.26	3.26	0.00
75% LSAT	165	165	0
Median LSAT	164	164	0
25% LSAT	156	156	0

Grants and Scholarships (from prior year)

	Total		Full-Time		Part-Time	
	#	%	#	%	#	%
Total # of students	613		612		1	
Total # receiving grants	479	78.1	479	78.3	0	0.0
Less than 1/2 tuition	265	43.2	265	43.3	0	0.0
Half to full tuition	76	12.4	76	12.4	0	0.0
Full tuition	50	8.2	50	8.2	0	0.0
More than full tuition	88	14.4	88	14.4	0	0.0
Median grant amount			$12,000		$0	

Informational and Library Resources

Total amount spent on library materials	$1,639,866
Study seating capacity inside the library	684
# of full-time equivalent professional librarians	10
Hours per week library is open	115
# of open, wired connections available to students	164
# of networked computers available for use by students	79
Has wireless network?	Y
Require computer?	Y

JD Attrition (from prior year)

	Academic	Other	Total	
	#	#	#	%
1st year	0	13	13	6.4
2nd year	0	0	0	0.0
3rd year	0	0	0	0.0
4th year	0	0	0	0.0

Employment (9 months after graduation)

	Total	Percentage
Employment status known	212	100.0
Employment status unknown	0	0.0
Employed	196	92.5
Pursuing graduate degrees	6	2.8
Unemployed (seeking, not seeking, or studying for the bar)	8	3.8
Type of Employment		
# employed in law firms	89	45.4
# employed in business and industry	33	16.8
# employed in government	33	16.8
# employed in public interest	11	5.6
# employed as judicial clerks	22	11.2
# employed in academia	8	4.1
Geographic Location		
# employed in state	62	31.6
# employed in foreign countries	2	1.0
# of states where employed		31

Bar Passage Rates

First-time takers	185	Reporting %	70.81
Average school %	93.89	Average state %	86.69
Average pass difference	7.20		

Jurisdiction	Takers	Passers	Pass %	State %	Diff %
Indiana	85	81	95.29	84.39	10.90
Illinois	46	42	91.30	90.94	0.36

Indiana University Maurer School of Law—Bloomington

211 S. Indiana Avenue
Bloomington, IN 47405-7001
Phone: 812.855.4765; Fax: 812.855.1967
E-mail: lawadmis@indiana.edu; Website: www.law.indiana.edu

■ Introduction

The Indiana University Maurer School of Law—Bloomington provides the highest quality legal education in a relaxed, collegial setting. Founded in 1842, the law school is located on the beautifully wooded campus of one of the nation's largest teaching and research universities. The presence of the university, including the world-famous Jacobs School of Music, offers students cultural opportunities available in few urban areas, while retaining the advantages of a small university town. With a student body of fewer than 675 students, drawn from more than 200 undergraduate schools in the United States and abroad, the law school is small enough to retain its distinctive sense of community and collegiality, while large enough to facilitate a stimulating, cosmopolitan environment. The school is a charter member of the Association of American Law Schools (AALS) and is approved by the American Bar Association (ABA).

■ Library and Physical Facilities

With nearly 750,000 volumes, the law library is one of the 20 largest law libraries in the US, the largest in the state of Indiana, and was recently named one of the top law school libraries in the nation by a national law school magazine. Law-trained librarians give instruction in research techniques and provide reference assistance. While continuing its commitment to a high-quality print collection, the library is a national leader in computer applications in legal education. Through Internet access (from the School of Law or their homes), students can utilize systems specific to law, such as LexisNexis and Westlaw, or access the rapidly expanding array of global information sources. All students are required to possess a laptop computer. Students may write their examinations using their laptops, but are not required to do so. The law school building features wireless access throughout, laptop-ready classrooms, and an outstanding law library where students can enjoy spectacular views of the wooded campus as they study. Recent renovations added three new classrooms to the second floor, new technology and seating in all classrooms, and several faculty offices. Across the street, a brand-new professional skills building houses additional classrooms and clinical space, including offices, student workspace, interview rooms, and more.

■ Curriculum

Indiana Law faculty recently adopted the most extensive first-year curriculum change in more than 20 years. In 2008–2009, first-year law students enrolled for the first time in the Legal Profession, an innovative new course on the economics and values of the profession—one that responds to the most important study on legal education in decades. In the four-credit spring course, students explore the economic and sociolegal structure and substance of the modern legal profession through in-depth ethnographic studies of—among others—solo and large firm practice, in-house counsel, government agencies, judges, and public interest practice. With this integrated first-year foundation as a guide, decisions regarding areas of study and career goals become more meaningful. Upper-level courses support a formative education that develops skills alongside traditional scholarship, culminating in a meaningful capstone course.

The school also offers traditional specialized courses, such as intellectual property, communications and Internet law, law and biomedical advances, immigration law, international business transactions, and environmental law. The school offers intensive training in litigation and dispute resolution. Students may participate in clinics that enable them to deal with client problems and, in some cases, represent clients in local courts, all under close faculty supervision.

■ Joint-Degree Programs

Formal joint-degree programs combine the award of a JD degree with a master's degree in business, accounting, public affairs, environmental science, journalism, telecommunications, or library science. The duration of most joint-degree programs is four years. However, the School of Law and the Kelley School of Business have recently established an intensive three-year JD/MBA program. Informal concurrent-degree programs with other disciplines (pursuing a JD and a master's or doctoral degree) are frequently designed to meet students' learning and career goals.

■ Opportunities to Study Abroad

The School of Law provides students with a wide variety of opportunities to study abroad. A limited number of second- and third-year students can take advantage of the unique opportunity to study in and immerse themselves in the legal education system and culture of another country. Semester-long opportunities are available through the London Law Consortium and exchange programs with Université Panthéon-Assas (Paris II) Law School; ESADE Law School in Barcelona, Spain; Bucerius Law School in Hamburg, Germany; China University of Political Science and Law in Beijing (CUPL); Friedrich-Schiller University in Jena, Germany; Warsaw University in Warsaw, Poland; the University of Auckland in Auckland, New Zealand; University of Hong Kong, Hong Kong; and Zhejiang University in Hangzhou, China. All classes, with the exception of those taken at Bucerius, are taught in the school's respective native language. Finally, the law school offers all students the opportunity to participate in summer study-abroad programs hosted by the Institute on International and Comparative Law in England, France, Ireland, Italy, Russia, and Spain. All courses are taught in English.

■ Summer Start Program

A summer start program is offered for students who wish to begin their legal studies in the summer session. This program allows students to take one four-credit class in the summer in a small, intimate environment as they make the transition into the law school.

■ Admission

Generally, the quality and size of the applicant pool forces the Admissions Committee to rely heavily on the

Indiana University Maurer School of Law—Bloomington

undergraduate grade-point average and the LSAT score. However, numerical indicators are not the only considerations used in evaluating applications. The committee considers the quality of the applicant's undergraduate institution, level and rigor of coursework, letters of recommendation (particularly those from faculty), graduate work, employment during and after college, extracurricular activities, potential for service to the profession, educational/geographic/socioeconomic diversity, and personal statement. Applicants are encouraged to explain matters that may have adversely affected their undergraduate performance. Applicants who feel they have been disadvantaged because of economic, educational, racial, or cultural factors are urged to bring this to the attention of the Admissions Committee.

■ Housing

The Bloomington area offers a variety of housing options for students. There are numerous apartments and houses available as off-campus rentals as well as on-campus housing. Information regarding off-campus housing options is provided to admitted students throughout the spring and summer.

■ Student Activities

A variety of student organizations present opportunities for involvement in groups focused on specialized areas of the law and public service. Some of the most active groups include the Black Law Student Association, Women's Law Caucus, Public Interest Law Foundation, Latino Law Student Association, and the Environmental Law Society. Students

may also obtain practical experience through a number of clinical opportunities, including the Community Legal Clinic, Conservation Law Clinic, Criminal Law Externship, Disability Law Clinic, Elmore Entrepreneurship Law Clinic, Viola J. Taliaferro Children and Mediation Clinic, Inmate Legal Assistance Project, Tenant Assistance Project, Public Interest Internship Program, Federal Courts Clinic, Immigration Law Practicum, Indiana Legal Services Externship, Intellectual Property Practicum, Student Legal Services Externship, Washington, DC, Public Interest Program, and the Protective Order Project. Second- and third-year students are offered the opportunity to gain valuable writing, editing, and advocacy skills through participation in the Moot Court Competition or on one of our three journals. The *Indiana Law Journal* publishes articles by legal scholars, practitioners, jurists, and Indiana University law students. The *Federal Communications Law Journal* is the nation's oldest and largest-circulation communications law journal. The *Indiana Journal of Global Legal Studies* is a multidisciplinary journal that specializes in international and comparative law articles.

■ Career Placement

The Office of Career and Professional Development actively provides career planning and employment assistance to law students and alumni. Both on- and off-campus interviews are coordinated to facilitate contact between students and employers. In recent years, more than 98 percent of graduates have secured employment within nine months of graduation. More than one-half are located outside the state of Indiana. Graduates are found in all 50 states and in 31 foreign countries.

Applicant Profile

Indiana University Maurer School of Law—Bloomington
This grid includes only applicants who earned 120–180 LSAT scores under standard administrations.

LSAT Score	3.75 + Apps	3.75 + Adm	3.50–3.74 Apps	3.50–3.74 Adm	3.25–3.49 Apps	3.25–3.49 Adm	3.00–3.24 Apps	3.00–3.24 Adm	2.75–2.99 Apps	2.75–2.99 Adm	2.50–2.74 Apps	2.50–2.74 Adm	Below 2.50 Apps	Below 2.50 Adm	No GPA Apps	No GPA Adm	Total Apps	Total Adm
175–180	1	1	2	1	2	1	2	2	2	2	4	3	1	0	0	0	14	10
170–174	12	12	9	8	13	13	11	9	6	4	3	1	2	0	0	0	56	47
165–169	70	66	69	60	62	58	52	46	32	26	18	9	7	2	2	2	312	269
160–164	206	102	144	54	122	49	74	35	31	14	18	7	12	4	8	0	615	265
155–159	225	96	190	18	136	8	99	7	29	0	15	1	14	0	23	2	731	132
150–154	82	35	98	10	130	10	74	1	35	2	7	0	13	0	13	0	452	58
145–149	23	9	35	5	58	2	38	0	21	0	12	0	7	0	6	0	200	16
140–144	8	2	11	2	17	1	23	0	9	0	12	0	12	0	3	0	95	5
Below 140	2	0	3	0	3	0	4	0	7	0	11	0	4	0	2	0	36	0
Total	629	323	561	158	543	142	377	100	172	48	100	21	72	6	57	4	2511	802

Apps = Number of Applicants
Adm = Number Admitted
Reflects 99% of the total applicant pool; average LSAT data reported.

Indiana University School of Law—Indianapolis

530 West New York Street
Indianapolis, IN 46202-3225
Phone: 317.274.2459; Fax: 317.278.4780
E-mail: lawadmit@iupui.edu; Website: www.indylaw.indiana.edu

ABA
Approved
Since
1944

The Basics

Type of school	Public
Term	Semester
Application deadline	11/15 2/1 3/1
Application fee	$50
Financial aid deadline	3/10
Can first year start other than fall?	No
Student to faculty ratio	17.7 to 1
# of housing spaces available restricted to law students	
graduate housing for which law students are eligible	288

Faculty and Administrators

	Total		Men		Women		Minorities	
	Spr	Fall	Spr	Fall	Spr	Fall	Spr	Fall
Full-time	39	37	21	19	18	18	5	4
Other full-time	3	4	2	3	1	1	0	0
Deans, librarians, & others who teach	9	9	4	4	5	5	0	0
Part-time	44	38	29	24	15	14	1	3
Total	95	88	56	50	39	38	6	7

Curriculum

	Full-Time	Part-Time
Typical first-year section size	90	102
Is there typically a "small section" of the first-year class, other than Legal Writing, taught by full-time faculty	No	No
If yes, typical size offered last year		
# of classroom course titles beyond first-year curriculum	126	
# of upper division courses, excluding seminars, with an enrollment: Under 25	93	
25–49	50	
50–74	18	
75–99	16	
100+	1	
# of seminars	11	
# of seminar positions available	226	
# of seminar positions filled	119	40
# of positions available in simulation courses	450	
# of simulation positions filled	281	127
# of positions available in faculty supervised clinical courses	92	
# of faculty supervised clinical positions filled	60	16
# involved in field placements	141	22
# involved in law journals	114	25
# involved in moot court or trial competitions	136	24
# of credit hours required to graduate	90	

JD Enrollment and Ethnicity

	Men		Women		Full-Time		Part-Time		1st-Year		Total		JD Degs. Awd.
	#	%	#	%	#	%	#	%	#	%	#	%	
African Amer.	30	5.8	41	9.7	35	5.6	36	11.3	35	9.0	71	7.5	12
Amer. Indian	0	0.0	3	0.7	1	0.2	2	0.6	2	0.5	3	0.3	1
Asian Amer.	20	3.8	21	5.0	28	4.5	13	4.1	19	4.9	41	4.3	8
Mex. Amer.	5	1.0	2	0.5	6	1.0	1	0.3	4	1.0	7	0.7	0
Puerto Rican	3	0.6	2	0.5	2	0.3	3	0.9	2	0.5	5	0.5	0
Hispanic	9	1.7	7	1.7	11	1.8	5	1.6	4	1.0	16	1.7	5
Total Minority	67	12.9	76	17.9	83	13.3	60	18.8	66	17.0	143	15.1	26
For. Nation.	23	4.4	17	4.0	31	5.0	9	2.8	20	5.1	40	4.2	6
Caucasian	430	82.7	331	78.1	511	81.8	250	78.4	303	77.9	761	80.6	237
Unknown	0	0.0	0	0.0	0	0.0	0	0.0	0	0.0	0	0.0	0
Total	520	55.1	424	44.9	625	66.2	319	33.8	389	41.2	944		269

Transfers

Transfers in	18
Transfers out	14

Tuition and Fees

	Resident	Nonresident
Full-time	$18,163	$38,478
Part-time	$14,065	$29,640
Tuition Guarantee Program	N	

Living Expenses

Estimated living expenses for singles

Living on campus	Living off campus	Living at home
$21,124	$21,124	N/A

Indiana University School of Law—Indianapolis

ABA
Approved
Since
1944

GPA and LSAT Scores

	Total	Full-Time	Part-Time
# of apps	1,766	1,513	253
# of offers	710	570	140
# of matrics	297	195	102
75% GPA	3.70	3.73	3.56
Median GPA	3.50	3.59	3.33
25% GPA	3.15	3.23	3.04
75% LSAT	159	160	155
Median LSAT	156	158	152
25% LSAT	151	154	147

Grants and Scholarships (from prior year)

	Total		Full-Time		Part-Time	
	#	%	#	%	#	%
Total # of students	953		638		315	
Total # receiving grants	378	39.7	296	46.4	82	26.0
Less than 1/2 tuition	327	34.3	269	42.2	58	18.4
Half to full tuition	35	3.7	23	3.6	12	3.8
Full tuition	10	1.0	0	0.0	10	3.2
More than full tuition	6	0.6	4	0.6	2	0.6
Median grant amount			$5,000		$2,000	

Informational and Library Resources

Total amount spent on library materials	$1,189,129
Study seating capacity inside the library	470
# of full-time equivalent professional librarians	11
Hours per week library is open	105
# of open, wired connections available to students	1,140
# of networked computers available for use by students	153
Has wireless network?	Y
Require computer?	N

JD Attrition (from prior year)

	Academic	Other	Total	
	#	#	#	%
1st year	2	24	26	6.7
2nd year	2	12	14	4.3
3rd year	0	0	0	0.0
4th year	0	0	0	0.0

Employment (9 months after graduation)

	Total	Percentage
Employment status known	283	99.6
Employment status unknown	1	0.4
Employed	268	94.7
Pursuing graduate degrees	0	0.0
Unemployed (seeking, not seeking, or studying for the bar)	10	3.5
Type of Employment		
# employed in law firms	139	51.9
# employed in business and industry	52	19.4
# employed in government	48	17.9
# employed in public interest	14	5.2
# employed as judicial clerks	3	1.1
# employed in academia	11	4.1
Geographic Location		
# employed in state	214	79.9
# employed in foreign countries	1	0.4
# of states where employed	20	

Bar Passage Rates

First-time takers	284	Reporting %	80.63
Average school %	83.84	Average state %	84.39
Average pass difference	−0.55		

Jurisdiction	Takers	Passers	Pass %	State %	Diff %
Indiana	229	192	83.84	84.39	−0.55

Indiana University School of Law—Indianapolis

530 West New York Street
Indianapolis, IN 46202-3225
Phone: 317.274.2459; Fax: 317.278.4780
E-mail: lawadmit@iupui.edu; Website: www.indylaw.indiana.edu

■ Introduction

Founded in 1894 as the Indiana Law School, the IU School of Law—Indianapolis has emerged as a premier educational institution, located in the dynamic heart of Indiana on the Indianapolis campus of Indiana University–Purdue University. This campus is also home to the Schools of Medicine, Dentistry, Nursing, and Social Work. The law school building, Lawrence W. Inlow Hall, is a state-of-the-art facility, enabling the faculty to employ the latest technology and teaching methods. The building houses modern classrooms, private study areas, and an unparalleled law library. The school is just steps away from the state's courts, the legislature, and major law firms, giving students opportunities to observe the legal process in action and to participate in that process as law clerks, judicial externs, and legislative staff assistants. The school is the largest in the state of Indiana and one of the few Big Ten law schools to offer the cultural, recreational, and professional advantages of an urban educational environment.

■ Clinical Experiences

The law school offers several clinical programs. The Civil Practice Clinic allows students the opportunity to represent clients in a variety of cases including housing, divorce, child support, consumer, and administrative matters. In the Civil Practice Disability Clinic, students represent school-age children with special needs, as well as persons who are afflicted with HIV, Alzheimer's disease, and AIDS. In the Criminal Defense Clinic, students represent clients in criminal cases involving a variety of misdemeanor or class D felony charges. Additional clinical opportunities include the Immigration Law Clinic, the Appellate Practice Clinic, and the Wrongful Conviction Clinic, which involves claims of innocence in postconviction proceedings.

■ Externships and Special Programs

The school's research centers and programs make significant contributions to the profession, both locally and nationally. The William S. and Christine S. Hall Center for Law and Health is considered one of the top health law programs in the nation. The center serves as a preeminent information resource on health law issues for the bar, government, and health care community. Through the center, students may pursue a concentration in law and health and participate in the *Indiana Health Law Review*.

The Program on Law and State Government enriches the dialogue between the academic legal community and state government policymakers. The program offers externships with more than 40 government offices and also sponsors a mediation course that qualifies students to become registered civil mediators. Additionally, the program sponsors a fellowship that allows students to host an academic event and write a publishable academic paper on critical legal or regulatory issues pertinent to state government.

The Center for Intellectual Property Law and Innovation provides experience for students in the fast-growing area of intellectual property.

The Court Externship Program provides externships with federal, state, and local courts. Externs work closely with judges and law clerks, learning about the legal process by experiencing it firsthand.

■ International Law Program

Because the school recognizes that international considerations touch all areas of the law from human rights to economic issues, it established the Center for International and Comparative Law. A wide variety of international courses, combined with opportunities for overseas experiences, demonstrate our commitment to a legal education with a world view. Our Program in International Human Rights Law has placed students in internships with human rights organizations in locations from Argentina to Zimbabwe.

The law school sponsors a summer program in cooperation with the University of Zagreb School of Law near the ancient Croatian city of Dubrovnik, as well as a program in China. Established in 1987, the Chinese Law Summer Program is hosted by Renmin (People's) University of China School of Law and introduces students to the Chinese legal and lawyering systems, its dispute resolution mechanisms, and Chinese constitutional law.

In addition to offering several courses and seminars in the area of international law, the school sponsors the *Indiana International and Comparative Law Review* and a student organization, the International Law Society. It is also home to the editorial offices of the *European Journal of Law Reform*.

■ Joint-Degree Programs

The school offers seven joint-degree options in cooperation with IU's School of Business, School of Public and Environmental Affairs, School of Medicine, School of Library and Information Science, School of Liberal Arts, and School of Social Work. Available degrees are the Doctor of Jurisprudence and Master of Business Administration (JD/MBA), Master of Health Administration (JD/MHA), Master of Public Affairs (JD/MPA), Master of Public Health (JD/MPH), Master of Library Science (JD/MLS), Master of Arts in Philosophy (JD/MPhil), and Master of Social Work (JD/MSW).

■ Special Summer Program

Summer admission is offered to a select group of applicants who can benefit from a rigorous, individualized summer course. Applicants who have either an LSAT score or GPA that is outside of the median range of accepted students, persons who are returning to school after several years outside of the classroom, and students for whom English is a second language may be considered for the summer program. Summer admittees earn two credits toward their JD degrees. Continuation in the fall is not contingent upon performance in the summer program. There is no special application procedure. Applicants who are not presumptively admitted and whose files are completed by February 1 may be considered for this program.

Additionally, the school strongly supports the Indiana Conference for Legal Education Opportunity program, which

provides those who are currently underrepresented in the legal profession or underrepresented in practice areas with assistance in preparing for law school through a six-week summer institute.

■ Admission

LSAT and Credential Assembly Service are required.
    The law school seeks to attain a culturally rich and diverse student body. To this end, admission decisions are based on a variety of factors in addition to the LSAT score and undergraduate GPA.
    Indiana University School of Law—Indianapolis offers an early decision program. Early decision candidates must have their applications completed, with their Credential Assembly Service Law School Report, by November 15 and will be notified of the admission committee's decision by late December.

■ Academic Support Programs

Students are offered assistance through the Dean's Tutorial Society. Supervised by a tenured faculty member, the tutorial society is staffed by academically distinguished students who offer individual tutoring as well as assistance in case briefing and exam preparation.

■ Student Activities

Students can participate in any of 30 different interest groups and organizations, ranging from Amnesty International to Sports and Entertainment Law Society. The school also offers an extensive moot court program, a client counseling program, and three law reviews.

■ Office of Professional Development

The Office of Professional Development provides career counseling and job-search assistance to students and alumni. Services include an on-campus interview program, a résumé review service, a mock interview program, and a variety of workshops and seminars.

Applicant Profile

Indiana University School of Law—Indianapolis
This grid includes only applicants who earned 120–180 LSAT scores under standard administrations.

LSAT Score	GPA 3.75 +		3.50–3.74		3.25–3.49		3.00–3.24		2.75–2.99		2.50–2.74		2.25–2.49		2.00–2.24		Below 2.00		No GPA		Total	
	Apps	Adm	Apps	Adm	Apps	Adm	Apps	Adm	Apps	Adm	Apps	Adm	Apps	Adm	Apps	Adm	Apps	Adm	Apps	Adm	Apps	Adm
170–180	1	1	0	0	1	1	0	0	0	0	1	0	0	0	0	0	0	0	0	0	3	2
165–169	8	8	6	6	5	5	4	3	2	2	2	2	0	0	0	0	0	0	0	0	27	26
160–164	36	36	40	39	30	27	32	31	21	18	6	4	3	1	0	0	0	0	2	1	170	157
155–159	62	58	91	70	95	51	63	36	34	19	17	9	6	1	1	0	0	0	11	8	380	252
150–154	85	62	109	52	143	25	86	16	61	14	23	0	15	2	6	0	3	0	27	9	558	180
145–149	37	9	60	16	78	11	65	8	46	1	18	1	13	1	6	0	2	0	11	0	336	47
140–144	11	6	27	6	33	7	46	4	29	2	18	5	19	0	6	0	3	0	8	2	200	32
Below 140	4	1	5	0	10	1	11	1	15	0	10	2	11	0	8	0	2	0	3	0	79	5
Total	244	181	338	189	395	128	307	99	208	56	95	23	67	5	27	0	10	0	62	20	1753	701

Apps = Number of Applicants
Adm = Number Admitted
Reflects 99% of the total applicant pool; average LSAT data reported.

Inter American University School of Law

PO Box 70351
San Juan, PR 00936-8351
Phone: 787.751.1912, exts. 2011, 2012
Website: www.derecho.inter.edu

ABA
Approved
Since
1969

AMERICAN BAR ASSOCIATION
Section of Legal Education
and Admissions to the Bar

The Basics

Type of school	Private
Term	Semester
Application deadline	3/30
Application fee	$63
Financial aid deadline	10/19
Can first year start other than fall?	No
Student to faculty ratio	25.9 to 1
# of housing spaces available restricted to law students	
graduate housing for which law students are eligible	

Faculty and Administrators

	Total		Men		Women		Minorities	
	Spr	Fall	Spr	Fall	Spr	Fall	Spr	Fall
Full-time	24	22	14	14	10	8	24	22
Other full-time	1	1	0	0	1	1	1	1
Deans, librarians, & others who teach	4	4	2	2	2	2	4	4
Part-time	37	39	27	26	10	13	36	38
Total	66	66	43	42	23	24	65	65

Curriculum

		Full-Time	Part-Time
Typical first-year section size		45	60
Is there typically a "small section" of the first-year class, other than Legal Writing, taught by full-time faculty		No	No
If yes, typical size offered last year			
# of classroom course titles beyond first-year curriculum		65	
# of upper division courses, excluding seminars, with an enrollment:	Under 25	37	
	25–49	32	
	50–74	28	
	75–99	0	
	100+	0	
# of seminars		9	
# of seminar positions available		180	
# of seminar positions filled		60	40
# of positions available in simulation courses		100	
# of simulation positions filled		60	40
# of positions available in faculty supervised clinical courses		80	
# of faculty supervised clinical positions filled		24	11
# involved in field placements		0	0
# involved in law journals		16	4
# involved in moot court or trial competitions		0	0
# of credit hours required to graduate		92	

JD Enrollment and Ethnicity

	Men		Women		Full-Time		Part-Time		1st-Year		Total		JD Degs. Awd.
	#	%	#	%	#	%	#	%	#	%	#	%	
African Amer.	0	0.0	0	0.0	0	0.0	0	0.0	0	0.0	0	0.0	0
Amer. Indian	0	0.0	0	0.0	0	0.0	0	0.0	0	0.0	0	0.0	0
Asian Amer.	0	0.0	0	0.0	0	0.0	0	0.0	0	0.0	0	0.0	0
Mex. Amer.	0	0.0	0	0.0	0	0.0	0	0.0	0	0.0	0	0.0	0
Puerto Rican	389	100.0	459	100.0	430	100.0	418	100.0	241	100.0	848	100.0	227
Hispanic	0	0.0	0	0.0	0	0.0	0	0.0	0	0.0	0	0.0	0
Total Minority	389	100.0	459	100.0	430	100.0	418	100.0	241	100.0	848	100.0	227
For. Nation.	0	0.0	0	0.0	0	0.0	0	0.0	0	0.0	0	0.0	0
Caucasian	0	0.0	0	0.0	0	0.0	0	0.0	0	0.0	0	0.0	0
Unknown	0	0.0	0	0.0	0	0.0	0	0.0	0	0.0	0	0.0	0
Total	389	45.9	459	54.1	430	50.7	418	49.3	241	28.4	848		227

Transfers

Transfers in	17
Transfers out	3

Tuition and Fees

	Resident	Nonresident
Full-time	$13,491	$13,491
Part-time	$10,481	$10,481
Tuition Guarantee Program		Y

Living Expenses

Estimated living expenses for singles

Living on campus	Living off campus	Living at home
N/A	$18,684	$15,752

Inter American University School of Law

ABA
Approved
Since
1969

GPA and LSAT Scores

	Total	Full-Time	Part-Time
# of apps	0	585	459
# of offers	362	217	145
# of matrics	238	127	111
75% GPA	3.74	3.59	3.55
Median GPA	3.37	3.38	3.34
25% GPA	3.46	3.30	2.95
75% LSAT	146	144	142
Median LSAT	139	139	138
25% LSAT	142	138	136

Grants and Scholarships (from prior year)

	Total		Full-Time		Part-Time	
	#	%	#	%	#	%
Total # of students	869		427		442	
Total # receiving grants	55	6.3	43	10.1	12	2.7
Less than 1/2 tuition	2	0.2	2	0.5	0	0.0
Half to full tuition	5	0.6	4	0.9	1	0.2
Full tuition	45	5.2	36	8.4	9	2.0
More than full tuition	3	0.3	1	0.2	2	0.5
Median grant amount			$4,530		$5,677	

Informational and Library Resources

Total amount spent on library materials	$718,073
Study seating capacity inside the library	302
# of full-time equivalent professional librarians	7
Hours per week library is open	101
# of open, wired connections available to students	0
# of networked computers available for use by students	0
Has wireless network?	Y
Require computer?	N

JD Attrition (from prior year)

	Academic	Other	Total	
	#	#	#	%
1st year	0	4	4	1.5
2nd year	9	3	12	4.7
3rd year	0	0	0	0.0
4th year	0	0	0	0.0

Employment (9 months after graduation)

	Total	Percentage
Employment status known	184	98.4
Employment status unknown	3	1.6
Employed	168	91.3
Pursuing graduate degrees	3	1.6
Unemployed (seeking, not seeking, or studying for the bar)	13	7.1
Type of Employment		
# employed in law firms	73	43.5
# employed in business and industry	35	20.8
# employed in government	39	23.2
# employed in public interest	1	0.6
# employed as judicial clerks	15	8.9
# employed in academia	5	3.0
Geographic Location		
# employed in state	162	96.4
# employed in foreign countries	0	0.0
# of states where employed	0	

Bar Passage Rates

First-time takers	153	Reporting %	94.12
Average school %	47.92	Average state %	54.16
Average pass difference	−6.24		

Jurisdiction	Takers	Passers	Pass %	State %	Diff %
Puerto Rico	144	69	47.92	54.16	−6.24

Inter American University School of Law

PO Box 70351
San Juan, PR 00936-8351
Phone: 787.751.1912, exts. 2011, 2012
Website: www.derecho.inter.edu

■ Introduction

The Inter American University School of Law is one of the 11 units of the Inter American University of Puerto Rico, a private nonprofit educational corporation accredited by the Middle States Association of Colleges and Secondary Schools, the Puerto Rico Council of Higher Education, and the Commonwealth of Puerto Rico Department of Education. The School of Law is approved by the ABA and is located in San Juan, the capital city of Puerto Rico. Since its founding, the School of Law has succeeded in meeting the needs of the legal profession, in particular, and Puerto Rico's society in general.

■ Enrollment/Student Body

The incoming class for academic year 2009–2010 was composed of 238 students. The student body comes mainly from Puerto Rico, although applicants from the mainland are encouraged to apply.

■ Library and Physical Facilities

The law school has developed its library into a center of access to traditional library services as well as computerized legal research services.

In 1993, the school was relocated to a new building that features seven classrooms equipped with air conditioning, accessibility for students with disabilities, state-of-the-art audiovisual equipment, seminar rooms, a library, a legal clinic, faculty offices, a conference room, a lounge, a Continuing Legal Education Program office, *Law Review* offices, student organization offices, administrative offices, a chapel, a student center, a cafeteria, a bookstore, an auditorium with a seating capacity of 310, parking, and more. The site has been landscaped to achieve a sense of serenity and beauty compatible with the building's functions.

In January 1990, the library signed a collaboration agreement to establish a consortium with the law school library of the Catholic University of Puerto Rico and the library of the Supreme Court of Puerto Rico, with the purpose of coordinating collection development and sharing its resources through an automated bibliographic network, interlibrary loans, and telecommunication services.

■ Curriculum

The JD program covers three years in the day division and four years in the evening division. Candidates must complete a minimum of 92 credit hours with a GPA of at least 2.5 to qualify for graduation.

Inter American University School of Law offers a three-week preparation course to be taken during the summer on a compulsory basis by students admitted to the school. Students who enter law school must be willing to make a heavy commitment.

For its part, Inter American University is willing to provide the best possible professional educational experience through the careful recruitment of a first-rate faculty, the development of a progressive curriculum, and a willingness to create new and exciting programs of clinical studies and research.

■ Admission

Proficiency in Spanish is essential to the program. Applicants must have a minimum grade-point average of 2.5, an immunization certificate (for students ages 21 and below), and a police department certificate of good conduct; those seeking admission may also be required to appear for a personal interview.

Candidates are required to take the Examen de Admisión a Estudios de Posgrado (EXADEP), the Aptitude Test for Graduate Education, and the Law School Admission Test (LSAT). Students should attain a 575 minimum score on the EXADEP and a minimum score of 130 on the LSAT. Application forms and other relevant information concerning the EXADEP may be obtained from Educational Testing Service, American International Plaza, 250 Muñoz Rivera Avenue, Suite 315, Hato Rey, PR 00918.

■ Housing

The university does not provide housing for law students. However, the areas surrounding the School of Law contain many private houses, apartments, and condominiums for rent.

■ Student Activities

Student organizations include the student council, an organization that represents the student body and participates in matters of administrative policy related to students' interests. Council representatives serve on various faculty committees as well as the university senate and the board of trustees.

Other student organizations are the Law Student Division of the American Bar Association; the Phi Alpha Delta legal fraternity (composed not only of law students, but also of distinguished honorary members who are supreme court justices, federal district court judges, and prominent attorneys); the National Association of Law Students; the Women Law Students Association; United Students Forging an Environmental Consciousness; the Law Student Division of the Inter-American Federation of Lawyers; the Association of Trial Lawyers of America; the Hispanic National Bar Association; the Federal Bar Association; the Student's Cooperative Bookstore; and the Hispanic Notarial Bar Association.

The *Inter American School of Law Review* is the official publication of the School of Law. Its members work under the supervision of an editorial board of four students chosen on the basis of merit and dedication to the *Review* and an academic advisor who is a faculty member appointed by the dean.

■ Clinical Programs

The faculty's Legal Aid Clinical Program is integrated with the Community Law Office through a combined effort of the US Legal Services Corporation and Inter American University. Law students are provided with the opportunity to learn skills such as interviewing, negotiation, counseling, fact gathering and analysis, legal research and drafting, decision making about alternative strategies, and preparation for trial and field

practice. They also represent clients before administrative agencies and courts under the close supervision of the program's staff attorney-professors, pursuant to the rules of the Supreme Court of Puerto Rico. Students also gain practical experience by serving with Puerto Rico Legal Services, Inc.; the San Juan Community Law Office, Inc.; the Legal Aid Society of Puerto Rico; the district attorney's offices; and the Environmental Quality Board.

■ Career Services

The mission of the Career Placement Office is to prepare students and alumni for the legal job market by encouraging them to conduct self-assessments in an effort to focus their job searches, as well as to educate students and alumni on their legal and nonlegal options in today's competitive legal market. This is accomplished through a variety of services including, but not limited to, individual counseling, group seminars, self-assessment materials, interviewing programs, a career resource library, and the alumni network.

■ Continuing Legal Education Program

The Continuing Legal Education (CLE) Program offers advanced courses and seminars concerning different fields of law that may be of interest to practicing lawyers as well as to the community in general.

The CLE Program enjoys a good reputation and has been able to develop a consistent course offering, primarily in the following categories: courses designed for specialists; refresher courses for experienced lawyers; courses designed to provide information in nontraditional areas or stimulated by recent legislation, decisions, or agency rulings; and courses designed to develop lawyering skills.

■ Cost and Financial Aid

As of the date this report was published, the cost per credit is $450. Once admitted, the student pays $125 to reserve a place in the class and $400 for the preparatory course that takes place in July.

There is a deferred payment plan and financial aid options that include the Federal Guaranteed Loan Program, Stafford loans, the Commonwealth Education Fund, the Students Incentive Grant Program, the Institutional College Work-Study Program, and alternative loans for the regular academic program as well as for bar study (Alternative Bar Loans). The university also has an Honor Scholarship program for law students based on academic accomplishment and financial need.

Applicant Profile Not Available

The University of Iowa College of Law

320 Melrose Avenue
Iowa City, IA 52242
Phone: 800.553.4692, ext. 9095; 319.335.9095; Fax: 319.335.9646
E-mail: law-admissions@uiowa.edu; Website: www.law.uiowa.edu

*ABA
Approved
Since
1923*

The Basics

Type of school	Public
Term	Semester
Application deadline	3/1
Application fee	$60
Financial aid deadline	1/1
Can first year start other than fall?	No
Student to faculty ratio	15.5 to 1
# of housing spaces available restricted to law students	
graduate housing for which law students are eligible	

Faculty and Administrators

	Total		Men		Women		Minorities	
	Spr	Fall	Spr	Fall	Spr	Fall	Spr	Fall
Full-time	33	30	25	22	8	8	4	4
Other full-time	9	9	4	4	5	5	0	0
Deans, librarians, & others who teach	14	13	6	5	8	8	1	1
Part-time	17	9	10	5	7	4	0	0
Total	73	61	45	36	28	25	5	5

Curriculum

	Full-Time	Part-Time
Typical first-year section size	75	0
Is there typically a "small section" of the first-year class, other than Legal Writing, taught by full-time faculty	Yes	No
If yes, typical size offered last year	40	
# of classroom course titles beyond first-year curriculum	65	
# of upper division courses, excluding seminars, with an enrollment: Under 25	55	
25–49	29	
50–74	9	
75–99	9	
100+	0	
# of seminars	27	
# of seminar positions available	382	
# of seminar positions filled	343	0
# of positions available in simulation courses	341	
# of simulation positions filled	294	0
# of positions available in faculty supervised clinical courses	65	
# of faculty supervised clinical positions filled	51	0
# involved in field placements	80	0
# involved in law journals	176	0
# involved in moot court or trial competitions	183	0
# of credit hours required to graduate	84	

JD Enrollment and Ethnicity

	Men		Women		Full-Time		Part-Time		1st-Year		Total		JD Degs. Awd.
	#	%	#	%	#	%	#	%	#	%	#	%	
African Amer.	10	3.0	11	4.2	21	3.6	0	0.0	4	2.1	21	3.6	8
Amer. Indian	5	1.5	1	0.4	6	1.0	0	0.0	3	1.5	6	1.0	1
Asian Amer.	13	4.0	23	8.8	36	6.1	0	0.0	12	6.2	36	6.1	18
Mex. Amer.	16	4.9	12	4.6	28	4.7	0	0.0	8	4.1	28	4.7	13
Puerto Rican	0	0.0	0	0.0	0	0.0	0	0.0	0	0.0	0	0.0	0
Hispanic	0	0.0	0	0.0	0	0.0	0	0.0	0	0.0	0	0.0	0
Total Minority	44	13.4	47	18.0	91	15.4	0	0.0	27	13.8	91	15.4	40
For. Nation.	10	3.0	9	3.4	19	3.2	0	0.0	8	4.1	19	3.2	3
Caucasian	275	83.6	205	78.5	480	81.4	0	0.0	160	82.1	480	81.4	163
Unknown	0	0.0	0	0.0	0	0.0	0	0.0	0	0.0	0	0.0	0
Total	329	55.8	261	44.2	590	100.0	0	0.0	195	33.1	590		206

Transfers

Transfers in	3
Transfers out	4

Tuition and Fees

	Resident	Nonresident
Full-time	$21,432	$39,138
Part-time		
Tuition Guarantee Program	N	

Living Expenses

Estimated living expenses for singles

Living on campus	Living off campus	Living at home
$16,730	$16,730	$8,630

The University of Iowa College of Law

ABA
Approved
Since
1923

GPA and LSAT Scores

	Total	Full-Time	Part-Time
# of apps	1,291	1,291	0
# of offers	566	566	0
# of matrics	195	195	0
75% GPA	3.81	3.81	0.00
Median GPA	3.61	3.61	0.00
25% GPA	3.43	3.43	0.00
75% LSAT	164	164	0
Median LSAT	161	161	0
25% LSAT	158	158	0

Grants and Scholarships (from prior year)

	Total		Full-Time		Part-Time	
	#	%	#	%	#	%
Total # of students	616		616		0	
Total # receiving grants	198	32.1	198	32.1	0	0.0
Less than 1/2 tuition	39	6.3	39	6.3	0	0.0
Half to full tuition	47	7.6	47	7.6	0	0.0
Full tuition	110	17.9	110	17.9	0	0.0
More than full tuition	2	0.3	2	0.3	0	0.0
Median grant amount			$16,758		$0	

Informational and Library Resources

Total amount spent on library materials	$2,908,574
Study seating capacity inside the library	705
# of full-time equivalent professional librarians	15
Hours per week library is open	106
# of open, wired connections available to students	488
# of networked computers available for use by students	99
Has wireless network?	Y
Require computer?	N

JD Attrition (from prior year)

	Academic	Other	Total	
	#	#	#	%
1st year	0	8	8	4.1
2nd year	0	5	5	2.3
3rd year	0	0	0	0.0
4th year	0	0	0	0.0

Employment (9 months after graduation)

	Total	Percentage
Employment status known	205	100.0
Employment status unknown	0	0.0
Employed	194	94.6
Pursuing graduate degrees	9	4.4
Unemployed (seeking, not seeking, or studying for the bar)	0	0.0
Type of Employment		
# employed in law firms	100	51.5
# employed in business and industry	27	13.9
# employed in government	32	16.5
# employed in public interest	6	3.1
# employed as judicial clerks	23	11.9
# employed in academia	6	3.1
Geographic Location		
# employed in state	66	34.0
# employed in foreign countries	0	0.0
# of states where employed	30	

Bar Passage Rates

First-time takers	205	Reporting %	70.24
Average school %	93.06	Average state %	89.66
Average pass difference	3.40		

Jurisdiction	Takers	Passers	Pass %	State %	Diff %
Iowa	66	62	93.94	90.11	3.83
Illinois	37	37	100.00	90.94	9.06
Minnesota	13	12	92.31	91.09	1.22
Missouri	10	9	90.00	92.33	−2.33
Others (2)	18	14	77.78		

The University of Iowa College of Law

320 Melrose Avenue
Iowa City, IA 52242
Phone: 800.553.4692, ext. 9095; 319.335.9095; Fax: 319.335.9646
E-mail: law-admissions@uiowa.edu; Website: www.law.uiowa.edu

■ Introduction

The University of Iowa College of Law, founded in 1865, is the oldest law school in continuous operation west of the Mississippi River. Iowa enjoys a top national reputation, and its faculty is renowned for its outstanding scholarship and teaching.

The college is located in Iowa City, a cosmopolitan college town that is home to a dynamic teaching and research university and over 60,000 people. Students from all 50 states and roughly 100 countries attend the university. Iowa City offers a rich cultural life, Big Ten athletic events, and the world-famous Iowa Writers' Workshop.

The Boyd Law Building's central campus location on a bluff overlooking the Iowa River provides a professional enclave well-suited to the college's intensive style of education as well as easy access to the academic, cultural, social, and recreational resources of a major research university.

■ Admission

Iowa strives to enroll a student body that reflects the academic quality and diversity expected of a leading national law school. The college's numbers-plus policy looks beyond numerical indicators and utilizes a full file review to evaluate an applicant's potential contribution to enhancing classroom discussion. Factors such as maturity, work experience, ability to overcome adversity, and cultural background are considered.

■ Enrollment Date

Iowa offers only one starting date for entering students: August. All students may "accelerate" their course of study toward the JD degree by taking summer and intersession classes. The minimum time of study is no fewer than 27 months after the student has started law study at this law school or at a law school from which transfer credit has been accepted.

■ Curriculum

The students are the heart of our institution. A broad and wide-ranging curriculum, small classes, accessible professors, and caring administrators are just a few examples of Iowa's student-centered orientation.

Iowa's curriculum establishes a solid foundation for a lifetime of professional growth and personal development. Students take an active role in their professional training. We go the extra measure to ensure that our students have the proper resources and learning environment to maximize their individual development as professionals.

First-year students have at least one class each semester with approximately 40 students; courses taught in this small-section format allow extensive class participation and interaction with a faculty member. After completing the set of required first-year courses exploring fundamental legal concepts, students plan their own course of study from a rich menu of mainstream, specialized, and clinical offerings. Second- and third-year courses cover the range of specialties within the legal profession, allowing students to sample liberally and follow professional interests.

At Iowa, students benefit from the serious emphasis the college places on both interdisciplinary study and the study of international and comparative law. Interdisciplinary courses and research programs are actively encouraged; nearly one-third of the college's faculty members offer courses or conduct research in the international and comparative law fields.

■ Legal Analysis, Writing, and Research Program

The Legal Analysis, Writing, and Research (LAWR) Program at the College of Law is a two-semester, first-year course (two credits each semester), with classes of 20 students, and is designed to equip participants with effective skills in legal analysis, writing, and research.

■ Iowa Law Library

The University of Iowa College of Law Library is consistently recognized as one of the finest and largest law libraries anywhere. The library's international holdings are impressive; it includes a complete collection of United Nations documents since the UN's founding in 1945. The Law Library received significant and high praise in the 2004 *National Jurist* survey of law libraries that are located in the United States. Additionally, wireless Internet is available throughout the library.

■ Special Programs

The first writing center in the country established specifically for a law school community, Iowa's Writing Resource Center serves as an extension of the classroom and supplements the college's Legal Analysis, Writing, and Research Program. Members of the writing center's staff help law students with a broad range of writing, including class assignments, law journal articles, and résumés and cover letters. The center's staff teaches strategies for overcoming writer's block, adapting materials for various audiences, and generally improving the quality of students' writing.

The Academic Achievement Program (AAP) helps students achieve their full academic potential as they move from successful undergraduate careers to face the new challenges of law study. AAP presents a variety of programs, including a first-semester lecture series for new students. Individual study skills counseling is also available for all students.

■ Clinical Law Programs

The Clinical Law Programs give students opportunities to gain experience in many different areas of substantive law including criminal defense, disability rights, domestic violence, employment law, general civil, and immigration and asylum law. Externship opportunities are available with federal trial courts, the Iowa Attorney General, legal services offices, US Attorneys' offices, Federal Public Defenders' offices, and the Iowa City City Attorney, among others. Through the representation of real clients, students are able

to develop and hone a diverse complement of lawyering skills from interviewing, counseling, and drafting court papers to trial practice, appellate advocacy, legislative lobbying, and policy development.

■ International Law

Iowa offers one of the nation's strongest programs for the study of international and comparative law. The school offers four study-abroad programs. Iowa is the stateside home of the London Law Consortium through which seven US law schools conduct a study-abroad program for a spring semester in London. The Iowa/Bordeaux Summer Program offers one month of intensive coursework in Arcachon, France. Students also have the opportunity to participate in an exchange program with Bucerius Law School in Germany as well as to study at Católica University in Lisbon, Portugal. In addition, students may receive credit for participating in other study-abroad programs offered by ABA-approved law schools.

■ Student Activities

Student activities at the law school include the American Constitution Society; the Asian American Law Students Association; the Black Law Students Association; the Christian Legal Society; Client Counseling; the Environmental Law Society; the Equal Justice Foundation; the Federalist Society; the Intellectual Property Law Society; the International Law Society; the Iowa Campaign for Human Rights; the *Iowa Law Review*; the Iowa Student Bar Association; the J. Reuben Clark Law Society; the Jewish Law Students Association; the *Journal of Corporation Law*; the *Journal of Gender, Race and Justice*; the *Journal of Transnational Law and Contemporary Problems*; the Latino Law Student Association; Law Students for Reproductive Justice; the Middle Eastern Law Students Association; Moot Court; the National Lawyers Guild; the Native American Law Students Association; the Order of the Coif; the Organization for Women Law Students and Staff; the Outlaws; Parents/Partners Weekend; Phi Alpha Delta; Phi Delta Phi; the *Pro Bono* Society; the Stephenson Competition; Supreme Court Day; and Trial Advocacy.

■ Expenses and Financial Aid

All admitted students are automatically considered for merit scholarships and fellowships based on their academic achievements. A separate application is not required. The college administers its substantial financial aid program to advance the goals of its selective admission policy. More than 90 percent of our students receive some form of financial aid. Grants, scholarships, work-study funds, and loans are awarded on a need or merit basis for the purpose of providing access to legal education for the talented and diverse students admitted to the college. A number of part-time employment opportunities are also available to second- and third-year students; nonresident students with a quarter-time research assistant position (10 hours per week) are classified as residents for tuition purposes. Eligibility for financial aid based on need is established by completion of the FAFSA, available at *www.fafsa.ed.gov*.

■ Career Services

Admitted students are strongly encouraged to pursue career counseling, which helps them clarify and articulate career and life plans with the JD or LLM; participate in internships, externships, summer associate positions, and other experiential legal opportunities; and develop strategic job-search plans for a wide range of legal careers. Each year, many 1Ls participate in the Partner for a Day program with alumni and employers, which helps them make career decisions and develop professional networks. To facilitate interviewing for summer and full-time employment, the Career Services Office provides students with access to national job fairs, résumé collections, video interviews, and on-campus interviews. The law school's participation in interview consortia on the East Coast and West Coast provides students with many interview opportunities outside of the Midwest. Finally, the Career Services Office offers continued services to alumni seeking career advice.

Applicant Profile Not Available

The John Marshall Law School

315 South Plymouth Court
Chicago, IL 60604
Phone: 800.537.4280; 312.987.1406; Fax: 312.427.5136
E-mail: admission@jmls.edu; Website: www.jmls.edu

ABA
Approved
Since
1951

ABA
AMERICAN BAR ASSOCIATION
Section of Legal Education
and Admissions to the Bar

The Basics

Type of school	Private
Term	Semester
Application deadline	4/1 11/1
Application fee	$60
Financial aid deadline	6/4
Can first year start other than fall?	Yes
Student to faculty ratio	14.4 to 1
# of housing spaces available restricted to law students	
graduate housing for which law students are eligible	

Faculty and Administrators

	Total		Men		Women		Minorities	
	Spr	Fall	Spr	Fall	Spr	Fall	Spr	Fall
Full-time	69	73	44	47	25	26	9	11
Other full-time	0	0	0	0	0	0	0	0
Deans, librarians, & others who teach	9	9	5	5	4	4	2	2
Part-time	109	110	73	77	36	33	11	10
Total	187	192	122	129	65	63	22	23

Curriculum

		Full-Time	Part-Time
Typical first-year section size		75	60
Is there typically a "small section" of the first-year class, other than Legal Writing, taught by full-time faculty		No	No
If yes, typical size offered last year			
# of classroom course titles beyond first-year curriculum		270	
# of upper division courses, excluding seminars, with an enrollment:	Under 25	246	
	25–49	60	
	50–74	33	
	75–99	16	
	100+	1	
# of seminars		38	
# of seminar positions available		760	
# of seminar positions filled		362	241
# of positions available in simulation courses		2,490	
# of simulation positions filled		1,090	822
# of positions available in faculty supervised clinical courses		90	
# of faculty supervised clinical positions filled		62	12
# involved in field placements		232	18
# involved in law journals		201	28
# involved in moot court or trial competitions		129	12
# of credit hours required to graduate		90	

Transfers

Transfers in	16
Transfers out	38

Tuition and Fees

	Resident	Nonresident
Full-time	$35,380	$35,380
Part-time	$25,300	$25,300
Tuition Guarantee Program	N	

Living Expenses

Estimated living expenses for singles

Living on campus	Living off campus	Living at home
$24,904	$24,904	$24,904

JD Enrollment and Ethnicity

	Men		Women		Full-Time		Part-Time		1st-Year		Total		JD Degs. Awd.
	#	%	#	%	#	%	#	%	#	%	#	%	
African Amer.	35	4.7	74	11.8	64	6.2	45	13.3	48	9.7	109	7.9	23
Amer. Indian	7	0.9	5	0.8	9	0.9	3	0.9	2	0.4	12	0.9	3
Asian Amer.	41	5.5	36	5.8	59	5.7	18	5.3	34	6.8	77	5.6	30
Mex. Amer.	26	3.5	14	2.2	28	2.7	12	3.5	10	2.0	40	2.9	7
Puerto Rican	5	0.7	4	0.6	8	0.8	1	0.3	4	0.8	9	0.7	3
Hispanic	38	5.1	27	4.3	49	4.7	16	4.7	28	5.6	65	4.7	6
Total Minority	152	20.2	160	25.6	217	20.9	95	28.0	126	25.4	312	22.7	72
For. Nation.	3	0.4	12	1.9	10	1.0	5	1.5	4	0.8	15	1.1	3
Caucasian	546	72.6	405	64.8	735	70.8	216	63.7	329	66.2	951	69.1	298
Unknown	51	6.8	48	7.7	76	7.3	23	6.8	38	7.6	99	7.2	26
Total	752	54.6	625	45.4	1038	75.4	339	24.6	497	36.1	1377		399

The John Marshall Law School

ABA
Approved
Since
1951

GPA and LSAT Scores

	Total	Full-Time	Part-Time
# of apps	3,345	2,728	617
# of offers	1,553	1,328	225
# of matrics	519	394	125
75% GPA	3.51	3.53	3.44
Median GPA	3.22	3.25	3.20
25% GPA	2.98	3.00	2.88
75% LSAT	155	156	154
Median LSAT	153	153	152
25% LSAT	150	150	149

Grants and Scholarships (from prior year)

	Total		Full-Time		Part-Time	
	#	%	#	%	#	%
Total # of students	1,354		1,000		354	
Total # receiving grants	665	49.1	541	54.1	124	35.0
Less than 1/2 tuition	592	43.7	495	49.5	97	27.4
Half to full tuition	40	3.0	22	2.2	18	5.1
Full tuition	11	0.8	9	0.9	2	0.6
More than full tuition	22	1.6	15	1.5	7	2.0
Median grant amount			$8,000		$6,000	

Informational and Library Resources

Total amount spent on library materials	$1,702,983
Study seating capacity inside the library	750
# of full-time equivalent professional librarians	12
Hours per week library is open	94
# of open, wired connections available to students	0
# of networked computers available for use by students	74
Has wireless network?	Y
Require computer?	N

JD Attrition (from prior year)

	Academic	Other	Total	
	#	#	#	%
1st year	31	49	80	17.7
2nd year	9	21	30	7.3
3rd year	0	6	6	1.5
4th year	0	0	0	0.0

Employment (9 months after graduation)

	Total	Percentage
Employment status known	403	96.6
Employment status unknown	14	3.4
Employed	359	89.1
Pursuing graduate degrees	6	1.5
Unemployed (seeking, not seeking, or studying for the bar)	35	8.7
Type of Employment		
# employed in law firms	197	54.9
# employed in business and industry	82	22.8
# employed in government	54	15.0
# employed in public interest	8	2.2
# employed as judicial clerks	6	1.7
# employed in academia	12	3.3
Geographic Location		
# employed in state	301	83.8
# employed in foreign countries	0	0.0
# of states where employed	23	

Bar Passage Rates

First-time takers	420	Reporting %	90.24
Average school %	87.86	Average state %	90.94
Average pass difference −3.08			

Jurisdiction	Takers	Passers	Pass %	State %	Diff %
Illinois	379	333	87.86	90.94	−3.08

The John Marshall Law School

315 South Plymouth Court
Chicago, IL 60604
Phone: 800.537.4280; 312.987.1406; Fax: 312.427.5136
E-mail: admission@jmls.edu; Website: www.jmls.edu

■ Introduction

Since its founding in 1899, The John Marshall Law School has become one of the nation's largest free-standing institutions dedicated to the teaching of law. The school offers a curriculum, writing courses, and a trial advocacy program that prepare students in the theory and practice of law. Students attend both day and evening classes at the 315 South Plymouth Court location in Chicago's Loop.

The Law School's reputation has been built by alumni who work as attorneys in private practice, government, industry, and the judiciary. Among its graduates are the former US Secretary of Commerce, two members of the Illinois Supreme Court, and the chief judge of the Circuit Court of Cook County, the largest unified court system in the United States.

Students learn in rigorous classes taught by a highly regarded faculty and adjunct faculty. Coursework is supplemented with practical experience through clinical and externship experiences. Located in the heart of Chicago's legal, financial, and commercial districts, The John Marshall Law School offers a location that is steps from the federal courthouse and blocks from the central offices of the Circuit Court of Cook County. Its students clerk or find positions with Chicago's top law firms, as well as boutique firms.

The law school holds accreditations from the American Bar Association, the American Association of Law Schools, and the North Central Association. The ethnically and racially diverse student population reflects the law school's founding principles of access and opportunity.

■ Curriculum

The law school offers both day and evening programs for JD, MS, and LLM students. Students can be admitted into a joint JD/LLM curriculum after their second year. Students are admitted in both January and August. The law school's JD curriculum places major emphasis on legal foundation classes with required Lawyering Skills writing courses. Students have the option of earning a JD degree with a concentration in advocacy/dispute resolution, business, elder law, employee benefits, estate planning, general practice, information technology law, intellectual property law, international law, public interest law, or real estate law. Students also can earn a JD degree with a certificate of specialization in alternative dispute resolution, elder law, intellectual property law, and trial advocacy.

John Marshall offers students the option of earning a JD/MPA, JD/MA, or JD/MBA degree through relationships with area institutions. The law school also offers MS degrees for the nonlawyer in the areas of employee benefits, information technology and privacy law, real estate law, and tax law.

John Marshall offers the largest selection of LLM degrees in the Midwest. Lawyers interested in specializing in an area of law for an LLM degree can select from employee benefits, information technology and privacy law, intellectual property law, international business and trade law, real estate law, and tax law.

■ Clinics, Externships, and Special Programs

Clinical experience is one of the best hands-on learning techniques. John Marshall's Fair Housing Legal Clinic offers assistance to persons who have been discriminated against in their housing choices. Students learn interview techniques, claims investigation, pleadings, motions, and trial preparation. The Patent Law Clinic gives students the opportunity to assist needy inventors in preparing and securing patents. The Immigration Clinic gives students training through the Midwest Immigrant and Human Rights Center where they assist immigrants with asylum claims.

The Veterans Legal Support Center & Clinic gives students the opportunity to assist veterans filing medical and education claims with the United States Department of Veterans Affairs, as well as the opportunity to provide representation for veterans during the appeals process through a statewide network of pro bono attorneys.

Students also can gain hands-on experience through externships. Students are paired with attorneys and judges through Judicial Externships, Defenders Clinic, Local Government Clinic, and Prosecution Clinic.

■ Library

The recently renovated Louis L. Biro Law Library occupies the 6th–10th floors of the law school's State Street building. A team of over 20 professional librarians and staff members work to serve the students during the 96 hours/week that the library is open. The library holds over 410,000 volumes and microform equivalents and provides on-campus and remote access to over 4,000 titles via our specialty electronic databases. Students have wireless access throughout the law school and the library offers seating for 750, including eight group study rooms. In addition to supporting the research and instructional needs of the students, faculty, and staff of the law school, the library is also open to members of the Chicago Bar Association.

■ Admission

Students are admitted in August and January. Applications for August entrance may be filed between October 1 and March 1; for January entrance, between May 1 and October 15. The LSAT score is evaluated together with the cumulative grade-point average and other relevant factors, including difficulty of undergraduate program, postgraduate experience, leadership potential, business and professional background, and letters of recommendation. Applicants from minority and other disadvantaged groups will be given special consideration in cases where their overall records are competitive with other applicants. Minority representation in the class enrolled in 2009 was 31 percent. Applicants with a B average overall and an LSAT score in the 60th percentile may be presumed to be within the range for favorable consideration.

■ Student Activities

There are five honors programs: the *John Marshall Law Review*, the *Journal of Computer and Information Law*, the *Review of Intellectual Property Law* (an online journal), the

Moot Court Honors Program, and the Trial Advocacy and Dispute Resolution Honors Program. John Marshall has a long-standing tradition of success in interscholastic competitions and sends teams to more than 30 moot court and mock trial competitions annually.

The student community at the John Marshall Law School includes more than 40 student organizations engaging in social awareness, community service, legal discussions, and social activities. Every student group at John Marshall reflects the diversity, highlights the talents, and enhances the opportunities of our total student body.

John Marshall welcomes numerous well-known visitors and scholars each year. In addition to giving lectures and presentations, our distinguished guests can be found meeting with individual classes or holding roundtable discussions with interested students and faculty.

■ Career Opportunities

The Career Services Office (CSO) offers personal assistance to help students assess and refine their career goals. The CSO sponsors more than 60 career-related programs each year, many featuring alumni as panelists and speakers. A robust Alumni Mentor Program has mentors meeting with students one-on-one to provide real-world advice on practice areas, law school courses, and the day-to-day practice of law. The CSO also aggressively promotes John Marshall students to employers. John Marshall graduates are employed at 34 of Chicago's 35 largest firms. Public service is another favored career path, with graduates serving as attorneys in the courts and government. Nearly one-fifth of all Illinois judges (circuit, appellate, and state supreme court) are John Marshall alumni.

■ Correspondence

We encourage you to visit our website at *www.jmls.edu* and to visit the law school. Tour arrangements can be made through our Office of Admission and visitors are welcome to sit in a class and talk with students and faculty. An admission counselor can explain the admission process and a representative from our Financial Aid Office can help you understand what loans and scholarships are available.

Applicant Profile

The John Marshall Law School
This grid includes only applicants who earned 120–180 LSAT scores under standard administrations.

LSAT Score	GPA						
	3.75 +	3.50–3.74	3.25–3.49	3.00–3.24	2.75–2.99	2.50–2.74	Below 2.50
175–180							
170–174							
165–169							
160–164							
155–159							
150–154							
145–149							
140–144							
135–139							
130–134							
125–129							
120–124							

■ Likely   □ Possible   ▨ Unlikely

The University of Kansas School of Law

1535 West 15th Street
Lawrence, KS 66045-7608
Phone: 866.220.3654 (toll free), 785.864.4378; Fax: 785.864.5054
E-mail: admitlaw@ku.edu; Website: www.law.ku.edu

ABA
Approved
Since
1923

AMERICAN BAR ASSOCIATION
Section of Legal Education
and Admissions to the Bar

The Basics

Type of school	Public
Term	Semester
Application deadline	3/15
Application fee	$55
Financial aid deadline	3/1
Can first year start other than fall?	Yes
Student to faculty ratio	12.4 to 1
# of housing spaces available restricted to law students	
graduate housing for which law students are eligible	550

Faculty and Administrators

	Total		Men		Women		Minorities	
	Spr	Fall	Spr	Fall	Spr	Fall	Spr	Fall
Full-time	33	32	19	19	14	13	5	5
Other full-time	3	3	0	0	3	3	0	0
Deans, librarians, & others who teach	7	7	5	5	2	2	1	1
Part-time	24	14	18	9	6	5	1	0
Total	67	56	42	33	25	23	7	6

Curriculum

		Full-Time	Part-Time
Typical first-year section size		67	0
Is there typically a "small section" of the first-year class, other than Legal Writing, taught by full-time faculty		Yes	No
If yes, typical size offered last year		18	
# of classroom course titles beyond first-year curriculum		93	
# of upper division courses, excluding seminars, with an enrollment:	Under 25	93	
	25–49	33	
	50–74	5	
	75–99	5	
	100+	0	
# of seminars		11	
# of seminar positions available		244	
# of seminar positions filled		172	0
# of positions available in simulation courses		270	
# of simulation positions filled		230	0
# of positions available in faculty supervised clinical courses		191	
# of faculty supervised clinical positions filled		137	0
# involved in field placements		131	0
# involved in law journals		88	0
# involved in moot court or trial competitions		89	0
# of credit hours required to graduate		90	

JD Enrollment and Ethnicity

	Men		Women		Full-Time		Part-Time		1st-Year		Total		JD Degs. Awd.
	#	%	#	%	#	%	#	%	#	%	#	%	
African Amer.	8	2.7	7	3.5	15	3.0	0	0.0	4	2.5	15	3.0	3
Amer. Indian	12	4.0	7	3.5	19	3.8	0	0.0	6	3.7	19	3.8	6
Asian Amer.	17	5.7	10	5.0	27	5.4	0	0.0	7	4.3	27	5.4	7
Mex. Amer.	3	1.0	1	0.5	4	0.8	0	0.0	4	2.5	4	0.8	0
Puerto Rican	0	0.0	0	0.0	0	0.0	0	0.0	0	0.0	0	0.0	0
Hispanic	9	3.0	8	4.0	17	3.4	0	0.0	6	3.7	17	3.4	8
Total Minority	49	16.3	33	16.6	82	16.4	0	0.0	27	16.8	82	16.4	24
For. Nation.	10	3.3	12	6.0	22	4.4	0	0.0	0	0.0	22	4.4	9
Caucasian	223	74.3	142	71.4	365	73.1	0	0.0	134	83.2	365	73.1	123
Unknown	18	6.0	12	6.0	30	6.0	0	0.0	0	0.0	30	6.0	4
Total	300	60.1	199	39.9	499	100.0	0	0.0	161	32.3	499		160

Transfers

Transfers in	16
Transfers out	3

Tuition and Fees

	Resident	Nonresident
Full-time	$14,478	$25,375
Part-time		
Tuition Guarantee Program	N	

Living Expenses

Estimated living expenses for singles

Living on campus	Living off campus	Living at home
$16,186	$16,186	$16,186

The University of Kansas School of Law

ABA
Approved
Since
1923

GPA and LSAT Scores

	Total	Full-Time	Part-Time
# of apps	1,098	1,098	0
# of offers	387	387	0
# of matrics	163	163	0
75% GPA	3.71	3.71	0.00
Median GPA	3.50	3.50	0.00
25% GPA	3.25	3.25	0.00
75% LSAT	160	160	0
Median LSAT	157	157	0
25% LSAT	155	155	0

Grants and Scholarships (from prior year)

	Total #	Total %	Full-Time #	Full-Time %	Part-Time #	Part-Time %
Total # of students	489		489		0	
Total # receiving grants	393	80.4	393	80.4	0	0.0
Less than 1/2 tuition	293	59.9	293	59.9	0	0.0
Half to full tuition	80	16.4	80	16.4	0	0.0
Full tuition	6	1.2	6	1.2	0	0.0
More than full tuition	14	2.9	14	2.9	0	0.0
Median grant amount			$3,450		$0	

Informational and Library Resources

Total amount spent on library materials	$869,767
Study seating capacity inside the library	481
# of full-time equivalent professional librarians	8
Hours per week library is open	95
# of open, wired connections available to students	0
# of networked computers available for use by students	51
Has wireless network?	Y
Require computer?	N

JD Attrition (from prior year)

	Academic #	Other #	Total #	Total %
1st year	0	1	1	0.6
2nd year	0	5	5	3.1
3rd year	2	0	2	1.2
4th year	0	0	0	0.0

Employment (9 months after graduation)

	Total	Percentage
Employment status known	161	98.2
Employment status unknown	3	1.8
Employed	137	85.1
Pursuing graduate degrees	11	6.8
Unemployed (seeking, not seeking, or studying for the bar)	8	5.0
Type of Employment		
# employed in law firms	77	56.2
# employed in business and industry	20	14.6
# employed in government	24	17.5
# employed in public interest	5	3.6
# employed as judicial clerks	10	7.3
# employed in academia	1	0.7
Geographic Location		
# employed in state	61	44.5
# employed in foreign countries	3	2.2
# of states where employed	21	

Bar Passage Rates

First-time takers	145	Reporting %	71.03
Average school %	95.14	Average state %	89.17
Average pass difference	5.97		

Jurisdiction	Takers	Passers	Pass %	State %	Diff %
Kansas	69	65	94.20	89.33	4.87
Missouri	21	20	95.24	92.33	2.91
Colorado	13	13	100.00	83.29	16.71

The University of Kansas School of Law

1535 West 15th Street
Lawrence, KS 66045-7608
Phone: 866.220.3654 (toll free), 785.864.4378; Fax: 785.864.5054
E-mail: admitlaw@ku.edu; Website: www.law.ku.edu

■ Introduction

The University of Kansas (KU) School of Law is an excellent place to begin a legal career. It has a venerable history and a commitment to educating for the future. Legal education at KU began in 1878. The school was a charter member of the Association of American Law Schools, and since 1924, it has had a chapter of the Order of the Coif, a national law school honor society with chapters at leading law schools throughout the country. The law school is fully accredited by the American Bar Association.

The law school is on KU's main campus—one of the most beautiful in the country. It occupies Green Hall, named in honor of James Woods Green, first dean of the school. Green Hall is a five-story building with extensive clinical facilities, spacious and attractive classrooms, seminar rooms, a formal courtroom, and common areas. The school is equipped with a wireless network, allowing students to access the Internet and e-mail from anywhere in the law school.

The school's primary mission is to prepare its students to be outstanding members of the legal profession, well educated in the law, with a commitment to professional achievement and public service. The school educates students in both general principles of law and the skills needed for practice in a changing legal environment. Students develop technical competence, pride in legal craftsmanship, a sound sense of ethics and professionalism, and an appreciation for the role of law in society.

■ Faculty

KU Law faculty care about teaching. They are committed to excellence in the classroom and to serving as mentors for law students. This is the KU Law tradition. Students are encouraged to consult regularly with their teachers about their progress in the study of law as well as about career plans, job opportunities, and the professional responsibilities of lawyers. Law faculty offices are located throughout Green Hall, and doors are open to students.

Faculty members enrich their teaching by researching and writing about the areas of law they teach. They regularly participate in symposia, publish widely in legal journals, and enjoy national and international recognition for the quality of their scholarship. Many have written important treatises and casebooks used at law schools around the country.

■ Learning the Law

Entering students take basic courses that provide a solid foundation for upper-level classes and for the practice of law. The lawyering course focuses on the skills and values of the profession. Taught by faculty members with extensive practice experience, the course introduces students to the tools all lawyers use: an understanding of the legal system and legal institutions, case law and statutes, legal research and writing, and advocacy. First-year students take one of their other required courses in a small section of approximately 20 students, which provides an informal learning atmosphere and encourages in-depth discussions and critical analysis.

More than 100 courses are available to upper-level students, covering a broad range of practice areas from agricultural law to the law of cyberspace. Eleven clinical programs permit students, acting under faculty supervision, to develop legal skills and learn professional values in actual practice settings: the Criminal Prosecution Clinic, Paul E. Wilson Project for Innocence and Post-Conviction Remedies, Elder Law Clinic, Family Health Care Legal Services Clinic, Judicial Clerkship Clinic, Legal Aid Clinic, Legislative Clinic, Media Law Clinic, Public Policy Clinic, Tribal Judicial Support Clinic, and the Externship Clinic. The large number of clinical placements available means that every student can participate in at least one clinic and many participate in more than one.

The school's setting at the heart of a major university makes possible the 11 joint-degree programs open to law students. The most popular joint-degree programs are business, health services administration, and social welfare, but joint degrees are also available in East Asian languages and cultures, economics, indigenous nations studies, journalism, political science, philosophy, public administration, and urban planning. In addition, the school offers eight certification programs: advocacy, business and commercial law, elder law, environmental and natural resources law, international trade and finance, media law and policy, tax law, and tribal lawyering.

■ Library

The Wheat Law Library is the largest law library in Kansas. Its hallmark is excellent service for students and faculty. The law library is a wireless environment that allows students, faculty, and staff access to LexisNexis, Westlaw, CALI, HeinOnline, LLMC-Digital, the Internet, and numerous university-wide interdisciplinary databases. Access is also available on desktop computers in carrels and throughout the library. The law library's award-winning website, *www.law.ku.edu/library/*, is a comprehensive gateway that provides access to virtual resources beyond the scope of the physical collection as well as in-house topical research guides. Professional librarians and reference staff are eager to help with legal research ranging from the rich heritage of historical materials to cutting-edge digitized images.

■ Accelerated/Summer Program

The law school's unique summer school program is fully integrated with the curriculum of the fall and spring semesters. Students who begin law school in May and attend summer school each of the following two summers may complete degree requirements in just 27 months.

■ Student Life

Because the school seeks students with strong personal qualities in addition to high academic credentials, students learn the law with classmates who have the interpersonal skills, maturity, judgment, and ambition to succeed. The law school values diversity, and students have a wide range of education and work experience, enriching classroom discussions and student life.

The University of Kansas School of Law

KU Law students develop friendships that last a lifetime. They find as many opportunities for collaboration as for competition. They socialize and develop leadership skills and an appreciation for community service through membership in many student organizations. They hone research, writing, and editing skills through work on two student-edited publications: the *Kansas Law Review* and the *Kansas Journal of Law and Public Policy*. They participate regularly and successfully in moot court, mock trial, and client counseling competitions. Study abroad is available through the London Consortium, the school's Limerick and Istanbul programs, and other programs approved by the American Bar Association.

■ Career Services and Alumni

The school's Office of Career Services helps students define career goals and find employment that matches their interests. The office coordinates an extensive on-campus interviewing program, sponsors workshops exploring career options, and helps students develop job-seeking skills.

KU Law students and graduates are highly sought after by employers throughout the state, region, and nation. Most recent graduates chose employment in private law firms, but many chose government service, including work as prosecutors, public interest work, the military, graduate study, and nontraditional careers. A considerable number of graduates accept judicial clerkships. Recent graduates have been law clerks at all levels, including the Supreme Court of the United States.

KU graduates have been highly successful in passing Kansas and Missouri bar examinations and have performed extremely well on examinations in other states. The Office of Career Services provides up-to-date information on bar requirements for all states.

The school's 6,600-plus alumni live in all 50 states, the District of Columbia, Puerto Rico, and 17 foreign countries. Many participate in the law school's mentor program for first-year law students or in the Career Services Alumni Network, serving as sources of information about practice specialties and practice opportunities.

Applicant Profile

The University of Kansas School of Law
This grid includes applicants who earned 120–180 LSAT scores under standard administrations.

LSAT Score	3.75 +		3.50–3.74		3.25–3.49		3.00–3.24		2.75–2.99		2.50–2.74		2.25–2.49		2.00–2.24		Below 2.00		No GPA		Total	
	Apps	Adm	Apps	Adm	Apps	Adm	Apps	Adm	Apps	Adm	Apps	Adm	Apps	Adm	Apps	Adm	Apps	Adm	Apps	Adm	Apps	Adm
175–180	0	0	0	0	0	0	0	0	0	0	0	0	0	0	0	0	0	0	0	0	0	0
170–174	2	2	2	2	0	0	3	3	1	0	1	0	0	0	0	0	0	0	0	0	9	7
165–169	16	15	9	8	5	5	6	4	1	1	1	0	0	0	1	1	0	0	0	0	39	34
160–164	38	36	20	17	24	18	21	16	11	7	6	0	4	1	1	0	1	0	2	1	128	96
155–159	48	35	63	44	64	32	42	16	25	5	18	3	11	1	1	0	0	0	2	0	274	136
150–154	47	12	50	15	70	16	71	10	46	6	17	0	8	0	1	0	1	0	10	3	321	62
145–149	17	3	23	4	26	5	24	2	21	1	8	0	5	0	2	0	1	0	5	0	132	15
140–144	1	0	6	1	17	0	11	1	15	0	7	0	10	0	0	0	0	0	3	1	70	3
135–139	0	0	2	1	6	0	1	0	5	0	7	0	4	0	4	0	0	0	2	0	31	1
130–134	0	0	1	0	1	0	4	0	2	0	1	0	0	0	1	0	1	0	4	0	15	0
125–129	0	0	0	0	0	0	0	0	1	0	0	0	0	0	0	0	0	0	0	0	1	0
120–124	0	0	0	0	0	0	0	0	0	0	0	0	0	0	0	0	0	0	0	0	0	0
Total	169	103	176	92	213	76	183	52	128	20	66	3	42	2	11	1	4	0	28	5	1020	354

Apps = Number of Applicants
Adm = Number Admitted
Reflects 99% of the total applicant pool; average LSAT data reported.

University of Kentucky College of Law

209 Law Building, South Limestone Street
Lexington, KY 40506-0048
Phone: 859.257.1678; Fax: 859.323.1061
E-mail: lawadmissions@email.uky.edu; Website: www.law.uky.edu

ABA
Approved
Since
1925

ABA — Section of Legal Education and Admissions to the Bar

The Basics

Type of school	Public
Term	Semester
Application deadline	3/1
Application fee	$50
Financial aid deadline	4/1
Can first year start other than fall?	No
Student to faculty ratio	16.9 to 1
# of housing spaces available restricted to law students	
graduate housing for which law students are eligible	

Faculty and Administrators

	Total		Men		Women		Minorities	
	Spr	Fall	Spr	Fall	Spr	Fall	Spr	Fall
Full-time	16	23	12	16	4	7	3	4
Other full-time	0	0	0	0	0	0	0	0
Deans, librarians, & others who teach	11	13	3	4	8	9	3	4
Part-time	28	22	20	18	8	4	0	0
Total	55	58	35	38	20	20	6	8

Curriculum

		Full-Time	Part-Time
Typical first-year section size		56	0
Is there typically a "small section" of the first-year class, other than Legal Writing, taught by full-time faculty		Yes	No
If yes, typical size offered last year		43	
# of classroom course titles beyond first-year curriculum		72	
# of upper division courses, excluding seminars, with an enrollment:	Under 25	37	
	25–49	28	
	50–74	10	
	75–99	0	
	100+	0	
# of seminars		15	
# of seminar positions available		240	
# of seminar positions filled		206	0
# of positions available in simulation courses		150	
# of simulation positions filled		70	0
# of positions available in faculty supervised clinical courses		32	
# of faculty supervised clinical positions filled		32	0
# involved in field placements		67	0
# involved in law journals		50	0
# involved in moot court or trial competitions		51	0
# of credit hours required to graduate		90	

JD Enrollment and Ethnicity

	Men		Women		Full-Time		Part-Time		1st-Year		Total		JD Degs. Awd.
	#	%	#	%	#	%	#	%	#	%	#	%	
African Amer.	17	7.5	19	10.6	36	8.9	0	0.0	17	11.3	36	8.9	10
Amer. Indian	3	1.3	0	0.0	3	0.7	0	0.0	2	1.3	3	0.7	0
Asian Amer.	6	2.7	3	1.7	9	2.2	0	0.0	3	2.0	9	2.2	1
Mex. Amer.	2	0.9	0	0.0	2	0.5	0	0.0	0	0.0	2	0.5	0
Puerto Rican	1	0.4	0	0.0	1	0.2	0	0.0	1	0.7	1	0.2	0
Hispanic	3	1.3	2	1.1	5	1.2	0	0.0	3	2.0	5	1.2	1
Total Minority	32	14.2	24	13.3	56	13.8	0	0.0	26	17.2	56	13.8	12
For. Nation.	0	0.0	1	0.6	1	0.2	0	0.0	1	0.7	1	0.2	0
Caucasian	188	83.2	155	86.1	343	84.5	0	0.0	118	78.1	343	84.5	124
Unknown	6	2.7	0	0.0	6	1.5	0	0.0	6	4.0	6	1.5	0
Total	226	55.7	180	44.3	406	100.0	0	0.0	151	37.2	406		136

Transfers

Transfers in	6
Transfers out	5

Tuition and Fees

	Resident	Nonresident
Full-time	$16,020	$27,758
Part-time		
Tuition Guarantee Program	N	

Living Expenses

Estimated living expenses for singles

Living on campus	Living off campus	Living at home
$15,080	$15,080	$5,980

University of Kentucky College of Law

ABA
Approved
Since
1925

GPA and LSAT Scores

	Total	Full-Time	Part-Time
# of apps	1,080	1,080	0
# of offers	414	414	0
# of matrics	152	152	0
75% GPA	3.82	3.82	0.00
Median GPA	3.60	3.60	0.00
25% GPA	3.33	3.33	0.00
75% LSAT	161	161	0
Median LSAT	159	159	0
25% LSAT	156	156	0

Grants and Scholarships (from prior year)

	Total #	Total %	Full-Time #	Full-Time %	Part-Time #	Part-Time %
Total # of students	395		395		0	
Total # receiving grants	257	65.1	257	65.1	0	0.0
Less than 1/2 tuition	172	43.5	172	43.5	0	0.0
Half to full tuition	77	19.5	77	19.5	0	0.0
Full tuition	0	0.0	0	0.0	0	0.0
More than full tuition	8	2.0	8	2.0	0	0.0
Median grant amount			$4,000		$0	

Informational and Library Resources

Total amount spent on library materials	$1,157,857
Study seating capacity inside the library	354
# of full-time equivalent professional librarians	7
Hours per week library is open	100
# of open, wired connections available to students	103
# of networked computers available for use by students	48
Has wireless network?	Y
Require computer?	N

JD Attrition (from prior year)

	Academic #	Other #	Total #	Total %
1st year	1	13	14	10.4
2nd year	0	0	0	0.0
3rd year	0	1	1	0.7
4th year	0	0	0	0.0

Employment (9 months after graduation)

	Total	Percentage
Employment status known	160	100.0
Employment status unknown	0	0.0
Employed	150	93.7
Pursuing graduate degrees	4	2.5
Unemployed (seeking, not seeking, or studying for the bar)	3	1.9
Type of Employment		
# employed in law firms	86	57.3
# employed in business and industry	11	7.3
# employed in government	14	9.3
# employed in public interest	8	5.3
# employed as judicial clerks	29	19.3
# employed in academia	2	1.3
Geographic Location		
# employed in state	104	69.3
# employed in foreign countries	0	0.0
# of states where employed	24	

Bar Passage Rates

First-time takers	161	Reporting %	78.88
Average school %	93.70	Average state %	83.08

Average pass difference 10.62

Jurisdiction	Takers	Passers	Pass %	State %	Diff %
Kentucky	127	119	93.70	83.08	10.62

University of Kentucky College of Law

209 Law Building, South Limestone Street
Lexington, KY 40506-0048
Phone: 859.257.1678; Fax: 859.323.1061
E-mail: lawadmissions@email.uky.edu; Website: www.law.uky.edu

■ Introduction

The University of Kentucky College of Law is a small, state-supported law school on the main campus of the university in scenic Lexington, Kentucky, a city of approximately 250,000 in the center of the Bluegrass horse-farm region. Founded in 1908, the college has been a member of the AALS since 1912 and has been accredited by the ABA since 1925. The faculty has wide experience in law practice and government service, as well as teaching and research. UK Law has a strong tradition of faculty concern about their students' progress and success. The curriculum offers broad training in the law and legal methods, drawing upon sources from all jurisdictions. Accordingly, UK Law graduates are prepared to practice in any of the 50 states.

■ Library and Physical Facilities

The college is self-contained in a contemporary building that provides all facilities for a complete program of legal education. All classrooms have been renovated with the addition of state-of-the-art teaching technology. Classrooms provide for student use of laptop computers with wired and wireless Internet access. The law library is on the college's wireless network with a number of attractive study areas, and laptops are available for you to check out and use in the library.

■ Curriculum

UK Law offers a full-time program only, designed to be completed over three academic years or two and one-half years if you take classes during both summer sessions. Several first-year classes are divided into three sections to give you more individual attention, and you will be in a small legal writing section. As an upper-level student, you can select from a full range of elective courses in both traditional and newly developing legal fields. After the first year, the only specific requirements are that you take a course in professional ethics and complete a seminar that involves substantial writing.

■ Legal Clinic

UK Law's Legal Clinic is located in its own building near the college. As a third-year student in the clinic course, you would represent low-income clients in a variety of civil legal matters. The clinic is supervised by a faculty member who was a very successful trial attorney for 10 years.

■ Externships

UK Law offers eight externships for course credit. The Judicial Clerkship Externship enables you to serve as a law clerk for a local state or federal judge. The Fayette Commonwealth Attorney's Office externship enables you to participate in criminal prosecutions. The Federal Correctional Institute Externship permits you to counsel federal inmates in civil and criminal matters. In the Externship with the Kentucky Innocence Project, you work on selected criminal appeals where a claim of factual innocence is made. The Externship with the US

Attorney's Office gives you the opportunity to work on federal appellate briefs in both criminal and civil cases. The Children's Law Center externship allows you to work on high-conflict custody cases representing children. The Department of Public Advocacy Externship enables you to work with the defense in criminal trials. The Externship with the UK HealthCare Risk Management Office gives you firsthand experience with hospital risk management issues and procedures.

■ Joint Degrees

The **JD/MBA** joint degree can be obtained in as little time as four years. You must apply and be admitted to both the UK College of Law and UK's Gatton College of Business and Economics.

If you are interested in a career in public administration, public service, or politics, you should consider the four-year **JD/MPA** joint-degree program with UK's Martin School of Public Policy. You must apply and be admitted to both programs.

If you are interested in a career in international law, public or private law, international business, or in government service in the international sector, you should consider the four-year **JD/MA** dual-degree program with UK's Patterson School of Diplomacy and International Commerce. You must apply and be admitted to both programs.

■ Student Activities

There are a variety of cocurricular activities in which you may earn course credit. The *Kentucky Law Journal* is the 10th oldest American law review and is edited entirely by students, as is the *Kentucky Journal for Equine, Agricultural, and Natural Resources Law*. The college fields several moot court teams that participate in both national and international competitions. UK Law's Trial Advocacy Team advanced to national title competitions in five of the last six years, placing second nationally in 2009. The Mock Trial Team for UK's Black Law Students Association won the Southeast Region of the Thurgood Marshall Moot Court Competition in both 2006 and 2008, placing second in the nation in 2006.

UK Law's Student Bar Association (SBA) serves as the law student governing body and student activities board. The SBA publishes a weekly student newspaper and sponsors regular student social events and community service activities. UK's SBA was recognized by the ABA as the best student bar association in the nation in 2002.

The Student Public Interest Law Foundation, through grants and fundraising, sponsors 15–20 summer internships with public interest and public service organizations selected by the students who apply. Other active student groups include the Black Law Students Association, the Latino/a Law Student Association, the Asian-Pacific Islander Law Student Association, OUTLaw, the Women's Law Caucus, the International Law Society, the Environmental Law Society, the Equine Law Society, the Federalist Society, the Health Law Society, and the Intellectual Property Law Society.

■ Admission

Admission is considered and granted by the faculty Admissions Committee. Each file is reviewed completely and is voted on by the full committee. While your undergraduate academic record and LSAT score(s) are the primary indicators for potential success in law school, all other factors you present will be considered. You are urged to read the full description of the admission process on our website and to provide full information about your intellectual and nonacademic achievements. The February LSAT is the last examination accepted by the Admissions Committee for that year. Admission as a first-year student is for the fall term only.

■ Scholarships and Financial Aid

UK Law offers a number of three-year scholarships based on merit and/or contributions to diversity, for which you will be considered automatically after admission. For the two largest and most prestigious awards, the Combs Scholarship and Ashland Scholarship, you must be selected for an interview. UK Law also offers three-year merit and diversity tuition-reduction fellowships for nonresidents. You may include a brief statement about your eligibility for merit and/or diversity awards with your admission application but a separate application is not required. Over 50 percent of the 2009 entering class received some form of scholarship award.

UK Law students are eligible for loan assistance through the Federal Direct Student Loan Program and federal graduate PLUS loan program, as well as through national private loan programs. Admitted candidates are mailed complete information on financial aid. To receive forms and information prior to admission, contact UK's Student Financial Aid Office, 128 Funkhouser Building, University of Kentucky, Lexington, KY 40506-0054.

■ Career Services

UK Law students have the benefit of a large on-campus job interview program for regional employers, as well as national placement through the college's participation in numerous off-campus interviewing conferences. The Career Services Office also uses alumni contacts to connect students with employers nationwide. In response to new job market conditions, UK Law is adding an additional attorney to the Career Services professional staff.

UK Law's job placement rate consistently exceeds national averages. For the 2008 graduating class, 96 percent were employed or in advanced-degree programs within nine months after graduation. A majority of UK Law graduates choose private practice, with 15–25 percent of each graduating class selected for prestigious state and federal judicial clerkships.

Applicant Profile

University of Kentucky College of Law
Probability of admission to the University of Kentucky College of Law, based on admission decisions for the 2009 entering class.

LSAT Score	3.75–4.00	3.50–3.74	3.25–3.49	3.00–3.24	2.75–2.99	2.50–2.74	2.25–2.49	Below 2.25	GPA not scaled
165 & Above									
160–164									
157–159									
155–156									
153–154									
150–152									
145–149									
Below 145									

Legend: Probable | Very Competitive | Somewhat Competitive | Possible | Unlikely

Average LSAT data reported.

University of La Verne College of Law

320 East D Street
Ontario, CA 91764
Phone: 877.858.4529; Fax: 909.460.2082
E-mail: lawadm@laverne.edu; Website: http://law.laverne.edu

Provisional ABA Approved Since 2006

The Basics

Type of school	Private
Term	Semester
Application deadline	7/1
Application fee	$50
Financial aid deadline	3/2
Can first year start other than fall?	Yes
Student to faculty ratio	16.4 to 1
# of housing spaces available restricted to law students	
graduate housing for which law students are eligible	36

Faculty and Administrators

	Total		Men		Women		Minorities	
	Spr	Fall	Spr	Fall	Spr	Fall	Spr	Fall
Full-time	15	18	8	9	7	9	4	6
Other full-time	0	0	0	0	0	0	0	0
Deans, librarians, & others who teach	7	8	3	4	4	4	2	2
Part-time	18	16	13	11	5	5	3	4
Total	40	42	24	24	16	18	9	12

Curriculum

		Full-Time	Part-Time
Typical first-year section size		55	35
Is there typically a "small section" of the first-year class, other than Legal Writing, taught by full-time faculty		No	No
If yes, typical size offered last year			
# of classroom course titles beyond first-year curriculum		54	
# of upper division courses, excluding seminars, with an enrollment:	Under 25	32	
	25–49	40	
	50–74	2	
	75–99	0	
	100+	0	
# of seminars		7	
# of seminar positions available		105	
# of seminar positions filled		50	12
# of positions available in simulation courses		349	
# of simulation positions filled		193	93
# of positions available in faculty supervised clinical courses		17	
# of faculty supervised clinical positions filled		12	4
# involved in field placements		48	16
# involved in law journals		33	4
# involved in moot court or trial competitions		6	4
# of credit hours required to graduate		88	

JD Enrollment and Ethnicity

	Men		Women		Full-Time		Part-Time		1st-Year		Total		JD Degs. Awd.
	#	%	#	%	#	%	#	%	#	%	#	%	
African Amer.	4	1.8	8	4.6	5	1.8	7	6.0	6	4.2	12	3.1	1
Amer. Indian	2	0.9	0	0.0	2	0.7	0	0.0	1	0.7	2	0.5	0
Asian Amer.	25	11.5	27	15.4	35	12.7	17	14.5	19	13.3	52	13.3	6
Mex. Amer.	25	11.5	29	16.6	37	13.5	17	14.5	16	11.2	54	13.8	10
Puerto Rican	0	0.0	0	0.0	0	0.0	0	0.0	0	0.0	0	0.0	0
Hispanic	0	0.0	0	0.0	0	0.0	0	0.0	0	0.0	0	0.0	0
Total Minority	56	25.8	64	36.6	79	28.7	41	35.0	42	29.4	120	30.6	17
For. Nation.	4	1.8	4	2.3	8	2.9	0	0.0	7	4.9	8	2.0	1
Caucasian	112	51.6	71	40.6	123	44.7	60	51.3	65	45.5	183	46.7	48
Unknown	45	20.7	36	20.6	65	23.6	16	13.7	29	20.3	81	20.7	10
Total	217	55.4	175	44.6	275	70.2	117	29.8	143	36.5	392		76

Transfers

Transfers in	4
Transfers out	5

Tuition and Fees

	Resident	Nonresident
Full-time	$36,320	$36,320
Part-time	$27,450	$27,450
Tuition Guarantee Program		N

Living Expenses

Estimated living expenses for singles

Living on campus	Living off campus	Living at home
$23,104	$23,104	$23,104

University of La Verne College of Law

ABA
Approved
Since
2006

GPA and LSAT Scores

	Total	Full-Time	Part-Time
# of apps	1,651	1,335	316
# of offers	665	576	89
# of matrics	147	114	33
75% GPA	3.31	3.31	3.27
Median GPA	3.06	3.14	2.90
25% GPA	2.77	2.86	2.60
75% LSAT	155	155	154
Median LSAT	151	151	151
25% LSAT	149	149	149

Grants and Scholarships (from prior year)

	Total #	Total %	Full-Time #	Full-Time %	Part-Time #	Part-Time %
Total # of students	354		241		113	
Total # receiving grants	230	65.0	175	72.6	55	48.7
Less than 1/2 tuition	162	45.8	124	51.5	38	33.6
Half to full tuition	60	16.9	46	19.1	14	12.4
Full tuition	8	2.3	5	2.1	3	2.7
More than full tuition	0	0.0	0	0.0	0	0.0
Median grant amount			$15,500		$7,782	

Informational and Library Resources

Total amount spent on library materials	$854,093
Study seating capacity inside the library	297
# of full-time equivalent professional librarians	10
Hours per week library is open	94
# of open, wired connections available to students	100
# of networked computers available for use by students	35
Has wireless network?	Y
Require computer?	N

JD Attrition (from prior year)

	Academic #	Other #	Total #	Total %
1st year	9	16	25	17.7
2nd year	2	2	4	3.6
3rd year	0	0	0	0.0
4th year	0	0	0	0.0

Employment (9 months after graduation)

	Total	Percentage
Employment status known	77	100.0
Employment status unknown	0	0.0
Employed	59	76.6
Pursuing graduate degrees	1	1.3
Unemployed (seeking, not seeking, or studying for the bar)	5	6.5
Type of Employment		
# employed in law firms	43	72.9
# employed in business and industry	10	16.9
# employed in government	3	5.1
# employed in public interest	2	3.4
# employed as judicial clerks	0	0.0
# employed in academia	1	1.7
Geographic Location		
# employed in state	55	93.2
# employed in foreign countries	0	0.0
# of states where employed	5	

Bar Passage Rates

First-time takers	71	Reporting %	100.00
Average school %	60.57	Average state %	78.67
Average pass difference	−18.10		

Jurisdiction	Takers	Passers	Pass %	State %	Diff %
California	66	40	60.61	78.07	−17.46
Illinois	2	1	50.00	90.94	−40.94
Connecticut	1	1	100.00	88.28	11.72
New York	1	1	100.00	88.98	11.02
Washington	1	0	0.00	74.40	−74.40

University of La Verne College of Law

320 East D Street
Ontario, CA 91764
Phone: 877.858.4529; Fax: 909.460.2082
E-mail: lawadm@laverne.edu; Website: http://law.laverne.edu

■ A Sense of Community

The University of La Verne College of Law, located in the heart of Southern California, prides itself on offering students not only an excellent legal education, but also a sense of community. At La Verne Law, you will be more than just a number. Our small class sizes and low student-to-faculty ratio ensure that you will get individualized attention from people who genuinely care about your success as both a student and a legal professional. Our professors, administrators, and staff have an open-door policy; you will never have to fight to get noticed. Additionally, our excellent student body offers a spirit of collegiality, in which individuals work together toward a common goal: learning to become the best attorneys they can be. Come and see for yourself the La Verne Law difference.

■ Hit the Ground Running

At La Verne Law, we strive to ensure that you will have the skills you need to be a stellar attorney the moment you graduate. Our faculty are not only superb legal scholars, but also boast years of practical experience. This allows us to provide a curriculum that offers a solid foundation in legal theory as well as a strong focus on practical training. Our required Lawyering Skills Practicum (LSP) course is unique in offering law students the chance to simulate the practice of law under the guidance of accomplished attorneys. Many of our other course offerings will give you similar opportunities to hone your legal skills not just by hearing lectures but by actually using them.

La Verne Law also houses two campus-based clinics that allow you to actually work on legal issues with real-life clients. Our Disability Rights Legal Center (DRLC) focuses on disability civil rights litigation and special-education issues for low-income and minority families. Our Justice and Immigration Clinic (JIC) allows students to represent asylum applicants who cannot return to their home countries because of persecution based on race, religion, nationality, political opinion, or membership in a particular social group.

Outside of class, La Verne Law students have the opportunity to do externships with a multitude of regional organizations that provide them with the solid practical training they will need to be successful attorneys. Our students have participated in externships with the San Bernardino County District Attorney's Office, Inland County Legal Services, the Harriet Buhai Center for Family Law, and dozens of other organizations focusing on everything from the legal rights of Holocaust survivors to entertainment law.

■ A Focus on Your Career

La Verne Law's Career Services and Professional Development Office (CSPDO) is dedicated to ensuring that you have the resources and opportunities to make the most of your legal education and reach your career goals. As the only ABA-approved law school in the Inland Empire, an area severely underserved by attorneys, La Verne Law graduates are well-poised to take on the challenge of the new legal market.

In addition to a commitment to developing solid relationships with potential employers, CSPDO offers:

- Individualized career counseling and résumé and cover letter review for both students and alumni;
- Career and professional development workshops on topics ranging from interviewing skills to negotiating a job offer;
- On-campus interview and networking opportunities with representatives from law firms, corporations, government agencies, and public interest organizations;
- A constantly updated database of job postings featuring opportunities for law clerk positions, externships, judicial clerkships, and postgraduate positions;
- The opportunity, through our Mentor Program and Mock Interview Program, to connect with practicing attorneys who will give you advice, help you explore the areas of practice in which you are interested, and assist you in learning to put your best foot forward in an interview;
- Panels and receptions where students hear from and mingle with attorneys and potential employers from a huge variety of practice areas; and
- Career fairs and consortium events cosponsored with other Southern California ABA-approved law schools.

Our alumni have been successful in obtaining positions with large and small law firms, corporations, government agencies, and public interest organizations. Several have started their own thriving practices, and we are particularly proud of our alumni who currently sit or have sat on the bench.

■ A Commitment to Your Success

La Verne Law is committed to ensuring your success as both a law student and a legal professional. To that end, we have an excellent academic support program for students who may need extra help. Our faculty are admired for their accessible demeanor and open-door policy, allowing you to obtain additional assistance with challenging subject matter. High-performing upper-level students offer free tutoring services, and our staff of bar exam professionals, all licensed attorneys, is dedicated to helping you prepare for the bar exam.

■ Location, Location, Location!

In addition to the amazing weather, La Verne Law students enjoy a wide variety of amenities due to the law school's location in the heart of Southern California. Where else can you lie in the sun in the morning and ski in the late afternoon with time for shopping in between? Located just east of Los Angeles and just north of Orange County, the Law School campus is under an hour away from beautiful beaches, majestic mountains, world-class concert halls and museums, and much more. Disneyland and Knott's Berry Farm are only a short drive away, and students can even take the opportunity to unwind on the weekends by heading three hours north to Las Vegas. The Inland Empire itself offers a wide variety of entertainment opportunities from hot air balloon festivals to wine country tours, while boasting one of the lowest costs of living in Southern California.

■ Student Groups for Every Interest

La Verne Law students have the opportunity to participate in a wide variety of extra and cocurricular activities. The

University of La Verne Law Review is subscribed to by the United States Supreme Court, state and local courts, individuals, and academic law libraries throughout the world. Our traveling moot court and mock trial teams compete and place well in both regional and national competitions, focusing on such areas as criminal procedure, entertainment law, cybercrime, and international law. We also have a number of student organizations, both social and career-focused, such as the Student Bar Association, the Sports and Entertainment Law Society, the Public Interest Law Foundation, and many more. Collectively, they provide you with the opportunity to engage in community service, network among your peers, participate in professional events, or just take a well-deserved break from your studies.

■ Facilities to Enhance Your Law School Experience

La Verne Law's 64,000-square-foot building sits on a seven-acre site in the city of Ontario. The facility, designed to give students ready access to technology, includes a state-of-the-art computer lab and on-campus Internet access via a combination of hardwired and wireless connections. Classrooms are equipped with the latest audiovisual technologies, and La Verne Law's mock courtroom includes a custom-designed audiovideo system used for trial and appellate exercises. A large, grassy park provides shade trees where students can study, throw around a Frisbie, or just relax. Additionally, the campus includes a small picnic area where student groups often host barbecues and other events.

■ A Thriving Law Library

La Verne Law is proud of its excellent law library, which boasts 300,000-plus print and microform resources, including federal and California statutory law, court opinions, administrative rules and regulations, major treatises on a variety of legal topics, form and practice books, numerous legal periodicals, and access to a huge variety of electronic databases. The Law Library also serves as a selective depository for federal and California government documents, including legislative materials. Our law librarians are expert legal researchers who hold both the JD and the MLS degrees, and they are available for assistance seven days a week. The Law Library staff also hosts a free series of short courses allowing law students the opportunity to obtain a Certificate in Legal Research.

■ Chart Your Own Academic Course

La Verne Law provides a variety of options to enhance your academic experience based on your own individual goals and needs. We offer both a full-time day and a part-time evening program in addition to summer classes. We also offer courses in a wide variety of subject areas spanning from the core first-year curriculum to a cutting-edge, first in the nation of its kind, course in computer game law.

Additionally, La Verne Law and the College of Business and Public Management offer dual Juris Doctor/Master of Business Administration (JD/MBA) and Juris Doctor/Master of Public Administration (JD/MPA) degree programs. Applicants must meet the admission standards of each degree program and should consult with each college for specific entrance requirements.

■ A Commitment to Diversity

La Verne Law believes that a diverse classroom is not only beneficial to all students but essential to a well-rounded learning experience. To that end, we strive to admit a class of students from a wide variety of cultural, ethnic, religious, and socioeconomic backgrounds, as well as students of diverse age, geographical origins, and academic and professional experience. To further ensure an accepting and welcoming campus, our students can participate in affinity groups such as the Black Law Students Association, the Hispanic National Bar Association, Pride Law Alliance, the J. Reuben Clark Society, and more.

Applicant Profile

At La Verne Law, we strive to provide you with the personalized attention you need to achieve your goals and become a successful member of the legal community. This philosophy extends to our admission process, during which we will consider you as an individual whose unique attributes should be evaluated independently from those of other applicants. Selection criteria include, but are not limited to, your educational and professional achievements, academic ability, motivation for entering the legal profession, individual background, work ethic, letters of recommendation, leadership skills, dedication to community service, and core values. By evaluating each application on a case-by-case basis, we are able to shape our incoming class with diverse personalities and a collective aptitude for success in the law. If you seek a unique legal education tailored to your individual aspirations and providing you with all of the theoretical and practical skills you will need to succeed as an attorney, we invite you to visit us in person or on the Web.

Lewis & Clark Law School

10015 SW Terwilliger Boulevard
Portland, OR 97219-7799
Phone: 800.303.4860 or 503.768.6613; Fax: 503.768.6793
E-mail: lawadmss@lclark.edu; Website: www.lclark.edu/law/

ABA
Approved
Since
1970

The Basics

Type of school	Private
Term	Semester
Application deadline	3/1
Application fee	$50
Financial aid deadline	3/1
Can first year start other than fall?	No
Student to faculty ratio	10.0 to 1
# of housing spaces available restricted to law students	22
graduate housing for which law students are eligible	

Faculty and Administrators

	Total		Men		Women		Minorities	
	Spr	Fall	Spr	Fall	Spr	Fall	Spr	Fall
Full-time	52	53	29	30	23	23	7	7
Other full-time	1	0	1	0	0	0	0	0
Deans, librarians, & others who teach	15	15	6	6	9	9	1	1
Part-time	42	33	28	21	14	12	14	11
Total	110	101	64	57	46	44	22	19

Curriculum

		Full-Time	Part-Time
Typical first-year section size		70	67
Is there typically a "small section" of the first-year class, other than Legal Writing, taught by full-time faculty		Yes	Yes
If yes, typical size offered last year		37	34
# of classroom course titles beyond first-year curriculum		131	
# of upper division courses, excluding seminars, with an enrollment:	Under 25	105	
	25–49	42	
	50–74	12	
	75–99	5	
	100+	1	
# of seminars		30	
# of seminar positions available		540	
# of seminar positions filled		271	132
# of positions available in simulation courses		545	
# of simulation positions filled		279	138
# of positions available in faculty supervised clinical courses		200	
# of faculty supervised clinical positions filled		114	32
# involved in field placements		42	23
# involved in law journals		103	40
# involved in moot court or trial competitions		91	33
# of credit hours required to graduate		86	

JD Enrollment and Ethnicity

	Men		Women		Full-Time		Part-Time		1st-Year		Total		JD Degs. Awd.
	#	%	#	%	#	%	#	%	#	%	#	%	
African Amer.	10	2.7	12	3.5	12	2.3	10	5.2	8	3.5	22	3.1	5
Amer. Indian	8	2.2	9	2.6	8	1.5	9	4.6	9	3.9	17	2.4	6
Asian Amer.	28	7.6	36	10.4	46	8.8	18	9.3	21	9.1	64	9.0	24
Mex. Amer.	4	1.1	8	2.3	9	1.7	3	1.5	4	1.7	12	1.7	3
Puerto Rican	1	0.3	1	0.3	0	0.0	2	1.0	0	0.0	2	0.3	0
Hispanic	15	4.1	8	2.3	15	2.9	8	4.1	7	3.0	23	3.2	12
Total Minority	66	17.9	74	21.3	90	17.3	50	25.8	49	21.3	140	19.6	50
For. Nation.	13	3.5	6	1.7	14	2.7	5	2.6	8	3.5	19	2.7	3
Caucasian	255	69.3	252	72.6	382	73.3	125	64.4	157	68.3	507	70.9	156
Unknown	34	9.2	15	4.3	35	6.7	14	7.2	16	7.0	49	6.9	29
Total	368	51.5	347	48.5	521	72.9	194	27.1	230	32.2	715		238

Transfers

Transfers in	21
Transfers out	3

Tuition and Fees

	Resident	Nonresident
Full-time	$31,984	$31,984
Part-time	$23,998	$23,998
Tuition Guarantee Program		N

Living Expenses

Estimated living expenses for singles

Living on campus	Living off campus	Living at home
N/A	$17,700	$17,700

Lewis & Clark Law School

ABA
Approved
Since
1970

GPA and LSAT Scores

	Total	Full-Time	Part-Time
# of apps	3,181	2,946	235
# of offers	1,107	1,034	73
# of matrics	231	176	55
75% GPA	3.71	3.72	3.68
Median GPA	3.52	3.52	3.48
25% GPA	3.20	3.21	3.12
75% LSAT	164	164	160
Median LSAT	161	161	157
25% LSAT	157	158	153

Grants and Scholarships (from prior year)

	Total		Full-Time		Part-Time	
	#	%	#	%	#	%
Total # of students	716		523		193	
Total # receiving grants	308	43.0	265	50.7	43	22.3
Less than 1/2 tuition	243	33.9	210	40.2	33	17.1
Half to full tuition	54	7.5	45	8.6	9	4.7
Full tuition	11	1.5	10	1.9	1	0.5
More than full tuition	0	0.0	0	0.0	0	0.0
Median grant amount			$10,000		$9,000	

Informational and Library Resources

Total amount spent on library materials	$1,446,400
Study seating capacity inside the library	385
# of full-time equivalent professional librarians	8
Hours per week library is open	113
# of open, wired connections available to students	943
# of networked computers available for use by students	100
Has wireless network?	Y
Require computer?	N

JD Attrition (from prior year)

	Academic	Other	Total	
	#	#	#	%
1st year	1	14	15	6.8
2nd year	1	3	4	1.8
3rd year	1	0	1	0.4
4th year	0	0	0	0.0

Employment (9 months after graduation)

	Total	Percentage
Employment status known	216	94.3
Employment status unknown	13	5.7
Employed	200	92.6
Pursuing graduate degrees	8	3.7
Unemployed (seeking, not seeking, or studying for the bar)	3	1.4
Type of Employment		
# employed in law firms	89	44.5
# employed in business and industry	40	20.0
# employed in government	34	17.0
# employed in public interest	22	11.0
# employed as judicial clerks	12	6.0
# employed in academia	3	1.5
Geographic Location		
# employed in state	128	64.0
# employed in foreign countries	4	2.0
# of states where employed	19	

Bar Passage Rates

First-time takers	190	Reporting %	78.42
Average school %	80.54	Average state %	78.64
Average pass difference	1.90		

Jurisdiction	Takers	Passers	Pass %	State %	Diff %
Oregon	149	120	80.54	78.64	1.90

Lewis & Clark Law School

10015 SW Terwilliger Boulevard
Portland, OR 97219-7799
Phone: 800.303.4860 or 503.768.6613; Fax: 503.768.6793
E-mail: lawadmss@lclark.edu; Website: www.lclark.edu/law/

■ Introduction

Lewis & Clark Law School believes in a balanced approach to legal education that ensures a solid theoretical foundation along with hands-on experience in practice. Situated next to a state park, the campus is one of the most beautiful in the nation. Students are only a moment away from an extensive trail system used by joggers, walkers, and bicyclists.

■ Enrollment/Student Body

The approximately 750 students attending the Law School represent a spectrum of ages, experiences, and priorities. Business executives, scientists, students of politics, musicians, and school teachers—people from many disciplines—meet at the Law School in a common pursuit. The atmosphere is one of mutual support during a time of academic challenge. Students and faculty can often be found discussing questions long after class has ended.

■ Faculty

The full-time faculty were educated at the nation's most distinguished law schools. They reflect a breadth of experience and interests that give depth and creative energy to their teaching. A number of faculty members have spent sabbaticals in recent years teaching in other countries; several have been Fulbright professors in such places as China, Greece, Germany, and Venezuela.

■ Library and Physical Facilities

The resources and staff of the Paul L. Boley Law Library, the largest law library in the state and the second largest in the Northwest, well exceed the standards set by the Association of American Law Schools.

Our collection includes extensive materials in environmental law, federal legislative history, tax law, commercial law, intellectual property, and legal history. We are also the only academic law library in the country to be a Patent and Trademark Depository Library. Supporting our collection is a sophisticated computer infrastructure of instruction labs and local area networks.

The Law School library is an exquisite study space with computer labs equipped with the latest technology. Wireless access is available on the entire campus.

Framed by majestic fir trees, the campus is composed of contemporary buildings with classrooms and a large state park within a moment's walk from the library. Traditional student needs and those of individuals with disabilities are met through a variety of facilities.

■ Curriculum

The Law School confers both the JD degree and a specialized LLM in Environmental and Natural Resources Law. Students may also apply for a joint JD/LLM degree. To earn a JD, a student must take a prescribed first-year set of courses. In the upper division, students must take a seminar, Constitutional Law II, and Professionalism, and fulfill two writing

requirements. Students choose between a three-year day program and a four-year evening program. Admission criteria, faculty, academic opportunities, and graduation requirements are the same for each.

Because the Law School offers both a full-time and a part-time program, students have great flexibility in scheduling courses and in determining the pace at which they want to pursue law school. Classes are offered both during the day and in the evening. Many students transfer between divisions and use the summer school program to accelerate progress toward graduation. Regardless of the division in which a student is enrolled, students may select courses from either the day or evening schedule as they find appropriate.

■ Specific Special Programs

Certificates: By taking a group of upper-division courses approved by the faculty, and by maintaining a superior grade-point average in those courses, a student may earn a certificate showing a concentration in environmental and natural resources law, public interest law, business law, tax law, intellectual property law, or criminal law.

The Law School has nationally recognized natural resources/environmental law and public interest law programs. The school is also home to an incredibly strong business and commercial law program. The intellectual property law program is particularly dynamic, and our criminal law program houses the first national organization in the United States to study and enhance the effectiveness of victim's rights law. Lewis & Clark is also a national leader of animal law programs and curriculums. All the traditional areas of legal study are fully covered. Students who do not wish to pursue a certificate may choose to study another area of particular interest.

Clinical Opportunities, Externships, and Simulations: A student may create a schedule with precisely the mix of practical skills courses that fit that student's interests and needs. Students may choose among live client clinical experience, externships and internships, or simulation courses. The legal clinic located in downtown Portland offers students the opportunity to interview and counsel real clients, prepare documents, conduct trials, negotiate settlements, and prepare appeals. Other established clinics at Lewis & Clark are the small business legal clinic, an environmental law clinic, an international environmental law clinic, a low-income taxpayer clinic, an animal law clinic, a crime victim advocacy clinic, and a business law practicum. Externships place a student in full-time work for a semester or for a summer and require a substantial research paper and attendance at a special seminar. Externs are placed throughout the United States and in foreign countries. Clinical internship seminars are similar to externships but the student works only part-time, attending other classes during the semester. Clinical internship seminars include placements with in-house counsel, government agencies, law firms, and public interest, nonprofit organizations. Other courses, such as moot courts, advanced advocacy, trial advocacy, criminal law seminar, estate planning seminar, corporate transactions seminar, and family mediation seminar, involve extensive simulations.

■ Admission

Lewis & Clark affirmatively seeks a diverse student body. The Admissions Committee makes a serious effort to consider each applicant as an individual. Factors such as college, program of study, length of time since the degree was obtained, experience, writing ability, and community activities are taken into consideration. Only those candidates with excellent professional promise are admitted. Academic attrition is low, averaging two to four percent.

■ Student Activities

Activities include three law reviews, *Environmental Law, Animal Law,* and *Lewis & Clark Law Review;* nine distinct moot court teams; numerous speakers on campus; programs that bring outstanding legal scholars to campus for lectures and seminars; and many student organizations reflecting the diverse makeup of the student body.

■ Expenses and Financial Aid

Approximately 40 percent of the students at Lewis & Clark receive some scholarship support during their law school career. The school annually awards renewable merit-based

Dean's Scholarships to incoming students. In addition, loan money and work-study funds are available. There is no separate application procedure for scholarship funds. Scholarship consideration is part of the admission process. Students are reviewed on the basis of undergraduate record, LSAT score, writing ability, and activities.

Students interested in loans need to apply for financial aid as early as possible and should not wait for an admission decision to begin the financial aid application. Applicants should submit the FAFSA (Free Application for Federal Student Aid) at *www.fafsa.ed.gov.*

■ Career Services

The Career Services Office maintains and runs an extraordinary number and variety of programs. In addition to posting clerk positions for law students and running the on-campus interviews, the office maintains an extensive mentoring program, runs dozens of panels each year on various areas of practice, and counsels individual students from the first year onward. The Career Services staff consists of experienced administrators, counselors, and professionals, including a full-time coordinator to assist public interest-minded students.

Applicant Profile

Lewis & Clark Law School

LSAT Score	3.75 +		3.50–3.74		3.25–3.49		3.00–3.24		2.75–2.99		2.50–2.74		Below 2.50		No GPA		Total	
	Apps	Adm	Apps	Adm	Apps	Adm	Apps	Adm	Apps	Adm	Apps	Adm	Apps	Adm	Apps	Adm	Apps	Adm
170–180	13	12	17	15	10	7	9	4	9	5	2	2	3	1	2	2	65	48
165–169	68	60	76	66	60	44	45	31	28	10	16	4	10	1	5	4	308	220
160–164	140	114	181	141	174	98	143	72	73	30	35	11	16	2	7	5	769	473
155–159	130	83	225	83	207	27	159	31	79	8	41	0	27	3	12	3	880	238
150–154	75	17	130	23	165	19	168	21	78	5	31	0	20	1	14	4	681	90
145–149	22	6	53	7	58	5	65	6	39	1	29	1	18	1	5	0	289	27
140–144	5	1	14	3	21	0	25	0	27	0	10	0	10	0	4	0	116	4
Below 140	2	0	4	0	7	0	8	0	12	0	7	0	21	0	3	0	64	0
Total	455	293	700	338	702	200	622	165	345	59	171	18	125	9	52	18	3172	1100

Apps = Number of Applicants
Adm = Number Admitted
Reflects 99% of the total applicant pool; average LSAT data reported.

This chart is to be used as a guide only. Nonnumerical factors are strongly considered for all applicants.

Liberty University School of Law

1971 University Boulevard
Lynchburg, VA 24502
Phone: 434.592.5300; Fax: 434.592.5400
E-mail: law@liberty.edu; Website: www.law.liberty.edu

The Basics

Type of school	Private
Term	Semester
Application deadline	10/1 5/1
Application fee	$50
Financial aid deadline	
Can first year start other than fall?	No
Student to faculty ratio	12.1 to 1
# of housing spaces available restricted to law students	
graduate housing for which law students are eligible	

Faculty and Administrators

	Total		Men		Women		Minorities	
	Spr	Fall	Spr	Fall	Spr	Fall	Spr	Fall
Full-time	16	17	12	12	4	5	1	2
Other full-time	1	1	1	1	0	0	0	0
Deans, librarians, & others who teach	5	5	4	4	1	1	0	0
Part-time	5	7	4	5	1	2	0	1
Total	27	30	21	22	6	8	1	3

Curriculum

		Full-Time	Part-Time
Typical first-year section size		58	0
Is there typically a "small section" of the first-year class, other than Legal Writing, taught by full-time faculty		No	No
If yes, typical size offered last year			
# of classroom course titles beyond first-year curriculum		43	
# of upper division courses, excluding seminars, with an enrollment:	Under 25	28	
	25–49	9	
	50–74	19	
	75–99	0	
	100+	0	
# of seminars		3	
# of seminar positions available		45	
# of seminar positions filled		22	0
# of positions available in simulation courses		445	
# of simulation positions filled		387	0
# of positions available in faculty supervised clinical courses		8	
# of faculty supervised clinical positions filled		5	0
# involved in field placements		21	0
# involved in law journals		44	0
# involved in moot court or trial competitions		17	0
# of credit hours required to graduate		90	

JD Enrollment and Ethnicity

	Men		Women		Full-Time		Part-Time		1st-Year		Total		JD Degs. Awd.
	#	%	#	%	#	%	#	%	#	%	#	%	
African Amer.	9	5.4	9	9.1	18	6.7	0	0.0	7	6.0	18	6.7	4
Amer. Indian	2	1.2	3	3.0	5	1.9	0	0.0	2	1.7	5	1.9	0
Asian Amer.	4	2.4	3	3.0	7	2.6	0	0.0	5	4.3	7	2.6	1
Mex. Amer.	1	0.6	1	1.0	2	0.7	0	0.0	0	0.0	2	0.7	0
Puerto Rican	0	0.0	1	1.0	1	0.4	0	0.0	0	0.0	1	0.4	0
Hispanic	7	4.2	0	0.0	7	2.6	0	0.0	5	4.3	7	2.6	1
Total Minority	23	13.7	17	17.2	40	15.0	0	0.0	19	16.4	40	15.0	6
For. Nation.	3	1.8	0	0.0	3	1.1	0	0.0	0	0.0	3	1.1	0
Caucasian	124	73.8	75	75.8	199	74.5	0	0.0	83	71.6	199	74.5	38
Unknown	18	10.7	7	7.1	25	9.4	0	0.0	14	12.1	25	9.4	11
Total	168	62.9	99	37.1	267	100.0	0	0.0	116	43.4	267		55

Transfers

Transfers in	2
Transfers out	8

Tuition and Fees

	Resident	Nonresident
Full-time	$27,847	
Part-time		
Tuition Guarantee Program		N

Living Expenses

Estimated living expenses for singles

Living on campus	Living off campus	Living at home
$16,513	$16,513	$16,513

Liberty University School of Law

ABA
Approved
Since
2006

GPA and LSAT Scores

	Total	Full-Time	Part-Time
# of apps	466	466	0
# of offers	201	201	0
# of matrics	119	119	0
75% GPA	3.53	3.53	0.00
Median GPA	3.15	3.15	0.00
25% GPA	2.80	2.80	0.00
75% LSAT	154	154	0
Median LSAT	151	151	0
25% LSAT	148	148	0

Grants and Scholarships (from prior year)

	Total		Full-Time		Part-Time	
	#	%	#	%	#	%
Total # of students	219		219		0	
Total # receiving grants	222	101.4	222	101.4	0	0.0
Less than 1/2 tuition	79	36.1	79	36.1	0	0.0
Half to full tuition	104	47.5	104	47.5	0	0.0
Full tuition	39	17.8	39	17.8	0	0.0
More than full tuition	0	0.0	0	0.0	0	0.0
Median grant amount			$13,952		$0	

Informational and Library Resources

Total amount spent on library materials	$1,110,903
Study seating capacity inside the library	290
# of full-time equivalent professional librarians	5
Hours per week library is open	95
# of open, wired connections available to students	0
# of networked computers available for use by students	40
Has wireless network?	Y
Require computer?	N

JD Attrition (from prior year)

	Academic	Other	Total	
	#	#	#	%
1st year	7	10	17	16.2
2nd year	6	4	10	17.2
3rd year	0	0	0	0.0
4th year	0	0	0	0.0

Employment (9 months after graduation)

	Total	Percentage
Employment status known	33	89.2
Employment status unknown	4	10.8
Employed	26	78.8
Pursuing graduate degrees	2	6.1
Unemployed (seeking, not seeking, or studying for the bar)	5	15.2
Type of Employment		
# employed in law firms	10	38.5
# employed in business and industry	6	23.1
# employed in government	4	15.4
# employed in public interest	2	7.7
# employed as judicial clerks	2	7.7
# employed in academia	2	7.7
Geographic Location		
# employed in state	12	46.2
# employed in foreign countries	0	0.0
# of states where employed	12	

Bar Passage Rates

First-time takers	44	Reporting %	86.36
Average school %	94.71	Average state %	84.63
Average pass difference	10.08		

Jurisdiction	Takers	Passers	Pass %	State %	Diff %
Virginia	19	17	89.47	82.70	6.77
Florida	5	5	100.00	80.76	19.24
Georgia	2	2	100.00	89.27	10.73
Illinois	2	2	100.00	90.94	9.06
Others (5)	10	10	100.00		

Liberty University School of Law

1971 University Boulevard
Lynchburg, VA 24502
Phone: 434.592.5300; Fax: 434.592.5400
E-mail: law@liberty.edu; Website: www.law.liberty.edu

■ Introduction

First-time takers from Liberty University School of Law achieved a 94.4 percent Virginia bar passage rate in July 2008. The class of 2008 had a pass rate of 91.4 percent overall in 13 states, topping the nearly 90 percent national pass rate of the class of 2007. Distinctively Christian, the law school has attracted national attention for its innovative program of legal education, competitive teams, and practice opportunities for its students. The student body will reach, and cap at, approximately 450 within a few years to maintain the small classes and collegiality that students and faculty now enjoy. With wireless connectivity throughout, the law school and adjoining law library are advantageously located on one level in LU's million-square-foot Campus North complex. The 330-seat ceremonial courtroom features a nine-seat bench, which replicates the US Supreme Court bench. Two other mock trial courtrooms, all classrooms, and the law library feature the latest technologies. The 6,549-acre campus of Liberty University rests in the eastern foothills of the Blue Ridge Mountains in Central Virginia, within easy driving distance of Washington, DC.

■ Program of Legal Education

Liberty's groundbreaking law program has three distinct but related components: foundations of law, substantive law courses, and lawyering skills. In keeping with the law school's mission "to equip future leaders in law with a superior legal education in fidelity to the Christian faith expressed through the Holy Scriptures," the foundations courses explore the thoughts and writings of those who shaped the American legal system. The Christian worldview permeates the curriculum. The six-semester skills program has two threads: a litigation thread and a planning thread. Each student moves a simulated case from the initial client interview to the court verdict and develops the practice skills essential to planning client affairs. While the core courses look much the same as at other law schools—same course names, same subject matter coverage, same casebooks—Liberty's distinction is in the linkage of the substantive law courses to the foundations and lawyering skills courses. The law faculty is highly accessible to students throughout each day. In addition to academic advising and support from faculty, many Liberty law students take advantage of the academic support program.

■ Academic Support

The Academic Support Program begins with an intensive four-day Barristers' Orientation for entering students. During the academic year, the program staff assists law students in achieving their full academic potential, helping them with class preparation, class participation, and examination strategies. Support includes post-class reviews prior to taking law school examinations and practice-exam workshops. All students may take advantage of one-on-one tutorials to help them assimilate course materials and apply classroom knowledge to law school examinations. The Academic Support Program also assists students with bar examination preparation.

■ Clinics, Externships, and Centers

The law school places a high priority on equipping students with the skills necessary to practice law, as evidenced in its Lawyering Skills program. Its externship and clinical programs provide the next step in the continuum of classroom learning, from simulation to live-client and other real-life practice experience. The Constitutional Litigation Clinic works in conjunction with Liberty Counsel, a nonprofit legal organization specializing in constitutional law, which has offices on the Liberty University campus. Students work on cases with a heavy constitutional law component. The School of Law has formed a partnership with Liberty Counsel in founding the Liberty Center for Law and Policy. The Center trains law students who have career plans in public interest litigation with a focus on constitutional and religious liberty advocacy.

The Criminal Law Externship Program is the flagship of the law school's externship offerings. It places law students as externs in county and federal prosecutors' offices, and in public defenders' offices, under the supervision of experienced practitioners. Students are placed in a host of field-study venues including state and US attorneys' offices; local, state, and federal courts; state supreme courts; and in public interest organizations. The public service externship component gives students a wide variety of individualized experiences in public service law and pro bono legal assistance. In addition, Liberty students obtain externships and summer positions ranging from the White House and the Department of Homeland Security, to private law firms and corporations.

■ Cocurricular and Student Activities

In addition to the Student Bar Association (SBA) and other student organizations such as the International Law Society and Federalist Society, the law school has competitive teams in moot court, negotiation, and alternative dispute resolution, along with a developing transactional competition program.

Students produce the *Liberty University Law Review*. Student life includes attending the wide range of events on the campus of Liberty University and enjoying the sociability of the law school community. Law students have access to all of the university's recreational facilities. Many law students volunteer their time in pro bono activities, such as the Street Law program, which is designed for local youth involved in the juvenile justice system. The law school also matches students with private practitioners engaged in pro bono work and notifies students of opportunities to intern in legal aid offices, public defender offices, and prosecutorial offices.

■ Career Services

The Center for Career and Professional Development serves law students and alumni by providing tools to develop skills essential for career development, by cultivating a life-long commitment to professionalism and community service, and by promoting regional and national awareness of the law school's distinctive program of legal study. The Center cultivates internship and pro bono opportunities and works cooperatively with the school's clinical and externship

programs to foster relationships with members of the bench and bar to the benefit of students and alumni. Alumni are working in all sectors of law practice, and placement statistics to date are available at the Center.

■ Information Resources and Technologies

With many comfortable seating areas and easy access from the classrooms, Ehrhorn Law Library provides an environment conducive to research, study, and writing. To its growing collection of over 260,000 volumes and volume equivalents, the law library is continually adding titles that support the curriculum and undergird the law school's mission. Along with its extensive microform archives, the law library provides access to law-related and general databases via the Internet through any Web browser. These electronic databases are available to law students on or off campus. Reliable wired and wireless access to the Internet is provided throughout the law school facility. Every classroom has SMART technology. The law school community benefits from a high level of university support for its state-of-the-art computing, instructional, informational, and audiovisual technologies.

■ Admission and Financial Aid

Many law schools have developed courses of study that give expression to a particular jurisprudential perspective, be it law and economics, legal realism, or policy-oriented jurisprudence. Liberty University School of Law has chosen to do the same, developing its curriculum and standards of conduct consistent with the Christian worldview. Its admission process is designed to identify those who desire to receive a legal education from this perspective. Each completed applicant file is reviewed by a law faculty committee. That committee gives careful attention to a full range of factors that indicate the applicant's likelihood of success in law school and the legal profession. It attempts to identify strengths and indicators of success that may not show up in test scores and to ensure that students make fully informed decisions in deciding to attend Liberty University School of Law. Written applications and letters of recommendation are used to identify applicants with strong communication skills, levels of interest, personal traits, and life experiences that exhibit a calling to law and potential for success in legal education and the practice of law. The personal statement, which addresses prescribed discussion points noted in the application for admission, is of particular importance in the admission decision.

Institutional scholarships are awarded on the basis of prior academic excellence and indicators of law school success, and for demonstrated leadership and service in keeping with the law school's mission. Committed to debt management, the law school assists each student with a financial aid package to meet individual needs.

The Office of Admissions and Financial Aid assists prospective students and law students with the law school admission process, financial aid, and other matters related to relocation and matriculation. To schedule a visit, call 434.592.5300 or e-mail *lawadmissions@liberty.edu*.

Applicant Profile

Liberty University School of Law

Entering Class	2004–2005	2005–2006	2006–2007	2007–2008	2008–2009
Completed Applications	157	192	203	293	491
Admits	71	84	102	118	188
Matriculants	60	50	70	72	109
LSAT 25%–75%	148–157	150–155	148–153	148–154	148–153
LSAT Median	153	152	150	150	150
GPA 25%–75%	2.98–3.65	2.97–3.61	2.75–3.57	2.85–3.49	2.88–3.57
GPA Median	3.27	3.26	3.35	3.16	3.17
Average Age	27	25	28	25	25
Minorities	10%	18%	16%	18%	13%
Women	40%	34%	38%	32%	43%
Advanced Degrees	18%	10%	10%	10%	9%
Enrolled from outside VA	73%	74%	80%	68%	78%

Louisiana State University, Paul M. Hebert Law Center

202 Law Center
Baton Rouge, LA 70803
Phone: 225.578.8646; Fax: 225.578.8647
E-mail: admissions@law.lsu.edu; Website: www.law.lsu.edu

ABA Approved Since 1926

The Basics

Type of school	Public
Term	Semester
Application deadline	3/1
Application fee	$50
Financial aid deadline	
Can first year start other than fall?	No
Student to faculty ratio	17.5 to 1
# of housing spaces available restricted to law students	
graduate housing for which law students are eligible	

Faculty and Administrators

	Total		Men		Women		Minorities	
	Spr	Fall	Spr	Fall	Spr	Fall	Spr	Fall
Full-time	28	27	20	20	8	7	2	2
Other full-time	5	5	2	2	3	3	1	0
Deans, librarians, & others who teach	7	7	6	6	1	1	0	0
Part-time	31	26	29	22	2	4	2	1
Total	71	65	57	50	14	15	5	3

Curriculum

	Full-Time	Part-Time
Typical first-year section size	78	0
Is there typically a "small section" of the first-year class, other than Legal Writing, taught by full-time faculty	Yes	No
If yes, typical size offered last year	39	
# of classroom course titles beyond first-year curriculum	77	
# of upper division courses, excluding seminars, with an enrollment: Under 25	130	
25–49	48	
50–74	17	
75–99	8	
100+	1	
# of seminars	16	
# of seminar positions available	312	
# of seminar positions filled	211	0
# of positions available in simulation courses	507	
# of simulation positions filled	468	0
# of positions available in faculty supervised clinical courses	60	
# of faculty supervised clinical positions filled	51	0
# involved in field placements	74	0
# involved in law journals	49	0
# involved in moot court or trial competitions	125	0
# of credit hours required to graduate	97	

Transfers

Transfers in	1
Transfers out	5

Tuition and Fees

	Resident	Nonresident
Full-time	$14,350	$25,446
Part-time		
Tuition Guarantee Program		N

Living Expenses

Estimated living expenses for singles

Living on campus	Living off campus	Living at home
$15,054	$17,246	$9,642

JD Enrollment and Ethnicity

	Men #	Men %	Women #	Women %	Full-Time #	Full-Time %	Part-Time #	Part-Time %	1st-Year #	1st-Year %	Total #	Total %	JD Degs. Awd.
African Amer.	10	3.0	16	5.9	25	4.3	1	9.1	11	4.7	26	4.3	4
Amer. Indian	3	0.9	4	1.5	7	1.2	0	0.0	4	1.7	7	1.2	1
Asian Amer.	8	2.4	6	2.2	14	2.4	0	0.0	10	4.3	14	2.3	2
Mex. Amer.	0	0.0	0	0.0	0	0.0	0	0.0	0	0.0	0	0.0	0
Puerto Rican	0	0.0	0	0.0	0	0.0	0	0.0	0	0.0	0	0.0	0
Hispanic	13	4.0	20	7.4	32	5.5	1	9.1	13	5.5	33	5.5	6
Total Minority	34	10.3	46	17.1	78	13.3	2	18.2	38	16.2	80	13.4	13
For. Nation.	1	0.3	2	0.7	3	0.5	0	0.0	2	0.9	3	0.5	0
Caucasian	255	77.5	202	75.1	449	76.5	8	72.7	169	71.9	457	76.4	149
Unknown	39	11.9	19	7.1	57	9.7	1	9.1	26	11.1	58	9.7	17
Total	329	55.0	269	45.0	587	98.2	11	1.8	235	39.3	598		179

Louisiana State University, Paul M. Hebert Law Center

ABA
Approved
Since
1926

GPA and LSAT Scores

	Total	Full-Time	Part-Time
# of apps	1,408	1,408	0
# of offers	527	527	0
# of matrics	233	233	0
75% GPA	3.66	3.66	0.00
Median GPA	3.44	3.44	0.00
25% GPA	3.22	3.22	0.00
75% LSAT	159	159	0
Median LSAT	157	157	0
25% LSAT	155	155	0

Grants and Scholarships (from prior year)

	Total #	Total %	Full-Time #	Full-Time %	Part-Time #	Part-Time %
Total # of students	576		565		11	
Total # receiving grants	383	66.5	383	67.8	0	0.0
Less than 1/2 tuition	216	37.5	216	38.2	0	0.0
Half to full tuition	78	13.5	78	13.8	0	0.0
Full tuition	40	6.9	40	7.1	0	0.0
More than full tuition	49	8.5	49	8.7	0	0.0
Median grant amount			$3,913		$0	

Informational and Library Resources

Total amount spent on library materials	$1,053,802
Study seating capacity inside the library	468
# of full-time equivalent professional librarians	11
Hours per week library is open	104
# of open, wired connections available to students	60
# of networked computers available for use by students	49
Has wireless network?	Y
Require computer?	N

JD Attrition (from prior year)

	Academic #	Other #	Total #	Total %
1st year	17	14	31	14.8
2nd year	0	0	0	0.0
3rd year	0	0	0	0.0
4th year	0	0	0	0.0

Employment (9 months after graduation)

	Total	Percentage
Employment status known	185	98.4
Employment status unknown	3	1.6
Employed	170	91.9
Pursuing graduate degrees	6	3.2
Unemployed (seeking, not seeking, or studying for the bar)	5	2.7
Type of Employment		
# employed in law firms	87	51.2
# employed in business and industry	19	11.2
# employed in government	25	14.7
# employed in public interest	4	2.4
# employed as judicial clerks	30	17.6
# employed in academia	3	1.8
Geographic Location		
# employed in state	136	80.0
# employed in foreign countries	0	0.0
# of states where employed	13	

Bar Passage Rates

First-time takers	160	Reporting %	91.88
Average school %	80.95	Average state %	67.32
Average pass difference 13.63			

Jurisdiction	Takers	Passers	Pass %	State %	Diff %
Louisiana	147	119	80.95	67.32	13.63

Louisiana State University, Paul M. Hebert Law Center

202 Law Center
Baton Rouge, LA 70803
Phone: 225.578.8646; Fax: 225.578.8647
E-mail: admissions@law.lsu.edu; Website: www.law.lsu.edu

■ Introduction

The Louisiana State University (LSU) Law Center was originally established as the Louisiana State University Law School in 1906, pursuant to an authorization contained in the university charter. In 1979, the Law Center was renamed the Paul M. Hebert Law Center of Louisiana State University. The Law Center holds membership in the Association of American Law Schools (AALS) and is on the approved list of the American Bar Association (ABA).

■ Library and Physical Facilities

The Law Center, completed in October 1969, added extensive facilities to the original Law Center building, dedicated in 1938. Both buildings were vastly renovated over several years at a cost in excess of $17 million and were completed in 2004. The renovated complex provides classroom areas, seminar and discussion rooms, and meeting areas, as well as a courtroom and Law Clinic. The Law Clinic is a self-contained legal services office located in the Law Center where students are certified to practice law pursuant to Louisiana Supreme Court Rule XX. Separate offices for student research and student activities, such as the *Louisiana Law Review*, Moot Court Board, and Student Bar Association, are included in the facility. The law library, housed in the complex, provides one of the most complete collections of Roman and modern civil law reports and materials in the country. Library resources include reading and discussion rooms, study carrels, computer labs, and audiovisual facilities. Students also have access to other campus facilities, including the LSU Student Health Center, residential housing, and the Student Recreation Complex. The Law Center is located on the main campus of LSU in close proximity to the undergraduate campus and other units with which the Law Center has joint-degree or cocurricular programs.

■ Curriculum

The LSU Law Center has established a JD/DCL program through which all graduates receive the Juris Doctor (JD) degree and a Diploma in Comparative Law (DCL). First-year students follow a prescribed curriculum and, thereafter, may choose from a wide variety of courses to complete their degrees, including skills training courses and a newly expanded clinical program designed to take full advantage of the Law Center's location in Louisiana's capital city. The Law Center's dedication to the study of both civil and common law prepares its graduates to practice in any state and in many foreign countries. Six semesters of resident study are required for the degree. In addition to its full-time law faculty, the LSU Law Center invites a number of distinguished lecturers, including practicing attorneys and legal scholars, to teach courses in their areas of specialty each semester. A number of faculty members have law degrees from foreign countries.

■ Summer Session Abroad

The Law Center conducts a summer program in Lyon, France, and, when student interest warrants, in Buenos Aires,

Argentina. All classes are conducted in English and are designed to meet the requirements of the ABA and AALS.

■ Special Programs

A wide variety of courses afford each student the opportunity to participate in the preparation and trial of mock cases, both civil and criminal, and also to develop skills in legal negotiation and counseling. LSU sponsors and encourages student participation in national trial and appellate competitions throughout the school year.

In cooperation with the Center for Continuing Professional Development, the Law Center presents seminars, institutes, and conferences for practicing lawyers.

The LSU Law Center admits candidates for the degrees of Master of Laws (LLM) and Master of Civil Law (MCL). These programs are highly selective and admit students with exceptional ability.

■ Admission

The Admissions Committee considers many factors in reaching admission decisions. While the quantitative predictors of success in law school (performance on the LSAT and the undergraduate GPA of applicants) are typically the most important factors in the admission decision, the Admissions Committee considers many other factors, such as the ability to analyze and write well, as demonstrated by the personal statement and the written portion of the LSAT; two letters of recommendation from teachers or others who can express an opinion on the applicant's aptitude for the study of law; the rigor of the undergraduate program of study and grade trends; extracurricular activities; work experience or military service; social and economic background; and other evidence of an applicant's aptitude for the study of law and likely contribution to academic and community life. A baccalaureate degree from an accredited college or university is required for admission.

Applicants are advised to take the LSAT in October, and not later than December, prior to the year in which they seek admission to the Law Center. The Law Center admits students only in the fall and only for full-time study. There are no night courses offered. Transfer applications are considered.

Louisiana State University assures equal opportunity for all qualified persons without regard to race, color, religion, sexual orientation, national origin, age, disability, marital status, or veteran's status in the admission to, participation in, or employment in the programs and activities that the university operates.

■ Joint Programs

In addition to earning a JD/DCL, LSU Law students may also earn a Master of Mass Communication (MMC) degree through the LSU Manship School of Mass Communication, or a Master of Business Administration (MBA) or Master of Public Administration (MPA) through the LSU E.J. Ourso College of Business. The combined-degree programs are typically completed in four years. Applicants must apply to each institution separately.

Louisiana State University, Paul M. Hebert Law Center

■ Student Activities

The *Louisiana Law Review* was established to encourage high quality legal scholarship in the student body, to contribute to the development of the law through scholarly criticism and analysis, and to serve the bar of Louisiana through comments and discussion of current cases and legal problems. It is edited by a board of student editors with faculty cooperation.

The Louisiana Chapter of the Order of the Coif, a national honorary law fraternity, was established at the Law Center in 1942. Election to the Order of the Coif is recognized as the highest honor a law student may receive.

Because a large number of graduates of the Law Center go directly into practice, the LSU Law Center has an extensive Trial Advocacy Program in which moot court training is offered both for trial work and in appellate argument.

Students have an opportunity to join student organizations representing a variety of interests, including, but not limited to, the Public Interest Law Society (PILS), the International Law Society, the Federalist Society, the American Constitution Society, the Environmental Law Society, and the Tax Club.

All students at the Law Center are members of the Student Bar Association. This association promotes and coordinates student activities within the Law Center and serves as an instructional medium for postgraduate bar association activities.

■ Expenses and Financial Aid

The Scholarship Committee automatically considers all admitted students for scholarship support. Most scholarships range in size from $2,000 to full-tuition awards. Awards are offered to applicants whom the committee believes will best contribute to the academic and community life of the Law Center. The Law Center will recognize in each entering class, on a highly selective basis, Louisiana residents with very strong entrance credentials through its new scholarship program, Louisiana Distinguished Public Service Scholars. This program will afford participants significant financial assistance and an opportunity to integrate challenging public service internships and externships into their law school experiences.

A number of loan funds are available to help deserving students who need financial assistance to continue their education. All such funds are subject to the policies and regulations authorized by the LSU Student Loan Fund Committee. Detailed information on all loan funds may be secured by contacting the Student Loan Section, LSU Office of Financial Aid and Scholarships, 1146 Pleasant Hall, Baton Rouge, LA 70803.

■ Career Services

The Career Services Office is dedicated to enhancing the personal growth and professional opportunities for law students and alumni through individual counseling, workshops, and resources. More than 1,000 employers in the United States, including private firms, government agencies, judges, nonprofits, and corporations, recruit students yearly from the LSU Law Center through visits to the campus, consortiums, job fairs, and electronic postings. More than 165 legal employers from Louisiana, Texas, Georgia, Tennessee, Mississippi, Alabama, Florida, New York, and Washington, DC, visit the school each year to recruit LSU Law Center students.

Applicant Profile

Louisiana State University, Paul M. Hebert Law Center
This grid includes only applicants who earned 120–180 LSAT scores under standard administrations.

LSAT Score	3.75 +		3.50–3.74		3.25–3.49		3.00–3.24		2.75–2.99		2.50–2.74		2.25–2.49		2.00–2.24		Below 2.00		No GPA		Total	
	Apps	Adm	Apps	Adm	Apps	Adm	Apps	Adm	Apps	Adm	Apps	Adm	Apps	Adm	Apps	Adm	Apps	Adm	Apps	Adm	Apps	Adm
175–180	0	0	0	0	0	0	0	0	0	0	0	0	0	0	0	0	0	0	0	0	0	0
170–174	2	1	1	1	2	2	1	1	1	1	0	0	0	0	0	0	0	0	0	0	7	6
165–169	8	8	6	6	2	2	3	3	3	2	0	0	0	0	0	0	0	0	0	0	22	21
160–164	19	19	28	27	25	23	28	24	8	8	7	4	3	2	3	0	0	0	1	1	122	108
155–159	58	51	76	68	102	79	65	34	43	13	28	10	7	1	4	2	0	0	3	0	386	258
150–154	56	26	94	33	102	23	90	13	55	8	21	1	15	1	6	3	2	0	11	2	452	110
145–149	32	9	42	5	63	7	42	2	36	2	20	2	7	0	5	0	0	0	1	0	248	27
140–144	5	0	10	0	17	0	32	0	20	1	16	0	7	0	2	0	0	0	0	0	109	1
135–139	2	0	3	0	3	0	6	0	9	0	13	0	3	0	1	0	1	0	0	0	41	0
130–134	0	0	0	0	2	0	1	0	1	0	4	0	2	0	0	0	0	0	1	0	11	0
125–129	0	0	0	0	2	0	0	0	0	0	1	0	0	0	0	0	0	0	0	0	3	0
120–124	0	0	0	0	0	0	0	0	0	0	1	0	0	0	0	0	0	0	0	0	1	0
Total	182	114	260	140	320	136	268	77	176	35	111	17	44	4	21	5	3	0	17	3	1402	531

Apps = Number of Applicants
Adm = Number Admitted
Reflects 99% of the total applicant pool; average LSAT data reported.

University of Louisville's Brandeis School of Law

University of Louisville
Louisville, KY 40292
Phone: 502.852.6364; Fax: 502.852.8971
E-mail: lawadmissions@louisville.edu; Website: www.law.louisville.edu

ABA
Approved
Since
1931

The Basics

Type of school	Public
Term	Semester
Application deadline	4/1
Application fee	$50
Financial aid deadline	3/1
Can first year start other than fall?	No
Student to faculty ratio	15.5 to 1
# of housing spaces available restricted to law students	
graduate housing for which law students are eligible	102

Faculty and Administrators

	Total		Men		Women		Minorities	
	Spr	Fall	Spr	Fall	Spr	Fall	Spr	Fall
Full-time	20	24	12	13	8	11	1	2
Other full-time	2	2	1	0	1	2	1	1
Deans, librarians, & others who teach	10	9	8	6	2	3	1	1
Part-time	17	12	11	8	6	3	1	0
Total	49	47	32	27	17	19	4	4

Curriculum

	Full-Time	Part-Time
Typical first-year section size	62	22
Is there typically a "small section" of the first-year class, other than Legal Writing, taught by full-time faculty	No	No
If yes, typical size offered last year		
# of classroom course titles beyond first-year curriculum		67
# of upper division courses, excluding seminars, with an enrollment: Under 25		48
25–49		27
50–74		17
75–99		0
100+		0
# of seminars		18
# of seminar positions available		324
# of seminar positions filled	219	41
# of positions available in simulation courses	519	
# of simulation positions filled	301	166
# of positions available in faculty supervised clinical courses	6	
# of faculty supervised clinical positions filled	6	0
# involved in field placements	110	18
# involved in law journals	66	4
# involved in moot court or trial competitions	51	3
# of credit hours required to graduate	90	

JD Enrollment and Ethnicity

	Men		Women		Full-Time		Part-Time		1st-Year		Total		JD Degs. Awd.
	#	%	#	%	#	%	#	%	#	%	#	%	
African Amer.	8	3.4	9	4.6	17	4.6	0	0.0	3	2.0	17	3.9	3
Amer. Indian	0	0.0	0	0.0	0	0.0	0	0.0	0	0.0	0	0.0	0
Asian Amer.	3	1.3	7	3.6	10	2.7	0	0.0	3	2.0	10	2.3	1
Mex. Amer.	5	2.1	4	2.0	9	2.4	0	0.0	1	0.7	9	2.1	0
Puerto Rican	0	0.0	0	0.0	0	0.0	0	0.0	0	0.0	0	0.0	0
Hispanic	0	0.0	0	0.0	0	0.0	0	0.0	0	0.0	0	0.0	0
Total Minority	16	6.7	20	10.2	36	9.8	0	0.0	7	4.8	36	8.3	4
For. Nation.	2	0.8	4	2.0	6	1.6	0	0.0	3	2.0	6	1.4	0
Caucasian	214	89.9	168	85.3	316	85.9	66	98.5	134	91.2	382	87.8	109
Unknown	6	2.5	5	2.5	10	2.7	1	1.5	3	2.0	11	2.5	2
Total	238	54.7	197	45.3	368	84.6	67	15.4	147	33.8	435		115

Transfers

Transfers in	4
Transfers out	5

Tuition and Fees

	Resident	Nonresident
Full-time	$14,632	$29,172
Part-time	$7,412	$15,172
Tuition Guarantee Program		N

Living Expenses

Estimated living expenses for singles

Living on campus	Living off campus	Living at home
$16,730	$16,730	$8,236

University of Louisville's Brandeis School of Law

*ABA
Approved
Since
1931*

GPA and LSAT Scores

	Total	Full-Time	Part-Time
# of apps	0	1,162	93
# of offers	465	432	33
# of matrics	141	118	23
75% GPA	3.73	3.75	3.67
Median GPA	3.50	3.50	3.45
25% GPA	3.14	3.15	3.04
75% LSAT	159	159	155
Median LSAT	156	157	154
25% LSAT	153	154	151

Grants and Scholarships (from prior year)

	Total		Full-Time		Part-Time	
	#	%	#	%	#	%
Total # of students	419		351		68	
Total # receiving grants	182	43.4	162	46.2	20	29.4
Less than 1/2 tuition	152	36.3	143	40.7	9	13.2
Half to full tuition	30	7.2	19	5.4	11	16.2
Full tuition	0	0.0	0	0.0	0	0.0
More than full tuition	0	0.0	0	0.0	0	0.0
Median grant amount			$4,000		$4,000	

Informational and Library Resources

Total amount spent on library materials	$1,436,700
Study seating capacity inside the library	357
# of full-time equivalent professional librarians	6
Hours per week library is open	89
# of open, wired connections available to students	5
# of networked computers available for use by students	35
Has wireless network?	Y
Require computer?	N

JD Attrition (from prior year)

	Academic	Other	Total	
	#	#	#	%
1st year	9	1	10	7.0
2nd year	1	6	7	4.3
3rd year	0	0	0	0.0
4th year	0	0	0	0.0

Employment (9 months after graduation)

	Total	Percentage
Employment status known	124	97.6
Employment status unknown	3	2.4
Employed	116	93.5
Pursuing graduate degrees	4	3.2
Unemployed (seeking, not seeking, or studying for the bar)	4	3.2
Type of Employment		
# employed in law firms	66	56.9
# employed in business and industry	19	16.4
# employed in government	12	10.3
# employed in public interest	9	7.8
# employed as judicial clerks	6	5.2
# employed in academia	4	3.4
Geographic Location		
# employed in state	92	79.3
# employed in foreign countries	3	2.6
# of states where employed	15	

Bar Passage Rates

First-time takers	125	Reporting %	86.40
Average school %	87.96	Average state %	83.08
Average pass difference	4.88		

Jurisdiction	Takers	Passers	Pass %	State %	Diff %
Kentucky	108	95	87.96	83.08	4.88

University of Louisville's Brandeis School of Law

University of Louisville
Louisville, KY 40292
Phone: 502.852.6364; Fax: 502.852.8971
E-mail: lawadmissions@louisville.edu; Website: www.law.louisville.edu

■ Introduction

Founded in 1846, the University of Louisville's Brandeis School of Law is Kentucky's oldest law school and America's fifth oldest law school in continuous operation. Heir to the legacy of Justice Louis D. Brandeis, the school is distinguished by a rich history, national outreach, and profound dedication to public service. It is an integral part of the University of Louisville, a public institution and major research center founded in 1798. The metropolitan area, with a population of approximately one million, combines the gracious ambience of southern hospitality with cultural, aesthetic, and recreational attractions (including historic Churchill Downs, the Actors Theatre of Louisville, the Speed Art Museum, and the Muhammad Ali Institute for Peace and Justice).

■ Enrollment/Student Body

The School of Law enrolls first-year students beginning in the fall semester, which starts in August. Candidates may apply for admission to either the full-time (three-year) division or the part-time (four- to five-year) division.

Candidates must have completed a bachelor's degree at an accredited college or university prior to enrollment. All undergraduate majors are acceptable, with courses that emphasize critical reasoning, writing, and communication skills recognized as good preparation for the study of law.

With an entering class numbering about 140 each fall, first-year class size seldom exceeds 70. Basic Legal Skills (the first-year writing course) has classes of approximately 22 students each.

The entire student body, composed of almost as many women as men, numbers about 400, enabling every student to be a name, not just a number, and presenting students with the opportunity to develop close relationships with their professors.

■ Faculty

Many UofL Law professors have practiced law, worked in government, or clerked for federal judges. Our faculty excels in teaching, scholarship, and service to the community. They collaborate with UofL colleagues in business, medicine, public policy, and social work. Public officials throughout the United States routinely rely upon their expertise.

With 33 full-time faculty members (including 12 women and 4 faculty members of color) and numerous part-time or adjunct teachers, the faculty-to-student ratio is at 1 to 14. Students have the opportunity to explore issues important to them through close cooperation with individual members of the faculty.

■ Curriculum

The law school's full-time and part-time division share the same curriculum, faculty, and academic standards. As of fall 2009, full-time and part-time students will enroll in the same sections of courses rather than being separated into day and evening divisions. After completing the foundational first-year curriculum, students choose from core courses in doctrinal subjects, advanced research and writing, and professional responsibility. Students also may take advantage of a rich variety of specialized and interdisciplinary electives. The School of Law conducts a Summer Enrichment Program for a limited number of newly admitted students.

A highly successful Academic Success Program provides structured study groups, academic success seminars, a library with aids, and individual academic counseling.

■ Samuel L. Greenebaum Public Service Program

Reflecting the spirit of Justice Louis D. Brandeis, the School of Law was one of America's first five law schools to adopt public service as part of the prescribed course of study. Through this public service work, students develop practical skills, serve their communities, and establish professional values. All students are required to complete 30 hours of pro bono services as a condition of graduation.

In the 2009–2010 academic year, over 200 placements were maintained, 7 of which were new to the program. At the University of Louisville, your first job is waiting for you.

■ Library and Physical Facilities

The law school is housed in Wilson W. Wyatt Hall, a gracious colonial-style building overlooking the formal entrance to the University of Louisville's Belknap Campus—a traditional college campus located in an urban setting. The University of Louisville also includes two other campuses: the Health Sciences Center (housing the medical, dental, public health, and nursing schools) and the Shelby Campus, which offers continuing education classes.

The school's law library houses a collection of more than 400,000 volumes and microform volume equivalents, carefully selected to aid student instruction and promote research. The library still receives original briefs of the US Supreme Court—a rare distinction for a law school and a practice originated by Justice Brandeis that continues today.

State-of-the-art instructional and research technologies; two computer labs; the Allen Courtroom's contemporary litigation environment; wireless access in the library, classrooms, and common areas; and a full-time technology staff provide a wealth of services to every law student. The school's website serves as our community bulletin board. Students can download course syllabi, assignments, handouts, old exams, and other materials; browse job listings from the Career Services Office; review the Academic Support Program's catalog of study aids; and get news, calendars, schedules, and more. Technology is increasingly part of law teaching and learning as the faculty incorporate presentations and Internet resources into the classroom experience.

■ Special Programs

The School of Law offers several dual-degree programs designed to enhance the student's understanding, skills, and career opportunities in both areas of study. Each requires application and admission to both participating schools: Master of Business Administration/Juris Doctor; Master of Science in Social Work/Juris Doctor; Juris Doctor/Master of Arts in Humanities; Juris Doctor/Master of Divinity—at the

University of Louisville's Brandeis School of Law

Louisville Presbyterian Theological Seminary; Juris Doctor/Master of Arts in Political Science; Juris Doctor/Master of Urban Planning; and Juris Doctor/Master of Arts in Bioethics.

The school also operates clinical externship programs in which upper-class students, with supervision, represent clients and appear in court. A third-year student may receive credit by working in the criminal arena (DA or PD), the tax arena (IRS), the judicial branch (various judges), family law (Center for Women and Families or Legal Aid Society), or technology (University of Louisville Office of Technology Transfer).

The law school operates a live-client clinic, housed in the same building as the Legal Aid Society. Under the direction and supervision of faculty, students in the clinic gain experience interacting with and representing clients.

International experience is another unique opportunity. The Brandeis School offers faculty or student exchanges with law schools in France, England, Germany, Finland, Australia, and South Africa.

■ Practical Success

Participating annually in about a dozen moot court and skills competitions, the law school has won several regional and national championships; most recently the 2008 ABA National Negotiations Competition.

Students are also actively involved in writing for and publishing the *University of Louisville Law Review*, the *Journal of Law and Education*, and the *Journal of Animal and Environmental Law*. Graduates of the University of Louisville's Brandeis School of Law consistently achieve high employment rates.

■ Admission

Applicants may apply beginning **October 1** and prior to **April 1**. Both full-time and part-time first-year students must start classes in the fall semester.

For the best chance of consideration, it is recommended that the LSAT be taken no later than December. Scores from the LSAT taken in June, prior to the first semester of enrollment, will be considered only under extraordinary circumstances.

Applicant Profile

University of Louisville's Brandeis School of Law
This grid includes only applicants who earned 120–180 LSAT scores under standard administrations.

LSAT Score	3.75 +		3.50–3.74		3.25–3.49		3.00–3.24		2.75–2.99		2.50–2.74		2.25–2.49		2.00–2.24		Below 2.00		No GPA		Total	
	Apps	Adm	Apps	Adm	Apps	Adm	Apps	Adm	Apps	Adm	Apps	Adm	Apps	Adm	Apps	Adm	Apps	Adm	Apps	Adm	Apps	Adm
175–180	0	0	0	0	0	0	0	0	0	0	0	0	0	0	0	0	0	0	0	0	0	0
170–174	0	0	0	0	0	0	0	0	0	0	0	0	0	0	0	0	0	0	0	0	0	0
165–169	6	5	2	2	3	3	1	0	4	4	0	0	0	0	1	1	0	0	0	0	17	15
160–164	23	22	11	9	12	11	9	7	6	5	8	5	4	2	5	3	2	0	0	0	80	64
155–159	59	53	67	58	66	54	61	40	37	18	13	6	9	4	3	0	0	0	1	0	316	233
150–154	48	29	97	62	90	23	81	8	58	13	24	4	16	1	4	0	2	0	8	2	428	142
145–149	24	9	40	11	56	4	64	4	29	1	21	0	9	0	7	0	1	0	2	0	253	29
140–144	3	0	10	2	19	2	27	1	15	1	19	1	13	0	4	0	0	0	2	0	112	7
135–139	0	0	5	1	8	0	6	0	7	0	9	0	5	0	2	0	1	0	1	0	44	1
130–134	1	0	1	0	2	0	2	0	4	0	3	0	0	0	2	1	0	0	0	0	15	1
125–129	0	0	0	0	0	0	0	0	1	0	0	0	0	0	0	0	1	0	1	0	3	0
120–124	0	0	0	0	1	0	0	0	0	0	0	0	0	0	0	0	0	0	0	0	1	0
Total	164	118	233	145	257	97	251	60	161	42	97	16	56	7	28	5	7	0	15	2	1269	492

Apps = Number of Applicants
Adm = Number Admitted
Reflects 100% of the total applicant pool; average LSAT data reported.

The faculty admission committee reads all files very carefully. Beyond numerical indicators (LSAT scores and grade-point averages), the committee looks for individuals with unique attributes who will bring diversity to the entering class and good character to the legal profession. Numerical quantifiers are not automatic grounds for admission or denial.

Loyola Law School, Loyola Marymount University

919 Albany Street
Los Angeles, CA 90015
Phone: 213.736.1074; Fax: 213.736.6523
E-mail: admissions@lls.edu; Website: www.lls.edu

ABA
Approved
Since
1935

The Basics

Type of school	Private
Term	Semester
Application deadline	2/1 4/15
Application fee	
Financial aid deadline	3/15
Can first year start other than fall?	No
Student to faculty ratio	14.8 to 1
# of housing spaces available restricted to law students	
graduate housing for which law students are eligible	

Faculty and Administrators

	Total		Men		Women		Minorities	
	Spr	Fall	Spr	Fall	Spr	Fall	Spr	Fall
Full-time	64	68	36	36	28	32	10	11
Other full-time	1	0	1	0	0	0	0	0
Deans, librarians, & others who teach	15	15	7	8	8	7	4	4
Part-time	62	61	45	46	17	15	26	23
Total	142	144	89	90	53	54	40	38

Curriculum

	Full-Time	Part-Time
Typical first-year section size	86	58
Is there typically a "small section" of the first-year class, other than Legal Writing, taught by full-time faculty	No	No
If yes, typical size offered last year		
# of classroom course titles beyond first-year curriculum		162
# of upper division courses, excluding seminars, with an enrollment:	Under 25	122
	25–49	48
	50–74	7
	75–99	11
	100+	10
# of seminars		31
# of seminar positions available		624
# of seminar positions filled	268	163
# of positions available in simulation courses		1,426
# of simulation positions filled	682	437
# of positions available in faculty supervised clinical courses		410
# of faculty supervised clinical positions filled	127	27
# involved in field placements	190	35
# involved in law journals	187	17
# involved in moot court or trial competitions	119	7
# of credit hours required to graduate		87

JD Enrollment and Ethnicity

	Men		Women		Full-Time		Part-Time		1st-Year		Total		JD Degs. Awd.
	#	%	#	%	#	%	#	%	#	%	#	%	
African Amer.	20	3.1	35	5.5	41	4.1	14	4.9	20	5.0	55	4.3	12
Amer. Indian	2	0.3	4	0.6	2	0.2	4	1.4	2	0.5	6	0.5	1
Asian Amer.	131	20.2	158	24.8	232	23.2	57	20.0	76	19.0	289	22.5	99
Mex. Amer.	48	7.4	58	9.1	90	9.0	16	5.6	37	9.3	106	8.2	25
Puerto Rican	1	0.2	7	1.1	6	0.6	2	0.7	5	1.3	8	0.6	3
Hispanic	27	4.2	25	3.9	45	4.5	7	2.5	18	4.5	52	4.0	14
Total Minority	229	35.3	287	45.0	416	41.5	100	35.1	158	39.5	516	40.1	154
For. Nation.	0	0.0	0	0.0	0	0.0	0	0.0	0	0.0	0	0.0	0
Caucasian	378	58.2	304	47.6	519	51.8	163	57.2	218	54.5	682	53.0	201
Unknown	42	6.5	47	7.4	67	6.7	22	7.7	24	6.0	89	6.9	41
Total	649	50.4	638	49.6	1002	77.9	285	22.1	400	31.1	1287		396

Transfers

Transfers in	48
Transfers out	11

Tuition and Fees

	Resident	Nonresident
Full-time	$40,530	$40,530
Part-time	$27,165	$27,165
Tuition Guarantee Program		N

Living Expenses

Estimated living expenses for singles

Living on campus	Living off campus	Living at home
N/A	$25,358	$13,612

Loyola Law School, Loyola Marymount University

ABA
Approved
Since
1935

GPA and LSAT Scores

	Total	Full-Time	Part-Time
# of apps	5,262	4,994	2,485
# of offers	1,712	1,602	110
# of matrics	396	339	57
75% GPA	3.67	3.68	3.66
Median GPA	3.53	3.54	3.44
25% GPA	3.31	3.33	3.20
75% LSAT	163	163	163
Median LSAT	160	160	159
25% LSAT	157	157	155

Grants and Scholarships (from prior year)

	Total		Full-Time		Part-Time	
	#	%	#	%	#	%
Total # of students	1,287		992		295	
Total # receiving grants	368	28.6	334	33.7	34	11.5
Less than 1/2 tuition	147	11.4	138	13.9	9	3.1
Half to full tuition	193	15.0	174	17.5	19	6.4
Full tuition	0	0.0	0	0.0	0	0.0
More than full tuition	28	2.2	22	2.2	6	2.0
Median grant amount			$20,500		$16,500	

Informational and Library Resources

Total amount spent on library materials	$2,244,309
Study seating capacity inside the library	550
# of full-time equivalent professional librarians	13
Hours per week library is open	108
# of open, wired connections available to students	930
# of networked computers available for use by students	179
Has wireless network?	Y
Require computer?	N

JD Attrition (from prior year)

	Academic	Other	Total	
	#	#	#	%
1st year	16	31	47	11.5
2nd year	3	6	9	2.2
3rd year	1	1	2	0.5
4th year	0	0	0	0.0

Employment (9 months after graduation)

	Total	Percentage
Employment status known	396	100.0
Employment status unknown	0	0.0
Employed	377	95.2
Pursuing graduate degrees	4	1.0
Unemployed (seeking, not seeking, or studying for the bar)	10	2.5
Type of Employment		
# employed in law firms	222	58.9
# employed in business and industry	68	18.0
# employed in government	26	6.9
# employed in public interest	45	11.9
# employed as judicial clerks	9	2.4
# employed in academia	5	1.3
Geographic Location		
# employed in state	359	95.2
# employed in foreign countries	0	0.0
# of states where employed	9	

Bar Passage Rates

First-time takers	390	Reporting %	97.18
Average school %	85.49	Average state %	78.07
Average pass difference	7.42		

Jurisdiction	Takers	Passers	Pass %	State %	Diff %
California	379	324	85.49	78.07	7.42

Loyola Law School, Loyola Marymount University

919 Albany Street
Los Angeles, CA 90015
Phone: 213.736.1074; Fax: 213.736.6523
E-mail: admissions@lls.edu; Website: www.lls.edu

■ Law School and Campus

Loyola Law School was founded in 1920 and is one of California's largest law schools. Having graduated more than 16,000 men and women, Loyola has had a profound effect on the legal profession and on American history. Known best for producing many of our nation's most exciting and influential attorneys, Loyola instills in its graduates a deep commitment to public service and ethical practice while emphasizing the philosophical, analytical, and professional skills essential to the lawyering process.

The Law School, a division of Loyola Marymount University (LMU), includes nearly 1,300 full-time day and part-time evening students, nearly 140 full-time and adjunct faculty, and 110 administrative and technical staff. Housed on a modern, innovative campus, including eight buildings, a spacious parking facility, green lawns, and athletic courts, Loyola encompasses an entire city block in downtown Los Angeles. The academic and social spaces are dedicated solely to the law school community—the environment is warm and welcoming. World-renowned architect Frank Gehry has received national and international recognition for the campus design.

The cornerstone of the campus, the William M. Rains Law Library, is one of the largest private law libraries in the western United States, providing extensive research capabilities with a collection of over 600,000 volumes and the latest advances in information technology.

Our central location, just minutes away from many courts, major law firms, and public interest agencies, provides excellent opportunities for our students. Students also have easy access to LA Live, an entertainment and sports venue that includes the Staples Center, Nokia Theatre, Grammy Museum, a movie theatre, and restaurants.

■ Juris Doctor

The Juris Doctor prepares students to be effective lawyers and judges in any jurisdiction in the United States. Loyola recognizes that a quality education must do more than simply prepare a student to file a lawsuit or draft a contract. The program is designed to teach students to think and reason critically. The faculty strives to instill in students a respect and appreciation for the law and a desire to improve the society in which we live. The Juris Doctor is offered in both a full-time, three-year day division and a part-time, four-year evening division.

■ JD/MBA and JD/International MBA

Loyola Law School and the Graduate Program of the College of Business Administration of Loyola Marymount University offer a dual-degree program in law and business. Graduates of the program receive the Juris Doctor degree (JD) and the Master of Business Administration (MBA). The International Master of Business Administration program may also be completed concurrently with the Law School curriculum. A graduate certificate in International Business will be awarded with the MBA.

The dual-degree program provides for the achievement of both degrees in four years instead of the five normally required to complete the degree programs separately. The program is only open to full-time day students. Students may receive up to 12 units of business classes toward the 87 units required to earn a JD, and may be allowed to count up to 12 units of law classes toward the 54 units required to earn an MBA.

Applicants must apply and be accepted separately to the Law School and the MBA program. Applicants must also apply and be accepted to the JD/MBA program. Applications for the JD/MBA program may be submitted after the first year of law school. Interested applicants should contact the LMU College of Business Administration to request an application for the MBA program and the Law School Office of Admissions to request an application for the JD/MBA program.

■ Master of Laws in Taxation and JD/Tax LLM

Loyola also offers the Master of Laws (LLM) degree in Taxation. This degree distinguishes tax specialists by its advanced legal theory, tax policy, and scholarship. Students may earn both the JD degree and the LLM in Taxation in three years (rather than the four years typically required to complete the degree programs separately) by completing an intensive summer tax session and by taking advanced tax courses that count for double credit toward both the Juris Doctor and the LLM in Taxation.

■ Faculty

The faculty is composed of scholars who publish innovative theories, influencing the development and direction of the legal profession. They draft hundreds of scholarly articles and books, advise law firms and agencies on recent developments, and lecture at universities around the world. They also include seasoned attorneys with extensive and varied practice experience as United States Supreme Court clerks, public interest lawyers, agency chiefs, and law firm partners. But most importantly, the Loyola faculty are exceptional teachers who maintain an open door policy to encourage free and continuous interaction with their students.

■ Curriculum

The curriculum is designed to provide the knowledge and skills that will enable students to become excellent practicing lawyers. The curriculum integrates traditional instruction in legal doctrine and theory with a special commitment to the development of legal skills.

The Law School has a wide variety of course offerings and seminars in business/corporate law, commercial law, constitutional and civil rights law, criminal law, environmental law, entertainment/sports law, intellectual property law, international law, jurisprudence, law and social policy, litigation and legal skills, property law, public interest law, and tax law.

■ Innovative Programs

Loyola demonstrates its commitment to public service by requiring all students to donate 40 hours to working in the public interest sector. The **Public Interest Law Department** coordinates public interest activities, counsels students about

law practice and fellowships, and administers five public service programs. The **Entertainment Law Practicum** provides students with an opportunity to get hands-on experience through field placements at television networks, major movie studios, record companies, talent agencies, and entertainment law firms. Loyola's newest program, the **Business Law Practicum** offers an innovative approach to educating business lawyers with practical, real-world training. **International programs** allow upper division students to study abroad in Costa Rica, China, Italy, and London. The **Center for Ethical Lawyering** is one of Loyola's greatest strengths, featuring specialized training courses and externships designed to prepare students for the courtroom. Through our excellent **trial advocacy programs**, upper division students receive extensive training in all aspects of trial work. Loyola students have won numerous international and national trial advocacy and moot court competitions in recent years.

■ Admission and Financial Aid/Scholarships

Admission to the law school is based on a comprehensive evaluation that includes LSAT performance, undergraduate academic record, the personal statement, and letters of recommendation. Professional experience, extracurricular activities, community involvement, and qualities such as motivation, maturity, and focus are also closely evaluated. A prospective student may also submit a résumé.

Applications for admission are accepted on a rolling basis. The committee begins reading complete files in December.

Deadlines are **February 1** for the day program and **April 15** for the evening program. Early applicants have greater prospects for gaining admission and receiving scholarship awards.

All admitted students are considered for our scholarship programs. The committee uses the merits of the file to evaluate the admitted student's potential to contribute to our community. In addition to the general scholarship program, Loyola offers the **Public Interest Scholars Program** for students interested in having a career in public service. For graduates working at public interest organizations or with government agencies, a **Loan Repayment Assistance Program** is also available. Entering students can work with our dedicated financial aid staff to find other sources (primarily loans) to help fund their educational and personal expenses.

■ Career Services

The Office of Career Services offers a wealth of services, programs, and resources to students and alumni. A large professional staff counsels and assists students and graduates in the job development process. Hundreds of national, international, and regional employers recruit from Loyola annually. Graduates are employed by the nation's most prestigious private and public legal organizations. Overall placement figures are consistently strong—recent classes have employment rates (within nine months of graduation) above 90 percent.

Applicant Profile

Loyola Law School, Loyola Marymount University
This grid includes only applicants who earned 120–180 LSAT scores under standard administrations.

LSAT Score	3.75 +		3.50–3.74		3.25–3.49		3.00–3.24		2.75–2.99		2.50–2.74		2.25–2.49		2.00–2.24		Below 2.00		No GPA		Total	
	Apps	Adm	Apps	Adm	Apps	Adm	Apps	Adm	Apps	Adm	Apps	Adm	Apps	Adm	Apps	Adm	Apps	Adm	Apps	Adm	Apps	Adm
175–180	0	0	2	1	1	0	1	1	0	0	1	0	0	0	0	0	0	0	0	0	5	2
170–174	10	10	14	14	10	9	9	7	3	3	4	2	2	0	0	0	1	0	0	0	53	45
165–169	66	64	88	83	82	72	53	32	29	12	18	5	5	0	1	0	0	0	1	1	343	269
160–164	187	179	294	272	248	179	155	65	83	24	42	11	17	4	4	1	2	0	13	8	1045	743
155–159	185	140	383	224	393	90	262	33	125	11	48	5	26	1	7	0	3	0	31	1	1463	505
150–154	99	19	240	44	320	30	283	14	136	0	58	2	28	0	12	0	2	0	28	2	1206	111
145–149	43	2	92	6	148	4	149	1	101	0	69	0	31	0	10	0	1	0	16	0	660	13
140–144	12	0	25	0	50	0	79	0	67	0	44	0	20	0	10	0	3	0	8	0	318	0
135–139	0	0	9	0	12	0	29	0	17	0	15	0	9	0	8	0	1	0	5	0	105	0
130–134	0	0	3	0	2	0	6	0	6	0	5	0	6	0	3	0	2	0	3	0	36	0
125–129	1	0	1	0	2	0	0	0	1	0	0	0	2	0	0	0	0	0	0	0	7	0
120–124	0	0	0	0	0	0	0	0	0	0	0	0	0	0	0	0	0	0	2	0	2	0
Total	603	414	1151	644	1268	384	1026	153	568	50	304	25	146	5	55	1	15	0	107	12	5243	1688

Apps = Number of Applicants
Adm = Number Admitted
Represents 99% of applicant pool; average LSAT data reported.

Loyola University Chicago School of Law

25 East Pearson Street, Suite 1440
Chicago, IL 60611
Phone: 312.915.7170; Fax: 312.915.7906
E-mail: law-admissions@luc.edu; Website: www.luc.edu/law

ABA Approved Since 1925

The Basics

Type of school	Private
Term	Semester
Application deadline	4/1
Application fee	$0
Financial aid deadline	3/1
Can first year start other than fall?	No
Student to faculty ratio	14.3 to 1
# of housing spaces available restricted to law students	96
graduate housing for which law students are eligible	106

Faculty and Administrators

	Total		Men		Women		Minorities	
	Spr	Fall	Spr	Fall	Spr	Fall	Spr	Fall
Full-time	43	48	24	30	19	18	4	6
Other full-time	7	6	3	2	4	4	1	1
Deans, librarians, & others who teach	14	15	5	5	9	10	1	1
Part-time	102	113	51	62	51	51	3	8
Total	166	182	83	99	83	83	9	16

Curriculum

	Full-Time	Part-Time
Typical first-year section size	65	75
Is there typically a "small section" of the first-year class, other than Legal Writing, taught by full-time faculty	Yes	No
If yes, typical size offered last year	25	
# of classroom course titles beyond first-year curriculum	183	
# of upper division courses, excluding seminars, with an enrollment: Under 25	193	
25–49	54	
50–74	31	
75–99	7	
100+	1	
# of seminars	41	
# of seminar positions available	510	
# of seminar positions filled	322	80
# of positions available in simulation courses	1,487	
# of simulation positions filled	780	247
# of positions available in faculty supervised clinical courses	155	
# of faculty supervised clinical positions filled	119	25
# involved in field placements	136	30
# involved in law journals	158	43
# involved in moot court or trial competitions	48	11
# of credit hours required to graduate	86	

JD Enrollment and Ethnicity

	Men		Women		Full-Time		Part-Time		1st-Year		Total		JD Degs. Awd.
	#	%	#	%	#	%	#	%	#	%	#	%	
African Amer.	17	4.3	30	6.8	34	5.2	13	6.9	11	4.1	47	5.6	14
Amer. Indian	3	0.8	1	0.2	4	0.6	0	0.0	0	0.0	4	0.5	1
Asian Amer.	15	3.8	26	5.9	31	4.8	10	5.3	11	4.1	41	4.9	21
Mex. Amer.	9	2.3	17	3.8	22	3.4	4	2.1	2	0.7	26	3.1	8
Puerto Rican	1	0.3	3	0.7	1	0.2	3	1.6	2	0.7	4	0.5	0
Hispanic	10	2.5	6	1.4	14	2.1	2	1.1	6	2.2	16	1.9	0
Total Minority	55	13.9	83	18.7	106	16.3	32	17.0	32	11.9	138	16.4	44
For. Nation.	5	1.3	4	0.9	8	1.2	1	0.5	2	0.7	9	1.1	4
Caucasian	322	81.3	342	77.0	517	79.3	147	78.2	233	86.3	664	79.0	240
Unknown	14	3.5	15	3.4	21	3.2	8	4.3	3	1.1	29	3.5	16
Total	396	47.1	444	52.9	652	77.6	188	22.4	270	32.1	840		304

Transfers

Transfers in	13
Transfers out	19

Tuition and Fees

	Resident	Nonresident
Full-time	$36,770	$36,770
Part-time	$27,720	$27,720
Tuition Guarantee Program		N

Living Expenses

Estimated living expenses for singles

Living on campus	Living off campus	Living at home
$19,998	$19,998	$19,998

Loyola University Chicago School of Law

ABA
Approved
Since
1925

GPA and LSAT Scores

	Total	Full-Time	Part-Time
# of apps	4,236	3,565	671
# of offers	1,284	1,133	151
# of matrics	268	203	65
75% GPA	3.60	3.62	3.50
Median GPA	3.47	3.50	3.31
25% GPA	3.24	3.29	3.06
75% LSAT	161	162	158
Median LSAT	160	160	155
25% LSAT	156	158	153

Grants and Scholarships (from prior year)

	Total #	Total %	Full-Time #	Full-Time %	Part-Time #	Part-Time %
Total # of students	887		638		249	
Total # receiving grants	569	64.1	465	72.9	104	41.8
Less than 1/2 tuition	401	45.2	300	47.0	101	40.6
Half to full tuition	158	17.8	156	24.5	2	0.8
Full tuition	9	1.0	8	1.3	1	0.4
More than full tuition	1	0.1	1	0.2	0	0.0
Median grant amount			$12,600		$4,783	

Informational and Library Resources

Total amount spent on library materials	$912,308
Study seating capacity inside the library	436
# of full-time equivalent professional librarians	9
Hours per week library is open	101
# of open, wired connections available to students	328
# of networked computers available for use by students	64
Has wireless network?	Y
Require computer?	N

JD Attrition (from prior year)

	Academic #	Other #	Total #	Total %
1st year	0	19	19	7.0
2nd year	0	2	2	0.8
3rd year	0	0	0	0.0
4th year	0	1	1	1.7

Employment (9 months after graduation)

	Total	Percentage
Employment status known	232	100.0
Employment status unknown	0	0.0
Employed	204	87.9
Pursuing graduate degrees	4	1.7
Unemployed (seeking, not seeking, or studying for the bar)	14	6.0
Type of Employment		
# employed in law firms	126	61.8
# employed in business and industry	35	17.2
# employed in government	26	12.7
# employed in public interest	8	3.9
# employed as judicial clerks	6	2.9
# employed in academia	3	1.5
Geographic Location		
# employed in state	167	81.9
# employed in foreign countries	1	0.5
# of states where employed	22	

Bar Passage Rates

First-time takers	217	Reporting %	89.40
Average school %	94.33	Average state %	90.94
Average pass difference	3.39		

Jurisdiction	Takers	Passers	Pass %	State %	Diff %
Illinois	194	183	94.33	90.94	3.39

Loyola University Chicago School of Law

25 East Pearson Street, Suite 1440
Chicago, IL 60611
Phone: 312.915.7170; Fax: 312.915.7906
E-mail: law-admissions@luc.edu; Website: www.luc.edu/law

■ Introduction

The School of Law is located on the Water Tower Campus of the university, a few blocks north of the Chicago Loop. This campus adjoins Michigan Avenue at the historical Water Tower, a Chicago landmark, in approximately the center of the renowned Magnificent Mile, a commercial center over which the John Hancock Center towers. This location provides ready access to the state and federal courts and to the offices of most other institutions of federal, state, and local government, as well as the cultural centers of Chicago. The school is a member of the AALS and is approved by the ABA. The School of Law celebrated its 100th anniversary in 2008.

■ Library and Facilities

The Philip H. Corboy Law Center, at 25 East Pearson Street, provides Loyola's law students with a modern and enhanced learning environment. The School of Law library is located on floors 3–5 of the Law Center. More than 400,000 volumes enhance Loyola's broad-based law curriculum and support the varied research needs of students and faculty. Offering custom-designed furnishings and custom carrels, the 43,900-square-foot facility creates a comfortable and accommodating atmosphere for users. The library is open 100 hours each week, with expanded hours during examination periods. The law library is fully staffed with professional librarians and paraprofessionals to assist students and faculty.

Across the street from the Law Center is a 25-story, 600-bed residence hall, Baumhart Hall, which opened in fall 2006. This structure enables graduate, professional, and undergraduate student residents to experience contemporary living in fully furnished apartments. Amenities include a 24-hour security staff, a food court and late-night café, a state-of-the-art fitness center, wireless access in apartment bedrooms and public areas, a laundry room equipped with "smart system" washers and dryers, and rent includes all utilities, heat and air-conditioning, cable, and high-speed Internet access.

■ Foreign Study Programs

Since 1983, the School of Law has offered a program of international and comparative law courses at the Rome Center for Liberal Arts, the university's campus in Rome, Italy. Each summer, for approximately four weeks, law students from the United States and elsewhere can take one or more of the courses offered in Rome by members of the full-time Loyola law faculty and visiting faculty. In 2009, Supreme Court Justice Ruth Bader Ginsberg participated in the Rome Program.

In 1997, the law school added a program in Strasbourg, France. This one-week optional field study follows the summer program in Rome.

In summer 2008, Loyola inaugurated a three-week program in China. In addition to time in the classroom, students hear from guest lecturers and experience guided excursions to sites in Bejing and the surrounding areas.

In 1989, Loyola inaugurated its London Comparative Advocacy Program in which students travel to London between semesters for approximately 15 days to become immersed in the world of the British barrister.

In spring 2003, Loyola inaugurated an immersion program at Universidad Alberto Hurtado, a Jesuit law school in Santiago, Chile.

■ Clinical Legal Education

For students, faculty, and alumni, Loyola's four legal clinics represent a valuable bridge between theory and practice, classroom and career. Through the clinics, the School of Law offers service to others in a way that gives them dignity while providing students with practical legal experience. In spring 2003, the law school celebrated the 20th anniversary of its clinical program that began with the founding of its Community Law Center Clinic, followed in later years by the Federal Tax, Child and Family Law, and Business Law clinics.

■ Special Opportunities

The School of Law has dual-degree programs with the School of Social Work, the Department of Political Science, the School of Education, and the Graduate School of Business. Automatic acceptance into the masters of political science program is granted to candidates admitted to the law school. Provisional admission to the MBA program is granted based upon LSAT score and law school grades. The multidegree programs are structured to allow completion after four years. Loyola offers accelerated LLM programs in health law, child and family law, and taxation to JD students who fulfill program requirements. Recognizing the increasing need for specialization in legal education and practice, the school offers specialized curricula in five key areas: International Law and Practice, Health Law, Child and Family Law, Advocacy, and Tax Law.

■ Child and Family Law Center

The Loyola ChildLaw Center was created in 1993 to prepare law students to represent abused and neglected children. The center is the first of its kind at any American law school; it was the recipient of the National Association of Counsel for Children 1996 Outstanding Legal Advocacy Award; and it draws on the full resources of Loyola University, including the schools of medicine, social work, and education. The program includes an LLM degree and a master's degree program for nonlawyers.

The Center houses our renowned ChildLaw and Education Institute, offering students an integrated curriculum in education law, interdisciplinary research, and outreach experiences, with the opportunity to represent children confronting barriers to educational equality. Law students also may obtain a unique dual degree with the School of Education, which will result in a JD and MA in Comparative Education.

The law school and Teach for America (TFA) have entered into a partnership. TFA corps members who are interested in using their legal education to advocate for children's legal interests and well-being will receive matching AmeriCorps Awards.

Annually, Child and Family Law Fellows are selected from the entering law class. One fellowship is reserved for a TFA corps member. Each fellow receives financial support.

■ Institute for Health Law

The Beazley Institute for Health Law was created in 1984 in recognition of the need for an academic forum to study the field of health law and to act as a vehicle to foster dialogue between the law and the health sciences. Through the institute, the law school offers an SJD in Health Law and Policy and an LLM in Health Law. In addition, it offers the first Master of Jurisprudence (MJ) in Health Law and Doctor of Law (DLaw) in Health Law and Policy, providing health care professionals with an intensive overview in health law. More than two dozen health law classes are offered at the law school.

■ Center for Business and Corporate Governance Law

The Center for Business and Corporate Governance Law was created in 1996 to further enhance Loyola's corporate law curriculum by offering more specialized and practical skills classes to its students. The center offers corporate externships for law students, sponsors continuing education programs for both corporate attorneys and employees, and includes a legal clinic for small businesses.

■ Institute for Consumer Antitrust Studies

The Institute for Consumer Antitrust Studies is an independent, academically-based institute designed to explore the effect of antitrust and consumer law enforcement on the individual consumer and the general public. The institute was founded by a grant from the US District Court for the Northern District of Illinois and is supported by Loyola and private donors.

■ Advocacy

Loyola prepares its students for careers of leadership at the bar and on the bench. For over 100 years, Loyola's tradition of educating and training top litigators has produced some of the country's most accomplished and recognized trial attorneys and judges. The advocacy program is composed of a second-year required course in advocacy, courses in beginning and advanced trial advocacy, numerous moot court competitions, the Corboy Fellowship Program in Trial Advocacy for mock trial competitions, and a wide variety of litigation-related courses. A certificate in advocacy is available for students who complete a menu of advocacy courses.

Symbolic of our advocacy success is our selection by the National Institute for Trial Advocacy as the site for two of its largest advocacy training programs, the Midwest Regional Trial Advocacy Program and the Midwest Regional Deposition Training Program.

■ Admission

Factors other than LSAT scores and college grades are considered. Such factors include work experience, personal goals, specialized education, and other evidence of the ability to contribute invaluable insight to law classes.

■ Career Services

The Career Resources Office assists students and alumni with career planning and employment selection. Seminars by practicing attorneys and alumni, résumé preparation, interviewing techniques, individual counseling, and job-search strategies are just some of the programs administered by the Career Resources Office.

A year-round, on-campus employer interview and recruitment program provides employment opportunities.

The School of Law is a member of NALP.

■ Cocurricular Activities

Students are encouraged to participate in cocurricular activities. There are six student-edited publications, including the *Annals of Health Law, Children's Legal Rights Journal, Consumer Law Review, International Law Review, Loyola University Chicago Law Journal,* and *Public Interest Law Reporter.* Students compete in more than 20 moot court and mock trial national and international competitions. All students are members of the Loyola Student Bar Association, the principal instrument of student government. There are over 30 student organizations devoted to legal practice, ethnic groups, or law student chapters of professional bar associations.

Applicant Profile

Loyola University Chicago School of Law
This grid includes only applicants who earned 120–180 LSAT scores under standard administrations.

LSAT Score	3.75 +		3.50–3.74		3.25–3.49		3.00–3.24		2.50–2.99		2.00–2.49		Below 2.00		No GPA		Total	
	Apps	Adm	Apps	Adm	Apps	Adm	Apps	Adm	Apps	Adm	Apps	Adm	Apps	Adm	Apps	Adm	Apps	Adm
165–180	41	38	59	55	50	47	22	19	25	18	5	3	0	0	1	1	203	181
160–164	133	129	215	202	156	127	120	88	63	32	13	5	0	0	6	2	706	585
155–159	166	72	318	113	322	96	190	44	153	34	20	5	3	0	15	1	1187	365
145–154	158	20	314	34	436	44	332	19	374	20	88	1	5	1	20	0	1727	139
120–144	22	1	52	1	78	1	100	0	176	1	58	0	6	0	14	1	506	5
Total	520	260	958	405	1042	315	764	170	791	105	184	14	14	1	56	5	4329	1275

Apps = Number of Applicants   Adm = Number Admitted   Reflects 99% of the total applicant pool; average LSAT data reported.

Loyola University New Orleans College of Law

7214 St. Charles Avenue, Box 904
New Orleans, LA 70118
Phone: 504.861.5575; Fax: 504.861.5772
E-mail: ladmit@loyno.edu; Website: http://law.loyno.edu/

The Basics

Type of school	Private
Term	Semester
Application deadline	
Application fee	$40
Financial aid deadline	
Can first year start other than fall?	No
Student to faculty ratio	17.1 to 1
# of housing spaces available restricted to law students	55
graduate housing for which law students are eligible	55

Faculty and Administrators

	Total		Men		Women		Minorities	
	Spr	Fall	Spr	Fall	Spr	Fall	Spr	Fall
Full-time	39	39	23	22	16	17	11	11
Other full-time	8	9	4	5	4	4	1	1
Deans, librarians, & others who teach	4	3	4	3	0	0	0	0
Part-time	25	22	22	18	3	4	3	1
Total	76	73	53	48	23	25	15	13

Curriculum

	Full-Time	Part-Time
Typical first-year section size	74	48
Is there typically a "small section" of the first-year class, other than Legal Writing, taught by full-time faculty	No	No
If yes, typical size offered last year		
# of classroom course titles beyond first-year curriculum	102	

# of upper division courses, excluding seminars, with an enrollment:		
Under 25	37	
25–49	32	
50–74	19	
75–99	12	
100+	1	

# of seminars	101	
# of seminar positions available	995	
# of seminar positions filled	700	138
# of positions available in simulation courses	0	
# of simulation positions filled	0	0
# of positions available in faculty supervised clinical courses	152	
# of faculty supervised clinical positions filled	82	70
# involved in field placements	11	7
# involved in law journals	72	6
# involved in moot court or trial competitions	16	1
# of credit hours required to graduate	90	

Transfers

Transfers in	8
Transfers out	12

Tuition and Fees

	Resident	Nonresident
Full-time	$34,166	$34,166
Part-time	$23,096	$23,096
Tuition Guarantee Program		N

JD Enrollment and Ethnicity

	Men		Women		Full-Time		Part-Time		1st-Year		Total		JD Degs. Awd.
	#	%	#	%	#	%	#	%	#	%	#	%	
African Amer.	43	9.5	86	20.0	104	14.3	25	16.0	53	16.3	129	14.6	25
Amer. Indian	3	0.7	2	0.5	2	0.3	3	1.9	3	0.9	5	0.6	3
Asian Amer.	16	3.5	19	4.4	32	4.4	3	1.9	11	3.4	35	4.0	15
Mex. Amer.	4	0.9	8	1.9	11	1.5	1	0.6	6	1.8	12	1.4	2
Puerto Rican	3	0.7	6	1.4	6	0.8	3	1.9	4	1.2	9	1.0	1
Hispanic	28	6.2	25	5.8	44	6.1	9	5.8	20	6.1	53	6.0	16
Total Minority	97	21.5	146	33.9	199	27.4	44	28.2	97	29.8	243	27.6	62
For. Nation.	0	0.0	4	0.9	4	0.6	0	0.0	2	0.6	4	0.5	1
Caucasian	324	71.8	259	60.1	476	65.6	107	68.6	203	62.3	583	66.1	170
Unknown	30	6.7	22	5.1	47	6.5	5	3.2	24	7.4	52	5.9	14
Total	451	51.1	431	48.9	726	82.3	156	17.7	326	37.0	882		247

Living Expenses

Estimated living expenses for singles

Living on campus	Living off campus	Living at home
$20,300	$20,300	$15,000

Loyola University New Orleans College of Law

ABA
Approved
Since
1931

GPA and LSAT Scores

	Total	Full-Time	Part-Time
# of apps	1,827	1,671	156
# of offers	928	825	103
# of matrics	323	254	69
75% GPA	3.51	3.52	3.46
Median GPA	3.26	3.29	3.14
25% GPA	3.01	3.05	2.84
75% LSAT	155	155	155
Median LSAT	153	153	152
25% LSAT	150	151	149

Grants and Scholarships (from prior year)

	Total		Full-Time		Part-Time	
	#	%	#	%	#	%
Total # of students	835		687		148	
Total # receiving grants	352	42.2	318	46.3	34	23.0
Less than 1/2 tuition	217	26.0	185	26.9	32	21.6
Half to full tuition	121	14.5	119	17.3	2	1.4
Full tuition	9	1.1	9	1.3	0	0.0
More than full tuition	5	0.6	5	0.7	0	0.0
Median grant amount			$13,000		$2,525	

Informational and Library Resources

Total amount spent on library materials	$1,274,066
Study seating capacity inside the library	366
# of full-time equivalent professional librarians	1
Hours per week library is open	106
# of open, wired connections available to students	40
# of networked computers available for use by students	79
Has wireless network?	Y
Require computer?	N

JD Attrition (from prior year)

	Academic	Other	Total	
	#	#	#	%
1st year	6	19	25	10.1
2nd year	4	2	6	1.9
3rd year	0	2	2	0.8
4th year	0	0	0	0.0

Employment (9 months after graduation)

	Total	Percentage
Employment status known	234	95.1
Employment status unknown	12	4.9
Employed	215	91.9
Pursuing graduate degrees	9	3.8
Unemployed (seeking, not seeking, or studying for the bar)	4	1.7

Type of Employment

# employed in law firms	134	62.3
# employed in business and industry	23	10.7
# employed in government	26	12.1
# employed in public interest	8	3.7
# employed as judicial clerks	22	10.2
# employed in academia	2	0.9

Geographic Location

# employed in state	149	69.3
# employed in foreign countries	6	2.8
# of states where employed	19	

Bar Passage Rates

First-time takers	251	Reporting %	73.31
Average school %	67.39	Average state %	67.32
Average pass difference	0.07		

Jurisdiction	Takers	Passers	Pass %	State %	Diff %
Louisiana	184	124	67.39	67.32	0.07

Loyola University New Orleans College of Law

7214 St. Charles Avenue, Box 904
New Orleans, LA 70118
Phone: 504.861.5575; Fax: 504.861.5772
E-mail: ladmit@loyno.edu; Website: http://law.loyno.edu/

■ Introduction

It is a rare combination of wide-ranging programs of study, real life opportunities, and a commitment to the community that makes Loyola University New Orleans College of Law stand apart. It is an institution that trains lawyers to think critically and be advocates for social justice. The entire Loyola law school community provides an atmosphere for our students to excel, succeed, and become productive members of legal communities across the country. It is a school where students have the opportunity to learn from a prestigious faculty, participate in many extracurricular activities to hone their practical lawyering skills, and serve the New Orleans community through our many clinical offerings.

Loyola New Orleans is a Catholic institution of higher learning in the Jesuit tradition. The College of Law was established in 1914, approved by the ABA in 1931, and has been a member of the AALS since 1934. The College of Law is committed to excellence in legal education in the tradition of its spiritual heritage, with the goal being wisdom, not mere technical competence. The law school welcomes all persons who strive for the truth and who are prepared to challenge all assumptions in light of this commitment.

■ Physical Facilities and Library

Loyola University has two campuses, both located approximately five miles from the historic French Quarter. The 20-acre main campus, in the heart of the uptown residential community, faces the nationally recognized Audubon Park and Zoo. The 4.2-acre Broadway campus is the home of the College of Law, including the new 16,000-square-foot wing that was dedicated in April 2007, providing more classroom, office, and library space.

The law library's collection of 385,000 volumes and microform equivalents supports the curriculum and research needs of the students. In addition to conventional resources, the library has extensive computer facilities in place to access information outside its confines. The Online Catalog Library Center service permits the library to access a national bibliographic database of over 10 million publications. The law library houses remote-controlled viewing/listening rooms, a computerized legal research room, and two computer labs equipped with 59 personal computers on a network with access to the Internet, LexisNexis, Westlaw, e-mail, and other computer resources.

■ Curriculum and Special Programs

The curricula have been shaped by Louisiana's unique role as the only state in the union that has a legal system based on significant elements of both the civil law and common law traditions. The civil law was imported into Louisiana during the eighteenth century, when it was first a colony of France, and later, Spain. As a result of Louisiana's unique legal heritage, Loyola New Orleans has developed three separate curricula: two full-time divisions—civil law and common law; and a part-time civil law division. It is important to note that the Loyola New Orleans JD degree will allow a graduate to sit for the bar in any of the 50 states, without regard for the curriculum chosen. Loyola offers a Certificate in Common Law

Studies and a Certificate in Civil Law Studies for students who wish to acquire a foundation in both disciplines. Full-time students are required to be in residence for a minimum of six full semesters. The normal time frame for part-time students is eight semesters and one summer session. At the graduate level, the law school offers an LLM for International Students for graduates of non-US law schools.

Practical Lawyering Skills Program—Loyola has one of the most unique and far-reaching professional lawyering skills programs in the country. Recognizing hands-on, learn-by-doing opportunities that develop the future practitioner's skills to be as important as traditional academic studies, the curriculum incorporates specialized courses and the expertise of attorneys and judges. Currently, over 100 members of the bench and bar teach in the skills curriculum. Skills courses are offered tuition-free and students may complete as many above those required as they choose.

International Law—Loyola has founded summer sessions on four continents and in six countries, established ties with a number of important foreign law schools, sent its professors to teach or lecture at law schools in more than a dozen foreign countries, and hosted lectures by a number of professors from non-US law schools. Summer courses are taught in special five-week, summer-abroad sessions in Mexico and Eastern Europe (Russia, Hungary, and Austria). There are also two- and three-week sessions offered each summer in Brazil or Costa Rica. Additionally, students may obtain a Certificate in International Legal Studies. There are also seminar courses that have short trips abroad to Austria, Italy, and Turkey.

Environmental Law—Loyola recently received a $2 million grant to establish a faculty chair for environmental law. The nationally renowned scholar in environmental law has created a Certificate in Environmental Law, which is part of the Loyola Center for Environmental Law and Land Use. The center was created to address legal issues relative to economic development, protection of the environment, and the public's role in environmental policy issues.

Public Interest Law—As part of Loyola's Jesuit commitment to social justice, the law school provides many courses and activities as part of this specialty, including the very active Law Clinic and Center for Social Justice. Most of the public interest focus falls under the umbrella of the Gillis Long Poverty Law Center. A loan forgiveness program is available for graduates working in eligible public interest employment.

Tax Law—Loyola recently established a certificate program designed to certify students in this area of law and assist those students who may choose to pursue an LLM in tax upon graduation.

Other Areas of Significant Emphasis—Other areas of significant emphasis include corporate law, maritime law, and a new entertainment law specialty incorporating resources from Loyola's Music Industry Studies Program as well as the Thelonious Monk Institute of Jazz.

Clinical Education—The law clinic is a vital component of the law school. Students chosen to participate in the senior-year program will be assigned cases, both civil and criminal, and will be expected to prepare them for trial prior to actually participating in the trial process. The areas of law practiced in the clinic are criminal (both prosecution and

defense), immigration, family law, civil rights, and landlord/tenant. Additionally, the Katrina clinic and construction fraud mediation clinic give our students special opportunities to help our community. Upper-division students also have an opportunity to serve as judicial clerks in the federal extern program.

Joint-Degree Programs—Loyola offers three combined degrees: JD/Master of Business Administration, JD/Master of Public Administration, and JD/Master of Urban and Regional Planning.

■ Scholarly Publications and Student Activities

The *Loyola Law Review* is published by a student editorial board and includes student work and articles written by specialists from the practicing bar and academic community. Staff membership is based on scholarship and interest in legal writing.

The *Loyola University New Orleans Journal of Public Interest Law* is devoted to issues faced by the poor, children, the elderly, and all others who are unable to afford legal representation.

The *Loyola Intellectual Property and High Technology Law Annual* is a scholarly publication focusing on current legal issues in patents, copyrights, trademarks, and technology law.

The *Loyola Maritime Law Journal* provides an avenue for research and writing in the field of maritime law. Staff membership is based on scholarship.

The Moot Court Board, selected from prior years' competitions, is responsible for the Moot Court Program. Teams are entered each year in competitions. Loyola teams have an impressive winning record in a wide variety of local, regional, national, and international competitions.

There are a number of student organizations, including three legal fraternities. Other organizations include the Environmental Law Society, Sports and Entertainment Law Society, St. Thomas More Law Club, and the American Association for Justice.

■ Admission

The law school begins processing applications for admission on September 1 each year. The first decision letters are generally released in December. The admission decision is based on an initial evaluation of a combination of the LSAT score and the undergraduate cumulative grade-point average. Additionally, the undergraduate institution attended, the undergraduate major, and any grade trends will be taken into consideration. Also included in the evaluation will be the required personal statement, letters of recommendation, and résumés, all of which may present a more illuminating portrait of the applicant's skills and accomplishments. Competition for acceptance to the law school is high, thus all information provided is used to make the final admission decision.

■ Career Services

The College of Law Office of Career Services offers a variety of services to both students and alumni. The office maintains and operates a career-planning center, assists students in preparing résumés, videotapes mock interviews, and conducts seminars on career planning, employment opportunities, and interviewing techniques. The office actively solicits job opportunities for summer and school-term clerkships, as well as employment options for each year's graduating class.

Applicant Profile

Loyola University New Orleans College of Law
This grid includes only applicants who earned 120–180 LSAT scores under standard administrations.

LSAT Score	GPA								
	3.75 +	3.50–3.74	3.25–3.49	3.00–3.24	2.75–2.99	2.50–2.74	2.25–2.49	2.00–2.24	Below 2.00
175–180									
170–174									
165–169									
160–164									
155–159									
150–154									
145–149									
140–144									
135–139									
130–134									
125–129									
120–124									

■ Excellent   ▦ Possible   ☐ Unlikely

The College of Law considers many factors beyond LSAT score and GPA. This chart should be used only as a general guide.

University of Maine School of Law

246 Deering Avenue
Portland, ME 04102
Phone: 207.780.4341; Fax: 207.780.5647
E-mail: mainelaw@usm.maine.edu; Website: http://mainelaw.maine.edu

ABA
Approved
Since
1962
Section of Legal Education
and Admissions to the Bar

The Basics

Type of school	Public
Term	Semester
Application deadline	3/1
Application fee	$50
Financial aid deadline	2/15
Can first year start other than fall?	No
Student to faculty ratio	14.2 to 1
# of housing spaces available restricted to law students	
graduate housing for which law students are eligible	275

Faculty and Administrators

	Total		Men		Women		Minorities	
	Spr	Fall	Spr	Fall	Spr	Fall	Spr	Fall
Full-time	15	16	10	11	5	5	0	0
Other full-time	1	1	0	1	1	0	0	1
Deans, librarians, & others who teach	7	7	3	3	4	4	0	0
Part-time	18	13	12	10	6	3	1	0
Total	41	37	25	25	16	12	1	1

JD Enrollment and Ethnicity

	Men		Women		Full-Time		Part-Time		1st-Year		Total		JD Degs. Awd.
	#	%	#	%	#	%	#	%	#	%	#	%	
African Amer.	0	0.0	5	4.5	5	1.9	0	0.0	3	3.3	5	1.9	0
Amer. Indian	3	2.0	1	0.9	4	1.5	0	0.0	3	3.3	4	1.5	0
Asian Amer.	3	2.0	4	3.6	7	2.7	0	0.0	4	4.4	7	2.7	2
Mex. Amer.	1	0.7	0	0.0	1	0.4	0	0.0	1	1.1	1	0.4	0
Puerto Rican	2	1.3	0	0.0	2	0.8	0	0.0	0	0.0	2	0.8	0
Hispanic	2	1.3	1	0.9	3	1.1	0	0.0	2	2.2	3	1.1	0
Total Minority	11	7.2	11	9.8	22	8.3	0	0.0	13	14.4	22	8.3	2
For. Nation.	1	0.7	2	1.8	3	1.1	0	0.0	1	1.1	3	1.1	0
Caucasian	140	92.1	99	88.4	239	90.5	0	0.0	76	84.4	239	90.5	91
Unknown	0	0.0	0	0.0	0	0.0	0	0.0	0	0.0	0	0.0	0
Total	152	57.6	112	42.4	264	100.0	0	0.0	90	34.1	264		93

Curriculum

	Full-Time	Part-Time
Typical first-year section size	91	0
Is there typically a "small section" of the first-year class, other than Legal Writing, taught by full-time faculty	Yes	No
If yes, typical size offered last year	47	
# of classroom course titles beyond first-year curriculum	73	
# of upper division courses, excluding seminars, with an enrollment: Under 25	44	
25–49	12	
50–74	6	
75–99	1	
100+	0	
# of seminars	10	
# of seminar positions available	138	
# of seminar positions filled	121	0
# of positions available in simulation courses	139	
# of simulation positions filled	126	0
# of positions available in faculty supervised clinical courses	60	
# of faculty supervised clinical positions filled	57	0
# involved in field placements	34	0
# involved in law journals	47	0
# involved in moot court or trial competitions	20	0
# of credit hours required to graduate	90	

Transfers

Transfers in	4
Transfers out	2

Tuition and Fees

	Resident	Nonresident
Full-time	$20,702	$31,202
Part-time		
Tuition Guarantee Program		N

Living Expenses

Estimated living expenses for singles

Living on campus	Living off campus	Living at home
$15,472	$15,472	$7,438

University of Maine School of Law

*ABA
Approved
Since
1962*

GPA and LSAT Scores

	Total	Full-Time	Part-Time
# of apps	705	705	0
# of offers	341	341	0
# of matrics	90	90	0
75% GPA	3.61	3.61	0.00
Median GPA	3.37	3.37	0.00
25% GPA	3.06	3.06	0.00
75% LSAT	158	158	0
Median LSAT	154	154	0
25% LSAT	152	152	0

Grants and Scholarships (from prior year)

	Total		Full-Time		Part-Time	
	#	%	#	%	#	%
Total # of students	269		269		0	
Total # receiving grants	80	29.7	80	29.7	0	0.0
Less than 1/2 tuition	75	27.9	75	27.9	0	0.0
Half to full tuition	3	1.1	3	1.1	0	0.0
Full tuition	0	0.0	0	0.0	0	0.0
More than full tuition	2	0.7	2	0.7	0	0.0
Median grant amount			$3,133		$0	

Informational and Library Resources

Total amount spent on library materials	$740,522
Study seating capacity inside the library	218
# of full-time equivalent professional librarians	7
Hours per week library is open	97
# of open, wired connections available to students	0
# of networked computers available for use by students	15
Has wireless network?	Y
Require computer?	N

JD Attrition (from prior year)

	Academic	Other	Total	
	#	#	#	%
1st year	0	9	9	9.9
2nd year	0	0	0	0.0
3rd year	0	0	0	0.0
4th year	0	0	0	0.0

Employment (9 months after graduation)

	Total	Percentage
Employment status known	70	98.6
Employment status unknown	1	1.4
Employed	61	87.1
Pursuing graduate degrees	4	5.7
Unemployed (seeking, not seeking, or studying for the bar)	5	7.1
Type of Employment		
# employed in law firms	33	54.1
# employed in business and industry	7	11.5
# employed in government	7	11.5
# employed in public interest	4	6.6
# employed as judicial clerks	10	16.4
# employed in academia	0	0.0
Geographic Location		
# employed in state	43	70.5
# employed in foreign countries	1	1.6
# of states where employed	9	

Bar Passage Rates

First-time takers	78	Reporting %	75.64
Average school %	91.53	Average state %	90.74
Average pass difference	0.79		

Jurisdiction	Takers	Passers	Pass %	State %	Diff %
Maine	59	54	91.53	90.74	0.79

University of Maine School of Law

246 Deering Avenue
Portland, ME 04102
Phone: 207.780.4341; Fax: 207.780.5647
E-mail: mainelaw@usm.maine.edu; Website: http://mainelaw.maine.edu

■ Introduction

Maine Law is a vibrant and distinctive place to study law. Students study law in a supportive and personalized environment and are prepared for success in today's global economy.

Maine Law holds a pivotal place in state and regional affairs and is a destination point for students, scholars, and civic leaders from near and far. The state's only law school, and one of the smallest in the nation, Maine Law fosters educational and scholarly excellence, professionalism, and public service through a close community of faculty members and students. Our location in the vibrant coastal city of Portland, Maine—the largest city in the state and two hours north of Boston—allows students to benefit from a multitude of hands-on training opportunities offered through clinical programs, externships, community service projects, and employment. We have a tradition of training remarkably distinguished graduates—governors, federal and state judges, prominent lawyers, and civic leaders—who remain close to the law school. We are the law school of the University of Maine System and an administrative unit of the University of Southern Maine (USM).

■ Location

The law school is located in Portland, one of the most livable cities in the United States, and the largest city in Maine. It has the charm of a small town with the cultural activities of a large city. Opportunities to participate in year-round outdoor activities are abundant.

■ Faculty

Faculty members are well-regarded for their commitment to teaching, for their accessibility to students, and for their cutting-edge scholarship. They come from a variety of backgrounds and have extensive experience in private practice and public service. They make significant contributions to legislative, judicial, and professional institutions; community organizations; and policy and economic development initiatives. Their research spans matters of state, national, and international interest and examines topics as varied as international treaty practice, Maine tort law, coastal zone management, federal tax elections, constitutional controls over the military, intellectual property, and commercial practice.

■ Curriculum

Maine Law offers a broad-based curriculum that helps prepare students for practice in all states. The school's strengths are in business and commercial law, environmental and marine law, international law, intellectual property, clinical training, and trial advocacy. Ninety credit hours are required for graduation.

The first-year curriculum is a prescribed program consisting of courses that allow students to develop legal analytical skills as well as the ability to read and understand cases and statutory material. The program provides the foundation course in legal research and writing, including a moot court experience. Most courses after the first year are elective. All students are required to complete Professional Responsibility; Constitutional Law II; and a perspective course—one that places the law in a broader philosophical, historical, or comparative context. Each student must fulfill an upper-level writing requirement through a substantial research paper under the direction of a member of the faculty, through a seminar or independent study, or through membership on the *Maine Law Review* or *Ocean and Coastal Law Journal*. Maine Law's practical skills program includes courses in trial practice, negotiation, and alternative dispute resolution. The course in advanced trial advocacy has fielded award-winning teams.

■ Special Programs

Cumberland Legal Aid Clinic—Third-year students represent clients under faculty supervision in this approved legal assistance office. Students work on family law and domestic matters, juvenile justice, and criminal, consumer, housing, employment, and probate issues at both the trial and appellate levels. The clinic also provides representation for prisoners in a variety of civil matters. All clinical courses work with the state's domestic violence project.

Intellectual Property Law Clinic—Students have the rare opportunity to work with clients involved with developing new products and businesses. Under the supervision of intellectual property lawyers at the Center for Law and Innovation, students work directly with independent inventors, entrepreneurs, and research scientists engaged in technology transfer.

Externships—Students have access to numerous clinical externship opportunities, for academic credit, in many areas. Externships are available with government agencies and nonprofit organizations.

Center for Law and Innovation—The Center for Law and Innovation provides students with courses, conferences, and hands-on experiences to enhance their understanding of the role of law in the development of technological progress and innovation. In addition to offering courses in intellectual property and Internet law, the center provides summer-session technology law courses that bring distinguished scholars and practitioners to the school. Externship opportunities are available with the Maine Patent Program, a unique service program established by the Maine legislature to provide education and legal assistance regarding the patent process to Maine inventors, entrepreneurs, and businesses.

Marine Law Institute (MLI)—The MLI is an ocean and coastal law program that conducts research on laws and policies affecting ocean and coastal resources. The program also supports a student-edited journal and offers courses and seminars in coastal zone law, marine resources law, port security, law of the sea, and admiralty.

Pro Bono Program—The faculty has established a voluntary standard of 80 hours of pro bono legal service for each student during his or her three years of law school and has instituted a means of encouraging students to fulfill that standard while recognizing those who follow through with it.

Joint-Degree Programs—Maine Law and the University of Southern Maine offer the following joint-degree programs: JD/MCP in Community Planning and Development, JD/MS in Health Policy and Management, JD/MA in Public Policy and

University of Maine School of Law

Management with the Edmund S. Muskie School of Public Service, and a JD/MBA with the School of Business.

International-Exchange Programs—Semester-exchange programs are available with Dalhousie University Schulich School of Law, University of New Brunswick Faculty of Law, National University of Ireland, Université du Maine, and University of Buckingham.

■ Student Activities

The Student Bar Association performs the varied functions of student government and acts as an umbrella organization of other student organizations, such as the American Constitution Society, Animal Legal Defense Fund, Black Law Students Association, Business Law Association, Environmental Law Society, Federalist Society, Health Law Association, International Law Society, Latino/Latina Law Students Association, Lesbian/Gay/Bisexual Law Caucus, Maine Association for Public Interest Law, Maine Law and Technology Association, National Lawyers Guild, Native American Law Association, Prisoner Justice Project, Sports and Entertainment Law Society, and the Women's Law Association.

The *Maine Law Review* and the *Ocean and Coastal Law Journal* are scholarly journals managed, edited, and published by students. Students interested in developing written and oral advocacy skills participate in Moot Court and/or the Trial Advocacy Team.

■ Career Services

The Career Services Office provides a full range of services, including counseling; career resource materials; specific summer, full-time, part-time, and work-study job listings; and extensive on-campus recruiting. The small size of the law school ensures services tailored to meet the specific needs of its students. A number of workshops, speakers, and panel discussions throughout the year assist students in learning about the diverse opportunities available to them.

■ Expenses, Financial Aid, and Housing

Maine Law offers a reasonable tuition charge to both residents and nonresidents. For tuition rates for the current year, please visit our website, *www.mainelaw.maine.edu*. The FAFSA priority deadline is February 15. A number of scholarships are available for entering students. Candidates for admission will automatically be considered for all scholarships for which they are eligible. There are no dorms for law students, however, there are plenty of rental properties situated around the law school. There is also a privately owned and operated student housing complex located less than five minutes from the law school.

Applicant Profile

University of Maine School of Law
This grid includes only applicants who earned 120–180 LSAT scores under standard administrations.

LSAT Score	3.75 + Apps	Adm	3.50–3.74 Apps	Adm	3.25–3.49 Apps	Adm	3.00–3.24 Apps	Adm	2.75–2.99 Apps	Adm	2.50–2.74 Apps	Adm	2.25–2.49 Apps	Adm	2.00–2.24 Apps	Adm	Below 2.00 Apps	Adm	No GPA Apps	Adm	Total Apps	Adm
175–180	1	1	0	0	0	0	0	0	0	0	1	1	0	0	0	0	0	0	0	0	2	2
170–174	0	0	0	0	2	2	0	0	0	0	0	0	0	0	0	0	0	0	0	0	2	2
165–169	0	0	7	7	4	4	4	3	3	2	1	1	0	0	0	0	0	0	1	1	20	18
160–164	12	12	10	9	12	12	11	8	6	6	4	4	2	2	0	0	0	0	1	0	58	53
155–159	16	16	37	36	26	25	32	26	22	20	9	7	3	2	0	0	0	0	2	2	147	134
150–154	17	11	41	31	49	31	33	12	30	13	10	5	6	2	2	0	0	0	2	1	190	106
145–149	14	3	33	6	38	8	38	12	15	0	9	0	7	2	1	0	0	0	5	1	160	32
140–144	3	0	7	1	14	2	12	1	8	0	7	0	2	0	1	0	2	0	0	0	56	4
135–139	0	0	1	0	6	1	1	1	3	0	5	0	1	0	0	0	0	0	0	0	17	2
130–134	0	0	1	0	1	0	1	0	0	0	1	0	0	0	0	0	0	0	0	0	4	0
125–129	0	0	0	0	0	0	0	0	0	0	2	0	0	0	0	0	0	0	0	0	2	0
120–124	0	0	0	0	0	0	0	0	0	0	0	0	0	0	0	0	0	0	0	0	0	0
Total	63	43	137	90	152	85	132	63	87	41	49	18	21	8	4	0	2	0	11	5	658	353

Apps = Number of Applicants
Adm = Number Admitted
Reflects 99% of the total applicant pool; average LSAT data reported.

This chart is to be used as a general guide only. Nonnumerical factors are strongly considered for all applicants.

Marquette University Law School

Office of Admissions, PO Box 1881
Milwaukee, WI 53201-1881
Phone: 414.288.6767; Fax: 414.288.0676
E-mail: law.admission@marquette.edu; Website: http://law.marquette.edu

ABA Approved Since 1925 — **ABA** Section of Legal Education and Admissions to the Bar

The Basics

Type of school	Private
Term	Semester
Application deadline	4/1 6/1
Application fee	$50
Financial aid deadline	3/1
Can first year start other than fall?	No
Student to faculty ratio	20.5 to 1
# of housing spaces available restricted to law students	
graduate housing for which law students are eligible	

Curriculum

	Full-Time	Part-Time
Typical first-year section size	81	35
Is there typically a "small section" of the first-year class, other than Legal Writing, taught by full-time faculty	Yes	Yes
If yes, typical size offered last year	42	35
# of classroom course titles beyond first-year curriculum	153	
# of upper division courses, excluding seminars, with an enrollment: Under 25	77	
25–49	44	
50–74	13	
75–99	7	
100+	0	
# of seminars	31	
# of seminar positions available	462	
# of seminar positions filled	259	86
# of positions available in simulation courses	523	
# of simulation positions filled	392	131
# of positions available in faculty supervised clinical courses	77	
# of faculty supervised clinical positions filled	46	15
# involved in field placements	167	56
# involved in law journals	95	31
# involved in moot court or trial competitions	55	17
# of credit hours required to graduate	90	

Faculty and Administrators

	Total Spr	Total Fall	Men Spr	Men Fall	Women Spr	Women Fall	Minorities Spr	Minorities Fall
Full-time	26	29	17	19	9	10	4	5
Other full-time	10	10	2	2	8	8	0	0
Deans, librarians, & others who teach	9	9	3	3	6	6	0	0
Part-time	45	28	29	20	16	8	3	1
Total	90	76	51	44	39	32	7	6

JD Enrollment and Ethnicity

	Men #	Men %	Women #	Women %	Full-Time #	Full-Time %	Part-Time #	Part-Time %	1st-Year #	1st-Year %	Total #	Total %	JD Degs. Awd.
African Amer.	15	3.6	19	5.8	29	5.2	5	2.8	11	5.0	34	4.6	3
Amer. Indian	5	1.2	2	0.6	4	0.7	3	1.7	2	0.9	7	0.9	2
Asian Amer.	10	2.4	17	5.2	16	2.8	11	6.1	5	2.3	27	3.6	4
Mex. Amer.	5	1.2	5	1.5	8	1.4	2	1.1	7	3.2	10	1.3	1
Puerto Rican	5	1.2	1	0.3	6	1.1	0	0.0	1	0.5	6	0.8	0
Hispanic	16	3.8	9	2.8	21	3.7	4	2.2	10	4.6	25	3.4	6
Total Minority	56	13.5	53	16.2	84	14.9	25	13.9	36	16.4	109	14.7	16
For. Nation.	0	0.0	0	0.0	0	0.0	0	0.0	0	0.0	0	0.0	0
Caucasian	358	86.1	274	83.8	477	84.7	155	86.1	183	83.6	632	85.1	196
Unknown	2	0.5	0	0.0	2	0.4	0	0.0	0	0.0	2	0.3	0
Total	416	56.0	327	44.0	563	75.8	180	24.2	219	29.5	743		212

Transfers

Transfers in	15
Transfers out	13

Tuition and Fees

	Resident	Nonresident
Full-time	$32,410	$32,410
Part-time	$19,425	$19,425
Tuition Guarantee Program	N	

Living Expenses

Estimated living expenses for singles

Living on campus	Living off campus	Living at home
$19,240	$19,240	$19,240

Marquette University Law School

ABA
Approved
Since
1925

GPA and LSAT Scores

	Total	Full-Time	Part-Time
# of apps	2,084	1,905	179
# of offers	927	868	59
# of matrics	219	185	34
75% GPA	3.61	3.61	3.60
Median GPA	3.39	3.40	3.35
25% GPA	3.07	3.09	2.88
75% LSAT	159	159	158
Median LSAT	157	157	154
25% LSAT	154	155	151

Grants and Scholarships (from prior year)

	Total		Full-Time		Part-Time	
	#	%	#	%	#	%
Total # of students	748		563		185	
Total # receiving grants	296	39.6	244	43.3	52	28.1
Less than 1/2 tuition	221	29.5	174	30.9	47	25.4
Half to full tuition	53	7.1	48	8.5	5	2.7
Full tuition	22	2.9	22	3.9	0	0.0
More than full tuition	0	0.0	0	0.0	0	0.0
Median grant amount			$8,000		$3,500	

Informational and Library Resources

Total amount spent on library materials	$1,559,606
Study seating capacity inside the library	406
# of full-time equivalent professional librarians	11
Hours per week library is open	117
# of open, wired connections available to students	102
# of networked computers available for use by students	61
Has wireless network?	Y
Require computer?	N

JD Attrition (from prior year)

	Academic	Other	Total	
	#	#	#	%
1st year	3	18	21	9.4
2nd year	1	0	1	0.4
3rd year	0	0	0	0.0
4th year	0	0	0	0.0

Employment (9 months after graduation)

	Total	Percentage
Employment status known	191	97.9
Employment status unknown	4	2.1
Employed	177	92.7
Pursuing graduate degrees	3	1.6
Unemployed (seeking, not seeking, or studying for the bar)	11	5.8
Type of Employment		
# employed in law firms	113	63.8
# employed in business and industry	25	14.1
# employed in government	17	9.6
# employed in public interest	9	5.1
# employed as judicial clerks	7	4.0
# employed in academia	6	3.4
Geographic Location		
# employed in state	131	74.0
# employed in foreign countries	1	0.6
# of states where employed		16

Bar Passage Rates

First-time takers	212	Reporting %	100.00
Average school %	100.00	Average state %	91.79
Average pass difference	8.21		

Jurisdiction	Takers	Passers	Pass %	State %	Diff %
Wisconsin	212	212	100.00	91.79	8.21

Marquette University Law School

Office of Admissions, PO Box 1881
Milwaukee, WI 53201-1881
Phone: 414.288.6767; Fax: 414.288.0676
E-mail: law.admission@marquette.edu; Website: http://law.marquette.edu

■ Introduction

For more than a century, Marquette University Law School has been committed to training men and women to serve the public interest by becoming highly skilled and ethical attorneys. Traditionally, the curriculum has emphasized the practical aspects of legal education. In recent years, that emphasis has expanded to include particular excellence in the areas of intellectual property, dispute resolution, sports law, labor and employment law, criminal law, family law, and litigation-related courses. The National Sports Law Institute, the premier sports law program in the US, is a part of the Law School. Our nearly 7,000 alumni serve in a broad range of legal, public, and corporate positions throughout the US.

The Law School is located on the university campus—two blocks from the state courthouse and a short walk from the federal courthouse and downtown Milwaukee. Marquette is the only law school in southeast Wisconsin. Marquette—a Catholic, Jesuit, and urban university—is the largest private university in the state. The Catholic and Jesuit nature of the school translates into a specific concern for the well-being of each individual, whether he or she is a student, a legal client, or the victim of a crime. Persons of all religious backgrounds attend Marquette, serve on our faculty, and are valued in our community. The Law School is committed to academic freedom, the broadest possible scope of inquiry, and the examination of any subject.

Milwaukee is a lively city on Lake Michigan, 90 miles north of Chicago. Wisconsin's largest city, with a metropolitan-area population of about 1.5 million, Milwaukee retains the appeal of a small town. Clean and well run, it is known for its many ethnic festivals and the variety of its cuisine.

■ Enrollment/Student Body

Within the Marquette Law School community, people know and care about one another. Our students come together from almost 200 different colleges and universities. They hail from more than 40 states, as well as from a handful of foreign countries. Our faculty includes 40 full-time professors in addition to prominent practicing attorneys and judges who serve as adjunct professors.

Law students at Marquette represent a broad range of backgrounds, beliefs, and life experiences. Students of color comprise about 13 percent of the student body. We respect our different traditions and believe diversity enriches the legal education we offer.

■ Library and Physical Facilities

In Summer 2010, the Law School moves into an entirely new structure, Eckstein Hall. This state-of-the-art "green" building is roughly twice the size of, and located just one block south of, the former facility. Eckstein Hall features the latest technology, and houses a full-service café, a conference center, a fitness center, and two courtrooms. For more information on this exciting project, including the path-breaking four-level "library without borders," please visit http://law.marquette.edu/ecksteinhall/plans.

■ Curriculum

The Law School offers full- and part-time programs leading to the JD degree. The Law School's curriculum is rooted in core courses that include consideration of the theoretical underpinnings of the law as well as the practical application of substantive legal concepts. The curriculum is national in focus and scope and emphasizes the skills and values necessary to be a competent and ethical lawyer as well as a contributing citizen and community leader. Our adjunct faculty includes many of the state's outstanding practitioners who supplement required and core courses by teaching a broad range of electives.

Students may earn a **JD/MBA** through the Law School and the College of Business Administration; of special note is the JD/MBA with a **sports business** concentration. Joint programs with the graduate school allow students to earn a **JD/MA** in **international affairs**, the **history of philosophy**, **social and applied philosophy**, or **political science**. The Law School offers a joint program with Marquette University's graduate program in dispute resolution that allows a student to graduate with a **JD** and a **certificate** in **dispute resolution**. In conjunction with the Medical College of Wisconsin, we offer the **JD/MA** in **bioethics**. Each joint-degree program requires meeting all requirements of both the Law School and the other degree-granting institution; typically, each program can be completed in four years. As an alternative to a joint degree, law students may take up to six hours of coursework in a related graduate program at Marquette, such as public policy, sociology, philosophy, or history.

■ Special Programs

Our comprehensive trial practice courses provide an exceptional opportunity for students to develop trial skills. Distinctive clinics include the prosecutor and defender clinics, judicial internships, and numerous supervised field work opportunities.

Marquette University Law School's sports law program provides a comprehensive offering of sports law courses and student internships with sports organizations, as well as opportunities for membership on the *Marquette Sports Law Review* and the sports law moot court team. Our broad, well-rounded curriculum is designed to provide students with both theoretical and practical education concerning legal regulation of the amateur and professional sports industries. Law students who fulfill certain requirements are eligible to earn a **sports law certificate** in addition to the **JD**. More information on the program and the certificate may be found at *http://law.marquette.edu/jw/sports*.

The Law School's Restorative Justice Initiative (RJI) gives law students the opportunity to work with victims of crime, offenders, and community members toward repairing the harm that crime has caused. More information on the RJI may be found at *http://law.marquette.edu/jw/restorative*.

■ Admission and Financial Aid

Review of completed applications begins after October 1 and continues through the spring. Although the applicant's LSAT score and academic record are important considerations in the selection process, the Admissions Committee also

considers qualitative factors, such as letters of recommendation, essays, work experience, extracurricular activities, and personal accomplishments and characteristics that contribute to the diversity of the school, the legal community, and the profession. Admitted applicants are required to submit nonrefundable tuition deposits in April and June. These deposits are applied to the student's fall semester tuition. Interviews are not part of the application process.

Although most students finance their education through a combination of federal and private loan programs, all applicants offered admission are automatically considered for merit scholarship awards. Additionally, the Law School has recently established a Loan Repayment Assistance Program (LRAP) to help graduates in government service or public interest practice repay the cost of their educational loans. More information on LRAP may be found at *http://law.marquette.edu/jw/lrap*.

■ Diploma Privilege

Since 1933, graduates of the Law School who qualify have been admitted to the practice of law in Wisconsin without having to take the Wisconsin Bar Examination. Marquette graduates are entitled to sit for bar examinations in any American jurisdiction.

■ Student Activities

The Law School publishes the *Marquette Law Review*, the *Marquette Sports Law Review*, the *Marquette Intellectual Property Law Review*, and the *Marquette Elder's Advisor* (elder law journal). Students may develop advocacy skills in moot court competitions. Marquette moot court teams have won regional titles and championships in national competitions. A wide variety of student organizations are active at the Law School. A listing of student groups and descriptions of their activities may be found on the Law School's website.

■ Career Services

The Career Planning Center (CPC) processes hundreds of listings of employment opportunities, coordinates campus interviews, and provides counseling assistance to students. In recent years, approximately 95 percent of our graduates secured employment within nine months of graduation. Our on-campus interview program includes a broad range of legal employers. The CPC will help students network with Marquette alumni and other potential resource persons. Our goals are to keep our placement rate high and to ensure a good fit and job satisfaction for all our graduates.

■ Housing

Ample, affordable housing is available throughout Milwaukee and its suburbs. Information and assistance on securing housing may be obtained from the Office of University Apartments and Off-campus Student Services; telephone: 414.288.7281, Web: *www.marquette.edu/orl/apartments/services.shtml*.

Applicant Profile

Marquette University Law School
This grid includes only applicants who earned 120–180 LSAT scores under standard administrations.

LSAT Score	3.75 +		3.50–3.74		3.25–3.49		3.00–3.24		2.75–2.99		2.50–2.74		2.25–2.49		2.00–2.24		Below 2.00		No GPA		Total	
	Apps	Adm	Apps	Adm	Apps	Adm	Apps	Adm	Apps	Adm	Apps	Adm	Apps	Adm	Apps	Adm	Apps	Adm	Apps	Adm	Apps	Adm
175–180	0	0	1	1	0	0	0	0	0	0	0	0	0	0	0	0	0	0	0	0	1	1
170–174	0	0	1	1	3	1	0	0	2	2	1	1	1	0	0	0	0	0	0	0	8	5
165–169	7	7	4	4	9	8	4	4	2	1	4	3	3	2	0	0	0	0	0	0	33	29
160–164	32	29	46	41	64	56	36	31	20	15	28	17	8	4	2	0	3	0	2	1	241	194
155–159	86	79	137	121	139	103	131	83	64	43	29	8	20	5	3	0	1	0	7	5	617	447
150–154	97	50	151	68	166	44	132	38	75	11	36	4	14	1	5	0	3	0	3	0	682	216
145–149	22	4	67	8	71	6	59	6	47	2	28	1	14	1	5	0	2	0	5	1	320	29
140–144	6	0	10	0	28	1	43	0	21	0	20	0	11	0	4	0	1	0	3	1	147	2
135–139	1	0	4	0	4	0	7	0	11	0	6	0	2	0	2	0	0	0	2	0	39	0
130–134	1	0	0	0	2	0	0	0	5	0	2	0	3	0	1	0	2	0	1	0	17	0
125–129	0	0	0	0	0	0	0	0	0	0	0	0	1	0	0	0	1	0	3	0	5	0
120–124	0	0	0	0	0	0	0	0	0	0	0	0	0	0	1	0	0	0	0	0	1	0
Total	252	169	421	244	486	219	412	162	247	74	154	34	77	13	23	0	13	0	26	8	2111	923

Apps = Number of Applicants
Adm = Number Admitted
Reflects 99% of the total applicant pool; average LSAT data reported.

University of Maryland School of Law

500 West Baltimore Street
Baltimore, MD 21201-1786
Phone: 410.706.3492; Fax: 410.706.1793
E-mail: admissions@law.umaryland.edu; Website: www.law.umaryland.edu

The Basics

Type of school	Public
Term	Semester
Application deadline	3/15
Application fee	$70
Financial aid deadline	3/1
Can first year start other than fall?	No
Student to faculty ratio	11.7 to 1
# of housing spaces available restricted to law students graduate housing for which law students are eligible	425

Faculty and Administrators

	Total		Men		Women		Minorities	
	Spr	Fall	Spr	Fall	Spr	Fall	Spr	Fall
Full-time	57	64	26	28	31	36	14	12
Other full-time	1	2	0	0	1	2	0	0
Deans, librarians, & others who teach	12	12	5	5	7	7	1	2
Part-time	89	50	62	35	27	15	6	5
Total	159	128	93	68	66	60	21	19

Curriculum

	Full-Time	Part-Time
Typical first-year section size	78	74
Is there typically a "small section" of the first-year class, other than Legal Writing, taught by full-time faculty	Yes	Yes
If yes, typical size offered last year	26	25
# of classroom course titles beyond first-year curriculum	223	

# of upper division courses, excluding seminars, with an enrollment:		
Under 25	131	
25–49	20	
50–74	10	
75–99	2	
100+	2	

# of seminars	87	
# of seminar positions available	1,212	
# of seminar positions filled	893	125
# of positions available in simulation courses	753	
# of simulation positions filled	572	78
# of positions available in faculty supervised clinical courses	380	
# of faculty supervised clinical positions filled	291	16
# involved in field placements	246	26
# involved in law journals	195	8
# involved in moot court or trial competitions	58	5
# of credit hours required to graduate	85	

JD Enrollment and Ethnicity

	Men		Women		Full-Time		Part-Time		1st-Year		Total		JD Degs. Awd.
	#	%	#	%	#	%	#	%	#	%	#	%	
African Amer.	52	10.9	68	14.3	87	12.0	33	14.3	32	10.6	120	12.6	26
Amer. Indian	2	0.4	2	0.4	3	0.4	1	0.4	0	0.0	4	0.4	2
Asian Amer.	50	10.5	53	11.1	81	11.2	22	9.6	38	12.6	103	10.8	30
Mex. Amer.	1	0.2	0	0.0	1	0.1	0	0.0	0	0.0	1	0.1	0
Puerto Rican	0	0.0	0	0.0	0	0.0	0	0.0	0	0.0	0	0.0	0
Hispanic	30	6.3	42	8.8	58	8.0	14	6.1	19	6.3	72	7.6	21
Total Minority	135	28.3	165	34.7	230	31.8	70	30.4	89	29.6	300	31.5	79
For. Nation.	7	1.5	5	1.1	10	1.4	2	0.9	3	1.0	12	1.3	5
Caucasian	324	67.9	291	61.1	459	63.5	156	67.8	202	67.1	615	64.5	154
Unknown	11	2.3	15	3.2	24	3.3	2	0.9	7	2.3	26	2.7	4
Total	477	50.1	476	49.9	723	75.9	230	24.1	301	31.6	953		242

Transfers

Transfers in	25
Transfers out	7

Tuition and Fees

	Resident	Nonresident
Full-time	$23,762	$35,041
Part-time	$18,053	$26,512
Tuition Guarantee Program	N	

Living Expenses

Estimated living expenses for singles

Living on campus	Living off campus	Living at home
$20,889	$26,559	$14,199

University of Maryland School of Law

ABA
Approved
Since
1930

GPA and LSAT Scores

	Total	Full-Time	Part-Time
# of apps	3,608	3,073	535
# of offers	699	588	111
# of matrics	298	226	72
75% GPA	3.66	3.67	3.61
Median GPA	3.46	3.50	3.31
25% GPA	3.21	3.29	3.12
75% LSAT	166	167	161
Median LSAT	161	162	158
25% LSAT	159	161	154

Grants and Scholarships (from prior year)

	Total #	Total %	Full-Time #	Full-Time %	Part-Time #	Part-Time %
Total # of students	897		714		183	
Total # receiving grants	461	51.4	415	58.1	46	25.1
Less than 1/2 tuition	385	42.9	342	47.9	43	23.5
Half to full tuition	75	8.4	72	10.1	3	1.6
Full tuition	1	0.1	1	0.1	0	0.0
More than full tuition	0	0.0	0	0.0	0	0.0
Median grant amount			$3,571		$3,000	

Informational and Library Resources

Total amount spent on library materials	$1,465,063
Study seating capacity inside the library	490
# of full-time equivalent professional librarians	11
Hours per week library is open	107
# of open, wired connections available to students	1,209
# of networked computers available for use by students	193
Has wireless network?	Y
Require computer?	Y

JD Attrition (from prior year)

	Academic #	Other #	Total #	Total %
1st year	2	9	11	3.6
2nd year	1	2	3	1.0
3rd year	0	0	0	0.0
4th year	0	0	0	0.0

Employment (9 months after graduation)

	Total	Percentage
Employment status known	249	96.5
Employment status unknown	9	3.5
Employed	234	94.0
Pursuing graduate degrees	4	1.6
Unemployed (seeking, not seeking, or studying for the bar)	7	2.8
Type of Employment		
# employed in law firms	93	39.7
# employed in business and industry	36	15.4
# employed in government	34	14.5
# employed in public interest	14	6.0
# employed as judicial clerks	43	18.4
# employed in academia	14	6.0
Geographic Location		
# employed in state	136	58.1
# employed in foreign countries	0	0.0
# of states where employed	27	

Bar Passage Rates

First-time takers	247	Reporting %	77.33
Average school %	90.05	Average state %	85.51
Average pass difference	4.54		

Jurisdiction	Takers	Passers	Pass %	State %	Diff %
Maryland	191	172	90.05	85.51	4.54

University of Maryland School of Law

500 West Baltimore Street
Baltimore, MD 21201-1786
Phone: 410.706.3492; Fax: 410.706.1793
E-mail: admissions@law.umaryland.edu; Website: www.law.umaryland.edu

■ Introduction

The University of Maryland School of Law was established in 1816, making it one of the oldest law schools in the nation. Currently, its innovative programs, renowned faculty, and superb student body make it one of the liveliest, most vibrant, and diverse law schools today.

Maryland School of Law offers a wide range of course offerings, which incorporates cutting-edge legal issues into a well-established and nationally recognized legal curriculum. The law school offers a variety of highly regarded programs and initiatives including Environmental, Healthcare, Business, and International Law. Additionally, Maryland has an institutional commitment to preparing students for career success, and a welcoming community dedicated to developing each student's talents fully. The law school is also committed to instilling a spirit of public service in all its students and provides unparalleled opportunities for experiential learning in pursuit of the public interest. The law school's new, state-of-the-art facility is ideally located in the Baltimore-Washington corridor, presenting a broad range of educational and career opportunities.

Maryland students are recruited by many of the nation's most respected law firms. They assume positions of leadership as lawyers and judges; business executives and community advocates; legislators and policymakers; and other agents of social, political, and economic progress.

Maryland School of Law is fully accredited by the ABA, is a member of the AALS, and has a chapter of the Order of the Coif.

■ Community of Students, Faculty, and Alumni

At Maryland, entering students quickly become part of a supportive community. We are diverse in age, gender, race, academic background, and prior employment, and this diversity is reflected in our students and in our faculty and deans. Our faculty are national leaders in a wide range of subject areas, and they are readily available to support and advise students. Smaller classes and an 11:1 student-to-faculty ratio enable close working relationships to develop in a professional and intellectually vibrant setting.

Many resources are available to students to ease their transition to law school. Students also directly benefit from a wide network of engaged alumni who occupy positions of professional leadership throughout the state, region, and nation. By acting as mentors, volunteer judges, and adjunct faculty, alumni help connect each student's law school experience with the professional life of the surrounding legal community.

■ Location

Maryland Law's location in the Baltimore-Washington corridor is among our greatest assets. Our state-of-the-art facility sits just a few blocks from Baltimore's beautiful Inner Harbor and Camden Yards, and—along with the rest of the burgeoning University of Maryland, Baltimore (UMB) campus—is playing a vital role in the city's downtown renaissance.

The law school is also a short commute from Capitol Hill and Maryland's capital in Annapolis, providing our students unique access to all levels of the federal and state government and judiciary. Students take full advantage of our proximity to Washington, DC, pursuing externships and careers with leading national law firms, public interest groups, government agencies, and other organizations of prominence.

Our proximity to the other professional schools on the UMB campus allows us to offer an array of interdisciplinary course and joint-degree programs. These offerings produce sophisticated graduates who are prepared to practice in an environment of increasing complexity.

■ Law School Complex and Library

The School of Law and the Thurgood Marshall Law Library occupy a state-of-the-art complex that supports the school's programs integrating classroom and experiential learning. The facility boasts three courtrooms, including the Ceremonial Courtroom, where state and federal trial and appellate courts regularly sit in session to hear cases. Our classrooms and courtrooms are equipped with the latest in educational technology, as well as wired and wireless Internet access for student use. In addition to their own notebook computers, students can use public computers located throughout the facility for writing and research.

The Thurgood Marshall Law Library houses a collection of about 508,800 volumes and equivalents accessible through the online catalog. A staff of 25, including 11 librarians, provides customized reference and consulting services to faculty and students. In addition to LexisNexis and Westlaw, the library offers an extensive array of legal and nonlegal Web-based electronic databases. Seating in the library includes carrels, tables in attractive reading rooms, and comfortable lounge areas, all located in spaces full of natural light.

■ Curriculum and Specialty Programs

The rigorous core curriculum at Maryland forms the basis for more specialized study through over 200 elective courses, seminars, independent studies, simulations, clinics, and externships. Also, each student must satisfy an advanced writing requirement by producing a substantial paper based on extensive research. Full-time students generally complete the Juris Doctor curriculum in three years; evening students typically complete the program in four years.

Maryland Law is home to several nationally recognized specialty programs. These programs are a magnet for leading faculty from across the country as they provide opportunities for in-depth scholarship and teaching. Three of our specialty programs—Law and Health Care, Environmental Law, and Clinical Law—have established national reputations for excellence. Our other specialty areas include Advocacy; Business Law; Intellectual Property Law; International and Comparative Law; Legislation and Public Policy; and Women, Leadership, and Equality.

Regardless of what course of study they pursue, students can expect a challenging law school experience that will cultivate depth of understanding and clarity of thought, the hallmarks of the most successful lawyers.

Clinical Law Program

Through the Cardin Requirement, named after our alumnus US Senator Benjamin Cardin, each full-time day student gains hands-on legal experience by representing actual clients who would otherwise lack access to justice. Our legal clinic is among the best and largest teaching law firms in the nation. In addition to in-house clinical work, students may gain experience in public and private nonprofit externships in the Baltimore-Washington region.

Dual Degrees and Interdisciplinary Study

Today's lawyer must practice in an environment of increasing sophistication. Maryland Law offers several dual-degree programs in partnership with other leading academic institutions in the region. Dual-degree programs include Business Administration, Community Planning, Criminal Justice, Liberal Arts, Pharmacy, Public Policy, Public Health, Public Management, Nursing, and Social Work.

Admission

Maryland School of Law's faculty believe that the quality of legal education is directly affected by the diversity of our students. The admission committee selects applicants who have the greatest potential for succeeding in law school studies and whose background, character, and experience will contribute to the diversity that we believe is important.

The factors we consider in the admissions file evaluation process include geographic origin; cultural and language background; barriers overcome; and extracurricular pursuits, work, leadership activities, and service or social experiences. The personal statement and letters of recommendation are the primary means for candidates to convey this information.

First-year students are admitted only in the fall. The School of Law uses a rolling admission process, reviewing applications in the order in which files are completed. Applications should be filed as early as possible after September 1 of the year preceding enrollment and before March 1. Applicants are encouraged to complete the application early; applications completed later may be at a competitive disadvantage. Residency may be a factor in close cases. Applicants are encouraged to visit the school, but interviews are not part of the admission process.

Student Activities

The law school is home to over 40 active and diverse student-run organizations. Students enforce the law school's honor code, participate in inter- and intraschool advocacy competitions, and volunteer in the local community and in gulf regions affected by Hurricane Katrina. Students can further their writing and editing expertise by participating in one of the five student-edited scholarly journals or serving as a writing center fellow. The Office of Student Affairs provides group and one-on-one academic advising to students at all stages of their legal education, leadership education to student leaders, and financial literacy workshops for all interested students.

Scholarships and Need-Based Financial Assistance

The School of Law offers a limited number of scholarships and traditional need-based financial aid assistance. All applicants are considered for the scholarship program based on the totality of the information available in the applicant's admission file and evidence of potential unique contributions to the academic and cocurricular programs, as well as student life. Such potential should be clearly described in the personal statement, résumé, and other admission documents. All admitted applicants **must** file the FAFSA as soon after January 1 as possible in order to be considered for scholarships or need-based financial assistance.

Career Development

Students at Maryland benefit from extensive connections to the bar, judiciary, business and industry, government, and community organizations in Maryland; Washington, DC; and beyond. Our Career Development Office offers a multitude of expert services and professional resources to help students and alumni launch their legal careers.

In the most recent survey, 94 percent of our 2008 graduates were employed, pursuing advanced degrees, or not seeking immediate employment. Graduates chose a variety of professional positions: 40 percent were in private practice, 18 percent in judicial clerkships, 15 percent in government and other public service, 15 percent in business and industry, 6 percent in public interest organizations, and 6 percent in academia.

Applicant Profile

The University of Maryland School of Law's admission policy focuses on the academic potential of applicants coupled with a flexible assessment of applicants' talents, experiences, and potential to contribute to the learning of those around them. Each applicant is evaluated on the basis of all the information available in their file, including UPGA, LSAT score, a personal statement, letters of recommendation, résumé, advanced degrees, professional accomplishments, and other related information.

The University of Memphis—Cecil C. Humphreys School of Law

One North Front Street
Memphis, TN 38103-2189
Phone: 901.678.5403; Fax: 901.678.0741
E-mail: lawadmissions@memphis.edu; Website: www.memphis.edu/law

ABA
Approved
Since
1965

The Basics

Type of school	Public
Term	Semester
Application deadline	3/1
Application fee	$25
Financial aid deadline	4/15
Can first year start other than fall?	No
Student to faculty ratio	17.7 to 1
# of housing spaces available restricted to law students	
graduate housing for which law students are eligible	125

Faculty and Administrators

	Total		Men		Women		Minorities	
	Spr	Fall	Spr	Fall	Spr	Fall	Spr	Fall
Full-time	20	18	13	11	7	7	2	2
Other full-time	1	1	0	0	1	1	0	0
Deans, librarians, & others who teach	4	4	3	3	1	1	0	0
Part-time	26	26	19	18	7	8	5	3
Total	51	49	35	32	16	17	7	5

Curriculum

		Full-Time	Part-Time
Typical first-year section size		75	0
Is there typically a "small section" of the first-year class, other than Legal Writing, taught by full-time faculty		No	No
If yes, typical size offered last year			
# of classroom course titles beyond first-year curriculum		62	
# of upper division courses, excluding seminars, with an enrollment:	Under 25	29	
	25–49	24	
	50–74	10	
	75–99	7	
	100+	1	
# of seminars		9	
# of seminar positions available		108	
# of seminar positions filled		90	0
# of positions available in simulation courses		197	
# of simulation positions filled		176	0
# of positions available in faculty supervised clinical courses		40	
# of faculty supervised clinical positions filled	39	0	
# involved in field placements	26	0	
# involved in law journals	58	0	
# involved in moot court or trial competitions	36	0	
# of credit hours required to graduate		90	

JD Enrollment and Ethnicity

	Men		Women		Full-Time		Part-Time		1st-Year		Total		JD Degs. Awd.
	#	%	#	%	#	%	#	%	#	%	#	%	
African Amer.	12	4.9	28	15.8	23	5.9	17	60.7	16	10.0	40	9.5	12
Amer. Indian	3	1.2	0	0.0	1	0.3	2	7.1	2	1.3	3	0.7	2
Asian Amer.	4	1.6	5	2.8	7	1.8	2	7.1	6	3.8	9	2.1	4
Mex. Amer.	0	0.0	0	0.0	0	0.0	0	0.0	0	0.0	0	0.0	0
Puerto Rican	0	0.0	0	0.0	0	0.0	0	0.0	0	0.0	0	0.0	0
Hispanic	4	1.6	3	1.7	6	1.5	1	3.6	3	1.9	7	1.7	0
Total Minority	23	9.5	36	20.3	37	9.4	22	78.6	27	16.9	59	14.0	18
For. Nation.	0	0.0	0	0.0	0	0.0	0	0.0	0	0.0	0	0.0	0
Caucasian	213	87.7	135	76.3	342	87.2	6	21.4	124	77.5	348	82.9	99
Unknown	7	2.9	6	3.4	13	3.3	0	0.0	9	5.6	13	3.1	0
Total	243	57.9	177	42.1	392	93.3	28	6.7	160	38.1	420		117

Transfers

Transfers in	2
Transfers out	3

Tuition and Fees

	Resident	Nonresident
Full-time	$13,570	$35,442
Part-time	$12,800	$32,680
Tuition Guarantee Program		N

Living Expenses

Estimated living expenses for singles

Living on campus	Living off campus	Living at home
$14,620	$14,620	$9,215

The University of Memphis—Cecil C. Humphreys School of Law

ABA
Approved
Since
1965

GPA and LSAT Scores

	Total	Full-Time	Part-Time
# of apps	951	905	46
# of offers	303	293	10
# of matrics	143	136	7
75% GPA	3.68	3.68	3.69
Median GPA	3.43	3.43	3.44
25% GPA	3.16	3.17	3.22
75% LSAT	158	158	156
Median LSAT	156	156	154
25% LSAT	153	153	150

Grants and Scholarships (from prior year)

	Total #	Total %	Full-Time #	Full-Time %	Part-Time #	Part-Time %
Total # of students	414		395		19	
Total # receiving grants	128	30.9	114	28.9	14	73.7
Less than 1/2 tuition	49	11.8	41	10.4	8	42.1
Half to full tuition	59	14.3	54	13.7	5	26.3
Full tuition	13	3.1	12	3.0	1	5.3
More than full tuition	7	1.7	7	1.8	0	0.0
Median grant amount			$8,891		$4,633	

Informational and Library Resources

Total amount spent on library materials	$938,530
Study seating capacity inside the library	203
# of full-time equivalent professional librarians	3
Hours per week library is open	100
# of open, wired connections available to students	71
# of networked computers available for use by students	50
Has wireless network?	Y
Require computer?	N

JD Attrition (from prior year)

	Academic #	Other #	Total #	Total %
1st year	3	7	10	6.8
2nd year	3	2	5	3.6
3rd year	0	0	0	0.0
4th year	0	0	0	0.0

Employment (9 months after graduation)

	Total	Percentage
Employment status known	127	97.7
Employment status unknown	3	2.3
Employed	112	88.2
Pursuing graduate degrees	3	2.4
Unemployed (seeking, not seeking, or studying for the bar)	6	4.7
Type of Employment		
# employed in law firms	78	69.6
# employed in business and industry	12	10.7
# employed in government	10	8.9
# employed in public interest	4	3.6
# employed as judicial clerks	6	5.4
# employed in academia	2	1.8
Geographic Location		
# employed in state	99	88.4
# employed in foreign countries	0	0.0
# of states where employed	12	

Bar Passage Rates

First-time takers	122	Reporting %	95.08
Average school %	93.10	Average state %	88.10
Average pass difference	5.00		

Jurisdiction	Takers	Passers	Pass %	State %	Diff %
Tennessee	116	108	93.10	88.10	5.00

The University of Memphis—Cecil C. Humphreys School of Law

One North Front Street
Memphis, TN 38103-2189
Phone: 901.678.5403; Fax: 901.678.0741
E-mail: lawadmissions@memphis.edu; Website: www.memphis.edu/law

■ History of the School of Law

The Cecil C. Humphreys School of Law at the University of Memphis was established in response to widespread interest in developing a full-time accredited legal preparation program to serve Memphis and West Tennessee. The Cecil C. Humphreys School of Law opened in 1962 and was accredited by the American Bar Association (ABA) in 1965. The school was named in honor of Cecil C. Humphreys, then-president of Memphis State University and an educator of great distinction. Dr. Humphreys led the group that worked with the state legislature and the ABA to accredit the law school. The school is also an active member of the Association of American Law Schools (AALS).

Since its inception, the School of Law has graduated over 5,000 students and continues its tradition of preparing competent and ethical attorneys. Our graduates can be found throughout the United States, employed in private practice, federal and state judiciaries, corporate boardrooms, government agencies, and public service organizations.

■ Memphis and the School of Law

Memphis is one of the South's largest, most beautiful, and most diverse cities. Memphis has one of the lowest cost-of-living rates of any major US city, and its temperate climate provides ample opportunity for year-round activities. Memphis has a rich history and an unmatched musical heritage.

The School of Law brings together unique individuals with a wide variety of cultural, geographical, employment, and academic backgrounds. Many of its students come to law school immediately after finishing their undergraduate education; however, a significant number have been in the workforce or have completed advanced degrees. The diversity within the student body enriches the classroom experience for all students and enhances the overall quality of the educational program.

The University of Memphis has been rated by *preLaw* magazine as one of its "best value" law schools. This publication recognizes that Memphis is among schools that can boast a high bar exam passage rate, a strong job placement rate for graduates, and affordable tuition.

In January 2010, the School of Law began classes in the newly renovated US Custom House and Post Office located in the heart of legal, business, and cultural districts in downtown Memphis. This beautiful state-of-the-art building offers a magnificent view of the Mississippi River and is within blocks of numerous law offices and both state and federal courthouses.

■ The University of Memphis

The University of Memphis serves as a regional center for education, service, and research, and is linked historically, intellectually, and emotionally with its community. It is a learner-centered metropolitan research university that enrolls over 21,000 students and is accredited by the Commission on Colleges of the Southern Association of Colleges and Schools.

■ Curriculum

The School of Law offers a full-time day program and a part-time day program. The challenging curriculum prepares our students for the practice of law. The curriculum reflects a commitment to traditional legal education, and academic emphasis is placed on fundamental lawyering skills and areas of knowledge.

■ Lawyering Skills, Legal Clinics, and Externships

The School of Law provides the opportunity to take upper-level courses in lawyering skills, including trial advocacy, mediation, and alternative dispute resolution. Upper-division students may receive class credit and practical experience through our Externship and Clinic Programs. Externship positions are offered in US District Courts, including the Bankruptcy Court, the US Attorney's Office, state and federal judicial offices, the National Labor Relations Board (NLRB), the Shelby County District Attorney General's Office and Public Defender's Office, and the Memphis Area Legal Services (MALS) Office. Spring 2010 clinic offerings include Child and Family Litigation, Civil Litigation, Elder Law, and Small Business. Students enrolled in the legal clinic courses are specially admitted to practice by the Tennessee Supreme Court and represent indigent clients referred through Memphis Area Legal Services or children in abuse and neglect cases, terminations of parental rights, adoptions, and other civil legal matters as referred through appointment by the juvenile court.

■ Joint- and Dual-Degree Programs

The School of Law and the Fogelman College of Business and Economics offer a coordinated degree program leading to both the JD and MBA degrees. The purpose of this program is to allow students to study both business management and law. This joint degree enables students to complete both the JD and MBA in considerably less time than would be required to complete each degree separately.

The School of Law and the Department of Political Science offer a dual degree leading to both the JD and MA degrees. Credit toward degrees in these disciplines can be earned simultaneously if admission and curricula are carefully structured. Students can complete both degrees in less time than would normally be required to complete each degree separately.

■ Library and Information Technology

The University of Memphis law library serves students, faculty, the legal community, and the public with reference services and access to its collection of print and electronic resources. The law library occupies five levels of the historic School of Law building and offers students many options for study—from study rooms to a three-sided glass reading room overlooking the Mississippi River. Students have access to computers in labs and open study areas. There is wireless access throughout the building.

■ Student Programs and Activities

The *University of Memphis Law Review* is a scholarly journal edited and staffed entirely by students. Law review members

The University of Memphis—Cecil C. Humphreys School of Law

have numerous opportunities to improve their legal research, writing, and editing skills.

The Moot Court Board (MCB) is composed of 20 third-year students who are dedicated to the development of advocacy skills. In addition to intraschool competitions, the law school fields several teams in national moot court and mock trial competitions. In recent years, the University of Memphis teams have earned national recognition by finishing in the final round of both major national moot court competitions. This national recognition garnered an invitation to the Moot Court National Championship in 2009.

The Student Bar Association (SBA) is the student government of the law school. The SBA coordinates a wide variety of activities, ranging from social events to a Speaker Series. Students can also choose from many other student groups, ranging from legal fraternities to special interest organizations.

■ Admission

Applicants are initially evaluated by the Admissions Office based on a weighed combination of LSAT score and cumulative undergraduate GPA as calculated by the Law School Admission Council. Those not admitted, or rejected, as a result of this evaluation will be reviewed by the Faculty Admission Committee using nonquantifiable factors such as quality of the applicant's undergraduate institution, level and rigor of coursework, letters of recommendation, graduate work, employment during and after college, extracurricular activities, educational diversity, and state of residence. In an attempt to attract a diverse student population, the school has developed a selection process that reviews the merits of all qualified applicants but assures that admission is based on a comprehensive range of criteria demonstrated to be predictive of success in law school.

■ Career Services

The Career Services Office actively assists students and alumni by helping them develop their interest in specific areas of the law, enhancing their professional skills, and providing information about opportunities for legal employment. A comprehensive national Internet job bank as well as a network of alumni mentors are available to help students who are interested in law careers beyond the Memphis area.

In addition to hosting a large number of firms, corporations, and public interest/governmental employers for on-campus interviewing and seminars, the School of Law is a member of several organizations that conduct annual recruiting conferences.

Employment statistics for Memphis law graduates have remained consistently high during the last decade. Of those known graduates seeking legal employment in the graduating class of 2008, 95 percent were employed within nine months of graduation, as reported to the Association for Legal Career Professionals (NALP). Memphis has graduates practicing in all 50 states and in several foreign countries.

■ Tennessee Institute for Pre-Law

Applicants from Tennessee, as well as Crittenden County, Arkansas, and De Soto, Marshall, Tate, and Tunica counties in Mississippi are eligible to apply for the Tennessee Institute for Pre-Law (TIP) program, which facilitates law school admission for students from diverse backgrounds who do not meet traditional academic standards for admission. Participants who successfully complete the program will be guaranteed admission to the law school. The TIP program is available to all applicants who will have met the requirements for a baccalaureate degree prior to May 31. The TIP program is a five-week program of classroom instruction that simulates the first-year law school curriculum. The program is held at the University of Memphis School of Law and begins the first week of June.

Applicant Profile

The University of Memphis—Cecil C. Humphreys School of Law
This grid includes only applicants who earned 120–180 LSAT scores under standard administrations.

LSAT Score	GPA																				
	3.75 +		3.50–3.74		3.25–3.49		3.00–3.24		2.75–2.99		2.50–2.74		2.25–2.49		2.00–2.24		Below 2.00		No GPA		Total	
	Apps	Adm	Apps	Adm	Apps	Adm	Apps	Adm	Apps	Adm	Apps	Adm	Apps	Adm	Apps	Adm	Apps	Adm	Apps	Adm	Apps	Adm
175–180	0	0	0	0	0	0	0	0	0	0	0	0	0	0	0	0	0	0	0	0	0	0
170–174	1	1	0	0	0	0	0	0	0	0	1	1	0	0	0	0	0	0	0	0	2	2
165–169	6	5	3	3	1	1	4	2	3	2	1	1	0	0	0	0	0	0	0	0	18	14
160–164	9	9	9	9	6	4	11	8	6	5	5	4	1	0	3	0	0	0	1	0	51	39
155–159	30	23	38	34	49	31	41	27	15	6	11	5	10	3	6	0	0	0	0	0	200	129
150–154	33	25	55	31	63	28	51	14	28	7	20	3	13	1	2	0	1	0	0	0	266	109
145–149	17	1	22	2	47	2	49	3	25	0	14	1	12	0	5	0	1	0	1	0	193	9
140–144	5	0	15	0	22	1	27	2	16	0	21	0	13	0	5	0	1	0	1	0	126	3
135–139	1	0	7	0	6	0	13	0	9	0	16	0	5	0	3	0	0	0	3	0	63	0
130–134	2	0	4	0	1	0	7	0	3	0	3	0	4	0	3	0	0	0	0	0	27	0
125–129	0	0	0	0	1	0	1	0	2	0	2	0	1	0	1	0	0	0	0	0	8	0
120–124	0	0	0	0	0	0	0	0	0	0	0	0	0	0	1	0	0	0	0	0	1	0
Total	104	64	153	79	196	67	204	56	107	20	94	15	59	4	29	0	3	0	6	0	955	305

Apps = Number of Applicants   Adm = Number Admitted   Reflects 99% of the total applicant pool; average LSAT data reported.

Mercer University—Walter F. George School of Law

Office of Admissions, 1021 Georgia Avenue
Macon, GA 31207
Phone: 478.301.2605; Fax: 478.301.2989
E-mail: martin_sv@law.mercer.edu; Website: www.law.mercer.edu

ABA
Approved
Since
1925

AMERICAN BAR ASSOCIATION
Section of Legal Education
and Admissions to the Bar

The Basics

Type of school	Private
Term	Semester
Application deadline	3/15
Application fee	$50
Financial aid deadline	4/1
Can first year start other than fall?	No
Student to faculty ratio	13.0 to 1
# of housing spaces available restricted to law students	
graduate housing for which law students are eligible	32

Faculty and Administrators

	Total		Men		Women		Minorities	
	Spr	Fall	Spr	Fall	Spr	Fall	Spr	Fall
Full-time	27	29	18	19	9	10	3	3
Other full-time	0	0	0	0	0	0	0	0
Deans, librarians, & others who teach	8	8	4	4	4	4	0	0
Part-time	33	17	26	13	7	4	1	1
Total	68	54	48	36	20	18	4	4

Curriculum

		Full-Time	Part-Time
Typical first-year section size		73	0
Is there typically a "small section" of the first-year class, other than Legal Writing, taught by full-time faculty		Yes	No
If yes, typical size offered last year		25	
# of classroom course titles beyond first-year curriculum		112	
# of upper division courses, excluding seminars, with an enrollment:	Under 25	117	
	25–49	23	
	50–74	13	
	75–99	3	
	100+	0	
# of seminars		18	
# of seminar positions available		270	
# of seminar positions filled		190	0
# of positions available in simulation courses		903	
# of simulation positions filled		811	0
# of positions available in faculty supervised clinical courses		36	
# of faculty supervised clinical positions filled	28		0
# involved in field placements	101		0
# involved in law journals	48		0
# involved in moot court or trial competitions	59		0
# of credit hours required to graduate		91	

JD Enrollment and Ethnicity

	Men		Women		Full-Time		Part-Time		1st-Year		Total		JD Degs. Awd.
	#	%	#	%	#	%	#	%	#	%	#	%	
African Amer.	8	3.5	31	15.4	39	9.0	0	0.0	14	8.8	39	9.0	21
Amer. Indian	1	0.4	2	1.0	3	0.7	0	0.0	0	0.0	3	0.7	1
Asian Amer.	15	6.5	7	3.5	22	5.1	0	0.0	12	7.5	22	5.1	3
Mex. Amer.	0	0.0	0	0.0	0	0.0	0	0.0	0	0.0	0	0.0	0
Puerto Rican	2	0.9	0	0.0	2	0.5	0	0.0	0	0.0	2	0.5	2
Hispanic	2	0.9	3	1.5	5	1.2	0	0.0	4	2.5	5	1.2	5
Total Minority	28	12.2	43	21.4	71	16.5	0	0.0	30	18.8	71	16.5	32
For. Nation.	0	0.0	0	0.0	0	0.0	0	0.0	0	0.0	0	0.0	0
Caucasian	178	77.4	147	73.1	325	75.4	0	0.0	123	76.9	325	75.4	106
Unknown	24	10.4	11	5.5	35	8.1	0	0.0	7	4.4	35	8.1	21
Total	230	53.4	201	46.6	431	100.0	0	0.0	160	37.1	431		159

Transfers

Transfers in	6
Transfers out	12

Tuition and Fees

	Resident	Nonresident
Full-time	$34,330	$34,330
Part-time		
Tuition Guarantee Program		N

Living Expenses

Estimated living expenses for singles

Living on campus	Living off campus	Living at home
$16,000	$16,000	$16,000

Mercer University—Walter F. George School of Law

ABA
Approved
Since
1925

GPA and LSAT Scores

	Total	Full-Time	Part-Time
# of apps	1,571	1,571	0
# of offers	600	600	0
# of matrics	157	157	0
75% GPA	3.67	3.67	0.00
Median GPA	3.43	3.43	0.00
25% GPA	3.13	3.13	0.00
75% LSAT	158	158	0
Median LSAT	156	156	0
25% LSAT	153	153	0

Grants and Scholarships (from prior year)

	Total		Full-Time		Part-Time	
	#	%	#	%	#	%
Total # of students	443		443		0	
Total # receiving grants	134	30.2	134	30.2	0	0.0
Less than 1/2 tuition	57	12.9	57	12.9	0	0.0
Half to full tuition	22	5.0	22	5.0	0	0.0
Full tuition	33	7.4	33	7.4	0	0.0
More than full tuition	22	5.0	22	5.0	0	0.0
Median grant amount			$20,000		$0	

Informational and Library Resources

Total amount spent on library materials	$801,544
Study seating capacity inside the library	390
# of full-time equivalent professional librarians	6
Hours per week library is open	68
# of open, wired connections available to students	748
# of networked computers available for use by students	40
Has wireless network?	Y
Require computer?	Y

JD Attrition (from prior year)

	Academic	Other	Total	
	#	#	#	%
1st year	3	17	20	13.9
2nd year	0	0	0	0.0
3rd year	0	0	0	0.0
4th year	0	0	0	0.0

Employment (9 months after graduation)

	Total	Percentage
Employment status known	145	100.0
Employment status unknown	0	0.0
Employed	126	86.9
Pursuing graduate degrees	2	1.4
Unemployed (seeking, not seeking, or studying for the bar)	11	7.6
Type of Employment		
# employed in law firms	83	65.9
# employed in business and industry	6	4.8
# employed in government	23	18.3
# employed in public interest	4	3.2
# employed as judicial clerks	10	7.9
# employed in academia	0	0.0
Geographic Location		
# employed in state	102	81.0
# employed in foreign countries	0	0.0
# of states where employed	12	

Bar Passage Rates

First-time takers	144	Reporting %	83.33
Average school %	95.83	Average state %	89.27
Average pass difference	6.56		

Jurisdiction	Takers	Passers	Pass %	State %	Diff %
Georgia	120	115	95.83	89.27	6.56

Mercer University—Walter F. George School of Law

Office of Admissions, 1021 Georgia Avenue
Macon, GA 31207
Phone: 478.301.2605; Fax: 478.301.2989
E-mail: martin_sv@law.mercer.edu; Website: www.law.mercer.edu

■ Introduction

The Walter F. George School of Law of Mercer University is located in Macon, Georgia, about 80 miles south of Atlanta. Founded in 1873, it is one of the oldest private law schools in the nation. Named for a distinguished alumnus who served as a United States senator for 36 years, the school became a member of AALS in 1923 and has been ABA-approved since 1925. Mercer's distinctive Woodruff curriculum emphasizes small classes which create an educational environment that fosters genuine, meaningful relationships with faculty, fellow students, and Mercer Law alumni. The curriculum also provides an innovative progression in the course of study and a unique sixth semester designed to facilitate the transition from student to practicing lawyer.

■ Admission

Mercer University's Walter F. George School of Law accepts applications between September 1 and March 15 from prospective students wishing to begin their studies in the fall semester. Applicants must have completed a bachelor's degree prior to law school enrollment. They must register with the Credential Assembly Service (CAS) and take the LSAT, preferably in the summer or fall before application is made. Applicants must submit two letters of recommendation, an application fee, and a personal statement candidly discussing their strengths and weaknesses as prospective law students.

LSAT performance and undergraduate grades are very important in determining admission to Mercer Law School, but other factors will be considered to arrive at a fair evaluation of an applicant's potential to become a competent and ethical attorney. Postgraduate work, employment, community and military service, leadership ability, personal circumstances, and other relevant background information will be evaluated.

■ Library Facilities

The Furman Smith Law Library is the primary resource center of the law school. The law library and computing facilities are accessible to students 24 hours a day. The library's collection of over 350,000 volumes is enhanced by a wide array of online services. Students are able to access network resources from any of the numerous network drops and wireless access points throughout the law school. In addition, each first-year student receives a laptop computer to use during his or her legal education at Mercer Law School. The law library staff of 15 includes 6 professional law librarians who teach legal research courses and provide superior service to students and the legal community.

■ Curriculum

Mercer's Woodruff Curriculum and the atmosphere of the law school work together to provide students with a thorough intellectual foundation, strong practical skills, professional relationships, and a commitment to ethical behavior. Mercer is one of a few select schools in the country to receive the prestigious Gambrell Professionalism Award from the American Bar Association. The award cites the depth and excellence of the Woodruff Curriculum and its obvious commitment to professionalism.

The practice-oriented Woodruff Curriculum helps ensure that Mercer graduates develop problem-solving, counseling, and trial and appellate advocacy skills, and acquire the legal knowledge to become exceptional practicing attorneys. Each year begins with an introductory week-long course exploring one role of the practicing lawyer.

All students take research and writing courses during at least four semesters of law study, and many take a research or writing course each term. Mercer is the first law school in the nation to offer a Certificate in Advanced Legal Writing, Research, and Drafting. Students are selected for the Certificate Program through an application process. In 2003, in recognition of Mercer's nationally known Legal Writing Program, the Legal Writing Institute selected Mercer as its host school. The Legal Writing Institute is the world's largest organization of lawyers, judges, and law professors devoted to improving legal writing.

The last semester of study is the most distinctive component of the Woodruff Curriculum, as it offers students a unique opportunity to make the transition from law school to law practice. An intensive session features advanced courses in a variety of practical lawyering skills.

■ Joint JD/MBA Program

Mercer's School of Law and Mercer's School of Business and Economics offer a joint program leading to both the Juris Doctor and Master of Business Administration degrees. An applicant to the program should indicate on the application to the law school his or her intent to also apply to the School of Business and Economics. The applicant must be admitted separately to each school.

■ Business Certificate Program

Students in good standing in the Walter F. George School of Law may choose to take up to three graduate courses in the School of Business and Economics without applying for admission to the MBA program. Currently, two specific combinations of courses can be taken for a Certificate in Practice Management or a Certificate in Corporate Finance.

■ Special Programs

Law school provides a foundation upon which lawyers build successful careers and meaningful lives. At Mercer Law, that foundation includes rigorous intellectual training anchored by nationally recognized programs in legal writing, ethics and professionalism, and public service.

The Law and Public Service Program offers students the opportunity to earn academic credit while helping to represent clients in one of the law school's clinics, such as the Habeas Project or Public Defender's Clinic, in judges' chambers through the Judicial Field Placement Program, and summer externships through various agencies. Students may also be selected as fellows through the Public Interest Fellowship Program. After completing the fellowship, the

Mercer University—Walter F. George School of Law

fellows are offered a one-time loan forgiveness grant conditional on their making a two-year commitment to a public interest employer in Georgia after graduation.

Since 1985, the National Criminal Defense College (NCDC) has held its Summer Trial Practice Institute every year on the Mercer Law School campus. NCDC conducts two, two-week trial skills sessions for nearly 200 public defenders and criminal defense attorneys from across the country.

■ Student Activities

At Mercer University's Walter F. George School of Law, excellence is measured by more than what happens inside the classroom. You will find a broad array of activities outside the classroom that have been designed to engage the members of our academic community and enable our students to stand out once they enter the professional world.

In Mercer's moot court and mock trial programs, students improve their written and oral advocacy, negotiation, and client counseling skills. Recently, Mercer Law's Moot Court program was ranked among the top 20 in the nation, based on our record of wins in national competitions. In addition, Mercer Law's Mock Trial Team won the 2009 ABA National Criminal Justice Trial Advocacy Competition.

The *Mercer Law Review* (the oldest continually published law review in Georgia) has been edited and published quarterly by law students since 1949.

Students may also gain editorial experience in connection with the *Journal of Southern Legal History*, which is published by the law school.

In addition to moot court and *Law Review*, Mercer offers its students the opportunity to participate in over two dozen student organizations where they can gain valuable leadership and relationship-building experiences.

■ Financial Aid

Mercer awards over $3 million in scholarship aid every year to students whose academic records, LSAT scores, and personal achievements demonstrate the potential for outstanding performance in the study of law. Two of our most prestigious scholarships are the George W. Woodruff Scholarship (full tuition plus a $5,000 stipend) and the Walter F. George Foundation Public Service Scholarship (full tuition plus a $6,000 summer community service scholarship). In order to be considered for the George W. Woodruff scholarship, you must have your admission application and scholarship application completed and received in our office no later than February 1. A complete list of scholarships is available on our website at *www.law.mercer.edu* under Prospective Students. In addition to scholarship aid, students may qualify for student loans, and work-study is available after the first year of law school.

■ Career Services

Mercer Law School has an active career services office. Alumni and faculty members support students in their efforts to find satisfying employment. The office assists students in obtaining permanent, summer, and part-time employment.

Services of the office include arranging on-campus interviews with employers, career-planning seminars, and off-campus interviewing consortia. Individual career counseling and résumé and cover-letter writing workshops also comprise much of the work of the office. An extensive library of career resources is available for student use.

The Office of Career Services reports that 88.28 percent of the Class of 2008 was employed or pursuing LLM degrees within six to nine months after graduation.

Applicant Profile

Mercer University—Walter F. George School of Law
This grid includes only applicants who earned 120–180 LSAT scores under standard administrations.

LSAT Score	3.75 +		3.50–3.74		3.25–3.49		3.00–3.24		2.75–2.99		2.50–2.74		2.25–2.49		2.00–2.24		Below 2.00		No GPA		Total	
	Apps	Adm	Apps	Adm	Apps	Adm	Apps	Adm	Apps	Adm	Apps	Adm	Apps	Adm	Apps	Adm	Apps	Adm	Apps	Adm	Apps	Adm
175–180	0	0	0	0	0	0	0	0	0	0	0	0	0	0	0	0	0	0	0	0	0	0
170–174	0	0	0	0	1	1	0	0	2	2	0	0	0	0	0	0	1	0	0	0	4	3
165–169	1	1	4	4	4	3	2	2	1	1	2	2	0	0	1	0	0	0	0	0	15	13
160–164	25	22	12	11	23	22	16	16	13	12	5	5	2	1	3	1	0	0	0	0	99	90
155–159	57	56	75	70	68	63	59	46	41	30	32	19	4	3	6	1	0	0	1	0	343	288
150–154	56	29	102	58	120	33	122	19	81	16	41	3	12	3	2	0	1	0	6	2	543	163
145–149	26	8	51	9	72	13	73	4	44	4	40	1	15	0	4	0	2	0	5	1	332	40
140–144	8	0	17	0	35	1	33	1	25	0	23	0	6	0	7	0	1	0	2	0	157	2
135–139	2	0	3	0	16	0	12	0	9	0	16	0	11	0	6	0	1	0	2	0	78	0
130–134	1	0	2	0	2	0	4	0	4	0	3	0	8	0	0	0	0	0	1	0	25	0
125–129	0	0	0	0	0	0	0	0	1	0	2	0	1	0	0	0	0	0	0	0	4	0
120–124	0	0	0	0	0	0	0	0	1	0	0	0	0	0	0	0	0	0	0	0	1	0
Total	176	116	266	152	341	136	321	88	222	65	164	30	59	7	29	2	6	0	17	3	1601	599

Apps = Number of Applicants   Adm = Number Admitted   Reflects 99% of the total applicant pool; average LSAT data reported.
This chart is to be used as a general guide only. Nonnumerical factors are strongly considered for all applicants.

University of Miami School of Law

PO Box 248087
Coral Gables, FL 33124-8087
Phone: 305.284.2523; Fax: 305.284.3084
E-mail: admissions@law.miami.edu; Website: www.law.miami.edu

ABA
Approved
Since
1941

The Basics

Type of school	Private
Term	Semester
Application deadline	7/31
Application fee	$60
Financial aid deadline	3/1
Can first year start other than fall?	No
Student to faculty ratio	16.5 to 1
# of housing spaces available restricted to law students	
graduate housing for which law students are eligible	

Faculty and Administrators

	Total		Men		Women		Minorities	
	Spr	Fall	Spr	Fall	Spr	Fall	Spr	Fall
Full-time	63	65	39	41	24	24	11	12
Other full-time	0	0	0	0	0	0	0	0
Deans, librarians, & others who teach	14	15	4	4	10	11	3	4
Part-time	104	106	74	75	28	29	18	21
Total	181	186	117	120	62	64	32	37

JD Enrollment and Ethnicity

	Men		Women		Full-Time		Part-Time		1st-Year		Total		JD Degs. Awd.
	#	%	#	%	#	%	#	%	#	%	#	%	
African Amer.	44	5.6	50	8.4	93	6.9	1	3.0	36	6.9	94	6.8	24
Amer. Indian	1	0.1	3	0.5	4	0.3	0	0.0	2	0.4	4	0.3	0
Asian Amer.	28	3.6	33	5.5	60	4.4	1	3.0	19	3.6	61	4.4	6
Mex. Amer.	0	0.0	0	0.0	0	0.0	0	0.0	0	0.0	0	0.0	0
Puerto Rican	0	0.0	0	0.0	0	0.0	0	0.0	0	0.0	0	0.0	0
Hispanic	73	9.3	89	14.9	160	11.8	2	6.1	62	11.8	162	11.7	52
Total Minority	146	18.6	175	29.3	317	23.5	4	12.1	119	22.7	321	23.2	82
For. Nation.	28	3.6	31	5.2	54	4.0	5	15.2	16	3.0	59	4.3	26
Caucasian	552	70.1	352	59.0	882	65.3	22	66.7	365	69.5	904	65.3	238
Unknown	61	7.8	39	6.5	98	7.3	2	6.1	25	4.8	100	7.2	28
Total	787	56.9	597	43.1	1351	97.6	33	2.4	525	37.9	1384		374

Curriculum

	Full-Time	Part-Time
Typical first-year section size	100	0
Is there typically a "small section" of the first-year class, other than Legal Writing, taught by full-time faculty	Yes	No
If yes, typical size offered last year	50	
# of classroom course titles beyond first-year curriculum		82
# of upper division courses, excluding seminars, with an enrollment: Under 25		39
25–49		47
50–74		19
75–99		9
100+		17
# of seminars		43
# of seminar positions available		645
# of seminar positions filled	382	0
# of positions available in simulation courses		890
# of simulation positions filled	698	0
# of positions available in faculty supervised clinical courses		120
# of faculty supervised clinical positions filled	77	0
# involved in field placements	153	0
# involved in law journals	194	0
# involved in moot court or trial competitions	93	0
# of credit hours required to graduate		88

Transfers

Transfers in	30
Transfers out	18

Tuition and Fees

	Resident	Nonresident
Full-time	$38,012	$38,012
Part-time		
Tuition Guarantee Program		N

Living Expenses

Estimated living expenses for singles

Living on campus	Living off campus	Living at home
$20,178	$20,178	$11,251

University of Miami School of Law

ABA Approved Since 1941

GPA and LSAT Scores

	Total	Full-Time	Part-Time
# of apps	4,605	4,605	0
# of offers	2,409	2,409	0
# of matrics	530	530	0
75% GPA	3.66	3.66	0.00
Median GPA	3.46	3.46	0.00
25% GPA	3.25	3.25	0.00
75% LSAT	159	159	0
Median LSAT	157	157	0
25% LSAT	155	155	0

Grants and Scholarships (from prior year)

	Total		Full-Time		Part-Time	
	#	%	#	%	#	%
Total # of students	1,235		1,205		30	
Total # receiving grants	417	33.8	417	34.6	0	0.0
Less than 1/2 tuition	196	15.9	196	16.3	0	0.0
Half to full tuition	191	15.5	191	15.9	0	0.0
Full tuition	14	1.1	14	1.2	0	0.0
More than full tuition	16	1.3	16	1.3	0	0.0
Median grant amount			$20,000		$0	

Informational and Library Resources

Total amount spent on library materials	$2,399,688
Study seating capacity inside the library	698
# of full-time equivalent professional librarians	10
Hours per week library is open	111
# of open, wired connections available to students	28
# of networked computers available for use by students	164
Has wireless network?	Y
Require computer?	N

JD Attrition (from prior year)

	Academic	Other	Total	
	#	#	#	%
1st year	3	26	29	7.7
2nd year	0	0	0	0.0
3rd year	0	0	0	0.0
4th year	0	0	0	0.0

Employment (9 months after graduation)

	Total	Percentage
Employment status known	362	96.8
Employment status unknown	12	3.2
Employed	332	91.7
Pursuing graduate degrees	15	4.1
Unemployed (seeking, not seeking, or studying for the bar)	4	1.1
Type of Employment		
# employed in law firms	219	66.0
# employed in business and industry	34	10.2
# employed in government	33	9.9
# employed in public interest	11	3.3
# employed as judicial clerks	18	5.4
# employed in academia	4	1.2
Geographic Location		
# employed in state	221	66.6
# employed in foreign countries	1	0.3
# of states where employed	26	

Bar Passage Rates

First-time takers	373	Reporting %	73.46
Average school %	90.51	Average state %	80.76
Average pass difference	9.75		

Jurisdiction	Takers	Passers	Pass %	State %	Diff %
Florida	274	248	90.51	80.76	9.75

University of Miami School of Law

PO Box 248087
Coral Gables, FL 33124-8087
Phone: 305.284.2523; Fax: 305.284.3084
E-mail: admissions@law.miami.edu; Website: www.law.miami.edu

■ Introduction

Established in 1926 in Coral Gables, Florida, the University of Miami School of Law is part of one of the largest private research universities in the United States. The school's location on the main campus enables students to attend law school in a beautiful, subtropical setting while taking advantage of the opportunities available in one of the most dynamic and rapidly expanding legal communities in the country. Miami is accredited by the ABA, is a member of the AALS, and has a chapter of the prestigious scholastic society, the Order of the Coif.

■ Faculty

The faculty of the University of Miami have exceptional credentials. They are graduates of the world's top universities and law schools, have completed prestigious judicial clerkships, and have significant work experience in private practice and government and with nongovernmental organizations. They are leading scholars in their fields. Their expertise is especially strong in international and foreign law (with half of them having written or taught in those fields), taxation, commercial and securities regulation, immigration, the Internet, legal theory, evidence, and legal ethics.

■ Library

With over 630,000 volumes in print and microform, and a wide array of electronic resources, the Law Library is one of the largest in the Southeast. The library has liberal hours, a superb service-oriented staff, computer labs, and ample seating for individual and group study. The campus is wireless.

■ Curriculum

The school provides a solid foundation in all the traditional subjects basic to understanding and practicing the law throughout the nation. It also offers ambitious programs designed to teach the craft as well as the theory of law, to develop the research and writing skills critical to the legal profession, and to expose students to other skills necessary for effective professional service.

Choosing from more than 160 courses, workshops, and seminars, students ordinarily complete the JD degree in three academic years of full-time study. Summer sessions are available. Miami's course offerings in inter-American, international, and comparative law are outstanding. Joint JD/Master's programs are offered in business administration, public health, and marine affairs, and JD/LLM degrees are offered in taxation, real property development, international law, inter-American law, and ocean and coastal law.

Master of Laws (LLM) programs include inter-American law, international law, ocean and coastal law, taxation, estate planning, real property development, and comparative law. A JD degree (or equivalent degree from a foreign law school) is required for entrance into an LLM program.

■ Special Programs

The school offers one of the most comprehensive and sophisticated skills training programs in the nation, integrating trial, pretrial, litigation, and clinical experiences. Directed by a full-time faculty member, distinguished trial attorneys and judges from both state and federal courts assist with the trial and pretrial courses and help supervise the clinical placements. The school's growing array of clinical programs allows students to participate in environmental protection advocacy; representation of abused and neglected children, immigrants, the elderly, or other persons in need of health care who are facing complicated legal issues; representation of prisoners appealing federal sentencing rulings and tenants caught up in housing disputes; and advocacy for community legal needs in economically challenged neighborhoods. Additional skills training is available in transactional skills, alternative dispute resolution, mediation, international arbitration, and domestic and international legal research.

The Center for Ethics and Public Service is an interdisciplinary project teaching the values of ethical judgment, professional responsibility, and public service.

HOPE (Helping Others Through Pro Bono Efforts) is the law school's public interest resource center, linking students, faculty, and alumni with community outreach projects, public interest lecture series, clinics, direct service legal advocacy projects, and fellowships in the public sector.

Study-abroad options consist of six separate segments presented in two sessions that are held in England, Spain, Greece, and Italy. Students may enroll solely in any of the six segments offered. A maximum of six credits will be awarded.

■ Admission

Admission is competitive. Undergraduate grade-point averages are used in the review process. While all LSAT scores are considered, the highest score is given the greatest weight. Letters of recommendation are required and a personal statement is strongly encouraged. Work experience, extracurricular activities, special skills, and background are also considered. First-year students are admitted only in the fall semester. Applicants are urged to apply as early as possible after September 1. Applications received after February 1 will be considered on a space-available basis until July 31.

■ The Student Body and Student Life

Miami's student body is highly talented and exceptionally diverse. The school is consistently among the leaders in numbers of Hispanic, African American, and foreign students graduated from its JD program. The school's many student activities include an active Student Bar Association, Honor Council, Moot Court Board, and International Moot Court Board, as well as more than 40 diverse student organizations, including the Black, Hispanic, Caribbean, South Asian, Middle Eastern, and Asian/Pacific American law student organizations; OUTLaw; Miami Law Women; Federalist Society; International Law Society; Entertainment and Sports Law Society; the Student Animal Legal Defense Fund; and

many more. Students regularly take part in a wide range of pro bono activities in the South Florida community. Miami's law journals include the *University of Miami Law Review*, the *University of Miami Inter-American Law Review*, the *University of Miami International and Comparative Law Review*, the *Business Law Review*, and *Psychology, Public Policy, and Law Review*.

■ Expenses and Financial Aid

Scholarship aid available through the school does not exceed the cost of tuition. Most scholarships are merit based, although need is sometimes considered. Admitted applicants are automatically considered for most scholarship awards. Applicants who wish to be considered for a merit scholarship should complete their admission files prior to January 4. Most scholarships are awarded on a rolling basis. Those admitted by February 1 are considered for the prestigious Harvey T. Reid and Soia Mentschikoff scholarships. In addition, admitted students are eligible to apply for the public interest-related Miami Scholars Program, which requires a separate application

with a deadline of March 1. The law school assists students in applying for federal and private loans.

Federal loans may be applied for by first completing the FAFSA online at *www.fafsa.ed.gov*. Our Federal School Code is E00532. Any additional financial information can be found on our website at *www.law.miami.edu/finaid*.

■ Career Services

The Career Development Office (CDO) offers extraordinary individual career counseling to law students and alumni, with nine attorneys in different areas of specialty providing guidance. The CDO offers a wide range of job-related programming and job fairs, networking opportunities with attorneys in varied practice areas, and access to a resource library and national job postings via the Internet. The On Campus Interview Program attracts national and local employers, providing opportunities with law firms, government agencies, public service organizations, corporate counsel, and the judiciary.

Applicant Profile

University of Miami School of Law
This grid includes only applicants who earned 120–180 LSAT scores under standard administrations.

LSAT Score	GPA									
	3.75 +	3.50–3.74	3.25–3.49	3.00–3.24	2.75–2.99	2.50–2.74	2.25–2.49	2.00–2.24	Below 2.00	No GPA
175–180										
170–174										
165–169										
160–164										
155–159										
150–154										
145–149										
140–144										
135–139										
130–134										
125–129										
120–124										

Good Possibility   Possible   Unlikely

When reviewing the grid, it is important to note that admission to the school is based upon all aspects of an applicant's background, and not limited to the LSAT and undergraduate grade-point average.

The University of Michigan Law School

Hutchins Hall, 625 South State Street
Ann Arbor, MI 48109-1215
Phone: 734.764.1358
E-mail: law.jd.admissions@umich.edu; Website: www.law.umich.edu

ABA Approved Since 1923
American Bar Association
Section of Legal Education and Admissions to the Bar

The Basics

Type of school	Public
Term	Semester
Application deadline	11/15 2/15
Application fee	$60
Financial aid deadline	
Can first year start other than fall?	Yes
Student to faculty ratio	11.4 to 1
# of housing spaces available restricted to law students	258
graduate housing for which law students are eligible	1,200

Curriculum

	Full-Time	Part-Time
Typical first-year section size	91	0
Is there typically a "small section" of the first-year class, other than Legal Writing, taught by full-time faculty	Yes	No
If yes, typical size offered last year	46	
# of classroom course titles beyond first-year curriculum	191	
# of upper division courses, excluding seminars, with an enrollment: Under 25	85	
25–49	43	
50–74	16	
75–99	14	
100+	8	
# of seminars	74	
# of seminar positions available	1,127	
# of seminar positions filled	1,009	0
# of positions available in simulation courses	423	
# of simulation positions filled	342	0
# of positions available in faculty supervised clinical courses	287	
# of faculty supervised clinical positions filled	279	0
# involved in field placements	33	0
# involved in law journals	468	0
# involved in moot court or trial competitions	78	0
# of credit hours required to graduate	82	

Faculty and Administrators

	Total Spr	Total Fall	Men Spr	Men Fall	Women Spr	Women Fall	Minorities Spr	Minorities Fall
Full-time	88	81	58	57	30	24	10	8
Other full-time	5	3	2	1	3	2	1	1
Deans, librarians, & others who teach	3	3	2	2	1	1	0	0
Part-time	38	33	23	22	14	11	4	1
Total	134	120	85	82	48	38	15	10

JD Enrollment and Ethnicity

	Men #	Men %	Women #	Women %	Full-Time #	Full-Time %	Part-Time #	Part-Time %	1st-Year #	1st-Year %	Total #	Total %	JD Degs. Awd.
African Amer.	24	3.8	33	6.8	57	5.1	0	0.0	17	4.6	57	5.1	23
Amer. Indian	13	2.1	4	0.8	17	1.5	0	0.0	6	1.6	17	1.5	9
Asian Amer.	52	8.2	83	17.1	135	12.1	0	0.0	47	12.7	135	12.1	53
Mex. Amer.	0	0.0	0	0.0	0	0.0	0	0.0	0	0.0	0	0.0	0
Puerto Rican	0	0.0	0	0.0	0	0.0	0	0.0	0	0.0	0	0.0	0
Hispanic	23	3.6	24	4.9	47	4.2	0	0.0	13	3.5	47	4.2	19
Total Minority	112	17.7	144	29.6	256	22.9	0	0.0	83	22.4	256	22.9	104
For. Nation.	20	3.2	18	3.7	38	3.4	0	0.0	11	3.0	38	3.4	12
Caucasian	412	65.3	283	58.2	695	62.2	0	0.0	235	63.3	695	62.2	252
Unknown	87	13.8	41	8.4	128	11.5	0	0.0	42	11.3	128	11.5	42
Total	631	56.5	486	43.5	1117	100.0	0	0.0	371	33.2	1117		410

Transfers

Transfers in	25
Transfers out	6

Tuition and Fees

	Resident	Nonresident
Full-time	$43,250	$46,250
Part-time		
Tuition Guarantee Program	N	

Living Expenses

Estimated living expenses for singles

Living on campus	Living off campus	Living at home
$15,650	$15,650	$6,260

The University of Michigan Law School

ABA
Approved
Since
1923

GPA and LSAT Scores

	Total	Full-Time	Part-Time
# of apps	5,414	5,414	0
# of offers	1,178	1,178	0
# of matrics	371	371	0
75% GPA	3.84	3.84	0.00
Median GPA	3.70	3.70	0.00
25% GPA	3.55	3.55	0.00
75% LSAT	170	170	0
Median LSAT	169	169	0
25% LSAT	167	167	0

Grants and Scholarships (from prior year)

	Total #	Total %	Full-Time #	Full-Time %	Part-Time #	Part-Time %
Total # of students	1,151		1,151		0	
Total # receiving grants	667	57.9	667	57.9	0	0.0
Less than 1/2 tuition	596	51.8	596	51.8	0	0.0
Half to full tuition	29	2.5	29	2.5	0	0.0
Full tuition	30	2.6	30	2.6	0	0.0
More than full tuition	12	1.0	12	1.0	0	0.0
Median grant amount			$11,300		$0	

Informational and Library Resources

Total amount spent on library materials	$2,663,457
Study seating capacity inside the library	854
# of full-time equivalent professional librarians	12
Hours per week library is open	112
# of open, wired connections available to students	332
# of networked computers available for use by students	203
Has wireless network?	Y
Require computer?	N

JD Attrition (from prior year)

	Academic #	Other #	Total #	Total %
1st year	0	1	1	0.3
2nd year	0	6	6	1.6
3rd year	0	1	1	0.2
4th year	0	0	0	0.0

Employment (9 months after graduation)

	Total	Percentage
Employment status known	385	99.7
Employment status unknown	1	0.3
Employed	376	97.7
Pursuing graduate degrees	6	1.6
Unemployed (seeking, not seeking, or studying for the bar)	0	0.0
Type of Employment		
# employed in law firms	273	72.6
# employed in business and industry	19	5.1
# employed in government	10	2.7
# employed in public interest	20	5.3
# employed as judicial clerks	51	13.6
# employed in academia	3	0.8
Geographic Location		
# employed in state	38	10.1
# employed in foreign countries	7	1.9
# of states where employed	31	

Bar Passage Rates

First-time takers	406	Reporting %	99.01
Average school %	92.05	Average state %	86.88
Average pass difference	5.17		

Jurisdiction	Takers	Passers	Pass %	State %	Diff %
New York	147	134	91.16	88.98	2.18
Illinois	86	84	97.67	90.94	6.73
California	65	53	81.54	78.07	3.47
Michigan	38	36	94.74	82.13	12.61
Others (11)	66	63	95.45		

The University of Michigan Law School

Hutchins Hall, 625 South State Street
Ann Arbor, MI 48109-1215
Phone: 734.764.1358
E-mail: law.jd.admissions@umich.edu; Website: www.law.umich.edu

■ Introduction

The University of Michigan Law School, founded in 1859, is one of the nation's finest institutions of legal education. The school's distinguished and diverse faculty, many preeminent in their fields, have a history of devotion to both scholarship and teaching. Our students come from around the globe to contribute their remarkable talents and accomplishments and make the Law School a collegial community that exudes a sense of serious purpose, academic achievement, and social commitment. Never restricted to the privileged, in 1870, Michigan—then the largest law school in the country—became the second American university to confer a law degree on an African American. That same year, Michigan became the first major law school to admit a woman, and in 1871, its graduate, Sarah Killgore, became the first woman with a law degree in the nation to be admitted to the bar.

■ Faculty

Michigan has almost 80 full-time faculty members, with many distinguished visiting scholars further enhancing course offerings. While maintaining a long tradition of eminence in constitutional, criminal, international, and comparative law, the interdisciplinary breadth of the faculty is reflected in an extraordinary range of expertise, including classics, economics, feminist theory, history, life sciences, philosophy, political theory, and public policy. The depth is reflected by multiple measures, such as the large number of faculty (almost 20%) who are governing members of a world-class department in another discipline, the number (more than one quarter) who hold doctorates in nonlaw fields, and the number (more than 10%) who are Fellows of the American Academy of Arts and Sciences.

■ Physical Facilities and Library

The location of residential and academic buildings within the strikingly beautiful Gothic architecture of the William W. Cook Law Quadrangle fosters the integration of activities for both students and faculty. Construction of a new four-story, 100,000-square-foot building south of the Quad, and a 16,000-square-foot Commons that will become the Quad's vibrant new heart, was begun in Summer 2009; completion is anticipated in January 2012.

With over one million volumes, the Law Library's comprehensive collection covers Anglo-American, foreign, comparative, and international law, and includes legislation, court reports, and administrative material from all US jurisdictions, Great Britain, Europe, and most Asian and South American countries. In 1957, the Library became the first depository of EU documents at an American university. It is also a selective depository for US government publications, and extensively collects documents of international intergovernmental organizations. There is special depth in the collections relating to indigenous peoples. Law students also have access to all other University libraries.

■ Curriculum

Recognized as preeminent in interdisciplinary legal studies, the insights and methods of many other fields are apparent throughout our broad curriculum. Formal dual-degree programs are available in 13 disciplines, while others are created ad hoc, sometimes with other institutions. Alternatively, students may count 12 credits of graduate-level work in other departments toward their JD. With the Law School located at the center of the University, it is easy for students to take advantage of these options, and about 15% of second- and third-year students do so.

A key component of the first year is our exceptional Legal Practice Program. This comprehensive class provides individualized instruction in legal writing, research, and oral advocacy by full-time faculty to first-year students.

Particularly renowned for international scholarship, Michigan's leadership is evident in its requirement that all students complete Transnational Law—the first elite law school to so recognize the centrality of the field to modern lawyering. The Geneva Externship Program provides 20 students annually with a unique "in" to extremely competitive jobs in the public international field, while other programs, such as the South Africa externship program, the Program for Cambodian Law and Development, and our AIRE Centre internships, provide students with advanced training in international areas of interest.

Bottom line, as one of the leaders in American legal education, Michigan's curriculum is strong across the board. Students with interest in business, corporate, and securities; intellectual property; criminal; international; environmental; and public interest law should pay special attention to Michigan's extensive offerings.

■ Clinical Opportunities

Michigan is committed to the union of theory and practice, and our clinical practice program, with more than thirty years of experience, is unquestionably one of the nation's best. Michigan is one of only two states to allow students to appear in court as early as second year, meaning that our students have more opportunities to represent clients selected from a rich pool of cases—often in smaller jurisdictions, where a faster timetable allows students to handle many cases from beginning to end. Beyond the General Clinic, where students are involved in civil and criminal trial work, as well as immigration and refugee cases, our diverse offerings include litigation clinics in Child Advocacy Law, Juvenile Justice, Criminal Appellate Practice, Human Trafficking, as well as our groundbreaking non-DNA Innocence Clinic; transactional clinics such as Urban Communities, International Transactions, International Tax, and Low Income Tax; the interdisciplinary medicolegal Pediatric Advocacy Clinic; an Environmental Law Clinic run in cooperation with the National Wildlife Federation; and a Mediation Clinic. Students can also participate in the Family Law Project, a student-run advocacy program for victims of domestic violence, as well as a variety of practicums, in fields ranging from copyright to bankruptcy, in which real cases are dissected in a classroom setting.

■ Admission and Student Body

Please refer to Applicant Profile for more information.

■ Student Activities

Approximately 450 students participate in six journals: the *Michigan Law Review*, the *Journal of Law Reform*, the *Michigan Journal of International Law*, the *Michigan Journal of Gender and Law*, the *Michigan Telecommunications and Technology Law Review*, and the *Michigan Journal of Race and Law*. Students interested in honing advocacy skills may choose to enter numerous moot court competitions. The Law School Student Senate funds more than 50 student organizations dedicated to affinity group membership and legal interests; students also participate in groups throughout the larger University community. Our voluntary Pro Bono Pledge gives students yet one more outlet to serve the world outside the Law School with their developing legal skills; projects range from local to global in providing underrepresented individuals with valuable expertise.

■ Expenses and Financial Aid

Our financial aid resources are substantial, and we distribute more than $3.5 million in grants annually to each entering class. Grants range in size from $5,000 to as much as full tuition plus a stipend, and average about $15,000 annually. Our resources are divided between grants made with reference to financial need, and merit awards made to outstanding candidates who are remarkable for their anticipated contribution to the Law School and the profession.

Michigan's Debt Management Program (LRAP) is a resource that only a very few law schools offer. It provides graduates with the flexibility to choose jobs from an unlimited range of law-related opportunities, including lower-paying public interest positions, while still maintaining a reasonable lifestyle and remaining current on outstanding loan obligations.

■ Career Services/Public Service

Repeatedly rated by multiple publications among the top three law schools for career prospects, Michigan offers unparalleled opportunity. Our location in the center of the country means that employers from all major markets target our graduates, and our on-campus recruiting program is consistently one of the largest in the country, even in comparison to other top schools—both in absolute numbers of employers recruiting and in relative terms of interviews per student. While the majority of our graduates go to the best and largest private-sector firms across the nation, the range of work performed by our alumni is truly extraordinary. Michigan has, for example, the third largest number of state and federal judges, the third largest number of legal academics, and the fourth largest number of Skadden Fellows; we are also leaders in judicial clerkships (about 15 percent of each class obtains positions in federal, state, and international courts), as well as government and public-interest employment (on average, about 10 percent). And as one of only a handful of schools regularly sending its graduates to more than 30 states and abroad, our students have confidence that their degree will be portable wherever they choose to live. The largest number of our graduates go to New York City and Chicago, followed closely by California and Washington, DC. Our reach extends well beyond these cities, though; the most recent class sent graduates to markets ranging from Seattle to Miami, London to Madrid, and to Hanoi, to name just a few.

Our six attorney-counselors have experience across the legal spectrum, and can advise students about the full range of professional opportunities. Both when the market is flourishing and when it contracts, the breadth of Michigan's recruiting program and depth of its counselors' expertise serves students exceptionally well.

■ Housing

Ann Arbor combines ease of living with superb cultural, athletic, and entertainment offerings. Approximately half of our first-year students (along with some upper-class and LLM students) reside in the Lawyers Club, enjoying the easy access and camaraderie of life in the Quad. High-quality, off-campus housing is available in a wide variety of choices. Economical University family housing is also available a short (and free) bus ride away, in northeast Ann Arbor.

Applicant Profile

We choose not to provide an applicant profile because we do not believe a grid based on undergraduate GPA and LSAT scores can accurately reflect our comprehensive admission process, which focuses on many elements in an application in order to determine an applicant's particular intellectual strengths, nonacademic achievements, and unique personal circumstances. We view our student body as one of our greatest assets, and our goal is to admit a group of students who, individually and collectively, are among the best applying to US law schools in a given year. We seek a mix of students with varying backgrounds and experiences who will respect and learn from each other. Our most general measures are an applicant's LSAT score and undergraduate GPA. As measured by those statistics, Michigan is among a handful of the most selective law schools in the country. However, each of these measures is far from perfect. Even the highest possible scores will not guarantee admission, and low scores will likewise not automatically result in a denial, as both circumstances may have significant offsetting considerations.

Michigan State University College of Law

Office of Admissions & Financial Aid, 300 Law College Building
East Lansing, MI 48824-1300
Phone: 800.844.9352, 517.432.0222; Fax: 517.432.0098
E-mail: admiss@law.msu.edu; Website: www.law.msu.edu

ABA Approved Since 1941

The Basics

Type of school	Private
Term	Semester
Application deadline	4/30
Application fee	$60
Financial aid deadline	5/1
Can first year start other than fall?	No
Student to faculty ratio	16.6 to 1
# of housing spaces available restricted to law students	
graduate housing for which law students are eligible	1,049

Faculty and Administrators

	Total		Men		Women		Minorities	
	Spr	Fall	Spr	Fall	Spr	Fall	Spr	Fall
Full-time	44	46	25	27	19	19	3	6
Other full-time	2	5	1	2	1	3	0	0
Deans, librarians, & others who teach	17	19	7	9	10	10	1	1
Part-time	53	54	43	39	10	15	10	9
Total	116	124	76	77	40	47	14	16

JD Enrollment and Ethnicity

	Men		Women		Full-Time		Part-Time		1st-Year		Total		JD Degs. Awd.
	#	%	#	%	#	%	#	%	#	%	#	%	
African Amer.	16	2.7	35	9.4	43	4.8	8	12.3	23	8.1	51	5.3	16
Amer. Indian	5	0.9	9	2.4	12	1.3	2	3.1	4	1.4	14	1.5	4
Asian Amer.	20	3.4	16	4.3	33	3.7	3	4.6	14	4.9	36	3.8	11
Mex. Amer.	2	0.3	1	0.3	3	0.3	0	0.0	1	0.4	3	0.3	1
Puerto Rican	0	0.0	0	0.0	0	0.0	0	0.0	0	0.0	0	0.0	0
Hispanic	14	2.4	9	2.4	18	2.0	5	7.7	7	2.5	23	2.4	6
Total Minority	57	9.8	70	18.7	109	12.2	18	27.7	49	17.3	127	13.3	38
For. Nation.	54	9.3	20	5.3	55	6.2	19	29.2	19	6.7	74	7.7	15
Caucasian	429	73.6	263	70.3	665	74.6	27	41.5	196	69.3	692	72.3	192
Unknown	43	7.4	21	5.6	63	7.1	1	1.5	19	6.7	64	6.7	9
Total	583	60.9	374	39.1	892	93.2	65	6.8	283	29.6	957		254

Curriculum

	Full-Time	Part-Time
Typical first-year section size	74	80
Is there typically a "small section" of the first-year class, other than Legal Writing, taught by full-time faculty	No	No
If yes, typical size offered last year		
# of classroom course titles beyond first-year curriculum	175	

# of upper division courses, excluding seminars, with an enrollment:		
	Under 25	120
	25–49	43
	50–74	15
	75–99	2
	100+	10

# of seminars	67
# of seminar positions available	1,407
# of seminar positions filled	770 · 43
# of positions available in simulation courses	1,198
# of simulation positions filled	912 · 64
# of positions available in faculty supervised clinical courses	161
# of faculty supervised clinical positions filled	107 · 3
# involved in field placements	267 · 40
# involved in law journals	150 · 3
# involved in moot court or trial competitions	123 · 6
# of credit hours required to graduate	88

Transfers

Transfers in	15
Transfers out	27

Tuition and Fees

	Resident	Nonresident
Full-time	$33,054	$33,054
Part-time	$27,394	$27,394
Tuition Guarantee Program		N

Living Expenses

Estimated living expenses for singles		
Living on campus	Living off campus	Living at home
$16,472	$16,472	$16,472

Michigan State University College of Law

ABA
Approved
Since
1941

GPA and LSAT Scores

	Total	Full-Time	Part-Time
# of apps	2,736	2,547	189
# of offers	1,266	1,214	52
# of matrics	288	264	24
75% GPA	3.61	3.61	3.53
Median GPA	3.36	3.37	2.90
25% GPA	3.07	3.09	2.67
75% LSAT	159	159	153
Median LSAT	155	156	148
25% LSAT	153	153	144

Grants and Scholarships (from prior year)

	Total		Full-Time		Part-Time	
	#	%	#	%	#	%
Total # of students	955		812		143	
Total # receiving grants	302	31.6	278	34.2	24	16.8
Less than 1/2 tuition	25	2.6	20	2.5	5	3.5
Half to full tuition	141	14.8	135	16.6	6	4.2
Full tuition	136	14.2	123	15.1	13	9.1
More than full tuition	0	0.0	0	0.0	0	0.0
Median grant amount			$23,814		$15,912	

Informational and Library Resources

Total amount spent on library materials	$1,083,727
Study seating capacity inside the library	455
# of full-time equivalent professional librarians	9
Hours per week library is open	109
# of open, wired connections available to students	1,209
# of networked computers available for use by students	66
Has wireless network?	Y
Require computer?	Y

JD Attrition (from prior year)

	Academic	Other	Total	
	#	#	#	%
1st year	6	36	42	14.5
2nd year	4	0	4	1.0
3rd year	0	0	0	0.0
4th year	0	0	0	0.0

Employment (9 months after graduation)

	Total	Percentage
Employment status known	311	97.5
Employment status unknown	8	2.5
Employed	271	87.1
Pursuing graduate degrees	16	5.1
Unemployed (seeking, not seeking, or studying for the bar)	21	6.8
Type of Employment		
# employed in law firms	129	47.6
# employed in business and industry	62	22.9
# employed in government	27	10.0
# employed in public interest	8	3.0
# employed as judicial clerks	25	9.2
# employed in academia	16	5.9
Geographic Location		
# employed in state	148	54.6
# employed in foreign countries	11	4.1
# of states where employed	32	

Bar Passage Rates

First-time takers	332	Reporting %	72.29
Average school %	84.16	Average state %	83.93
Average pass difference	0.23		

Jurisdiction	Takers	Passers	Pass %	State %	Diff %
Michigan	172	144	83.72	82.13	1.59
Illinois	36	34	94.44	90.94	3.50
New Jersey	14	11	78.57	84.69	−6.12
New York	10	5	50.00	88.98	−38.98
Colorado	8	8	100.00	83.29	16.71

Michigan State University College of Law

Office of Admissions & Financial Aid, 300 Law College Building
East Lansing, MI 48824-1300
Phone: 800.844.9352, 517.432.0222; Fax: 517.432.0098
E-mail: admiss@law.msu.edu; Website: www.law.msu.edu

■ Introduction

With a broad and rigorous curriculum that provides extensive opportunities for students to gain valuable practical experience, Michigan State University (MSU) College of Law successfully prepares graduates for legal employment in settings across the nation—litigation, transactional law, business and industry, alternative dispute resolution, and public interest—to mention just a few.

As a law school with a 100-plus year tradition of graduating outstanding lawyers, judges, and entrepreneurs, students at MSU Law benefit from the college's status as a private law school located in the heart of a Big 10, world-class research university. The College of Law's location in East Lansing provides students with convenient access to externships and employment with state and federal agencies and courts, and an array of law firms and corporations. MSU Law is fully accredited by the ABA and is a member of the AALS.

■ Academic Programs

The College of Law curriculum provides a thorough education in all principal areas of law and practice. A total of 88 credit hours is required for graduation, with 40 of these credits being proscribed by the College of Law. The Law College teaches core legal skills, supplemented with academic concentrations, programmatic initiatives, and scholarly research and exchanges. The educational program of the college teaches and reinforces the ethical core of good lawyering, the values of professionalism and service, the art of client representation and trial advocacy, and the understanding of legal principles, private rights, and public policy.

The Law College strives to continuously strengthen academic quality in all programs and activities of the college. The college is committed to fostering flexible opportunities for professional growth, innovation, research, and scholarship by the faculty. The faculty is committed to excellence in instruction, to making significant contributions to legal research, and to engaging in public service and community outreach. The staff is committed to providing necessary service, support, and creativity.

The elective and required curriculum of the Law College integrates theory and practice, thereby helping to ensure that graduates of MSU Law are well prepared for their first professional positions and the professional responsibilities for decades to come.

Focus Areas: Law students at MSU have the opportunity to choose a focus area or certificate program when selecting elective courses. Focus areas include Alternative Dispute Resolution (ADR), Corporate Law, Criminal Law, Environmental and Natural Resource Law, Family Law, Health Law, Intellectual Property and Communications Law, International and Comparative Law, Public Law and Regulation, and Taxation Law.

Certificate Programs: MSU Law students may elect to participate in one of three certificate programs, thereby developing greater expertise in an area of law. MSU Law certificate programs are Child and Family Advocacy, Trial Practice at the Geoffrey Fieger Trial Practice Institute, and Indigenous Law.

Joint JD/LLB with the University of Ottawa: A joint JD/LLB degree prepares students to practice law in Canada and the United States. Students spend two years of study at MSU Law and two years attending the University of Ottawa Faculty of Law.

Study-Abroad Programs: The MSU Law Canadian study-abroad program provides students with the opportunity to study US-Canadian and international law and gain legal work experience in Ottawa. Additionally, the Law College offers study-abroad programs in Japan and Mexico.

Dual-Degree Options: Law students with an interest in broadening their skills set have the opportunity to pursue a dual degree with another graduate program at Michigan State University. Dual degrees are established with more than a dozen graduate programs, with the typical dual-degree student being able to earn the law degree and a master's degree in just four years.

Master of Laws (LLM) Program: An LLM is offered for foreign lawyers. An LLM/MJ (Master of Jurisprudence) is offered in Intellectual Property and Communications Law for domestic and foreign students.

■ Experiential Learning

MSU Law Clinics: The Law College operates law clinics to benefit low-income persons and to give law students an opportunity to put their legal knowledge into practice. Students in the clinics may handle cases from start to finish and gain much satisfaction—as well as résumé-building experience—from their clinical experiences, all while helping members of their own community. Law clinics available to students are the Housing Clinic, Immigration Clinic, Plea and Sentencing Clinic, Small Business and Nonprofit Law Clinic, Tax Clinic, and the Chance at Childhood Law and Social Work Clinic.

Spring Semester in Washington, DC: The Law College's Washington, DC, Semester Program provides the opportunity for 25 students to spend a full spring semester in our nation's capital, working 24 hours weekly for federal agencies while also enrolling in several law courses taught by MSU Law faculty. The DC program provides valuable practical experience and insights into employment with the federal government.

Externships: Externships, which are field placements that provide practical legal training under the supervision of practicing attorneys and faculty members, may be completed with a variety of legal employers—judicial, legal aid, nonprofit, and governmental. Two of the most innovative and exciting externship opportunities are in Washington, DC, and Ottawa, Canada.

MSU Law Journals: The *Michigan State Law Review*, *Journal of International Law*, *Journal of Medicine and Law*, *Journal of Business and Securities Law*, *Journal of Gender Law*, and *MSU Entertainment and Sports Law Journal*.

Trial Practice Institute: MSU Law alumnus Geoffrey N. Fieger has partnered with the Law College to establish a premier trial practice institute, designed specifically to train law students as successful trial lawyers. Students interview at the end of their first year of law school, and selected students start the program at the beginning of their second year. The institute offers hands-on learning experiences through clinics, externships, field placements, and simulations.

Career Services

Graduates of the College of Law can be found in all regions of the country and abroad. In a typical year, graduates accept employment in 25 or more states. The most common career path of recent graduates is private practice, with graduates accepting employment with law firms of all sizes. Other recent MSU Law graduates have accepted judicial clerkships (4–8 percent), employment in business or industry (15–25 percent), governmental employment (10–15 percent), and public interest work (3–5 percent). Placement rates for new graduates consistently exceed 90 percent.

Admission

MSU Law has an admission process designed to identify individuals who have the potential to excel in their legal studies and the practice of law. The College of Law seeks to enroll students who are academically talented and who bring to the classroom a diversity of personal and professional experiences and perspectives. The Law College's Admission Committee considers many variables in addition to the applicant's undergraduate grade-point average and score on the LSAT.

The Admission Committee encourages candidates for the Juris Doctor program to apply for admission at the earliest possible date after October 1 and prior to March 1. The Admission Office accepts applications through late spring, with a final deadline of April 30. Candidates whose applications are received prior to March 1 will be given priority consideration for scholarship assistance. Applications for admission are reviewed on a rolling-admission basis beginning in early November and continuing through late spring. Applications generally are reviewed according to the date they are complete with all supporting materials. Admission to Michigan State University College of Law is granted for the fall term only for both the full-time and part-time programs.

Scholarship Assistance

The College of Law offers one of the most generous scholarship programs among law schools nationally, with as many as 45 full-tuition scholarships awarded to members of each incoming class. Additionally, the Law College annually awards 50 scholarships ranging in value up to $25,000. Every applicant who is offered admission to the Law College is considered for scholarship assistance, though grants based on financial need require an application. Law students who achieve a GPA of 3.60 or higher at the end of their first year at MSU Law (29 credit hours) automatically qualify for scholarship assistance that covers one-half, three-quarters, or 100 percent of tuition.

Applicant Profile

Michigan State University College of Law
This grid includes only applicants who earned 120–180 LSAT scores under standard administrations.

LSAT Score	3.75 +		3.50–3.74		3.25–3.49		3.00–3.24		2.75–2.99		2.50–2.74		2.25–2.49		2.00–2.24		Below 2.00		No GPA		Total	
	Apps	Adm	Apps	Adm	Apps	Adm	Apps	Adm	Apps	Adm	Apps	Adm	Apps	Adm	Apps	Adm	Apps	Adm	Apps	Adm	Apps	Adm
175–180	0	0	0	0	0	0	2	2	0	0	0	0	0	0	0	0	0	0	0	0	2	2
170–174	5	5	1	1	3	3	1	1	0	0	0	0	2	2	0	0	0	0	0	0	12	12
165–169	11	11	16	16	8	8	6	6	2	2	4	4	0	0	2	2	0	0	3	3	52	52
160–164	46	46	58	58	44	44	26	25	16	15	5	4	6	5	1	0	3	2	4	3	209	202
155–159	79	77	109	107	109	104	102	96	64	53	40	30	12	2	8	2	3	0	13	9	539	480
150–154	86	66	157	118	196	122	164	71	107	25	65	7	25	5	11	1	8	0	13	4	832	419
145–149	35	16	95	26	126	19	105	2	90	6	61	3	30	1	7	0	0	0	6	0	555	73
140–144	17	3	37	5	58	2	78	2	55	2	48	4	25	0	14	0	1	0	10	0	343	18
135–139	2	0	2	0	22	0	21	0	26	0	24	1	15	0	7	0	4	0	5	1	128	2
130–134	1	0	1	0	3	0	3	0	9	0	9	0	2	0	4	0	1	0	5	0	38	0
125–129	0	0	0	0	0	0	2	0	1	0	2	0	3	0	1	0	1	0	0	0	10	0
120–124	0	0	0	0	0	0	0	0	0	0	0	0	0	0	0	0	0	0	0	0	0	0
Total	282	224	476	331	569	302	510	205	370	103	258	53	120	15	55	5	21	2	59	20	2720	1260

Apps = Number of Applicants
Adm = Number Admitted
Reflects 99% of the total applicant pool; average LSAT data reported.

University of Minnesota Law School

290 Walter F. Mondale Hall, 229 19th Avenue South
Minneapolis, MN 55455
Phone: 612.625.3487; Fax: 612.626.1874
E-mail: jdadmissions@umn.edu; Website: www.law.umn.edu

ABA Approved Since 1923

The Basics

Type of school	Public
Term	Semester
Application deadline	4/1
Application fee	$75
Financial aid deadline	5/1
Can first year start other than fall?	No
Student to faculty ratio	12.0 to 1
# of housing spaces available restricted to law students	
graduate housing for which law students are eligible	

Faculty and Administrators

	Total		Men		Women		Minorities	
	Spr	Fall	Spr	Fall	Spr	Fall	Spr	Fall
Full-time	54	50	32	27	22	23	4	4
Other full-time	3	5	3	3	0	2	0	0
Deans, librarians, & others who teach	8	8	4	4	4	4	1	1
Part-time	137	114	72	60	65	53	5	4
Total	202	177	111	94	91	82	10	9

Curriculum

		Full-Time	Part-Time
Typical first-year section size		96	0
Is there typically a "small section" of the first-year class, other than Legal Writing, taught by full-time faculty		Yes	No
If yes, typical size offered last year		48	
# of classroom course titles beyond first-year curriculum		178	
# of upper division courses, excluding seminars, with an enrollment:	Under 25	64	
	25–49	28	
	50–74	12	
	75–99	10	
	100+	2	
# of seminars		62	
# of seminar positions available		864	
# of seminar positions filled		823	0
# of positions available in simulation courses		403	
# of simulation positions filled		388	0
# of positions available in faculty supervised clinical courses		331	
# of faculty supervised clinical positions filled		325	0
# involved in field placements		164	0
# involved in law journals		195	0
# involved in moot court or trial competitions		65	0
# of credit hours required to graduate		88	

JD Enrollment and Ethnicity

	Men		Women		Full-Time		Part-Time		1st-Year		Total		JD Degs. Awd.
	#	%	#	%	#	%	#	%	#	%	#	%	
African Amer.	14	3.1	8	2.5	22	2.9	0	0.0	10	4.7	22	2.9	3
Amer. Indian	6	1.3	5	1.6	11	1.4	0	0.0	3	1.4	11	1.4	3
Asian Amer.	40	8.9	23	7.2	63	8.2	0	0.0	15	7.0	63	8.2	22
Mex. Amer.	0	0.0	0	0.0	0	0.0	0	0.0	0	0.0	0	0.0	0
Puerto Rican	0	0.0	0	0.0	0	0.0	0	0.0	0	0.0	0	0.0	0
Hispanic	16	3.6	10	3.1	26	3.4	0	0.0	10	4.7	26	3.4	10
Total Minority	76	17.0	46	14.4	122	15.9	0	0.0	38	17.8	122	15.9	38
For. Nation.	11	2.5	10	3.1	21	2.7	0	0.0	4	1.9	21	2.7	2
Caucasian	327	73.2	248	77.7	575	75.1	0	0.0	156	73.2	575	75.1	196
Unknown	33	7.4	15	4.7	48	6.3	0	0.0	15	7.0	48	6.3	19
Total	447	58.4	319	41.6	766	100.0	0	0.0	213	27.8	766		255

Transfers

Transfers in	41
Transfers out	5

Tuition and Fees

	Resident	Nonresident
Full-time	$28,203	$37,605
Part-time		
Tuition Guarantee Program		N

Living Expenses

Estimated living expenses for singles

Living on campus	Living off campus	Living at home
N/A	$14,028	$7,286

University of Minnesota Law School

*ABA
Approved
Since
1923*

GPA and LSAT Scores

	Total	Full-Time	Part-Time
# of apps	3,594	3,594	0
# of offers	911	911	0
# of matrics	213	213	0
75% GPA	3.85	3.85	0.00
Median GPA	3.64	3.64	0.00
25% GPA	3.30	3.30	0.00
75% LSAT	168	168	0
Median LSAT	167	167	0
25% LSAT	160	160	0

Grants and Scholarships (from prior year)

	Total #	Total %	Full-Time #	Full-Time %	Part-Time #	Part-Time %
Total # of students	780		780		0	
Total # receiving grants	500	64.1	500	64.1	0	0.0
Less than 1/2 tuition	346	44.4	346	44.4	0	0.0
Half to full tuition	128	16.4	128	16.4	0	0.0
Full tuition	4	0.5	4	0.5	0	0.0
More than full tuition	22	2.8	22	2.8	0	0.0
Median grant amount			$8,150		$0	

Informational and Library Resources

Total amount spent on library materials	$2,195,208
Study seating capacity inside the library	775
# of full-time equivalent professional librarians	12
Hours per week library is open	81
# of open, wired connections available to students	0
# of networked computers available for use by students	78
Has wireless network?	Y
Require computer?	Y

JD Attrition (from prior year)

	Academic #	Other #	Total #	Total %
1st year	0	14	14	6.1
2nd year	0	8	8	2.7
3rd year	0	0	0	0.0
4th year	0	0	0	0.0

Employment (9 months after graduation)

	Total	Percentage
Employment status known	252	99.6
Employment status unknown	1	0.4
Employed	227	90.1
Pursuing graduate degrees	11	4.4
Unemployed (seeking, not seeking, or studying for the bar)	8	3.2
Type of Employment		
# employed in law firms	136	59.9
# employed in business and industry	17	7.5
# employed in government	25	11.0
# employed in public interest	10	4.4
# employed as judicial clerks	38	16.7
# employed in academia	0	0.0
Geographic Location		
# employed in state	118	52.0
# employed in foreign countries	3	1.3
# of states where employed	28	

Bar Passage Rates

First-time takers	252	Reporting %	73.02
Average school %	96.19	Average state %	90.77
Average pass difference	5.42		

Jurisdiction	Takers	Passers	Pass %	State %	Diff %
Minnesota	137	133	97.08	91.09	5.99
New York	26	23	88.46	88.98	–0.52
Illinois	21	21	100.00	90.94	9.06

University of Minnesota Law School

290 Walter F. Mondale Hall, 229 19th Avenue South
Minneapolis, MN 55455
Phone: 612.625.3487; Fax: 612.626.1874
E-mail: jdadmissions@umn.edu; Website: www.law.umn.edu

■ Introduction

The University of Minnesota Law School, founded in 1888, is one of the country's premier law schools. Under the leadership of international scholar Dean David Wippman, the quality of Minnesota's faculty, the academic credentials of its students, and the caliber of its library and physical facilities are the strongest in the history of the school. For over 120 years, the school's tradition of excellence and innovation in legal education has made it among the best in the nation. In keeping with its Midwestern traditions, the Law School provides a personal, collegial environment for the study of law. At the same time, the school's location in the midst of a thriving cosmopolitan area provides a variety of academic, employment, cultural, and recreational opportunities. Students have easy access to the resources of a world-class research university and to the Twin Cities of Minneapolis and St. Paul, one of the most progressive and livable metropolitan communities in the country.

■ Faculty

The faculty's wide-ranging expertise allows students to choose from an academically rich and innovative curriculum that integrates theory and doctrine with skills, ethics, and practice.

Faculty members are prolific and influential scholars, having published over 250 books and close to 2,500 articles. Thirty-six percent of the tenured faculty are invited members of the prestigious American Law Institute, and 63 percent of them have been honored with chair-level appointments. Members of the faculty include a recent chair of the United Nations Sub-Commission on the Promotion and Protection of Human Rights (the first US citizen to chair the commission since Eleanor Roosevelt), a member of the American Academy of Arts and Sciences, and a former counselor on international law for the US Department of State.

But while the faculty's scholarship has earned them national acclaim, their equally energetic passion for teaching and mentoring, along with a 11:1 student-to-faculty ratio, have earned them the respect and appreciation of their students.

■ Student Body/Admission

With 213 students in the entering class, the student body is large enough to enjoy the benefits of diverse backgrounds, perspectives, and interests, while remaining small enough to foster the kind of collegial and supportive community that is a hallmark of Minnesota life.

Although the atmosphere and camaraderie reflect distinctly Minnesotan values, 45 states, 12 countries, and over 200 undergraduate institutions are represented in the current JD student body. The admissions committee looks beyond a simple evaluation of LSAT and undergraduate GPA to compose a class that will produce leaders in the legal profession. Many students have advanced degrees and prior work experience.

■ Library and Physical Facilities

The award-winning Walter F. Mondale Hall was substantially expanded in 2001. The building houses all faculty offices, 10 law school research institutes, model classrooms in varying sizes, a beautiful auditorium, the law clinics, a cafeteria, the law school bookstore, student lockers, offices for student organizations and publications, a variety of lounge areas, and a computer lab. All incoming JD students are issued laptops, and wireless access is available in all student areas of the building.

Mondale Hall also houses the law library, which is the seventh largest in the United States with over one million volumes. The library offers students 24-hour access. The professional staff takes pride in the outstanding collection of materials and in the individualized service it provides to students and faculty.

■ Curriculum

Minnesota is implementing curriculum innovations that are designed to merge traditionally doctrinal pedagogy with clinical instruction. Beginning in the first year, students will build on basic lawyering skills, doctrinal concepts, and ethical considerations to craft professional solutions to realistic problems in the new Work of the Lawyer class. First-year students will also enjoy Minnesota's rich curriculum with the opportunity to choose an elective in their second semester. Minnesota continues to be one of only a handful of schools with three years of writing requirements and enjoys one of the smallest first-year writing section sizes, with 10–12 students per section. Second-year students are required to participate in a journal or competitive moot court.

Drawing on the strength of our world-class university, qualified students may pursue dual or joint degrees with a myriad of nationally ranked graduate and professional schools. Especially noteworthy is Minnesota's unique joint-degree program in law, health, and the life sciences. Students also enjoy the opportunity to specialize in various subject areas. Currently, concentrations are available in health law and bioethics, human rights, and labor and employment law.

■ Clinical Programs

With 19 separate clinics, Minnesota has one of the country's largest and most active clinical programs. Through the clinics, students represent real clients under the close tutelage of the clinic faculty. Over 50 percent of the student body participates in a live-client clinic prior to graduation, providing more than 18,000 hours of pro bono legal work for the Twin Cities community each year.

■ Special Programs

Minnesota hosts international exchange programs in France, Germany, Ireland, Italy, the Netherlands, Spain, Sweden, and Uruguay. The University of Minnesota Law School also hosts a six-week Summer Study-Abroad Program in Beijing, China. These programs enable interested students to study abroad and allow our students to benefit from the international perspectives students from these countries bring to our classrooms.

Through the Law School Public Service Program, students are asked to perform 50 hours of pro bono legal service for low-income and disadvantaged Minnesotans. Those who complete at least 50 hours of service are recognized for their

dedication with a notation on their transcript and at the graduation ceremony.

Ten major research institutes are housed in the law school: Human Rights Center; Institute on Race and Poverty; Kommerstad Center for Business Law and Entrepreneurship; Consortium on Law and Values in Health, Environment, and the Life Sciences; Institute on Crime and Public Policy; Institute on Intellectual Property; Institute on Law and Economics; Institute on Law and Politics; Institute on Law and Rationality; and Minnesota Center for Legal Studies. These institutes enrich the school's intellectual life, contribute to policy debate and formation, and provide research and employment opportunities for selected law students.

■ Student Activities

Minnesota hosts four student-edited journals: *Minnesota Law Review*; *Law and Inequality: A Journal of Theory and Practice*; *Minnesota Journal of International Law*; and *Minnesota Journal of Law, Science, and Technology*. Students receive academic credit for their journal work.

Students also receive credit for moot court participation. The breadth of Minnesota's moot court program is unusual, with eight programs spanning a wide variety of subject areas: Civil Rights Moot Court, Intellectual Property Moot Court, International Moot Court, Environmental Moot Court, Wagner Labor Law Moot Court, National Moot Court, ABA Moot Court, and Maynard Pirsig Moot Court.

Student extracurricular activities include 50 separate student organizations, spanning the full spectrum of political viewpoints, social interests, and intellectual and recreational activities (not to mention a full-blown musical theatre production).

■ Expenses and Financial Aid

In recent years, over 90 percent of the student body has received financial aid and approximately 65 percent of each incoming class received a scholarship of some kind. Second- and third-year students also may apply for research assistantships.

■ Career and Professional Development

With alumni in all 50 states and over 260 federal and state court judges nationwide, our graduates are leaders in the judiciary, government, law practice, business, and academics. Employers interview on campus, at regional interview programs sponsored by the Career and Professional Development Center, and at job fairs for nearly 700 offices, including law firms, corporations, and governmental agencies from around the United States. Employers nationwide regularly solicit résumés from our students for job postings. Each year, 15–20 percent of our graduates accept prestigious judicial clerkships, and 98 percent are employed within nine months of graduation.

Applicant Profile

University of Minnesota Law School

LSAT Score	GPA																				
	3.75 +		3.50–3.74		3.25–3.49		3.00–3.24		2.75–2.99		2.50–2.74		2.25–2.49		2.00–2.24		Below 2.00		No GPA		Total
	Apps	Adm	Apps	Adm	Apps	Adm	Apps	Adm	Apps	Adm	Apps	Adm	Apps	Adm	Apps	Adm	Apps	Adm	Apps	Adm	Apps Adm
175–180	12	11	15	9	7	3	4	0	5	0	6	3	2	0	1	0	0	0	0	0	52 26
170–174	51	39	61	48	55	36	24	12	15	10	8	1	4	1	1	1	0	0	4	1	223 149
165–169	178	134	192	112	167	103	93	45	56	14	28	7	8	2	3	0	0	0	14	6	739 423
160–164	228	111	247	28	215	27	115	16	50	3	28	0	10	0	3	0	2	0	36	2	934 187
155–159	135	44	209	22	184	13	119	4	65	1	31	0	21	0	7	0	2	0	32	0	805 84
150–154	81	23	118	4	113	3	99	2	44	0	29	0	15	0	3	0	0	0	15	0	517 32
145–149	27	3	30	2	48	0	38	0	17	0	9	0	5	0	2	0	0	0	6	0	182 5
140–144	6	0	5	0	15	0	18	0	8	0	12	0	1	0	3	0	1	0	7	0	76 0
135–139	2	0	0	0	2	0	5	0	3	0	6	0	2	0	1	0	0	0	2	0	23 0
130–134	1	0	0	0	0	0	0	0	2	0	2	0	2	0	0	0	0	0	2	0	9 0
125–129	0	0	0	0	0	0	0	0	0	0	3	0	0	0	1	0	0	0	0	0	4 0
120–124	0	0	0	0	0	0	0	0	0	0	0	0	0	0	1	0	0	0	0	0	1 0
Total	721	365	877	225	806	185	515	79	265	28	162	11	70	3	26	1	5	0	118	9	3565 906

Apps = Number of Applicants
Adm = Number Admitted
Reflects 99% of the total applicant pool; average LSAT data reported.

This grid includes all applicants who earned 120–180 LSAT scores.
This chart is to be used as a general guide only. Nonnumerical factors are strongly considered for all applicants.

The University of Mississippi School of Law

Lamar Law Center, PO Box 1848
University, MS 38677
Phone: Admission: 662.915.6910, Main: 662.915.7361; Fax: 662.915.1289
E-mail: bvinson@olemiss.edu; Website: www.law.olemiss.edu

ABA Approved Since 1930

The Basics

Type of school	Public
Term	Semester
Application deadline	3/1
Application fee	$40
Financial aid deadline	3/15
Can first year start other than fall?	Yes
Student to faculty ratio	18.2 to 1
# of housing spaces available restricted to law students	
graduate housing for which law students are eligible	

Faculty and Administrators

	Total		Men		Women		Minorities	
	Spr	Fall	Spr	Fall	Spr	Fall	Spr	Fall
Full-time	22	22	16	17	6	5	4	3
Other full-time	7	7	5	5	2	2	1	1
Deans, librarians, & others who teach	7	6	5	5	2	1	0	0
Part-time	16	12	10	6	6	6	2	2
Total	52	47	36	33	16	14	7	6

Curriculum

	Full-Time	Part-Time
Typical first-year section size	57	0
Is there typically a "small section" of the first-year class, other than Legal Writing, taught by full-time faculty	No	No
If yes, typical size offered last year		
# of classroom course titles beyond first-year curriculum	89	
# of upper division courses, excluding seminars, with an enrollment: Under 25	43	
25–49	21	
50–74	6	
75–99	7	
100+	1	
# of seminars	24	
# of seminar positions available	460	
# of seminar positions filled	370	0
# of positions available in simulation courses	231	
# of simulation positions filled	188	0
# of positions available in faculty supervised clinical courses	69	
# of faculty supervised clinical positions filled	65	0
# involved in field placements	34	0
# involved in law journals	79	0
# involved in moot court or trial competitions	35	0
# of credit hours required to graduate	90	

JD Enrollment and Ethnicity

	Men		Women		Full-Time		Part-Time		1st-Year		Total		JD Degs. Awd.
	#	%	#	%	#	%	#	%	#	%	#	%	
African Amer.	15	5.4	45	20.9	60	12.1	0	0.0	23	13.3	60	12.1	23
Amer. Indian	2	0.7	2	0.9	4	0.8	0	0.0	0	0.0	4	0.8	1
Asian Amer.	2	0.7	2	0.9	4	0.8	0	0.0	1	0.6	4	0.8	1
Mex. Amer.	0	0.0	0	0.0	0	0.0	0	0.0	0	0.0	0	0.0	0
Puerto Rican	0	0.0	0	0.0	0	0.0	0	0.0	0	0.0	0	0.0	0
Hispanic	3	1.1	1	0.5	4	0.8	0	0.0	1	0.6	4	0.8	2
Total Minority	22	7.9	50	23.3	72	14.5	0	0.0	25	14.5	72	14.5	27
For. Nation.	0	0.0	0	0.0	0	0.0	0	0.0	0	0.0	0	0.0	0
Caucasian	258	92.1	164	76.3	422	85.3	0	0.0	148	85.5	422	85.3	149
Unknown	0	0.0	1	0.5	1	0.2	0	0.0	0	0.0	1	0.2	0
Total	280	56.6	215	43.4	495	100.0	0	0.0	173	34.9	495		176

Transfers

Transfers in	0
Transfers out	3

Tuition and Fees

	Resident	Nonresident
Full-time	$9,350	$20,440
Part-time		
Tuition Guarantee Program		N

Living Expenses

Estimated living expenses for singles

Living on campus	Living off campus	Living at home
$18,760	$18,760	$18,760

The University of Mississippi School of Law

ABA
Approved
Since
1930

GPA and LSAT Scores

	Total	Full-Time	Part-Time
# of apps	1,164	1,164	0
# of offers	472	472	0
# of matrics	173	173	0
75% GPA	3.71	3.71	0.00
Median GPA	3.49	3.49	0.00
25% GPA	3.27	3.27	0.00
75% LSAT	157	157	0
Median LSAT	154	154	0
25% LSAT	151	151	0

Grants and Scholarships (from prior year)

	Total		Full-Time		Part-Time	
	#	%	#	%	#	%
Total # of students	494		494		0	
Total # receiving grants	144	29.1	144	29.1	0	0.0
Less than 1/2 tuition	62	12.6	62	12.6	0	0.0
Half to full tuition	59	11.9	59	11.9	0	0.0
Full tuition	4	0.8	4	0.8	0	0.0
More than full tuition	19	3.8	19	3.8	0	0.0
Median grant amount			$1,000		$0	

Informational and Library Resources

Total amount spent on library materials	$805,581
Study seating capacity inside the library	305
# of full-time equivalent professional librarians	7
Hours per week library is open	105
# of open, wired connections available to students	737
# of networked computers available for use by students	62
Has wireless network?	Y
Require computer?	N

JD Attrition (from prior year)

	Academic	Other	Total	
	#	#	#	%
1st year	5	7	12	7.3
2nd year	1	1	2	1.2
3rd year	0	0	0	0.0
4th year	0	0	0	0.0

Employment (9 months after graduation)

	Total	Percentage
Employment status known	168	95.5
Employment status unknown	8	4.5
Employed	152	90.5
Pursuing graduate degrees	1	0.6
Unemployed (seeking, not seeking, or studying for the bar)	12	7.1
Type of Employment		
# employed in law firms	76	50.0
# employed in business and industry	17	11.2
# employed in government	21	13.8
# employed in public interest	7	4.6
# employed as judicial clerks	26	17.1
# employed in academia	5	3.3
Geographic Location		
# employed in state	90	59.2
# employed in foreign countries	0	0.0
# of states where employed		17

Bar Passage Rates

First-time takers	147	Reporting %	81.63
Average school %	90.00	Average state %	88.14
Average pass difference	1.86		

Jurisdiction	Takers	Passers	Pass %	State %	Diff %
Mississippi	120	108	90.00	88.14	1.86

The University of Mississippi School of Law

Lamar Law Center, PO Box 1848
University, MS 38677
Phone: Admission: 662.915.6910, Main: 662.915.7361; Fax: 662.915.1289
E-mail: bvinson@olemiss.edu; Website: www.law.olemiss.edu

■ Introduction

Recognizing the need for formal law instruction in the state of Mississippi, the legislature, in 1854, established the Department of Law at the University of Mississippi. Located in Oxford, on the main campus of the University of Mississippi, the School of Law is housed in Lamar Hall, named in honor of the late Mississippian, L.Q.C. Lamar, former Associate Justice of the United States Supreme Court and one of the first law professors at the university. Oxford, a small town of approximately 19,000 people, lies nestled in the quiet hills of North Mississippi, just 75 miles southeast of bustling Memphis, Tennessee, and 180 miles north of the state capital of Jackson.

A new law building is under construction with planned occupancy in fall 2010. The new building will have traditional Greek Revival architecture to match the architectural style of the campus, and it will be state-of-the-art in terms of instructional space.

The University of Mississippi is the fourth oldest state-supported law school in the nation. The School of Law is fully approved by the American Bar Association and is a long-standing member of the Association of American Law Schools.

■ Library and Physical Facilities

The library houses one of the most extensive federal, state, and international law collections in the Southeast. The library's experienced, service-oriented staff is available to assist patrons with these materials and to provide training in all aspects of traditional and computer-assisted legal research. Other library features include open stacks, an online catalog, two state-of-the-art computer labs, and private study rooms and carrels that may be reserved. The library has a strong commitment to new information technologies and has recently added additional multimedia support, along with enhanced wired and wireless network access for patrons.

■ Admission

Admission to law school is gained by committee approval based upon an applicant's credentials. These credentials include a satisfactory LSAT score and an acceptable academic record at the undergraduate level. A bachelor's degree from an accredited school is required before an applicant can register for law school.

There are no prelaw requisites. Every applicant must take the LSAT and register with LSAC's Credential Assembly Service. An LSAT score obtained more than three years before application is not valid, and the applicant will be required to retake the test. Applications are available the September preceding admission, with the application completion deadline for both summer and fall enrollment being March 1. However, early application is encouraged. Applicants who file late risk being placed on a waiting list.

Although the LSAT and GPA are the most important factors in the admission process, other considerations are (1) grade patterns and progression; (2) quality of undergraduate institution; (3) difficulty of major field of study; (4) number of years since bachelor's degree was earned; (5) job experience;

(6) social, personal, or economic circumstances that may have affected college grades or performance on the LSAT or academic record; (7) nonacademic achievements; (8) letters of recommendation; and (9) residency.

■ Entrance Dates

Students are given the option to enter in the summer or fall of each admission year. Because summer and fall enrollees are considered as one class, the same standards are applied in the decision-making process.

■ Curriculum

First-year students complete a predetermined curriculum that focuses on the development of analytical skills and a foundation of substantive knowledge. Largely, second- and third-year students are free to select their own courses of study and emphasis, although a number of courses are recommended to ensure a broad-based substantive and procedural background. Students may select from a large number of elective courses, including seminars, clinical, and trial advocacy courses. The elective curriculum offers generous opportunities for students to pursue special interests such as constitutional and individual rights, business and commercial transactions, federal taxation, international law, and environmental law.

■ Clinical Programs

Civil Legal Clinic—Under the supervision of the director of the clinic, students provide legal counseling for low-income clients on civil matters. The program includes clinical units in Elder Law, Consumer Law, Child Advocacy, Legislation, and Domestic Violence.

Criminal Appeals Clinic—The Criminal Appeals Clinic was established by the National Center for Justice and the Rule of Law. The course of study is designed to give students practical experience representing clients in criminal appellate cases and includes direct student participation in the pro bono representation of indigent persons in their cases on appeal.

Prosecution Externship Program—The Prosecution Externship was established by the National Center for Justice and the Rule of Law. It is designed to prepare law students for careers in criminal law by combining academic training with placements as externs in local, state, and federal prosecutor offices.

■ Student Activities

The *Mississippi Law Journal*, edited and published by law students three times each year, includes articles by distinguished professors, judges, and practitioners.

The *Journal of Space Law* is the oldest journal dedicated to space law and is the only one of its kind in the United States. The National Center for Remote Sensing, Air and Space Law faculty regularly supervise an editorial team of 15–18 law student editors, staff, and authors on this journal.

The **Moot Court Board** oversees several moot court competitions, including the Steen, Reynolds, and Dalehite

trial competition each fall and the McGlinchey Stafford oral-advocacy competition each spring.

Summer-Abroad Programs

The School of Law offers an opportunity to earn up to six semester credit hours in its summer session held annually in England at Downing College, Cambridge University. Classes offered are for full academic credit and are subject to the same academic standards maintained in the domestic program.

Special Programs

One of the most active organizations is the **Public Interest Law Foundation**. The student-run organization focuses its efforts on community groups that need legal assistance—victims of domestic violence, children, and defendants who cannot afford an attorney. The organization raises money to support students working in public interest jobs.

The **National Center for Justice and the Rule of Law** is a component of the law center funded by a multimillion dollar grant from the Department of Justice. The center works cooperatively with agencies in sponsoring research, hosting international and national conferences, and presenting educational programs on issues related to criminal justice, such as international and domestic terrorism, drug-trafficking, and the role of the proposed International Criminal Court. Advanced courses in criminal law and procedure are offered to students who may choose a criminal law concentration and receive official recognition of that achievement upon graduation.

The **National Center for Remote Sensing, Air and Space Law** is funded by a grant from NASA. The only center of its kind in the United States, it serves as a research, advisory, and training resource for the emerging commercial geospatial industry, the international legal community, and related user groups. A concentration in remote sensing, air and space law is available through the center. Courses include US Space Law, International Space Law, Remote Sensing Law, Independent Study, US Aviation Law, International Aviation Law, and Journal of Space Law.

Mississippi Innocence Project—Established in 2007 and housed at the School of Law, the Mississippi Innocence Project is committed to providing the highest quality legal representation to its clients: state prisoners serving significant periods of incarceration who have cognizable claims of wrongful conviction.

Housing

The majority of law students live off campus in rental units. On-campus housing is available, and students who are interested in living on campus should make early application to the Housing Office.

Career Services

A full-time director of career services assists students in finding employment. Seventy-five to 100 law firms and other prospective employers interview at the law school each year. Approximately 60 percent of graduating seniors are employed prior to graduation, with the remaining number being placed within six months of graduation. The law school is an active member of the National Association for Law Placement (NALP) and annually participates in the Atlanta Legal Hiring Conference, the Equal Justice Works Public Interest Career Fair, the Patent Law Interview Program, and the Southeastern Minority Job Fair.

Applicant Profile

The University of Mississippi School of Law
This grid includes only applicants who earned 120–180 LSAT scores under standard administrations.

LSAT Score	GPA 3.75 +		3.50–3.74		3.25–3.49		3.00–3.24		2.75–2.99		2.50–2.74		2.25–2.49		2.00–2.24		Below 2.00		No GPA		Total	
	Apps	Adm	Apps	Adm	Apps	Adm	Apps	Adm	Apps	Adm	Apps	Adm	Apps	Adm	Apps	Adm	Apps	Adm	Apps	Adm	Apps	Adm
175–180	0	0	0	0	0	0	0	0	0	0	0	0	0	0	0	0	0	0	0	0	0	0
170–174	2	2	0	0	0	0	0	0	2	1	0	0	0	0	0	0	0	0	0	0	4	3
165–169	4	4	3	3	2	1	2	2	3	3	1	1	0	0	0	0	0	0	0	0	15	14
160–164	15	15	17	17	14	14	17	15	10	7	6	1	1	0	3	1	0	0	0	0	83	70
155–159	52	52	38	38	61	48	52	28	24	9	16	1	4	0	0	0	0	0	1	0	248	176
150–154	67	59	78	41	96	33	73	13	40	3	27	1	10	0	0	0	0	0	0	0	391	150
145–149	30	10	33	11	49	10	49	5	31	3	16	0	11	0	5	0	1	0	4	0	229	39
140–144	6	2	22	4	22	2	32	4	16	0	11	1	1	0	5	0	0	0	2	0	117	13
135–139	1	0	6	1	9	1	6	0	4	0	4	0	5	0	5	0	0	0	0	0	40	2
130–134	0	0	0	0	1	0	5	0	4	0	1	0	3	0	1	0	0	0	0	0	15	0
125–129	0	0	0	0	3	0	0	0	1	0	2	0	1	0	0	0	0	0	1	0	8	0
120–124	0	0	0	0	0	0	0	0	0	0	0	0	0	0	0	0	0	0	0	0	0	0
Total	177	144	197	115	257	109	236	67	135	26	84	5	36	0	19	1	1	0	8	0	1150	467

Apps = Number of Applicants
Adm = Number Admitted
Reflects 99% of the total applicant pool; average LSAT data reported.

Mississippi College School of Law

151 E. Griffith Street
Jackson, MS 39201
Phone: 601.925.7152
E-mail: lawadmissions@mc.edu; Website: http://law.mc.edu

ABA Approved Since 1980

The Basics

Type of school	Private
Term	Semester
Application deadline	6/1
Application fee	
Financial aid deadline	6/1
Can first year start other than fall?	No
Student to faculty ratio	18.2 to 1
# of housing spaces available restricted to law students	
graduate housing for which law students are eligible	

Faculty and Administrators

	Total		Men		Women		Minorities	
	Spr	Fall	Spr	Fall	Spr	Fall	Spr	Fall
Full-time	23	25	11	11	12	14	3	5
Other full-time	0	0	0	0	0	0	0	0
Deans, librarians, & others who teach	8	8	5	5	3	3	1	1
Part-time	74	85	53	48	20	36	5	9
Total	105	118	69	64	35	53	9	15

Curriculum

	Full-Time	Part-Time
Typical first-year section size	87	0
Is there typically a "small section" of the first-year class, other than Legal Writing, taught by full-time faculty	Yes	No
If yes, typical size offered last year	48	
# of classroom course titles beyond first-year curriculum	84	

# of upper division courses, excluding seminars, with an enrollment:		
Under 25	78	
25–49	22	
50–74	19	
75–99	4	
100+	1	

	Full-Time	Part-Time
# of seminars	13	
# of seminar positions available	200	
# of seminar positions filled	157	0
# of positions available in simulation courses	880	
# of simulation positions filled	709	0
# of positions available in faculty supervised clinical courses	47	
# of faculty supervised clinical positions filled	39	0
# involved in field placements	148	0
# involved in law journals	48	0
# involved in moot court or trial competitions	86	0
# of credit hours required to graduate	90	

JD Enrollment and Ethnicity

	Men #	Men %	Women #	Women %	Full-Time #	Full-Time %	Part-Time #	Part-Time %	1st-Year #	1st-Year %	Total #	Total %	JD Degs. Awd.
African Amer.	13	4.2	37	16.4	48	9.2	2	13.3	23	11.6	50	9.3	16
Amer. Indian	2	0.6	0	0.0	2	0.4	0	0.0	1	0.5	2	0.4	0
Asian Amer.	4	1.3	3	1.3	7	1.3	0	0.0	2	1.0	7	1.3	0
Mex. Amer.	0	0.0	0	0.0	0	0.0	0	0.0	0	0.0	0	0.0	0
Puerto Rican	0	0.0	0	0.0	0	0.0	0	0.0	0	0.0	0	0.0	0
Hispanic	4	1.3	0	0.0	4	0.8	0	0.0	0	0.0	4	0.7	0
Total Minority	23	7.4	40	17.8	61	11.7	2	13.3	26	13.1	63	11.8	16
For. Nation.	1	0.3	0	0.0	1	0.2	0	0.0	1	0.5	1	0.2	0
Caucasian	283	91.0	177	78.7	447	85.8	13	86.7	166	83.8	460	85.8	152
Unknown	4	1.3	8	3.6	12	2.3	0	0.0	5	2.5	12	2.2	3
Total	311	58.0	225	42.0	521	97.2	15	2.8	198	36.9	536		171

Transfers

Transfers in	1
Transfers out	11

Tuition and Fees

	Resident	Nonresident
Full-time	$26,300	
Part-time		
Tuition Guarantee Program		Y

Living Expenses

Estimated living expenses for singles

Living on campus	Living off campus	Living at home
N/A	$18,825	$18,825

Mississippi College School of Law

ABA
Approved
Since
1980

GPA and LSAT Scores

	Total	Full-Time	Part-Time
# of apps	1,316	1,315	1
# of offers	745	744	1
# of matrics	194	193	1
75% GPA	3.53	3.53	0.00
Median GPA	3.30	3.30	4.01
25% GPA	3.01	3.01	0.00
75% LSAT	153	153	0
Median LSAT	150	150	153
25% LSAT	148	148	0

Grants and Scholarships (from prior year)

	Total		Full-Time		Part-Time	
	#	%	#	%	#	%
Total # of students	549		537		12	
Total # receiving grants	180	32.8	180	33.5	0	0.0
Less than 1/2 tuition	107	19.5	107	19.9	0	0.0
Half to full tuition	30	5.5	30	5.6	0	0.0
Full tuition	15	2.7	15	2.8	0	0.0
More than full tuition	28	5.1	28	5.2	0	0.0
Median grant amount			$5,000		$0	

Informational and Library Resources

Total amount spent on library materials	$977,536
Study seating capacity inside the library	394
# of full-time equivalent professional librarians	5
Hours per week library is open	108
# of open, wired connections available to students	0
# of networked computers available for use by students	24
Has wireless network?	Y
Require computer?	N

JD Attrition (from prior year)

	Academic	Other	Total	
	#	#	#	%
1st year	10	19	29	14.6
2nd year	1	2	3	1.5
3rd year	0	0	0	0.0
4th year	0	0	0	0.0

Employment (9 months after graduation)

	Total	Percentage
Employment status known	162	100.0
Employment status unknown	0	0.0
Employed	146	90.1
Pursuing graduate degrees	7	4.3
Unemployed (seeking, not seeking, or studying for the bar)	9	5.6
Type of Employment		
# employed in law firms	76	52.1
# employed in business and industry	29	19.9
# employed in government	22	15.1
# employed in public interest	0	0.0
# employed as judicial clerks	18	12.3
# employed in academia	1	0.7
Geographic Location		
# employed in state	97	66.4
# employed in foreign countries	2	1.4
# of states where employed	17	

Bar Passage Rates

First-time takers	150	Reporting %	70.00
Average school %	94.28	Average state %	88.19
Average pass difference	6.09		

Jurisdiction	Takers	Passers	Pass %	State %	Diff %
Mississippi	99	93	93.94	88.14	5.80
Alabama	6	6	100.00	89.02	10.98

Mississippi College School of Law

151 E. Griffith Street
Jackson, MS 39201
Phone: 601.925.7152
E-mail: lawadmissions@mc.edu; Website: http://law.mc.edu

■ Introduction

Mississippi College School of Law (MC Law), located in downtown Jackson, the state's capital and largest city, serves as a state-of-the-art legal center for the mid-South. Jackson, with a metropolitan population of 480,000, is the legal, political, cultural, and commercial center of Mississippi.

MC Law's innovative campus includes an administrative building; an 18,000-square-foot classroom building that houses high-tech classrooms, a multipurpose courtroom and lecture hall, seminar rooms, a jury room, judges' chambers, and teaching centers; a nationally recognized law library; and a Student Center. A safe and convenient student parking lot is located next to the law school. Within walking distance of the law school lies a vibrant, thriving legal community, as well as the legislature, federal and state administrative agencies, and courts.

Founded in 1826, Mississippi College is the oldest college in Mississippi and is located in Clinton, a suburb 12 miles west of Jackson. The law school was acquired by Mississippi College in 1975, is accredited by the American Bar Association, is a member of the Association of American Law Schools, and is a charter member of the International Association of Law Schools. Graduates of MC Law take the bar examination in all 50 states.

■ Admission

When admitting students, the Office of Admissions uses a whole-person concept. The law school has rolling admissions, with admission standards based on the college undergraduate grade-point average, the LSAT score, and personal or academic achievements or honors. A degree from an accredited four-year college or university is a prerequisite to admission. Every applicant must take the LSAT and register for the Credential Assembly Service (CAS) prior to being considered for admission. The school makes admission decisions without discrimination against any person on the basis of race, religion, gender, orientation, age, or national origin. The application deadline is June 1. When an applicant is accepted, a deposit of $250 is required to reserve a seat in the entering class. A second deposit of $250 must be received by June 1. Upon enrollment, these nonrefundable payments are credited to the applicant's tuition.

Tuition is locked-in so that a student pays the same tuition throughout law school with no subsequent increase. All applicants are automatically considered for merit-based scholarships that exceed $2 million.

■ Learning Environment

Our students receive one-on-one attention and interaction with professors that extend beyond the classroom. The school is dedicated to maintaining a supportive learning environment. Because of our small size and collegial atmosphere, students form lasting relationships with one another, collaborate on team projects, and are active in a variety of cocurricular and extracurricular activities.

■ Curriculum

MC Law is a foundational law school. Our course of study integrates the theoretical aspects of the law with practical, hands-on training. First-year law students are required to take fundamental courses that focus on the major doctrinal areas of law, as well as development of legal writing and research skills. The law school offers a diverse range of second- and third-year elective courses. Our curriculum emphasizes the following disciplines: litigation and dispute resolution, family law, business and tax law, bioethics and health law, international law, and advocacy. MC Law offers a Louisiana Civil Law Certificate program for those who want to practice in Louisiana or to study comparative law.

The law school's Child Advocacy Program is a premier training ground, equipping students with the skills required to shepherd children in need of an advocate through the court system. It gives second- and third-year students the opportunity to work under faculty supervision in handling numerous adoptions and other child-related cases.

The law school operates on a semester basis, and a beginning student must enter in the fall semester. A summer term is available to second- and third-year students who wish to accelerate or enrich their studies.

■ Externship Program

At MC Law, classroom theory and practical application go hand-in-hand. In addition to courses in legal doctrine, a wide range of instruction in the skills of modern practice is offered to second- and third-year students. Student externs work alongside practicing attorneys in government offices and public interest organizations. Depending on the particular externship, students present cases in court, interview witnesses, prepare pleadings, take depositions, negotiate with opposing parties, research legal issues, and draft court opinions. This program allows students to practice in the real world what they have learned in more traditional law school classes and gain experience prior to graduation. Many students secure employment as a result of this extern program.

■ Student Activities

The *Mississippi College Law Review* is a legal journal edited and published by law students who are selected on the basis of scholarship and the ability to do creative, scholarly research and writing. Membership on the *Law Review* staff is recognized as both an honor and a unique educational experience. The law school also provides an appellate advocacy program administered by the Moot Court Board, composed of second- and third-year students. This required program provides students with instruction and practice in both brief writing and oral argument. The school's legal aid office allows students to acquire client interviewing skills and substantive practical experience while providing a valuable pro bono service.

The Law Student Bar Association is the organized student government of the law school. All students are members and are eligible to hold office in the association. Other student activities include two national legal fraternity chapters, Phi

Alpha Delta and Phi Delta Phi; student chapters of the Mississippi Association for Justice and the American Association for Justice; the Women's Student Bar Association; and the Environmental Law Association, among others. Students are afforded the opportunity to participate on a number of national moot court teams and have enjoyed regional and national success.

■ Career Services

The Career Services Office assists in placement. In addition to the traditional on-campus interviews, the law school participates in regional interviews. Students are also encouraged to work in local or national public interest or government agencies through the MC Law/Federal Work-Study public interest program. Graduates are employed by major law firms, corporations, and government agencies throughout the United States, with a primary focus in the Southeast. Students have received clerkships with the United States Court of Appeals, United States District Courts, and the appellate and trial courts of various states. A number of graduates serve as JAG officers in the military services.

■ Minority Program

The law school offers a variety of programs to assist minority students: scholarships/stipends and an Academic Support Program. Minority students are strongly encouraged to apply, and each applicant's entire record will be carefully considered.

■ Faculty

Teaching is our strength. Our faculty members have impeccable credentials and are leaders in their fields of study. From insurance to international law and from constitutional law to ethics, our professors are regularly cited in courts,

scholarly journals, and the media. MC Law is renowned for the extraordinary level of interaction between faculty and students.

Because of our strategic location, federal and state judges and some of the best legal practitioners teach as adjunct professors, giving our students valuable practical training and enviable networking opportunities.

■ Library

The law library has a collection of more than 360,000 volumes and is committed to acquiring materials for both the immediate and the long-term needs of the law school. Emphasis is placed on development of the collections of statutes, legal periodicals, federal and state legislative materials, reports of all federal and all state appellate courts, federal administrative agency materials, specialized loose-leaf services, and microforms and treatises that support our mission. The library is a member of the American Association of Law Libraries. The technology division supports a WiFi system and a help desk for students.

■ International Law Center

The International Law Center permits our students to take a global focus in their legal education. In addition to the international law-related courses the center oversees, students can participate in the Korean Summer Legal Studies Program in Seoul, South Korea. The center coordinates a series of speakers and programs with an international theme.

■ Executive Law School Program

An Executive Law School Program permits professionals to continue their employment or business while completing their legal studies in a five year period on a part-time basis.

Applicant Profile

Mississippi College School of Law
This grid includes only applicants who earned 120–180 LSAT scores under standard administrations.

LSAT Score	GPA								
	3.75 +	3.50–3.74	3.25–3.49	3.00–3.24	2.75–2.99	2.50–2.74	2.25–2.49	2.00–2.24	Below 2.00
175–180									
170–174									
165–169									
160–164									
155–159									
150–154									
145–149									
140–144									
135–139									
130–134									
125–129									
120–124									

■ Good Possibility   □ Possibility   ▨ Unlikely

University of Missouri School of Law

Office of Admissions, 103 Hulston Hall
Columbia, MO 65211
Phone: 573.882.6042, toll-free: 888.MULaw4U; Fax: 573.882.9625
E-mail: mulawadmissions@missouri.edu; Website: www.law.missouri.edu

The Basics

Type of school	Public
Term	Semester
Application deadline	3/1
Application fee	$55
Financial aid deadline	3/1
Can first year start other than fall?	No
Student to faculty ratio	17.9 to 1
# of housing spaces available restricted to law students	
graduate housing for which law students are eligible	

Faculty and Administrators

	Total		Men		Women		Minorities	
	Spr	Fall	Spr	Fall	Spr	Fall	Spr	Fall
Full-time	19	22	15	16	4	6	3	3
Other full-time	0	0	0	0	0	0	0	0
Deans, librarians, & others who teach	9	9	6	6	3	3	0	0
Part-time	17	9	8	6	9	3	1	1
Total	45	40	29	28	16	12	4	4

JD Enrollment and Ethnicity

	Men		Women		Full-Time		Part-Time		1st-Year		Total		JD Degs. Awd.
	#	%	#	%	#	%	#	%	#	%	#	%	
African Amer.	13	4.7	16	9.4	28	6.3	1	25.0	11	7.1	29	6.5	6
Amer. Indian	0	0.0	3	1.8	3	0.7	0	0.0	0	0.0	3	0.7	4
Asian Amer.	8	2.9	8	4.7	15	3.4	1	25.0	4	2.6	16	3.6	12
Mex. Amer.	2	0.7	2	1.2	4	0.9	0	0.0	4	2.6	4	0.9	0
Puerto Rican	0	0.0	0	0.0	0	0.0	0	0.0	0	0.0	0	0.0	0
Hispanic	7	2.6	2	1.2	9	2.0	0	0.0	2	1.3	9	2.0	7
Total Minority	30	10.9	31	18.1	59	13.4	2	50.0	21	13.6	61	13.7	29
For. Nation.	0	0.0	1	0.6	1	0.2	0	0.0	0	0.0	1	0.2	0
Caucasian	238	86.9	136	79.5	372	84.4	2	50.0	132	85.7	374	84.0	114
Unknown	6	2.2	3	1.8	9	2.0	0	0.0	1	0.6	9	2.0	8
Total	274	61.6	171	38.4	441	99.1	4	0.9	154	34.6	445		151

Curriculum

	Full-Time	Part-Time
Typical first-year section size	73	0
Is there typically a "small section" of the first-year class, other than Legal Writing, taught by full-time faculty	Yes	No
If yes, typical size offered last year	37	
# of classroom course titles beyond first-year curriculum	119	
# of upper division courses, excluding seminars, with an enrollment: Under 25	82	
25–49	27	
50–74	12	
75–99	3	
100+	0	
# of seminars	3	
# of seminar positions available	65	
# of seminar positions filled	63	0
# of positions available in simulation courses	303	
# of simulation positions filled	246	0
# of positions available in faculty supervised clinical courses	46	
# of faculty supervised clinical positions filled	45	0
# involved in field placements	63	0
# involved in law journals	122	0
# involved in moot court or trial competitions	126	0
# of credit hours required to graduate	89	

Transfers

Transfers in	10
Transfers out	5

Tuition and Fees

	Resident	Nonresident
Full-time	$16,017	$30,519
Part-time		
Tuition Guarantee Program		N

Living Expenses

Estimated living expenses for singles

Living on campus	Living off campus	Living at home
$15,610	$15,610	$15,610

University of Missouri School of Law

ABA
Approved
Since
1923

GPA and LSAT Scores

	Total	Full-Time	Part-Time
# of apps	914	914	0
# of offers	400	400	0
# of matrics	147	147	0
75% GPA	3.70	3.70	0.00
Median GPA	3.47	3.47	0.00
25% GPA	3.24	3.24	0.00
75% LSAT	161	161	0
Median LSAT	158	158	0
25% LSAT	156	156	0

Grants and Scholarships (from prior year)

	Total		Full-Time		Part-Time	
	#	%	#	%	#	%
Total # of students	453		448		5	
Total # receiving grants	258	57.0	258	57.6	0	0.0
Less than 1/2 tuition	218	48.1	218	48.7	0	0.0
Half to full tuition	33	7.3	33	7.4	0	0.0
Full tuition	0	0.0	0	0.0	0	0.0
More than full tuition	7	1.5	7	1.6	0	0.0
Median grant amount			$4,025		$0	

Informational and Library Resources

Total amount spent on library materials	$782,015
Study seating capacity inside the library	472
# of full-time equivalent professional librarians	7
Hours per week library is open	70
# of open, wired connections available to students	6
# of networked computers available for use by students	54
Has wireless network?	Y
Require computer?	N

JD Attrition (from prior year)

	Academic	Other	Total	
	#	#	#	%
1st year	2	11	13	8.9
2nd year	1	0	1	0.7
3rd year	0	1	1	0.6
4th year	0	0	0	0.0

Employment (9 months after graduation)

	Total	Percentage
Employment status known	138	98.6
Employment status unknown	2	1.4
Employed	123	89.1
Pursuing graduate degrees	5	3.6
Unemployed (seeking, not seeking, or studying for the bar)	7	5.1
Type of Employment		
# employed in law firms	66	53.7
# employed in business and industry	14	11.4
# employed in government	17	13.8
# employed in public interest	6	4.9
# employed as judicial clerks	16	13.0
# employed in academia	2	1.6
Geographic Location		
# employed in state	98	79.7
# employed in foreign countries	1	0.8
# of states where employed	13	

Bar Passage Rates

First-time takers	140	Reporting %	87.86
Average school %	91.87	Average state %	92.33
Average pass difference	−0.46		

Jurisdiction	Takers	Passers	Pass %	State %	Diff %
Missouri	123	113	91.87	92.33	−0.46

University of Missouri School of Law

Office of Admissions, 103 Hulston Hall
Columbia, MO 65211
Phone: 573.882.6042, toll-free: 888.MULaw4U; Fax: 573.882.9625
E-mail: mulawadmissions@missouri.edu; Website: www.law.missouri.edu

■ Introduction

The University of Missouri School of Law (MU) is a dynamic and collegial community. Founded in 1839, MU was the first state university west of the Mississippi River. Established in 1872, the School of Law has had an enviable history of service to the state and the nation. Graduates include judges, governors, attorneys general, and legislators who serve locally and nationwide. The law school is a charter member of the Association of American Law Schools (AALS) and is fully accredited.

Located in Columbia, MU is 35 miles from Jefferson City, the state capital. The location provides law students with easy access to the legislature, the Supreme Court, and the various offices of state government. In addition to living and studying in one of America's most livable cities, students are within two hours of the cultural, athletic, and entertainment centers of St. Louis and Kansas City. Students and their families enjoy Columbia's Midwestern friendliness. It combines a small town feel with the diversity and opportunities often found only in larger cities. Columbia truly offers something for everyone.

■ Faculty

The faculty at MU is strong and vibrant. The faculty focus is on teaching, research, and service. MU is among the top 10 percent of law schools in American Law Institute membership. Multiple members of the faculty serve as commissioners and reporters for the National Conference of Commissioners on Uniform State Laws. Faculty maintain an open-door policy for students. Faculty scholarship regularly appears in the finest national law publications.

■ Enrollment/Student Body

The law school student body is composed of students from numerous states and foreign countries. This diverse, but collegial, group of students provides a wealth of experience and fosters a stimulating learning environment.

■ Curriculum

The academic program leading to the JD degree traditionally consists of six semesters of study. One seven-week semester is offered each summer. The first-year curriculum is proscribed, as is a portion of the second-year curriculum.

To graduate, students must complete 89 semester hours, including a writing requirement and a professional perspectives requirement. Students must have a minimum average of 77.5 on a scale of 65 to 100 to graduate.

■ Library and Physical Facilities

John K. Hulston Hall is dominated by windows, skylights, and large open spaces. It is a magnificent laboratory in which to study the law. The law school is part of the campus wireless network and law students can access the Internet and computer-assisted legal services throughout Hulston Hall or anywhere on campus. Exams are offered on laptop computers.

The law library houses an extensive collection of legal volumes and reference materials and a significant rare book collection. A staff of specialized librarians, researchers, and computer support personnel are available to assist students. Faculty and students have 24-hour access to the law library.

■ Special Programs: Alternative Dispute Resolution

The Center for the Study of Dispute Resolution is a unique feature of the law school and provides national leadership in this rapidly developing area of the law. First-year law students are exposed to an overview of dispute resolution processes. MU also offers a variety of dispute resolution courses and other educational opportunities for second- and third-year students.

One of the first programs of its kind in the country, the center houses a Master of Laws in Dispute Resolution degree program.

■ Dual-Degree Programs

The School of Law offers several dual-degree programs, including Business Administration (JD/MBA), Public Administration (JD/MPA), Health Administration (JD/MHA), Library Science (JD/MLS), and Journalism (JD/MA and JD/PhD). The law school has established other dual-degree programs to meet individual interests. Traditionally, dual-degree students spend their first year in the School of Law. (Students must fulfill the entrance requirements of both schools.)

■ Certificate Programs

The law school offers a certificate in Alternative Dispute Resolution. Students can complete this certificate by concentrating their elective hours in this area of the law.

In addition, a certificate in Journalism, the Digital Globe, or the European Union is available to law students through the Graduate School.

MU hosts one of 10 European Union (EU) centers in the United States. The EU Center is working to develop a better understanding of the transatlantic agenda between the EU and the United States.

■ Study-Abroad Programs

The School of Law offers two opportunities to study abroad. Since 2004, MU has offered a summer program in Cape Town, South Africa. The program is available to all law students and consists of three, two-credit courses in different areas of comparative law. Students reside in De Waterkant Village, one of Cape Town's trendiest neighborhoods, and are transported to their classes at the University of the Western Cape. Field trips to the Cape of Good Hope, the Stellenbosch wine region, Robben Island (the prison home of Nelson Mandela), and other scenic and historical locales are included in the itinerary. MU is also part of the London Law Consortium. This group of six American Bar Association (ABA)-approved schools offers second- and third-year law students a culturally enriching spring semester in London. With law school approval, students also can obtain academic credit

while studying in another ABA-approved law school international program.

Clinics and Externships

MU provides students with practical experience to enhance lawyering skills and to promote awareness of ethical issues. An active externship and judicial clerkship program and five clinical programs—the Criminal Prosecution Clinic, Family Violence Clinic, Legislative Clinic, Mediation Clinic, and the Innocence Clinic—have been developed to enrich student skills. Students, subject to the rules of the Missouri Supreme Court, are able to practice law in these programs.

Student Activities

All students are eligible to participate in the writing competition for membership on the *Missouri Law Review*, the *Journal of Dispute Resolution*, or the *Missouri Environmental Law and Policy Review*. Also open to all students, the Board of Advocates sponsors a wide variety of advocacy competitions. The school has chapters of the Order of Barristers, the Student Bar Association, and two legal fraternities. In addition, MU is one of only 75 law schools with a chapter of the Order of the Coif, the national law school honor society. Other student organizations, encompassing almost every aspect of social and academic life, are also offered.

Admission

A faculty committee reviews all applications. In many cases, factors other than the GPA or LSAT score have proven to be determinative. If the LSAT is repeated, the committee will consider all scores in its evaluation. Applications from disadvantaged students are especially encouraged.

Students are encouraged to apply early and to visit the law school. The Admissions Office can arrange for students to meet with an admission counselor, attend a class, and tour the facility.

Expenses and Financial Aid

Although costly, law school is a career investment. MU offers an outstanding value for the cost, and the accompanying housing, utility, and related living expenses in Columbia are low when compared to more urban settings.

Financial assistance is available to students.

Career Services

The Office of Career Services and Professional Development serves as a liaison between students or alumni and prospective employers. Students are taught to use their analytical and advocacy skills to achieve career goals. Workshops, seminars, and individual counseling are offered to help students successfully employ their lawyering skills. Typically, between 90 and 95 percent of each graduating class accepts employment within nine months of graduation.

Applicant Profile

University of Missouri School of Law
This grid includes only applicants who earned 120–180 LSAT scores under standard administrations.

LSAT Score	GPA								
	3.75 +	3.50–3.74	3.25–3.49	3.00–3.24	2.75–2.99	2.50–2.74	2.25–2.49	2.00–2.24	Below 2.00
175–180									
170–174									
165–169									
160–164									
155–159									
150–154									
145–149									
140–144									
135–139									
130–134									
125–129									
120–124									

■ Good Possibility   ■ Possible   □ Unlikely

This chart is to be used as a general guide only. Nonnumerical factors are strongly considered for all applicants. Average LSAT data reported.

University of Missouri—Kansas City School of Law

5100 Rockhill Road
Kansas City, MO 64110
Phone: 816.235.1644; Fax: 816.235.5276
E-mail: law@umkc.edu; Website: www.law.umkc.edu; http://twitter.com/UMKCLaw

*ABA
Approved
Since
1936*

The Basics

Type of school	Public
Term	Semester
Application deadline	
Application fee	$50
Financial aid deadline	3/1
Can first year start other than fall?	No
Student to faculty ratio	14.1 to 1
# of housing spaces available restricted to law students	
graduate housing for which law students are eligible	

Faculty and Administrators

	Total		Men		Women		Minorities	
	Spr	Fall	Spr	Fall	Spr	Fall	Spr	Fall
Full-time	29	28	18	17	11	11	5	4
Other full-time	4	5	3	3	1	2	0	0
Deans, librarians, & others who teach	9	9	5	5	4	4	0	0
Part-time	27	14	21	11	6	3	0	0
Total	69	56	47	36	22	20	5	4

Curriculum

		Full-Time	Part-Time
Typical first-year section size		56	0
Is there typically a "small section" of the first-year class, other than Legal Writing, taught by full-time faculty		No	No
If yes, typical size offered last year			
# of classroom course titles beyond first-year curriculum		114	
# of upper division courses, excluding seminars, with an enrollment:	Under 25	84	
	25–49	19	
	50–74	11	
	75–99	11	
	100+	0	
# of seminars		18	
# of seminar positions available		327	
# of seminar positions filled		245	0
# of positions available in simulation courses		384	
# of simulation positions filled		303	0
# of positions available in faculty supervised clinical courses		112	
# of faculty supervised clinical positions filled		82	0
# involved in field placements		70	0
# involved in law journals		182	0
# involved in moot court or trial competitions		54	0
# of credit hours required to graduate		91	

JD Enrollment and Ethnicity

	Men		Women		Full-Time		Part-Time		1st-Year		Total		JD Degs. Awd.
	#	%	#	%	#	%	#	%	#	%	#	%	
African Amer.	14	4.6	17	8.2	23	4.7	8	30.8	12	6.4	31	6.0	2
Amer. Indian	2	0.7	2	1.0	4	0.8	0	0.0	1	0.5	4	0.8	0
Asian Amer.	7	2.3	6	2.9	12	2.5	1	3.8	5	2.7	13	2.5	4
Mex. Amer.	0	0.0	0	0.0	0	0.0	0	0.0	0	0.0	0	0.0	0
Puerto Rican	0	0.0	0	0.0	0	0.0	0	0.0	0	0.0	0	0.0	0
Hispanic	8	2.6	9	4.3	16	3.3	1	3.8	5	2.7	17	3.3	4
Total Minority	31	10.1	34	16.3	55	11.2	10	38.5	23	12.3	65	12.6	10
For. Nation.	2	0.7	5	2.4	6	1.2	1	3.8	1	0.5	7	1.4	1
Caucasian	234	76.2	151	72.6	371	75.9	14	53.8	143	76.5	385	74.8	116
Unknown	40	13.0	18	8.7	57	11.7	1	3.8	20	10.7	58	11.3	27
Total	307	59.6	208	40.4	489	95.0	26	5.0	187	36.3	515		154

Transfers

Transfers in	9
Transfers out	6

Tuition and Fees

	Resident	Nonresident
Full-time	$14,242	$27,262
Part-time	$10,248	$19,548
Tuition Guarantee Program		N

Living Expenses

Estimated living expenses for singles

Living on campus	Living off campus	Living at home
$28,430	$28,641	$20,118

University of Missouri—Kansas City School of Law

ABA
Approved
Since
1936

GPA and LSAT Scores

	Total	Full-Time	Part-Time
# of apps	950	914	36
# of offers	451	437	14
# of matrics	164	155	9
75% GPA	3.58	3.58	3.54
Median GPA	3.30	3.30	2.88
25% GPA	2.99	3.03	2.70
75% LSAT	157	156	161
Median LSAT	154	154	154
25% LSAT	152	152	148

Grants and Scholarships (from prior year)

	Total #	Total %	Full-Time #	Full-Time %	Part-Time #	Part-Time %
Total # of students	475		448		27	
Total # receiving grants	178	37.5	178	39.7	0	0.0
Less than 1/2 tuition	101	21.3	101	22.5	0	0.0
Half to full tuition	50	10.5	50	11.2	0	0.0
Full tuition	19	4.0	19	4.2	0	0.0
More than full tuition	8	1.7	8	1.8	0	0.0
Median grant amount			$6,023		$0	

Informational and Library Resources

Total amount spent on library materials	$658,507
Study seating capacity inside the library	377
# of full-time equivalent professional librarians	5
Hours per week library is open	100
# of open, wired connections available to students	46
# of networked computers available for use by students	55
Has wireless network?	Y
Require computer?	N

JD Attrition (from prior year)

	Academic #	Other #	Total #	Total %
1st year	9	12	21	13.0
2nd year	0	1	1	0.6
3rd year	0	0	0	0.0
4th year	0	0	0	0.0

Employment (9 months after graduation)

	Total	Percentage
Employment status known	150	98.7
Employment status unknown	2	1.3
Employed	133	88.7
Pursuing graduate degrees	9	6.0
Unemployed (seeking, not seeking, or studying for the bar)	5	3.3
Type of Employment		
# employed in law firms	77	57.9
# employed in business and industry	11	8.3
# employed in government	22	16.5
# employed in public interest	6	4.5
# employed as judicial clerks	15	11.3
# employed in academia	1	0.8
Geographic Location		
# employed in state	98	73.7
# employed in foreign countries	1	0.8
# of states where employed	15	

Bar Passage Rates

First-time takers	140	Reporting %	90.00
Average school %	97.62	Average state %	92.33
Average pass difference	5.29		

Jurisdiction	Takers	Passers	Pass %	State %	Diff %
Missouri	126	123	97.62	92.33	5.29

University of Missouri—Kansas City School of Law

5100 Rockhill Road
Kansas City, MO 64110
Phone: 816.235.1644; Fax: 816.235.5276
E-mail: law@umkc.edu; Website: www.law.umkc.edu; http://twitter.com/UMKCLaw

■ Introduction

The University of Missouri—Kansas City School of Law (UMKC) takes pride in being the urban public law school with the small liberal arts feel. UMKC serves and collaborates with the legal communities in two major metropolitan areas of the states of Missouri and Kansas. Students, faculty, and alumni actively lead and participate in professional activities with area bar associations, lawyers, and law firms, as well as government agencies and the judiciary.

UMKC law school graduates hold important positions in legal arenas across the country, distinguishing themselves in private practice, government service, academia, and corporate roles. UMKC is one of only six law schools to have educated both a president of the United States and a US Supreme Court justice. Many other UMKC alumni currently serve as judges at the federal, state, and local levels.

UMKC School of Law is committed to providing a high-quality legal education in a professional and supportive environment, concentrating always on the foundations of good lawyering: respect for people, knowledge, ideas, and justice. UMKC is one of the most student-friendly law schools in the country, with outstanding student-faculty interaction and alumni providing mentoring to our students through the UMKC Inns of Court program.

Founded in 1895, the school is accredited by the American Bar Association (ABA) and is a member of the Association of American Law Schools (AALS).

■ Faculty

Our faculty are outstanding scholars who have extensive practice experience and national renown. For example, Professor Doug Linder's Famous Trials website, www.umkc.edu/famoustrials, receives seven to nine million hits per month. Professor Bill Eckhardt was the chief prosecutor in the My Lai massacre case. Professor Kris Kobach is one of the nation's leading conservative voices on immigration policy, while Professor Bill Black's experience and expertise in bank regulation has led him to major roles in a Barack Obama campaign documentary and a Michael Moore film about America's financial crisis.

Faculty at UMKC are actively engaged with students both inside and outside the classroom—in competitions as well as activities and events. Under faculty supervision, students write and edit a substantial portion of the *UMKC Law Review*, a scholarly legal journal, and also serve as assistant editors of *The Urban Lawyer*, published by the ABA Section of State and Local Government Law, and the national and international *Journal of the American Academy of Matrimonial Lawyers*.

■ Library and Physical Facilities

Office suites shared by faculty and students are designed to foster the exchange of ideas and to promote collegiality between faculty and students. The school has over 121,000 square feet of usable space, which includes wireless computer access throughout the building, and a newly remodeled courtroom with state-of-the-art technology and an innovative viewing theater.

The Leon E. Bloch Law Library combines the traditions of print media with emerging electronic media in preparing the lawyer for the future and supporting the legal community.

■ Curriculum

Courses are taught in a variety of formats. Many of the substantive courses include problem solving, simulations, service learning, and the development of skills components essential to the practice of law. The first-year JD program offers a year-long intensive Introduction to Law and Lawyering Processes. The upper-level program includes a combination of required courses, as well as a broad selection of elective courses.

All first-year sections have 60 or fewer students, and first-year legal research and writing classes have approximately 25 students each. Among the 114 upper division courses offered each year, 84 have an enrollment of fewer than 25 students, and 19 more have an enrollment of between 25 and 49 students. A law school strategies program that includes supervised, structured study groups, lecture series, and weekly workshops is open to all students. Additional opportunities include a week-long summer program, which is available on a limited basis.

While the school's innovative Solo and Small Firm Initiative prepares students for general practice, those seeking more focused study can pursue one of our five emphasis areas: Litigation; Business and Entrepreneurial Law; Urban, Land Use and Environmental Law; International, Comparative, and Foreign Law, and Law in Service to Children and Families. These emphases build on our long-standing tradition of excellence in these areas and prepare students to enter the job market with specialized knowledge and skills.

A part-time day program is available for those students with family or career responsibilities who are unable to enroll on a full-time basis. Full-time students may graduate in two and one-half years by attending two summer sessions.

■ JD/MBA and JD/MPA Programs

The School of Law has established dual-degree programs with the Henry W. Bloch School of Business and Public Administration. The program allows students to earn a JD degree and a Master of Business Administration or Master of Public Administration degree on an accelerated basis through cross-acceptance of some credit hours. Applicants must satisfy the admission requirements of each school.

■ JD/LLM and Combined-Degree Programs

The School of Law has adopted combined-degree programs that allow qualified JD students to apply, with approval, up to 12 credit hours of UMKC tax or estate planning courses toward an LLM on an accelerated basis, generally requiring only one additional semester (or two summer sessions) beyond that required for the JD degree.

■ Student Activities

The law school's location in a metropolitan area provides many opportunities for students to engage in real-life representation

University of Missouri—Kansas City School of Law

of clients in clinical programs. More than 50 percent of our students take advantage of internships and clinics that include UMKC's Child and Family Services Clinic, Tax Clinic, Entrepreneurial Legal Services Clinic, and The Innocence Project Clinic. The school also offers a number of field placements. Students may also participate in our Pro Bono/Public Service Program designed to instill a sense of civic responsibility and meet the needs of those with limited means in the community.

Students obtain advanced skills development in trial and appellate advocacy through sequenced upper-level courses and competition participation. Students also participate in client counseling and negotiation competitions. UMKC teams frequently win regional and national honors in these competitions.

UMKC benefits from an active Student Bar Association, which represents students and plays an important role in establishing school policy. Three national legal fraternities have chapters at the school, as do Black Law Students, Hispanic Law Students, Jewish Law Students, Asian Pacific Islander Law Students, Women Law Students, and Nontraditional Law Students. Additional student organizations specialize in many areas of interest, with over 30 total student groups. Students also have the opportunity to participate in study-abroad programs that visit China, Ireland, and Oxford. The school provides many opportunities for development of personal relationships that will last throughout one's career.

■ Admission

The School of Law restricts the number of students admitted each year to achieve a favorable faculty-to-student ratio,

providing the best possible legal education for each student enrolled. Because many more people apply to the law school than there are seats available, admission is highly competitive. While substantial weight is given to the LSAT score and undergraduate GPA, the law school and its faculty believe that using factors in addition to the LSAT and GPA contribute to an intellectually stimulating and diverse environment. These factors include racial, ethnic, cultural, gender, age, or other forms of diversity; triumphs over challenges and barriers based on societal discrimination or economic disadvantage; outstanding leadership qualities; serious and sustained commitment to significant public or community service; advanced or specialized educational achievements; accomplishments or qualities indicative of potential for contributing to scholarly and creative initiatives; and potential to provide high-quality legal services to clients.

Students may be admitted with a bachelor's degree from an approved institution, or in appropriate cases, with 90 hours of acceptable academic work. Arrangements can be made to meet with students and faculty, visit a class, or tour the school.

■ Career Services

The Office of Career Services assists law students in exploring and defining career options. It also provides advice and assistance in résumé preparation and interviewing skills. The office sponsors a series of programs to introduce students to a variety of career opportunities. Participants in the school's Judicial Clerkship Initiative have enjoyed a high placement rate in pursuing clerkships with state and federal judges.

Applicant Profile

University of Missouri—Kansas City School of Law

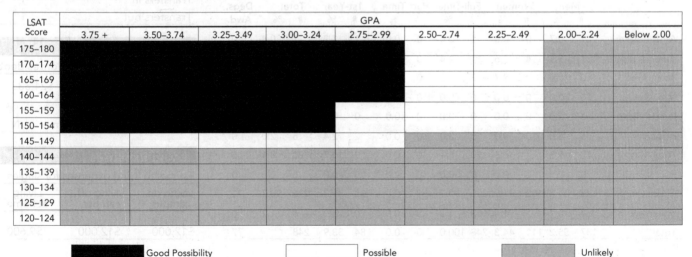

Average LSAT data reported.

University of Montana School of Law

32 Campus Drive
Missoula, MT 59812
Phone: 406.243.4311
E-mail: lawadmis@umontana.edu; Website: www.umt.edu/law

ABA
Approved
Since
1923

The Basics

Type of school	Public
Term	Semester
Application deadline	3/12
Application fee	$60
Financial aid deadline	3/1
Can first year start other than fall?	No
Student to faculty ratio	12.3 to 1
# of housing spaces available restricted to law students	
graduate housing for which law students are eligible	245

Faculty and Administrators

	Total		Men		Women		Minorities	
	Spr	Fall	Spr	Fall	Spr	Fall	Spr	Fall
Full-time	17	16	9	9	8	7	4	4
Other full-time	2	2	1	1	1	1	0	0
Deans, librarians, & others who teach	7	6	3	2	4	4	0	0
Part-time	14	10	10	8	4	2	0	0
Total	40	34	23	20	17	14	4	4

Curriculum

		Full-Time	Part-Time
Typical first-year section size		42	0
Is there typically a "small section" of the first-year class, other than Legal Writing, taught by full-time faculty		No	No
If yes, typical size offered last year			
# of classroom course titles beyond first-year curriculum		72	
# of upper division courses, excluding seminars, with an enrollment:	Under 25	24	
	25–49	4	
	50–74	2	
	75–99	5	
	100+	1	
# of seminars		35	
# of seminar positions available		450	
# of seminar positions filled	399		0
# of positions available in simulation courses		97	
# of simulation positions filled	97		0
# of positions available in faculty supervised clinical courses		25	
# of faculty supervised clinical positions filled	22		0
# involved in field placements	51		0
# involved in law journals	33		0
# involved in moot court or trial competitions	33		0
# of credit hours required to graduate		90	

JD Enrollment and Ethnicity

	Men		Women		Full-Time		Part-Time		1st-Year		Total		JD Degs. Awd.
	#	%	#	%	#	%	#	%	#	%	#	%	
African Amer.	1	0.7	0	0.0	1	0.4	0	0.0	1	1.2	1	0.4	0
Amer. Indian	7	5.1	4	3.6	11	4.4	0	0.0	4	4.8	11	4.4	4
Asian Amer.	0	0.0	3	2.7	3	1.2	0	0.0	2	2.4	3	1.2	2
Mex. Amer.	0	0.0	0	0.0	0	0.0	0	0.0	0	0.0	0	0.0	0
Puerto Rican	0	0.0	0	0.0	0	0.0	0	0.0	0	0.0	0	0.0	0
Hispanic	5	3.6	0	0.0	5	2.0	0	0.0	2	2.4	5	2.0	0
Total Minority	13	9.5	7	6.3	20	8.1	0	0.0	9	10.7	20	8.1	6
For. Nation.	0	0.0	0	0.0	0	0.0	0	0.0	0	0.0	0	0.0	0
Caucasian	123	89.8	102	91.9	225	90.7	0	0.0	75	89.3	225	90.7	71
Unknown	1	0.7	2	1.8	3	1.2	0	0.0	0	0.0	3	1.2	0
Total	137	55.2	111	44.8	248	100.0	0	0.0	84	33.9	248		77

Transfers

Transfers in	1
Transfers out	1

Tuition and Fees

	Resident	Nonresident
Full-time	$10,620	$24,333
Part-time		
Tuition Guarantee Program		N

Living Expenses

Estimated living expenses for singles

Living on campus	Living off campus	Living at home
$12,000	$12,000	$9,600

University of Montana School of Law

ABA
Approved
Since
1923

GPA and LSAT Scores

	Total	Full-Time	Part-Time
# of apps	396	396	0
# of offers	199	199	0
# of matrics	84	84	0
75% GPA	3.69	3.69	0.00
Median GPA	3.44	3.44	0.00
25% GPA	3.26	3.26	0.00
75% LSAT	157	157	0
Median LSAT	154	154	0
25% LSAT	151	151	0

Grants and Scholarships (from prior year)

	Total		Full-Time		Part-Time	
	#	%	#	%	#	%
Total # of students	245		245		0	
Total # receiving grants	98	40.0	98	40.0	0	0.0
Less than 1/2 tuition	85	34.7	85	34.7	0	0.0
Half to full tuition	12	4.9	12	4.9	0	0.0
Full tuition	1	0.4	1	0.4	0	0.0
More than full tuition	0	0.0	0	0.0	0	0.0
Median grant amount			$2,200		$0	

Informational and Library Resources

Total amount spent on library materials	$616,866
Study seating capacity inside the library	360
# of full-time equivalent professional librarians	6
Hours per week library is open	98
# of open, wired connections available to students	224
# of networked computers available for use by students	26
Has wireless network?	Y
Require computer?	N

JD Attrition (from prior year)

	Academic	Other	Total	
	#	#	#	%
1st year	0	2	2	2.4
2nd year	0	4	4	4.9
3rd year	0	2	2	2.5
4th year	0	0	0	0.0

Employment (9 months after graduation)

	Total	Percentage
Employment status known	79	96.3
Employment status unknown	3	3.7
Employed	69	87.3
Pursuing graduate degrees	5	6.3
Unemployed (seeking, not seeking, or studying for the bar)	4	5.1
Type of Employment		
# employed in law firms	32	46.4
# employed in business and industry	3	4.3
# employed in government	7	10.1
# employed in public interest	7	10.1
# employed as judicial clerks	17	24.6
# employed in academia	0	0.0
Geographic Location		
# employed in state	50	72.5
# employed in foreign countries	0	0.0
# of states where employed	11	

Bar Passage Rates

First-time takers	73	Reporting %	80.82
Average school %	88.14	Average state %	92.47
Average pass difference	−4.33		

Jurisdiction	Takers	Passers	Pass %	State %	Diff %
Montana	59	52	88.14	92.47	−4.33

University of Montana School of Law

32 Campus Drive
Missoula, MT 59812
Phone: 406.243.4311
E-mail: lawadmis@umontana.edu; Website: www.umt.edu/law

■ Introduction

The University of Montana (UM) School of Law is located in Missoula on the west slopes of the Rocky Mountains. Missoula is situated halfway between Yellowstone and Glacier national parks and is surrounded by several of the largest designated wilderness areas in the continental United States. The city is known for its outdoor opportunities and quality of life.

The School of Law was established in 1911 and serves as a legal center for the state. It has been accredited by the Association of American Law Schools (AALS) since 1914 and by the American Bar Association (ABA) since 1923. As one of the smallest law schools in the nation, the University of Montana School of Law offers students a congenial academic, intellectual, and social environment.

As the School of Law enters its second century of preparing students for the practice of law and community leadership, we have expanded and substantially renovated our building. Students now enjoy new classrooms, formal and informal study spaces, clinic and student-group offices, and community areas.

■ UM's Program

The University of Montana School of Law integrates theory and practice throughout its curriculum to instill entry-level practice and competence in its graduates. The School of Law's curriculum, teaching methodology, and assessment techniques are designed to address the following components of a lawyer's work: (1) knowledge of the law, (2) ability to apply legal rules to solve problems, (3) ability to use lawyering skills (e.g., negotiation and client counseling), (4) perspective on the societal role and responsibility of lawyers, and (5) sensitivity to the dynamics of social and interpersonal interaction.

The school has created three distinctive programs to acquaint first-year students with the ways lawyers think and work: (1) the Introductory Program, (2) the Lawyer Skills Program, and (3) the Law Firm Program. In the Introductory Program, students are initiated into the legal culture by surveying legal history, the American legal system, the litigation process, legal writing, and legal analysis and jurisprudence. The School of Law is one of the few to introduce first-year students to the skills involved in dispute resolution, including client counseling, legal document drafting, and oral argument. UM's program encourages students to cooperate and collaborate rather than compete as they begin to think and work as lawyers. Entering students belong to *law firms*—groups of seven students directed by upper-class students.

The school has long emphasized performance in its curriculum. The school's Legal Writing and Dispute Resolution programs represent a comprehensive approach to lawyering skills. Students master specific transactional skills such as planning an estate, drafting a contract, and creating a small business.

The upper-division clinical training program provides students with a wide range of opportunities to earn required academic credit by working on cases under the supervision of faculty and practicing attorneys in Missoula. The clinical offerings include ACLU, Associated Students of UM Legal Services, Child Support Enforcement Division, Criminal Defense, DNRC Forestry and Trust Land Management

Divisions, Federal Judicial, Indian Law, Innocence Project, Land Use, Mediation, Missoula City Attorney's Office, Missoula County Attorney's Office, Montana Legal Services Association, National Wildlife Federation, Natural Resource, Office of State Public Defender, Rocky Mountain Elk Foundation, UM Legal Counsel, USDA General Counsel, and US Department of Justice.

■ Special Programs

The School of Law offers three certificate programs: (1) Environmental and Natural Resource Law and the opportunity to participate in natural resource clinics, the *Public Land and Resources Law Review*, the Environmental Law Group, and the Environmental Law Moot Court Team; (2) Alternative Dispute Resolution and the opportunity to participate in the Mediation Clinic; and (3) American Indian Law and the opportunity to participate in the Indian Law Clinic, the Native American Law Student Association (NALSA), and the NALSA Moot Court Team.

In conjunction with the School of Law, UM's graduate school offers a certificate in Natural Resources Conflict Resolution. It is the only graduate-level certificate program in the Rocky Mountain West specifically designed to provide students a working knowledge of the theory and practice of collaboration, consensus building, and conflict resolution as they apply to natural resources and the environment.

The School of Law offers three joint-degree programs. Students can combine their law degrees with a Master of Science in Environmental Studies, a Master of Business Administration, or a Master of Public Administration. These programs can lead to completion of the joint degree in as little as three years. The School of Law also offers concentrations in the areas of Trial Advocacy, Business, and Tax Law.

■ Admission

A committee of law faculty reviews applications. Candidates must be of good moral character, have intellectual promise, and have a baccalaureate degree from an approved college or university prior to matriculation. Applicants are considered in resident or nonresident pools. The School of Law seeks a diverse student body and welcomes applications from members of groups historically underrepresented in the legal profession.

The School of Law recommends that you submit your application as soon as possible. We begin reviewing completed applications as they are submitted. Applications are not considered complete until all application materials, including the LSAC Law School Report, are received. If your file is completed by February 15, you will be notified of a decision (admit, deny, or retain for further review) by March 15. If your file is completed by March 15, you will be notified of a decision by April 15. Files completed after March 15 may be considered on a space-available basis.

The most important admission criteria are the cumulative undergraduate GPA and the LSAT score. If the LSAT is repeated, all scores will be used in evaluating the applicant. The admission committee weighs such factors as writing ability; college attended; trend in grades; quality of work in difficult courses; experience prior to application to law school,

including graduate study; ability to overcome economic or other disadvantages; and change in performance after an absence from school.

The school recognizes a commitment to provide full opportunities for the study of law and entry into the legal profession of qualified members of groups (notably racial and ethnic minorities) who have been victims of discrimination.

■ Student Activities

All students are members of the Student Bar Association (SBA). The SBA contributes to the professional development and the social life of the student body. Other student organizations include the American Association for Justice (AAJ), ACLU, Animal Legal Defense Fund, Christian Legal Society, Environmental Law Group, Federalist Society, International Law Student Association, Military Law Society, Montana Public Interest Law Coalition, Native American Law Student Association, Clayberg Inn of Phi Delta Phi national

law fraternity, Rural Advocacy League, and Women's Law Caucus. The *Montana Law Review* and the *Public Land and Resources Law Review* afford supplementary training in analyzing legal problems precisely and presenting legal issues cogently.

The School of Law is proud of its performance in interscholastic competitions. Nearly every year, the School of Law fields teams that compete at the national level. Most recently, UM won the 2000 National Moot Court Championship. UM won the ATLA trial competition national championship in 1992 and the national ABA Client Counseling Competition championship in 1990. Additionally, the Environmental Law Moot Court Team, which competes at the Pace Moot Court Competition each year, won the Best Oralist Award in 2002, and competed in the final round in 2005. Likewise, the Indian Law and Jessop International Law Moot Court teams have won oralist and brief honors in their respective national and, in the case of the Jessop team, international competitions.

Applicant Profile

University of Montana School of Law

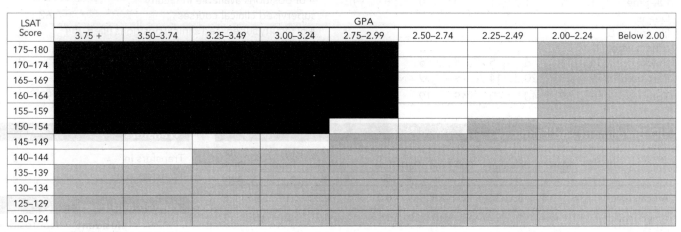

Good Possibility   Possible   Unlikely

Average LSAT data reported.

University of Nebraska College of Law

PO Box 830902
Lincoln, NE 68583-0902
Phone: 402.472.2161; Fax: 402.472.5185
E-mail: lawadm@unl.edu; Website: http://law.unl.edu/

ABA
Approved
Since
1923

The Basics

Type of school	Public
Term	Semester
Application deadline	3/1
Application fee	$25
Financial aid deadline	5/1
Can first year start other than fall?	No
Student to faculty ratio	13.6 to 1
# of housing spaces available restricted to law students	
graduate housing for which law students are eligible	295

Faculty and Administrators

	Total		Men		Women		Minorities	
	Spr	Fall	Spr	Fall	Spr	Fall	Spr	Fall
Full-time	24	24	19	20	5	4	1	1
Other full-time	1	1	1	1	0	0	0	0
Deans, librarians, & others who teach	11	11	6	5	5	6	1	1
Part-time	29	23	20	14	9	9	0	0
Total	65	59	46	40	19	19	2	2

Curriculum

	Full-Time	Part-Time
Typical first-year section size	70	0
Is there typically a "small section" of the first-year class, other than Legal Writing, taught by full-time faculty	Yes	No
If yes, typical size offered last year	35	
# of classroom course titles beyond first-year curriculum		91
# of upper division courses, excluding seminars, with an enrollment: Under 25		65
25–49		26
50–74		9
75–99		1
100+		0
# of seminars		12
# of seminar positions available		152
# of seminar positions filled	149	0
# of positions available in simulation courses		479
# of simulation positions filled	410	0
# of positions available in faculty supervised clinical courses		62
# of faculty supervised clinical positions filled	54	0
# involved in field placements	21	0
# involved in law journals	42	0
# involved in moot court or trial competitions	54	0
# of credit hours required to graduate		93

JD Enrollment and Ethnicity

	Men		Women		Full-Time		Part-Time		1st-Year		Total		JD Degs. Awd.
	#	%	#	%	#	%	#	%	#	%	#	%	
African Amer.	6	2.5	5	3.2	11	2.8	0	0.0	3	2.2	11	2.8	6
Amer. Indian	1	0.4	1	0.6	2	0.5	0	0.0	1	0.7	2	0.5	1
Asian Amer.	4	1.7	3	1.9	7	1.8	0	0.0	1	0.7	7	1.8	2
Mex. Amer.	3	1.3	1	0.6	4	1.0	0	0.0	1	0.7	4	1.0	7
Puerto Rican	0	0.0	0	0.0	0	0.0	0	0.0	0	0.0	0	0.0	0
Hispanic	5	2.1	0	0.0	5	1.3	0	0.0	3	2.2	5	1.3	3
Total Minority	19	8.0	10	6.4	29	7.4	0	0.0	9	6.6	29	7.4	19
For. Nation.	1	0.4	1	0.6	2	0.5	0	0.0	1	0.7	2	0.5	0
Caucasian	217	91.6	146	93.0	363	92.1	0	0.0	127	92.7	363	92.1	115
Unknown	0	0.0	0	0.0	0	0.0	0	0.0	0	0.0	0	0.0	0
Total	237	60.2	157	39.8	394	100.0	0	0.0	137	34.8	394		134

Transfers

Transfers in	2
Transfers out	3

Tuition and Fees

	Resident	Nonresident
Full-time	$12,154	$26,600
Part-time		
Tuition Guarantee Program		N

Living Expenses

Estimated living expenses for singles

Living on campus	Living off campus	Living at home
$13,308	$12,778	$7,474

University of Nebraska College of Law

ABA
Approved
Since
1923

GPA and LSAT Scores

	Total	Full-Time	Part-Time
# of apps	712	712	0
# of offers	369	369	0
# of matrics	137	137	0
75% GPA	3.82	3.82	0.00
Median GPA	3.55	3.55	0.00
25% GPA	3.29	3.29	0.00
75% LSAT	158	158	0
Median LSAT	156	156	0
25% LSAT	154	154	0

Grants and Scholarships (from prior year)

	Total		Full-Time		Part-Time	
	#	%	#	%	#	%
Total # of students	404		404		0	
Total # receiving grants	160	39.6	160	39.6	0	0.0
Less than 1/2 tuition	60	14.9	60	14.9	0	0.0
Half to full tuition	63	15.6	63	15.6	0	0.0
Full tuition	0	0.0	0	0.0	0	0.0
More than full tuition	37	9.2	37	9.2	0	0.0
Median grant amount			$10,000		$0	

Informational and Library Resources

Total amount spent on library materials	$815,301
Study seating capacity inside the library	372
# of full-time equivalent professional librarians	7
Hours per week library is open	109
# of open, wired connections available to students	16
# of networked computers available for use by students	16
Has wireless network?	Y
Require computer?	N

JD Attrition (from prior year)

	Academic	Other	Total	
	#	#	#	%
1st year	9	4	13	8.9
2nd year	0	4	4	3.4
3rd year	0	0	0	0.0
4th year	0	0	0	0.0

Employment (9 months after graduation)

	Total	Percentage
Employment status known	116	95.1
Employment status unknown	6	4.9
Employed	105	90.5
Pursuing graduate degrees	7	6.0
Unemployed (seeking, not seeking, or studying for the bar)	3	2.6
Type of Employment		
# employed in law firms	43	41.0
# employed in business and industry	16	15.2
# employed in government	27	25.7
# employed in public interest	4	3.8
# employed as judicial clerks	11	10.5
# employed in academia	4	3.8
Geographic Location		
# employed in state	69	65.7
# employed in foreign countries	0	0.0
# of states where employed		15

Bar Passage Rates

First-time takers	116	Reporting %	72.41
Average school %	92.85	Average state %	88.64
Average pass difference	4.21		

Jurisdiction	Takers	Passers	Pass %	State %	Diff %
Nebraska	65	59	90.77	89.15	1.62
Iowa	10	10	100.00	90.11	9.89
Colorado	9	9	100.00	83.29	16.71

University of Nebraska College of Law

PO Box 830902
Lincoln, NE 68583-0902
Phone: 402.472.2161; Fax: 402.472.5185
E-mail: lawadm@unl.edu; Website: http://law.unl.edu/

■ Introduction

Founded in 1888, the University of Nebraska College of Law offers an excellent legal education at a reasonable cost. It is large enough to provide students with a diverse curriculum, yet small enough to ensure that students are not lost in a faceless crowd. The College of Law is a charter member of the AALS and is accredited by the ABA. The University of Nebraska College of Law is located on the East Campus of the University of Nebraska in Lincoln, a city with a population of approximately 235,000 and the state capital.

■ Curriculum

The College of Law's academic year runs from late August to early May. A two-day orientation before the beginning of the fall semester introduces first-year students to the law school. Each incoming student is assigned a faculty advisor who can answer questions about law school, course selections, and career goals. The first-year curriculum is 15 hours the first semester and 18 hours the second semester and includes civil procedure, contracts, criminal law, legal writing, property, and torts. Courses in the second and third years are elective, with the exception of required courses in constitutional law, professional responsibility, a research seminar, and a professional skills course. The curriculum encompasses a broad range of areas. The curriculum offers particular depth in the areas of litigation, alternative dispute resolution, taxation, environmental, employment, international, space and telecommunications, corporate and commercial law. Students who wish to focus on a particular area of the law may pursue the Litigation Skills Program of Concentrated Studies or the Business Program of Concentrated Studies or develop an individualized program of concentrated study.

The College of Law provides an Academic Resource Program for first-year students to assist them in developing and improving fundamental skills such as note taking, briefing cases, legal analysis, outlining, and writing examinations. The program provides weekly skills classes as well as a series of lectures and individual academic counseling.

Although completing the requirements for a JD degree normally takes three years, it is possible to graduate in two and one-half years by attending summer school. The college offers no night classes and rarely accepts part-time students. Students receiving the JD degree are qualified to practice in any state upon passage of that state's bar examination.

■ Skills and Clinical Education

The College of Law recognizes that becoming a lawyer involves more than learning legal theory. Students need to be able to develop practical skills to effectively represent clients and function as lawyers. The College of Law has offered courses that emphasize "learning by doing" since the early 1970s. The college offers professional skills courses in pretrial litigation, trial advocacy, appellate advocacy, mediation, negotiations, alternative dispute resolution, client interviewing and counseling, construction law, business planning, civil law, and criminal law. These classes allow second- and third-year students to develop lawyering skills in simulated settings or in the handling of real cases for actual clients. In the Civil Clinic, third-year students represent clients in and out of court in matters such as bankruptcy, domestic relations, immigration, and landlord-tenant disputes. Students in the Criminal Clinic prosecute misdemeanor cases in Lancaster County.

■ Joint-Degree Programs

The college's interdisciplinary program in law and psychology is recognized as one of the finest in the nation. The college also participates in seven other joint-degree programs and will work with students to individually design programs in disciplines not covered by a formal program. In each program, students will earn two degrees with fewer credit hours and in less time than if the degrees were pursued separately. The formal joint-degree programs include JD/MBA (Business), JD/MPA (Accounting), JD/PhD (Psychology), JD/MA (Political Science), JD/MA or MS (Economics), JD/MCRP (Community and Regional Planning), JD/PhD (Educational Administration), and JD/MA (Journalism).

■ Library and Physical Facilities

The Schmid Law Library has a collection of about 395,000 volumes and a full complement of the latest developments in information technology. The library provides seating for 335 students and has 14 group-study rooms, each with full access to power and fast data connections, both wired and wireless, for the best access to the Internet from any place in the library. The five professional librarians and their staff strive to create a service-oriented environment for legal research and scholarship. All these attributes combine to make the Schmid Law Library not only the largest, but the most effective, efficient, and friendliest law library in the region.

The College of Law's classrooms and Welpton Courtroom include attractive decor, adjustable chairs, laptop compatibility, and state-of-the-art technology.

■ Student Activities

The *Nebraska Law Review*, published by a student editorial board, publishes leading articles from well-known authorities in their fields, as well as student notes and comments. Other extracurricular academic programs include the National Moot Court Competition, Client Counseling Competition, and National Trial Competition.

Students can become involved in over 25 activities and organizations, including the Student Bar Association, Women's Law Caucus, Black Law Students Association, Nebraska Entertainment and Sports Law Association, Equal Justice Society, Federalist Society, Multicultural Legal Society, and two national legal fraternities.

■ Career Services

The College of Law operates its own Career Services Office for students seeking full-time employment or summer clerkships. The office provides students with a variety of placement-related services and also organizes on-campus

interviews by private law firms, governmental agencies, corporations, and other potential employers. As reported to the ABA, the post-graduation survey indicated 93 percent of the Class of 2008 graduates were employed, enrolled in a full-time degree program, or not seeking employment.

■ Admission

The College of Law starts reviewing applications in early January, and the application deadline is March 1. Admission decisions are made on a rolling basis. Students are required to have a bachelor's degree from an accredited institution, take the LSAT, and register with LSAC's Credential Assembly Service. In making its decisions, the Admissions Committee seeks to identify those individuals who have the ability to compete successfully in a rigorous academic environment. The major factors that the committee considers are the applicant's LSAT score and the applicant's undergraduate grade-point average. However, admission decisions are not simply a function of the numbers. The committee also takes into account any upward (or downward) trend in the applicant's academic performance over time, quality of the applicant's undergraduate institution, course of study, personal statement, work experience, graduate study, extracurricular activities, letters of recommendation, and other information supplied by the applicant.

The College of Law will waive the application fee upon demonstration of financial need. To visit a law class, meet with admission personnel, or tour the law college, contact the admission office.

Applicant Profile

University of Nebraska College of Law
This grid includes only applicants who earned 120–180 LSAT scores under standard administrations.

LSAT Score	3.75 +		3.50–3.74		3.25–3.49		3.00–3.24		2.75–2.99		2.50–2.74		2.25–2.49		2.00–2.24		Below 2.00		No GPA		Total	
	Apps	Adm	Apps	Adm	Apps	Adm	Apps	Adm	Apps	Adm	Apps	Adm	Apps	Adm	Apps	Adm	Apps	Adm	Apps	Adm	Apps	Adm
175–180	0	0	0	0	0	0	0	0	0	0	0	0	0	0	0	0	0	0	0	0	0	0
170–174	2	2	2	2	2	1	2	2	0	0	0	0	0	0	0	0	0	0	0	0	8	7
165–169	5	5	3	3	0	0	2	0	2	2	1	1	0	0	0	0	0	0	0	0	13	11
160–164	27	26	16	16	10	8	9	8	2	2	7	7	5	3	0	0	0	0	0	0	76	70
155–159	46	44	55	52	38	33	26	21	12	7	10	8	5	4	1	0	1	0	0	0	194	169
150–154	51	39	49	29	41	20	34	13	30	3	7	0	9	1	0	0	1	0	8	2	230	107
145–149	16	2	27	2	26	2	20	0	13	0	7	0	3	0	0	0	0	0	3	1	115	7
140–144	5	0	8	0	13	0	9	0	9	0	5	0	4	0	1	0	0	0	1	0	55	0
135–139	0	0	3	0	4	0	5	0	4	0	1	0	2	0	2	0	1	0	1	0	23	0
130–134	0	0	1	0	0	0	0	0	0	0	2	0	1	0	2	0	0	0	0	0	6	0
125–129	0	0	0	0	0	0	0	0	0	0	0	0	0	0	0	0	0	0	0	0	0	0
120–124	0	0	0	0	0	0	0	0	0	0	0	0	0	0	0	0	0	0	0	0	0	0
Total	152	118	164	104	134	64	107	44	72	14	40	16	29	8	6	0	3	0	13	3	720	371

Apps = Number of Applicants
Adm = Number Admitted
Reflects 98% of the total applicant pool; average LSAT data reported.

University of Nevada, Las Vegas, William S. Boyd School of Law

4505 Maryland Parkway, Box 451003
Las Vegas, NV 89154-1003
Phone: 702.895.2440; Fax: 702.895.2414
E-mail: request@law.unlv.edu; Website: www.law.unlv.edu

ABA
Approved
Since
2000

The Basics

Type of school	Public
Term	Semester
Application deadline	3/15
Application fee	$50
Financial aid deadline	2/1
Can first year start other than fall?	No
Student to faculty ratio	16.8 to 1
# of housing spaces available restricted to law students	
graduate housing for which law students are eligible	

Curriculum

	Full-Time	Part-Time
Typical first-year section size	65	34
Is there typically a "small section" of the first-year class, other than Legal Writing, taught by full-time faculty	No	No
If yes, typical size offered last year		
# of classroom course titles beyond first-year curriculum		79
# of upper division courses, excluding seminars, with an enrollment: Under 25		94
25–49		20
50–74		11
75–99		3
100+		0
# of seminars		8
# of seminar positions available		144
# of seminar positions filled	100	12
# of positions available in simulation courses		289
# of simulation positions filled	224	23
# of positions available in faculty supervised clinical courses		67
# of faculty supervised clinical positions filled	73	7
# involved in field placements	134	14
# involved in law journals	31	8
# involved in moot court or trial competitions	18	6
# of credit hours required to graduate		89

Faculty and Administrators

	Total Spr	Total Fall	Men Spr	Men Fall	Women Spr	Women Fall	Minorities Spr	Minorities Fall
Full-time	22	21	9	9	13	12	7	4
Other full-time	12	2	8	1	4	1	1	0
Deans, librarians, & others who teach	10	11	6	6	4	5	2	2
Part-time	14	14	9	10	5	3	0	0
Total	58	48	32	26	26	21	10	6

JD Enrollment and Ethnicity

	Men #	Men %	Women #	Women %	Full-Time #	Full-Time %	Part-Time #	Part-Time %	1st-Year #	1st-Year %	Total #	Total %	JD Degs. Awd.
African Amer.	11	4.2	16	7.1	15	4.1	12	10.2	11	6.9	27	5.6	6
Amer. Indian	8	3.1	3	1.3	10	2.7	1	0.8	2	1.3	11	2.3	2
Asian Amer.	22	8.5	32	14.3	45	12.3	9	7.6	13	8.2	54	11.2	14
Mex. Amer.	1	0.4	1	0.4	0	0.0	2	1.7	0	0.0	2	0.4	10
Puerto Rican	0	0.0	1	0.4	0	0.0	1	0.8	0	0.0	1	0.2	2
Hispanic	18	6.9	27	12.1	38	10.4	7	5.9	21	13.2	45	9.3	5
Total Minority	60	23.1	80	35.7	108	29.5	32	27.1	47	29.6	140	28.9	39
For. Nation.	0	0.0	2	0.9	1	0.3	1	0.8	0	0.0	2	0.4	0
Caucasian	181	69.6	126	56.3	229	62.6	78	66.1	102	64.2	307	63.4	89
Unknown	19	7.3	16	7.1	28	7.7	7	5.9	10	6.3	35	7.2	12
Total	260	53.7	224	46.3	366	75.6	118	24.4	159	32.9	484		140

Transfers

Transfers in	7
Transfers out	4

Tuition and Fees

	Resident	Nonresident
Full-time	$18,838	$30,838
Part-time	$12,328	$20,032
Tuition Guarantee Program		N

Living Expenses

Estimated living expenses for singles

Living on campus	Living off campus	Living at home
$16,790	$18,920	$11,000

University of Nevada, Las Vegas, William S. Boyd School of Law

ABA
Approved
Since
2000

GPA and LSAT Scores

	Total	Full-Time	Part-Time
# of apps	1,737	1,511	226
# of offers	381	333	48
# of matrics	158	122	36
75% GPA	3.66	3.67	3.64
Median GPA	3.48	3.50	3.43
25% GPA	3.18	3.19	3.13
75% LSAT	160	160	158
Median LSAT	158	158	155
25% LSAT	155	156	152

Grants and Scholarships (from prior year)

	Total		Full-Time		Part-Time	
	#	%	#	%	#	%
Total # of students	487		371		116	
Total # receiving grants	148	30.4	138	37.2	10	8.6
Less than 1/2 tuition	68	14.0	67	18.1	1	0.9
Half to full tuition	28	5.7	22	5.9	6	5.2
Full tuition	52	10.7	49	13.2	3	2.6
More than full tuition	0	0.0	0	0.0	0	0.0
Median grant amount			$7,000		$3,500	

Informational and Library Resources

Total amount spent on library materials	$1,088,763
Study seating capacity inside the library	313
# of full-time equivalent professional librarians	6
Hours per week library is open	101
# of open, wired connections available to students	1,215
# of networked computers available for use by students	67
Has wireless network?	Y
Require computer?	N

JD Attrition (from prior year)

	Academic	Other	Total	
	#	#	#	%
1st year	2	12	14	9.0
2nd year	4	1	5	3.2
3rd year	0	0	0	0.0
4th year	0	0	0	0.0

Employment (9 months after graduation)

	Total	Percentage
Employment status known	140	100.0
Employment status unknown	0	0.0
Employed	131	93.6
Pursuing graduate degrees	2	1.4
Unemployed (seeking, not seeking, or studying for the bar)	3	2.1
Type of Employment		
# employed in law firms	72	55.0
# employed in business and industry	16	12.2
# employed in government	13	9.9
# employed in public interest	5	3.8
# employed as judicial clerks	21	16.0
# employed in academia	3	2.3
Geographic Location		
# employed in state	109	83.2
# employed in foreign countries	1	0.8
# of states where employed	11	

Bar Passage Rates

First-time takers	132	Reporting %	81.82
Average school %	81.48	Average state %	76.94
Average pass difference	4.54		

Jurisdiction	Takers	Passers	Pass %	State %	Diff %
Nevada	108	88	81.48	76.94	4.54

University of Nevada, Las Vegas, William S. Boyd School of Law

4505 Maryland Parkway, Box 451003
Las Vegas, NV 89154-1003
Phone: 702.895.2440; Fax: 702.895.2414
E-mail: request@law.unlv.edu; Website: www.law.unlv.edu

■ Introduction

The William S. Boyd School of Law, the first and only public law school in Nevada history, commenced classes in fall 1998 and now has graduated over 1,000 students. Located in a unique, dynamic, and continually growing metropolitan area, BSL offers its students an evolving social climate in which to study the law and observe and participate in its application. The law school is fully accredited by the American Bar Association and is a member of the Association of American Law Schools.

■ Faculty

The full-time faculty consists of experienced, accomplished, and well-respected legal educators. All faculty members have excellent credentials, experience, and reputations; all are people for whom teaching and mentoring of students is very important; and all are people who are eager to serve their community through scholarship, civic involvement, and various outreach programs. The law school also taps into the wealth of talent in the local bar for adjunct faculty who teach a variety of specialized courses.

■ Curriculum

The Boyd School of Law offers and encourages its students to undertake a generalist curriculum. Specific course offerings are constantly reviewed and revised as societal needs, student interest, and faculty resources change. The curriculum generally emphasizes the responsibilities, skills, and values required of members of the legal profession. This emphasis comes to the fore in Lawyering Process, a three-semester required course that offers students the opportunity to examine the relationship between legal analysis and other legal skills such as research, writing, oral advocacy, and client interviewing and counseling, with significant emphasis on professionalism and ethics.

■ Programs of Study

The law school offers a traditional three-year, full-time JD program, as well as a four-year, part-time JD program during evening hours and a four-year, part-time JD program during day hours. Additionally, three dual-degree programs have been established: Juris Doctor/Master of Business Administration, Juris Doctor/Master of Social Work, and Juris Doctor/PhD in Education.

■ Community Service

Students are afforded a valuable opportunity to help people in need during their first year through the law school's community service program. Working with representatives of Legal Aid Services of Southern Nevada and Nevada Legal Services, teams of students prepare and conduct weekly workshops for unrepresented people on basic procedures in family or small claims court and on paternity, custody, guardianship, immigration, mediation, and bankruptcy matters. In addition to providing direct assistance to others, the program is intended to acquaint students with the large unmet need for legal services and to instill a lasting commitment to community service and pro bono work.

■ Hands-on Experience

The Thomas and Mack Legal Clinic houses the school's "law firm" and offers an integrated academic and practice-based educational experience that teaches students to be reflective practitioners and community-oriented professionals. The clinic currently focuses on six specific areas: appellate litigation, child welfare, juvenile justice, education, innocence, and immigration. Additionally, the law school provides an extensive externship program. Working closely with the legal community, the law school has established a year-round program offering opportunities for students to extern with the federal and state judiciary, government and public service agencies, and Nevada and US legislatures.

■ Saltman Center for Conflict Resolution

The Saltman Center for Conflict Resolution was established in 2003 to provide a venue for advanced study of the nature of conflict and the methods through which conflicts may be resolved. The work of the center encompasses conflicts arising out of regional, national, and international concerns, in both the public and private sectors. Recognizing that a sophisticated understanding of conflict necessarily requires insights derived from disciplines other than law, the center places particular emphasis on interdisciplinary approaches to understanding and resolving disputes. The center's faculty teach courses on mediation, negotiations, alternative dispute resolution, and arbitration as well as a clinical offering in the area of mediation.

■ Student Activities

The Nevada Law Journal is a publication devoted to scholarly research on the subject of national legal interest as well as on issues of particular interest to the Nevada legal community.

The Society of Advocates is the school's appellate and trial forensic program. The society consists of an executive board and team members who participate in interscholastic competitions. Teams compete in mock trial, client counseling, negotiation, mediation, and alternative dispute resolution competitions, as well as traditional appellate advocacy. Boyd's teams have been very successful in winning regional, national, and international competitions.

Students also participate in over 20 student organizations.

■ Career Services

The Department of Career Services offers personalized career counseling, employment workshops, a job opportunity board, on-campus interviewing programs, and a state-of-the-art online job-search program to assist students.

■ Academic Success Program

The Boyd School of Law Academic Success Program provides students a comprehensive network of presentations,

activities, tutorials, and workshops designed to stimulate learning and to amplify the classroom experience. The program supplements the curriculum with opportunities to enhance learning skills and develop more efficient and effective methods of studying, comprehending, and writing. As part of this program, the student-operated Center for Academic Success and Enrichment (CASE) offers students mentoring, advising, and tutoring.

■ Facility

The Boyd School of Law facility includes the William S. Boyd Hall, the James E. Rogers Center for Administration and Justice, and the Thomas and Mack Moot Court Facility. Classrooms include state-of-the art technology for presentations using PowerPoint, video, and document cameras, and are equipped to facilitate video conferencing and distance learning. Classroom, lounge, and study space offer students indoor and outdoor wireless access seating areas where they can make productive use of their time between classes.

■ Library

The Wiener-Rogers Law Library holds the most substantial collection of legal materials in the state of Nevada. The

library is staffed by excellent, service-oriented librarians who have come from major libraries across the country. Patrons and students have access to a core collection of important material in printed and micro formats. The library houses two computer labs and provides numerous carrels for individual study, as well as group study rooms. The growing library collection now exceeds 300,000 volumes and microform volume equivalents.

■ Admission

The Boyd School of Law seeks to enroll an academically well-qualified, accomplished, and diverse group of individuals who will contribute to the vitality of the school's educational program, the community, and the legal profession after graduation. Applicants for admission may demonstrate qualification and accomplishment through distinguished academic records as undergraduate or graduate students, successful careers, meaningful contributions to their communities, or successful efforts to meet challenges associated with race, ethnicity, gender, economic status, or disability. Students of diverse backgrounds, attitudes, and interests contribute to the breadth and quality of the classroom and nonclassroom dialogues which are critical elements of legal education.

Applicant Profile

The Boyd School of Law has elected not to publish an applicant profile based on LSAT score and undergraduate GPA. Those two factors, while certainly important, are not the only factors taken into consideration. The Boyd School of Law uses no form of indexing system in reaching its admission decisions. Each completed application file is reviewed in its entirety.

New England Law | Boston

154 Stuart Street
Boston, MA 02116
Phone: 617.422.7210; Fax: 617.422.7201
E-mail: admit@nesl.edu; Website: www.nesl.edu

ABA
Approved
Since
1969

The Basics

Type of school	Private
Term	Semester
Application deadline	3/15
Application fee	$65
Financial aid deadline	4/8
Can first year start other than fall?	No
Student to faculty ratio	23.2 to 1
# of housing spaces available restricted to law students	
graduate housing for which law students are eligible	

Faculty and Administrators

	Total		Men		Women		Minorities	
	Spr	Fall	Spr	Fall	Spr	Fall	Spr	Fall
Full-time	35	34	23	24	12	10	3	3
Other full-time	3	2	1	1	2	1	1	0
Deans, librarians, & others who teach	6	6	3	3	3	3	0	0
Part-time	68	76	41	50	27	26	11	14
Total	112	118	68	78	44	40	15	17

JD Enrollment and Ethnicity

	Men		Women		Full-Time		Part-Time		1st-Year		Total		JD Degs. Awd.
	#	%	#	%	#	%	#	%	#	%	#	%	
African Amer.	5	1.0	16	2.6	17	2.3	4	1.1	10	2.5	21	1.9	7
Amer. Indian	2	0.4	0	0.0	2	0.3	0	0.0	0	0.0	2	0.2	0
Asian Amer.	21	4.3	38	6.3	48	6.5	11	3.1	21	5.3	59	5.4	32
Mex. Amer.	3	0.6	5	0.8	6	0.8	2	0.6	4	1.0	8	0.7	2
Puerto Rican	4	0.8	0	0.0	4	0.5	0	0.0	1	0.3	4	0.4	1
Hispanic	5	1.0	10	1.6	13	1.8	2	0.6	8	2.0	15	1.4	3
Total Minority	40	8.2	69	11.3	90	12.2	19	5.3	44	11.0	109	9.9	45
For. Nation.	0	0.0	0	0.0	0	0.0	0	0.0	0	0.0	0	0.0	0
Caucasian	372	76.2	446	73.4	540	73.3	278	77.4	295	73.9	818	74.6	230
Unknown	76	15.6	93	15.3	107	14.5	62	17.3	61	15.3	169	15.4	38
Total	488	44.5	608	55.5	737	67.2	359	32.8	399	36.4	1096		313

Curriculum

	Full-Time	Part-Time
Typical first-year section size	110	105
Is there typically a "small section" of the first-year class, other than Legal Writing, taught by full-time faculty	No	No
If yes, typical size offered last year		
# of classroom course titles beyond first-year curriculum	121	

# of upper division courses, excluding seminars, with an enrollment:		
Under 25	97	
25–49	52	
50–74	14	
75–99	11	
100+	3	

# of seminars	51	
# of seminar positions available	1,324	
# of seminar positions filled	376	231
# of positions available in simulation courses	1,044	
# of simulation positions filled	328	417
# of positions available in faculty supervised clinical courses	60	
# of faculty supervised clinical positions filled	53	6
# involved in field placements	191	35
# involved in law journals	112	19
# involved in moot court or trial competitions	11	0
# of credit hours required to graduate	86	

Transfers

Transfers in	1
Transfers out	32

Tuition and Fees

	Resident	Nonresident
Full-time	$38,580	$38,580
Part-time	$28,960	$28,960
Tuition Guarantee Program	N	

Living Expenses

Estimated living expenses for singles

Living on campus	Living off campus	Living at home
N/A	$16,650	$8,776

New England Law | Boston

ABA
Approved
Since
1969

GPA and LSAT Scores

	Total	Full-Time	Part-Time
# of apps	3,163	2,678	765
# of offers	1,990	1,599	391
# of matrics	403	296	107
75% GPA	3.45	3.45	3.40
Median GPA	3.22	3.24	3.13
25% GPA	2.97	3.00	2.80
75% LSAT	154	154	155
Median LSAT	152	152	151
25% LSAT	150	151	149

Grants and Scholarships (from prior year)

	Total		Full-Time		Part-Time	
	#	%	#	%	#	%
Total # of students	1,077		703		374	
Total # receiving grants	478	44.4	381	54.2	97	25.9
Less than 1/2 tuition	354	32.9	292	41.5	62	16.6
Half to full tuition	69	6.4	51	7.3	18	4.8
Full tuition	55	5.1	38	5.4	17	4.5
More than full tuition	0	0.0	0	0.0	0	0.0
Median grant amount			$5,000		$5,000	

Informational and Library Resources

Total amount spent on library materials	$1,201,397
Study seating capacity inside the library	473
# of full-time equivalent professional librarians	9
Hours per week library is open	104
# of open, wired connections available to students	176
# of networked computers available for use by students	66
Has wireless network?	Y
Require computer?	N

JD Attrition (from prior year)

	Academic	Other	Total	
	#	#	#	%
1st year	22	55	77	20.3
2nd year	3	12	15	4.9
3rd year	0	4	4	1.3
4th year	0	2	2	2.5

Employment (9 months after graduation)

	Total	Percentage
Employment status known	276	87.3
Employment status unknown	40	12.7
Employed	233	84.4
Pursuing graduate degrees	14	5.1
Unemployed (seeking, not seeking, or studying for the bar)	28	10.1
Type of Employment		
# employed in law firms	91	39.1
# employed in business and industry	62	26.6
# employed in government	35	15.0
# employed in public interest	10	4.3
# employed as judicial clerks	31	13.3
# employed in academia	4	1.7
Geographic Location		
# employed in state	146	62.7
# employed in foreign countries	1	0.4
# of states where employed		28

Bar Passage Rates

First-time takers	297	Reporting %	75.08
Average school %	91.48	Average state %	91.91

Average pass difference −0.43

Jurisdiction	Takers	Passers	Pass %	State %	Diff %
Massachusetts	195	177	90.77	92.33	−1.56
New York	28	27	96.43	88.98	7.45

New England Law | Boston

154 Stuart Street
Boston, MA 02116
Phone: 617.422.7210; Fax: 617.422.7201
E-mail: admit@nesl.edu; Website: www.nesl.edu

■ Introduction

New England Law | Boston offers an exceptional academic program; an engaged, welcoming community; and a menu of experiential learning opportunities that's among the most varied in the nation—all in the heart of Boston's legal community. Founded in 1908 as Portia Law School, the first law school in the nation exclusively for women, New England Law has been coeducational since 1938.

The law school officially announced the shortening of its name from New England School of Law to New England Law | Boston during its centennial celebrations in 2008. The law school is accredited by the American Bar Association (ABA) and is a member of the Association of American Law Schools (AALS).

■ The Faculty

The faculty brings elite academic credentials, a wealth of legal practice experience, and a strong desire to help students reach their goals. Because of the school's location in the heart of the legal community, the school's adjunct professors are drawn from a pool of outstanding practitioners, including more than a dozen judges.

Even US Supreme Court justices provide their points of view in the school's classrooms, with visits last academic year from four High Court justices. During her visit, retired Justice Sandra Day O'Connor remarked, "It's a tremendous honor to be here to celebrate the start of the second 100 years of this amazing law school, and it's a privilege to be here with America's favorite dean. In a real sense this is a pioneering law school ..."

■ Academic Program

The law school offers one of the most wide-ranging, experiential-learning programs in the country. Through 16 clinics, three academic centers, and multiple cocurricular activities, students gain hands-on experience with the benefit of consistent faculty supervision. Programs include a variety of judicial clerkship opportunities. The school places recent graduates in postgraduate judicial clerkships at a rate 38 percent higher than the average at law schools nationally (from 2009 NALP data).

The law school is one of a handful in the country to place students regularly at a variety of international criminal tribunals (International Criminal Tribunals for the former Yugoslavia and Rwanda, Special Court for Sierra Leone, Extraordinary Chambers in the Courts of Cambodia, International Criminal Court) and at UN headquarters.

The law school has three nationally distributed journals, the *New England Law Review*, the *New England Journal on Criminal and Civil Confinement*, and the *Journal of International and Comparative Law*. The curriculum at New England Law prepares students to practice in any jurisdiction in the United States.

■ Academic Centers

The law school has three academic centers.

The Center for International Law and Policy provides students with the opportunity to move beyond the walls of the classroom, confront critical social and legal issues, interact directly with senior international officials and victims of international crises, and apply what they are learning to actual cases. A few recent efforts include a project on Afghan women's access to justice, which was undertaken on behalf of Amnesty International; recent work on secret renditions is being done at the request of the Council of Europe.

The center's 2008 conference, "African Voices, Global Choices: The Impact on Human Rights," was honored with the Best Academic Event award by the International Law Students Association.

The Center for Law and Social Responsibility engages students and faculty in public interest work in areas such as the environment, children and families, and wrongful convictions. Some recent environmental projects include representing townspeople who are fighting the construction of a carbon-polluting power plant near an elementary school and building a case against an environmentally damaging hydroelectric dam in South America.

The Center for Business Law offers a wide range of challenging opportunities, with placements at organizations like the Boston Stock Exchange and insurance giant Liberty Mutual. Faculty and students helped draft a comprehensive revision of the Massachusetts Business Corporation Law and their proposal assisted in the enactment of Massachusetts General Laws Chapter 15D.

■ Diversity

The law school's earliest alumnae broke major barriers blocking the entry of women into the legal profession (Blanche Braxton '21, for example, was the first African American woman admitted to the Massachusetts Bar). The school's pioneering roots are evident today as it continues to offer a quality legal education to students from a broad range of backgrounds. The school is one of only a few in the United States offering a program that provides parents with primary child-rearing responsibilities an opportunity to pursue a legal education.

New England Law fosters a comfortable and supportive atmosphere for students of color. A cornerstone of that commitment is the Charles Hamilton Houston Enrichment Program. The program seeks to address racial bias in the legal profession and the law, promote diversity in the student body, and reduce isolation. The program combines discussion groups with guest speakers and community-building activities.

■ Study Options

Students may enroll in the full-time day division, the part-time day or evening divisions, or the Special Part-Time Program. New England Law accepts foreign lawyers in an advanced placement JD program or an LLM program in Advanced Legal Studies.

■ Study Abroad

Students may study in summer-abroad programs in Galway, Ireland; London; Malta; Chile; or Prague; or in semester-abroad programs in Denmark, the Netherlands, Tanzania, Switzerland, Nepal, Paris X-Nanterre, or Cambodia. An international

criminal process clinic in The Hague enrolls students for a summer or semester.

Financial Aid

Financial aid consists of a combination of federal loan programs, private loans, and institutional aid. Students are automatically considered upon admission for our generous merit-based scholarship program. Nearly two-thirds of the entering class receives merit- or need-based grants or scholarships. Federal work-study is also available by application.

Student Activities

New England Law has a Student Bar Association, which oversees more than two dozen student groups. These organizations sponsor speakers, social events, and volunteer activities during the year. Student representatives sit on most faculty committees.

Career Services

The Career Services Office (CSO) provides students with individual career counseling, job-search resources, and career programs and workshops. The office maintains an extensive resource library and an online Recruitment and Programming Center with services that include a searchable job-posting database, employer recruitment programs, an e-mail service that sends students job postings, an alumni networking and mentoring program, and postings of job-related programs sponsored by the CSO and outside organizations.

As a member of the Massachusetts Law School Consortium, New England Law participates in recruitment programs with the state's six other ABA-accredited law schools. The school is also a member of the Northeast Law School Consortium and participates in recruitment programs with eight ABA-accredited law schools in the region.

Most students take the Massachusetts bar exam, while many take exams in New York, the District of Columbia, Florida, New Hampshire, and New Jersey.

Applicant Profile

New England Law | Boston
This grid includes only applicants who earned 120–180 LSAT scores under standard administrations.

LSAT Score	3.75 +		3.50–3.74		3.25–3.49		3.00–3.24		2.75–2.99		2.50–2.74		2.25–2.49		2.00–2.24		Below 2.00		No GPA		Total	
	Apps	Adm	Apps	Adm	Apps	Adm	Apps	Adm	Apps	Adm	Apps	Adm	Apps	Adm	Apps	Adm	Apps	Adm	Apps	Adm	Apps	Adm
175–180	0	0	0	0	0	0	0	0	0	0	0	0	0	0	0	0	0	0	0	0	0	0
170–174	0	0	1	1	0	0	1	1	0	0	0	0	0	0	0	0	0	0	0	0	2	2
165–169	2	2	4	4	4	4	9	8	9	9	1	0	1	1	0	0	0	0	0	0	30	28
160–164	11	11	25	23	26	26	31	31	22	22	12	11	9	7	0	0	1	0	0	0	137	131
155–159	30	30	78	77	85	83	102	98	57	54	47	45	21	15	9	4	2	0	6	4	437	410
150–154	68	67	177	172	256	250	230	219	155	136	84	72	42	26	17	8	4	0	8	5	1041	955
145–149	50	20	114	47	224	75	239	89	142	48	94	22	53	6	8	0	2	0	12	3	938	310
140–144	15	0	34	0	67	0	110	0	73	0	47	0	24	0	13	0	2	0	9	0	394	0
135–139	3	0	9	0	24	0	32	0	31	0	23	0	20	0	9	0	2	0	6	0	159	0
130–134	1	0	2	0	7	0	3	0	11	0	12	0	5	0	4	0	1	0	6	0	52	0
125–129	0	0	1	0	0	0	0	0	2	0	1	0	4	0	0	0	2	0	1	0	11	0
120–124	0	0	0	0	0	0	0	0	0	0	0	0	0	0	0	0	0	0	1	0	1	0
Total	180	130	445	324	693	438	757	446	502	269	321	150	179	55	60	12	16	0	49	12	3202	1836

Apps = Number of Applicants
Adm = Number Admitted
Reflects 99% of the total applicant pool; average LSAT data reported.

The University of New Mexico School of Law

MSC11-6070, 1 University of New Mexico
Albuquerque, NM 87131-0001
Phone: 505.277.2146; Fax: 505.277.9958
E-mail: admissions@law.unm.edu; Website: http://lawschool.unm.edu

ABA
Approved
Since
1948

The Basics

Type of school	Public
Term	Semester
Application deadline	2/15
Application fee	
Financial aid deadline	3/1
Can first year start other than fall?	No
Student to faculty ratio	11.3 to 1
# of housing spaces available restricted to law students	
graduate housing for which law students are eligible	

Faculty and Administrators

	Total		Men		Women		Minorities	
	Spr	Fall	Spr	Fall	Spr	Fall	Spr	Fall
Full-time	24	27	11	11	13	16	12	13
Other full-time	3	3	1	1	2	2	0	0
Deans, librarians, & others who teach	13	10	5	4	8	6	5	3
Part-time	27	20	14	12	13	8	3	4
Total	67	60	31	28	36	32	20	20

Curriculum

		Full-Time	Part-Time
Typical first-year section size		56	0
Is there typically a "small section" of the first-year class, other than Legal Writing, taught by full-time faculty		Yes	No
If yes, typical size offered last year		37	
# of classroom course titles beyond first-year curriculum		81	
# of upper division courses, excluding seminars, with an enrollment:	Under 25	48	
	25–49	17	
	50–74	8	
	75–99	0	
	100+	0	
# of seminars		29	
# of seminar positions available		345	
# of seminar positions filled		330	0
# of positions available in simulation courses		430	
# of simulation positions filled		418	0
# of positions available in faculty supervised clinical courses		124	
# of faculty supervised clinical positions filled		123	0
# involved in field placements		57	0
# involved in law journals		62	0
# involved in moot court or trial competitions		26	0
# of credit hours required to graduate		86	

JD Enrollment and Ethnicity

	Men		Women		Full-Time		Part-Time		1st-Year		Total		JD Degs. Awd.
	#	%	#	%	#	%	#	%	#	%	#	%	
African Amer.	7	4.3	6	3.2	13	3.7	0	0.0	6	4.8	13	3.7	5
Amer. Indian	10	6.2	25	13.2	35	10.0	0	0.0	12	9.7	35	10.0	10
Asian Amer.	4	2.5	6	3.2	10	2.8	0	0.0	2	1.6	10	2.8	4
Mex. Amer.	0	0.0	0	0.0	0	0.0	0	0.0	0	0.0	0	0.0	35
Puerto Rican	0	0.0	0	0.0	0	0.0	0	0.0	0	0.0	0	0.0	0
Hispanic	48	29.8	51	26.8	99	28.2	0	0.0	34	27.4	99	28.2	0
Total Minority	69	42.9	88	46.3	157	44.7	0	0.0	54	43.5	157	44.7	54
For. Nation.	0	0.0	0	0.0	0	0.0	0	0.0	0	0.0	0	0.0	0
Caucasian	75	46.6	83	43.7	158	45.0	0	0.0	52	41.9	158	45.0	54
Unknown	17	10.6	19	10.0	36	10.3	0	0.0	18	14.5	36	10.3	4
Total	161	45.9	190	54.1	351	100.0	0	0.0	124	35.3	351		112

Transfers

Transfers in	4
Transfers out	3

Tuition and Fees

	Resident	Nonresident
Full-time	$12,620	$28,235
Part-time		
Tuition Guarantee Program		N

Living Expenses

Estimated living expenses for singles

Living on campus	Living off campus	Living at home
$13,412	$13,846	$8,452

The University of New Mexico School of Law

ABA
Approved
Since
1948

GPA and LSAT Scores

	Total	Full-Time	Part-Time
# of apps	1,039	1,039	0
# of offers	254	254	0
# of matrics	117	117	0
75% GPA	3.67	3.67	0.00
Median GPA	3.51	3.51	0.00
25% GPA	3.12	3.12	0.00
75% LSAT	158	158	0
Median LSAT	155	155	0
25% LSAT	152	152	0

Grants and Scholarships (from prior year)

	Total #	Total %	Full-Time #	Full-Time %	Part-Time #	Part-Time %
Total # of students	346		346		0	
Total # receiving grants	82	23.7	82	23.7	0	0.0
Less than 1/2 tuition	40	11.6	40	11.6	0	0.0
Half to full tuition	9	2.6	9	2.6	0	0.0
Full tuition	29	8.4	29	8.4	0	0.0
More than full tuition	4	1.2	4	1.2	0	0.0
Median grant amount			$6,498		$0	

Informational and Library Resources

Total amount spent on library materials	$738,272
Study seating capacity inside the library	275
# of full-time equivalent professional librarians	7
Hours per week library is open	90
# of open, wired connections available to students	331
# of networked computers available for use by students	80
Has wireless network?	Y
Require computer?	Y

JD Attrition (from prior year)

	Academic #	Other #	Total #	Total %
1st year	1	3	4	3.5
2nd year	0	0	0	0.0
3rd year	0	0	0	0.0
4th year	0	0	0	0.0

Employment (9 months after graduation)

	Total	Percentage
Employment status known	105	100.0
Employment status unknown	0	0.0
Employed	98	93.3
Pursuing graduate degrees	2	1.9
Unemployed (seeking, not seeking, or studying for the bar)	4	3.8
Type of Employment		
# employed in law firms	34	34.7
# employed in business and industry	14	14.3
# employed in government	17	17.3
# employed in public interest	16	16.3
# employed as judicial clerks	13	13.3
# employed in academia	3	3.1
Geographic Location		
# employed in state	77	78.6
# employed in foreign countries	1	1.0
# of states where employed	11	

Bar Passage Rates

First-time takers	92	Reporting %	95.65
Average school %	92.05	Average state %	91.59
Average pass difference	0.46		

Jurisdiction	Takers	Passers	Pass %	State %	Diff %
New Mexico	88	81	92.05	91.59	0.46

The University of New Mexico School of Law

MSC11-6070, 1 University of New Mexico
Albuquerque, NM 87131-0001
Phone: 505.277.2146; Fax: 505.277.9958
E-mail: admissions@law.unm.edu; Website: http://lawschool.unm.edu

■ Introduction

Located in Albuquerque, the School of Law is known for its small classes, easy student-faculty interaction, and programs in clinical law, natural resources law, and Indian law. The excellent student-to-faculty ratio, one of the best in the country, facilitates a sense of community in the educational experience. It also allows the school to offer more courses with smaller enrollments. The school is a member of the Association of American Law Schools (AALS) and is approved by the American Bar Association (ABA). The University of New Mexico is the state's flagship institution with approximately 33,000 students on its main and branch campuses.

■ Curriculum

The Juris Doctor (JD) program offers a full-time day curriculum. Students normally complete the required 86 hours of law credit for the JD degree in three academic years (six semesters). A limited number of entering students may be admitted to the Flexible Time Program, which allows students to take fewer credit hours per semester and graduate in five academic years. All students must take the standard first-year curriculum, including basic courses in torts, contracts, civil procedure, property, criminal law, and constitutional law. Emphasis is also placed on the skills of advocacy: legal writing, oral argument, litigation, counseling, and negotiation. First-year classes range in size from approximately 13 to 59 students. After completion of the first-year curriculum, courses are elective except for Ethics and a clinical program. Typically, one half of the electives have fewer than 15 students. Every student must complete the advanced writing requirement.

■ Special Programs

Clinical Law. UNM's program in Clinical Law is regarded as one of the finest practical lawyering programs in the country and includes the Law Practice Clinic, the Business and Tax Clinic, the Community Lawyering Clinic, and the Southwest Indian Law Clinic. Students may participate in the extern placement program and elect assignment to a judge's office, the public defender's office, federal and state administrative offices, and private practitioners. The school also offers an innovative course in Criminal Law in Practice, in which students receive hands-on experience in either prosecution or defense of criminal cases at both the misdemeanor and felony levels. Unlike most other law schools, UNM requires six credit hours of clinical work for graduation. In 1970, the New Mexico Supreme Court adopted a rule permitting students to practice before state courts.

Indian Law. UNM has long been a leader in Indian law and has developed one of the most comprehensive programs in the country. The school offers students the Southwest Indian Law Clinic, the *Tribal Law Journal*, the Indian Law Certificate (ILC), scholarly research, guest lectures, seminars, and social activities. An ILC student completes the JD while enrolling in 21 hours of required and elective Indian law courses.

Natural Resources Law. The UNM School of Law is widely known for its strength in the areas of natural resources and environmental law and offers a number of electives in these subjects. Students who want to gain a more comprehensive understanding of resource problems may participate in the Natural Resources Certificate Program, which may include work on the *Natural Resources Journal*, an internationally recognized quarterly.

Business Law. UNM's Economic Development Program gives students the training they need to become well-prepared business lawyers. An enhanced curriculum includes the Business and Tax Clinic, which offers services to small businesses, start-ups, nonprofit organizations, and economic development programs. Students learn how to advise entrepreneurs on a wide range of business issues.

International Law. The school has developed a variety of programs and courses that provide opportunities for students interested in international law. Students may expand their experience through coursework at the law school and through the study-abroad and exchange programs.

- *Guanajuato Summer Law Institute.* The School of Law, in conjunction with the Universidad de Guanajuato, Southwestern University, and Texas Tech University, offers four to six weeks of summer law study in Guanajuato, Mexico. The institute features an introduction to Mexican law and international law subjects related to Latin America. The institute is ABA-approved.
- *North American Exchange Program.* Students can participate in a semester exchange with a Canadian or Mexican law school. Students may visit for a semester in their second or third year and receive up to 12 credits.
- *Tasmania.* Students have the opportunity to study for one semester at the University of Tasmania School of Law and receive up to 12 credits.
- *Visiting Programs.* Students may visit at other ABA-approved programs around the world.

■ Dual-Degree Programs

Three established dual JD and master's degree programs are offered: the JD and MPA in Public Administration, the JD and MBA, and the JD and MA in Latin American Studies. Students can also earn the JD degree and an MA, MS, or PhD in other academic fields. Students must satisfy the admission and academic requirements of both the School of Law and the graduate school.

■ Facilities

The School of Law, a state-of-the-art facility, is located on the northern edge of the UNM campus. The building is wireless and laptop friendly. The law school includes classroom and seminar rooms, all faculty offices, student organization and publication offices, a computer lab, the Clinical Program, and the law library. The law school is also home to the American Indian Law Center, Inc., and the Utton Transboundary Resources Center. The Utton Center uses multidisciplinary scholarship to address complex resource issues, focusing primarily on the Rio Bravo/Rio Grande and the Mexican–US border. Adjacent to the law school is the New Mexico Law Center in which the Institute of Public Law and the Albuquerque branch of the New Mexico Court of Appeals are located.

The University of New Mexico School of Law

Law Library. The UNM Law Library is the largest legal research facility in New Mexico. The library offers a wide variety of electronic products, and its book and microform collection of 433,064 includes special collections in American Indian law, Mexican and Latin American law, land grant law, and natural resources law. The library's 32,443 square feet of space provides 359 seats, including 106 student carrels and 253 noncarrel seats, plus numerous areas for study, lounging, and browsing. Wireless Internet broadcasters, group study rooms equipped with audiovisual equipment, photocopy facilities, the school's computer lab for student use, and a classroom for legal research instruction are found in the library. The library is also home to the Governor Bruce King Archives and Reading Room, which serves as a meeting space for special events.

Career and Student Services. The school's smaller size allows for individualized attention in all aspects of career development and job-search methodology. Regular workshops are provided on résumé and cover letter writing, interviewing, and job-search strategies. In addition, the law school sponsors on-campus interviews, a mock interview program, and presentations on various practice opportunities. Career advisement for students and graduates is provided by two full-time attorney career advisors.

■ Student Activities

Extracurricular activities include the *Natural Resources Journal*, the *New Mexico Law Review*, the *Tribal Law Journal*, and several moot court and mock trial competitions. All law students are members of the university's Graduate/Professional Student Association and the Student Bar Association. Students may participate in over 30 law student organizations.

■ Admission and Financial Aid

Applicants must take the LSAT, register for the LSAC Credential Assembly Service, and have a bachelor's degree from an accredited university or college before registration in the fall. A five-member committee reviews applications. Substantial weight is given to the applicant's personal statement, prior work experience, extracurricular activities, letters of recommendation, and other information supplied by the applicant. Applications from New Mexico residents are given a preference. Students apply for financial aid by filing the FAFSA. Types of financial aid include loans, grants, and work study. The school awards grants to students based on the Access Group's Need Access application.

■ Albuquerque

The Albuquerque metropolitan area has a population of approximately 750,000. Located along the Rio Grande, the city is located at a high desert elevation of 5,000–7,000 feet and is surrounded by the Sandia Mountains.

From golf to skiing to hiking to fly-fishing, students have access to outdoor New Mexico. In addition, students have the opportunity to visit museums and art galleries and take in concerts and theater. The combination of multiple cultures reflected in food, music, art, architecture, and local customs heightens Albuquerque's appeal.

Applicant Profile

The University of New Mexico School of Law
This grid includes only applicants who earned 120–180 LSAT scores under standard administrations.

LSAT Score	GPA 3.75 + Apps	Adm	3.50–3.74 Apps	Adm	3.25–3.49 Apps	Adm	3.00–3.24 Apps	Adm	2.75–2.99 Apps	Adm	2.50–2.74 Apps	Adm	2.25–2.49 Apps	Adm	2.00–2.24 Apps	Adm	Below 2.00 Apps	Adm	No GPA Apps	Adm	Total Apps	Adm
175–180	0	0	0	0	0	0	0	0	1	1	0	0	0	0	0	0	0	0	0	0	1	1
170–174	2	2	1	1	1	1	0	0	0	0	0	0	0	0	0	0	0	0	0	0	4	4
165–169	4	4	4	3	3	3	3	2	3	2	2	0	1	1	0	0	0	0	0	0	20	15
160–164	17	13	19	16	21	15	23	12	5	2	6	1	0	0	1	0	1	0	2	1	95	60
155–159	30	18	51	27	41	13	42	14	24	7	15	3	11	2	0	0	0	0	1	0	215	84
150–154	48	18	56	15	86	18	68	5	43	2	21	3	6	0	8	0	2	0	9	2	347	63
145–149	22	3	41	10	47	2	44	5	26	4	25	2	10	0	1	0	0	0	3	0	219	26
140–144	8	0	18	0	23	0	15	0	22	0	13	0	6	0	3	0	0	0	4	0	112	0
135–139	3	0	5	0	6	0	17	0	3	0	11	0	5	0	3	0	0	0	2	0	55	0
130–134	0	0	2	0	1	0	3	0	4	0	2	0	1	0	4	0	0	0	0	0	17	0
125–129	0	0	0	0	0	0	0	0	0	0	2	0	2	0	0	0	1	0	1	0	6	0
120–124	0	0	0	0	0	0	0	0	0	0	0	0	0	0	0	0	0	0	0	0	0	0
Total	134	58	197	72	229	52	215	38	131	18	97	9	42	3	20	0	4	0	22	3	1091	253

Apps = Number of Applicants
Adm = Number Admitted
Reflects 99% of the total applicant pool; average LSAT data reported.

New York Law School

185 West Broadway
New York, NY 10013
Phone: 212.431.2888; Fax: 212.966.1522
E-mail: admissions@nyls.edu; Website: www.nyls.edu

ABA
Approved
Since
1954

ABA — AMERICAN BAR ASSOCIATION — Section of Legal Education and Admissions to the Bar

The Basics

Type of school	Private
Term	Semester
Application deadline	4/1
Application fee	$65
Financial aid deadline	4/1
Can first year start other than fall?	No
Student to faculty ratio	23.6 to 1
# of housing spaces available restricted to law students	99
graduate housing for which law students are eligible	

Faculty and Administrators

	Total Spr	Total Fall	Men Spr	Men Fall	Women Spr	Women Fall	Minorities Spr	Minorities Fall
Full-time	55	55	40	39	15	16	7	8
Other full-time	6	6	3	3	3	3	0	0
Deans, librarians, & others who teach	14	14	7	6	7	8	1	0
Part-time	128	123	81	76	47	47	9	13
Total	203	198	131	124	72	74	17	21

JD Enrollment and Ethnicity

	Men #	Men %	Women #	Women %	Full-Time #	Full-Time %	Part-Time #	Part-Time %	1st-Year #	1st-Year %	Total #	Total %	JD Degs. Awd.
African Amer.	40	4.3	74	7.9	75	5.3	39	8.7	40	5.5	114	6.1	21
Amer. Indian	4	0.4	0	0.0	2	0.1	2	0.4	3	0.4	4	0.2	2
Asian Amer.	34	3.7	58	6.2	74	5.3	18	4.0	1	0.1	92	5.0	49
Mex. Amer.	4	0.4	9	1.0	8	0.6	5	1.1	0	0.0	13	0.7	4
Puerto Rican	16	1.7	15	1.6	16	1.1	15	3.3	11	1.5	31	1.7	5
Hispanic	57	6.2	58	6.2	80	5.7	35	7.8	40	5.5	115	6.2	27
Total Minority	155	16.8	214	22.9	255	18.1	114	25.4	95	13.1	369	19.9	108
For. Nation.	0	0.0	0	0.0	0	0.0	0	0.0	0	0.0	0	0.0	0
Caucasian	600	65.2	547	58.4	887	63.0	260	58.0	485	66.7	1147	61.8	268
Unknown	165	17.9	175	18.7	266	18.9	74	16.5	147	20.2	340	18.3	61
Total	920	49.6	936	50.4	1408	75.9	448	24.1	727	39.2	1856		437

Curriculum

	Full-Time	Part-Time
Typical first-year section size	114	80
Is there typically a "small section" of the first-year class, other than Legal Writing, taught by full-time faculty	Yes	Yes
If yes, typical size offered last year	38	40
# of classroom course titles beyond first-year curriculum	245	
# of upper division courses, excluding seminars, with an enrollment: Under 25	118	
25–49	57	
50–74	24	
75–99	10	
100+	36	
# of seminars	89	
# of seminar positions available	1,619	
# of seminar positions filled	928	324
# of positions available in simulation courses	174	
# of simulation positions filled	108	40
# of positions available in faculty supervised clinical courses	88	
# of faculty supervised clinical positions filled	80	0
# involved in field placements	162	20
# involved in law journals	210	10
# involved in moot court or trial competitions	113	8
# of credit hours required to graduate	86	

Transfers

Transfers in	22
Transfers out	18

Tuition and Fees

	Resident	Nonresident
Full-time	$44,800	$44,800
Part-time	$34,500	$34,500
Tuition Guarantee Program		Y

Living Expenses

Estimated living expenses for singles

Living on campus	Living off campus	Living at home
$22,765	$22,765	$10,105

ABA
Approved
Since
1954

AMERICAN BAR ASSOCIATION
Section of Legal Education
and Admissions to the Bar

New York Law School

GPA and LSAT Scores

	Total	Full-Time	Part-Time
# of apps	4,188	3,403	785
# of offers	2,246	1,936	310
# of matrics	736	569	167
75% GPA	3.48	3.48	3.46
Median GPA	3.23	3.25	3.07
25% GPA	2.96	3.02	2.79
75% LSAT	157	157	155
Median LSAT	154	154	152
25% LSAT	152	152	149

Grants and Scholarships (from prior year)

	Total		Full-Time		Part-Time	
	#	%	#	%	#	%
Total # of students	1,596		1,190		406	
Total # receiving grants	526	33.0	433	36.4	93	22.9
Less than 1/2 tuition	461	28.9	370	31.1	91	22.4
Half to full tuition	61	3.8	60	5.0	1	0.2
Full tuition	4	0.3	3	0.3	1	0.2
More than full tuition	0	0.0	0	0.0	0	0.0
Median grant amount			$10,000		$5,000	

Informational and Library Resources

Total amount spent on library materials	$1,657,279
Study seating capacity inside the library	700
# of full-time equivalent professional librarians	13
Hours per week library is open	98
# of open, wired connections available to students	95
# of networked computers available for use by students	140
Has wireless network?	Y
Require computer?	N

JD Attrition (from prior year)

	Academic	Other	Total	
	#	#	#	%
1st year	29	35	64	11.4
2nd year	0	2	2	0.4
3rd year	0	1	1	0.2
4th year	0	0	0	0.0

Employment (9 months after graduation)

	Total	Percentage
Employment status known	450	97.2
Employment status unknown	13	2.8
Employed	409	90.9
Pursuing graduate degrees	9	2.0
Unemployed (seeking, not seeking, or studying for the bar)	24	5.3
Type of Employment		
# employed in law firms	176	43.0
# employed in business and industry	94	23.0
# employed in government	57	13.9
# employed in public interest	25	6.1
# employed as judicial clerks	17	4.2
# employed in academia	16	3.9
Geographic Location		
# employed in state	289	70.7
# employed in foreign countries	2	0.5
# of states where employed		14

Bar Passage Rates

First-time takers	436	Reporting %	97.25
Average school %	91.27	Average state %	88.98
Average pass difference	2.29		

Jurisdiction	Takers	Passers	Pass %	State %	Diff %
New York	424	387	91.27	88.98	2.29

New York Law School

185 West Broadway
New York, NY 10013
Phone: 212.431.2888; Fax: 212.966.1522
E-mail: admissions@nyls.edu; Website: www.nyls.edu

■ Introduction

New York Law School has developed a unique approach to legal education that it calls *The Right Program for Each Student*. At its core is an acknowledgment that different practice settings require different levels of training. For example, students working in larger organizations with extensive in-house training programs have less need for hands-on training than those who will open a solo practice. Those in larger organizations may need training in a specialized area, while those in general practice may need more breadth and less specialized expertise. The following components of *The Right Program for Each Student* are described on our website: Harlan Scholars Program, Individual Program, Comprehensive Curriculum, and the Professional Development Project.

Founded in 1891, New York Law School is one of the oldest independent law schools in the country. The school is fully accredited by the American Bar Association and is a member of the Association of American Law Schools.

■ Location/Physical Facilities/Library

New York Law School is located in Manhattan's historic district, TriBeCa, in Lower Manhattan. It is an extraordinary setting for the study of law and one of the city's most colorful and dynamic neighborhoods. Lower Manhattan is the site of New York's largest concentration of government agencies, courts, law firms, banks, corporate headquarters, and securities exchanges. Federal Courts, New York State Civil and Criminal Courts, Family Court, and the Court of International Trade are within a four-block radius of the Law School.

The opening of a striking new building during the 2009–2010 academic year doubles the size of the school's facilities and provides the most modern and technologically advanced law building in New York City. This new building houses a four story library—containing more than 500,000 volumes and periodicals, individual and group study space, an auditorium, classrooms, student activity space, and a penthouse dining facility for students.

■ Student Life

We are committed to giving students a first-rate law school experience—in and out of the classroom. In return, we demand of them the seriousness of purpose necessary to become ethical professionals—the kind of lawyers sought by clients, law firms, government agencies, advocacy groups, and corporations.

New York Law School has a long-standing and continuing interest in enrolling students from varied backgrounds, including older students, minority students, women, career-changers, and public servants. Students range in age from 20 to 57, with the average age being 25.

■ Faculty

The Law School's distinguished full-time faculty is composed of productive scholars who are dedicated educators and who share a strong commitment to the school's vision and philosophy embodied in its core values: embracing innovation, fostering integrity and professionalism, and advancing justice for a diverse society. A national survey of law faculty scholarship includes them among the 50 most prolific law faculties in the country and notes the significant number of their books that are published by university presses. Leading jurists and attorneys who work in nearby offices are members of the adjunct faculty.

■ Curriculum and Special Programs

The required curriculum, composed of the entire first year and part of the second year, provides a foundation in legal reasoning and in areas of law that are considered indispensable building blocks of a legal education. In the second year and thereafter, students may design their programs with elective courses chosen from an extraordinarily rich array.

Elements such as legal analysis and legal writing, counseling, interviewing, negotiating, advocacy, planning, and strategizing form the core subject areas of the school's Lawyering Skills Program. Six clinical programs offer students the opportunity to represent real clients.

Externship and judicial internship programs permit students to do actual lawyering work in law offices.

■ Admission

In the admission process, a number of factors are taken into account, including the applicant's academic record and LSAT scores. The admission committee also looks for those applicants who have demonstrated leadership ability, motivation, and a sense of service and responsibility to society. Excellence in a particular field of study, progression of grades, strength of undergraduate curriculum, work and community service experience, graduate study in other disciplines, and extracurricular activities all are considered as well. Writing ability receives particular attention, and the admission committee strongly urges applicants to submit the optional writing sample.

The school seeks to enroll students who, through their diversity of backgrounds, experiences, perspectives, and ambitions, promise to enrich the law school community and, ultimately, the larger society.

■ Academic Centers

The Institute for Information Law and Policy is the home for the study of technology, intellectual property, and information law. It includes our Media Law Center and the Program on Law and Journalism. The Institute offers a certificate of mastery in law office technology and a patent bar preparation curriculum.

The Center for New York City Law focuses on governmental and legal processes in the urban setting.

The Center for International Law focuses on legal issues relating to international trade and finance.

The Justice Action Center seeks to develop students' expertise in civil rights and civil liberties law and international human rights.

The Center on Business Law and Policy focuses on business and corporate law.

The Center on Financial Services Law focuses on law in financial services including regulatory reforms and other current issues in this global industry.

The Center for Professional Values serves as a vehicle through which to examine the role of the legal profession and alternative approaches to the practice of law.

The Center for Real Estate Studies enables students to study both the private practice and public regulation of real estate.

■ Moot Court/Law Journals/Student Organizations

New York Law School students exhibit well-honed courtroom skills, in recent years winning outright three national moot court competitions and earning awards in many others. The school's annual Robert F. Wagner Sr. Labor and Employment Law Competition is one of the nation's largest student-run moot court competitions.

The Law School currently has three scholarly publications, edited and staffed by students, that are an integral part of the Law School's program: *Law Review, Journal of International and Comparative Law*, and *Journal of Human Rights*.

Students have established some 35 interest organizations as well.

■ Expenses and Financial Aid

New York Law School has established a program of financial aid to assist students in meeting the costs of a legal education through grants, scholarships, work-study awards, and loans. Scholarships are awarded on the basis of academic merit and financial need.

■ Office of Professional Development

The Office of Professional Development brings together three key student services: Student Life, Career Services, and Public Interest and Community Service. This innovative structure allows us to offer students personal attention from their first day of study to help them pursue their professional goals. The Career Services Office offers a wide array of services, including individual career counseling, on-campus interview programs, career panels and workshops, alumni network and mentoring programs, online employer databases, and information on summer, full- and part-time positions, and alternative career opportunities.

Applicant Profile

New York Law School
This grid includes only applicants who earned 120–180 LSAT scores under standard administrations.

LSAT Score	3.75 +		3.50–3.74		3.25–3.49		3.00–3.24		2.75–2.99		2.50–2.74		Below 2.50		No GPA		Total	
	Apps	Adm	Apps	Adm	Apps	Adm	Apps	Adm	Apps	Adm	Apps	Adm	Apps	Adm	Apps	Adm	Apps	Adm
170–180	0	0	0	0	1	1	0	0	0	0	2	2	0	0	0	0	3	3
165–169	7	7	10	10	10	8	5	5	5	5	0	0	4	3	0	0	41	38
160–164	36	35	55	54	56	56	48	48	38	38	27	26	20	19	6	4	286	280
155–159	69	66	149	145	194	190	164	158	112	106	60	55	43	27	12	9	803	756
150–154	94	88	231	203	319	242	286	196	177	84	96	29	71	14	21	11	1295	867
145–149	50	33	134	46	193	51	209	62	163	31	85	9	71	2	15	3	920	237
140–144	17	1	62	9	96	7	99	4	111	6	69	1	59	0	17	0	530	28
Below 140	7	0	24	0	48	0	47	0	53	0	52	0	68	0	19	1	318	1
Total	280	230	665	467	917	555	858	473	659	270	391	122	336	65	90	28	4196	2210

Apps = Number of Applicants
Adm = Number Admitted
Reflects 98% of the total applicant pool; average LSAT data reported.

New York University School of Law

40 Washington Square South
New York, NY 10012
Phone: 212.998.6060; Fax: 212.995.4527
E-mail: law.moreinfo@nyu.edu; Website: www.law.nyu.edu

ABA Approved Since 1930

The Basics

Type of school	Private
Term	Semester
Application deadline	2/1
Application fee	$75
Financial aid deadline	4/15
Can first year start other than fall?	No
Student to faculty ratio	9.4 to 1
# of housing spaces available restricted to law students graduate housing for which law students are eligible	810

Faculty and Administrators

	Total		Men		Women		Minorities	
	Spr	Fall	Spr	Fall	Spr	Fall	Spr	Fall
Full-time	125	125	92	89	33	36	22	21
Other full-time	32	25	16	14	16	11	2	1
Deans, librarians, & others who teach	15	15	6	6	9	9	1	1
Part-time	104	70	71	47	32	23	35	24
Total	276	235	185	156	90	79	60	47

Curriculum

	Full-Time	Part-Time
Typical first-year section size	89	0
Is there typically a "small section" of the first-year class, other than Legal Writing, taught by full-time faculty	No	No
If yes, typical size offered last year		

# of classroom course titles beyond first-year curriculum		326
# of upper division courses, excluding seminars, with an enrollment:	Under 25	122
	25–49	73
	50–74	33
	75–99	17
	100+	16
# of seminars		174
# of seminar positions available		3,562
# of seminar positions filled	2,479	0
# of positions available in simulation courses		78
# of simulation positions filled	78	0
# of positions available in faculty supervised clinical courses		223
# of faculty supervised clinical positions filled	214	0
# involved in field placements	151	0
# involved in law journals	634	0
# involved in moot court or trial competitions	141	0
# of credit hours required to graduate		83

JD Enrollment and Ethnicity

	Men		Women		Full-Time		Part-Time		1st-Year		Total		JD Degs. Awd.
	#	%	#	%	#	%	#	%	#	%	#	%	
African Amer.	32	4.0	56	8.9	88	6.2	0	0.0	34	7.6	88	6.2	37
Amer. Indian	3	0.4	0	0.0	3	0.2	0	0.0	1	0.2	3	0.2	0
Asian Amer.	83	10.4	67	10.7	150	10.5	0	0.0	48	10.7	150	10.5	44
Mex. Amer.	8	1.0	8	1.3	16	1.1	0	0.0	2	0.4	16	1.1	2
Puerto Rican	2	0.3	10	1.6	12	0.8	0	0.0	5	1.1	12	0.8	1
Hispanic	33	4.1	30	4.8	63	4.4	0	0.0	20	4.5	63	4.4	13
Total Minority	161	20.2	171	27.2	332	23.3	0	0.0	110	24.5	332	23.3	97
For. Nation.	22	2.8	22	3.5	44	3.1	0	0.0	17	3.8	44	3.1	20
Caucasian	404	50.6	282	44.9	686	48.1	0	0.0	221	49.2	686	48.1	258
Unknown	212	26.5	153	24.4	365	25.6	0	0.0	101	22.5	365	25.6	96
Total	799	56.0	628	44.0	1427	100.0	0	0.0	449	31.5	1427		471

Transfers

Transfers in	37
Transfers out	3

Tuition and Fees

	Resident	Nonresident
Full-time	$46,196	
Part-time		
Tuition Guarantee Program		N

Living Expenses

Estimated living expenses for singles

Living on campus	Living off campus	Living at home
$23,854	$23,854	$23,854

New York University School of Law

ABA
Approved
Since
1930

GPA and LSAT Scores

	Total	Full-Time	Part-Time
# of apps	7,272	7,272	0
# of offers	1,644	1,644	0
# of matrics	450	450	0
75% GPA	3.86	3.86	0.00
Median GPA	3.72	3.72	0.00
25% GPA	3.57	3.57	0.00
75% LSAT	173	173	0
Median LSAT	171	171	0
25% LSAT	169	169	0

Grants and Scholarships (from prior year)

	Total		Full-Time		Part-Time	
	#	%	#	%	#	%
Total # of students	1,423		1,423		0	
Total # receiving grants	495	34.8	495	34.8	0	0.0
Less than 1/2 tuition	327	23.0	327	23.0	0	0.0
Half to full tuition	54	3.8	54	3.8	0	0.0
Full tuition	114	8.0	114	8.0	0	0.0
More than full tuition	0	0.0	0	0.0	0	0.0
Median grant amount		$20,000		$0		

Informational and Library Resources

Total amount spent on library materials	$2,550,284
Study seating capacity inside the library	850
# of full-time equivalent professional librarians	40
Hours per week library is open	101
# of open, wired connections available to students	775
# of networked computers available for use by students	185
Has wireless network?	Y
Require computer?	Y

JD Attrition (from prior year)

	Academic	Other	Total	
	#	#	#	%
1st year	0	3	3	0.7
2nd year	0	7	7	1.4
3rd year	0	0	0	0.0
4th year	0	0	0	0.0

Employment (9 months after graduation)

	Total	Percentage
Employment status known	484	100.0
Employment status unknown	0	0.0
Employed	458	94.6
Pursuing graduate degrees	18	3.7
Unemployed (seeking, not seeking, or studying for the bar)	4	0.8
Type of Employment		
# employed in law firms	344	75.1
# employed in business and industry	10	2.2
# employed in government	10	2.2
# employed in public interest	42	9.2
# employed as judicial clerks	48	10.5
# employed in academia	4	0.9
Geographic Location		
# employed in state	315	68.8
# employed in foreign countries	13	2.8
# of states where employed	28	

Bar Passage Rates

First-time takers	461	Reporting %	84.60
Average school %	97.18	Average state %	88.98
Average pass difference	8.20		

Jurisdiction	Takers	Passers	Pass %	State %	Diff %
New York	390	379	97.18	88.98	8.20

New York University School of Law

40 Washington Square South
New York, NY 10012
Phone: 212.998.6060; Fax: 212.995.4527
E-mail: law.moreinfo@nyu.edu; Website: www.law.nyu.edu

■ Introduction

Founded in 1835, New York University School of Law has a record of academic excellence and national scholarly influence extending back into the nineteenth century. More than 100 years ago, it became one of the first law schools to routinely admit women and those from groups discriminated against by many other institutions.

NYU School of Law has been a pioneer in such widely diverse programs as clinical education, law and business, public service, interdisciplinary colloquia, and global studies.

These traditions remain vibrant today as the School of Law, located on the university's campus in Greenwich Village, continues to use its position in New York City to create a twenty-first century legal education in global justice, grounded in solid sociological and jurisprudential training and reflected in sensitive professional service to the world's peoples.

■ Library and Physical Facilities

As one of the largest academic law libraries in the world, NYU School of Law's collection boasts widely recognized strengths in tax, legal history, intellectual property, constitutional law, and the law of democratic institutions. The extensive public law collection is complemented by primary law materials for over 20 non-US jurisdictions. The library's award-winning home page is a gateway to specialized legal research guides, e-journals, annotated foreign and international law sites, and commercial databases.

In 2004, the School of Law opened Furman Hall, its first new academic building in 50 years. Furman Hall is adjacent to the recently renovated Vanderbilt Hall and connects underground via the law library. The law school also owns two apartment buildings that provide housing for more than 800 law students, many with spouses, partners, and children.

■ Curriculum

NYU School of Law's curriculum is distinguished by its strength in traditional areas of legal study, interdisciplinary study, and clinical education, and has long been committed to educating lawyers who will use their degrees to serve the public. Students enjoy the intellectual and pedagogical diversity of the law school by mixing traditional courses with colloquia, global courses, clinics, independent research, journal work, study abroad, fellowships, and more.

The JD program is enriched by the graduate program, which offers advanced degrees in corporation law, environmental law, international business regulation, international legal studies, international taxation, taxation, and trade regulation.

■ Institutes and Centers

The curriculum is complemented by over 20 institutes and centers, which represent the law school's extraordinary commitment of resources and energy to the collegial study of law at the most advanced level. These include the Brennan Center for Justice, the Hauser Global Law School Program, the Institute for International Law and Justice, the Center for Environmental and Land Use Law, and the Pollack Center for Law and Business.

■ Admission

The admission process is highly selective and seeks to enroll men and women of exceptional ability. The Committee on Admissions makes decisions after considering all the information in an application. It reviews the undergraduate transcript closely, with attention to factors such as trends in the applicant's grades, class rank, the ratio of pass/fail to graded courses, the diversity and depth of coursework, and the length of time since graduation. Factors other than undergraduate grades and LSAT scores may be particularly significant for applicants who have experienced educational or socioeconomic disadvantage. In all cases, however, other aspects of the application significantly influence the decision. The committee evaluates work experience and extracurricular and community activities for evidence of advancement, leadership, and capacity for assuming responsibility. A recommendation letter is particularly valuable when the writer provides substantive information about the applicant's abilities, activities, and personal qualities. The personal statement provides an opportunity for the applicant to supplement the information supplied in the application.

The committee seeks to enroll an entering class of students with diverse experience, backgrounds, and points of view. Applicants are encouraged to provide information to help the committee reach thoughtful, informed decisions on their applications.

■ Student Activities

There are several student-edited publications: *New York University Law Review*, *Annual Survey of American Law*, *Environmental Law Journal*, *Journal of International Law and Politics*, *Journal of Law and Business*, *Journal of Law and Liberty*, *Journal of Legislation and Public Policy*, and the *Review of Law and Social Change*, as well as the Moot Court Board. The *Commentator* is the law school newspaper. There are more than 60 student organizations.

■ Financial Aid

NYU School of Law will award a number of Root-Tilden-Kern Scholarships, full-tuition scholarships, to entering students chosen for their intellectual potential, capacity for, and demonstrated commitment to public service through law. A limited number of awards will also be made on the basis of outstanding intellectual potential or substantial records indicating that the student will enrich the educational experience at the law school. The AnBryce Scholarship will be awarded to outstanding students who are among the first in their immediate families to pursue a graduate degree. The Furman Academic Scholarship will be awarded to students who show promise in becoming legal academics. Scholarships are also available in the areas of business law, criminal law, environmental law, housing and urban policy, intellectual property, international law, Latino human rights, and law and economics. Federal and private loans also provide funding.

Graduates who pursue careers in public service may be eligible for postgraduation benefits through the Loan Repayment Assistance Program.

■ Career Services

NYU School of Law has an extensive career services program. Career planning for first-year students includes personal career counseling, workshops on all aspects of the job search, specialty panels featuring speakers from all areas of practice, and a videotape mock interview program. Each year, more than 500 private law firms, public interest organizations, government agencies, corporations, and public accounting firms visit the law school to interview students. Over 60 percent of these employers are from outside New York.

The focal point of the law school's public service activities is the Public Interest Law Center, which provides students interested in public service with comprehensive support, including advice on courses and career opportunities. The Public Interest Summer Scholarship Program guarantees funding to all first- and second-year students who work in public interest positions. The Public Interest Law Center, with area law schools, also annually sponsors a public interest legal career fair.

Applicant Profile

NYU School of Law does not provide a profile chart because we believe that while an applicant's undergraduate record and LSAT are important, they are not the sole determinants for admission to the law school. No index or cutoff is used in reviewing applications. There is no combination of grades or scores, therefore, that assures admission or denial.

An applicant's transcripts are analyzed for breadth and depth of coursework, trend in grades, and rank; the competitiveness of the school and major are taken into consideration, as are special honors, awards and activities. Other aspects of the application significantly influence the decision, such as letters of recommendation, the personal statement, and work experience.

In making its decision, the Committee on Admissions aims to enroll an entering class of students with the strongest combination of qualifications and the greatest potential to contribute to NYU School of Law and to the legal profession.

University of North Carolina School of Law

Campus Box 3380, 5026 Van Hecke-Wettach Hall
Chapel Hill, NC 27599-3380
Phone: 919.962.5109; Fax: 919.843.7939
E-mail: law_admissions@unc.edu; Website: www.law.unc.edu

ABA Approved Since 1923

The Basics

Type of school	Public
Term	Semester
Application deadline	3/1
Application fee	$75
Financial aid deadline	3/1
Can first year start other than fall?	No
Student to faculty ratio	15.4 to 1
# of housing spaces available restricted to law students	
graduate housing for which law students are eligible	

Curriculum

	Full-Time	Part-Time
Typical first-year section size	85	0
Is there typically a "small section" of the first-year class, other than Legal Writing, taught by full-time faculty	Yes	No
If yes, typical size offered last year	28	
# of classroom course titles beyond first-year curriculum	117	

# of upper division courses, excluding seminars, with an enrollment:		
Under 25	53	
25–49	28	
50–74	8	
75–99	7	
100+	4	

	Full-Time	Part-Time
# of seminars	32	
# of seminar positions available	484	
# of seminar positions filled	418	0
# of positions available in simulation courses	1,122	
# of simulation positions filled	1,039	0
# of positions available in faculty supervised clinical courses	52	
# of faculty supervised clinical positions filled	50	0
# involved in field placements	126	0
# involved in law journals	218	0
# involved in moot court or trial competitions	68	0
# of credit hours required to graduate	86	

Faculty and Administrators

	Total Spr	Total Fall	Men Spr	Men Fall	Women Spr	Women Fall	Minorities Spr	Minorities Fall
Full-time	39	42	24	27	15	15	5	7
Other full-time	0	0	0	0	0	0	0	0
Deans, librarians, & others who teach	13	14	6	6	7	8	3	3
Part-time	32	35	20	24	12	11	5	5
Total	84	91	50	57	34	34	13	15

JD Enrollment and Ethnicity

	Men #	Men %	Women #	Women %	Full-Time #	Full-Time %	Part-Time #	Part-Time %	1st-Year #	1st-Year %	Total #	Total %	JD Degs. Awd.
African Amer.	19	5.3	39	9.7	58	7.6	0	0.0	22	8.5	58	7.6	13
Amer. Indian	8	2.2	11	2.7	19	2.5	0	0.0	3	1.2	19	2.5	4
Asian Amer.	23	6.4	29	7.2	52	6.8	0	0.0	27	10.5	52	6.8	21
Mex. Amer.	5	1.4	0	0.0	5	0.7	0	0.0	5	1.9	5	0.7	0
Puerto Rican	0	0.0	0	0.0	0	0.0	0	0.0	0	0.0	0	0.0	0
Hispanic	21	5.8	28	6.9	49	6.4	0	0.0	21	8.1	49	6.4	13
Total Minority	76	21.1	107	26.5	183	23.9	0	0.0	78	30.2	183	23.9	51
For. Nation.	0	0.0	1	0.2	1	0.1	0	0.0	1	0.4	1	0.1	0
Caucasian	204	56.5	223	55.2	427	55.8	0	0.0	159	61.6	427	55.8	161
Unknown	81	22.4	73	18.1	154	20.1	0	0.0	20	7.8	154	20.1	15
Total	361	47.2	404	52.8	765	100.0	0	0.0	258	33.7	765		227

Transfers

Transfers in	4
Transfers out	8

Tuition and Fees

	Resident	Nonresident
Full-time	$16,014	$29,332
Part-time		
Tuition Guarantee Program	N	

Living Expenses

Estimated living expenses for singles

Living on campus	Living off campus	Living at home
$18,932	$18,932	$7,302

University of North Carolina School of Law

ABA
Approved
Since
1923

GPA and LSAT Scores

	Total	Full-Time	Part-Time
# of apps	2,905	2,905	0
# of offers	426	426	0
# of matrics	262	262	0
75% GPA	3.73	3.73	0.00
Median GPA	3.58	3.58	0.00
25% GPA	3.43	3.43	0.00
75% LSAT	164	164	0
Median LSAT	162	162	0
25% LSAT	157	157	0

Grants and Scholarships (from prior year)

	Total #	Total %	Full-Time #	Full-Time %	Part-Time #	Part-Time %
Total # of students	735		735		0	
Total # receiving grants	614	83.5	614	83.5	0	0.0
Less than 1/2 tuition	514	69.9	514	69.9	0	0.0
Half to full tuition	76	10.3	76	10.3	0	0.0
Full tuition	2	0.3	2	0.3	0	0.0
More than full tuition	22	3.0	22	3.0	0	0.0
Median grant amount			$3,900		$0	

Informational and Library Resources

Total amount spent on library materials	$1,779,247
Study seating capacity inside the library	530
# of full-time equivalent professional librarians	12
Hours per week library is open	109
# of open, wired connections available to students	560
# of networked computers available for use by students	111
Has wireless network?	Y
Require computer?	N

JD Attrition (from prior year)

	Academic #	Other #	Total #	Total %
1st year	0	9	9	3.5
2nd year	1	0	1	0.4
3rd year	0	1	1	0.4
4th year	0	0	0	0.0

Employment (9 months after graduation)

	Total	Percentage
Employment status known	217	98.6
Employment status unknown	3	1.4
Employed	196	90.3
Pursuing graduate degrees	3	1.4
Unemployed (seeking, not seeking, or studying for the bar)	9	4.1
Type of Employment		
# employed in law firms	124	63.3
# employed in business and industry	17	8.7
# employed in government	14	7.1
# employed in public interest	17	8.7
# employed as judicial clerks	19	9.7
# employed in academia	3	1.5
Geographic Location		
# employed in state	108	55.1
# employed in foreign countries	0	0.0
# of states where employed	22	

Bar Passage Rates

First-time takers	203	Reporting %	63.05
Average school %	89.84	Average state %	82.61
Average pass difference	7.23		

Jurisdiction	Takers	Passers	Pass %	State %	Diff %
North Carolina	128	115	89.84	82.61	7.23

University of North Carolina School of Law

Campus Box 3380, 5026 Van Hecke-Wettach Hall
Chapel Hill, NC 27599-3380
Phone: 919.962.5109; Fax: 919.843.7939
E-mail: law_admissions@unc.edu; Website: www.law.unc.edu

■ Introduction

The University of North Carolina, the first state university chartered in the United States, has offered degrees in law since 1845. The School of Law has been a member of the American Association of Law Schools since 1920 and has been an approved school since the American Bar Association began its accreditation activities in 1923. The School of Law is one of the outstanding institutions in the United States, and the University of North Carolina is recognized as being among the nation's leaders in graduate and professional education. The programs at the School of Law reflect a powerful, active commitment to the goals of teaching, scholarship, and public service. The town of Chapel Hill, a university community, is close to the Research Triangle Park, the metropolitan and industrial centers of Greensboro and Durham, and the state capital, Raleigh. The immediate area offers an attractive blend of a strong academic atmosphere in a multicultural, cosmopolitan setting.

■ Library and Physical Facilities

Housed on five floors within the law school, the library provides critical support to the school's academic program and to lawyers and members of the public throughout the state. Its collection, which totals over 488,000 volumes, includes court reports for American and English appellate courts, current codes and session laws for all states, and other primary legal materials. Within the library, a university computer lab provides Internet access, electronic mail, and word processing capabilities and is easily accessible to law students. Additionally, students may bring their own laptop computers and connect to the university's network in many of the high-technology classrooms, library study carrels, and other areas in the building.

The School of Law aims to provide a quality legal education that will prepare students to practice successfully in any jurisdiction. The three-year Juris Doctor program begins with a first-year core curriculum designed to provide a theoretical and analytical foundation for law students. The second-year curriculum provides an important bridge between the core instruction of the first year and the culminating electives, seminars, and skills-oriented instruction of the third year. Finally, in the third year, the curriculum is designed to provide a capstone for students' legal education and begin the transition into practice.

■ Dual-Degree Programs/Certificate Programs

Ten formal dual JD and master's degree programs are available: JD/MPP (in conjunction with Duke University), JD/MBA, JD/MPA, JD/MPH, JD/MRP, JD/MSW, JD/MASA, JD/MAMC, JD/MSLS, or MSIS.

The Nonprofit Leadership Certificate Program prepares graduate students for leadership roles in North Carolina's rapidly growing nonprofit sector. The program provides an in-depth examination of leadership issues within human services, education, the arts, and other nonprofit organizations.

■ International Study Opportunities

In addition to the regularly taught courses in international business and human rights and the *International Law Journal*, students interested in international law can enhance their legal experience further with foreign study during the school year in France, the Netherlands, Mexico, England, and Scotland. Additionally, after the first year, students may also participate in the school's Summer Law Programs in Sydney, Australia or Augsburg, Germany.

■ Centers and Initiatives

Carolina boasts nationally recognized centers in banking and financial services; civil rights; poverty, work, and opportunity; our new Center for Law, Environment, Adaptation and Resources (CLEAR); and the Center for Law and Government. All are key areas tied to our history and the unique opportunities unfolding in North Carolina, the South, and the world. These centers and initiatives expand and enliven our curriculum, push the frontiers of teaching and research, and open new channels of scholarship for students.

■ Student Activities

Outside of the classroom, student organizations provide a forum for the enormous talent and energy characteristic of Carolina law students. Students can write for five prominent student publications—the *North Carolina Law Review*, the *North Carolina Journal of International Law and Commercial Regulation*, the *North Carolina Banking Institute Journal*, the *First Amendment Law Review*, and the *North Carolina Journal of Law and Technology*. The Student Bar Association sponsors a full range of professional, athletic, and social events; a speakers program; minority recruitment events; a legal research service for practicing lawyers; and participation in school governance. The Moot Court Program is student operated and fields a number of successful teams in regional, national, and international competitions. Over 50 student organizations are active in the School of Law, including the Black Law Students Association, Parents as Law Students, the Federalist Society, the Hispanic/Latino Law Students Association, the Native American Law Students Association, ACLU, Women in Law, American Constitution Society, and our nationally recognized Pro Bono Program.

■ Expenses and Financial Aid

Full-time tuition and fees in 2009–2010—North Carolina resident, $16,014; nonresident, $29,332. Estimated additional expenses—$17,932. Chancellors' Scholars Program scholarships are available, as well as other merit-based scholarships. Need-based assistance is awarded on the basis of FAFSA information. Students must submit parental information to FAFSA to be considered for need-based grants.

Admitted applicants are automatically considered for merit-based scholarships. Awards range from $1,000 to full tuition. Scholarship offers are made beginning in February.

University of North Carolina School of Law

■ Housing

There are graduate dormitories near the law school for single students; however, most students live off campus. University student family housing and private apartments are available. Information may be obtained from the University Housing Office, Carr Building CB 5500, Chapel Hill, NC 27399-5580; 919.962.5401.

■ Career Services Office

The Career Services Office staff assists students and alumni with summer and permanent positions. Each year, approximately 200 employers from across the nation interview at the School of Law. Of those 2008 graduates reporting to the Career Services Office, 95 percent had accepted employment or were in graduate school within nine months of graduation. Of those 2008 graduates who entered into the practice arena, 63 percent entered private practice; 16 percent entered public sector work, including public interest; 10 percent accepted judicial clerkships; 9 percent entered business/corporate-related practice; and 2 percent entered academia. Regarding job location, 58 percent were employed in North Carolina; 6 percent were employed in New York, New Jersey, and Pennsylvania; and 1 percent were employed in Alaska, California, Hawaii, Oregon, and Washington. Almost 80 percent of our students are employed in the South Atlantic region of the country, which includes Delaware; Washington, DC; Florida; Georgia; Maryland; North Carolina; South Carolina; Virginia; and West Virginia.

Applicant Profile

University of North Carolina School of Law
This grid includes only applicants who earned 120–180 LSAT scores under standard administrations.

LSAT Score	3.75 +		3.50–3.74		3.25–3.49		3.00–3.24		2.75–2.99		2.50–2.74		2.25–2.49		2.00–2.24		Below 2.00		No GPA		Total	
	Apps	Adm	Apps	Adm	Apps	Adm	Apps	Adm	Apps	Adm	Apps	Adm	Apps	Adm	Apps	Adm	Apps	Adm	Apps	Adm	Apps	Adm
175–180	3	3	1	1	2	2	1	1	0	0	1	1	1	0	1	0	0	0	0	0	10	8
170–174	14	10	13	5	17	5	8	1	6	0	1	0	0	0	0	0	0	0	0	0	59	21
165–169	62	34	60	22	53	19	25	4	15	2	7	0	4	0	0	0	0	0	1	0	227	81
160–164	172	51	255	77	167	38	97	15	37	2	14	0	5	0	2	0	0	0	9	0	758	183
155–159	173	24	285	36	208	24	122	4	53	3	16	1	13	0	1	0	0	0	21	0	892	92
150–154	77	16	134	17	130	19	104	6	54	0	18	0	13	0	7	0	2	0	5	0	544	58
145–149	29	0	28	5	50	2	51	1	28	0	17	0	7	0	1	0	1	0	4	0	216	8
140–144	6	0	18	2	18	0	22	0	16	0	13	0	4	0	1	0	0	0	5	0	103	2
135–139	1	0	8	0	13	0	10	0	11	0	5	0	2	0	2	0	0	0	2	0	54	0
130–134	0	0	2	0	3	0	2	0	1	0	1	0	3	0	0	0	0	0	1	0	13	0
125–129	0	0	0	0	0	0	1	0	0	0	0	0	0	0	1	0	0	0	0	0	2	0
120–124	0	0	0	0	0	0	0	0	0	0	0	0	0	0	0	0	0	0	0	0	0	0
Total	537	138	804	165	661	109	443	32	221	7	93	2	52	0	16	0	3	0	48	0	2878	453

Apps = Number of Applicants
Adm = Number Admitted
Reflects 99% of the total applicant pool; average LSAT data reported.

North Carolina Central University School of Law

640 Nelson Street
Durham, NC 27707
Phone: 919.530.6333; Fax: 919.530.6339
E-mail: sbrownb@nccu.edu; Website: www.nccu.edu/law

ABA
Approved
Since
1950

The Basics

Type of school	Public
Term	Semester
Application deadline	3/31
Application fee	$40
Financial aid deadline	7/1
Can first year start other than fall?	No
Student to faculty ratio	16.5 to 1
# of housing spaces available restricted to law students	
graduate housing for which law students are eligible	32

Faculty and Administrators

	Total		Men		Women		Minorities	
	Spr	Fall	Spr	Fall	Spr	Fall	Spr	Fall
Full-time	29	29	12	11	17	18	18	19
Other full-time	6	6	3	3	3	3	3	3
Deans, librarians, & others who teach	13	13	3	3	10	10	9	9
Part-time	18	20	6	11	12	9	12	8
Total	66	68	24	28	42	40	42	39

Curriculum

	Full-Time	Part-Time
Typical first-year section size	65	65
Is there typically a "small section" of the first-year class, other than Legal Writing, taught by full-time faculty	No	No
If yes, typical size offered last year		
# of classroom course titles beyond first-year curriculum	77	

# of upper division courses, excluding seminars, with an enrollment:		
Under 25	51	
25–49	32	
50–74	10	
75–99	5	
100+	3	

# of seminars	23	
# of seminar positions available	460	
# of seminar positions filled	359	8
# of positions available in simulation courses	333	
# of simulation positions filled	249	42
# of positions available in faculty supervised clinical courses	346	
# of faculty supervised clinical positions filled	235	20
# involved in field placements	27	2
# involved in law journals	65	15
# involved in moot court or trial competitions	25	1
# of credit hours required to graduate	88	

JD Enrollment and Ethnicity

	Men		Women		Full-Time		Part-Time		1st-Year		Total		JD Degs. Awd.
	#	%	#	%	#	%	#	%	#	%	#	%	
African Amer.	92	38.8	201	55.2	268	55.8	25	20.7	119	57.8	293	48.8	83
Amer. Indian	2	0.8	2	0.5	4	0.8	0	0.0	1	0.5	4	0.7	2
Asian Amer.	12	5.1	8	2.2	14	2.9	6	5.0	1	0.5	20	3.3	3
Mex. Amer.	0	0.0	0	0.0	0	0.0	0	0.0	0	0.0	0	0.0	1
Puerto Rican	0	0.0	0	0.0	0	0.0	0	0.0	0	0.0	0	0.0	0
Hispanic	9	3.8	9	2.5	13	2.7	5	4.1	4	1.9	18	3.0	4
Total Minority	115	48.5	220	60.4	299	62.3	36	29.8	125	60.7	335	55.7	93
For. Nation.	7	3.0	13	3.6	15	3.1	5	4.1	4	1.9	20	3.3	7
Caucasian	113	47.7	129	35.4	163	34.0	79	65.3	76	36.9	242	40.3	81
Unknown	2	0.8	2	0.5	3	0.6	1	0.8	1	0.5	4	0.7	8
Total	237	39.4	364	60.6	480	79.9	121	20.1	206	34.3	601		189

Transfers

Transfers in	0
Transfers out	5

Tuition and Fees

	Resident	Nonresident
Full-time	$8,097	$20,835
Part-time	$8,097	$20,835
Tuition Guarantee Program	N	

Living Expenses

Estimated living expenses for singles

Living on campus	Living off campus	Living at home
$14,756	$19,956	$9,910

North Carolina Central University School of Law

ABA
Approved
Since
1950

GPA and LSAT Scores

	Total	Full-Time	Part-Time
# of apps	2,089	2,013	806
# of offers	480	353	127
# of matrics	204	169	35
75% GPA	3.49	3.43	3.67
Median GPA	3.24	3.21	3.48
25% GPA	3.02	2.99	3.16
75% LSAT	150	148	155
Median LSAT	145	145	151
25% LSAT	143	142	148

Grants and Scholarships (from prior year)

	Total		Full-Time		Part-Time	
	#	%	#	%	#	%
Total # of students	644		519		125	
Total # receiving grants	293	45.5	293	56.5	0	0.0
Less than 1/2 tuition	139	21.6	139	26.8	0	0.0
Half to full tuition	41	6.4	41	7.9	0	0.0
Full tuition	113	17.5	113	21.8	0	0.0
More than full tuition	0	0.0	0	0.0	0	0.0
Median grant amount		$0		$0		

Informational and Library Resources

Total amount spent on library materials	$1,221,989
Study seating capacity inside the library	370
# of full-time equivalent professional librarians	9
Hours per week library is open	100
# of open, wired connections available to students	78
# of networked computers available for use by students	258
Has wireless network?	Y
Require computer?	N

JD Attrition (from prior year)

	Academic	Other	Total	
	#	#	#	%
1st year	31	21	52	23.3
2nd year	1	0	1	0.5
3rd year	0	0	0	0.0
4th year	0	0	0	0.0

Employment (9 months after graduation)

	Total	Percentage
Employment status known	121	84.0
Employment status unknown	23	16.0
Employed	100	82.6
Pursuing graduate degrees	7	5.8
Unemployed (seeking, not seeking, or studying for the bar)	10	8.3
Type of Employment		
# employed in law firms	53	53.0
# employed in business and industry	6	6.0
# employed in government	22	22.0
# employed in public interest	7	7.0
# employed as judicial clerks	6	6.0
# employed in academia	1	1.0
Geographic Location		
# employed in state	68	68.0
# employed in foreign countries	0	0.0
# of states where employed	9	

Bar Passage Rates

First-time takers	145	Reporting %	86.90
Average school %	82.54	Average state %	83.12
Average pass difference −0.58			

Jurisdiction	Takers	Passers	Pass %	State %	Diff %
North Carolina	113	91	80.53	82.61	−2.08
Georgia	8	8	100.00	89.27	10.73
New Jersey	5	5	100.00	84.69	15.31

North Carolina Central University School of Law

640 Nelson Street
Durham, NC 27707
Phone: 919.530.6333; Fax: 919.530.6339
E-mail: sbrownb@nccu.edu; Website: www.nccu.edu/law

■ Introduction

The mission of the North Carolina University School of Law is to produce competent and socially responsible members of the legal profession. NCCU School of Law accomplishes its mission by providing a challenging and broad-based educational program which stimulates intellectual inquiry of the highest order, and which fosters in each student a deep sense of professional responsibility and personal integrity. Founded in 1939 to provide an opportunity for a legal education to African-Americans, the School of Law now provides this opportunity to one of the most diverse student bodies in the nation. This environment of diversity better prepares our students to effect positive change in the broader society.

The School of Law has been accredited by the North Carolina State Bar Council and the ABA since 1950. Today, NCCU School of Law remains one of the most affordable and diverse in the country. The School of Law offers two programs leading to the Juris Doctor degree: a full-time day program and the oldest ABA-accredited part-time evening program between Atlanta, Georgia, and Washington, DC. The School of Law participates in an interinstitutional agreement with Duke University and the University of North Carolina at Chapel Hill that permits students to enroll in electives at any member law school without an increase in tuition.

■ Facilities, Library, and Technology

The Albert L. Turner Law School building is a state-of-the-art facility that provides the law school community with an attractive, comfortable, and technology-friendly environment in which to work and study. The entire building is wireless. Students are provided a laptop and software for use throughout their matriculation. All classrooms are equipped with state-of-the-art multimedia resources, including smart boards, video and teleconferencing capabilities, and lectern computers with Internet access. The School of Law has several state-of-the-art group-study rooms, a moot courtroom, and a Great Hall for gatherings.

The law library, with more than 378,233 volumes and volume equivalents, provides the resources needed to support the Juris Doctor program, the JD/MLS and JD/MBA dual-degree programs, and the legal community. The law library is a selective North Carolina and United States government depository and has a special collection in civil rights law.

■ Special Academic Programs

- **Joint-Degree Options**—There are two joint-degree programs available to Day Program students. The joint-degree JD/MBA Program allows students who are interested in a career in law and business to receive both degrees in four years. The joint-degree JD/MLS Program allows students who are interested in a career in law librarianship to simultaneously pursue both degrees. Students must apply and be accepted to each program separately.
- **Evening Program**—The Evening Program is a four-year, year-round program that offers a unique opportunity for motivated professionals to pursue a legal education while maintaining their current daytime work commitments.
- **Academic Support Program**—The Academic Support Program is available to assist students with the rigors of law school. Through the tutorial program, workshops, one-on-one guidance, and readily available resources, all students have access to information to enable them to become effective and successful law students.
- **Faculty Advising Program**—Each student is assigned a faculty advisor who is available to discuss questions or problems related to the School of Law experience, career choices, and personal problems that might affect academic performance. They also advise students on taking appropriate classes and monitor their progress.
- **Clinical Program**—The award-winning Clinical Program is rated highly by *National Jurist Magazine*. It operates year-round from a state-of-the-art model law office. The program offers as many as 13 innovative clinical experiences that provide law students with the opportunity to gain practical skills in the area of law that interests them the most. It is the most comprehensive program of any law school in the state. In-house clinical professors teach skills courses and supervise clinical students who represent real clients with real legal issues.
- **Invest in Success Program**—This bar preparation program is a joint effort with the faculty and academic support staff. Various faculty members conduct weekly substantive law reviews during the summer. The Office of Academic Support conducts workshops on various topics and works with students to improve their essay exam writing skills. Special attention is given to those students who underperformed in NC Distinctions, the School of Law's bar-prep-for-credit course.
- **Institutes**—The law school offers special programs and certificates through our Biotechnology and Pharmaceutical Law Institute and the Dispute Resolution Institute.

■ Admission

Admission to the School of Law is competitive, with more than 3,000 applicants competing for approximately 180–190 seats in the Day Program and 40–45 seats in the Evening Program. Students are admitted for the fall semester only on a rolling admission basis. Applicants are evaluated for admission based on a range of attributes, including academic achievement, performance on the LSAT, personal and professional experiences, intelligence and reasoning ability, individuality of thought and creativity, initiative and motivation, judgment and maturity, oral and written communication skills, integrity, leadership ability, and their potential contribution to the legal profession.

Because it is presumed that Evening Program students will have full-time employment, the Admissions Committee places greater weight on the quantifiable performance predictors for applicants to the Evening Program. Electronic applications for admission are accepted from October 1 through March 31 via our website at *www.nccu.edu/law* or the Law School Admission Council's website at *www.LSAC.org*.

Please note: Prospective applicants should view the School of Law website at *www.nccu.edu/law* for information regarding the School of Law.

Performance-Based Admission Program (PBAP)

As part of its commitment to the school's mission, North Carolina Central offers prospective students opportunities to gain admission through its Performance-Based Admission Program (PBAP). The PBAP enables applicants whose numerical predictors fall below the presumptively admissible range to demonstrate their ability through a rigorous two-week, noncredit program in the spring. The Office of Admissions selects PBAP participants based on a number of factors, including, but not limited to, a history of below-average standardized test scores followed by academic achievement, work experience, a significant time lapse between the undergraduate degree and law school application, and students who come from socially disadvantaged backgrounds. Students who successfully complete PBAP are then offered admission to NCCU's Day or Evening Program.

Student Organizations

The *North Carolina Central Law Review* is devoted to a broad range of legal topics submitted by legal scholars, attorneys, and law students. Students are selected for membership based upon GPA and performance in the annual Law Review Writing Competition. The School of Law also has a student-run *Biotechnology and Pharmaceutical Law Review*. The Moot Court Board consists of upper-class students who have demonstrated exceptional ability in appellate skills. The Trial Advocacy Board consists of student teams who participate in mock jury trial competitions. The board has gained regional and national recognition for its excellence in trial advocacy. Other student organizations include the Black Law Students Association, Christian Legal Society, Environmental Law Society, Hispanic Law Student

Association, Innocence Project, Native American Law Student Association, OutLaw Alliance, Public Interest Law Organization, Sports and Entertainment Law Society, Women's Caucus, and various legal fraternities.

Career Services

The Office of Career Services offers a range of career planning and development services, including career counseling, résumé workshops, interview preparation, job postings and information sessions, and panel discussions on legal careers. Graduates find employment in law firms, corporations, state and federal government agencies, public interest organizations, the judiciary, and the military.

Financial Aid

For information about financial aid, please visit our website at *www.nccu.edu/law/admissions/financial.html*.

Tuition and Expenses

NCCU School of Law provides one of the most cost effective legal educations in the country. For information on tuition, fees, and expenses, please visit our website at *www.nccu.edu/law/admissions/expenses.html* or contact Student Accounting at 919.530.5071.

Housing

Limited on-campus housing is available for single law students. Write the Department of Residential Life, North Carolina Central University, PO Box 19382, Durham, NC 27707, or call 919.530.6227.

Applicant Profile

North Carolina Central University School of Law
This grid includes only applicants with 120–180 LSAT scores earned under standard administrations.

LSAT Score	3.75 +		3.50–3.74		3.25–3.49		3.00–3.24		2.75–2.99		2.50–2.74		2.25–2.49		2.00–2.24		Below 2.00		No GPA		Totals	
	Apps	Adm	Apps	Adm	Apps	Adm	Apps	Adm	Apps	Adm	Apps	Adm	Apps	Adm	Apps	Adm	Apps	Adm	Apps	Adm	Apps	Adm
175–180	0	0	0	0	0	0	0	0	0	0	0	0	1	0	0	0	0	0	0	0	1	0
170–174	1	1	0	0	1	1	1	0	0	0	0	0	0	0	0	0	0	0	0	0	3	2
165–169	2	2	2	1	2	1	2	1	3	0	3	2	1	0	0	0	0	0	0	0	15	7
160–164	3	1	7	2	12	2	12	2	6	0	2	0	1	0	3	0	0	0	0	0	46	7
155–159	16	9	17	7	30	7	38	12	18	3	17	2	13	1	5	0	0	0	1	0	155	41
150–154	24	11	41	18	67	23	62	21	61	17	28	1	23	2	17	2	4	0	5	0	332	95
145–149	33	10	73	22	102	26	133	30	102	17	61	2	45	3	25	1	4	0	10	2	588	113
140–144	15	4	78	30	107	31	109	25	137	15	95	6	53	2	22	1	4	0	20	0	640	114
135–139	12	2	20	5	60	13	70	8	61	1	62	1	44	0	11	0	2	0	5	1	347	31
130–134	1	0	10	0	17	0	24	1	24	0	15	0	13	0	6	0	0	0	5	0	115	1
125–129	0	0	1	0	2	0	3	0	6	0	1	0	3	0	3	0	0	0	0	0	19	0
120–124	0	0	0	0	0	0	0	0	0	0	1	0	0	0	0	0	0	0	0	0	1	0
Total	107	40	249	85	400	104	454	100	418	53	285	14	197	8	92	4	14	0	46	3	2262	411

Apps = Number of Applicants   Adm = Number Admitted   Reflects 99% of the total applicant pool; average LSAT data reported.

This chart is to be used as a general guide only. Nonnumerical factors are strongly considered for all applicants.

University of North Dakota School of Law

215 Centennial Drive, Stop 9003
Grand Forks, ND 58202
Phone: 701.777.2104; Fax: 701.777.6447
E-mail: hoffman@law.und.edu; Website: www.law.und.edu

ABA
Approved
Since
1923

The Basics

Type of school	Public
Term	Semester
Application deadline	7/15
Application fee	$35
Financial aid deadline	4/15
Can first year start other than fall?	No
Student to faculty ratio	21.7 to 1
# of housing spaces available restricted to law students	
graduate housing for which law students are eligible	236

Faculty and Administrators

	Total		Men		Women		Minorities	
	Spr	Fall	Spr	Fall	Spr	Fall	Spr	Fall
Full-time	9	10	6	7	3	3	1	2
Other full-time	1	2	1	2	0	0	0	0
Deans, librarians, & others who teach	7	7	2	2	5	5	0	0
Part-time	9	7	6	6	3	1	0	0
Total	26	26	15	17	11	9	1	2

Curriculum

	Full-Time	Part-Time
Typical first-year section size	85	0
Is there typically a "small section" of the first-year class, other than Legal Writing, taught by full-time faculty	No	No
If yes, typical size offered last year		
# of classroom course titles beyond first-year curriculum	53	

# of upper division courses, excluding seminars, with an enrollment:		
	Under 25	31
	25–49	16
	50–74	8
	75–99	1
	100+	0

	Full-Time	Part-Time
# of seminars	6	
# of seminar positions available	118	
# of seminar positions filled	68	0
# of positions available in simulation courses	68	
# of simulation positions filled	53	0
# of positions available in faculty supervised clinical courses	32	
# of faculty supervised clinical positions filled	32	0
# involved in field placements	38	0
# involved in law journals	32	0
# involved in moot court or trial competitions	16	0
# of credit hours required to graduate	90	

JD Enrollment and Ethnicity

	Men		Women		Full-Time		Part-Time		1st-Year		Total		JD Degs. Awd.
	#	%	#	%	#	%	#	%	#	%	#	%	
African Amer.	4	3.0	2	1.8	6	2.4	0	0.0	3	3.5	6	2.4	0
Amer. Indian	5	3.7	4	3.6	9	3.6	0	0.0	4	4.7	9	3.6	4
Asian Amer.	2	1.5	1	0.9	3	1.2	0	0.0	3	3.5	3	1.2	1
Mex. Amer.	3	2.2	0	0.0	3	1.2	0	0.0	1	1.2	3	1.2	0
Puerto Rican	0	0.0	0	0.0	0	0.0	0	0.0	0	0.0	0	0.0	0
Hispanic	3	2.2	1	0.9	4	1.6	0	0.0	1	1.2	4	1.6	2
Total Minority	17	12.6	8	7.1	25	10.1	0	0.0	12	14.0	25	10.1	7
For. Nation.	12	8.9	6	5.4	18	7.3	0	0.0	7	8.1	18	7.3	2
Caucasian	103	76.3	97	86.6	200	81.0	0	0.0	63	73.3	200	81.0	74
Unknown	3	2.2	1	0.9	4	1.6	0	0.0	4	4.7	4	1.6	0
Total	135	54.7	112	45.3	247	100.0	0	0.0	86	34.8	247		83

Transfers

Transfers in	7
Transfers out	5

Tuition and Fees

	Resident	Nonresident
Full-time	$9,461	$20,476
Part-time		
Tuition Guarantee Program		N

Living Expenses

Estimated living expenses for singles

Living on campus	Living off campus	Living at home
$14,400	$14,400	$14,400

University of North Dakota School of Law

ABA
Approved
Since
1923

GPA and LSAT Scores

	Total	Full-Time	Part-Time
# of apps	534	534	0
# of offers	187	187	0
# of matrics	86	86	0
75% GPA	3.73	3.73	0.00
Median GPA	3.30	3.30	0.00
25% GPA	3.00	3.00	0.00
75% LSAT	155	155	0
Median LSAT	152	152	0
25% LSAT	149	149	0

Grants and Scholarships (from prior year)

	Total		Full-Time		Part-Time	
	#	%	#	%	#	%
Total # of students	243		243		0	
Total # receiving grants	81	33.3	81	33.3	0	0.0
Less than 1/2 tuition	45	18.5	45	18.5	0	0.0
Half to full tuition	28	11.5	28	11.5	0	0.0
Full tuition	0	0.0	0	0.0	0	0.0
More than full tuition	8	3.3	8	3.3	0	0.0
Median grant amount		$4,000		$0		

Informational and Library Resources

Total amount spent on library materials	$649,781
Study seating capacity inside the library	222
# of full-time equivalent professional librarians	5
Hours per week library is open	99
# of open, wired connections available to students	173
# of networked computers available for use by students	21
Has wireless network?	Y
Require computer?	N

JD Attrition (from prior year)

	Academic	Other	Total	
	#	#	#	%
1st year	1	5	6	7.2
2nd year	0	0	0	0.0
3rd year	0	0	0	0.0
4th year	0	0	0	0.0

Employment (9 months after graduation)

	Total	Percentage
Employment status known	85	100.0
Employment status unknown	0	0.0
Employed	69	81.2
Pursuing graduate degrees	4	4.7
Unemployed (seeking, not seeking, or studying for the bar)	8	9.4
Type of Employment		
# employed in law firms	30	43.5
# employed in business and industry	12	17.4
# employed in government	7	10.1
# employed in public interest	4	5.8
# employed as judicial clerks	15	21.7
# employed in academia	1	1.4
Geographic Location		
# employed in state	44	63.8
# employed in foreign countries	0	0.0
# of states where employed	14	

Bar Passage Rates

First-time takers	71	Reporting %	100.00
Average school %	87.33	Average state %	87.03
Average pass difference	0.30		

Jurisdiction	Takers	Passers	Pass %	State %	Diff %
North Dakota	47	43	91.49	85.48	6.01
Minnesota	17	14	82.35	91.09	–8.74
Wisconsin	3	3	100.00	91.79	8.21
Nevada	2	0	0.00	76.94	–76.94
Others (2)	2	2	100.00		

University of North Dakota School of Law

215 Centennial Drive, Stop 9003
Grand Forks, ND 58202
Phone: 701.777.2104; Fax: 701.777.6447
E-mail: hoffman@law.und.edu; Website: www.law.und.edu

■ Introduction

Founded in 1899, the University of North Dakota (UND) School of Law blends quality, opportunity, and a sense of community in its education of approximately 245 students. The school is a fully accredited graduate professional school awarding the JD degree. It has been a member of the AALS since 1910 and was approved by the ABA in 1923. UND Law is part of a highly respected, nationally recognized university, located in Grand Forks, North Dakota. Grand Forks, a community of nearly 60,000, is in the heart of the Red River Valley on the North Dakota/Minnesota border. It offers a small-town feel with all the opportunities of an urban area and has a large legal community including county, state, and federal trial courts.

■ Library and Physical Facilities

The Thormodsgard Law Library manages a growing collection of comprehensive resources necessary for the study of law and provides a home for students. The school and library are linked everywhere with high-speed Ethernet and wireless access points. The Computer Services office supports the Web, e-mail, file sharing, database, group scheduling, servers, the in-house video system, as well as student laptops. The elegant, traditionally appointed Baker Courtroom provides facilities for trial and appellate arguments and is used by the North Dakota Supreme Court and occasionally by other federal and district courts.

■ Curriculum

The curriculum of the School of Law covers a period of three full academic years. All the work of the first year is prescribed. Courses in the second and third years are elective, except for the course in Professional Responsibility.

■ Special Programs

The size of the student body is ideally suited for close professional contact with faculty, the visiting courts, legal professionals, and alumni. Students are given ample opportunity to participate in the governance of the school. Elected members of the Student Bar Association attend regularly scheduled faculty meetings and are active voting participants in most law school committees.

In consultation with area tribes and Indian leaders, the UND School of Law has established the region's first Northern Plains Indian Law Center. The center is a clearinghouse for American Indian legal materials and provides a forum for discussing and resolving legal issues confronting Indian tribes, the states, and the federal government. It also supports tribal advocacy training programs. Among the center's programs are the Tribal Judicial Institute, the Institute for the Study of Tribal Gaming Law and Policy, the Native American Law Project, and the Tribal Environmental Law Project.

The Clinical Education Program of the UND School of Law provides students with the opportunity to integrate the theory and practice of law in a real law office setting. In the clinic, students assume the role of lawyers and, in doing so, move beyond the classroom into the world of law practice. In the course of representing their clients, students gain firsthand experience with substantive law, the many skills of lawyering, and the rules of professional ethics. Students reflect on their experiences during clinic class discussions, "case-rounds" sessions, one-on-one faculty supervision, and legal research and writing assignments.

A comprehensive Externship Program allows students an opportunity to earn academic credit while gaining practical experience in a variety of placements. Externship students receive local and state field placements throughout the academic year, as well as during the summer in the Federal Externship Program.

The school has an extensive Trial Advocacy Program in which students learn trial skills in a simulated advocacy setting under the close supervision of experienced trial lawyers. Each student in this course is responsible, with one student advocate cocounsel, for the trial of at least one full civil or criminal case during the semester.

During sessions of the state legislature, selected students serve as legislative interns at the North Dakota state capital in Bismarck.

Central Legal Research (CLR) provides select students with opportunities to work with attorneys and judges across North Dakota on the issues and problems faced in practice. Focusing primarily on criminal law and procedure issues, CLR students work closely with an experienced lawyer and with each other, honing their skills by writing, researching, analyzing, and discussing their individual projects. CLR students receive a full in-state tuition waiver and develop a broad writing portfolio.

UND offers a joint Juris Doctor/Master of Business Administration (JD/MBA) as well as a Juris Doctor/Master of Public Administration (JD/MPA) degree. Utilizing free summer time, these joint-degree programs could be completed in four years or less.

The UND School of Law is one of approximately 80 law schools throughout the United States that have a chapter of the national legal honorary society, the Order of the Coif. The Order of the Coif was founded to encourage legal scholarship and advance the ethical standards of the legal profession.

UND law students may receive credit for summer law study at the University of Oslo Faculty of Law, Oslo, Norway. The program provides six weeks of instruction and offers students specialized instruction in such areas as the Norwegian legal system, comparative criminal justice, and European law. As part of this exchange program, up to 15 Norwegian law students also attend the UND School of Law during the spring semester.

■ Admission

The School of Law has no specific undergraduate course prerequisites and agrees with the observations in the introduction to this guide. The school admits students only in August and only for full-time study. Applications are available upon request. The policy of the faculty of the School of Law is to admit those applicants who, in the determination of the faculty, will be able to satisfactorily complete the law school program. The admission committee utilizes the following criteria to achieve this goal: (1) LSAT score; (2) undergraduate GPA; (3) past performance in an academic environment; (4) past performance in activities that would tend to predict the applicant's ability to complete successfully the law school

program; and (5) other evidence relevant to predicted success and prospective professional responsibility. The total number of students admitted is, of course, limited by considerations involving space and faculty courseload.

The law school does not have a nonresident quota; however, preference is given to residents.

Students who have begun the study of law in other accredited law schools may be admitted in exceptional circumstances to advanced standing, provided they have fulfilled the requirements for admission to the University of North Dakota School of Law. Ordinarily, no transfer credit will be allowed for more than two semesters of work completed elsewhere, nor will transfer credit be given for any courses in which an unsatisfactory or failing grade has been received. Moreover, admission may be conditioned upon meeting such additional requirements as the faculty may prescribe. No student will be admitted as a transfer student with advanced standing who is not eligible to continue as a student at his or her present law school.

■ Student Activities

The *North Dakota Law Review* provides research and writing opportunities. Students participate in various moot court activities, with the North Dakota Supreme Court judging the moot court finals. Student organizations include the Environmental Law Society, Law Women's Caucus, Native American Law Students Association, Public Interest Law Students Association, Student Trial Lawyers Association, and an active Student Bar Association. One of the more popular activities during the year is the Malpractice Bowl, pitting law students against medical school students in an annual football game. The School of Law also has chapters of the Order of the Coif and legal fraternities.

■ Expenses and Financial Aid

Tuition and fees per semester for students averaging 15 credit hours in 2009–2010 are $4,730 per resident, $6,379 per contiguous states, and $10,238 per nonresident. The semester fees include student activity and university fees totaling $552 per semester and an $800 per semester professional fee. The student activity and university fees cover payment for health services, the university center, campus publications, and drama and athletic events. The professional fee is assessed by the School of Law and is used to support and improve the law school program. Fees are subject to change without notice. Loan funds for all qualified students are available through the university Student Financial Aid Office, PO Box 8371, Grand Forks, ND 58202.

■ Housing

The university has a comprehensive housing system with options including family housing facilities, student apartment housing, and traditional residence halls for single students. For more detailed information, visit *www.housing.und.edu.*

■ Career Services

The Career Services Office serves students and alumni by assisting with the job-search process and employment information, and provides job seekers with knowledge about types of employment, specific employers, positions available, and wage and salary information. The office also assists in job-search strategies and skills such as résumé writing, interviewing techniques, and electronic job-search strategies. More than 94 percent of graduates find employment within six months of graduation. While a majority choose employment in North Dakota and Minnesota, graduates are employed nationally and internationally.

Applicant Profile

University of North Dakota School of Law
This grid includes only applicants who earned 120–180 LSAT scores under standard administrations.

LSAT Score	3.75 +		3.50–3.74		3.25–3.49		3.00–3.24		2.75–2.99		2.50–2.74		2.25–2.49		2.00–2.24		Below 2.00		No GPA		Total	
	Apps	Adm	Apps	Adm	Apps	Adm	Apps	Adm	Apps	Adm	Apps	Adm	Apps	Adm	Apps	Adm	Apps	Adm	Apps	Adm	Apps	Adm
175–180	0	0	0	0	0	0	0	0	0	0	0	0	0	0	0	0	0	0	0	0	0	0
170–174	0	0	1	0	0	0	0	0	0	0	0	0	0	0	0	0	0	0	0	0	1	0
165–169	2	2	1	1	0	0	0	0	0	0	0	0	0	0	0	0	0	0	0	0	3	3
160–164	4	4	3	3	4	3	1	1	0	0	0	0	1	1	1	1	0	0	1	1	15	14
155–159	10	10	8	8	10	10	11	10	4	4	4	2	0	0	2	0	1	0	0	0	50	44
150–154	21	19	16	13	17	9	23	13	16	9	5	2	3	1	3	2	0	0	2	1	106	69
145–149	10	8	35	4	44	8	30	9	25	5	17	5	8	2	2	0	2	0	4	0	177	41
140–144	5	1	12	0	18	4	25	1	21	0	17	0	6	0	4	0	0	0	5	0	113	6
135–139	3	0	0	0	5	0	4	0	8	0	4	0	3	0	2	0	0	0	2	0	31	0
130–134	1	0	2	0	1	0	2	0	5	0	1	0	0	0	0	0	0	0	0	0	12	0
125–129	0	0	0	0	0	0	1	0	1	0	1	0	0	0	0	0	0	0	0	0	3	0
120–124	0	0	0	0	0	0	0	0	0	0	0	0	0	0	0	0	0	0	0	0	0	0
Total	56	44	78	29	99	34	97	34	80	18	49	9	21	4	14	3	3	0	14	2	511	177

Apps = Number of Applicants   Adm = Number Admitted   Reflects 99% of the total applicant pool.; average LSAT data reported.

Northeastern University School of Law

400 Huntington Avenue
Boston, MA 02115
Phone: 617.373.2395; Fax: 617.373.8865
E-mail: lawadmissions@neu.edu; Website: www.northeastern.edu/law

ABA
Approved
Since
1969

The Basics

Type of school	Private
Term	Quarter
Application deadline	11/15 3/1
Application fee	$75
Financial aid deadline	2/15
Can first year start other than fall?	No
Student to faculty ratio	15.5 to 1
# of housing spaces available restricted to law students graduate housing for which law students are eligible	46

Faculty and Administrators

	Total		Men		Women		Minorities	
	Spr	Fall	Spr	Fall	Spr	Fall	Spr	Fall
Full-time	29	36	13	18	16	18	6	8
Other full-time	0	0	0	0	0	0	0	0
Deans, librarians, & others who teach	7	7	3	1	4	6	1	0
Part-time	32	45	17	27	15	18	1	7
Total	68	88	33	46	35	42	8	15

JD Enrollment and Ethnicity

	Men		Women		Full-Time		Part-Time		1st-Year		Total		JD Degs. Awd.
	#	%	#	%	#	%	#	%	#	%	#	%	
African Amer.	15	6.1	47	13.1	62	10.3	0	0.0	24	11.2	62	10.3	11
Amer. Indian	2	0.8	6	1.7	8	1.3	0	0.0	4	1.9	8	1.3	1
Asian Amer.	17	6.9	35	9.7	52	8.6	0	0.0	19	8.8	52	8.6	17
Mex. Amer.	0	0.0	0	0.0	0	0.0	0	0.0	0	0.0	0	0.0	0
Puerto Rican	0	0.0	0	0.0	0	0.0	0	0.0	0	0.0	0	0.0	0
Hispanic	21	8.6	47	13.1	68	11.3	0	0.0	25	11.6	68	11.3	18
Total Minority	55	22.4	135	37.6	190	31.6	0	0.0	72	33.5	190	31.5	47
For. Nation.	0	0.0	0	0.0	0	0.0	0	0.0	0	0.0	0	0.0	0
Caucasian	149	60.8	172	47.9	320	53.2	1	50.0	113	52.6	321	53.1	120
Unknown	41	16.7	52	14.5	92	15.3	1	50.0	30	14.0	93	15.4	55
Total	245	40.6	359	59.4	602	99.7	2	0.3	215	35.6	604		222

Curriculum

	Full-Time	Part-Time
Typical first-year section size	70	0
Is there typically a "small section" of the first-year class, other than Legal Writing, taught by full-time faculty	Yes	No
If yes, typical size offered last year	14	
# of classroom course titles beyond first-year curriculum	93	
# of upper division courses, excluding seminars, with an enrollment: Under 25	42	
25–49	33	
50–74	9	
75–99	4	
100+	1	
# of seminars	20	
# of seminar positions available	305	
# of seminar positions filled	257	0
# of positions available in simulation courses	284	
# of simulation positions filled	251	0
# of positions available in faculty supervised clinical courses	102	
# of faculty supervised clinical positions filled	84	0
# involved in field placements	524	0
# involved in law journals	110	0
# involved in moot court or trial competitions	29	0
# of credit hours required to graduate	87	

Transfers

Transfers in	10
Transfers out	9

Tuition and Fees

	Resident	Nonresident
Full-time	$39,866	
Part-time		
Tuition Guarantee Program		N

Living Expenses

Estimated living expenses for singles

Living on campus	Living off campus	Living at home
$17,700	$17,700	$17,700

Northeastern University School of Law

ABA
Approved
Since
1969

GPA and LSAT Scores

	Total	Full-Time	Part-Time
# of apps	3,798	3,798	0
# of offers	1,280	1,280	0
# of matrics	214	214	0
75% GPA	3.63	3.63	0.00
Median GPA	3.40	3.40	0.00
25% GPA	3.20	3.20	0.00
75% LSAT	163	163	0
Median LSAT	161	161	0
25% LSAT	155	155	0

Grants and Scholarships (from prior year)

	Total		Full-Time		Part-Time	
	#	%	#	%	#	%
Total # of students	616		615		1	
Total # receiving grants	473	76.8	473	76.9	0	0.0
Less than 1/2 tuition	452	73.4	452	73.5	0	0.0
Half to full tuition	18	2.9	18	2.9	0	0.0
Full tuition	3	0.5	3	0.5	0	0.0
More than full tuition	0	0.0	0	0.0	0	0.0
Median grant amount			$9,200		$0	

Informational and Library Resources

Total amount spent on library materials	$971,841
Study seating capacity inside the library	333
# of full-time equivalent professional librarians	8
Hours per week library is open	88
# of open, wired connections available to students	370
# of networked computers available for use by students	55
Has wireless network?	Y
Require computer?	N

JD Attrition (from prior year)

	Academic	Other	Total	
	#	#	#	%
1st year	0	3	3	1.5
2nd year	0	11	11	5.7
3rd year	0	0	0	0.0
4th year	0	0	0	0.0

Employment (9 months after graduation)

	Total	Percentage
Employment status known	192	97.0
Employment status unknown	6	3.0
Employed	173	90.1
Pursuing graduate degrees	1	0.5
Unemployed (seeking, not seeking, or studying for the bar)	14	7.3
Type of Employment		
# employed in law firms	58	33.5
# employed in business and industry	46	26.6
# employed in government	14	8.1
# employed in public interest	27	15.6
# employed as judicial clerks	23	13.3
# employed in academia	5	2.9
Geographic Location		
# employed in state	119	68.8
# employed in foreign countries	3	1.7
# of states where employed	21	

Bar Passage Rates

First-time takers	194	Reporting %	73.20
Average school %	93.66	Average state %	92.33
Average pass difference	1.33		

Jurisdiction	Takers	Passers	Pass %	State %	Diff %
Massachusetts	142	133	93.66	92.33	1.33

Northeastern University School of Law

400 Huntington Avenue
Boston, MA 02115
Phone: 617.373.2395; Fax: 617.373.8865
E-mail: lawadmissions@neu.edu; Website: www.northeastern.edu/law

■ Introduction

Northeastern University School of Law, located in Boston, offers the nation's premier Cooperative Legal Education Program. Combining classroom theory with work experience, Northeastern law students receive their JD degrees in the same three-year time period as students at other law schools, but graduate with one full year of hands-on legal employment, gained through four, 11-week work experiences (called co-ops) in the legal workplace. More than 900 employers, including private firms, legal services, public defender offices, judicial clerkships, government agencies, corporate legal departments, unions, and special interest advocacy organizations, in 40 states and a number of foreign countries participate in the co-op program.

Northeastern was cited as the best public interest law school in the nation by *The National Jurist* and *preLaw Magazine*. The school's commitment to social justice extends through the curriculum, co-op program, clinics and institutes, and student group activism. The law school provides financial support through several public interest initiatives, from the Loan Deferral and Forgiveness Program to co-op stipends to the generous Public Interest Law Scholarship.

Northeastern provides a supportive, student-centered learning environment. In lieu of traditional letter grades and class rank, students receive detailed written evaluations from professors and co-op employers. The school cultivates a culture of cooperation, collaboration, and mutual respect.

■ Cooperative Legal Education

Northeastern's Cooperative Legal Education Program alternates periods of academic study with equal periods of workplace experience during the second and third years of law school. During the first year of law school, students follow a traditional, full-time academic schedule. At the end of the first year, half of the class begins, during the summer, the first academic quarter of their second year. The other half of the class starts their first co-op. For the remaining two years, students alternate every three months between working full time as legal interns and attending classes. By participating in four, 11-week co-op placements with four different legal employers, students are provided with an extraordinary opportunity to experience the actual practice of law and to determine their career paths based on practical training.

More than 900 employers worldwide currently participate in the co-op program, representing virtually every practice area, including law firms of all sizes, trial and appellate judges in federal and state courts, public defender and legal services organizations, government agencies, corporate and union legal departments, and a variety of advocacy groups. While many co-op placements are in the Greater Boston area, students work with employers in more than 40 states and countries in any given quarter. In recent years, students have increasingly developed their own co-ops both in the United States and abroad. All students are required to successfully complete four full-time legal work experiences in order to graduate.

While the co-op program is not intended as a financial aid program, earnings from co-op employment may somewhat reduce the net cost of attending law school during the second and third years. Salaries range from nominal amounts for public interest jobs to $3,100 per week in major law firms. To assist students in low-paying co-ops in the public interest area and the judiciary, the school provides approximately $700,000 in co-op stipends each year.

■ Clinics and Institutes

Nationally recognized for its clinical education program, Northeastern offers students the opportunity to engage in advocacy on behalf of individuals and community organizations too often unacknowledged or underrepresented by the justice system. Students can participate with faculty and staff in the work of outstanding research and service centers: the Civil Rights and Restorative Justice Project, the Domestic Violence Institute, the Marshall-Brennan Constitutional Literacy Project, the Public Health Advocacy Institute, and the Program on Human Rights and the Global Economy. Together, the clinics, institutes, and special programs reflect and fulfill a commitment to social and economic justice that distinguishes Northeastern as one of the nation's foremost public interest law schools. Northeastern offers five clinics: Criminal Advocacy, Domestic Violence, Poverty Law and Practice, Prisoners' Rights, and Public Health. The clinics differ from one another by substantive legal focus, advocacy experience, and the primary skills each seeks to impart. Students engage in challenging legal practice with the support of clinical faculty who provide the requisite training, close supervision, and opportunity for reflection.

■ Legal Skills in Social Context

Every Northeastern first-year student participates in Legal Skills in Social Context, a one-of-a-kind, year-long signature course introducing the central skills of effective lawyering: legal research, objective and persuasive legal writing, client representation, critical analysis and oral skills—all heavily grounded in the social contexts in which the law is practiced. The Legal Skills in Social Context course operates in small "law offices" of approximately 14 students, each taught by a team of full-time faculty, adjunct professors and upper-level student fellows and teaching assistants. These law offices plan and execute a social justice project—an extensive real-world legal research project on behalf of a community-based or public service organization.

■ Dual-Degree Programs

Northeastern University School of Law offers six dual-degree programs. In cooperation with Tufts University School of Medicine, students may pursue both the JD and the Master of Public Health degrees. With a specialized curriculum, the two institutions enhance the training of law students who seek to understand the role advocacy and public action can play in reducing risk and ameliorating conditions that threaten community health. Completion of the dual-degree program takes three and one-half years, rather than the average five years if the degrees were obtained sequentially. Northeastern University School of Law has also partnered with Brandeis University's Heller School of Social Policy and Management to offer a JD/MA in Sustainable International

Development. The accelerated four-year program, including combined law/international development co-ops, gives students experience in applying the law in an international development context. For students interested in environmental law, Northeastern University School of Law, in conjunction with Vermont Law School—a national leader in environmental law—offers its law students the opportunity to earn both a JD and a master's degree in Environmental Law and Policy (MELP) in the same three-year period it would take to earn just the JD. Dual-degrees are also available from other schools and colleges at Northeastern University. A four-year program coordinates the academic and cooperative features of the School of Law and the Graduate School of Business Administration, enabling students to earn both the JD and the MBA in 45 months rather than the 54 months required if undertaken sequentially. Law students with nonaccounting undergraduate degrees are eligible for admission to a program leading to a concurrent JD/MSA/MBA. The program enables students to earn these degrees in 45 months rather than the 48 months required if undertaken sequentially. The Law, Policy, and Society JD/MS/PhD interdisciplinary graduate program is designed to offer students in the School of Law the opportunity to study policy, social issues, and the law in pursuit of an MS or PhD in Law, Policy, and Society. The program is based in the Graduate School of Arts and Sciences and is affiliated with graduate schools throughout the university.

Student Life

The student body is diverse and active. Sixty percent of the first-year class are women, and 33 percent are people of color. Students are active participants in the law school community, serving on all of the school's standing committees, including the Admissions Committee. Students also run a wide variety of more than 30 organizations, ranging from the American Civil Liberties Union to the Queer Caucus to the Northeastern University Law Journal.

Career Services

The Office of Career Services actively assists students and graduates in their pursuit of professionally rewarding careers. The school's bar passage rate is impressive: for the most recent exam in Massachusetts (July 2009), more than 97 percent of students taking the bar for the first time passed. Students also generally find their postgraduate employment prospects to be substantially enhanced through the co-op program; on average, 40 percent accept postgraduate employment with one of their former co-op employers. Northeastern graduates are employed throughout the world in every practice area. They may be found teaching at distinguished law schools, sitting on the bench at both the state and federal levels, practicing as partners in prominent law firms, and serving as directors of legal aid and public defender programs throughout the nation. The school is also well known for its emphasis on public service. Graduates of Northeastern enter public service careers at a rate that is three to five times the national average. In addition, graduates have been awarded prestigious postgraduate fellowships, including those granted by Skadden, Equal Justice Works, Georgetown, and the Center for Constitutional Rights.

Financial Aid

Northeastern University School of Law is committed to providing access to all admitted students. Each year, the School of Law awards more than $1,000,000 to first-year students based on a combination of need and merit. Scholarships include the Dean's Scholarship, Academic Excellence Scholarship, Public Interest Law Scholarship, Social Justice Scholarship, Peace Corps Scholarship, Teach For America Scholarship, and Designated Law Scholarship. These scholarships represent a three-year commitment, with awards guaranteed for the upper-level years as long as the student remains in good academic standing. The law school also provides co-op stipends, endowed scholarships for upper-level students and a Loan Deferral and Forgiveness Program for graduates pursuing careers in public interest.

Applicant Profile Not Available

Northern Illinois University College of Law

Swen Parson Hall, Room 151
DeKalb, IL 60115-2890
Phone: 800.892.3050 or 815.753.8595; Fax: 815.753.5680
E-mail: Lawadm@niu.edu; Website: http://www.niu.edu/law

ABA Approved Since 1978

The Basics

Type of school	Public
Term	Semester
Application deadline	5/15
Application fee	$50
Financial aid deadline	3/1
Can first year start other than fall?	No
Student to faculty ratio	20.3 to 1
# of housing spaces available restricted to law students	
graduate housing for which law students are eligible	300

Faculty and Administrators

	Total		Men		Women		Minorities	
	Spr	Fall	Spr	Fall	Spr	Fall	Spr	Fall
Full-time	13	12	9	7	4	5	5	5
Other full-time	3	4	0	1	3	3	0	0
Deans, librarians, & others who teach	10	10	7	7	3	3	1	1
Part-time	7	7	5	4	2	3	2	1
Total	33	33	21	19	12	14	8	7

JD Enrollment and Ethnicity

	Men		Women		Full-Time		Part-Time		1st-Year		Total		JD Degs. Awd.
	#	%	#	%	#	%	#	%	#	%	#	%	
African Amer.	5	3.0	16	11.3	20	6.7	1	9.1	8	7.3	21	6.8	8
Amer. Indian	1	0.6	1	0.7	2	0.7	0	0.0	1	0.9	2	0.6	0
Asian Amer.	6	3.6	15	10.6	21	7.0	0	0.0	8	7.3	21	6.8	1
Mex. Amer.	15	8.9	10	7.1	25	8.4	0	0.0	12	11.0	25	8.1	10
Puerto Rican	0	0.0	0	0.0	0	0.0	0	0.0	0	0.0	0	0.0	0
Hispanic	5	3.0	3	2.1	7	2.3	1	9.1	6	5.5	8	2.6	1
Total Minority	32	19.0	45	31.9	75	25.2	2	18.2	35	32.1	77	24.9	20
For. Nation.	0	0.0	0	0.0	0	0.0	0	0.0	0	0.0	0	0.0	0
Caucasian	121	72.0	94	66.7	206	69.1	9	81.8	67	61.5	215	69.6	70
Unknown	15	8.9	2	1.4	17	5.7	0	0.0	7	6.4	17	5.5	1
Total	168	54.4	141	45.6	298	96.4	11	3.6	109	35.3	309		91

Curriculum

	Full-Time	Part-Time
Typical first-year section size	49	0
Is there typically a "small section" of the first-year class, other than Legal Writing, taught by full-time faculty	No	No
If yes, typical size offered last year		
# of classroom course titles beyond first-year curriculum		59
# of upper division courses, excluding seminars, with an enrollment: Under 25		42
25–49		12
50–74		10
75–99		4
100+		0
# of seminars		6
# of seminar positions available		84
# of seminar positions filled	85	0
# of positions available in simulation courses		144
# of simulation positions filled	143	0
# of positions available in faculty supervised clinical courses		31
# of faculty supervised clinical positions filled	31	0
# involved in field placements	25	0
# involved in law journals	19	0
# involved in moot court or trial competitions	22	0
# of credit hours required to graduate		90

Transfers

Transfers in	1
Transfers out	1

Tuition and Fees

	Resident	Nonresident
Full-time	$14,847	$27,351
Part-time		
Tuition Guarantee Program		N

Living Expenses

Estimated living expenses for singles

Living on campus	Living off campus	Living at home
$15,612	$16,112	$5,580

Northern Illinois University College of Law

ABA
Approved
Since
1978

GPA and LSAT Scores

	Total	Full-Time	Part-Time
# of apps	1,169	1,169	14
# of offers	474	472	2
# of matrics	107	105	2
75% GPA	3.51	3.51	3.74
Median GPA	3.23	3.23	3.65
25% GPA	2.93	2.93	3.57
75% LSAT	156	156	153
Median LSAT	154	154	151
25% LSAT	153	153	150

Grants and Scholarships (from prior year)

	Total #	Total %	Full-Time #	Full-Time %	Part-Time #	Part-Time %
Total # of students	297		288		9	
Total # receiving grants	140	47.1	136	47.2	4	44.4
Less than 1/2 tuition	65	21.9	65	22.6	0	0.0
Half to full tuition	27	9.1	23	8.0	4	44.4
Full tuition	22	7.4	22	7.6	0	0.0
More than full tuition	26	8.8	26	9.0	0	0.0
Median grant amount			$5,846		$9,105	

Informational and Library Resources

Total amount spent on library materials	$970,417
Study seating capacity inside the library	213
# of full-time equivalent professional librarians	5
Hours per week library is open	98
# of open, wired connections available to students	14
# of networked computers available for use by students	43
Has wireless network?	Y
Require computer?	N

JD Attrition (from prior year)

	Academic #	Other #	Total #	Total %
1st year	2	3	5	5.0
2nd year	0	1	1	1.0
3rd year	0	2	2	2.2
4th year	0	0	0	0.0

Employment (9 months after graduation)

	Total	Percentage
Employment status known	106	95.5
Employment status unknown	5	4.5
Employed	93	87.7
Pursuing graduate degrees	2	1.9
Unemployed (seeking, not seeking, or studying for the bar)	8	7.5
Type of Employment		
# employed in law firms	54	58.1
# employed in business and industry	12	12.9
# employed in government	18	19.4
# employed in public interest	5	5.4
# employed as judicial clerks	2	2.2
# employed in academia	2	2.2
Geographic Location		
# employed in state	75	80.6
# employed in foreign countries	2	2.2
# of states where employed	11	

Bar Passage Rates

First-time takers	106	Reporting %	96.23
Average school %	96.08	Average state %	90.94
Average pass difference	5.14		

Jurisdiction	Takers	Passers	Pass %	State %	Diff %
Illinois	102	98	96.08	90.94	5.14

Northern Illinois University College of Law

Swen Parson Hall, Room 151
DeKalb, IL 60115-2890
Phone: 800.892.3050 or 815.753.8595; Fax: 815.753.5680
E-mail: Lawadm@niu.edu; Website: http://www.niu.edu/law

■ Introduction

Northern Illinois University was founded in 1895, and the College of Law was established in 1978. The College of Law seeks to prepare its graduates not only for the traditional role of lawyers, but also for the tasks we can assume will be performed in the future by lawyers. The school has a diverse and professionally distinguished faculty dedicated to teaching and scholarship.

■ Our Campus

The College of Law is located in DeKalb, a community conveniently located approximately 65 miles west of Chicago and 25 miles from the suburban area on the Ronald Reagan Memorial Tollway (I-88). DeKalb is close enough to the Chicago metropolitan area to draw on its many resources, yet retain its own college town flavor—a safe and affordable environment with a high quality of life.

The University's main campus is set on 755 acres of rolling country land. The lush campus features two lagoons, museums, and a vast variety of cultural opportunities. It ultimately provides an excellent environment for the study of law.

Though on a relatively large campus with all of the associated activities and opportunities, the College of Law is a small oasis at its center. For an online tour go to our website at *www.niu.edu/law.*

■ Libraries

The David C. Shapiro Memorial Law Library provides one of the best ratios of library materials to students of any American law school. The law library offers in-depth, research-level coverage of more than 32 areas of American law and study-level coverage of almost all other areas. Coverage of international, European Union, and British law is provided at study level. As a federally designated depository, the law library also receives selected government documents. In addition to its physical collection of over 262,000 volumes and volume equivalents, the library also offers access to Westlaw, LexisNexis, and a wide range of other Web-based legal resources. Laptop users enjoy convenient access to these electronic products anywhere in the law school through the College of Law's wireless network. Access to most of these resources is available off campus as well. The library also features a student computer lab that offers desktop high-speed Internet access and laser printing.

Further research support is provided through Founders Memorial Library, the University's main library, which is conveniently located adjacent to the College of Law. Founders Memorial Library contains over 2 million volumes and an additional 1.3 million federal, state, and international government documents. It also subscribes to diverse collections of nonlegal web-based resources that may be accessed either on or off campus.

■ Enrollment/Student Body

The student body represents universities from coast-to-coast and reflects a broad spectrum of ethnic, cultural, and geographic diversity. Our low student-to-faculty ratio, which is normally 15 to 1, facilitates a supportive environment with a lively exchange of ideas. The law school provides an atmosphere of shared goals and achievement and a genuine sense of community.

■ Curriculum and Clinical Experience Opportunities

The College of Law provides its students with a curriculum that will make them well-rounded legal professionals. The first-year program consists of the traditional ABA-required courses. After the first year, the only required courses are Constitutional Law II, Professional Responsibility, and a seminar; the remaining 90 hours are from a wide range of electives. Northern offers an Academic Support Program during the first year of classes. The ultimate goal is to help students succeed in law school.

During the summer, electives are offered on the main campus. Also during the summer, NIU offers an international law program in France. During this program, students receive six hours of credit in international and comparative law.

The clinical lawyering skills programs offer students the opportunity to acquire essential techniques needed in pretrial and trial work through structured simulations and experiences in an array of legal settings. The externship programs provide students with sound experience under the supervision of a highly qualified practicing attorney or the opportunity to be a law clerk for a state or federal judge. The Zeke Giorgi Legal Clinic in Rockford gives students the opportunity to apply legal theory by representing clients and resolving disputes in a real-world setting.

■ Admission

Considering the College of Law's small entering class size of between 110 and 120 out of an applicant pool ranging from 1,200 to 1,500, we are a relatively selective institution. The College of Law grants admission on a competitive basis through an evaluation of an applicant's aptitude and professional promise. Factors of most importance to the admission committee are the applicant's undergraduate record, LSAT score, reasons for seeking admission, school or community activities and accomplishments, employment background, and ability to add diversity to the law school community and the legal profession.

Applicants may submit their application either online at the Law School Admission Council's (LSAC) website at *www.LSAC.org.* In addition to the application, prospective students must submit a personal statement, résumé, and application fee directly through LSAC.org. The College of Law requires applicants to use the LSAC Credential Assembly Service. International students who do not have a degree from a United States institution must submit all foreign transcripts and TOEFL scores to LSAC's Credential Assembly Service. In order for Northern to receive LSAT scores, applicants need to submit official undergraduate and graduate transcripts as well as two letters of recommendation to LSAC's Credential Assembly Service. Applicants are encouraged to submit their application early, even if the LSAT has not yet been taken, due

to the limited number of seats in each entering class. Prospective students are encouraged to visit the College of Law.

■ Student Activities

Students are offered a wide variety of educational and professionally oriented activities. Among these are the *Law Review*, a forum for the expression of serious legal scholarship, and the Moot Court Society. Students compete in a wide selection of moot court and alternative dispute resolution competitions. Organizations range from the Asian American Law Student Organization to the Women's Law Caucus.

■ Expenses and Financial Aid

The College of Law offers its students small class sizes and a quality legal education all at an affordable cost. For the 2009–2010 academic year, in-state tuition is $12,504 and out-of-state tuition is $25,008. Out-of-state residents can also qualify for in-state tuition in six months, which is why so few students, after the first year, are classified as out-of-state residents.

Scholarships and grants are available for students from a variety of sources. After the first year, students may qualify for research assistantships.

Scholarship, grant, and loan information is on our website at *www.niu.edu/law*. The priority deadline for the FAFSA form is March 1.

■ Career Opportunities

The Career Opportunities Office has a strong track record in assisting and preparing our graduates for rewarding careers through references to prospective employers and on-campus interviews. The office assists current students in obtaining enriching summer legal employment. Due to Northern's small class size, personalized counseling, normally not available at larger law schools, is offered.

■ Housing

Affordable housing is available both on and off campus. Handicap-accessible housing is available. For information about on-campus housing, you may telephone 815.753.5125, or visit our website at *www.shds.niu.edu/housing*.

Many moderately priced apartments are available close to the university. The housing budget is $10,032. You may contact off-campus housing at, 815.753.9999 or visit our website at *www.niu.edu/comnontrad/housing/index.shtml*.

■ Correspondence

We encourage you to visit our campus and our website. Check our calendar on our website at *www.niu.edu* for activities, or call us toll free at 800.892.3050. Once you visit us, we are confident you will agree that Northern Illinois University College of Law is the school for you.

Applicant Profile

Northern Illinois University College of Law
This grid includes only applicants who earned 120–180 LSAT scores under standard administrations.

LSAT Score	3.75 +		3.50–3.74		3.25–3.49		3.00–3.24		2.75–2.99		2.50–2.74		2.25–2.49		2.00–2.24		Below 2.00		No GPA		Total	
	Apps	Adm	Apps	Adm	Apps	Adm	Apps	Adm	Apps	Adm	Apps	Adm	Apps	Adm	Apps	Adm	Apps	Adm	Apps	Adm	Apps	Adm
175–180	0	0	0	0	0	0	0	0	0	0	0	0	0	0	0	0	0	0	0	0	0	0
170–174	0	0	0	0	0	0	0	0	0	0	0	0	0	0	0	0	0	0	0	0	0	0
165–169	1	1	0	0	0	0	0	0	1	1	2	2	0	0	0	0	0	0	0	0	4	4
160–164	3	3	7	7	7	7	10	10	5	5	2	2	1	1	2	2	0	0	0	0	37	37
155–159	20	20	20	20	40	38	28	27	23	22	14	9	10	8	3	1	1	0	1	1	160	146
150–154	34	29	58	52	72	54	84	52	51	18	39	14	11	3	6	1	1	0	5	2	361	225
145–149	27	10	54	10	60	10	70	12	51	5	33	4	18	1	7	0	2	0	2	1	324	53
140–144	12	1	16	1	24	0	39	0	32	0	25	0	10	0	9	0	1	0	7	0	175	2
135–139	4	0	6	0	12	0	6	0	16	0	10	0	11	0	3	0	1	0	4	0	73	0
130–134	1	0	1	0	3	0	4	0	4	0	8	0	5	0	1	0	1	0	1	0	29	0
125–129	0	0	0	0	1	0	0	0	0	0	1	0	1	0	0	0	0	0	0	0	3	0
120–124	0	0	0	0	0	0	0	0	0	0	0	0	0	0	0	0	0	0	0	0	0	0
Total	102	64	162	90	219	109	241	101	183	51	134	31	67	13	31	4	7	0	20	4	1166	467

Apps = Number of Applicants
Adm = Number Admitted
Reflects 99% of the total applicant pool; average LSAT data reported.

Northern Kentucky University—Salmon P. Chase College of Law

Nunn Hall, Nunn Drive
Highland Heights, KY 41099
Phone: 859.572.5490; Fax: 859.572.6081
E-mail: chaseadmissions@nku.edu; Website: http://chaselaw.nku.edu/

ABA
Approved
Since
1954

The Basics

Type of school	Public
Term	Semester
Application deadline	4/1
Application fee	$40
Financial aid deadline	3/1
Can first year start other than fall?	No
Student to faculty ratio	15.1 to 1
# of housing spaces available restricted to law students	
graduate housing for which law students are eligible	

Faculty and Administrators

	Total		Men		Women		Minorities	
	Spr	Fall	Spr	Fall	Spr	Fall	Spr	Fall
Full-time	26	29	16	21	10	8	3	4
Other full-time	0	0	0	0	0	0	0	0
Deans, librarians, & others who teach	7	9	1	3	6	6	0	0
Part-time	16	14	10	10	5	4	1	0
Total	49	52	27	34	21	18	4	4

Curriculum

		Full-Time	Part-Time
Typical first-year section size		70	65
Is there typically a "small section" of the first-year class, other than Legal Writing, taught by full-time faculty		No	No
If yes, typical size offered last year			
# of classroom course titles beyond first-year curriculum		50	
# of upper division courses, excluding seminars, with an enrollment:	Under 25	54	
	25–49	28	
	50–74	21	
	75–99	3	
	100+	0	
# of seminars		5	
# of seminar positions available		129	
# of seminar positions filled		66	45
# of positions available in simulation courses		238	
# of simulation positions filled		138	84
# of positions available in faculty supervised clinical courses		56	
# of faculty supervised clinical positions filled		31	5
# involved in field placements		50	28
# involved in law journals		25	8
# involved in moot court or trial competitions		41	6
# of credit hours required to graduate		90	

JD Enrollment and Ethnicity

	Men		Women		Full-Time		Part-Time		1st-Year		Total		JD Degs. Awd.
	#	%	#	%	#	%	#	%	#	%	#	%	
African Amer.	8	2.5	25	8.8	22	5.9	11	4.7	12	6.3	33	5.4	4
Amer. Indian	1	0.3	1	0.4	1	0.3	1	0.4	0	0.0	2	0.3	0
Asian Amer.	4	1.2	11	3.9	11	2.9	4	1.7	6	3.2	15	2.5	2
Mex. Amer.	0	0.0	0	0.0	0	0.0	0	0.0	0	0.0	0	0.0	0
Puerto Rican	0	0.0	0	0.0	0	0.0	0	0.0	0	0.0	0	0.0	0
Hispanic	3	0.9	6	2.1	7	1.9	2	0.9	4	2.1	9	1.5	3
Total Minority	16	4.9	43	15.2	41	11.0	18	7.7	22	11.6	59	9.7	9
For. Nation.	0	0.0	0	0.0	0	0.0	0	0.0	0	0.0	0	0.0	0
Caucasian	284	87.1	226	79.9	306	81.8	204	86.8	160	84.2	510	83.7	125
Unknown	26	8.0	14	4.9	27	7.2	13	5.5	8	4.2	40	6.6	0
Total	326	53.5	283	46.5	374	61.4	235	38.6	190	31.2	609		134

Transfers

Transfers in	3
Transfers out	10

Tuition and Fees

	Resident	Nonresident
Full-time	$14,812	$32,232
Part-time	$5,740	$12,440
Tuition Guarantee Program		N

Living Expenses

Estimated living expenses for singles

Living on campus	Living off campus	Living at home
$9,956	$16,645	$16,645

Northern Kentucky University—Salmon P. Chase College of Law

ABA
Approved
Since
1954

GPA and LSAT Scores

	Total	Full-Time	Part-Time
# of apps	1,225	1,029	196
# of offers	526	439	87
# of matrics	194	135	59
75% GPA	3.56	3.64	3.41
Median GPA	3.35	3.39	3.27
25% GPA	3.19	3.16	3.07
75% LSAT	157	157	154
Median LSAT	153	154	152
25% LSAT	151	152	150

Grants and Scholarships (from prior year)

	Total		Full-Time		Part-Time	
	#	%	#	%	#	%
Total # of students	571		337		234	
Total # receiving grants	154	27.0	130	38.6	24	10.3
Less than 1/2 tuition	57	10.0	48	14.2	9	3.8
Half to full tuition	34	6.0	34	10.1	0	0.0
Full tuition	63	11.0	48	14.2	15	6.4
More than full tuition	0	0.0	0	0.0	0	0.0
Median grant amount			$12,000		$10,000	

Informational and Library Resources

Total amount spent on library materials	$627,611
Study seating capacity inside the library	260
# of full-time equivalent professional librarians	7
Hours per week library is open	168
# of open, wired connections available to students	31
# of networked computers available for use by students	46
Has wireless network?	Y
Require computer?	N

JD Attrition (from prior year)

	Academic	Other	Total	
	#	#	#	%
1st year	6	13	19	8.8
2nd year	4	14	18	10.2
3rd year	2	0	2	1.6
4th year	0	0	0	0.0

Employment (9 months after graduation)

	Total	Percentage
Employment status known	154	100.0
Employment status unknown	0	0.0
Employed	134	87.0
Pursuing graduate degrees	1	0.6
Unemployed (seeking, not seeking, or studying for the bar)	11	7.1
Type of Employment		
# employed in law firms	70	52.2
# employed in business and industry	28	20.9
# employed in government	14	10.4
# employed in public interest	9	6.7
# employed as judicial clerks	11	8.2
# employed in academia	1	0.7
Geographic Location		
# employed in state	59	44.0
# employed in foreign countries	0	0.0
# of states where employed	9	

Bar Passage Rates

First-time takers	153	Reporting %	97.39
Average school %	84.56	Average state %	85.87
Average pass difference −1.31			

Jurisdiction	Takers	Passers	Pass %	State %	Diff %
Ohio	83	71	85.54	88.09	−2.55
Kentucky	66	55	83.33	83.08	0.25

Northern Kentucky University—Salmon P. Chase College of Law

Nunn Hall, Nunn Drive
Highland Heights, KY 41099
Phone: 859.572.5490; Fax: 859.572.6081
E-mail: chaseadmissions@nku.edu; Website: http://chaselaw.nku.edu/

■ Introduction

Northern Kentucky University, Salmon P. Chase College of Law, founded in 1893, is located in Nunn Hall on the main campus of Northern Kentucky University. NKU is a learner-centered metropolitan university in a thriving legal and business community just seven miles south of Cincinnati, Ohio. NKU Chase offers both a full-time, day division and a part-time, evening division. Chase is accredited by the American Bar Association and is a member of the Association of American Law Schools.

■ Curriculum

The curriculum consists of required courses, core courses, and elective courses. Ninety credit hours are required to graduate, with forty-eight credits devoted to required courses. Full-time students complete the program in three years, while part-time students generally complete the program in four years. Chase offers a number of academic support and development programs designed to enhance the law school experience.

■ Evening Division

For the past 116 years, NKU Chase has been providing legal education to working professionals through its part-time, evening division. The evening class schedule allows students to meet their other obligations while attending law school. Classes usually meet three evenings per week from 6:30 PM to 9:15 PM.

■ Excellence Centers

Center for Excellence in Advocacy

The Center for Excellence in Advocacy continues NKU Chase's tradition of innovative advocacy skills training. Students learn the practical aspects of pretrial procedures, negotiations, mediations, trial techniques, appellate advocacy, and legislation. These programs encompass all aspects of advocacy skills training opportunities, ensuring that students develop the skills needed to handle a case from beginning to end. At the same time, a sharp focus on legal ethics and professionalism is maintained.

Transactional Law Practice Center

The Transactional Law Practice Center's mission is to provide students with multiple opportunities to develop the skill sets and knowledge employed by lawyers involved in the practice of business and transactional law. By partnering our faculty with practicing attorneys and business leaders, students are taught the practical skills that will turn them into the deal makers of tomorrow. The Center offers training in interviewing, negotiating, drafting, business planning, and client counseling. The Center also offers specialized courses and workshops in related disciplines including accounting, corporate finance, general business concepts, and economics, enabling students to understand the business aspects, as well as the legal aspects, of a corporate transaction.

Local Government Law Center

Attorneys are leaders in their communities and are often called upon to provide guidance and service to their local governments. The Local Government Law Center furthers this mission by promoting the development and study of government law through teaching, scholarship, and continuing education. The Local Government Law Center provides research services and technical assistance, and it delivers information through its newsletter, website, public speaking engagements, and community outreach to local governments throughout Kentucky.

■ Pro Bono Service Program

NKU Chase offers a Pro Bono Service Program that requires students to complete 50 hours of pro bono service prior to graduation. Pro bono work is broadly defined as law-related work performed in legal service organizations, government agencies, private law firms (pro bono cases), nonprofit organizations, and legislative offices.

Students select from a variety of organizations designated as approved placement sites, or they design their own pro bono project. In addition, NKU Chase offers several pro bono projects based at the law school. Service could include interviewing clients about legal problems, researching issues for public interest lawyers, engaging in legislative or policy analysis, teaching at-risk youth about the law, providing income tax assistance to low-income clients, or participating in legal aid clinics.

■ Joint-Degree Program

NKU Chase offers a Juris Doctor/Master of Business Administration (JD/MBA) degree program. This program is an attractive alternative for individuals who wish to practice law or business in an increasingly complex environment. Courses in the College of Law serve as electives for the MBA degree, and specific MBA courses serve as electives for the law degree. Thus, the number of hours required to obtain both degrees through the combined program is less than the number of hours required to complete each degree separately.

■ Student Activities

Moot Court promotes excellence in appellate advocacy through training, education, and development in legal research, brief writing, and oral advocacy.

The **National Trial Advocacy Team** promotes excellence in trial advocacy through training, education, and development of trial advocacy skills with one-on-one attention from expert practitioners.

The **Northern Kentucky Law Review** is published by NKU Chase students and includes scholarly legal writings by law professors, practitioners, jurists, and students.

The **Student Bar Association** sponsors professional, social, and community service events, and it selects students to participate on several faculty committees.

Student organizations bring prominent local, regional, and national speakers to campus to speak on topics of interest to the NKU Chase community, the university, and the community at large. Our student organizations also provide many opportunities for community service. These organizations include:

Northern Kentucky University—Salmon P. Chase College of Law

- American Constitution Society
- Black Law Students Association
- Chase Intellectual Property Society
- Chase Latino Law Association
- Chase Public Interest Group
- Chase Student Advocacy Society
- Christian Legal Society
- The Federalist Society for Law and Public Policy Studies
- International Law Student Association
- The Legal Association of Women
- Transactional Law Practice Group
- Phi Alpha Delta Law Fraternity International

■ Scholars Program

The NKU Chase Scholars Program recognizes the achievements of outstanding students and provides financial assistance that will allow them to explore a variety of professional opportunities after graduation.

Salmon P. Chase Scholars: Full-tuition scholarship each year plus a guaranteed paid research assistantship in the second and third years.

Henry Clay Scholars: Scholarship award amounts from $10,000 to $12,000 per year.

John Marshall Harlan Diversity Scholars: Scholarship award amounts ranging from $6,000 to full tuition. Diversity is defined as "the ability to enhance the multicultural and socioeconomic diversity at the College of Law through such characteristics as ethnicity, race, gender, age, abilities/limitations, and/or multicultural and socioeconomic background."

■ Career Development

The Career Development Office assists students and alumni with career planning, networking, and developing job-search skills and strategies. The director of career development and the career development coordinator are attorneys with diverse legal backgrounds. The office schedules fall and spring on-campus interviews; posts job notices daily; manages a student résumé database; conducts mock interviews; and holds seminars, workshops, and networking events to prepare students for the job market. Law students attend a variety of job fairs and recruiting programs throughout the country, and many obtain legal work experience for pay while in law school. Throughout the year, the office also coordinates information sessions with attorneys which enable students to network and learn about a wide variety of legal specialties and career options.

■ Library and Learning Environment

Students have access to the law library 24/7. The wireless environment gives students the ability to have ready access to the most up-to-date legal information. The classrooms and courtrooms feature the latest equipment, allowing faculty to use innovative technologies to enhance the learning experience.

■ Admission

NKU Chase seeks to admit applicants who have the best prospect of high-quality academic work. During the application review process, the Admissions Committee relies heavily on undergraduate grades and performance on the LSAT. Additional factors considered include: upward trend of undergraduate grades; time between college graduation and application to NKU Chase; college grading and course selection patterns; outside work while in college; letters of recommendation; graduate study; cultural, educational, or sociological disadvantages; employment background; leadership ability; speaking or linguistic ability; and demonstrated competence in another profession or vocation.

Applicant Profile

Northern Kentucky University—Salmon P. Chase College of Law
This grid includes only applicants who earned 120–180 LSAT scores under standard administrations.

LSAT Score	GPA																
	3.75 +		3.50–3.74		3.25–3.49		3.00–3.24		2.75–2.99		2.50–2.74		Below 2.50		No GPA		Total	
	Apps	Adm	Apps	Adm	Apps	Adm	Apps	Adm	Apps	Adm	Apps	Adm	Apps	Adm	Apps	Adm	Apps	Adm
170–180	0	0	0	0	0	0	1	1	0	0	0	0	0	0	0	0	1	1
165–169	1	1	2	2	1	1	0	0	0	0	1	1	0	0	0	0	5	5
160–164	17	15	14	11	15	13	16	12	10	6	2	0	5	2	1	0	80	59
155–159	49	45	52	49	53	45	46	37	20	13	16	7	13	5	2	1	251	202
150–154	49	36	56	45	91	51	69	31	43	11	32	6	26	4	3	0	369	184
145–149	31	13	42	11	56	12	55	10	35	2	37	4	22	2	5	1	283	55
140–144	6	1	12	0	22	1	42	5	20	1	22	0	26	0	3	2	153	10
Below 140	5	0	5	3	8	0	8	0	12	0	18	0	15	0	1	0	72	3
Total	158	111	183	121	246	123	237	96	140	33	128	18	107	13	15	4	1214	519

Apps = Number of Applicants
Adm = Number Admitted
Reflects 99% of the total applicant pool; average LSAT data reported.

Northwestern University School of Law

375 East Chicago Avenue
Chicago, IL 60611-3069
Phone: 312.503.3100; Fax: 312.503.0178
E-mail: admissions@law.northwestern.edu; Website: www.law.northwestern.edu

ABA
Approved
Since
1923

ABA
AMERICAN BAR ASSOCIATION
Section of Legal Education
and Admissions to the Bar

The Basics

Type of school	Private
Term	Semester
Application deadline	2/15
Application fee	$100
Financial aid deadline	2/15
Can first year start other than fall?	No
Student to faculty ratio	8.8 to 1
# of housing spaces available restricted to law students	
graduate housing for which law students are eligible	42

Faculty and Administrators

	Total		Men		Women		Minorities	
	Spr	Fall	Spr	Fall	Spr	Fall	Spr	Fall
Full-time	77	75	45	43	32	32	7	8
Other full-time	16	15	5	5	11	10	2	1
Deans, librarians, & others who teach	10	12	8	9	2	3	0	0
Part-time	82	64	58	53	23	11	31	6
Total	185	166	116	110	68	56	40	15

Curriculum

	Full-Time	Part-Time
Typical first-year section size	65	0
Is there typically a "small section" of the first-year class, other than Legal Writing, taught by full-time faculty	No	No
If yes, typical size offered last year		
# of classroom course titles beyond first-year curriculum	217	

# of upper division courses, excluding seminars, with an enrollment:		
Under 25	153	
25–49	70	
50–74	24	
75–99	3	
100+	0	

	Full-Time	Part-Time
# of seminars	78	
# of seminar positions available	1,702	
# of seminar positions filled	1,302	0
# of positions available in simulation courses	945	
# of simulation positions filled	826	0
# of positions available in faculty supervised clinical courses	329	
# of faculty supervised clinical positions filled	316	0
# involved in field placements	220	0
# involved in law journals	322	0
# involved in moot court or trial competitions	29	0
# of credit hours required to graduate	86	

JD Enrollment and Ethnicity

	Men #	Men %	Women #	Women %	Full-Time #	Full-Time %	Part-Time #	Part-Time %	1st-Year #	1st-Year %	Total #	Total %	JD Degs. Awd.
African Amer.	34	7.8	33	8.8	67	8.2	0	0.0	26	9.6	67	8.2	23
Amer. Indian	3	0.7	5	1.3	8	1.0	0	0.0	4	1.5	8	1.0	4
Asian Amer.	64	14.6	69	18.4	133	16.3	0	0.0	61	22.5	133	16.3	34
Mex. Amer.	11	2.5	17	4.5	28	3.4	0	0.0	9	3.3	28	3.4	0
Puerto Rican	2	0.5	3	0.8	5	0.6	0	0.0	3	1.1	5	0.6	1
Hispanic	14	3.2	21	5.6	35	4.3	0	0.0	11	4.1	35	4.3	19
Total Minority	128	29.2	148	39.4	276	33.9	0	0.0	114	42.1	276	33.9	81
For. Nation.	32	7.3	29	7.7	61	7.5	0	0.0	24	8.9	61	7.5	0
Caucasian	278	63.5	199	52.9	477	58.6	0	0.0	133	49.1	477	58.6	129
Unknown	0	0.0	0	0.0	0	0.0	0	0.0	0	0.0	0	0.0	44
Total	438	53.8	376	46.2	814	100.0	0	0.0	271	33.3	814		254

Transfers

Transfers in	37
Transfers out	6

Tuition and Fees

	Resident	Nonresident
Full-time	$47,472	$47,472
Part-time		
Tuition Guarantee Program		N

Living Expenses

Estimated living expenses for singles

Living on campus	Living off campus	Living at home
$20,349	$20,349	$7,973

Northwestern University School of Law

ABA
Approved
Since
1923

GPA and LSAT Scores

	Total	Full-Time	Part-Time
# of apps	5,205	5,205	0
# of offers	952	952	0
# of matrics	271	271	0
75% GPA	3.81	3.81	0.00
Median GPA	3.72	3.72	0.00
25% GPA	3.40	3.40	0.00
75% LSAT	172	172	0
Median LSAT	170	170	0
25% LSAT	166	166	0

Grants and Scholarships (from prior year)

	Total		Full-Time		Part-Time	
	#	%	#	%	#	%
Total # of students	781		779		2	
Total # receiving grants	274	35.1	274	35.2	0	0.0
Less than 1/2 tuition	161	20.6	161	20.7	0	0.0
Half to full tuition	109	14.0	109	14.0	0	0.0
Full tuition	0	0.0	0	0.0	0	0.0
More than full tuition	4	0.5	4	0.5	0	0.0
Median grant amount			$20,000		$0	

Informational and Library Resources

Total amount spent on library materials	$969,371
Study seating capacity inside the library	630
# of full-time equivalent professional librarians	12
Hours per week library is open	96
# of open, wired connections available to students	236
# of networked computers available for use by students	105
Has wireless network?	Y
Require computer?	Y

JD Attrition (from prior year)

	Academic	Other	Total	
	#	#	#	%
1st year	0	6	6	2.5
2nd year	0	0	0	0.0
3rd year	0	0	0	0.0
4th year	0	0	0	0.0

Employment (9 months after graduation)

	Total	Percentage
Employment status known	273	100.0
Employment status unknown	0	0.0
Employed	266	97.4
Pursuing graduate degrees	5	1.8
Unemployed (seeking, not seeking, or studying for the bar)	0	0.0
Type of Employment		
# employed in law firms	197	74.1
# employed in business and industry	12	4.5
# employed in government	4	1.5
# employed in public interest	14	5.3
# employed as judicial clerks	32	12.0
# employed in academia	5	1.9
Geographic Location		
# employed in state	109	41.0
# employed in foreign countries	2	0.8
# of states where employed	25	

Bar Passage Rates

First-time takers	197	Reporting %	87.82
Average school %	95.96	Average state %	90.34
Average pass difference	5.62		

Jurisdiction	Takers	Passers	Pass %	State %	Diff %
Illinois	120	118	98.33	90.94	7.39
New York	53	48	90.57	88.98	1.59

Northwestern University School of Law

375 East Chicago Avenue
Chicago, IL 60611-3069
Phone: 312.503.3100; Fax: 312.503.0178
E-mail: admissions@law.northwestern.edu; Website: www.law.northwestern.edu

■ Introduction

Guided by a visionary strategic plan and its recent update, "Plan 2008: Building Great Leaders for the Changing World," Northwestern University School of Law, founded in 1859, advances the understanding of law and produces graduates prepared to excel in a rapidly changing world. Northwestern Law uniquely blends a rigorous intellectual environment with a collegial and supportive community. With one of the lowest student-to-faculty ratios in the country—11:1—our students have exceptional access to their full-time professors, who comprise the most highly credentialed and interdisciplinary law faculty in the nation. The law school's lakefront location in the heart of downtown Chicago provides a wealth of part-time employment options for students while in school, and a spectacular setting in which to study law. Northwestern Law's proximity to courts, commerce, and public interest activities enables students to experience the practice of law, as well as its theory, in one of the most vibrant legal and business communities in the world.

■ Enrollment and Admission

Northwestern Law's close-knit community fosters collaborative learning, which enables students to develop outstanding leadership, team, organizational, and professional skills. We seek students with a wide variety of experience and backgrounds, and our Admissions Committee considers many factors beyond test scores and GPAs when evaluating applicants. Currently, more than 95 percent of entering JD students have at least one year of full-time work experience; approximately 80 percent have two years of experience; and approximately 60 percent have three or more years of experience. Through a unique interviewing program, Northwestern Law ensures it enrolls students with strong academic credentials as well as the interpersonal skills and maturity needed to thrive in the law school community.

■ Faculty

Our faculty is comprised of world-class scholars, diverse in background and perspective, whose research and writing contribute to resolving significant academic and public policy issues. Northwestern Law has a higher percentage of PhD-trained professors than any other law school, making it the most highly credentialed and interdisciplinary faculty in the country. The faculty includes scholars with advanced degrees in economics, history, philosophy, and political science, as well as law. It includes a former US Ambassador-at-Large for War Crimes Issues; a leading expert on race, gender, and the law; an author of more than 50 books on tax law; the coauthor of the most frequently cited book within legal scholarship; the first American attorney to argue before the European Court of Human Rights; and the senior author for the most widely used casebook on American legal history. The full-time research faculty is supplemented by a distinguished group of clinical professors who lead students in simulations, in representing clients, and in efforts to reform our legal system; as well as senior lecturers and adjunct professors, who teach a wide variety of specialized courses.

■ Curriculum

In the rigorous first year of study, Northwestern Law provides a superior foundation in legal reasoning, analysis, and writing, as well as a thorough understanding of the structures and policies of the law. Communication, teamwork, cross-training in business, and experiential learning are also hallmarks of Northwestern Law.

The law school's size enables students to have one-on-one relationships with professors, with required first-year courses taught in sections of approximately 60 students. The JD program requires 83 semester hours of credit.

The broad and flexible curriculum gives upper-level students the opportunity to specialize in particular areas, to pursue advanced research in legal theory, or to pursue a range of hands-on simulation, externship, and live-client opportunities. The Owen L. Coon/James A. Rahl Senior Research Program enables third-year students to do individual research under the supervision of a professor, using library, field, and interdisciplinary research methods.

■ Special Degree and International Programs

A limited number of highly motivated students are enrolled in Northwestern Law's Accelerated JD program—the first such program offered by a top law school. Accelerated JD students complete the same number of credit hours as traditional three-year JD students in five semesters over the course of two calendar years.

A combined program in law and business, jointly offered with Northwestern's Kellogg School of Management, enables students to earn both a JD from the law school and an MBA degree from Kellogg after only three years of study. Students may also enroll in a highly integrated six-year JD-PhD program with the law school and one of the graduate school departments.

Northwestern Law also offers a four-year joint-degree program leading to both a JD and an LLM in International Human Rights (JD-LLM IHR). We are the only law school in the country to offer such a program. Students enrolled in the program receive a thorough grounding in the norms and mechanisms of international human rights law and international criminal law. A distinctive feature of the new program is a requirement that students complete a semester-long externship with one of a number of designated international and hybrid criminal tribunals, foreign supreme courts, and international human rights organizations.

Students who wish to specialize in the study of tax law can earn an LLM in Taxation or jointly pursue a JD and an LLM in Taxation at the same time. Students educated outside the United States can earn an LLM through a nine-month program of advanced study, or an LLM degree and a certificate in business administration from Kellogg through a twelve-month program in law and business. Legal and business professionals abroad can earn an LLM degree from Northwestern through our Executive LLM Programs in Seoul, South Korea; Madrid, Spain; and Tel Aviv, Israel.

Clinical Programs

In Northwestern Law's comprehensive clinical program, students learn strong litigation and negotiation skills and gain direct experience with representing clients and reforming laws.

The innovative simulation-based curriculum, including the Program on Advocacy and Professionalism and the Program on Negotiation and Mediation, gives students the skills they need to negotiate and communicate effectively, solve problems, prepare briefs, examine witnesses, present evidence, and argue cases.

The **Bluhm Legal Clinic** is widely recognized as the best legal clinic facility in the country. The Clinic centers—Fred Bartlit Center for Trial Strategy, Children and Family Justice Center, Small Business Opportunity Center, Center for International Human Rights, Center on Wrongful Convictions, Roderick MacArthur Justice Center, and Investor Protection Center—are nationally recognized for their direct involvement in legal reform.

Students represent underserved clients as well as challenge the fairness of our legal institutions and propose solutions for reform. Working in teams, they assist small business owners and prepare cases in juvenile justice, immigration and asylum, and criminal matters. In addition to fine-tuning their skills as advocates, they often effect change in the law and legal institutions.

Library and Facilities

With more than a half million volumes and access to a wide range of electronic resources, the Pritzker Legal Research Center is one of the country's largest law libraries. It also provides students access to the 3.7 million volumes of the combined Northwestern University libraries.

Our modern facilities and recent additions support collaboration and interaction. Wireless technology is available throughout the law school, and recent renovations include a new 22,000-square-foot clinic center, more than 10 state-of-the-art classrooms and seminar rooms, and upgraded lighting.

Student Activities

Northwestern Law students take an intense and energetic interest in their community and education. Six scholarly journals are available for research, writing, and editing. Students automatically belong to the Student Bar Association, which gives them a voice in curriculum and administration, and they have an opportunity to participate in more than 50 student organizations. Our students also enjoy Chicago's sophisticated yet friendly atmosphere, along with its world-class cultural, sports, and entertainment offerings. Northwestern's 20-acre Chicago campus is nestled between the shores of Lake Michigan, the energy of Michigan Avenue's "Magnificent Mile," and the elegant Gold Coast residential area.

Career Services

The Center for Career Strategy and Advancement proactively cultivates relationships with potential employers while assisting students in focusing their goals and developing short- and long-term career strategies. In 2008, more than 820 national and international offices and organizations recruited our students. In recent years, nearly 80 percent of the recruiters were based in regions outside the Midwest and, typically, more than half of our students accept offers outside the Midwest.

Expenses and Financial Aid

Northwestern Law annually awards $6 million in grants and scholarships in addition to long-term, low-interest institutional loans. These resources enable the law school to cover 100 percent of a student's calculated financial need. Approximately 85 percent of our currently enrolled students receive financial aid.

Applicant Profile

At Northwestern Law, emphasis on teamwork, communication, and interpersonal skills begins during the admission process, in which every applicant is urged to interview. Currently, more than 75 percent of applicants are interviewed, and college seniors must be interviewed. We also place a heavy emphasis on work experience, which contributes to an environment where students learn a great deal from not only faculty, but also each other.

Notre Dame Law School

Admissions Office, PO Box 780
Notre Dame, IN 46556
Phone: 574.631.6626; Fax: 574.631.5474
E-mail: lawadmit@nd.edu; Website: http://law.nd.edu

ABA
Approved
Since
1925

The Basics

Type of school	Private
Term	Semester
Application deadline	3/15
Application fee	$60
Financial aid deadline	2/15
Can first year start other than fall?	No
Student to faculty ratio	11.0 to 1
# of housing spaces available restricted to law students graduate housing for which law students are eligible	192

Faculty and Administrators

	Total		Men		Women		Minorities	
	Spr	Fall	Spr	Fall	Spr	Fall	Spr	Fall
Full-time	39	40	29	30	10	10	6	7
Other full-time	1	1	0	0	1	1	0	0
Deans, librarians, & others who teach	12	12	7	7	5	5	1	1
Part-time	49	43	26	26	23	17	1	1
Total	101	96	62	63	39	33	8	9

JD Enrollment and Ethnicity

	Men		Women		Full-Time		Part-Time		1st-Year		Total		JD Degs. Awd.
	#	%	#	%	#	%	#	%	#	%	#	%	
African Amer.	12	3.8	16	6.9	28	5.1	0	0.0	9	4.9	28	5.1	6
Amer. Indian	6	1.9	1	0.4	7	1.3	0	0.0	3	1.6	7	1.3	4
Asian Amer.	18	5.7	28	12.1	46	8.4	0	0.0	25	13.6	46	8.4	14
Mex. Amer.	7	2.2	3	1.3	10	1.8	0	0.0	4	2.2	10	1.8	6
Puerto Rican	0	0.0	1	0.4	1	0.2	0	0.0	1	0.5	1	0.2	0
Hispanic	18	5.7	18	7.8	36	6.6	0	0.0	14	7.6	36	6.6	16
Total Minority	61	19.2	67	29.0	128	23.4	0	0.0	56	30.4	128	23.4	46
For. Nation.	1	0.3	3	1.3	4	0.7	0	0.0	2	1.1	4	0.7	0
Caucasian	212	66.9	137	59.3	349	63.7	0	0.0	108	58.7	349	63.7	122
Unknown	43	13.6	24	10.4	67	12.2	0	0.0	18	9.8	67	12.2	30
Total	317	57.8	231	42.2	548	100.0	0	0.0	184	33.6	548		198

Curriculum

		Full-Time	Part-Time
Typical first-year section size		64	0
Is there typically a "small section" of the first-year class, other than Legal Writing, taught by full-time faculty		No	No
If yes, typical size offered last year			
# of classroom course titles beyond first-year curriculum		128	
# of upper division courses, excluding seminars, with an enrollment:	Under 25	87	
	25–49	27	
	50–74	13	
	75–99	7	
	100+	1	
# of seminars		34	
# of seminar positions available		677	
# of seminar positions filled		464	0
# of positions available in simulation courses		188	
# of simulation positions filled		161	0
# of positions available in faculty supervised clinical courses		100	
# of faculty supervised clinical positions filled	97		0
# involved in field placements	31		0
# involved in law journals	167		0
# involved in moot court or trial competitions	70		0
# of credit hours required to graduate		90	

Transfers

Transfers in	13
Transfers out	1

Tuition and Fees

	Resident	Nonresident
Full-time	$39,320	$39,320
Part-time		
Tuition Guarantee Program	N	

Living Expenses

Estimated living expenses for singles

Living on campus	Living off campus	Living at home
$16,400	$16,400	$16,400

Notre Dame Law School

ABA
Approved
Since
1925

GPA and LSAT Scores

	Total	Full-Time	Part-Time
# of apps	3,178	3,178	0
# of offers	810	810	0
# of matrics	186	186	0
75% GPA	3.74	3.74	0.00
Median GPA	3.60	3.60	0.00
25% GPA	3.36	3.36	0.00
75% LSAT	167	167	0
Median LSAT	166	166	0
25% LSAT	163	163	0

Grants and Scholarships (from prior year)

	Total		Full-Time		Part-Time	
	#	%	#	%	#	%
Total # of students	558		558		0	
Total # receiving grants	439	78.7	439	78.7	0	0.0
Less than 1/2 tuition	356	63.8	356	63.8	0	0.0
Half to full tuition	81	14.5	81	14.5	0	0.0
Full tuition	2	0.4	2	0.4	0	0.0
More than full tuition	0	0.0	0	0.0	0	0.0
Median grant amount			$13,000		$0	

Informational and Library Resources

Total amount spent on library materials	$1,476,059
Study seating capacity inside the library	0
# of full-time equivalent professional librarians	9
Hours per week library is open	95
# of open, wired connections available to students	18
# of networked computers available for use by students	63
Has wireless network?	Y
Require computer?	N

JD Attrition (from prior year)

	Academic	Other	Total	
	#	#	#	%
1st year	0	2	2	1.1
2nd year	1	2	3	1.7
3rd year	1	2	3	1.5
4th year	0	0	0	0.0

Employment (9 months after graduation)

	Total	Percentage
Employment status known	184	98.9
Employment status unknown	2	1.1
Employed	180	97.8
Pursuing graduate degrees	3	1.6
Unemployed (seeking, not seeking, or studying for the bar)	1	0.5
Type of Employment		
# employed in law firms	109	60.6
# employed in business and industry	10	5.6
# employed in government	21	11.7
# employed in public interest	12	6.7
# employed as judicial clerks	26	14.4
# employed in academia	2	1.1
Geographic Location		
# employed in state	12	6.7
# employed in foreign countries	0	0.0
# of states where employed	34	

Bar Passage Rates

First-time takers	186	Reporting %	100.00
Average school %	96.25	Average state %	86.24
Average pass difference	10.01		

Jurisdiction	Takers	Passers	Pass %	State %	Diff %
Illinois	45	45	100.00	90.94	9.06
California	24	21	87.50	78.07	9.43
New York	23	22	95.65	88.98	6.67
Indiana	12	12	100.00	84.39	15.61
Others (25)	82	79	96.34		

Notre Dame Law School

Admissions Office, PO Box 780
Notre Dame, IN 46556
Phone: 574.631.6626; Fax: 574.631.5474
E-mail: lawadmit@nd.edu; Website: http://law.nd.edu

■ Introduction

With a rich history that dates to its founding in 1869, Notre Dame Law School today enjoys a national and international reputation for preparing consummate professionals—men and women who are extraordinarily competent in their professional endeavors and who commit themselves to serve their clients and the profession effectively and honorably. Distinctive among nationally regarded law schools as a result of the school's and the university's Catholic heritage and tradition, faith and values, and community spirit, the Law School inspires students to examine their practice of law within the context of their responsibilities as members of the bar, as leaders within their respective fields, and as citizens of the world community.

■ Enrollment/Student Body

The student body represents the national stature and international nature of the programs of the Law School and the university. Our student body of approximately 575 students represents nearly all states and a number of foreign countries. The small size of the student body fosters a sense of community and allows significant interaction between faculty and students.

■ Faculty

Faculty members come to Notre Dame Law School with experience in private practice and government service, and represent a wide range of undergraduate institutions, law schools, and state bars. Members of the faculty are well regarded for their commitment to teaching, as well as their accessibility to students outside of the classroom as advisors and mentors. At the same time, these premier scholars publish in leading journals and are invited to participate in academic conferences around the world.

■ Library and Physical Facilities

In January 2009, the Law School moved into the Eck Hall of Law, a beautiful and spacious, three-story, 85,000-square-foot building. It is connected to the existing building by a covered walkway and chapel, with a common area above. The design captures the Law School's commitment to shaping the minds, hearts, and souls of the next generation of Notre Dame lawyers. The equally beautiful gothic structure that has been home to the Law School since 1930 is currently undergoing renovation. When completed in June 2010, that building will house an expanded Kresge Law Library, several administrative offices, four journal offices, and additional classroom space.

The Kresge Law Library is among the top American law school research libraries. The staff of 29 is noted for its service to law school faculty, students, and staff, and the larger university community.

The Law School provides significant computing support for students and other members of the law school community. Five full-time technology professionals offer assistance for both hardware and software, in addition to other computing and technology needs.

■ Curriculum

The JD curriculum provides a strong foundation in those areas that have proven to be fundamental to the actual practice of law in every American jurisdiction, while giving students the opportunity to tailor coursework to particular career aspirations. Required courses, those that are critical to a mastery of specialized areas of the law, total 42 of the 90 credit hours needed for graduation. In addition to the JD degree, the Law School confers three graduate law degrees: an LLM in International and Comparative Law, an LLM in International Human Rights, and a JSD (also in International Human Rights). The LLM in International and Comparative Law is offered exclusively at the Law School's London Law Centre.

■ London Programs

Notre Dame Law School recognizes that today's legal practice increasingly involves problems that the law of no one nation can resolve. Hence, JD candidates may augment their legal education by participating in one of two programs offered by the Law School through its London Law Centre. Second-year students who wish to immerse themselves in comparative and international law, as well as in the traditions of the American and British common-law systems, can study in the only year-long overseas program offered by an American law school. Students who desire a shorter international-study experience and who have completed their first year of law school can spend six weeks in London during Notre Dame's summer program.

■ Student Life

The sense of community and the quality of student life at Notre Dame have developed out of long-standing traditions that make the Notre Dame Law School experience different: admission policies that emphasize the importance of qualitative factors such as service to others; a mission that focuses on teaching, scholarship, and service in the legal and Judeo-Christian traditions; and an emphasis on forming and nurturing collegial relationships between students and faculty. The Law School is centrally located on the Notre Dame campus, and law students fully participate in athletic, cultural, religious, and social events on the campus. Law students also manage to find a comfortable balance between their studies and involvement in the Law School's four law journals and any of 30 organizations that reflect the professional and personal interests of the student body.

■ Expenses and Financial Aid

Notre Dame is committed to providing a legal education of the highest quality at a tuition structure that compares favorably to other nationally regarded private law schools. Additionally, law students benefit from the low cost of living in northern Indiana.

In recent years, scholarship assistance has been provided annually to approximately 60–70 percent of entering students on the basis of merit, commitment to the Law School's

mission, and financial need. Fellowships range from $5,000 to full tuition and are renewable for all three years of legal study.

■ Housing

Many single law students choose to live on campus in graduate-student housing. Married students with children can live in the unfurnished University Village apartments. Students who wish to live off campus can find reasonably priced accommodations near the campus and can secure on-campus parking for a nominal additional charge.

■ Career Services

Notre Dame Law School graduates have, in recent years, found rewarding work all over the country and in a wide variety of practice areas. Historically, the employment rate has been at or above 95 percent within nine months of graduation. In a typical year, approximately 150–170 employers visit the campus to interview Notre Dame law students. Another 20–25 employers participate in interviews exclusive to Notre Dame law students in Los Angeles; Washington, DC; and New York. Employers are interested in interviewing Notre Dame law students because of the Law School's reputation for preparing extraordinarily competent lawyers. A national network of over 8,000 Law School alumni and friends assists students and graduates in finding employment opportunities across the country.

Graduates of Notre Dame Law School have been successful in terms of obtaining judicial clerkships, with 10–15 percent of recent graduating classes choosing this career option. These highly sought-after positions provide graduates with a unique opportunity to learn firsthand about the inner workings of the judicial system, while at the same time allowing them to hone important legal skills and problem-solving abilities.

The Career Services Office (CSO) also coordinates a variety of initiatives to encourage students who wish to be employed in public interest work following graduation. These include a variety of informational programs and services, including participation in our campus-wide, nonprofit career night. The CSO also participates in public interest law career fairs across the country and is a sponsoring and coordinating school for the Midwest Public Interest Law Career Conference in Chicago. Additionally, the office coordinates a comprehensive summer stipend program that provides funding for approximately 100 students working in public interest positions each summer. The Law School's Loan Repayment Assistance Program (LRAP) assists eligible law school graduates who choose to work in public interest, public service, or other similar positions after graduation. The Law School seeks to help reduce the financial pressures that can discourage graduates from pursuing positions in public interest and public service employment.

Please visit our website for the most current employment information.

Applicant Profile

Each year the Law School Admissions Committee employs a whole-person review philosophy to create a class from a large number of highly qualified applicants. We seek to enroll multidimensional students with a wide range of talents, backgrounds, experiences, accomplishments, and points of view. Academic ability, as reflected in the LSAT score and academic performance in college are important; however, the committee considers a broad array of elements in addition to

these two quantitative measures. Notre Dame Law School officials involved in the admission process are mindful of the school's objective to produce lawyers who are competent, compassionate, and committed to serving their clients with integrity. The admission process is highly selective and seeks to enroll men and women of exceptional ability. We do not provide an applicant profile grid because it would be based solely on LSAT and GPA.

Nova Southeastern University—Shepard Broad Law Center

3305 College Avenue
Fort Lauderdale, FL 33314-7721
Phone: 954.262.6117; Fax: 954.262.3844
E-mail: admission@nsu.law.nova.edu; Website: www.nsulaw.nova.edu

ABA Approved Since 1975 — Section of Legal Education and Admissions to the Bar

The Basics

Type of school	Private
Term	Semester
Application deadline	4/1
Application fee	$50
Financial aid deadline	4/15
Can first year start other than fall?	No
Student to faculty ratio	17.7 to 1
# of housing spaces available restricted to law students	
graduate housing for which law students are eligible	512

Faculty and Administrators

	Total		Men		Women		Minorities	
	Spr	Fall	Spr	Fall	Spr	Fall	Spr	Fall
Full-time	42	48	24	26	18	22	9	12
Other full-time	8	9	3	3	5	6	4	4
Deans, librarians, & others who teach	7	8	3	3	4	5	2	3
Part-time	41	50	32	36	9	13	8	6
Total	98	115	62	68	36	46	23	25

JD Enrollment and Ethnicity

	Men		Women		Full-Time		Part-Time		1st-Year		Total		JD Degs. Awd.
	#	%	#	%	#	%	#	%	#	%	#	%	
African Amer.	15	3.0	43	7.3	39	4.3	19	10.1	28	6.2	58	5.3	12
Amer. Indian	1	0.2	3	0.5	3	0.3	1	0.5	0	0.0	4	0.4	1
Asian Amer.	19	3.8	37	6.3	51	5.6	5	2.6	26	5.7	56	5.1	7
Mex. Amer.	3	0.6	5	0.8	6	0.7	2	1.1	4	0.9	8	0.7	0
Puerto Rican	6	1.2	6	1.0	9	1.0	3	1.6	8	1.8	12	1.1	5
Hispanic	85	16.9	108	18.3	139	15.4	54	28.6	80	17.7	193	17.7	36
Total Minority	129	25.6	202	34.3	247	27.4	84	44.4	146	32.2	331	30.3	61
For. Nation.	9	1.8	6	1.0	15	1.7	0	0.0	11	2.4	15	1.4	0
Caucasian	324	64.4	339	57.6	577	63.9	86	45.5	263	58.1	663	60.7	177
Unknown	41	8.2	42	7.1	64	7.1	19	10.1	33	7.3	83	7.6	20
Total	503	46.1	589	53.9	903	82.7	189	17.3	453	41.5	1092		258

Curriculum

	Full-Time	Part-Time
Typical first-year section size	63	51
Is there typically a "small section" of the first-year class, other than Legal Writing, taught by full-time faculty	No	No
If yes, typical size offered last year		
# of classroom course titles beyond first-year curriculum	119	
# of upper division courses, excluding seminars, with an enrollment: Under 25	130	
25–49	37	
50–74	34	
75–99	4	
100+	0	
# of seminars	19	
# of seminar positions available	380	
# of seminar positions filled	267	56
# of positions available in simulation courses	1,410	
# of simulation positions filled	935	172
# of positions available in faculty supervised clinical courses	190	
# of faculty supervised clinical positions filled	70	31
# involved in field placements	95	8
# involved in law journals	98	18
# involved in moot court or trial competitions	59	2
# of credit hours required to graduate	90	

Transfers

Transfers in	9
Transfers out	23

Tuition and Fees

	Resident	Nonresident
Full-time	$31,672	$31,672
Part-time	$23,878	$23,878
Tuition Guarantee Program	N	

Living Expenses

Estimated living expenses for singles

Living on campus	Living off campus	Living at home
$19,588	$25,225	$11,536

Nova Southeastern University—Shepard Broad Law Center

ABA
Approved
Since
1975

GPA and LSAT Scores

	Total	Full-Time	Part-Time
# of apps	2,543	2,122	421
# of offers	1,095	969	126
# of matrics	430	374	56
75% GPA	3.47	3.47	3.45
Median GPA	3.22	3.23	3.20
25% GPA	3.01	3.02	2.94
75% LSAT	152	152	151
Median LSAT	149	149	148
25% LSAT	147	147	145

Grants and Scholarships (from prior year)

	Total		Full-Time		Part-Time	
	#	%	#	%	#	%
Total # of students	1,000		829		171	
Total # receiving grants	125	12.5	96	11.6	29	17.0
Less than 1/2 tuition	73	7.3	54	6.5	19	11.1
Half to full tuition	10	1.0	6	0.7	4	2.3
Full tuition	42	4.2	36	4.3	6	3.5
More than full tuition	0	0.0	0	0.0	0	0.0
Median grant amount			$14,000		$9,000	

Informational and Library Resources

Total amount spent on library materials	$1,177,605
Study seating capacity inside the library	532
# of full-time equivalent professional librarians	10
Hours per week library is open	104
# of open, wired connections available to students	4
# of networked computers available for use by students	5
Has wireless network?	Y
Require computer?	Y

JD Attrition (from prior year)

	Academic	Other	Total	
	#	#	#	%
1st year	47	36	83	21.9
2nd year	5	8	13	4.1
3rd year	0	2	2	0.8
4th year	0	0	0	0.0

Employment (9 months after graduation)

	Total	Percentage
Employment status known	255	98.8
Employment status unknown	3	1.2
Employed	208	81.6
Pursuing graduate degrees	11	4.3
Unemployed (seeking, not seeking, or studying for the bar)	35	13.7
Type of Employment		
# employed in law firms	142	68.3
# employed in business and industry	20	9.6
# employed in government	21	10.1
# employed in public interest	15	7.2
# employed as judicial clerks	7	3.4
# employed in academia	3	1.4
Geographic Location		
# employed in state	183	88.0
# employed in foreign countries	1	0.5
# of states where employed	14	

Bar Passage Rates

First-time takers	245	Reporting %	92.65
Average school %	84.14	Average state %	80.76
Average pass difference	3.38		

Jurisdiction	Takers	Passers	Pass %	State %	Diff %
Florida	227	191	84.14	80.76	3.38

Nova Southeastern University—Shepard Broad Law Center

3305 College Avenue
Fort Lauderdale, FL 33314-7721
Phone: 954.262.6117; Fax: 954.262.3844
E-mail: admission@nsu.law.nova.edu; Website: www.nsulaw.nova.edu

■ Introduction

NSU Law Center is one of 16 graduate and professional schools of Nova Southeastern University, the largest private independent university in Florida and the sixth largest in the US. NSU Law is accredited by the ABA and is a member of the AALS. The Law Center is located in the suburbs of Fort Lauderdale, in the heart of South Florida's fast-growing Broward, Miami-Dade, Palm Beach area. We encourage applicants to tour the campus and speak with the staff of the Admissions Office.

■ Curriculum and Special Academic/Professional Programs

The Law Center offers a rigorous traditional academic program in three-year day and four-year evening versions. NSU Law prides itself on preparing graduates to make a smooth transition from the classroom to the courtroom or boardroom.

Lawyering Skills and Values (LSV)—Every student completes a four-semester LSV sequence that combines traditional legal reasoning, writing, and research with an introduction to lawyer interviewing, counseling, negotiating, mediating, advocating, and other critical skills in a simulated law firm experience.

Clinical Opportunities—Clinical education is an important part of the NSU Law experience. In fact, we think clinical education is so important that each and every student who meets the clinic criteria has the opportunity to participate in one of our clinics. The clinical semester brings the study of law to life. In seven clinical programs, students are introduced to a practice specialty under the guidance of a seasoned mentor. Each clinical semester begins with intensive classes that focus on advanced substantive law and lawyering skills in the clinic specialty plus interdisciplinary topics. For the rest of the term, faculty members supervise the students' representation of clients in Law Center clinics, government agencies, nonprofit organizations, and private law offices.

International Dual-Degree Opportunities—NSU Law students have an opportunity to study both common law and civil law through our dual-degree program with the University of Barcelona. With successful completion of the program and the appropriate bar requirements, students can qualify for admission to the bar in both Spain and the United States. As lawyers, dual-degree graduates will have an opportunity to practice in the United States and Spain, and to practice transactional law in the European Union. The dual degree will also assist those wishing to practice in Latin America. Opportunities are also available in the Czech Republic and Italy.

Joint Degrees—NSU Law offers students opportunities to earn a second graduate degree in a complementary discipline and in a compressed time frame.

Internships—In addition to an award-winning pro bono service program, the Law Center operates judicial internship, mediation, street law, consumer protection, and dependency workshop programs that provide valuable real-world experiences.

■ Two Admission Programs

The Law Center's Admissions Committee oversees two separate programs. The Regular Admission Program combines each applicant's undergraduate grades and LSAT score according to a weighted formula based on the academic success of NSU Law students. The committee also values the applicant's personal statement, writing sample, work experience, and letters of recommendation. While no single factor is determinative, if the LSAT/UGPA combination does not demonstrate the promise of academic achievement, an applicant is unlikely to be offered regular admission.

Selected applicants who are denied regular admission will be offered the opportunity to earn admission to the Law Center by successful performance in NSU Law's unique Alternative Admission Model Program for Legal Education (AAMPLE). In the 31 years of AAMPLE's operation, more than 1,000 students have qualified for admission. AAMPLE students who enroll in a six-week summer session and earn a C+ average in the two courses are offered admission to the Law Center. AAMPLE is presented in two formats, the traditional on-campus program and an innovative online model.

Approximately 40 percent of our applicants are offered seats through the Regular Admission Program. Another 26 percent are invited to the AAMPLE Program. Applicants are encouraged to review the charts that follow this narrative to evaluate the likelihood of being admitted to the Law Center via the Regular Admission or the AAMPLE Program. NSU Law's two admission programs produce a diverse student body. Recent classes were nearly evenly divided between men and women, with members of minority groups comprising approximately 33 percent of the class.

The Admissions Committee awards partial tuition scholarships on the basis of academic merit to approximately 35 percent of students admitted through the Regular Admission Program.

■ Faculty

NSU Law professors have a long tradition of teaching excellence. The faculty's open-door policy is enhanced by our sophisticated wireless communications system and pioneering laptop program. Limits on the size of first-year sections result in more individualized feedback. The faculty's expertise is reflected in rich classroom discussion and a wide range of scholarly publications and professional service.

■ Library and Physical Facilities

Nova Southeastern has been a technology pioneer for more than a decade. NSU Law Center installed the first wireless system in a law school in 1996 and was the first US law school to provide totally wireless access to all faculty, staff, and students. NSU Law leads the way in the use of technology in legal education.

The Law Library's extensive holdings include special collections in tax, criminal law, law and popular culture, admiralty, and international law. With over 340,000 volume/volume equivalents, the Law Library provides access to primary and secondary sources of US law as well as

case-finding and updating tools. The Law Library and Technology Center is designated as a United Nations depository and as a depository for US and Florida government documents.

Leo Goodwin Sr. Hall, which houses the Law Center, has two courtrooms used by students in the school's trial advocacy and moot court programs as well as by the National Institute for Trial Advocacy and state appellate court judges.

■ Student Activities

The Law Center is home to three significant publications: the *Nova Law Review*, the *Journal of International and Comparative Law*, and the *International Citator and Research Project*.

The Moot Court Society sponsors intramural competitions. Members of the society compete in major national events. The Association of Trial Lawyers of America and other student advocacy groups field teams in competitions around the country.

Students shape the life of the Law Center through their involvement in a wide range of service organizations and social clubs. Extremely active groups include the Asian Pacific American Law Students Association, Black Law Students Association, Jewish Law Students Association, Hispanic Law Student Association, Lambda, Student Bar Association, Florida Association for Women Lawyers, National Association for Public Interest Law, International Law Society, Native American Law Students Association, and a variety of practice specialty and sports clubs. Students also guide chapters of national legal fraternities, participate with lawyers and judges in the Inns of Court, and serve on faculty committees.

■ Career Services

Our Career Development Office assists students and alumni with career counseling and the employment process. In addition to facilitating on-campus interviews and résumé distributions, the director coordinates career-option seminars and interviewing workshops. The office also sponsors skill courses and assists students in finding pro bono experiences with law firms and legal agencies throughout the country.

Applicant Profile

Nova Southeastern University—Shepard Broad Law Center
Regular Admission Program

LSAT Score	GPA								
	3.75 +	3.50–3.74	3.25–3.49	3.00–3.24	2.75–2.99	2.50–2.74	2.25–2.49	2.00–2.24	Below 2.00
165–180									
160–164									
155–159									
150–154									
145–149									
140–144									
135–139									
130–134									
Below 130									

Good Possibility · Possible · Unlikely

Please use this chart as a general guide in determining admission chances for the Regular Admission Program. Nonnumerical factors are also considered during the file-evaluation process.

AAMPLE®
Enrolled/Successful

LSAT Score	GPA									
	3.75 +	3.50–3.74	3.25–3.49	3.00–3.24	2.75–2.99	2.50–2.74	2.25–2.49	2.00–2.24	Below 2.00	Un-known GPA
150–159					2/1	5/4	11/8	3/2		
145–149	1/0	2/2	5/4	9/3	29/13	16/11	2/1			
140–144		13/3	10/5	28/10	17/10	4/0	1/0			
135–139	3/0	2/1	9/2	3/2	2/1	1/0	1/1		1/0	1/1
130–134		1/0	1/0							

Please use this chart to determine the possibility of being admitted through AAMPLE® (Alternative Admission Model Program for Legal Education). The chart reflects combined admission data for the summer 2009 AAMPLE programs, including both on-campus and online. Overall, there were 145 students enrolled in the on-campus AAMPLE, with 72 successful, and 38 enrolled in the online AAMPLE, 13 of whom were successful.

Ohio Northern University—Claude W. Pettit College of Law

525 South Main Street
Ada, OH 45810
Phone: 877.452.9668, 419.772.2211; Fax: 419.772.3042
E-mail: lawadmissions@onu.edu; Website: www.law.onu.edu

ABA Approved Since 1948

Section of Legal Education and Admissions to the Bar

The Basics

Type of school	Private
Term	Semester
Application deadline	
Application fee	
Financial aid deadline	6/1
Can first year start other than fall?	No
Student to faculty ratio	12.8 to 1
# of housing spaces available restricted to law students	52
graduate housing for which law students are eligible	52

Faculty and Administrators

	Total		Men		Women		Minorities	
	Spr	Fall	Spr	Fall	Spr	Fall	Spr	Fall
Full-time	19	21	11	13	8	8	3	3
Other full-time	0	0	0	0	0	0	0	0
Deans, librarians, & others who teach	7	7	5	5	2	2	0	0
Part-time	8	8	6	6	2	2	0	0
Total	34	36	22	24	12	12	3	3

Curriculum

		Full-Time	Part-Time
Typical first-year section size		60	0
Is there typically a "small section" of the first-year class, other than Legal Writing, taught by full-time faculty		No	No
If yes, typical size offered last year			
# of classroom course titles beyond first-year curriculum		78	
# of upper division courses, excluding seminars, with an enrollment:	Under 25	49	
	25–49	25	
	50–74	5	
	75–99	0	
	100+	0	
# of seminars		12	
# of seminar positions available		144	
# of seminar positions filled		102	0
# of positions available in simulation courses		506	
# of simulation positions filled		319	0
# of positions available in faculty supervised clinical courses		75	
# of faculty supervised clinical positions filled		33	0
# involved in field placements		85	0
# involved in law journals		42	0
# involved in moot court or trial competitions		21	0
# of credit hours required to graduate		88	

JD Enrollment and Ethnicity

	Men		Women		Full-Time		Part-Time		1st-Year		Total		JD Degs. Awd.
	#	%	#	%	#	%	#	%	#	%	#	%	
African Amer.	6	3.4	16	12.4	22	7.2	0	0.0	6	5.3	22	7.2	5
Amer. Indian	1	0.6	1	0.8	2	0.7	0	0.0	1	0.9	2	0.7	0
Asian Amer.	6	3.4	5	3.9	11	3.6	0	0.0	6	5.3	11	3.6	2
Mex. Amer.	0	0.0	0	0.0	0	0.0	0	0.0	0	0.0	0	0.0	0
Puerto Rican	0	0.0	0	0.0	0	0.0	0	0.0	0	0.0	0	0.0	0
Hispanic	3	1.7	3	2.3	6	2.0	0	0.0	3	2.6	6	2.0	2
Total Minority	16	9.0	25	19.4	41	13.4	0	0.0	16	14.0	41	13.4	9
For. Nation.	0	0.0	0	0.0	0	0.0	0	0.0	0	0.0	0	0.0	0
Caucasian	153	86.0	94	72.9	247	80.5	0	0.0	88	77.2	247	80.5	82
Unknown	9	5.1	10	7.8	19	6.2	0	0.0	10	8.8	19	6.2	9
Total	178	58.0	129	42.0	307	100.0	0	0.0	114	37.1	307		100

Transfers

Transfers in	2
Transfers out	8

Tuition and Fees

	Resident	Nonresident
Full-time	$28,900	$28,900
Part-time		
Tuition Guarantee Program		N

Living Expenses

Estimated living expenses for singles

Living on campus	Living off campus	Living at home
$13,580	$14,750	$14,750

Ohio Northern University—Claude W. Pettit College of Law

ABA Approved Since 1948

GPA and LSAT Scores

	Total	Full-Time	Part-Time
# of apps	1,286	1,286	0
# of offers	464	464	0
# of matrics	113	113	0
75% GPA	3.65	3.65	0.00
Median GPA	3.40	3.49	0.00
25% GPA	2.90	2.96	0.00
75% LSAT	157	157	0
Median LSAT	154	154	0
25% LSAT	149	149	0

Grants and Scholarships (from prior year)

	Total #	Total %	Full-Time #	Full-Time %	Part-Time #	Part-Time %
Total # of students	309		309		0	
Total # receiving grants	166	53.7	166	53.7	0	0.0
Less than 1/2 tuition	25	8.1	25	8.1	0	0.0
Half to full tuition	131	42.4	131	42.4	0	0.0
Full tuition	9	2.9	9	2.9	0	0.0
More than full tuition	1	0.3	1	0.3	0	0.0
Median grant amount			$20,000		$0	

Informational and Library Resources

Total amount spent on library materials	$963,817
Study seating capacity inside the library	303
# of full-time equivalent professional librarians	3
Hours per week library is open	113
# of open, wired connections available to students	286
# of networked computers available for use by students	61
Has wireless network?	Y
Require computer?	N

JD Attrition (from prior year)

	Academic #	Other #	Total #	Total %
1st year	5	16	21	18.8
2nd year	0	0	0	0.0
3rd year	0	0	0	0.0
4th year	0	0	0	0.0

Employment (9 months after graduation)

	Total	Percentage
Employment status known	77	81.9
Employment status unknown	17	18.1
Employed	69	89.6
Pursuing graduate degrees	5	6.5
Unemployed (seeking, not seeking, or studying for the bar)	3	3.9
Type of Employment		
# employed in law firms	37	53.6
# employed in business and industry	4	5.8
# employed in government	21	30.4
# employed in public interest	1	1.4
# employed as judicial clerks	2	2.9
# employed in academia	3	4.3
Geographic Location		
# employed in state	30	43.5
# employed in foreign countries	0	0.0
# of states where employed		17

Bar Passage Rates

First-time takers	93	Reporting %	79.57
Average school %	85.14	Average state %	86.02
Average pass difference −0.88			

Jurisdiction	Takers	Passers	Pass %	State %	Diff %
Ohio	31	29	93.55	88.09	5.46
Pennsylvania	15	12	80.00	86.69	−6.69
New Jersey	8	8	100.00	84.69	15.31
Virginia	6	3	50.00	82.70	−32.70
Others (3)	14	11	78.57		

Ohio Northern University—Claude W. Pettit College of Law

525 South Main Street
Ada, OH 45810
Phone: 877.452.9668, 419.772.2211; Fax: 419.772.3042
E-mail: lawadmissions@onu.edu; Website: www.law.onu.edu

Introduction

Founded in 1885, the Ohio Northern University Pettit College of Law is the second oldest of the nine Ohio law schools. The college is accredited by the American Bar Association and is a member of the Association of American Law Schools. Annually, the college enrolls more than 320 students from more than 40 states in its full-time juris doctor degree and LLM programs. Dedicated to the rigorous pursuits of teaching and practicing law, the college's esteemed faculty is focused on providing one-on-one personal training to students with a passion for legal scholastic excellence. The College of Law is located in Ada, Ohio, with an off-campus legal clinic in Lima, Ohio.

The College and the University

The Claude W. Pettit College of Law is accredited by the American Bar Association and is a member of the Association of American Law Schools. The college is centered in newly renovated Tilton Hall, a modern building that houses all law classes and the Taggart Law Library.

The College of Law lies at the center of the tree-lined campus. The university's facilities are readily available to all law students and are located only steps away from the law building. These facilities include hiking and biking trails, a sports center, and the Freed Center for the Performing Arts. Law students may bowl, swim, and play handball, racquet sports, and basketball all year-round in indoor and outdoor facilities. The sports center houses a wide variety of modern fitness machines and one of the best indoor tracks in the Midwest.

Student Life

Community is part of your law school experience.

Your involvement in cocurricular activities plays an important role in your law school experience. By participating in any of 20 different student organizations, you will quickly see your communication, social, and leadership skills develop, and you'll build long-lasting relationships with peers and faculty. These activities also showcase your drive for excellence to prospective employers.

Improve your oral advocacy and brief writing skills by participating in moot court. The *Ohio Northern University Law Review*, a highly respected law journal of the College of Law, is edited and published by students three times a year.

While taking a break from studying, you'll discover the cultural side of the university. Theatre, dance, music, and other programs are hosted regularly at the acclaimed Freed Center for the Performing Arts. Permanent and provisional art collections are on display at the Elzay Gallery of Art. If sports are more your interest, you can attend a game at Dial-Roberson Stadium or participate in a number of intramural sports activities at King-Horn Sports Center. You can also watch Ohio Northern athletes compete in 21 varsity sports.

Faculty

With a 10:1 student-to-faculty ratio, our professors and staff will know you by name and interact with you on a personal level.

From the moment you arrive on campus, you will notice something different about our faculty. They are engaged in your education and truly interested in seeing you succeed. This is individualized attention you won't encounter at a larger school. Our goal is not only to educate, but also to ensure the development of practical skills, morals, and leadership needed to be successful in the practice of law.

Our professors have studied at some of the most prestigious schools in the United States—including Harvard, Columbia, Yale, and Duke—and practiced at some of the largest firms in the country. More than 50 percent of the faculty holds a PhD or LLM degree in addition to their JD degree. You learn your craft from renowned experts specializing in international law, law of war, commercial law, business law, bankruptcy law, criminal law, and tax law.

Curriculum

Ohio Northern takes learning beyond traditional theory and brings the practice of law to life in the classroom.

During your first year, your studies will focus on the foundations of the law. The school's innovative first-year curriculum, however, will also introduce you to modern practice. During the first year January term, practicing lawyers will demonstrate how legal theory shapes what they do in courtrooms and boardrooms. A court of appeals will actually hear cases in the law building during the term, giving students a chance to interact with the judges and lawyers. In the second and third years of study, students have the opportunity to take a wide array of electives.

CONCURRENT JD AND LLM: Our concurrent JD and LLM in Democratic Governance and the Rule of Law degree is designed for students who have a passion for bringing democracy and law reform to developing countries. You will build valuable international relationships through domestic and overseas externships. You will graduate in three years with both your juris doctor and a Master of Laws degree.

INTERNATIONAL LLM: Our one-year International LLM in Democratic Governance and the Rule of Law provides an opportunity for young lawyers from transitional democracies to study democracy and law at Ohio Northern. Each year, a group of lawyers travel from across the globe to study international law alongside our JD students in an effort to implement law reforms that can support democracy and the rule of law in their home countries.

PHARMACY/LAW DUAL DEGREE: Our pharmacy and law dual degree joins together two of ONU's elite programs into a combined seven-year curriculum. Following substantial educational, practice, and research experiences in both pharmacy and law, you will graduate with your doctor of pharmacy and juris doctor degrees.

Practical Skills

Get involved, apply your learning in a real-life scenario, and compete on a national stage.

CLINIC: By participating in a clinic, you can enhance your writing, analytical, and communication skills and garner valuable courtroom and client experience. Almost 70 percent of ONU

students choose to take advantage of this unique opportunity and participate in a clinic study before they graduate.

EXPERIENTIAL LEARNING: Inside and outside of the classroom, our academic and nonacademic experiential learning activities provide a valuable opportunity to engage in the practice of law prior to graduation.

■ Career Services

Exceeding the national average in job placement, for the past seven years ONU has a 94 percent employment rate nine months after graduation.

We realize legal training is only part of the equation; your ultimate goal is to find a job. Our skilled staff in the Office of Career Services is here to help. We provide workshops and coordinate individual meetings to help you with résumé preparation, interviewing skills, professional image, and other career development techniques. We also tap into our more than 4,500 distinguished alumni to offer networking options and further strengthen our recruiting channels across the country.

Each year, more than 600 employers look to ONU for assistance in hiring law clerks, summer associates, and attorneys. Whether you want to pursue a career in private practice, government, business, or judicial clerkships, ONU will prepare you for a successful career and work with you to find the right job.

■ Admission and Financial Aid

Ohio Northern University is committed to a culturally and socially diverse student body. While Ohio Northern gives significant weight to the LSAT and undergraduate GPA, the Admissions Committee may consider other factors such as candidates' undergraduate programs, grade trends, completion of other graduate degrees, professional accomplishments, and socioeconomic or cultural barriers faced by the applicant. Although letters of recommendation

are not required, letters from persons who have a basis to assess the candidate's intellectual ability and potential for success in law school, such as former professors or employers, are strongly recommended.

The Summer Starter Program is an opportunity for students whose outstanding undergraduate performance indicates probable academic success in law school, despite disproportionate LSAT scores. Candidates who qualify for the program, based on their application, will be invited to interview for the program on campus.

The College of Law also provides scholarship awards for students whose undergraduate records demonstrate academic excellence. The scholarship amounts range from $5,000 to $30,000 and are renewable provided the student remains in good academic standing. Additionally, substantial scholarships are awarded to students who excel in their first year of law school. In order to foster diversity in the student body and the legal profession, the university awards grants-in-aid to eligible students. The college generally awards approximately $3 million of institutional aid annually to all three classes.

Students are encouraged to schedule a campus visit where they can sit in on a class, meet with a financial aid counselor, tour the facilities, and talk with current students. Contact *lawadmissions@onu.edu* to make arrangements.

■ Facilities and Technology

The college contains state-of-the-art facilities including two moot court rooms, a technology classroom, wireless capabilities throughout the building, and classrooms equipped with plasma televisions and SMART Board technology.

The Taggart Law Library features an outstanding collection of federal, state, and international legal materials. The library is open seven days a week and provides seating for up to 303 students. In addition, the technology research center is available for research, training, and printing. The reading rooms of the library offer ideal locations for both quiet and group study.

Applicant Profile

Ohio Northern University—Claude W. Pettit College of Law
This grid includes only applicants who earned 120–180 LSAT scores under standard administrations.

LSAT Score	GPA								
	3.75 +	3.50–3.74	3.25–3.49	3.00–3.24	2.75–2.99	2.50–2.74	2.25–2.49	2.00–2.24	Below 2.00
175–180									
170–174									
165–169									
160–164									
155–159									
150–154									
145–149									
140–144									
135–139									
130–134									
125–129									
120–124									

Good Possibility   Possible   Unlikely

Average LSAT data reported.

The Ohio State University Moritz College of Law

John Deaver Drinko Hall, 55 West 12th Avenue
Columbus, OH 43210-1391
Phone: 614.292.8810; Fax: 614.292.1492
E-mail: lawadmit@osu.edu; Website: www.moritzlaw.osu.edu

ABA Approved Since 1923
Section of Legal Education and Admissions to the Bar

The Basics

Type of school	Public
Term	Semester
Application deadline	3/15
Application fee	$60
Financial aid deadline	3/1
Can first year start other than fall?	No
Student to faculty ratio	13.3 to 1
# of housing spaces available restricted to law students	
graduate housing for which law students are eligible	927

Faculty and Administrators

	Total		Men		Women		Minorities	
	Spr	Fall	Spr	Fall	Spr	Fall	Spr	Fall
Full-time	43	40	25	25	18	15	8	6
Other full-time	7	7	5	6	2	1	0	0
Deans, librarians, & others who teach	13	13	9	9	4	4	4	4
Part-time	21	17	15	15	6	2	3	1
Total	84	77	54	55	30	22	15	11

JD Enrollment and Ethnicity

	Men		Women		Full-Time		Part-Time		1st-Year		Total		JD Degs. Awd.
	#	%	#	%	#	%	#	%	#	%	#	%	
African Amer.	23	6.0	31	10.8	54	8.1	0	0.0	15	6.7	54	8.1	17
Amer. Indian	1	0.3	1	0.3	2	0.3	0	0.0	2	0.9	2	0.3	1
Asian Amer.	24	6.3	28	9.8	52	7.8	0	0.0	15	6.7	52	7.8	13
Mex. Amer.	4	1.0	2	0.7	6	0.9	0	0.0	1	0.4	6	0.9	0
Puerto Rican	2	0.5	2	0.7	4	0.6	0	0.0	2	0.9	4	0.6	0
Hispanic	14	3.7	11	3.8	25	3.7	0	0.0	10	4.5	25	3.7	8
Total Minority	68	17.8	75	26.2	143	21.4	0	0.0	45	20.1	143	21.4	39
For. Nation.	3	0.8	2	0.7	5	0.7	0	0.0	5	2.2	5	0.7	0
Caucasian	312	81.5	209	73.1	521	77.9	0	0.0	174	77.7	521	77.9	195
Unknown	0	0.0	0	0.0	0	0.0	0	0.0	0	0.0	0	0.0	0
Total	383	57.2	286	42.8	669	100.0	0	0.0	224	33.5	669		234

Curriculum

	Full-Time	Part-Time
Typical first-year section size	75	0
Is there typically a "small section" of the first-year class, other than Legal Writing, taught by full-time faculty	Yes	No
If yes, typical size offered last year	40	
# of classroom course titles beyond first-year curriculum	123	
# of upper division courses, excluding seminars, with an enrollment: Under 25	73	
25–49	34	
50–74	23	
75–99	1	
100+	0	
# of seminars	20	
# of seminar positions available	405	
# of seminar positions filled	316	0
# of positions available in simulation courses	162	
# of simulation positions filled	152	0
# of positions available in faculty supervised clinical courses	176	
# of faculty supervised clinical positions filled	163	0
# involved in field placements	72	0
# involved in law journals	297	0
# involved in moot court or trial competitions	70	0
# of credit hours required to graduate	88	

Transfers

Transfers in	12
Transfers out	6

Tuition and Fees

	Resident	Nonresident
Full-time	$22,433	$37,383
Part-time		
Tuition Guarantee Program		N

Living Expenses

Estimated living expenses for singles

Living on campus	Living off campus	Living at home
$18,112	$18,112	$18,112

The Ohio State University Moritz College of Law

ABA
Approved
Since
1923

GPA and LSAT Scores

	Total	Full-Time	Part-Time
# of apps	2,521	2,521	0
# of offers	857	857	0
# of matrics	225	225	0
75% GPA	3.81	3.81	0.00
Median GPA	3.64	3.64	0.00
25% GPA	3.49	3.49	0.00
75% LSAT	164	164	0
Median LSAT	162	162	0
25% LSAT	158	158	0

Grants and Scholarships (from prior year)

	Total		Full-Time		Part-Time	
	#	%	#	%	#	%
Total # of students	670		670		0	
Total # receiving grants	564	84.2	564	84.2	0	0.0
Less than 1/2 tuition	469	70.0	469	70.0	0	0.0
Half to full tuition	74	11.0	74	11.0	0	0.0
Full tuition	2	0.3	2	0.3	0	0.0
More than full tuition	19	2.8	19	2.8	0	0.0
Median grant amount				$5,500		$0

Informational and Library Resources

Total amount spent on library materials	$1,552,239
Study seating capacity inside the library	675
# of full-time equivalent professional librarians	8
Hours per week library is open	107
# of open, wired connections available to students	0
# of networked computers available for use by students	92
Has wireless network?	Y
Require computer?	N

JD Attrition (from prior year)

	Academic	Other	Total	
	#	#	#	%
1st year	0	5	5	2.2
2nd year	0	2	2	1.0
3rd year	0	1	1	0.4
4th year	0	0	0	0.0

Employment (9 months after graduation)

	Total	Percentage
Employment status known	215	99.5
Employment status unknown	1	0.5
Employed	201	93.5
Pursuing graduate degrees	6	2.8
Unemployed (seeking, not seeking, or studying for the bar)	3	1.4
Type of Employment		
# employed in law firms	108	53.7
# employed in business and industry	29	14.4
# employed in government	36	17.9
# employed in public interest	6	3.0
# employed as judicial clerks	12	6.0
# employed in academia	10	5.0
Geographic Location		
# employed in state	127	63.2
# employed in foreign countries	2	1.0
# of states where employed	24	

Bar Passage Rates

First-time takers	185	Reporting %	72.43
Average school %	90.30	Average state %	88.09
Average pass difference	2.21		

Jurisdiction	Takers	Passers	Pass %	State %	Diff %
Ohio	134	121	90.30	88.09	2.21

The Ohio State University Moritz College of Law

John Deaver Drinko Hall, 55 West 12th Avenue
Columbus, OH 43210-1391
Phone: 614.292.8810; Fax: 614.292.1492
E-mail: lawadmit@osu.edu; Website: www.moritzlaw.osu.edu

■ Introduction

Founded in 1891, the Ohio State University Moritz College of Law has played a leading role in the legal profession through countless contributions made by graduates and faculty. The administration of the College of Law is committed to advancing the quality and reputation of the college through ongoing improvements to the academic program and student services, thereby creating a learning environment that is second to none.

Ohio State's 9,600 law alumni are central to the college's national reputation. Graduates of the college include justices of the Ohio Supreme Court, current and former US senators and representatives, managing partners in law firms, chief executive officers, professors, and attorneys with nonprofit organizations and public interest law firms.

The comprehensive scope of the university and its location in the state capital provide law students with access to a wealth of educational, professional, cultural, and recreational resources and opportunities. Law students are able to pursue joint degrees with one of the university's more than 100 graduate programs and also may extern with federal and state judges or find employment with one of the more than 500 law firms located in central Ohio.

■ Academic Program

With approximately 140 classes offered annually, Ohio State students have a rich array of courses from which to choose. The curriculum is designed to provide a strong theoretical and analytical foundation, as well as multiple opportunities for developing and honing lawyering skills.

Alternative Dispute Resolution—The College of Law is widely regarded as having one of the nation's finest programs in the area of Alternative Dispute Resolution. The program emphasizes training in an array of dispute resolution methods beyond litigation, including negotiation, mediation, and arbitration. Students with an especially strong interest may want to serve as a member or editor of the *Ohio State Journal on Dispute Resolution* or pursue a certificate in Dispute Resolution.

Clinical Opportunities—The College of Law offers an extensive selection of clinics in civil law, criminal law, children's issues, housing, mediation, and legislation. Students enrolled in a clinic course benefit from working with real clients, the court, or other parties while receiving intensive feedback and supervision from one of the college's 15 clinical faculty members. The fieldwork component of each clinic course is augmented by a classroom component in which topics such as lawyering skills, legal doctrine, and ethical and strategic issues are addressed.

Judicial Externship Program—Ohio State law students have the opportunity to gain first-hand insight into the judicial system through the college's Judicial Externship Program. As externs, students earn academic credit for conducting legal research and drafting legal documents for justices of the Ohio Supreme Court and for judges at the federal and county levels.

A Global Perspective on the Law—Students with an interest in international law may select from a menu of approximately 20 courses that have an international law or comparative law focus, including semester-long and summer study-abroad programs in Oxford, England. The College of Law awards a Certificate in International Trade and Development to students who combine their law coursework with select courses in international economics, politics, history, culture, and foreign language.

■ Faculty

One of the most frequently cited strengths of the College of Law is the quality of the faculty. Faculty members are consistently recognized for the experiences they bring to the classroom, for the clarity of their teaching, and for their accessibility to students outside of the classroom. As a group, they are highly regarded for being committed teachers who care about students. Members of the Ohio State law faculty also have earned a reputation within the profession for their expertise in specific areas of the law. Faculty are regularly cited in court and in the national media; they serve on legal reform commissions, help draft model statutes, and provide testimony before Congress.

■ Moritz Law Library

The Moritz Law Library provides Ohio State law students with one of the largest collections among law school libraries in the nation and access to a vast array of electronic databases. Law students with a laptop and network card can tap into online resources from virtually any point within the Moritz Law Library or the law building. All classrooms are wired for use of laptop computers.

■ Extracurricular Opportunities

Learning Outside of the Classroom—Recognizing that a student's legal education rests on what occurs in the classroom as well as the intellectual interchange and professional development outside of the classroom, the College of Law strives to provide an environment that is rich with extracurricular and cocurricular opportunities. Each year, the college brings to campus more than 100 speakers to address students, law faculty, and members of the bar.

The Program on Law and Leadership seeks to increase the awareness and understanding of leadership development among lawyers as well as excite and equip students for future leadership roles both in and beyond the profession. It has multiple components: education, a speaker series, skills workshops, scholarships, career assessment, and mentoring.

Ohio State law students have the opportunity to refine their legal writing skills through participation in one of the college's five highly regarded law journals: the *Ohio State Law Journal*, the *Ohio State Journal on Dispute Resolution*, the *Ohio State Journal of Criminal Law*, the *I/S: A Journal of Law and Policy for the Information Society*, and the *Entrepreneurial Business Law Journal*. Students are able to refine their skills in the areas of oral advocacy and legal writing through a variety of intramural and interscholastic competitions. In recent years, Ohio State law students have competed in approximately 14 interscholastic moot court competitions including the National Moot Court Competition, the Jessup International Law Moot

The Ohio State University Moritz College of Law

Court Competition, the Frederick Douglass Moot Court Competition, the National Health Law Moot Court Competition, the Civil Rights Moot Court Competition, the Corporate Law Competition, and the Criminal Procedure Moot Court Competition.

Service to the Public—The College of Law enjoys a strong reputation for its commitment to public service as part of the educational mission of the college. Ohio State law students are encouraged to become involved in the Leadership Program or in one or more of the college's many public interest initiatives, such as the Pro Bono Research Group. To encourage Ohio State law students to accept low-paying or volunteer positions with public interest organizations during the summer, the college and the Public Interest Law Foundation annually offer several student-funded fellowships.

■ Placement Opportunities

Moritz College of Law students and graduates are provided with an array of career and professional development services by a staff of six full- and part-time professionals, three of whom have JDs. Students and alumni have access to an online job-posting system and a wide variety of programs, workshops, and events. All programming and counseling services are designed to teach skills and to provide a foundation for gaining legal and professional career experience. The on-campus recruiting program, which brings over 120 employers to campus to interview students annually, is conducted through a state-of-the-art Web-based recruiting system that allows students access at all hours. Alumni and practitioners interact with students through many avenues, including a practice interview program and a mentoring program. Each year, students find employment across the country. Ohio State is a member of the National Law School Consortium, which hosts job fairs in nine major legal markets outside Ohio. Cutting-edge technology, current resources, talented staff, and creative initiatives give College of Law students a sound professional development foundation.

■ Admission and Financial Aid

The Moritz College of Law is committed to enrolling highly motivated men and women who have excelled academically and who bring to the College of Law a diversity of personal and professional backgrounds. In selecting members of each entering class, the Admissions Committee seeks to enroll individuals who represent all segments of society, as well as those who, as attorneys, will respect the profession's public service obligations.

An Ohio State legal education offers one of the best values among nationally regarded law schools. The annual cost of tuition for residents of Ohio is roughly half the tuition charged by comparably ranked private law schools. Columbus also boasts a cost of living that compares favorably to major cities across the country. Nonresidents of Ohio who relocate to the state may be reclassified as Ohio residents after residing in the state for 12 months. Each year, the College of Law awards more than $3 million in need-based and merit-based financial aid to members of the student body.

Applicant Profile

The Ohio State University Moritz College of Law
This grid includes only applicants who earned 120–180 LSAT scores under standard administrations.

LSAT Score	3.75 +		3.50–3.74		3.25–3.49		3.00–3.24		2.75–2.99		2.50–2.74		2.25–2.49		2.00–2.24		Below 2.00		No GPA		Total	
	Apps	Adm	Apps	Adm	Apps	Adm	Apps	Adm	Apps	Adm	Apps	Adm	Apps	Adm	Apps	Adm	Apps	Adm	Apps	Adm	Apps	Adm
175–180	3	3	2	2	2	2	0	0	0	0	0	0	0	0	0	0	0	0	0	0	7	7
170–174	10	10	10	10	7	6	4	2	3	1	2	0	3	0	0	0	0	0	0	0	39	29
165–169	91	88	63	58	36	33	21	17	16	3	11	1	5	0	1	0	0	0	1	1	245	201
160–164	192	162	198	143	152	71	60	19	20	1	14	0	5	1	0	0	0	0	12	5	653	402
155–159	145	68	231	52	175	26	101	11	36	2	17	0	6	0	3	0	0	0	20	5	734	164
150–154	79	11	124	15	105	10	84	5	48	1	16	1	5	0	3	0	0	0	12	0	476	43
145–149	25	0	40	5	47	4	46	0	17	0	8	0	8	0	5	0	0	0	4	0	200	9
140–144	12	0	6	0	23	0	23	0	13	0	17	0	5	0	1	0	0	0	7	0	107	0
135–139	2	0	4	0	7	0	4	0	8	0	11	0	3	0	4	0	0	0	1	0	44	0
130–134	0	0	0	0	3	0	0	0	4	0	4	0	2	0	0	0	0	0	0	0	13	0
125–129	0	0	0	0	1	0	0	0	1	0	0	0	0	0	1	0	0	0	0	0	3	0
120–124	0	0	0	0	0	0	0	0	0	0	0	0	0	0	0	0	0	0	0	0	0	0
Total	559	342	678	285	558	152	343	54	166	8	100	2	42	1	18	0	0	0	57	11	2521	855

Apps = Number of Applicants
Adm = Number Admitted
Reflects 99% of total applicant pool; average LSAT data reported.

University of Oklahoma College of Law

Andrew M. Coats Hall, 300 Timberdell Road
Norman, OK 73019
Phone: 405.325.4726; Fax: 405.325.0502
E-mail: admissions@law.ou.edu; Website: www.law.ou.edu

ABA Approved Since 1923

The Basics

Type of school	Public
Term	Semester
Application deadline	3/15
Application fee	$50
Financial aid deadline	3/1
Can first year start other than fall?	No
Student to faculty ratio	14.2 to 1
# of housing spaces available restricted to law students graduate housing for which law students are eligible	549

Faculty and Administrators

	Total		Men		Women		Minorities	
	Spr	Fall	Spr	Fall	Spr	Fall	Spr	Fall
Full-time	33	31	20	18	13	13	5	3
Other full-time	0	1	0	0	0	1	0	0
Deans, librarians, & others who teach	5	5	4	4	1	1	0	0
Part-time	16	18	11	13	5	5	1	1
Total	54	55	35	35	19	20	6	4

Curriculum

	Full-Time	Part-Time
Typical first-year section size	44	0
Is there typically a "small section" of the first-year class, other than Legal Writing, taught by full-time faculty	No	No
If yes, typical size offered last year		
# of classroom course titles beyond first-year curriculum	108	
# of upper division courses, excluding seminars, with an enrollment: Under 25	48	
25–49	23	
50–74	17	
75–99	9	
100+	0	
# of seminars	11	
# of seminar positions available	176	
# of seminar positions filled	168	0
# of positions available in simulation courses	241	
# of simulation positions filled	236	0
# of positions available in faculty supervised clinical courses	42	
# of faculty supervised clinical positions filled	27	0
# involved in field placements	51	0
# involved in law journals	125	0
# involved in moot court or trial competitions	95	0
# of credit hours required to graduate	90	

JD Enrollment and Ethnicity

	Men		Women		Full-Time		Part-Time		1st-Year		Total		JD Degs. Awd.
	#	%	#	%	#	%	#	%	#	%	#	%	
African Amer.	10	3.2	13	5.5	23	4.2	0	0.0	5	2.6	23	4.2	11
Amer. Indian	27	8.7	20	8.4	47	8.5	0	0.0	16	8.2	47	8.5	13
Asian Amer.	12	3.8	13	5.5	25	4.5	0	0.0	9	4.6	25	4.5	7
Mex. Amer.	11	3.5	9	3.8	20	3.6	0	0.0	9	4.6	20	3.6	6
Puerto Rican	0	0.0	0	0.0	0	0.0	0	0.0	0	0.0	0	0.0	0
Hispanic	0	0.0	0	0.0	0	0.0	0	0.0	0	0.0	0	0.0	0
Total Minority	60	19.2	55	23.1	115	20.9	0	0.0	39	20.0	115	20.9	37
For. Nation.	1	0.3	1	0.4	2	0.4	0	0.0	0	0.0	2	0.4	0
Caucasian	248	79.5	179	75.2	427	77.6	0	0.0	154	79.0	427	77.6	128
Unknown	3	1.0	3	1.3	6	1.1	0	0.0	2	1.0	6	1.1	0
Total	312	56.7	238	43.3	550	100.0	0	0.0	195	35.5	550		165

Transfers

Transfers in	15
Transfers out	0

Tuition and Fees

	Resident	Nonresident
Full-time	$16,976	$26,904
Part-time		
Tuition Guarantee Program	N	

Living Expenses

Estimated living expenses for singles

Living on campus	Living off campus	Living at home
$15,218	$17,047	$11,543

University of Oklahoma College of Law

ABA
Approved
Since
1923

GPA and LSAT Scores

	Total	Full-Time	Part-Time
# of apps	1,137	1,137	0
# of offers	355	355	0
# of matrics	199	199	0
75% GPA	3.72	3.72	0.00
Median GPA	3.51	3.51	0.00
25% GPA	3.29	3.29	0.00
75% LSAT	161	161	0
Median LSAT	158	158	0
25% LSAT	155	155	0

Grants and Scholarships (from prior year)

	Total #	Total %	Full-Time #	Full-Time %	Part-Time #	Part-Time %
Total # of students	517		517		0	
Total # receiving grants	405	78.3	405	78.3	0	0.0
Less than 1/2 tuition	342	66.2	342	66.2	0	0.0
Half to full tuition	46	8.9	46	8.9	0	0.0
Full tuition	0	0.0	0	0.0	0	0.0
More than full tuition	17	3.3	17	3.3	0	0.0
Median grant amount		$3,000			$0	

Informational and Library Resources

Total amount spent on library materials	$792,337
Study seating capacity inside the library	442
# of full-time equivalent professional librarians	7
Hours per week library is open	99
# of open, wired connections available to students	105
# of networked computers available for use by students	109
Has wireless network?	Y
Require computer?	N

JD Attrition (from prior year)

	Academic #	Other #	Total #	Total %
1st year	0	8	8	4.5
2nd year	0	0	0	0.0
3rd year	0	0	0	0.0
4th year	0	0	0	0.0

Employment (9 months after graduation)

	Total	Percentage
Employment status known	167	100.0
Employment status unknown	0	0.0
Employed	148	88.6
Pursuing graduate degrees	3	1.8
Unemployed (seeking, not seeking, or studying for the bar)	7	4.2
Type of Employment		
# employed in law firms	84	56.8
# employed in business and industry	22	14.9
# employed in government	30	20.3
# employed in public interest	3	2.0
# employed as judicial clerks	4	2.7
# employed in academia	5	3.4
Geographic Location		
# employed in state	113	76.4
# employed in foreign countries	0	0.0
# of states where employed	11	

Bar Passage Rates

First-time takers	161	Reporting %	83.23
Average school %	96.27	Average state %	92.80
Average pass difference	3.47		

Jurisdiction	Takers	Passers	Pass %	State %	Diff %
Oklahoma	134	129	96.27	92.80	3.47

University of Oklahoma College of Law

Andrew M. Coats Hall, 300 Timberdell Road
Norman, OK 73019
Phone: 405.325.4726; Fax: 405.325.0502
E-mail: admissions@law.ou.edu; Website: www.law.ou.edu

■ Introduction

The University of Oklahoma College of Law is located on the main campus of the university in Norman, a city of approximately 100,000 adjacent to the Oklahoma City metropolitan area. The college was founded in 1909 and joined the membership of the Association of American Law Schools in 1911. The law school has been accredited by the American Bar Association's Section of Legal Education and Admissions to the Bar since that list was first published in 1923.

The College of Law is housed in beautiful Andrew M. Coats Hall, located on the south part of the university campus. A substantial addition to the existing building was completed in 2002. It has the most significant law library in Oklahoma and houses three courtrooms for training and enrichment purposes. The entering classes are limited to 175 students so that the first-year sections consist of not more than 45 students. Admission is very competitive. More than 95 percent of the students admitted will graduate. More than 95 percent will pass the bar exam on their first try, and more than 95 percent will have employment using their legal skills within three months of graduation.

The College of Law benefits from being part of a strong university community. The University of Oklahoma, the state's flagship university, is a major doctoral degree-granting research university. Founded in 1890, the university has 18 colleges.

■ Admission

The College of Law utilizes a rolling admission process. A faculty committee meets regularly throughout the academic year to review applications. Admission to the College of Law is highly competitive, and many factors are considered in the selection process. Although considerable weight is given to undergraduate grade-point average and performance on the LSAT, thoughtful attention is also given to an applicant's extracurricular activities, employment experience, graduate studies, military service, adjustments to personal difficulties, and other relevant factors.

In addition to the regular fall entering class, the College of Law conducts a special Early Admission Program each summer. Admission is offered to a select group of approximately 20 students whose statistical scores may not meet the current standards for regular admission, but who have demonstrated a probable capacity for success in the study and practice of law. Students in the program receive five hours of credit for the summer study and then join the fall class.

■ International Programs

For the 35th year, the College of Law will conduct a summer program at Oxford University for American law students. The program affords students an opportunity to live and study in stimulating and beautiful surroundings under the guidance of American and English legal educators. Other opportunities exist for foreign study abroad in almost any country in which a student wishes to study.

■ Library and Physical Facilities

Andrew M. Coats Hall provides 170,000 square feet of instructional space for its programs. The modern facility provides wireless Internet access and multimedia technology in classrooms, the library, and student areas. The building features three courtrooms, one of which has seating for 250 persons and is equipped with the latest in technological innovations. The library offers access to electronic Web-based services and maintains over 350,000 volumes and equivalents and also contains one of the nation's largest Native People's collections.

■ Student Activities

The College of Law sponsors three major student-directed journals, the Oklahoma Law Review, the American Indian Law Review, and the recently created Oklahoma Journal of Law and Technology, an online review, which focuses on intellectual property law.

Since 1948, the Oklahoma Law Review has been published quarterly to give expression to legal scholarship nationally and to serve the profession and the public with timely discussion of important legal issues.

The American Indian Law Review, published biannually, serves as a nationwide scholarly forum for the presentation of important developments in Indian law and affairs. The Review offers in-depth articles written by nationally recognized experts on a wide range of issues in the rapidly expanding field of Indian law.

The Oklahoma Journal of Law and Technology is a Web-based collection of important articles on the various aspects of intellectual property. The student Board of Editors continually monitors and updates the articles and other material on the website.

The College of Law provides opportunities for students to participate in a wide range of extracurricular interscholastic appellate moot court, counseling and interviewing, negotiation, and trial advocacy competitions. The student Board of Advocates works closely with the students to facilitate participation in these competitions and provide intramural competitions for 1L and upper-level students.

All students at the College of Law may join a wide variety of organizations and participate in many kinds of extracurricular activities. The law school has an active Student Bar Association, affiliated with the Law Student Division of the American Bar Association. The student-elected Board of Governors supervises student activities and works with the faculty and administration of the law school.

■ Career Services

The College of Law's Office of Professional and Career Development provides comprehensive professional planning and placement services to all students. The director, the associate director, and the assistant dean for external affairs work personally with students on the entire range of career development services, including offering workshops on interviewing and résumé and cover letter writing, using Web-based resources, scheduling on-campus interviews, and providing individual counseling. The office works closely with

University of Oklahoma College of Law

law firms, government agencies, judges, and alumni around the country to expand employment opportunities for graduates.

Employment opportunities have continually expanded for University of Oklahoma law graduates, and the market placement has been very strong. In recent years, over 95 percent of graduates consistently are employed within nine months of graduation, placing the College of Law among the upper echelon of schools nationally. Approximately two-thirds of the college's graduates practice in Oklahoma. The other one-third are found in all 50 states and 14 foreign countries, with concentrations in Texas; Washington, DC; and California. In addition to traditional legal careers as attorneys, prosecutors, and judges, University of Oklahoma law graduates work in areas such as corporate management, banking, journalism, public service, government, entrepreneurial enterprises, teaching, and academia.

Applicant Profile

University of Oklahoma College of Law
This grid includes only applicants who earned 120–180 LSAT scores under standard administrations.

LSAT Score	3.75 +		3.50–3.74		3.25–3.49		3.00–3.24		2.75–2.99		2.50–2.74		2.25–2.49		2.00–2.24		Below 2.00		No GPA		Total	
	Apps	Adm	Apps	Adm	Apps	Adm	Apps	Adm	Apps	Adm	Apps	Adm	Apps	Adm	Apps	Adm	Apps	Adm	Apps	Adm	Apps	Adm
175–180	0	0	1	0	0	0	1	1	0	0	0	0	0	0	0	0	0	0	0	0	2	1
170–174	4	4	3	2	2	2	1	0	0	0	0	0	1	0	0	0	0	0	0	0	11	8
165–169	12	11	7	7	8	6	5	3	2	1	3	3	4	1	1	0	0	0	0	0	42	32
160–164	38	33	31	26	24	17	17	10	12	6	8	3	1	0	1	0	0	0	1	1	133	96
155–159	55	35	68	39	75	27	43	22	28	8	16	0	5	0	2	0	0	0	3	0	295	131
150–154	65	25	72	16	76	25	44	5	37	3	23	2	11	0	1	0	1	0	7	1	337	77
145–149	24	2	49	5	27	4	31	0	27	0	8	0	9	0	4	0	0	0	2	0	181	11
140–144	5	0	13	0	10	0	11	0	15	0	18	0	8	0	2	0	0	0	3	0	85	0
135–139	2	0	4	0	1	0	9	0	4	0	9	0	2	0	1	0	0	0	3	0	35	0
130–134	0	0	2	0	2	0	1	0	1	0	1	0	0	0	0	0	0	0	4	0	11	0
125–129	0	0	1	0	0	0	0	0	0	0	0	0	0	0	0	0	0	0	0	0	1	0
120–124	0	0	0	0	0	0	0	0	0	0	0	0	0	0	0	0	0	0	0	0	0	0
Total	205	110	251	95	225	81	163	41	126	18	86	8	41	1	12	0	1	0	23	2	1133	356

Apps = Number of Applicants
Adm = Number Admitted
Reflects 98% of the total applicant pool; average LSAT data reported.

Oklahoma City University School of Law

2501 North Blackwelder Avenue
Oklahoma City, OK 73106-1493
Phone: 866.529.6281 or 405.208.5354
E-mail: lawquestions@okcu.edu; Website: www.okcu.edu/law

ABA
Approved
Since
1960

The Basics

Type of school	Private
Term	Semester
Application deadline	8/1
Application fee	$50
Financial aid deadline	3/1
Can first year start other than fall?	No
Student to faculty ratio	17.6 to 1
# of housing spaces available restricted to law students	
graduate housing for which law students are eligible	200

Faculty and Administrators

	Total		Men		Women		Minorities	
	Spr	Fall	Spr	Fall	Spr	Fall	Spr	Fall
Full-time	27	27	16	16	11	11	4	3
Other full-time	4	3	2	2	2	1	0	0
Deans, librarians, & others who teach	6	6	3	3	3	3	2	2
Part-time	28	21	16	13	12	8	1	1
Total	65	57	37	34	28	23	7	6

Curriculum

		Full-Time	Part-Time
Typical first-year section size		70	72
Is there typically a "small section" of the first-year class, other than Legal Writing, taught by full-time faculty		No	No
If yes, typical size offered last year			
# of classroom course titles beyond first-year curriculum		128	
# of upper division courses, excluding seminars, with an enrollment:	Under 25	119	
	25–49	20	
	50–74	25	
	75–99	3	
	100+	0	
# of seminars		13	
# of seminar positions available		182	
# of seminar positions filled		123	20
# of positions available in simulation courses		336	
# of simulation positions filled		230	30
# of positions available in faculty supervised clinical courses		24	
# of faculty supervised clinical positions filled	19	0
# involved in field placements		45	5
# involved in law journals		98	7
# involved in moot court or trial competitions	29	2
# of credit hours required to graduate		90	

JD Enrollment and Ethnicity

	Men		Women		Full-Time		Part-Time		1st-Year		Total		JD Degs. Awd.
	#	%	#	%	#	%	#	%	#	%	#	%	
African Amer.	12	3.2	9	3.6	17	3.2	4	4.4	9	3.9	21	3.4	2
Amer. Indian	16	4.3	17	6.7	21	3.9	12	13.3	10	4.4	33	5.3	9
Asian Amer.	11	3.0	8	3.2	18	3.4	1	1.1	6	2.6	19	3.0	5
Mex. Amer.	1	0.3	0	0.0	1	0.2	0	0.0	0	0.0	1	0.2	0
Puerto Rican	1	0.3	1	0.4	1	0.2	1	1.1	0	0.0	2	0.3	0
Hispanic	18	4.9	8	3.2	22	4.1	4	4.4	9	3.9	26	4.2	5
Total Minority	59	15.9	43	17.0	80	15.0	22	24.4	34	14.8	102	16.4	21
For. Nation.	4	1.1	2	0.8	5	0.9	1	1.1	1	0.4	6	1.0	3
Caucasian	298	80.5	203	80.2	438	82.2	63	70.0	189	82.5	501	80.4	142
Unknown	9	2.4	5	2.0	10	1.9	4	4.4	5	2.2	14	2.2	1
Total	370	59.4	253	40.6	533	85.6	90	14.4	229	36.8	623		167

Transfers

Transfers in	3
Transfers out	20

Tuition and Fees

	Resident	Nonresident
Full-time	$31,870	$31,870
Part-time	$21,270	$21,270
Tuition Guarantee Program		N

Living Expenses

Estimated living expenses for singles

Living on campus	Living off campus	Living at home
$17,300	$17,300	$17,300

Oklahoma City University School of Law

ABA
Approved
Since
1960

GPA and LSAT Scores

	Total	Full-Time	Part-Time
# of apps	1,334	1,214	120
# of offers	721	675	46
# of matrics	224	200	24
75% GPA	3.47	3.47	3.30
Median GPA	3.20	3.22	3.11
25% GPA	2.88	2.90	2.87
75% LSAT	152	152	153
Median LSAT	150	150	148
25% LSAT	148	148	148

Grants and Scholarships (from prior year)

	Total		Full-Time		Part-Time	
	#	%	#	%	#	%
Total # of students	607		513		94	
Total # receiving grants	217	35.7	203	39.6	14	14.9
Less than 1/2 tuition	140	23.1	127	24.8	13	13.8
Half to full tuition	63	10.4	62	12.1	1	1.1
Full tuition	2	0.3	2	0.4	0	0.0
More than full tuition	12	2.0	12	2.3	0	0.0
Median grant amount			$13,000		$5,300	

Informational and Library Resources

Total amount spent on library materials	$649,727
Study seating capacity inside the library	384
# of full-time equivalent professional librarians	7
Hours per week library is open	103
# of open, wired connections available to students	147
# of networked computers available for use by students	40
Has wireless network?	Y
Require computer?	N

JD Attrition (from prior year)

	Academic	Other	Total	
	#	#	#	%
1st year	17	25	42	17.7
2nd year	5	5	10	5.6
3rd year	0	0	0	0.0
4th year	0	0	0	0.0

Employment (9 months after graduation)

	Total	Percentage
Employment status known	176	97.8
Employment status unknown	4	2.2
Employed	146	83.0
Pursuing graduate degrees	4	2.3
Unemployed (seeking, not seeking, or studying for the bar)	10	5.7
Type of Employment		
# employed in law firms	91	62.3
# employed in business and industry	21	14.4
# employed in government	22	15.1
# employed in public interest	8	5.5
# employed as judicial clerks	0	0.0
# employed in academia	4	2.7
Geographic Location		
# employed in state	96	65.8
# employed in foreign countries	1	0.7
# of states where employed	17	

Bar Passage Rates

First-time takers	182	Reporting %	79.67
Average school %	81.38	Average state %	90.98
Average pass difference	−9.60		

Jurisdiction	Takers	Passers	Pass %	State %	Diff %
Oklahoma	113	102	90.27	92.80	−2.53
Texas	32	16	50.00	84.54	−34.54

Oklahoma City University School of Law

2501 North Blackwelder Avenue
Oklahoma City, OK 73106-1493
Phone: 866.529.6281 or 405.208.5354
E-mail: lawquestions@okcu.edu; Website: www.okcu.edu/law

■ Introduction

At Oklahoma City University School of Law (OCU LAW) we introduce students to an educational philosophy that purposefully and carefully blends the theory and practice of law in all of its forms. Located within minutes of some of Oklahoma's largest law firms, corporations, banks, city and state government agencies, the state capital, and state and federal courts, our location enables our students to gain valuable experience before graduation.

Oklahoma City, the capital of Oklahoma, boasts a metropolitan population that numbers over one million and covers 625 square miles. In the past 10 years, Oklahoma City has undergone a revitalization resulting in a new NBA team, a new AAA baseball stadium, the establishment of Bricktown as a premier historic entertainment district, a new public library, creation of a new riverfront recreation area, and increased investment in public schools. It is considered an easy, comfortable, and friendly place to live.

■ Faculty

The faculty at OCU LAW are committed to the intellectual and professional growth of every student. They hold law degrees from a variety of law schools, including the nation's most prestigious. Many faculty members also hold advanced degrees in law and other fields of study, and most have significant practice-based experience.

■ Library and Physical Facilities

Classes at OCU LAW are held in the Sarkeys Law Center. It houses two moot courtrooms and classrooms equipped with contemporary technology. The building features several common areas that foster interaction between students and faculty. The OCU LAW Library, located in the nearby historic Gold Star Memorial Building, houses a collection of over 321,561 volumes and volume equivalents and features computer labs with access to all online research databases. A wireless network is available in all law school facilities.

■ Scheduling Options

The School of Law offers a full-time JD program with either a traditional day or sunset (late afternoon/early evening) schedule. Our part-time program is available with day or evening classes. By attending summer sessions, full-time students may complete their degree requirements (90 semester hours) in as little as two-and-a-half years and part-time students in three-and-a-half years.

■ Special Programs

In Oklahoma, students who have completed just 45 course hours are eligible for a limited license, and those who qualify may appear in court under certain circumstances. As a companion to this state licensing policy, OCU LAW has created a range of externship opportunities where academic credit can be earned in a variety of practice placement sites with field supervisors, operating under the guidance of a full-time director of externship programs.

The School of Law operates three legal centers for its students and the legal community. The Center on Alternative Dispute Resolution provides coherence and structure for the varied activities of OCU LAW in the areas of negotiation, mediation, and arbitration. The Native American Legal Resource Center focuses on Native American law and provides legal services to tribes and tribal courts, frequently through federal grants. The Center for the Study of State Constitutional Law and Government promotes scholarship and discussion on important issues relating to state government.

OCU LAW cosponsors (with Stetson University) summer international programs in Buenos Aires, Argentina; Granada, Spain; Freiberg, Germany; The Hague, the Netherlands; and Tianjin, China.

■ Office of Admission

OCU LAW seeks serious, motivated students who value education and demonstrate a commitment to the values and ethics of the legal profession. Many factors are considered in the evaluation of applications. Reviewers look for evidence of analytical and critical thinking, as well as reading, research, and writing skills that suggest the applicant is prepared for law school. Additionally, the committee considers factors such as work and life experience, cultural and economic background, advanced degrees, and extracurricular and community activities.

The Alternate Summer Admission Program (ASAP) offers a limited number of applicants who do not meet traditional admission requirements an opportunity to demonstrate their capacity for law study and to earn admission for the fall by attending and passing two summer classes. Any applicant not offered direct admission will automatically be considered for admission through the summer program.

OCU LAW uses a rolling admission review process and will review applications until the class is filled. Applications received by February 1, with LSAT scores on record, will receive priority consideration for admission and scholarship assistance. To be eligible for priority review, applicants should take the June, October, or December LSAT in the year prior to which they are applying.

■ Scholarships

Each year OCU LAW awards over one million dollars in scholarships. New applicants are evaluated and encouraged to apply for our generous scholarships ranging from $5,000 to full-tuition awards. The Hatton W. Sumners Scholarship, for example, is a full-tuition award that includes a book and living expense stipend. The Sumners Scholarships are competitive and awarded based on academic and leadership potential demonstrated within the scholarship application and during an on-campus interview. Applications for the Sumners award are due February 1. Incoming students are also invited to apply for additional scholarships. Additional scholarship assistance is available to returning upper-division students based on academic performance.

Student Services

OCU LAW actively provides law students with opportunities to be engaged with the larger legal community. Numerous guest speakers, programs, and activities are sponsored to provide students with exposure to local, state, and national leaders; scholars; and legal professionals.

The entire staff at the law school is committed to assisting law students. The associate dean for students offers broad support to students and student organizations. An in-house financial aid advisor provides loan and debt management counseling, and a student technology coordinator assists students with their computing needs. A very accessible professional library staff, which includes five librarians with JD degrees, aids students in the development of important research skills.

Professional and Career Development Center

The Professional and Career Development Center (PCDC) hosts a wide range of workshops and guest speakers in addition to offering personal career counseling and employer cultivation efforts. The center seeks to expose law students to various areas of the law, to provide the resources needed to successfully conduct an employment search, and to guide them in developing the skills, ethics, and values of a legal professional. Details of services provided, contact information for career counselors, and a list of programs and workshops are available on the Professional and Career Development section of the OCU LAW website.

Curriculum

The School of Law offers a joint JD/MBA program and specialized certificate programs in alternative dispute resolution, public law, and business law (with concentrations in e-commerce or in financial services and commercial law). The core curriculum for every OCU LAW student includes a purposeful balance of legal theory and practical application. It provides a well-grounded foundation in the basic doctrines, functions, and ethical principles that underlie law and law practice, and is designed to produce graduates who have a breadth of understanding that enables them to become leaders in law, business, government, and civic life.

Applicant Profile

Oklahoma City University School of Law
This grid includes only applicants who earned 120–180 LSAT scores under standard administrations.

LSAT Score	3.75 +		3.50–3.74		3.25–3.49		3.00–3.24		2.75–2.99		2.50–2.74		2.25–2.49		2.00–2.24		Below 2.00		No GPA		Total	
	Apps	Adm	Apps	Adm	Apps	Adm	Apps	Adm	Apps	Adm	Apps	Adm	Apps	Adm	Apps	Adm	Apps	Adm	Apps	Adm	Apps	Adm
175–180	0	0	0	0	0	0	1	1	0	0	0	0	0	0	0	0	0	0	0	0	1	1
170–174	0	0	1	1	1	1	0	0	0	0	0	0	0	0	0	0	0	0	0	0	2	2
165–169	2	2	1	1	1	1	2	2	0	0	1	1	3	3	0	0	0	0	0	0	10	10
160–164	3	3	5	5	9	9	5	4	1	0	5	5	0	0	2	1	0	0	1	1	31	28
155–159	19	17	24	23	28	25	17	15	19	18	10	10	9	6	2	1	0	0	0	0	128	115
150–154	27	26	44	41	55	53	68	64	46	39	40	32	16	8	8	1	2	0	1	1	307	265
145–149	22	18	61	48	73	56	85	64	88	49	50	23	22	4	7	0	2	0	3	0	413	262
140–144	9	0	31	9	37	3	55	9	55	9	38	0	28	0	14	0	2	0	13	2	282	32
135–139	3	0	3	0	9	0	17	0	23	0	27	1	16	0	9	0	1	0	3	0	111	1
130–134	1	0	1	0	2	0	7	0	4	0	6	0	0	0	2	0	1	0	2	0	26	0
125–129	0	0	1	0	0	0	1	0	1	0	1	0	2	0	1	0	1	0	1	0	9	0
120–124	0	0	0	0	0	0	0	0	0	0	0	0	0	0	1	0	0	0	0	0	1	0
Total	86	66	172	128	215	148	258	159	237	115	178	72	96	21	46	3	9	0	24	4	1321	716

Apps = Number of Applicants
Adm = Number Admitted
Reflects 99% of the total applicant pool; average LSAT data reported.

University of Oregon School of Law

Office of Admissions, 1221 University of Oregon
Eugene, OR 97403-1221
Phone: 541.346.3846; Fax: 541.346.3984
E-mail: admissions@law.uoregon.edu; Website: lawadmissions.uoregon.edu

ABA
Approved
Since
1923

The Basics

Type of school	Public
Term	Semester
Application deadline	3/1
Application fee	$50
Financial aid deadline	3/1
Can first year start other than fall?	No
Student to faculty ratio	16.4 to 1
# of housing spaces available restricted to law students graduate housing for which law students are eligible	72

Faculty and Administrators

	Total		Men		Women		Minorities	
	Spr	Fall	Spr	Fall	Spr	Fall	Spr	Fall
Full-time	27	27	15	14	12	13	5	7
Other full-time	4	4	1	0	3	4	0	0
Deans, librarians, & others who teach	5	5	1	1	4	4	0	0
Part-time	31	25	19	11	12	14	6	6
Total	67	61	36	26	31	35	11	13

Curriculum

	Full-Time	Part-Time
Typical first-year section size	61	0
Is there typically a "small section" of the first-year class, other than Legal Writing, taught by full-time faculty	No	No
If yes, typical size offered last year		
# of classroom course titles beyond first-year curriculum	103	

# of upper division courses, excluding seminars, with an enrollment:		
Under 25	80	
25–49	27	
50–74	11	
75–99	4	
100+	0	

# of seminars	17	
# of seminar positions available	340	
# of seminar positions filled	229	0
# of positions available in simulation courses	590	
# of simulation positions filled	491	0
# of positions available in faculty supervised clinical courses	199	
# of faculty supervised clinical positions filled	139	0
# involved in field placements	109	0
# involved in law journals	127	0
# involved in moot court or trial competitions	31	0
# of credit hours required to graduate	85	

JD Enrollment and Ethnicity

	Men		Women		Full-Time		Part-Time		1st-Year		Total		JD Degs. Awd.
	#	%	#	%	#	%	#	%	#	%	#	%	
African Amer.	9	3.0	7	2.9	16	2.9	0	0.0	5	2.7	16	2.9	6
Amer. Indian	5	1.7	6	2.5	11	2.0	0	0.0	2	1.1	11	2.0	3
Asian Amer.	27	9.0	25	10.3	52	9.6	0	0.0	18	9.8	52	9.6	14
Mex. Amer.	5	1.7	1	0.4	6	1.1	0	0.0	0	0.0	6	1.1	0
Puerto Rican	0	0.0	0	0.0	0	0.0	0	0.0	0	0.0	0	0.0	0
Hispanic	5	1.7	9	3.7	14	2.6	0	0.0	4	2.2	14	2.6	6
Total Minority	51	16.9	48	19.8	99	18.2	0	0.0	29	15.8	99	18.2	29
For. Nation.	0	0.0	4	1.6	4	0.7	0	0.0	0	0.0	4	0.7	0
Caucasian	219	72.8	168	69.1	387	71.1	0	0.0	139	76.0	387	71.1	115
Unknown	31	10.3	23	9.5	54	9.9	0	0.0	15	8.2	54	9.9	19
Total	301	55.3	243	44.7	544	100.0	0	0.0	183	33.6	544		163

Transfers

Transfers in	5
Transfers out	5

Tuition and Fees

	Resident	Nonresident
Full-time	$22,328	$27,818
Part-time		
Tuition Guarantee Program	N	

Living Expenses

Estimated living expenses for singles

Living on campus	Living off campus	Living at home
$13,866	$13,866	$6,801

University of Oregon School of Law

*ABA
Approved
Since
1923*

GPA and LSAT Scores

	Total	Full-Time	Part-Time
# of apps	2,093	2,093	0
# of offers	888	888	0
# of matrics	182	182	0
75% GPA	3.56	3.56	0.00
Median GPA	3.34	3.34	0.00
25% GPA	3.12	3.12	0.00
75% LSAT	161	161	0
Median LSAT	159	159	0
25% LSAT	157	157	0

Grants and Scholarships (from prior year)

	Total #	Total %	Full-Time #	Full-Time %	Part-Time #	Part-Time %
Total # of students	531		531		0	
Total # receiving grants	266	50.1	266	50.1	0	0.0
Less than 1/2 tuition	241	45.4	241	45.4	0	0.0
Half to full tuition	17	3.2	17	3.2	0	0.0
Full tuition	0	0.0	0	0.0	0	0.0
More than full tuition	8	1.5	8	1.5	0	0.0
Median grant amount			$5,941		$0	

Informational and Library Resources

Total amount spent on library materials	$698,945
Study seating capacity inside the library	322
# of full-time equivalent professional librarians	7
Hours per week library is open	107
# of open, wired connections available to students	1,354
# of networked computers available for use by students	26
Has wireless network?	Y
Require computer?	Y

JD Attrition (from prior year)

	Academic #	Other #	Total #	Total %
1st year	1	8	9	4.9
2nd year	0	0	0	0.0
3rd year	0	0	0	0.0
4th year	0	0	0	0.0

Employment (9 months after graduation)

	Total	Percentage
Employment status known	180	98.4
Employment status unknown	3	1.6
Employed	161	89.4
Pursuing graduate degrees	1	0.6
Unemployed (seeking, not seeking, or studying for the bar)	15	8.3
Type of Employment		
# employed in law firms	73	45.3
# employed in business and industry	17	10.6
# employed in government	25	15.5
# employed in public interest	18	11.2
# employed as judicial clerks	22	13.7
# employed in academia	6	3.7
Geographic Location		
# employed in state	100	62.1
# employed in foreign countries	2	1.2
# of states where employed	17	

Bar Passage Rates

First-time takers	158	Reporting %	82.28
Average school %	83.84	Average state %	78.53
Average pass difference	5.31		

Jurisdiction	Takers	Passers	Pass %	State %	Diff %
Oregon	105	89	84.76	78.64	6.12
California	25	20	80.00	78.07	1.93

University of Oregon School of Law

Office of Admissions, 1221 University of Oregon
Eugene, OR 97403-1221
Phone: 541.346.3846; Fax: 541.346.3984
E-mail: admissions@law.uoregon.edu; Website: lawadmissions.uoregon.edu

■ Introduction

Founded in 1884, the University of Oregon School of Law is one of the oldest and smallest law schools in the West. It is situated in Eugene, the state's second largest city, on the historic campus of the University of Oregon. A state-supported university, Oregon is one of only 62 research institutions to hold membership in the prestigious Association of American Universities. The School of Law is the state's only law school with membership in the Order of the Coif. Oregon was also one of the first law schools to be accredited by the American Bar Association. About 540 students are engaged in full-time study at the University of Oregon School of Law. The law school community is collegial and informal and demonstrates a spirited commitment to public service.

■ Environs

An active legal community in Eugene mentors and employs law students as clerks and externs. Eugene is the county seat and home to an office of the US Attorney and a federal courthouse. The law school partners with local entities to provide students clinical and pro bono opportunities. Eugene's 146,000 residents enjoy urban amenities, but with the friendliness and affordability of a smaller city. These include the Hult Center for the Performing Arts, Saturday Market, Shedd Institute for the Arts, and Cuthbert Amphitheater. In 2012, "Track City USA" will again host the US Olympic Track and Field Trials. The Pacific Coast, Cascade Mountains, and Salem, the state capital, are within a one-hour drive. Two hours north is Portland, where many alumni practice. It is home to the University of Oregon in Portland, which houses several University initiatives, including the School of Law Green Business Initiative and the business law externship program.

Built in 1999, the William W. Knight Law Center is both inspiring and accessible. The John E. Jaqua Law Library, at the south end of the Law Center, is part of the University Libraries and its 2.6 million-volume collection. The law library supports specialized research in international law and ocean and coastal law, as well as several other interdisciplinary areas.

■ Curriculum

Oregon's curriculum offers student many program options. A broad base of common understanding is established in the first year of study with the core curriculum emphasizing traditional legal subjects. The law school awards the JD, undertaken on a full-time basis, and offers four concurrent master's/JD programs and 12 specialized statements of completion, as well as multiple clinical and externship opportunities in Eugene and Portland. The University of Oregon School of Law also awards an LLM in Environmental and Natural Resources Law.

■ Centers and Programs

Academic centers and programs provide students with the choice to specialize in particular areas of the law. Among them are the Appropriate Dispute Resolution Center, Environmental and Natural Resources Law Center, Center for Law and Entrepreneurship, Ocean and Coastal Law Center, the UO in Portland Program, Public Interest-Public Service Program (PIPS), and the Wayne Morse Center for Law and Politics. The Oregon Child Advocacy Project is also housed in the law school. In addition, the law school has a long-standing commitment to American Indian law and legal scholarship.

Appropriate Dispute Resolution: The Appropriate Dispute Resolution program is integrated into the law school's traditional legal curriculum. The ADR Center also provides specialized training in the skills of mediation, counseling, and negotiation and creates domestic and international opportunities to practice those skills. "Competition not Conflict" is an ADR initiative that seeks to reduce destructive conflict in sport and to promote the positive values of competition. The Master's Degree in Conflict and Dispute Resolution (CRES) is an interdisciplinary University graduate program housed in the School of Law. Through the CRES program, law students are engaged in exploring profound personal and global subjects of conflict and their resolution, competition and cooperation, war and peace, communication and consciousness, and relationship and responsibility.

Concurrent Degrees: Oregon law students also can concurrently pursue one of several master's degree options through other graduate programs at the University of Oregon. A JD student can achieve a master's degree in just one additional year. The concurrent-degree programs include business administration (JD/MBA), environmental studies (JD/MA or JD/MS), international studies (JD/MA), and conflict and dispute resolution (JD/MA or JD/MS). Students apply separately to the master's program of their choice.

Statements of Completion: Statements of completion enable Oregon students to concentrate their legal study in the second and third year. Statements include business law, law and entrepreneurship, appropriate dispute resolution, criminal practice, environmental and natural resources law, estate planning, tax law, intellectual property, public interest and public service law, international law, ocean and coastal law, and sustainable business law. The newly established sustainable business law program enables students to study in Portland and is designed to respond to the needs of new and emerging businesses and to the related complexities of the regulation of energy and environment.

Clinics and Skills Training: Valuable skills training and real-world experience are provided to students through extensive clinical opportunities. In addition, legal writing and research skills are honed in an intensive, required, year-long research and writing program. The course culminates with students presenting final oral arguments in a courtroom setting.

International Exchange Program: Students may apply to a semester-long international exchange program at the University of Adelaide School of Law, situated in South Australia's capital city. The coursework selected must meet academic standards established by the law school and the American Bar Association.

Oregon LLM Program: The master of laws program offers a concentration in environmental and natural resources law, preparing graduates for national and international leadership careers working with governments, companies, and civil society organizations. Applicants must possess a US or foreign law degree.

■ Class Profile, Costs, and Financial Aid

For fall 2009, 2,093 students competed for 180 first-year seats. The Oregon admission committee uses a holistic approach in its application review, evaluating the full range of an applicant's accomplishments. The 75th/25th percentile cumulative undergraduate GPAs are 3.56/3.12. The 75th/25th percentile LSAT scores are 161/157. The median LSAT score is 159 and the median GPA is 3.34. Diversity in the classroom is part of the mission statement of the School of Law. For example, 65 percent of the first year class are residents of states other than Oregon. Thirty-four states are represented, as are 100 different colleges and universities. More than 80 percent majored in an academic area other than political science. Women comprise 43 percent of the class and students of color, 16 percent. Thirty percent speak more than one language and 45 percent have lived abroad. Notably, 82 percent entered the School of Law with public interest or public service experience.

For the 2009–2010 academic year, nonresident tuition is $27,818. Residents of Oregon pay tuition of $22,328. The UO School of Law supports many students through merit-based scholarships. More than 60 percent of the first-year class were recipients of such scholarships. No additional application is required for scholarship consideration. The Free Application for Federal Student Aid (FAFSA), however, is required for federal and private loan evaluation. A loan repayment assistance program (LRAP) is available to Oregon alumni practicing public interest/public service law.

■ Student Activities

The School of Law enjoys the reputation for being a committed and energetic community, attracting students with strong public interest, public service, and international experience. Since 2001, Oregon School of Law students have contributed the most pro bono hours of any law school in Oregon, winning an annual competition of the Oregon State Bar. There are 40 active and diverse law student organizations including American Constitution Society, Green Business Initiative, and six multicultural groups. Each spring, the Land, Air, and Water (LAW) student organization, the oldest of its kind among American law schools, hosts "PIELC," the largest public interest environmental law conference in the world. The School of Law supports four student-run publications: *Oregon Law Review*, *Journal of Environmental Law and Litigation*, *Oregon Review of International Law*, and online, the *Legality*. The Moot Court Board sponsors five in-house school competitions. Law students also readily participate in the intellectual, social, and athletic activities of the larger University of Oregon community.

■ Career Services and Bar Passage

The staff of the Career Services Office (CSO) has a strong reputation for providing comprehensive and personalized career counseling to law students, including assistance with job-search strategies, interviewing, and résumé development. The Oregon CSO utilizes a network of more than 5,500 alumni and oversees a busy on-campus interview program. Students take advantage of the popular Portland Interview Program and the Portland Mentorship Program. More than half of the most recent graduating class chose to remain in Oregon, but alumni work on Wall Street; in Washington, DC; and throughout the West. Graduates have risen to prominent positions, particularly in Portland and Seattle, and in the federal and state courts. For 10 of the last 11 years, Oregon graduates have passed the Oregon state bar examination at rates that most frequently have exceeded the state average. In 2009, the bar pass rate for the University of Oregon School of Law was 84 percent for first-time test takers. The state's average was 77 percent.

Applicant Profile

University of Oregon School of Law

LSAT Score	GPA								
	3.75 +	3.50–3.74	3.25–3.49	3.00–3.24	2.75–2.99	2.50–2.74	2.25–2.49	2.00–2.24	Below 2.00
175–180									
170–174									
165–169									
160–164									
155–159									
150–154									
145–149									
140–144									
135–139									
130–134									
125–129									
120–124									

■ Good Possibility   □ Possible   ▨ Unlikely

Pace University School of Law

78 North Broadway
White Plains, NY 10603
Phone: 914.422.4210; Fax: 914.989.8714
E-mail: admissions@law.pace.edu; Website: www.law.pace.edu

ABA Approved Since 1978

The Basics

Type of school	Private
Term	Semester
Application deadline	3/1
Application fee	$65
Financial aid deadline	2/15
Can first year start other than fall?	Yes
Student to faculty ratio	12.7 to 1
# of housing spaces available restricted to law students	
graduate housing for which law students are eligible	110

Faculty and Administrators

	Total		Men		Women		Minorities	
	Spr	Fall	Spr	Fall	Spr	Fall	Spr	Fall
Full-time	43	46	25	28	18	18	6	4
Other full-time	2	2	2	2	0	0	0	0
Deans, librarians, & others who teach	10	11	5	5	5	6	1	1
Part-time	36	36	22	24	14	12	5	2
Total	91	95	54	59	37	36	12	7

JD Enrollment and Ethnicity

	Men		Women		Full-Time		Part-Time		1st-Year		Total		JD Degs. Awd.
	#	%	#	%	#	%	#	%	#	%	#	%	
African Amer.	9	2.9	22	5.0	23	4.1	8	4.3	19	7.3	31	4.1	9
Amer. Indian	0	0.0	1	0.2	1	0.2	0	0.0	0	0.0	1	0.1	0
Asian Amer.	22	7.1	29	6.6	39	6.9	12	6.5	16	6.1	51	6.8	24
Mex. Amer.	0	0.0	1	0.2	1	0.2	0	0.0	1	0.4	1	0.1	0
Puerto Rican	0	0.0	1	0.2	1	0.2	0	0.0	1	0.4	1	0.1	0
Hispanic	18	5.8	28	6.4	30	5.3	16	8.6	17	6.5	46	6.2	6
Total Minority	49	15.8	82	18.8	95	16.9	36	19.5	54	20.7	131	17.5	39
For. Nation.	1	0.3	7	1.6	8	1.4	0	0.0	1	0.4	8	1.1	4
Caucasian	210	67.7	295	67.5	380	67.6	125	67.6	161	61.7	505	67.6	204
Unknown	50	16.1	53	12.1	79	14.1	24	13.0	45	17.2	103	13.8	6
Total	310	41.5	437	58.5	562	75.2	185	24.8	261	34.9	747		253

Curriculum

	Full-Time	Part-Time
Typical first-year section size	52	63
Is there typically a "small section" of the first-year class, other than Legal Writing, taught by full-time faculty	Yes	Yes
If yes, typical size offered last year	21	20
# of classroom course titles beyond first-year curriculum		148
# of upper division courses, excluding seminars, with an enrollment: Under 25		137
25–49		34
50–74		19
75–99		4
100+		0
# of seminars		36
# of seminar positions available		540
# of seminar positions filled	315	140
# of positions available in simulation courses	352	
# of simulation positions filled	241	94
# of positions available in faculty supervised clinical courses		111
# of faculty supervised clinical positions filled	70	37
# involved in field placements	140	37
# involved in law journals	89	28
# involved in moot court or trial competitions	51	10
# of credit hours required to graduate		88

Transfers

Transfers in	4
Transfers out	18

Tuition and Fees

	Resident	Nonresident
Full-time	$39,794	$39,794
Part-time	$29,858	$29,858
Tuition Guarantee Program		N

Living Expenses

Estimated living expenses for singles

Living on campus	Living off campus	Living at home
$18,518	$20,200	$7,288

Pace University School of Law

ABA
Approved
Since
1978

GPA and LSAT Scores

	Total	Full-Time	Part-Time
# of apps	3,016	2,527	489
# of offers	1,173	1,035	138
# of matrics	262	204	58
75% GPA	3.60	3.61	3.43
Median GPA	3.36	3.39	3.27
25% GPA	3.15	3.20	3.08
75% LSAT	157	157	155
Median LSAT	154	154	153
25% LSAT	152	152	149

Grants and Scholarships (from prior year)

	Total		Full-Time		Part-Time	
	#	%	#	%	#	%
Total # of students	785		543		242	
Total # receiving grants	513	65.4	388	71.5	125	51.7
Less than 1/2 tuition	450	57.3	346	63.7	104	43.0
Half to full tuition	53	6.8	32	5.9	21	8.7
Full tuition	10	1.3	10	1.8	0	0.0
More than full tuition	0	0.0	0	0.0	0	0.0
Median grant amount			$8,000		$7,000	

Informational and Library Resources

Total amount spent on library materials	$1,425,161
Study seating capacity inside the library	553
# of full-time equivalent professional librarians	10
Hours per week library is open	101
# of open, wired connections available to students	320
# of networked computers available for use by students	85
Has wireless network?	Y
Require computer?	N

JD Attrition (from prior year)

	Academic	Other	Total	
	#	#	#	%
1st year	5	27	32	12.9
2nd year	0	6	6	2.4
3rd year	0	2	2	0.9
4th year	0	0	0	0.0

Employment (9 months after graduation)

	Total	Percentage
Employment status known	194	91.5
Employment status unknown	18	8.5
Employed	178	91.8
Pursuing graduate degrees	5	2.6
Unemployed (seeking, not seeking, or studying for the bar)	4	2.1
Type of Employment		
# employed in law firms	79	44.4
# employed in business and industry	31	17.4
# employed in government	31	17.4
# employed in public interest	12	6.7
# employed as judicial clerks	9	5.1
# employed in academia	13	7.3
Geographic Location		
# employed in state	111	62.4
# employed in foreign countries	0	0.0
# of states where employed	11	

Bar Passage Rates

First-time takers	212	Reporting %	87.74
Average school %	83.33	Average state %	88.98
Average pass difference	−5.65		

Jurisdiction	Takers	Passers	Pass %	State %	Diff %
New York	186	155	83.33	88.98	−5.65

Pace University School of Law

78 North Broadway
White Plains, NY 10603
Phone: 914.422.4210; Fax: 914.989.8714
E-mail: admissions@law.pace.edu; Website: www.law.pace.edu

■ A Well-Rounded Legal Education

Pace Law School is a national law school ranked among the top three environmental law schools in the country. Students can explore a range of subject matters or pursue one of our sixteen curriculum concentrations. Pace Law School also offers a variety of clinics, centers, externships, and simulation courses for hands-on practical experience. White Plains, New York, home to Pace Law School, not only ranks in the top ten nationwide for income and standard of living but is also just 20 miles north of the heart—and pulse—of New York City.

Founded in 1976, Pace Law School benefits from its network of over 7,000 alumni throughout the world. Pace Law School offers full-time and part-time day and evening JD programs, the Master of Laws in Environmental Law—including the nation's first Climate Change track, Real Estate Law and Comparative Legal Studies, and a Doctor of Laws in Environmental Law. The school is part of Pace University, a comprehensive, independent, and diversified university with campuses in New York City and Westchester County.

■ A Varied Curriculum

The JD program provides students with the fundamental skills necessary for the practice of law nationally, and the flexibility to shape their elective coursework based on particular career goals. The curriculum is based on the concept that rigorous standards and high-quality teaching can coexist with an atmosphere congenial to learning and enjoyment. Students can obtain certificates in Environmental Law and in International Law by completing a sequence of courses with a specified GPA in the applicable area. Pace offers the opportunity to pursue joint degrees in the JD/MBA and JD/MPA programs, as well as the JD/MEM with Yale University School of Forestry, the JD/MS in Environmental Policy with Bard College, and the JD/MA in Women's History with Sarah Lawrence College. These programs can be completed on a full-time or part-time basis. Graduate law degrees; an LLM in Comparative Legal Studies, Environmental Law, or Real Estate Law; and an SJD in Environmental Law attract attorneys from around the world. Pace JD candidates taking 12 credits of environmental or real estate law may earn LLM degrees in one additional semester.

The majority of classes have fewer than 25 students, which enables close faculty-student relationships. The range of scholarship reflects a faculty of diverse interests, and the curriculum offers courses in traditional areas of legal study, legal theory, and specialized studies. Curricular concentrations include constitutional law, commercial law, corporate law, civil litigation and dispute resolution, criminal law and criminal procedure, evidence, family law, intellectual property, real estate law, women's justice, and land use law. Faculty scholarship also covers such specialized areas as the Americans with Disabilities Act, children's legal representation, environmental and toxic torts, equal pay, hazardous waste, health care fraud, international commercial law, land use, legal and ethical issues in health care, nonprofit organizations, prosecutorial and judicial ethics, racially motivated violence, securities fraud, and white-collar crime.

■ Renowned Centers and Programs

Pace Law School offers many clinics, simulation courses, and externships through our on-campus centers, institutes, and lawyering skills programs.

Students can represent the underserved through the Family Court Externship with the Pace Women's Justice Center, preserve individual liberties through our John Jay Legal Services Immigration Justice Clinic, or work side-by-side with Assistant District Attorneys through a prosecution externship preparing and prosecuting criminal cases.

In the popular and growing field of environmental law, students work on conservation and development matters through the Land Use Law Center; help accelerate the world's transition to clean, efficient, and renewable energy alternatives through the Pace Energy and Climate Center; extern with a federal agency in Washington, DC; and help nation-states develop climate change policies through the country's only United Nations Environmental Diplomacy Externship.

Pace Law School's international programs allow students to spend a summer abroad with one of the United Nations War Crimes Tribunals, or intern locally through an international trade with law firms and corporate legal departments handling international trade matters.

Judicial externship programs allow students to hone their writing skills in a mentoring program with a faculty member and in the chambers of a state or United States district or circuit court judge.

Whatever your interests, Pace Law School has the facilities and resources to help you pursue them.

■ Modern Library and Physical Facilities

The Pace Law Library is housed in an airy, modern facility. The law library contains an extensive collection of law and law-related publications, provides access to materials in other libraries in metropolitan New York and throughout the United States, and subscribes to national online research systems such as LexisNexis, Westlaw, and HeinOnline. Pace Law School students have free access to these databases from computer terminals distributed throughout the law library as well as in the student lounge, and from their home computers. A wireless network is available in the law library, classroom buildings, and throughout the campus. The library was recently renovated and features attractive, comfortable space in which students can study individually or in groups.

■ Financial Aid

A comprehensive aid program has been developed to include scholarships, need-based grants, employment, loans, and a loan forgiveness program for graduates who choose a public interest career. Over 1.6 million dollars have been allocated for first-year students. These funds may be available on the basis of financial need and academic merit.

■ Supportive Career Development Services

The Center for Career Development and the Public Interest Law Center offer a number of services to students and

alumni, including one-on-one counseling and résumé review; panels and programs regarding the many areas of legal practice; specific job, internship, and fellowship opportunities (provided through our website); and on-campus interview and résumé collection programs. The centers publish and distribute to all first-year students a comprehensive *Legal Employment Guidebook*, which provides an overview of the legal employment market, descriptions of the various types of legal employers, and specific legal recruiting information. The centers also produce a monthly online newsletter and publish career guides on areas of legal practice. The staff actively solicits and identifies employment opportunities through an on-campus career fair, targeted mailings, and other outreach activities, as well as develops and maintains an extensive collection of resources for students and alumni to use in their job searches. Respondents to the 2008 class survey reported 91.8 percent employment within the nine months following graduation.

■ Student Activities

Pace Law School publishes three law reviews, the *Pace Law Review*, the *Pace Environmental Law Review*, and the *Pace International Law Review*. Students also work on the *Journal of Court Innovations*, a joint journal created by Pace Law School and the New York State Judicial Institute, and *GreenLaw*, a journal published by the Pace Law Center for Environmental Legal Studies. Students compete in interscholastic moot court competitions, host the largest environmental moot court competition in the country (the National Environmental Moot Court Competition), and participate in the Pace-sponsored and -directed international commercial arbitration moot court competition (the "Vis"), the first and largest of its kind, held annually in Vienna, Austria. The school also sponsors more than 26 organizations in which students can participate. Available activities include professional organizations, minority student groups, issue-centered organizations, political groups, social action groups, religious groups, a student bar association, and a student newspaper.

■ Admissions/Visits to Campus

Pace seeks students with demonstrated potential to contribute meaningfully to the diversity of the law school community and legal profession. Full-time students may apply to enter in September or January. The January entry program allows students to complete the program through an accelerated 2½-year program.

The law school hosts several open house programs which include tours; discussions with faculty, administrators, and students; and information regarding the admission process, financial aid, placement, and life at Pace Law School. For a complete list of our on-campus events, visit our website at *www.law.pace.edu*.

Applicant Profile

Pace University School of Law
This grid includes only applicants who earned 120–180 LSAT scores under standard administrations.

LSAT Score	3.75 +		3.50–3.74		3.25–3.49		3.00–3.24		2.75–2.99		2.50–2.74		2.25–2.49		2.00–2.24		Below 2.00		No GPA		Total	
	Apps	Adm	Apps	Adm	Apps	Adm	Apps	Adm	Apps	Adm	Apps	Adm	Apps	Adm	Apps	Adm	Apps	Adm	Apps	Adm	Apps	Adm
175–180	0	0	1	1	0	0	0	0	0	0	1	1	0	0	0	0	0	0	0	0	2	2
170–174	1	1	1	1	0	0	0	0	1	1	0	0	0	0	0	0	0	0	0	0	3	3
165–169	6	6	12	12	6	5	2	1	6	2	2	1	0	0	1	1	0	0	0	0	35	28
160–164	30	28	48	47	46	44	37	31	34	21	15	6	10	1	2	0	1	0	5	2	228	180
155–159	66	60	95	89	111	103	116	96	62	39	36	11	15	2	5	0	2	0	7	6	515	406
150–154	98	68	166	102	215	109	210	84	103	27	67	11	27	2	8	0	3	0	14	8	911	411
145–149	54	15	120	25	163	40	163	26	113	12	50	2	28	0	9	0	1	0	9	1	710	121
140–144	14	1	48	1	61	1	81	0	72	1	40	1	34	0	10	0	2	0	10	0	372	5
135–139	5	0	20	0	27	0	29	0	39	0	28	0	21	0	6	0	4	0	4	0	183	0
130–134	1	0	1	0	9	0	7	0	13	0	12	0	5	0	2	0	1	0	6	0	57	0
125–129	0	0	0	0	0	0	0	0	5	0	4	0	1	0	2	0	0	0	1	0	13	0
120–124	0	0	0	0	0	0	0	0	0	0	0	0	0	0	1	0	0	0	0	0	1	0
Total	275	179	512	278	638	302	645	238	448	103	255	33	141	5	46	1	14	0	56	17	3030	1156

Apps = Number of Applicants   Adm = Number Admitted   Reflects 99% of the total applicant pool; average LSAT data reported.

University of the Pacific, McGeorge School of Law

3200 Fifth Avenue
Sacramento, CA 95817
Phone: 916.739.7105; Fax: 916.739.7301
E-mail: mcgeorge@pacific.edu; Website: www.mcgeorge.edu

ABA Approved Since 1969

The Basics

Type of school	Private
Term	Semester
Application deadline	5/1
Application fee	$50
Financial aid deadline	
Can first year start other than fall?	No
Student to faculty ratio	14.0 to 1
# of housing spaces available restricted to law students	169
graduate housing for which law students are eligible	169

Faculty and Administrators

	Total		Men		Women		Minorities	
	Spr	Fall	Spr	Fall	Spr	Fall	Spr	Fall
Full-time	56	48	37	31	19	17	12	9
Other full-time	0	0	0	0	0	0	0	0
Deans, librarians, & others who teach	22	22	12	12	10	10	1	1
Part-time	46	33	29	23	17	10	7	3
Total	124	103	78	66	46	37	20	13

Curriculum

	Full-Time	Part-Time
Typical first-year section size	79	103
Is there typically a "small section" of the first-year class, other than Legal Writing, taught by full-time faculty	Yes	Yes
If yes, typical size offered last year	41	49
# of classroom course titles beyond first-year curriculum	176	

# of upper division courses, excluding seminars, with an enrollment:		
Under 25	116	
25–49	28	
50–74	12	
75–99	14	
100+	6	

# of seminars	17	
# of seminar positions available	503	
# of seminar positions filled	231	70
# of positions available in simulation courses	1,089	
# of simulation positions filled	593	257
# of positions available in faculty supervised clinical courses	252	
# of faculty supervised clinical positions filled	125	30
# involved in field placements	205	66
# involved in law journals	96	21
# involved in moot court or trial competitions	33	17
# of credit hours required to graduate	88	

JD Enrollment and Ethnicity

	Men		Women		Full-Time		Part-Time		1st-Year		Total		JD Degs. Awd.
	#	%	#	%	#	%	#	%	#	%	#	%	
African Amer.	16	3.1	17	3.3	13	2.0	20	5.3	6	1.8	33	3.2	11
Amer. Indian	4	0.8	7	1.3	8	1.2	3	0.8	1	0.3	11	1.1	4
Asian Amer.	65	12.6	89	17.0	99	15.0	55	14.6	62	18.8	154	14.9	26
Mex. Amer.	28	5.4	24	4.6	34	5.2	18	4.8	15	4.6	52	5.0	13
Puerto Rican	3	0.6	6	1.1	7	1.1	2	0.5	4	1.2	9	0.9	0
Hispanic	12	2.3	20	3.8	23	3.5	9	2.4	8	2.4	32	3.1	8
Total Minority	128	24.9	163	31.2	184	27.9	107	28.4	96	29.2	291	28.1	62
For. Nation.	0	0.0	0	0.0	0	0.0	0	0.0	0	0.0	0	0.0	0
Caucasian	387	75.1	359	68.8	476	72.1	270	71.6	233	70.8	746	71.9	196
Unknown	0	0.0	0	0.0	0	0.0	0	0.0	0	0.0	0	0.0	0
Total	515	49.7	522	50.3	660	63.6	377	36.4	329	31.7	1037		258

Transfers

Transfers in	9
Transfers out	23

Tuition and Fees

	Resident	Nonresident
Full-time	$38,629	$38,629
Part-time	$25,705	$25,705
Tuition Guarantee Program	N	

Living Expenses

Estimated living expenses for singles

Living on campus	Living off campus	Living at home
$20,394	$20,394	$20,394

University of the Pacific, McGeorge School of Law

ABA
Approved
Since
1969

GPA and LSAT Scores

	Total	Full-Time	Part-Time
# of apps	3,035	2,657	378
# of offers	1,287	1,138	149
# of matrics	321	236	85
75% GPA	3.58	3.60	3.51
Median GPA	3.38	3.41	3.29
25% GPA	3.05	3.07	3.05
75% LSAT	159	160	157
Median LSAT	157	158	155
25% LSAT	153	155	151

Grants and Scholarships (from prior year)

	Total		Full-Time		Part-Time	
	#	%	#	%	#	%
Total # of students	1,007		620		387	
Total # receiving grants	545	54.1	386	62.3	159	41.1
Less than 1/2 tuition	501	49.8	353	56.9	148	38.2
Half to full tuition	41	4.1	32	5.2	9	2.3
Full tuition	3	0.3	1	0.2	2	0.5
More than full tuition	0	0.0	0	0.0	0	0.0
Median grant amount			$10,000		$5,000	

Informational and Library Resources

Total amount spent on library materials	$1,472,412
Study seating capacity inside the library	345
# of full-time equivalent professional librarians	8
Hours per week library is open	108
# of open, wired connections available to students	271
# of networked computers available for use by students	59
Has wireless network?	Y
Require computer?	N

JD Attrition (from prior year)

	Academic	Other	Total	
	#	#	#	%
1st year	7	18	25	7.6
2nd year	3	31	34	10.6
3rd year	0	2	2	0.7
4th year	0	1	1	1.1

Employment (9 months after graduation)

	Total	Percentage
Employment status known	298	99.0
Employment status unknown	3	1.0
Employed	270	90.6
Pursuing graduate degrees	9	3.0
Unemployed (seeking, not seeking, or studying for the bar)	11	3.7
Type of Employment		
# employed in law firms	136	50.4
# employed in business and industry	24	8.9
# employed in government	69	25.6
# employed in public interest	23	8.5
# employed as judicial clerks	7	2.6
# employed in academia	9	3.3
Geographic Location		
# employed in state	242	89.6
# employed in foreign countries	1	0.4
# of states where employed		14

Bar Passage Rates

First-time takers	301	Reporting %	92.03
Average school %	79.78	Average state %	78.07
Average pass difference	1.71		

Jurisdiction	Takers	Passers	Pass %	State %	Diff %
California	277	221	79.78	78.07	1.71

University of the Pacific, McGeorge School of Law

3200 Fifth Avenue
Sacramento, CA 95817
Phone: 916.739.7105; Fax: 916.739.7301
E-mail: mcgeorge@pacific.edu; Website: www.mcgeorge.edu

■ Overview

The University of the Pacific, McGeorge School of Law is in Sacramento, California, capital of the nation's most populous state with one of the world's leading economies. The school is a member of the AALS, is accredited by the ABA, and has a chapter of the Order of the Coif.

Day- and evening-division programs provide flexibility to earn a JD degree in three, four, or five years of study. More than 1,000 students pursue a JD, LLM, or JSD on Pacific McGeorge's unique 13-acre law-school-only campus. The school's reputation for educating well-prepared, practice-ready lawyers grows from the vitality of students and faculty working together. The diversity of the student body is reflected in the 150 or more colleges and universities students attended as undergraduates, the 50 or more major fields, the range in years from age 20 to over 60, and the gender and ethnic diversity represented each year by the growing number of students from a wide range of ethnic and cultural heritages.

■ Library and Physical Facilities

Pacific McGeorge's students study on a campus designed exclusively for legal education that includes class and seminar rooms; a student center; a technologically equipped trial courtroom; a lecture hall; a clinical legal education center; a law library and computer center; administrative, faculty, and student services offices; recreational facilities; and student apartments.

The Gordon D. Schaber Law Library is a comprehensive legal research facility of over 500,000 volumes. The library includes a new state-of-the-art student study area, computer lab, group study rooms, and wireless Internet capabilities. Pacific McGeorge librarians are experts in legal research methodology and assist students in using the library's electronic and traditional resources.

■ Curriculum

Pacific McGeorge offers more than 100 advanced elective offerings, ranging from comprehensive courses in traditional areas such as business, constitutional law, criminal justice, and family and juvenile law, to a wide variety of courses in specialty areas such as environmental (both US and international), entertainment, labor, intellectual property, mass media, banking, and elder law. Certificate and concentration curricula are offered for those with specific career interests.

Clinical Experience: Pacific McGeorge believes that clinical education—working in a practice setting while guided by a faculty mentor—is a key part of the law school experience. On-campus clinics include Community Legal Services, Business and Community Development, Administrative Adjudication, Parole Representation, Victim's Rights, Civil Practice, Bankruptcy, Immigration, and Legislative Process. Off campus, the internship program makes available more than 125 placements.

■ Public Law & Policy Program

Pacific McGeorge's Public Law & Policy Program prepares students for private practice or public service and policy-making careers in governmental positions. Significant opportunities are offered for hands-on work and networking contacts with governmental entities. Graduates of the certificate program are practicing in law firms whose clients are involved with governmental regulatory matters as consultants, lobbyists, or in-house counsel with business and nonprofit organizations; and in staff and policy positions with legislative branches, executive departments, or administrative agencies at all levels of government. A one- or two-year LLM program in Public Law & Policy is available.

■ International Legal Studies

Law and accounting firms, government agencies, and corporations require lawyers who understand international law. Pacific McGeorge offers an international law certificate program. Students can also study in an international setting at the Center for International Legal Studies in Salzburg, Austria. The Summer Institute offers international and comparative law courses in Austria. Pacific McGeorge also offers LLMs in International Water Resources Law and Transnational Business Practice, and a JSD in International Water Resources Law.

■ Trial and Appellate Advocacy

In its broadest sense, advocacy is an integral part of any legal career, whether representing clients in civil and criminal litigation or at administrative hearings, negotiating business agreements, resolving disputes through alternative dispute-resolution mechanisms, or advising on legal matters to avoid litigation. Pacific McGeorge's curriculum offers the opportunity for all students to gain advanced advocacy skills. For those especially attracted to courtroom advocacy, Pacific McGeorge's certificate equips future litigators for success. In addition, the one-year LLM in Advocacy Practice and Teaching empowers international and domestic lawyers and law professors to implement advocacy methodology and principles in their practices and classrooms.

■ Intellectual Property

Intellectual property is one of the fastest growing practice areas. Pacific McGeorge graduates are practicing in diverse settings and areas of intellectual property law that include the entertainment industry; music and theater law; intellectual property litigation; sports, trademark, and domain-name law; patent and biotechnology law; and the rapidly emerging areas of computer and Internet law.

■ Taxation

Pacific McGeorge has responded to the need for tax expertise in a booming economy by creating a tax concentration within its JD program that provides students with the needed foundation to enter business or estate-planning practice.

University of the Pacific, McGeorge School of Law

Criminal Justice

Pacific McGeorge's criminal justice curriculum includes advanced electives in a wide range of subjects, including sentencing and post-conviction remedies, white-collar crime, capital punishment, criminal pretrial litigation, specialized evidence courses, juvenile law, family violence, and problems in criminal justice. Hands-on training is available through a rich program of internship opportunities. A concentration curriculum is structured for those who wish to specialize.

Student Activities

Over 40 professional, social, and academic student organizations at Pacific McGeorge represent the breadth of interests and diversity of the student community. Student staffs manage, edit, and write for the *McGeorge Law Review* and the *Pacific McGeorge Global Business and Development Law Journal*. Pacific McGeorge competition teams compete with notable success in a wide range of trial, appellate, counseling, and dispute-resolution competitions on the regional and national levels, as well as at the Willem C. Vis International Commercial Arbitration Moot Competition in Vienna, Austria.

Admission and Financial Aid

Admission is competitive. Prelegal education includes at least a bachelor's degree or senior standing from an accredited college or university. An applicant's undergraduate record and LSAT results are important factors in the decision process. When there are multiple LSAT scores, the highest may be accorded significant weight. Other factors considered are grade patterns or trends, employment and career accomplishments, graduate work, and extracurricular or community activities. Ethnic, cultural, and experiential backgrounds that contribute to student-body diversity are valued. Strong merit- and need-based financial aid programs provide scholarship awards and grants to entering and advanced students. A knowledgeable financial aid staff provides counseling to assist students in minimizing student loan indebtedness.

Housing

Pacific McGeorge has 150 on-campus apartments, furnished and unfurnished, including one- and two-bedroom units, studios, and townhouses. Early application is advised. The school's full-time housing coordinator also assists in locating off-campus accommodations that are readily available in Sacramento.

Career Services

The Pacific McGeorge Career Development Office (CDO) provides comprehensive career search assistance for permanent, part-time, and summer employment. The CDO staff is available to help students identify their interests, introduce them to the vast array of career development and employment opportunity resources, and assist with career decision making. The CDO focuses on career counseling, individualized review and critique of résumés and cover letters, and job search strategy development.

Pacific McGeorge faculty and alumni play a major role in our programs, sharing their experience and offering advice to students seeking career opportunities in their fields of expertise. Alumni participate in a Day in the Life Speakers Series, the Alumni Mentor Program, and mock interviews. In addition, the CDO hosts employer on-campus interviews for students and maintains up-to-date listings of specific employment opportunities, as well as an extensive library of resource materials.

Applicant Profile

University of the Pacific, McGeorge School of Law
This grid includes only applicants who earned 120–180 LSAT scores under standard administrations.

LSAT Score	3.75 +		3.50–3.74		3.25–3.49		3.00–3.24		2.75–2.99		2.50–2.74		2.25–2.49		2.00–2.24		Below 2.00		No GPA		Total	
	Apps	Adm	Apps	Adm	Apps	Adm	Apps	Adm	Apps	Adm	Apps	Adm	Apps	Adm	Apps	Adm	Apps	Adm	Apps	Adm	Apps	Adm
175–180	0	0	1	1	0	0	1	0	0	0	0	0	0	0	0	0	0	0	0	0	2	1
170–174	3	3	0	0	2	2	0	0	3	2	0	0	1	0	0	0	0	0	0	0	9	7
165–169	8	8	9	8	15	15	19	19	16	14	10	8	1	0	0	0	0	0	0	0	78	72
160–164	41	41	62	62	75	73	56	54	44	40	29	21	8	3	5	2	3	0	4	3	327	299
155–159	83	81	158	148	215	169	157	87	91	41	45	18	20	8	8	4	2	1	8	8	787	565
150–154	68	37	153	94	211	79	233	38	128	14	55	6	20	4	8	0	2	0	15	4	893	276
145–149	28	8	81	33	104	13	113	2	92	2	51	1	30	0	12	0	1	0	9	0	521	59
140–144	13	0	23	1	44	0	55	0	55	0	31	0	21	0	8	0	2	0	10	0	262	1
135–139	0	0	5	0	8	0	19	0	14	1	16	0	11	0	2	0	1	0	4	0	80	1
130–134	0	0	3	0	2	0	2	0	7	0	8	0	4	0	3	0	3	0	7	0	39	0
125–129	0	0	1	0	0	0	0	0	1	0	2	0	0	0	1	0	0	0	2	0	7	0
120–124	0	0	0	0	0	0	0	0	0	0	0	0	0	0	1	0	0	0	1	0	2	0
Total	244	178	496	347	676	351	655	200	451	114	247	54	116	15	48	6	14	1	60	15	3007	1281

Apps = Number of Applicants   Adm = Number Admitted   Reflects 98% of the total applicant pool; average LSAT data reported.

Penn State University, The Dickinson School of Law

Lewis Katz Building, University Park, PA 16802-1017; Phone: 814.867.1251; Fax: 814.867.0405
150 South College Street, Carlisle, PA 17013-2899; Phone: 717.240.5207; Fax: 717.241.3503
E-mail: dsladmit@psu.edu; Website: www.law.psu.edu; Phone: 800.840.1122

ABA Approved Since 1931

The Basics

Type of school	Public
Term	Semester
Application deadline	3/1
Application fee	$60
Financial aid deadline	3/1
Can first year start other than fall?	No
Student to faculty ratio	9.4 to 1
# of housing spaces available restricted to law students	
graduate housing for which law students are eligible	424

Faculty and Administrators

	Total		Men		Women		Minorities	
	Spr	Fall	Spr	Fall	Spr	Fall	Spr	Fall
Full-time	52	54	27	30	25	24	6	7
Other full-time	4	4	4	4	0	0	1	1
Deans, librarians, & others who teach	17	17	8	8	9	9	1	1
Part-time	21	14	15	8	6	6	1	1
Total	94	89	54	50	40	39	9	10

Curriculum

		Full-Time	Part-Time
Typical first-year section size		50	28
Is there typically a "small section" of the first-year class, other than Legal Writing, taught by full-time faculty		No	No
If yes, typical size offered last year			
# of classroom course titles beyond first-year curriculum		124	
# of upper division courses, excluding seminars, with an enrollment:	Under 25	201	
	25–49	40	
	50–74	10	
	75–99	3	
	100+	0	
# of seminars		21	
# of seminar positions available		405	
# of seminar positions filled		280	2
# of positions available in simulation courses		530	
# of simulation positions filled		338	0
# of positions available in faculty supervised clinical courses		392	
# of faculty supervised clinical positions filled		227	10
# involved in field placements		146	8
# involved in law journals		229	0
# involved in moot court or trial competitions		42	0
# of credit hours required to graduate		88	

JD Enrollment and Ethnicity

	Men		Women		Full-Time		Part-Time		1st-Year		Total		JD Degs. Awd.
	#	%	#	%	#	%	#	%	#	%	#	%	
African Amer.	14	3.9	19	7.9	32	5.5	1	9.1	7	3.4	33	5.5	16
Amer. Indian	1	0.3	1	0.4	2	0.3	0	0.0	1	0.5	2	0.3	0
Asian Amer.	30	8.4	20	8.4	48	8.2	2	18.2	22	10.7	50	8.4	16
Mex. Amer.	0	0.0	0	0.0	0	0.0	0	0.0	0	0.0	0	0.0	0
Puerto Rican	0	0.0	0	0.0	0	0.0	0	0.0	0	0.0	0	0.0	0
Hispanic	22	6.1	15	6.3	36	6.1	1	9.1	6	2.9	37	6.2	11
Total Minority	67	18.7	55	23.0	118	20.1	4	36.4	36	17.6	122	20.4	43
For. Nation.	0	0.0	0	0.0	0	0.0	0	0.0	0	0.0	0	0.0	3
Caucasian	265	74.0	170	71.1	430	73.4	5	45.5	164	80.0	435	72.9	147
Unknown	26	7.3	14	5.9	38	6.5	2	18.2	5	2.4	40	6.7	27
Total	358	60.0	239	40.0	586	98.2	11	1.8	205	34.3	597		220

Transfers

Transfers in	6
Transfers out	8

Tuition and Fees

	Resident	Nonresident
Full-time	$34,462	$34,462
Part-time		
Tuition Guarantee Program		N

Living Expenses

Estimated living expenses for singles

Living on campus	Living off campus	Living at home
$20,926	$20,926	$20,926

*The opening of Penn State's University Park location has been acquiesced in by the Council of the ABA Section of Legal Education and Admissions to the Bar (as required by Standard 105). This location is currently undergoing review for provisional/full approval.

ABA Data

Penn State University, The Dickinson School of Law

ABA
Approved
Since
1931

GPA and LSAT Scores

	Total	Full-Time	Part-Time
# of apps	4,047	4,047	0
# of offers	1,157	1,157	0
# of matrics	206	206	0
75% GPA	3.68	3.68	0.00
Median GPA	3.48	3.48	0.00
25% GPA	3.28	3.28	0.00
75% LSAT	160	160	0
Median LSAT	158	158	0
25% LSAT	157	157	0

Grants and Scholarships (from prior year)

	Total #	Total %	Full-Time #	Full-Time %	Part-Time #	Part-Time %
Total # of students	636		547		89	
Total # receiving grants	310	48.7	310	56.7	0	0.0
Less than 1/2 tuition	278	43.7	278	50.8	0	0.0
Half to full tuition	32	5.0	32	5.9	0	0.0
Full tuition	0	0.0	0	0.0	0	0.0
More than full tuition	0	0.0	0	0.0	0	0.0
Median grant amount			$6,500		$0	

Informational and Library Resources

Total amount spent on library materials	$1,635,770
Study seating capacity inside the library	443
# of full-time equivalent professional librarians	8
Hours per week library is open	94
# of open, wired connections available to students	24
# of networked computers available for use by students	161
Has wireless network?	Y
Require computer?	N

JD Attrition (from prior year)

	Academic #	Other #	Total #	Total %
1st year	9	15	24	11.9
2nd year	5	0	5	2.5
3rd year	1	1	2	0.9
4th year	0	0	0	0.0

Employment (9 months after graduation)

	Total	Percentage
Employment status known	181	95.8
Employment status unknown	8	4.2
Employed	158	87.3
Pursuing graduate degrees	7	3.9
Unemployed (seeking, not seeking, or studying for the bar)	11	6.1
Type of Employment		
# employed in law firms	62	39.2
# employed in business and industry	17	10.8
# employed in government	35	22.2
# employed in public interest	4	2.5
# employed as judicial clerks	32	20.3
# employed in academia	4	2.5
Geographic Location		
# employed in state	72	45.6
# employed in foreign countries	1	0.6
# of states where employed	24	

Bar Passage Rates

First-time takers	200	Reporting %	81.00
Average school %	80.87	Average state %	86.09
Average pass difference −5.22			

Jurisdiction	Takers	Passers	Pass %	State %	Diff %
Pennsylvania	113	96	84.96	86.69	−1.73
New Jersey	49	35	71.43	84.69	−13.26

Penn State University, The Dickinson School of Law

Lewis Katz Building, University Park, PA 16802-1017; Phone: 814.867.1251; Fax: 814.867.0405
150 South College Street, Carlisle, PA 17013-2899; Phone: 717.240.5207; Fax: 717.241.3503
E-mail: dsladmit@psu.edu; Website: www.law.psu.edu; Phone: 800.840.1122

■ Introduction

Founded in 1834, Penn State Law is the oldest law school in Pennsylvania and the fifth oldest in the nation. The law school embraces the university's mission to improve the lives of the people of Pennsylvania, the nation, and the world through legal teaching, scholarship, and service.

Our law school is an engaged, diverse, and multidisciplinary intellectual community that challenges students to research, think, and act like lawyers—and to ascend to new heights of academic excellence. Through an intensive and comprehensive program of study that includes both classroom-based and experiential learning, our students are prepared to practice law at the highest level in an increasingly global world. As part of a world-class research university, Penn State Law students have access to extensive academic and programmatic resources to enhance their learning experience. Courses are offered at Penn State's University Park campus in State College, Pennsylvania, and at the law school's traditional home in Carlisle, Pennsylvania.

■ Faculty

Penn State's faculty includes one of the nation's leading scholars of corporate mergers and acquisitions, the world's preeminent expert on Russian law, leading scholars of commercial arbitration, renowned scholars of antitrust and law and economics, former law clerks to United States Supreme Court Justices, a leading scholar of international banking and finance, the first legal counsel to the African Union, the legal counsel to the Greek Presidency of the European Union, and other active and influential teachers and scholars in a wide range of substantive areas.

Our faculty scholars value academic rigor and are committed to sharing their knowledge, engaging students, and sustaining an intense and comprehensive legal program. They encourage students to participate in vigorous in-class discussion and provide abundant opportunities for thoughtful discourse and research outside of the classroom.

■ Curriculum

Our curriculum is designed to produce leaders and lawyers with high professional and ethical standards and the ability to navigate legal, policy, and social developments in all areas of human endeavor. After completing required first-year coursework, students can explore professional and intellectual interests by choosing elective courses in a variety of areas, including criminal law, trial advocacy, government and politics, and science and intellectual property. Experiential learning programs, moot court teams, concentrated research opportunities, and law journals enhance the curriculum by providing opportunities for students to distinguish themselves and explore their strengths.

■ Academic Programs and Activities

Experiential Learning: The law school's curriculum includes a wide range of experiential learning opportunities, including semester-long government agency externships in Washington, DC, and clinics that focus on child advocacy,

immigrants' rights, appellate civil rights litigation, disability law, elder and consumer protection law, and family law. Clinical professors include the former deputy director of the Lawyers' Committee for Civil Rights Under Law and the former deputy director of the National Immigration Forum.

Centers: Students can pursue focused scholarship through academic centers that include the Center for the Study of Mergers and Acquisitions; Institute for Sports Law, Policy, and Research; Institute of Arbitration Law and Practice; and the Agricultural Law Resource and Reference Center.

Joint Degrees: Students can pursue joint-degree programs and other forms of multidisciplinary study with other graduate departments within the university, including the School of International Affairs, Smeal College of Business, College of Education, and College of Agricultural Sciences.

Public Interest: In addition to our clinics, students can explore service-oriented careers through field placements with legal services, public defenders, and nonprofit public interest offices. Our Miller Center for Public Interest Advocacy works with a network of attorneys to enable students to participate in pro bono cases.

■ International Programs

As citizens of a global society, we provide a rich and evocative international curriculum—complete with significant opportunities for immersion in international cultures and legal systems. Our relationship with Penn State's School of International Affairs has enriched the intellectual life of our law school and particularly our curriculum, which offers ever-expanding opportunities for international interactions and cross-border, interdisciplinary studies. Penn State law students may take electives from the School of International Affairs and learn from a faculty of former diplomats, national leaders, and government analysts, as well as scholars of international economics, agricultural development, and business.

Many of our law faculty have exceptional depth in international issues, enabling the law school to offer advanced coursework in comparative and international commercial law, constitutional law, corporate law, and humanitarian law, among other areas. Additionally, we have established student exchange programs with the University of Cape Town in South Africa, the University of Maastricht Faculty of Law in the Netherlands, and Yeditepe University in Turkey.

The law school also offers one of the oldest and most prestigious master of laws programs for foreign-trained lawyers, whose presence at the law school enriches the diversity of our educational experience.

■ Physical Facilities, Technology, and Library

The university has invested more than $120 million in new and renovated facilities for the law school in Carlisle and University Park. Our buildings reflect the serious academic nature of the study of law, with state-of-the-art libraries, classrooms, and gathering spaces that enhance opportunities for learning, spontaneous discussion, and passionate debate.

Our facilities are reciprocally designed and equipped with sophisticated and pervasive audiovisual technologies that provide our students with appropriate exposure to

technology, allow for the real-time delivery of classes and programs between Carlisle and University Park, and enable us to conduct courses and other collaborative projects with schools and institutions worldwide. In addition to modern electronic courtrooms, our facilities feature class and seminar rooms equipped with integrated high-definition video, personal video systems to complement the teaching experience, and advanced recording technologies. Consistent with Penn State's commitment to sustainability and "green" design, the law school buildings are also designed to meet Leadership in Energy and Environmental Design (LEED) certification requirements and to encourage efficient energy use.

With holdings of more than a half million volumes and access to a wealth of electronic resources, the Penn State Law library fully supports the research and study activities of students, faculty, and members of the bar. Additionally, legal and interdisciplinary research is greatly enhanced through access to the vast print and electronic collections held by other university libraries.

Our building initiatives, combined with an additional several million dollars annually for faculty and program development, represent one of the largest investments ever made in an American law school.

■ Student Activities

Law students may pursue activities in legal scholarship, trial advocacy, and public service to refine their legal skills and develop their leadership styles. Law students edit and publish four journals: the *Penn State Law Review*, the *Penn State Environmental Law Review*, the *Penn State International Law Review*, and the *Yearbook on Arbitration and Mediation*. Second- and third-year students can also pursue valuable trial experience by engaging in moot court team competitions at

both the regional and national levels. Our vibrant student body supports more than 40 active student groups that organize social events, serve the underrepresented, host speakers, and establish professional networks. Law students are also welcome to participate in the hundreds of organizations, events, and activities available at Penn State's flagship University Park campus.

■ Career Services

Dedicated to keeping in touch with a profession that is both fast-paced and nuanced, our Career Services Office offers a dynamic menu of programs and high-quality individual counseling sessions and programming to assist students in identifying and achieving their career goals. Our career services professionals maintain contact with employers across the country, resulting in two formal, on-campus interview programs and the posting of more than 1,500 positions annually. Students can participate in more than 20 job fairs, including one in the District of Columbia, two exclusively devoted to public interest, several minority job fairs, and one exclusively devoted to patent law.

■ Admission and Financial Aid

You can apply online at *www.law.psu.edu*. Admitted students may choose to attend first-year classes in University Park or Carlisle, Pennsylvania.

The Financial Aid Office works with accepted students to obtain the funding necessary to finance their education. All admitted students are considered for scholarship opportunities.

Applicant Profile

Penn State University, The Dickinson School of Law
This grid includes only applicants who earned 120–180 LSAT scores under standard administrations.

LSAT Score	GPA								
	3.75 +	3.50–3.74	3.25–3.49	3.00–3.24	2.75–2.99	2.50–2.74	2.25–2.49	2.00–2.24	Below 2.00
175–180									
170–174									
165–169									
160–164									
155–159									
150–154									
145–149									
140–144									
135–139									
130–134									
125–129									
120–124									

Good Possibility   Possible   Unlikely

Average LSAT data reported.

University of Pennsylvania Law School

3400 Chestnut Street
Philadelphia, PA 19104-6204
Phone: 215.898.7400; Fax: 215.898.9606
E-mail: admissions@law.upenn.edu; Website: www.law.upenn.edu

ABA
Approved
Since
1923

ABA
AMERICAN BAR ASSOCIATION
Section of Legal Education
and Admissions to the Bar

The Basics

Type of school	Private
Term	Semester
Application deadline	2/15 7/15
Application fee	$75
Financial aid deadline	3/1
Can first year start other than fall?	No
Student to faculty ratio	10.7 to 1
# of housing spaces available restricted to law students	
graduate housing for which law students are eligible	999

Faculty and Administrators

	Total		Men		Women		Minorities	
	Spr	Fall	Spr	Fall	Spr	Fall	Spr	Fall
Full-time	61	60	47	44	14	16	9	9
Other full-time	10	10	3	2	7	8	3	1
Deans, librarians, & others who teach	5	4	4	4	1	0	0	0
Part-time	51	39	44	25	7	14	7	4
Total	127	113	98	75	29	38	19	14

Curriculum

		Full-Time	Part-Time
Typical first-year section size		85	0
Is there typically a "small section" of the first-year class, other than Legal Writing, taught by full-time faculty		Yes	No
If yes, typical size offered last year		42	
# of classroom course titles beyond first-year curriculum		172	
# of upper division courses, excluding seminars, with an enrollment:	Under 25	59	
	25–49	37	
	50–74	20	
	75–99	10	
	100+	5	
# of seminars		64	
# of seminar positions available		896	
# of seminar positions filled		788	0
# of positions available in simulation courses		442	
# of simulation positions filled		427	0
# of positions available in faculty supervised clinical courses		124	
# of faculty supervised clinical positions filled	124		0
# involved in field placements	14		0
# involved in law journals	326		0
# involved in moot court or trial competitions	104		0
# of credit hours required to graduate		89	

JD Enrollment and Ethnicity

	Men		Women		Full-Time		Part-Time		1st-Year		Total		JD Degs. Awd.
	#	%	#	%	#	%	#	%	#	%	#	%	
African Amer.	31	7.4	27	7.2	58	7.3	0	0.0	20	7.9	58	7.3	20
Amer. Indian	1	0.2	1	0.3	2	0.3	0	0.0	0	0.0	2	0.3	1
Asian Amer.	52	12.4	58	15.5	110	13.9	0	0.0	42	16.6	110	13.9	29
Mex. Amer.	3	0.7	4	1.1	7	0.9	0	0.0	4	1.6	7	0.9	2
Puerto Rican	3	0.7	1	0.3	4	0.5	0	0.0	0	0.0	4	0.5	3
Hispanic	17	4.1	23	6.2	40	5.1	0	0.0	9	3.6	40	5.1	13
Total Minority	107	25.6	114	30.6	221	28.0	0	0.0	75	29.6	221	27.9	68
For. Nation.	13	3.1	6	1.6	19	2.4	0	0.0	4	1.6	19	2.4	10
Caucasian	280	67.0	233	62.5	512	64.8	1	100.0	161	63.6	513	64.9	167
Unknown	18	4.3	20	5.4	38	4.8	0	0.0	13	5.1	38	4.8	13
Total	418	52.8	373	47.2	790	99.9	1	0.1	253	32.0	791		258

Transfers

Transfers in	30
Transfers out	10

Tuition and Fees

	Resident	Nonresident
Full-time	$46,514	$46,514
Part-time		
Tuition Guarantee Program	N	

Living Expenses

Estimated living expenses for singles

Living on campus	Living off campus	Living at home
$19,096	$19,096	$9,242

University of Pennsylvania Law School

ABA
Approved
Since
1923

GPA and LSAT Scores

	Total	Full-Time	Part-Time
# of apps	6,205	6,205	0
# of offers	895	895	0
# of matrics	255	255	0
75% GPA	3.90	3.90	0.00
Median GPA	3.82	3.82	0.00
25% GPA	3.57	3.57	0.00
75% LSAT	171	171	0
Median LSAT	170	170	0
25% LSAT	166	166	0

Grants and Scholarships (from prior year)

	Total		Full-Time		Part-Time	
	#	%	#	%	#	%
Total # of students	787		786		1	
Total # receiving grants	314	39.9	314	39.9	0	0.0
Less than 1/2 tuition	241	30.6	241	30.7	0	0.0
Half to full tuition	54	6.9	54	6.9	0	0.0
Full tuition	18	2.3	18	2.3	0	0.0
More than full tuition	1	0.1	1	0.1	0	0.0
Median grant amount			$14,000		$0	

Informational and Library Resources

Total amount spent on library materials	$1,516,832
Study seating capacity inside the library	520
# of full-time equivalent professional librarians	14
Hours per week library is open	115
# of open, wired connections available to students	28
# of networked computers available for use by students	141
Has wireless network?	Y
Require computer?	N

JD Attrition (from prior year)

	Academic	Other	Total	
	#	#	#	%
1st year	0	7	7	2.8
2nd year	0	11	11	3.8
3rd year	0	2	2	0.8
4th year	0	0	0	0.0

Employment (9 months after graduation)

	Total	Percentage
Employment status known	257	100.0
Employment status unknown	0	0.0
Employed	254	98.8
Pursuing graduate degrees	1	0.4
Unemployed (seeking, not seeking, or studying for the bar)	1	0.4
Type of Employment		
# employed in law firms	195	76.8
# employed in business and industry	10	3.9
# employed in government	0	0.0
# employed in public interest	7	2.8
# employed as judicial clerks	42	16.5
# employed in academia	0	0.0
Geographic Location		
# employed in state	41	16.1
# employed in foreign countries	5	2.0
# of states where employed	22	

Bar Passage Rates

First-time takers	254	Reporting %	70.08
Average school %	98.32	Average state %	88.22
Average pass difference	10.10		

Jurisdiction	Takers	Passers	Pass %	State %	Diff %
New York	127	125	98.43	88.98	9.45
Pennsylvania	42	41	97.62	86.69	10.93
New Jersey	9	9	100.00	84.69	15.31

University of Pennsylvania Law School

3400 Chestnut Street
Philadelphia, PA 19104-6204
Phone: 215.898.7400; Fax: 215.898.9606
E-mail: admissions@law.upenn.edu; Website: www.law.upenn.edu

■ Introduction

The hallmarks of the Penn Law experience are an extraordinary cross-disciplinary legal education and a vibrant and collegial community. Penn Law is one of the nation's leading law schools and takes advantage of its position at the University of Pennsylvania, one of the world's preeminent research universities. Penn Law faculty collaborate with world-renowned scholars throughout the University, and students enrich their legal education with study in other disciplines via courses, certificate programs (including at the Wharton School), and formal joint-degree programs.

Penn Law has a well-deserved reputation as a school where collegiality trumps competitiveness. We pride ourselves on the supportive environment we provide for students as they engage in the rigors of legal study. Students develop close relationships with their faculty and colleagues.

Minutes from downtown Philadelphia, Penn Law enjoys a university campus neighborhood and close proximity to one of the nation's most lively urban areas, providing an exciting, invigorating, and affordable world.

■ Faculty

Penn Law faculty are unparalleled in the depth and breadth of their intellectual interests, the quality of their scholarship, and their teaching excellence. More than 70 percent hold advanced degrees in addition to their JD, and more than 50 percent hold secondary appointments or have an affiliation with other schools throughout the University.

The Law School has a low student-to-faculty ratio that fosters the development of close personal and professional relationships. Faculty employ an open-door policy and encourage students to join in their research endeavors. It has become a Penn Law tradition for professors to host dinner parties at their homes for first-year students and to invite students to small-group lunches at neighborhood restaurants.

■ Libraries

Biddle Law Library, one of the world's premier law libraries, overlooks the Penn Law courtyard. It is a modern complex with expansive areas encompassing rooms for study groups, computer labs, and places for quiet study. Librarians teach legal research courses and work closely with students and faculty in identifying and accessing the legal and interdisciplinary materials that support their scholarship.

■ Curriculum

Penn Law's first-year curriculum includes foundational courses plus two electives. Students receive individualized legal writing and research instruction in small-group courses. In the upper years, students choose from electives that range from standards such as corporations and evidence, to introductory courses in specialized areas of the law, to seminars in emerging fields. Students may supplement their legal education with up to four courses at Penn's other esteemed graduate and professional schools as part of their JD degree.

Penn Law offers students a wide choice of clinical courses in which to develop their applied-lawyering skills under intensive faculty supervision. Students also enjoy participating in Penn's ABA award-winning mandatory pro bono program, which allows them to gain practical experience while working on behalf of underserved populations.

In addition to the JD, Penn Law offers the Master of Laws (LLM), Master of Comparative Law (LLCM), and Doctor of Juridical Science (SJD).

■ Special Programs

Penn Law's cross-disciplinary program is unrivaled among the leading law schools. Law students may take classes and earn certificates or joint degrees throughout the University.

Penn's three-year JD/MBA (Wharton) is the country's first fully integrated three-year program offered on one campus by elite law and business schools. Additional three-year interdisciplinary degrees include the JD/MSEd, JD/MSE, JD/MGA, JD/MA (International Studies), JD/MBioethics, MA/MS (Criminology), and JD/MS (Social Policy). Other programs include the JD/MCP, JD/MES (Environment), JD/MPH, JD/AM (Islamic Studies), JD/MSW, JD/MBA, JD/MA (Global Business Law), JD/PhD (American Legal History, Philosophy), JD/MD, JD/MS (Historic Preservation), JD/MA (Philosophy), and JD/EdD.

Students can also earn certificates in programs such as Business and Public Policy, Non-profit/NGO Leadership, Environmental Policy, and Middle East and Islamic Studies.

Penn Law's international and comparative law program offers formal study abroad in Tokyo, Hamburg, Beijing, Tel Aviv, Barcelona, and Paris. In addition, the Penn Law Global Initiative offers summer-abroad opportunities throughout the world.

Penn Law's Center on Professionalism provides a unique program for students to develop professional skills to complement their classroom learning. The Center gives students insight into their professional foundations and expands their knowledge of the skills necessary for leadership in the profession.

■ Student Body

Students come from all over the country and from more than 200 undergraduate institutions, creating one of the nation's most diverse student bodies. About 11 percent hold advanced degrees and, on average, 68 percent have taken one or more years before enrolling in law school. Approximately one third of the student body is composed of students of color. The diversity of the community creates a dynamic and engaging classroom environment and enriches every aspect of the school.

■ Student Activities

Over 90 student groups provide myriad opportunities for students to work and socialize together. Activities cover a wide spectrum of academic interest areas, identity groups, political affiliations, sports, journals, moot court and mock trial programs, and service organizations.

The *University of Pennsylvania Law Review* is the nation's oldest and among its most distinguished. Today, Penn Law's tradition of exceptional journal scholarship also includes the *Journal of Constitutional Law, Journal of International Law, Journal of Business Law,* and *Journal of Law and Social Change,* as well as the student-published *Journal of Animal Law and Ethics* and *East Asia Law Review.*

Penn Law's Moot Court program is nationally recognized and supported by faculty who appreciate its immense value to participants. Our Mock Trial Team travels for competitions throughout the country and invites trial professionals to lecture on trial advocacy.

■ Admission

The demand for a Penn Law legal education has risen dramatically in recent years. In the 2008–2009 admission cycle, over 6,200 applicants sought admission for the JD program. Fourteen percent of applicants were accepted, with a median LSAT score in the 98th percentile.

The Law School evaluates each application holistically. While academic excellence is of primary importance, we take all factors in each application into consideration and do not apply numeric cutoffs for LSAT or GPA. Instead, each individual file is read by two members of the Admissions Committee. In addition to an applicant's academic history, the Committee considers letters of recommendation, a personal statement, a supplemental essay, and a résumé, to develop a full picture of each applicant.

We begin processing applications on October 1. Applications received by November 15, and completed by December 1, will be considered for our early decision (binding) program; these applicants receive a decision by the end of December. The regular admission deadline is February 15. Our program is limited to fall semester, full-time students.

Current first-year JD students enrolled in a full-time program who have achieved excellent records at other law schools may apply as transfer students after completion of their first year only; we do not accept mid-semester or second-year transfer students. All applicants must apply by July 15. Transfer decisions are made on a rolling basis, beginning in mid-June.

■ Housing

Penn Law is located in a city that is both vibrant and affordable. Students select from a wide range of living arrangements on campus or in private housing.

■ Expenses and Financial Aid

The Law School maintains a substantial program of need-based grant and loan aid, with approximately 80 percent of the student body receiving financial assistance.

Penn Law extends merit-based scholarships to a select group of applicants. Every applicant admitted to the Law School is automatically considered for merit-based aid.

Penn Law nominates students with a demonstrated previous involvement in public service and who are committed to public sector employment following graduation for the Toll Public Interest Scholarship. We also have a strong loan forgiveness program to assist graduates who choose public sector work.

■ Career Services

The Career Planning and Professionalism Office has a successful record of assisting law students in finding employment coast-to-coast and counseling students and alumni on career opportunities. The Office offers specialized counseling for public interest work, first-year job searches, judicial clerkships, and alternate careers.

Penn Law graduates proceed to productive careers in every conceivable arena of practice, business, and advocacy. In recent years, 65–82 percent of graduates begin their careers in private practice, 17–22 percent in judicial clerkships, 4–8 percent in government or public interest positions, 1–2 percent in university or law school teaching or study, and 2–4 percent in the business world.

Applicant Profile

Penn Law has chosen not to include an applicant profile because LSAT and GPA figures alone do not capture the qualities that make our students so dynamic. We value our students' diverse backgrounds, rich life experiences, leadership, community service, professional accomplishments, advanced degrees and coursework, motivation, initiative, and exemplary writing skills. While admission to Penn Law requires an excellent academic record, the Admissions Committee approaches each application holistically and takes all of these factors into consideration.

Pepperdine University School of Law

24255 Pacific Coast Highway
Malibu, CA 90263
Phone: 310.506.4611; Fax: 310.506.7668
E-mail: soladmis@pepperdine.edu; Website: http://law.pepperdine.edu

ABA
Approved
Since
1972

The Basics

Type of school	Private
Term	Semester
Application deadline	2/1
Application fee	$60
Financial aid deadline	4/1
Can first year start other than fall?	No
Student to faculty ratio	17.1 to 1
# of housing spaces available restricted to law students	
graduate housing for which law students are eligible	251

Faculty and Administrators

	Total		Men		Women		Minorities	
	Spr	Fall	Spr	Fall	Spr	Fall	Spr	Fall
Full-time	32	30	23	20	9	10	3	4
Other full-time	1	1	1	1	0	0	0	0
Deans, librarians, & others who teach	11	11	7	7	4	4	0	0
Part-time	49	45	33	33	16	12	2	4
Total	93	87	64	61	29	26	5	8

JD Enrollment and Ethnicity

	Men		Women		Full-Time		Part-Time		1st-Year		Total		JD Degs. Awd.
	#	%	#	%	#	%	#	%	#	%	#	%	
African Amer.	7	2.1	17	5.1	24	3.6	0	0.0	5	2.2	24	3.6	8
Amer. Indian	0	0.0	3	0.9	3	0.4	0	0.0	0	0.0	3	0.4	1
Asian Amer.	28	8.3	28	8.5	56	8.4	0	0.0	19	8.2	56	8.4	10
Mex. Amer.	6	1.8	10	3.0	16	2.4	0	0.0	4	1.7	16	2.4	4
Puerto Rican	0	0.0	2	0.6	2	0.3	0	0.0	1	0.4	2	0.3	0
Hispanic	3	0.9	5	1.5	8	1.2	0	0.0	4	1.7	8	1.2	5
Total Minority	44	13.1	65	19.6	109	16.3	0	0.0	33	14.3	109	16.3	28
For. Nation.	0	0.0	0	0.0	0	0.0	0	0.0	0	0.0	0	0.0	0
Caucasian	202	60.1	192	58.0	394	59.1	0	0.0	135	58.4	394	59.1	132
Unknown	90	26.8	74	22.4	164	24.6	0	0.0	63	27.3	164	24.6	39
Total	336	50.4	331	49.6	667	100.0	0	0.0	231	34.6	667		199

Curriculum

		Full-Time	Part-Time
Typical first-year section size		75	0
Is there typically a "small section" of the first-year class, other than Legal Writing, taught by full-time faculty		No	No
If yes, typical size offered last year			
# of classroom course titles beyond first-year curriculum		125	
# of upper division courses, excluding seminars, with an enrollment:	Under 25	128	
	25–49	40	
	50–74	12	
	75–99	5	
	100+	6	
# of seminars		29	
# of seminar positions available		648	
# of seminar positions filled		430	0
# of positions available in simulation courses		1,577	
# of simulation positions filled		1,387	0
# of positions available in faculty supervised clinical courses		88	
# of faculty supervised clinical positions filled	78		0
# involved in field placements	178		0
# involved in law journals	156		0
# involved in moot court or trial competitions	57		0
# of credit hours required to graduate		88	

Transfers

Transfers in	10
Transfers out	10

Tuition and Fees

	Resident	Nonresident
Full-time	$39,340	$39,340
Part-time		
Tuition Guarantee Program	N	

Living Expenses

Estimated living expenses for singles

Living on campus	Living off campus	Living at home
$22,386	$22,386	$22,386

Pepperdine University School of Law

ABA
Approved
Since
1972

GPA and LSAT Scores

	Total	Full-Time	Part-Time
# of apps	3,244	3,244	0
# of offers	872	872	0
# of matrics	230	230	0
75% GPA	3.79	3.79	0.00
Median GPA	3.61	3.61	0.00
25% GPA	3.43	3.43	0.00
75% LSAT	163	163	0
Median LSAT	162	162	0
25% LSAT	160	160	0

Grants and Scholarships (from prior year)

	Total		Full-Time		Part-Time	
	#	%	#	%	#	%
Total # of students	640		640		0	
Total # receiving grants	533	83.3	533	83.3	0	0.0
Less than 1/2 tuition	363	56.7	363	56.7	0	0.0
Half to full tuition	143	22.3	143	22.3	0	0.0
Full tuition	0	0.0	0	0.0	0	0.0
More than full tuition	27	4.2	27	4.2	0	0.0
Median grant amount			$4,300		$0	

Informational and Library Resources

Total amount spent on library materials	$817,909
Study seating capacity inside the library	431
# of full-time equivalent professional librarians	9
Hours per week library is open	106
# of open, wired connections available to students	80
# of networked computers available for use by students	34
Has wireless network?	Y
Require computer?	N

JD Attrition (from prior year)

	Academic	Other	Total	
	#	#	#	%
1st year	10	11	21	8.9
2nd year	0	0	0	0.0
3rd year	0	0	0	0.0
4th year	0	0	0	0.0

Employment (9 months after graduation)

	Total	Percentage
Employment status known	205	98.6
Employment status unknown	3	1.4
Employed	192	93.7
Pursuing graduate degrees	8	3.9
Unemployed (seeking, not seeking, or studying for the bar)	5	2.4
Type of Employment		
# employed in law firms	127	66.1
# employed in business and industry	33	17.2
# employed in government	11	5.7
# employed in public interest	7	3.6
# employed as judicial clerks	9	4.7
# employed in academia	5	2.6
Geographic Location		
# employed in state	156	81.2
# employed in foreign countries	2	1.0
# of states where employed	21	

Bar Passage Rates

First-time takers	205	Reporting %	83.90
Average school %	87.21	Average state %	78.07
Average pass difference	9.14		

Jurisdiction	Takers	Passers	Pass %	State %	Diff %
California	172	150	87.21	78.07	9.14

Pepperdine University School of Law

24255 Pacific Coast Highway
Malibu, CA 90263
Phone: 310.506.4611; Fax: 310.506.7668
E-mail: soladmis@pepperdine.edu; Website: http://law.pepperdine.edu

■ Introduction

Pepperdine School of Law is located in Malibu, California, just 30 miles from downtown Los Angeles, making it a conducive environment for the intense study of law. Malibu offers an almost rural setting, yet it is an integral part of greater Los Angeles, providing access to one of the largest legal communities in the world. Pepperdine is a Christian university committed to the highest standards of academic excellence and Christian values, where students are strengthened for lives of purpose, service, and leadership.

■ Student Body

Pepperdine students bring a broad spectrum of backgrounds. They share a strong desire to attain high levels of achievement in academics, in their personal lives, and in their careers. Students come to Pepperdine from diverse socioeconomic, cultural, and religious backgrounds for the emphasis on integrity, service, and justice with a desire to become trusted leaders.

■ Faculty

Although the faculty have distinguished themselves through scholarly research and writing as well as leadership positions in prestigious legal organizations, the faculty's primary mission is to teach—to help students see the structure of legal thought and to be available as professional examples of a multifaceted profession. They demonstrate to their students that lawyers should be people-oriented individuals with strong moral character, capable of guiding their clients toward what is just and honorable as well as what is legally permissible.

■ Library and Physical Facilities

The School of Law occupies the Odell McConnell Law Center, located on the university's 830-acre campus overlooking the Pacific Ocean. The Jerene Appleby Harnish Library is the focal point of the school, housing a collection of over 400,000 volumes and volume equivalents. Students enjoy access to a multitude of leading online legal research services. Wireless network access is available throughout the Law Center. The facility contains two high-tech courtrooms, as well as lecture halls, seminar rooms, a bookstore, student dining area, and lounges.

■ Curriculum

Pepperdine offers a three-year, full-time JD program; four-year, full-time JD/MBA and JD/MPP dual-degree programs; a five-year, full-time JD/MDiv dual-degree program; a concurrent JD/MDR-degree program; and an LLM in Dispute Resolution. A student enrolled full time in a summer session can accelerate graduation by one semester. The required core courses are complemented by an extensive selection of elective courses.

■ The Palmer Center for Entrepreneurship and the Law

Unique in the nation, the Palmer Center prepares students for the modern hybrid role of lawyer, business consultant, financial strategist, and venture capitalist, and equips them with credentials and options in the field of entrepreneurship. Through carefully tailored coursework, the Palmer Center integrates multifaceted law and business disciplines into a distinctive and dynamic certificate program that supplements and complements the traditional JD degree.

■ Straus Institute for Dispute Resolution

The Straus Institute is the most comprehensive program of its type in the nation. Students studying in the field of dispute resolution can complete a special certificate program as part of their Juris Doctor degree program or a Master of Dispute Resolution. The LLM in Dispute Resolution began January 2003.

■ Nootbaar Institute on Law, Religion, and Ethics

The Nootbaar Institute was created to explore the nexus between these three disciplines, with particular emphasis on religion and the practice of law. While affirming Pepperdine's Christian identity, the institute draws from the largest possible pool of religious voices, seeking dialogue and common ground with other faith traditions.

■ Wm. Matthew Byrne Jr. Judicial Clerkship Institute

Each year, Pepperdine University School of Law brings law students from across the country to its campus for the Wm. Matthew Byrne Jr. Judicial Clerkship Institute (Byrne JCI). Through the Byrne JCI, students who have been accepted into federal judicial clerkship positions have the opportunity to gain distinctive, comprehensive training by federal judges.

■ Clinical Education

Clinical law programs provide students with the opportunity to refine their skills under the supervision of faculty, lawyers, and judges. The majority of clinical law opportunities are with the district attorneys, public defenders, and state and federal court judges. There are a number of programs offering experience in corporate and securities law, tax law, juvenile law, family law, labor law, consumer protection, environmental law, and trade regulation. Placements are also available within the film, television, and music industries.

■ Public Interest Opportunities

Pepperdine has partnered with the Los Angeles Union Rescue Mission to develop the Pepperdine/Union Rescue Mission Legal Aid Clinic. Located in downtown Los Angeles, the mission provides emergency food and shelter, health services, recovery programs, education, job training, and counseling within a Christian context. Students volunteer at the mission, where they meet with residents regarding legal concerns. The Pepperdine/Union Rescue Mission Family Law Clinic helps clients resolve issues such as child custody and support. The Special Education Advocacy Clinic gives students an opportunity to gain valuable experience advocating for children with disabilities.

Asylum Clinic

The Asylum Clinic, under the direction of retired United States immigration judge and now Pepperdine professor, Bruce J. Einhorn, provides law student representation to indigent and near-indigent foreign-born individuals who seek to legalize their status in the US based on their fear of religious and other persecution abroad. The clinic provides students real-world experience in immigration law and litigation, and also provides advocacy for persons of faith as well as other vulnerable persons.

London Program

Students have the opportunity to study law in London at Pepperdine's university-owned facility in the museum district of South Kensington. While in London, students may serve as externs in clinical placements.

Exchange Programs

Students have the opportunity to participate in exchange programs with the University of Copenhagen and the University of Augsburg. Classes are taught in English in both programs.

Career Development Office

The Career Development Office is committed to helping law students explore, define, and achieve their career goals through career-related workshops, guest-speaker programs, and one-on-one counseling sessions. The office also manages on-campus recruiting programs and cosponsors with the Alumni Office a robust Alumni Mentoring Program. Over 300 employers participated in Pepperdine's most recent fall recruiting programs.

Student Activities

Pepperdine has earned a national reputation for excellence in appellate advocacy and trial advocacy competitions. Editorial and staff positions are awarded with the *Pepperdine Law Review, Pepperdine Dispute Resolution Law Journal, National Association of Administrative Law Judges Journal*, and the *Journal of Business, Entrepreneurship, and the Law*.

Admission

Admission is based on the applicant's academic record, LSAT score, a written personal statement, as well as a response to the university's mission statement, and other information that reflects outstanding academic and professional promise. Applications are also evaluated on the basis of employment experience, extracurricular activities, community involvement, commitment to high standards of morality and ethics, maturity, initiative, and motivation. The admission process is guided by the view that a student body that reflects diversity provides a superior educational environment. Admission decisions may be based on consideration of factors that include racial and ethnic origin, unique work or service experience, a history of overcoming disadvantage, or unusual life experiences. First-year students are admitted only in the fall.

Expenses and Financial Aid

Pepperdine's active financial aid program provides over 85 percent of the student body with some type of assistance. Scholarships and grants are available to students with outstanding academic credentials and to those with demonstrated financial need. The deadline for completed applications for financial aid is April 1 of the entering year.

Housing

The George Page Residential Complex is located directly across the street from the Law Center. The 72-unit complex houses graduate students in four-bedroom apartments. The Admission Office also provides an extensive housing referral service.

Applicant Profile

Pepperdine University School of Law
This grid includes only applicants who earned 120–180 LSAT scores under standard administrations.

LSAT Score	3.75 +		3.50–3.74		3.25–3.49		3.00–3.24		2.75–2.99		2.50–2.74		Below 2.50		No GPA		Total	
	Apps	Adm	Apps	Adm	Apps	Adm	Apps	Adm	Apps	Adm	Apps	Adm	Apps	Adm	Apps	Adm	Apps	Adm
175–180	0	0	0	0	1	1	0	0	0	0	1	0	0	0	0	0	2	1
170–174	7	7	8	8	1	1	2	1	2	1	2	1	4	0	0	0	26	19
165–169	61	56	39	35	33	30	28	23	18	4	12	1	2	0	2	1	195	150
160–164	132	122	186	163	158	100	101	43	44	5	27	3	15	0	4	1	667	437
155–159	147	91	256	92	286	36	152	11	75	2	30	0	26	1	13	1	985	234
150–154	93	11	167	10	191	2	154	0	83	0	42	0	26	0	14	0	770	23
Below 150	41	0	78	0	140	1	150	2	102	0	64	0	71	0	16	0	662	3
Total	481	287	734	308	810	171	587	80	324	12	178	5	144	1	49	3	3307	867

Apps = Number of Applicants   Adm = Number Admitted   Reflects 99% of the total applicant pool; average LSAT data reported.

Phoenix School of Law

4041 North Central Avenue
Phoenix, AZ 85012
Phone: 602.682.6800; Fax: 602.682.6999
E-mail: admissions@phoenixlaw.edu; Website: www.phoenixlaw.edu

Provisional   *ABA* *Approved* *Since* *2007*

ABA — AMERICAN BAR ASSOCIATION — Section of Legal Education and Admissions to the Bar

The Basics

Type of school	Private
Term	Semester
Application deadline	
Application fee	$50
Financial aid deadline	
Can first year start other than fall?	Yes
Student to faculty ratio	12.4 to 1
# of housing spaces available restricted to law students	
graduate housing for which law students are eligible	

Faculty and Administrators

	Total		Men		Women		Minorities	
	Spr	Fall	Spr	Fall	Spr	Fall	Spr	Fall
Full-time	22	25	10	13	12	12	7	7
Other full-time	0	0	0	0	0	0	0	0
Deans, librarians, & others who teach	2	2	1	1	1	1	0	0
Part-time	9	17	7	12	2	5	1	0
Total	33	44	18	26	15	18	8	7

JD Enrollment and Ethnicity

	Men		Women		Full-Time		Part-Time		1st-Year		Total		JD Degs. Awd.
	#	%	#	%	#	%	#	%	#	%	#	%	
African Amer.	5	1.9	18	6.4	15	4.3	8	4.3	15	4.2	23	4.3	2
Amer. Indian	1	0.4	1	0.4	2	0.6	0	0.0	1	0.3	2	0.4	2
Asian Amer.	11	4.3	13	4.6	17	4.8	7	3.8	21	5.9	24	4.5	1
Mex. Amer.	6	2.3	12	4.3	12	3.4	6	3.2	12	3.4	18	3.4	2
Puerto Rican	1	0.4	0	0.0	1	0.3	0	0.0	1	0.3	1	0.2	0
Hispanic	12	4.7	25	8.9	21	6.0	16	8.6	21	5.9	37	6.9	5
Total Minority	36	14.0	69	24.6	68	19.3	37	20.0	71	19.8	105	19.6	12
For. Nation.	0	0.0	0	0.0	0	0.0	0	0.0	0	0.0	0	0.0	0
Caucasian	187	72.8	180	64.3	250	71.0	117	63.2	257	71.8	367	68.3	35
Unknown	34	13.2	31	11.1	34	9.7	31	16.8	44	12.3	65	12.1	12
Total	257	47.9	280	52.1	352	65.5	185	34.5	358	66.7	537		59

Curriculum

		Full-Time	Part-Time
Typical first-year section size		49	51
Is there typically a "small section" of the first-year class, other than Legal Writing, taught by full-time faculty		No	No
If yes, typical size offered last year			
# of classroom course titles beyond first-year curriculum		29	
# of upper division courses, excluding seminars, with an enrollment:	Under 25	15	
	25–49	8	
	50–74	1	
	75–99	0	
	100+	0	
# of seminars		1	
# of seminar positions available		0	
# of seminar positions filled		8	0
# of positions available in simulation courses		40	
# of simulation positions filled		29	10
# of positions available in faculty supervised clinical courses		48	
# of faculty supervised clinical positions filled		17	1
# involved in field placements		7	3
# involved in law journals		12	1
# involved in moot court or trial competitions		8	0
# of credit hours required to graduate		87	

Transfers

Transfers in	7
Transfers out	28

Tuition and Fees

	Resident	Nonresident
Full-time	$15,781	$15,781
Part-time	$12,763	$12,763
Tuition Guarantee Program	N	

Living Expenses

Estimated living expenses for singles

Living on campus	Living off campus	Living at home
N/A	$28,169	N/A

Phoenix School of Law

ABA
Approved
Since
2007

GPA and LSAT Scores

	Total	Full-Time	Part-Time
# of apps	1,807	1,557	249
# of offers	1,221	1,090	131
# of matrics	272	211	61
75% GPA	3.39	3.39	3.35
Median GPA	3.15	3.14	3.15
25% GPA	2.79	2.79	2.79
75% LSAT	154	154	154
Median LSAT	151	151	150
25% LSAT	148	148	147

Grants and Scholarships (from prior year)

	Total		Full-Time		Part-Time	
	#	%	#	%	#	%
Total # of students	336		196		140	
Total # receiving grants	177	52.7	118	60.2	59	42.1
Less than 1/2 tuition	152	45.2	109	55.6	43	30.7
Half to full tuition	21	6.3	8	4.1	13	9.3
Full tuition	4	1.2	1	0.5	3	2.1
More than full tuition	0	0.0	0	0.0	0	0.0
Median grant amount			$12,432		$15,576	

Informational and Library Resources

Total amount spent on library materials	$340,081
Study seating capacity inside the library	173
# of full-time equivalent professional librarians	5
Hours per week library is open	106
# of open, wired connections available to students	0
# of networked computers available for use by students	56
Has wireless network?	Y
Require computer?	Y

JD Attrition (from prior year)

	Academic	Other	Total	
	#	#	#	%
1st year	13	26	39	20.3
2nd year	2	9	11	13.6
3rd year	1	0	1	1.6
4th year	0	0	0	0.0

Employment (9 months after graduation)

	Total	Percentage
Employment status known	34	100.0
Employment status unknown	0	0.0
Employed	30	88.2
Pursuing graduate degrees	2	5.9
Unemployed (seeking, not seeking, or studying for the bar)	1	2.9
Type of Employment		
# employed in law firms	18	60.0
# employed in business and industry	5	16.7
# employed in government	1	3.3
# employed in public interest	3	10.0
# employed as judicial clerks	1	3.3
# employed in academia	2	6.7
Geographic Location		
# employed in state	28	93.3
# employed in foreign countries	0	0.0
# of states where employed	3	

Bar Passage Rates

First-time takers	32	Reporting %	100.00
Average school %	96.88	Average state %	84.00
Average pass difference	12.88		

Jurisdiction	Takers	Passers	Pass %	State %	Diff %
Arizona	31	30	96.77	84.03	12.74
Colorado	1	1	100.00	83.29	16.71

Phoenix School of Law

4041 North Central Avenue
Phoenix, AZ 85012
Phone: 602.682.6800; Fax: 602.682.6999
E-mail: admissions@phoenixlaw.edu; Website: www.phoenixlaw.edu

■ Introduction to Phoenix School of Law

Phoenix School of Law is dedicated to facilitating a student's legal education and pursuit of meaningful career options in traditional and other settings. Toward these ends, Phoenix School of Law offers a legal education calibrated to the needs of graduates in a changing market environment. Its program of study is responsive to significant change in the legal profession, particularly to the reality that most of today's graduates will practice in small- to medium-sized firms, and thus must be in a position to add immediate value to an organization.

Phoenix School of Law provides a traditional education but also imparts essential skills such as interviewing, counseling, negotiation, trial advocacy, and dispute resolution. The school also fosters an appreciation for the law's context and history and stresses professional responsibility. Phoenix School of Law welcomes qualified students, whatever their goals, and believes the educational process benefits from diversity in backgrounds and objectives.

Overall, the mission of Phoenix School of Law is to provide a legal education that is student-centered, facilitates practice readiness, and serves underserved communities. In furtherance of this mission, Phoenix School of Law is committed to achieving the following objectives: (1) provide a program of legal education that prepares graduates for admission to the bar, enables them to participate effectively and ethically in the legal profession, and is the basis for comprehensive professional development; (2) offer a "student-centered" educational experience that facilitates market-leading outcomes in bar examination performance, career placement, and minority success; (3) instill "best practices" processes that facilitate excellence in teaching and other key functions, and are the basis for continuous improvement; (4) recruit and develop a well-qualified and diverse faculty, staff, and student body who are committed to the institution's mission; (5) develop learning models that enable students, regardless of background or learning style, to succeed; and (6) provide the facilities, information resources, and technology to support the educational program and other institutional needs, and to provide service to the community.

■ Full- and Part-Time Programs

Phoenix School of Law is the only law school in Arizona to offer full-time and part-time (day or evening) programs.

■ Admission

Phoenix School of Law admits students after a careful and thorough evaluation process. Highly qualified applicants typically are admitted first. Admission decisions may include attention to factors that enhance the educational experience of the entire student body. The Admissions Committee weighs all characteristics bearing upon the ability of an applicant to study law successfully. Undergraduate grades and majors, the difficulty of the undergraduate field of study, LSAT scores, personal statements, and letters of recommendation are important. Phoenix School of Law also evaluates other criteria, such as experience, accomplishments, graduate study and degrees, the LSAT writing sample, and other factors that may provide meaningful insight into potential.

■ Curriculum

The Phoenix School of Law curriculum is designed to provide students with a solid grounding in the law and facilitate their capacity to graduate in a practice-ready status. These competencies are the primary reference points for a curriculum that correlates with an advanced state of practice-readiness for Phoenix School of Law graduates. The program of study thus responds directly to a market environment that demands not only a grasp of basic legal principles, but an ability to add immediate value to an existing organization or function in an independent and self-reliant manner. Courses are taught with the understanding that most law school graduates will practice in small- or medium-sized firms or on their own. Consistent with these realities, the curriculum provides exposure essential for success on the bar examination and effective performance in a contemporary market environment.

General Practice Skills: General Practice Skills is a unique course that exposes students to the multidimensional realities of a small law firm. Over the course of a semester, students will manage a wide array of problems and issues typifying experience in such a practice. Among other things, they will negotiate and make contracts, establish business entities, draft wills, handle pleadings in a divorce, factor tax implications in a business transaction, participate in pretrial discovery exercises such as composing and responding to interrogatories, engage in various methods of dispute resolution, and gain insight into creating and managing law firms.

Clinical Programs: Phoenix School of Law has clinical programs designed to develop and enhance practice skills. Courses are offered in trial and appellate practice, mediation, and alternative methods of dispute resolution. Clinical methods are used in various courses throughout the curriculum.

Externships: Phoenix School of Law offers qualified, upper-level students in good academic standing opportunities to participate in a for-credit externship program. Students attend a classroom component that provides a link between the placement setting and the learning process. A faculty member coordinates and supervises the externship program.

■ Faculty

Highly accomplished and dedicated to teaching the law, the faculty at Phoenix School of Law is exceptional. Our professors include attorneys and former judges, experienced in nearly every aspect of the legal profession, who have garnered awards and accolades for their accomplishments by the profession's top institutions. True legal educators, they serve as knowledgeable guides and mentors with a focus on providing a practical learning experience and preparing students to be professionally prepared upon graduation.

■ Academic Success

Phoenix School of Law has a comprehensive Academic Success Program to help students succeed in law school. The Academic Success Program provides workshops as well as small group and individual academic support counseling sessions to assist students in: adjusting to a rigorous legal learning environment; fostering time-management and stress-management skills; identifying individualized learning style preferences to enhance efficiency and effectiveness in academics and practice; developing the necessary study skills, classroom preparation, and exam-preparation tools to succeed in law school; maximizing effective writing, analytical, oratory, and legal reasoning skills; bar preparation; and increasing cultural awareness, both personally and professionally.

■ Career Services

The Center for Professional Development (CPD) is a full-service counseling and resource center that supports and assists students in all stages of the career planning and placement process. The CPD offers a wide range of services and programs that are responsive to a diverse student body and evolving market realities.

Personal assistance is offered to students so that they can identify, develop, and attain their individual goals. The CPD houses an extensive collection of books, directories, pamphlets, and other publications covering a wide variety of career-related topics, including self-assessment, career planning, job-search strategies, résumé preparation, interview skills, legal practice areas and alternatives, legal and nonlegal employers, public sector and public interest careers, and law firm practice and management, as well as online resources for career exploration and planning needs. The CPD offers a comprehensive program that brings students together with employers and provides other opportunities to gain practical experience.

■ Library and Information Technology

The Information Resources Center (IRC) continues to build a collection of legal information sources in a variety of formats, including print and online databases. The law book collection consists of core primary sources: cases, statutes, and regulations of the State of Arizona and the United States. The center also includes a range of secondary resources: periodicals, legal encyclopedias, and treatises devoted to legal topics. The IRC works continuously to update its collection with materials that students and faculty will use in legal research training and in law practice.

The Phoenix School of Law Information Technology (IT) Department provides students access to a campus-wide wireless network, a state-of-the-art computer lab, and Phoenix School of Law e-mail addresses, as well as to high-speed printers and copiers. IT also prides itself on giving first-class support to all students, faculty, and staff members.

Applicant Profile

Phoenix School of Law

LSAT Score	GPA									
	3.75 +	3.50–3.74	3.25–3.49	3.00–3.24	2.75–2.99	2.50–2.74	2.25–2.49	2.00–2.24	Below 2.00	No GPA
175–180	■	■	■	■	■	■	■	■		
170–174	■	■	■	■	■	■	■	■		
165–169	■	■	■	■	■	■	■	■		
160–164	■	■	■	■	■	■	■	■		
157–159	■	■	■	■	■	■	■	▨		
154–156	■	■	■	■	■	■	▨			
150–153	■	■	■	■	■	▨				
145–149	▨	▨	▨	▨	▨					
140–144										
135–139										
130–134										
125–129										
120–124										

■ Highly Possible   ▨ Possible   ☐ Unlikely

The information contained in this chart should be used as an estimated guide as to the likelihood of admission. The Admissions Committee engages in a holistic review of all information submitted by candidates for admission. LSAT and UGPA are not the sole determinants for admission.

University of Pittsburgh School of Law

3900 Forbes Avenue, Barco Law Building
Pittsburgh, PA 15260
Phone: 412.648.1413; Fax: 412.648.1318
E-mail: admitlaw@pitt.edu; Website: www.law.pitt.edu

ABA
Approved
Since
1923

 Section of Legal Education and Admissions to the Bar

The Basics

Type of school	Public
Term	Semester
Application deadline	3/1
Application fee	$55
Financial aid deadline	1/1 4/1
Can first year start other than fall?	No
Student to faculty ratio	12.9 to 1
# of housing spaces available restricted to law students	
graduate housing for which law students are eligible	

Faculty and Administrators

	Total		Men		Women		Minorities	
	Spr	Fall	Spr	Fall	Spr	Fall	Spr	Fall
Full-time	45	43	27	27	18	16	3	3
Other full-time	0	1	0	1	0	0	0	0
Deans, librarians, & others who teach	10	9	3	2	7	7	1	1
Part-time	61	46	44	31	15	14	3	6
Total	116	99	74	61	40	37	7	10

Curriculum

		Full-Time	Part-Time
Typical first-year section size		82	0
Is there typically a "small section" of the first-year class, other than Legal Writing, taught by full-time faculty		No	No
If yes, typical size offered last year			
# of classroom course titles beyond first-year curriculum		192	
# of upper division courses, excluding seminars, with an enrollment:	Under 25	135	
	25–49	31	
	50–74	18	
	75–99	3	
	100+	6	
# of seminars		25	
# of seminar positions available		313	
# of seminar positions filled		238	0
# of positions available in simulation courses		337	
# of simulation positions filled		195	0
# of positions available in faculty supervised clinical courses		168	
# of faculty supervised clinical positions filled	168		0
# involved in field placements		135	0
# involved in law journals		187	0
# involved in moot court or trial competitions	98		0
# of credit hours required to graduate		88	

JD Enrollment and Ethnicity

	Men		Women		Full-Time		Part-Time		1st-Year		Total		JD Degs. Awd.
	#	%	#	%	#	%	#	%	#	%	#	%	
African Amer.	21	5.7	25	8.0	46	6.7	0	0.0	20	8.6	46	6.7	10
Amer. Indian	0	0.0	1	0.3	1	0.1	0	0.0	0	0.0	1	0.1	0
Asian Amer.	14	3.8	29	9.3	43	6.3	0	0.0	14	6.0	43	6.3	16
Mex. Amer.	0	0.0	0	0.0	0	0.0	0	0.0	0	0.0	0	0.0	0
Puerto Rican	1	0.3	0	0.0	1	0.1	0	0.0	1	0.4	1	0.1	0
Hispanic	11	3.0	6	1.9	17	2.5	0	0.0	4	1.7	17	2.5	5
Total Minority	47	12.7	61	19.6	108	15.8	0	0.0	39	16.7	108	15.8	31
For. Nation.	0	0.0	0	0.0	0	0.0	0	0.0	0	0.0	0	0.0	0
Caucasian	247	66.6	193	62.1	440	64.5	0	0.0	146	62.7	440	64.5	142
Unknown	77	20.8	57	18.3	134	19.6	0	0.0	48	20.6	134	19.6	57
Total	371	54.4	311	45.6	682	100.0	0	0.0	233	34.2	682		230

Transfers

Transfers in	10
Transfers out	8

Tuition and Fees

	Resident	Nonresident
Full-time	$25,098	$33,094
Part-time		
Tuition Guarantee Program		N

Living Expenses

Estimated living expenses for singles

Living on campus	Living off campus	Living at home
$15,690	$15,690	$15,690

University of Pittsburgh School of Law

ABA
Approved
Since
1923

GPA and LSAT Scores

	Total	Full-Time	Part-Time
# of apps	2,177	2,177	0
# of offers	811	811	0
# of matrics	235	235	0
75% GPA	3.63	3.63	0.00
Median GPA	3.42	3.42	0.00
25% GPA	3.18	3.18	0.00
75% LSAT	161	161	0
Median LSAT	159	159	0
25% LSAT	157	157	0

Grants and Scholarships (from prior year)

	Total		Full-Time		Part-Time	
	#	%	#	%	#	%
Total # of students	698		698		0	
Total # receiving grants	393	56.3	393	56.3	0	0.0
Less than 1/2 tuition	287	41.1	287	41.1	0	0.0
Half to full tuition	88	12.6	88	12.6	0	0.0
Full tuition	8	1.1	8	1.1	0	0.0
More than full tuition	10	1.4	10	1.4	0	0.0
Median grant amount			$10,000		$0	

Informational and Library Resources

Total amount spent on library materials	$1,528,340
Study seating capacity inside the library	438
# of full-time equivalent professional librarians	15
Hours per week library is open	101
# of open, wired connections available to students	282
# of networked computers available for use by students	73
Has wireless network?	Y
Require computer?	N

JD Attrition (from prior year)

	Academic	Other	Total	
	#	#	#	%
1st year	1	10	11	4.5
2nd year	0	1	1	0.4
3rd year	0	0	0	0.0
4th year	0	0	0	0.0

Employment (9 months after graduation)

	Total	Percentage
Employment status known	239	99.6
Employment status unknown	1	0.4
Employed	216	90.4
Pursuing graduate degrees	8	3.3
Unemployed (seeking, not seeking, or studying for the bar)	13	5.4
Type of Employment		
# employed in law firms	133	61.6
# employed in business and industry	36	16.7
# employed in government	21	9.7
# employed in public interest	9	4.2
# employed as judicial clerks	16	7.4
# employed in academia	1	0.5
Geographic Location		
# employed in state	135	62.5
# employed in foreign countries	2	0.9
# of states where employed	24	

Bar Passage Rates

First-time takers	215	Reporting %	74.42
Average school %	90.63	Average state %	86.69
Average pass difference	3.94		

Jurisdiction	Takers	Passers	Pass %	State %	Diff %
Pennsylvania	160	145	90.63	86.69	3.94

University of Pittsburgh School of Law

3900 Forbes Avenue, Barco Law Building
Pittsburgh, PA 15260
Phone: 412.648.1413; Fax: 412.648.1318
E-mail: admitlaw@pitt.edu; Website: www.law.pitt.edu

■ Introduction

The University of Pittsburgh School of Law (Pitt Law), founded in 1895, is a leader in legal education. It features a broad and varied curriculum, an internationally accomplished faculty, state-of-the-art physical facilities, and a talented and diverse student body hailing from all over the globe. Pitt Law is located in its own six-story building on campus in Oakland, the cultural and educational center of Pittsburgh. State and federal courts, major corporate headquarters, and hundreds of law firms are located nearby in downtown Pittsburgh, only minutes from campus. The dynamic Oakland area is home to four colleges and universities, the world-renowned, multi-hospital University of Pittsburgh Medical Center, numerous scientific and high-tech offices and research centers, museums, art galleries, coffee houses, and libraries. The Pitt campus abuts a beautiful 429-acre city park. Desirable and affordable residential areas are situated nearby and all mass transit in the city is free to Pitt students.

■ Library and Physical Facilities

The Barco Law Library is an attractive, 450,000-volume, open-stack research facility, housed on three floors of the School of Law building. It contains several study rooms, a computer lab, and ample seating space. The Fawcett Student Commons in the library is a comfortable gathering spot for students, faculty, and staff. Faculty offices ring the perimeter of the two floors of the library, encouraging interaction between students and faculty. Classrooms with state-of-the-art technology are located on the first and ground floors of the School of Law building. A spacious and comfortable student lounge and the elegant Teplitz Memorial Courtroom are located on the ground floor. Student computing is supported through a wireless network and wired carrels and seating.

■ Special Programs

- *Clinical Programs*—Academics and reality meet head-on in our legal clinics. Pitt Law students have the opportunity to obtain hands-on experience in several clinical programs, including a Tax Clinic; an Environmental Law Clinic; a Civil Practice Clinic with a focus on either Health Law or Elder Law; a Family Law Clinic; and a Community Economic Development Clinic. With a supervising attorney, students do it all: pretrial preparation, negotiation, litigation, and counseling real-life clients about real-life legal concerns.
- *Certificate Programs*—One way to prepare for law practice in an increasingly complex society is to develop specialized expertise. Pitt Law students may seize that advantage through participation in our certificate programs, a collection of sharply focused courses of study in high-demand areas of practice. Pitt Law has certificate programs in the areas of civil litigation; environmental law, science, and policy; health law; international and comparative law; and intellectual property and technology law. These certificate programs can be completed within the regular 88 credits.
- *Joint-Degree Programs*—Prompted by the growing needs for attorneys and the increasingly intricate legal needs of society, we offer several joint-degree programs that

provide rigorous, integrated training, effectively merging law and a number of allied fields. They include the JD/MBA with both Pitt and Carnegie Mellon University; the JD/MPH with our Graduate School of Public Health; the JD/MPA, JD/MPIA, and JD/MID with our Graduate School of Public and International Affairs; the JD/MA (Bioethics); the JD/MSW (Social Work); and the JD/MS, PPM and JD/MAM with the Heinz School at Carnegie Mellon University.
- *Mellon Legal Writing Program*—The Mellon Program provides academic support to students at the law school who wish to improve their writing, exam-taking, and study skills. Exam preparation sessions include general discussion regarding the form and substance of law school exams as well as more specific guidance relating to particular topics and classes.
- *Semester in DC*—Pitt Law students can spend a semester working for a nonprofit or government agency in Washington DC, while earning a full semester's worth of academic credit. The DC Externship Program allows students to combine supervised field work with a government or nonprofit employer, a related academic seminar, and the option of earning additional credit by writing a paper related to the externship. Members of the Pitt Law alumni network are eager to serve as mentors to Pitt Law students, and many DC area employers are interested in receiving externship applications from Pitt Law students.
- *Innovation Practice Institute (IPI)*—Pitt Law is uniquely situated amid some of the world's leading innovators in fields ranging from regenerative medicine to robotics, to social and commercial infrastructure design and development. Taking advantage of this environment, IPI gives Pitt Law students the opportunity to immerse themselves in experiential, cross-disciplinary, project-based learning to develop the skills and confidence to participate as professionals in the innovation culture and economy.

■ Center for International Legal Education (CILE)

In today's world, legal transactions involve many nations and many sets of laws. Today's global lawyer understands the political, cultural, and social influences on the legal systems of other countries and uses that knowledge for the benefit of his or her clients. CILE faculty prepare Pitt Law students for successful futures in this modern world. Students study the workings of foreign legal systems and explore the wide array of issues facing practicing attorneys in the global marketplace. The center also coordinates international programs at Pitt with the University Center for International Studies and affiliated area studies programs, and it supervises a number of specialized language classes, for example, French for Lawyers, Spanish for Lawyers, German for Lawyers, and Chinese for Lawyers.

■ Admission and Financial Aid

Pitt Law has a highly competitive process, with decisions based upon several factors, with the GPA and LSAT serving as the most important academic factors. When evaluating an undergraduate degree, the committee pays careful attention to the strength of the major field of study, and looks for evidence of discipline and ability to handle a rigorous and

demanding program. The same assessment is made of graduate and professional work. A required personal statement provides a view into the nonacademic world of the applicant. This is critical to our ability to enroll a diverse class—students with various backgrounds and a range of experiences. Similarly, letters of recommendation and résumés provide a broader view of the applicant's accomplishments. Applicants are reviewed on a rolling notification basis.

Pitt Law assists accepted students in securing the financial resources needed to cover the cost of their legal education. Approximately half of the student body receives merit or need-based scholarships. Pitt Law also offers a Public Interest Scholarship and numerous named scholarships. All students admitted to Pitt Law are automatically considered for scholarships and notifications of awards are included in their acceptance letters.

■ Career Services

The Career Services Office provides year-round assistance to Pitt Law students and graduates. The office serves as a clearinghouse for information on summer, part-time, and permanent work with law firms, corporations, accounting firms, government agencies, judges, and other legal employers. It also helps students develop practical job-search strategies, helps demystify the dynamics of the legal job market, offers strategies for finding the perfect job in that market, and offers information and counseling regarding nontraditional careers utilizing professional skills gained in law school. The placement rate for the Class of 2008 was 93 percent.

■ Student Activities

The *Law Review*, the *Journal of Law and Commerce*, and the *Journal of Law and Technology* are among the journals published by law students. More than 30 law student organizations thrive at Pitt Law, reflecting the diverse social and intellectual interests and experiences of our students. They include the Asian Law Students Association, the Black Law Students Association, the Environmental Law Council, the Federalist Society, the Hispanic Law Society, the Jewish Law Students Association, the Lesbian-Gay Rights Organization (OUTLAW), the Pitt Law Women's Association, and the Pitt Legal Income Sharing Foundation, among others.

■ The City of Pittsburgh

Today Pittsburgh is spectacular—a thriving business center and a high-tech hotbed rated America's most livable city in 2009! Our campus is at the center of it all. We are a stroll away from wonderfully diverse neighborhoods, acres of parks, scores of restaurants and shops, three major league sports arenas, movies, museums, galleries, dance clubs, coffee houses, riverside cafes, and that's just the short list. A quick commute on your bike takes you to the nucleus of the law and business community in downtown Pittsburgh. You'll also find the heart of the cultural district downtown, offering world-class theater, opera, symphony, ballet, and dance. For a law student, Pittsburgh is a lot more than a livable city—it's a context for building a strong career. There is no finer preparation for law than learning in a setting that gives you a wealth of opportunity to put theory into practice. Pittsburgh is the global headquarters for Fortune 500 corporations, home to one of the nation's largest medical centers, a hub of public policy interest, and host to more than 2,500 high technology companies—all served by a robust and sophisticated practicing bar. Pitt Law's location near the heart of the legal community makes practitioners accessible as mentors in the classroom and models in the field.

Applicant Profile

University of Pittsburgh School of Law
This grid includes only applicants who earned 120–180 LSAT scores under standard administrations.

LSAT Score	GPA																
	3.75 +		3.50–3.74		3.25–3.49		3.00–3.24		2.75–2.99		2.50–2.74		Below 2.50		No GPA		Total
	Apps	Adm	Apps	Adm	Apps	Adm	Apps	Adm	Apps	Adm	Apps	Adm	Apps	Adm	Apps	Adm	Apps	Adm
165–180	24	20	26	20	20	14	12	7	9	5	5	3	3	1	0	0	99	70
160–164	101	77	113	88	102	71	78	38	34	14	11	2	8	1	6	4	453	295
155–159	114	80	188	106	169	88	127	46	47	15	27	8	11	0	11	7	694	350
150–154	68	11	112	14	153	22	100	18	49	12	18	2	12	0	11	1	523	80
145–149	24	1	63	3	41	1	42	4	33	2	20	1	8	1	6	0	237	13
Below 145	11	0	26	1	29	0	25	1	37	0	20	0	17	0	15	0	180	2
Total	342	189	528	232	514	196	384	114	209	48	101	16	59	3	49	12	2186	810

Apps = Number of Applicants
Adm = Number Admitted
Reflects 100% of the total applicant pool; average LSAT data reported.

Pontifical Catholic University of Puerto Rico School of Law

2250 Avenida Las Americas, Suite 633
Ponce, PR 00717-9997
Phone: 787.841.2000, exts. 1836, 1837; Fax: 787.841.4620
E-mail: derecho@email.pucpr.edu; Website: www.pucpr.edu/derecho

ABA
Approved
Since
1967

The Basics

Type of school	Private
Term	Semester
Application deadline	4/15 9/30
Application fee	
Financial aid deadline	4/8
Can first year start other than fall?	Yes
Student to faculty ratio	28.3 to 1
# of housing spaces available restricted to law students	
graduate housing for which law students are eligible	

Faculty and Administrators

	Total		Men		Women		Minorities	
	Spr	Fall	Spr	Fall	Spr	Fall	Spr	Fall
Full-time	17	17	13	12	4	5	17	17
Other full-time	4	3	4	3	0	0	3	3
Deans, librarians, & others who teach	8	8	5	5	3	3	8	8
Part-time	24	26	17	16	7	10	24	26
Total	53	54	39	36	14	18	52	54

Curriculum

	Full-Time	Part-Time
Typical first-year section size	41	39
Is there typically a "small section" of the first-year class, other than Legal Writing, taught by full-time faculty	Yes	Yes
If yes, typical size offered last year	21	21
# of classroom course titles beyond first-year curriculum	90	
# of upper division courses, excluding seminars, with an enrollment: Under 25	58	
25–49	57	
50–74	18	
75–99	1	
100+	0	
# of seminars	19	
# of seminar positions available	456	
# of seminar positions filled	137	264
# of positions available in simulation courses	200	
# of simulation positions filled	69	118
# of positions available in faculty supervised clinical courses	6	
# of faculty supervised clinical positions filled	6	0
# involved in field placements	0	0
# involved in law journals	50	5
# involved in moot court or trial competitions	0	0
# of credit hours required to graduate	94	

JD Enrollment and Ethnicity

	Men		Women		Full-Time		Part-Time		1st-Year		Total		JD Degs. Awd.
	#	%	#	%	#	%	#	%	#	%	#	%	
African Amer.	0	0.0	0	0.0	0	0.0	0	0.0	0	0.0	0	0.0	0
Amer. Indian	0	0.0	0	0.0	0	0.0	0	0.0	0	0.0	0	0.0	0
Asian Amer.	0	0.0	0	0.0	0	0.0	0	0.0	0	0.0	0	0.0	0
Mex. Amer.	0	0.0	0	0.0	0	0.0	0	0.0	0	0.0	0	0.0	0
Puerto Rican	324	100.0	372	100.0	474	100.0	222	100.0	260	100.0	696	100.0	147
Hispanic	0	0.0	0	0.0	0	0.0	0	0.0	0	0.0	0	0.0	0
Total Minority	324	100.0	372	100.0	474	100.0	222	100.0	260	100.0	696	100.0	147
For. Nation.	0	0.0	0	0.0	0	0.0	0	0.0	0	0.0	0	0.0	0
Caucasian	0	0.0	0	0.0	0	0.0	0	0.0	0	0.0	0	0.0	0
Unknown	0	0.0	0	0.0	0	0.0	0	0.0	0	0.0	0	0.0	0
Total	324	46.6	372	53.4	474	68.1	222	31.9	260	37.4	696		147

Transfers

Transfers in	0
Transfers out	24

Tuition and Fees

	Resident	Nonresident
Full-time	$13,806	
Part-time	$10,526	
Tuition Guarantee Program		N

Living Expenses

Estimated living expenses for singles

Living on campus	Living off campus	Living at home
$7,789	$9,020	$7,155

Pontifical Catholic University of Puerto Rico School of Law

ABA
Approved
Since
1967

GPA and LSAT Scores

	Total	Full-Time	Part-Time
# of apps	562	414	148
# of offers	318	227	91
# of matrics	266	187	79
75% GPA	3.54	3.54	3.53
Median GPA	3.22	3.16	3.31
25% GPA	2.93	2.93	2.93
75% LSAT	138	138	138
Median LSAT	135	135	135
25% LSAT	133	133	132

Grants and Scholarships (from prior year)

	Total		Full-Time		Part-Time	
	#	%	#	%	#	%
Total # of students	592		395		197	
Total # receiving grants	81	13.7	54	13.7	27	13.7
Less than 1/2 tuition	59	10.0	42	10.6	17	8.6
Half to full tuition	15	2.5	8	2.0	7	3.6
Full tuition	7	1.2	4	1.0	3	1.5
More than full tuition	0	0.0	0	0.0	0	0.0
Median grant amount			$2,100		$2,400	

Informational and Library Resources

Total amount spent on library materials	$642,333
Study seating capacity inside the library	184
# of full-time equivalent professional librarians	4
Hours per week library is open	98
# of open, wired connections available to students	42
# of networked computers available for use by students	30
Has wireless network?	Y
Require computer?	N

JD Attrition (from prior year)

	Academic	Other	Total	
	#	#	#	%
1st year	4	37	41	17.4
2nd year	3	3	6	3.2
3rd year	1	4	5	3.6
4th year	0	0	0	0.0

Employment (9 months after graduation)

	Total	Percentage
Employment status known	111	100.0
Employment status unknown	0	0.0
Employed	39	35.1
Pursuing graduate degrees	4	3.6
Unemployed (seeking, not seeking, or studying for the bar)	68	61.3
Type of Employment		
# employed in law firms	12	30.8
# employed in business and industry	22	56.4
# employed in government	2	5.1
# employed in public interest	0	0.0
# employed as judicial clerks	1	2.6
# employed in academia	2	5.1
Geographic Location		
# employed in state	39	100.0
# employed in foreign countries	0	0.0
# of states where employed	1	

Bar Passage Rates

First-time takers	531	Reporting %	30.51
Average school %	43.83	Average state %	54.16
Average pass difference −10.33			

Jurisdiction	Takers	Passers	Pass %	State %	Diff %
Puerto Rico	162	71	43.83	54.16	−10.33

Pontifical Catholic University of Puerto Rico School of Law

2250 Avenida Las Americas, Suite 633
Ponce, PR 00717-9997
Phone: 787.841.2000, exts. 1836, 1837; Fax: 787.841.4620
E-mail: derecho@email.pucpr.edu; Website: www.pucpr.edu/derecho

■ Introduction

The School of Law of the Pontifical Catholic University of Puerto Rico was founded in 1961. It is located within the main campus of the Pontifical Catholic University of Puerto Rico, on the southern part of the island in the historical city of Ponce, one of the most beautiful places in Puerto Rico.

The primary objective of the Pontifical Catholic University School of Law is the formation of lawyers imbued with a deep love and concern for their Catholic faith and imbedded in the redeeming truths of Christian philosophy and ethics. The law school of the Pontifical Catholic University of Puerto Rico hopes to contribute to upholding the high ethical, cultural, and literary accomplishments of the Puerto Rican bar, which historically represents a tradition of moral austerity, intellectual achievement, and professional competence.

■ Library and Physical Facilities

The School of Law occupies the Spellman Building. Its location on the campus of Pontifical Catholic University of Puerto Rico enables students to study related academic disciplines, to participate in the intellectual life, and to enjoy many other facilities of the university.

Among the materials in the library is a comprehensive and growing collection of legal treatises, tests, monographs, and periodicals, including the most important and recent publications in civil, common, and comparative law. Modern audiovisual equipment and computerized services are also available. The library is an authorized depository for United Nations documents as well as for United States government documents. In addition, it offers the services of the Westlaw and LexisNexis systems, which permit computer-assisted legal research.

■ Curriculum

The required subjects are:
- Administrative Law
- Advanced Legal Analysis
- Civil Procedure
- Constitutional Law
- Contracts
- Corporations
- Criminal Procedure
- Evidence
- Family Law
- Federal Jurisdiction
- Fundamentals of Research, Analysis, and Writing
- Intermediate Research, Analysis, and Writing
- Introduction to Law
- Legal Aid Clinic
- Legal Ethics and Professional Responsibility
- Mercantile Law
- Mortgages
- Notarial Law
- Obligations
- Penal Law
- Property Law
- Successions and Donations
- Theology
- Torts
- Trial Practice
- Workshop Bar Preparation

The basic program covers three years in the day division or four years in the evening division.

The school curriculum includes a clinical program for third-year students. Pursuant to a rule approved by the Supreme Court of the Commonwealth of Puerto Rico in 1974, students practice trial advocacy under the supervision of law school professors in the Courts of First Instance and in administrative agencies.

The Pontifical Catholic University of Puerto Rico also offers a combined JD/MBA degree. For the combined degree, students are required to complete 85 credit hours at the School of Law (79 required credits and 6 elective credits), plus 9 credit hours in electives completed at the Graduate Program of the School of Business Administration, for a total of 94 credit hours. In addition, the students must complete 34 credit hours at the School of Business Administration (31 required credits and 3 electives) and an additional 9 approved elective credits in JD, for a total of 43 credits, plus 4 hours of Theology.

■ Admission

Application for admission is open to men and women of good character who have received a bachelor's degree from a qualified institution and have obtained a 2.5 grade-point average.

The required forms for application for admission and all other information may be obtained from the registrar of the law school and should be filed with all supporting documents before April 15. The School of Law admits beginning students in August and January for both the full-time and part-time programs.

Applicants are required to take both the LSAT and the Examen de Admisión a Estudios de Posgrado (EXADEP) (formerly PAEG).

Test scores are not the only factor considered. Besides the objective factors, there are many intangible and personal considerations, such as strong motivation, disadvantaged circumstances, evidence of improving performance, and relevant work experience. A personal interview of the applicant by a committee is essential before a decision is made. Applicants of both sexes and from all religious, racial, social, and ethnic backgrounds are encouraged to apply.

All courses are offered only in Spanish. Consequently, students are required to be proficient in Spanish.

■ Student Activities

The law review, *Revista de Derecho Puertorriqueño*, is devoted to scholarly analysis and discussion of development of the law. It publishes student notes, comments, and surveys, as well as articles of outstanding quality submitted by attorneys, judges, and other members of the legal profession. The school has a student council, a chapter of the National Association of Law Students of Puerto Rico, and an Association for Women's Rights. Local chapters of Phi Alpha

Delta international law fraternity, the Delta Theta Phi law fraternity, and the Law Student Division of the ABA are also active and well organized in the law school.

■ Housing

Students live either in university residences or private housing. Inquiries concerning housing facilities should be addressed to the Housing Office, Pontifical Catholic University of Puerto Rico, 2250 Avenida Las Americas, Suite 545, Ponce, PR 00717-9997.

■ Expenses and Financial Aid

There is a deferred plan for students who have financial difficulties at the time of registration. The university has made available for law students several full-tuition scholarships to be awarded on the basis of scholastic excellence. The university also has an office for student loans and other types of financial services.

Applicant Profile Not Available

University of Puerto Rico School of Law

PO Box 23349, UPR Station
San Juan, PR 00931-3349
Phone: 787.999.9553; Fax: 787.999.9564
E-mail: admisiones@law.upr.edu; Website: www.law.upr.edu

The Basics

Type of school	Public
Term	Semester
Application deadline	2/15
Application fee	
Financial aid deadline	4/30
Can first year start other than fall?	No
Student to faculty ratio	23.0 to 1
# of housing spaces available restricted to law students	16
graduate housing for which law students are eligible	

Faculty and Administrators

	Total		Men		Women		Minorities	
	Spr	Fall	Spr	Fall	Spr	Fall	Spr	Fall
Full-time	24	24	16	16	8	8	23	23
Other full-time	6	2	5	2	1	0	6	2
Deans, librarians, & others who teach	15	16	4	5	11	11	15	16
Part-time	61	78	38	51	22	26	57	73
Total	106	120	63	74	42	45	101	114

Curriculum

	Full-Time	Part-Time
Typical first-year section size	70	36
Is there typically a "small section" of the first-year class, other than Legal Writing, taught by full-time faculty	No	No
If yes, typical size offered last year		
# of classroom course titles beyond first-year curriculum	105	

# of upper division courses, excluding seminars, with an enrollment:		
	Under 25	129
	25–49	36
	50–74	35
	75–99	8
	100+	1

	Full-Time	Part-Time
# of seminars	52	
# of seminar positions available	780	
# of seminar positions filled	325	219
# of positions available in simulation courses	245	
# of simulation positions filled	54	173
# of positions available in faculty supervised clinical courses	420	
# of faculty supervised clinical positions filled	252	104
# involved in field placements	56	4
# involved in law journals	21	0
# involved in moot court or trial competitions	5	0
# of credit hours required to graduate	92	

JD Enrollment and Ethnicity

	Men #	Men %	Women #	Women %	Full-Time #	Full-Time %	Part-Time #	Part-Time %	1st-Year #	1st-Year %	Total #	Total %	JD Degs. Awd.
African Amer.	0	0.0	0	0.0	0	0.0	0	0.0	0	0.0	0	0.0	0
Amer. Indian	0	0.0	0	0.0	0	0.0	0	0.0	0	0.0	0	0.0	0
Asian Amer.	0	0.0	0	0.0	0	0.0	0	0.0	0	0.0	0	0.0	0
Mex. Amer.	0	0.0	0	0.0	0	0.0	0	0.0	0	0.0	0	0.0	0
Puerto Rican	319	95.2	377	93.1	498	94.5	198	93.0	339	88.5	696	94.1	175
Hispanic	14	4.2	27	6.7	26	4.9	15	7.0	41	10.7	41	5.5	0
Total Minority	333	99.4	404	99.8	524	99.4	213	100.0	380	99.2	737	99.6	175
For. Nation.	2	0.6	1	0.2	3	0.6	0	0.0	3	0.8	3	0.4	5
Caucasian	0	0.0	0	0.0	0	0.0	0	0.0	0	0.0	0	0.0	0
Unknown	0	0.0	0	0.0	0	0.0	0	0.0	0	0.0	0	0.0	0
Total	335	45.3	405	54.7	527	71.2	213	28.8	383	51.8	740		180

Transfers

Transfers in	10
Transfers out	0

Tuition and Fees

	Resident	Nonresident
Full-time	$6,345	$8,105
Part-time	$5,125	$7,397
Tuition Guarantee Program		Y

Living Expenses

Estimated living expenses for singles

Living on campus	Living off campus	Living at home
$10,895	$15,155	$10,455

University of Puerto Rico School of Law

ABA Approved Since 1945

GPA and LSAT Scores

	Total	Full-Time	Part-Time
# of apps	569	389	180
# of offers	221	163	58
# of matrics	200	145	55
75% GPA	3.79	3.83	3.67
Median GPA	3.60	3.65	3.45
25% GPA	3.33	3.33	3.32
75% LSAT	149	150	147
Median LSAT	145	145	144
25% LSAT	141	141	141

Grants and Scholarships (from prior year)

	Total		Full-Time		Part-Time	
	#	%	#	%	#	%
Total # of students	718		536		182	
Total # receiving grants	0	0.0	0	0.0	0	0.0
Less than 1/2 tuition	0	0.0	0	0.0	0	0.0
Half to full tuition	0	0.0	0	0.0	0	0.0
Full tuition	0	0.0	0	0.0	0	0.0
More than full tuition	0	0.0	0	0.0	0	0.0
Median grant amount			$0		$0	

Informational and Library Resources

Total amount spent on library materials	$1,209,936
Study seating capacity inside the library	437
# of full-time equivalent professional librarians	8
Hours per week library is open	112
# of open, wired connections available to students	170
# of networked computers available for use by students	49
Has wireless network?	Y
Require computer?	N

JD Attrition (from prior year)

	Academic	Other	Total	
	#	#	#	%
1st year	12	9	21	5.5
2nd year	0	4	4	3.1
3rd year	6	4	10	5.2
4th year	0	0	0	0.0

Employment (9 months after graduation)

	Total	Percentage
Employment status known	72	36.7
Employment status unknown	124	63.3
Employed	55	76.4
Pursuing graduate degrees	0	0.0
Unemployed (seeking, not seeking, or studying for the bar)	6	8.3
Type of Employment		
# employed in law firms	32	58.2
# employed in business and industry	7	12.7
# employed in government	8	14.5
# employed in public interest	1	1.8
# employed as judicial clerks	6	10.9
# employed in academia	1	1.8
Geographic Location		
# employed in state	54	98.2
# employed in foreign countries	0	0.0
# of states where employed	0	

Bar Passage Rates

First-time takers	609	Reporting %	30.54
Average school %	69.35	Average state %	54.16
Average pass difference 15.19			

Jurisdiction	Takers	Passers	Pass %	State %	Diff %
Puerto Rico	186	129	69.35	54.16	15.19

University of Puerto Rico School of Law

PO Box 23349, UPR Station
San Juan, PR 00931-3349
Phone: 787.999.9553; Fax: 787.999.9564
E-mail: admisiones@law.upr.edu; Website: www.law.upr.edu

■ Introduction

The University of Puerto Rico School of Law was founded in 1913 at its present site on the University Campus at Río Piedras, within the metropolitan area of San Juan in the heart of the Caribbean. The University of Puerto Rico is accredited by the Middle States Colleges Association. The School of Law has been accredited by the American Bar Association since 1945 and by the Association of American Law Schools since 1948. It is also accredited by the Council on Higher Education and the Puerto Rico Supreme Court.

■ Academic and Special Programs

The Academic Program: The guiding principle behind our academic program is to increase and diversify the learning and development experiences of our students. That is the reason why half of our study program is elective. Our students can take courses ranging from theoretical to practical, to issues pertaining to civil rights, technology, feminism, business, international relations, and comparative law. In addition, our students, as part of their program, have to participate in a clinical program.

The study program consists of 92 credit hours. The majority of the courses are taught in Spanish.

Degree Offered: Juris Doctor
Joint-Degree Programs:
- Dual Juris Doctor and Law Degree Program (Licenciatura en Derecho) with the University of Barcelona, Spain
- Juris Doctor and Master of Business Administration with the University of Puerto Rico Graduate School of Business Administration
- Juris Doctor and Doctor of Medicine with the University of Puerto Rico School of Medicine
- Juris Doctor and Master of Public Policy with the Hubert Humphrey Institute of the University of Minnesota

Graduate: LLM for Latin American and Caribbean lawyers
Special Programs: The School of Law has student exchange programs with the University of Arizona James E. Rogers College of Law, the University of Connecticut School of Law, the University of Palermo in Argentina, the University of Chile Law School, the University of Ottawa Faculty of Law in Canada, and the University of Amberes in Belgium. Under these programs, students register at their home institution but will take a full courseload at the host institution. The credits and grades earned during a single semester will be awarded by the home institution according to the standard procedure of the home law school. Students also have a chance to participate in a summer law program at the University of Barcelona, Spain. Also, the school has a winter exchange program with the University of Ottawa Faculty of Law in Canada, through which students can earn four credits studying Law and Technology or Law, Technology, and Feminism for one week in Canada and two weeks in Puerto Rico.

■ Clinical Program

In March 1974, the Puerto Rico Supreme Court approved rules for the local courts to allow students to practice law and participate in judicial proceedings. The US District Court followed suit in 1991. Our curriculum requires that students in their last year of study complete a two-semester clinical program. The clinical program stands as clear testimony of our school's commitment to community service. The Legal Aid Clinic handles over 1,300 cases per year, offering assistance to those in need of legal aid. Our clinic offers our students the opportunity to practice law in a wide range of areas in an environment resembling the facilities of a modern, medium-sized law firm.
- Cyber Law
- Community Economic Development
- Criminal Law (Federal and State)
- Family Law
- Mediation
- Gay and Lesbian Rights
- Civil Rights
- Environmental Law
- Employment Law
- Civil Cases (in general)
- Juvenile Law
- Health Rights for Women Inmates

■ Admission

In order to be admitted to the University of Puerto Rico School of Law, applicants must take two aptitude tests: the Law School Admission Test (LSAT) and the Examen de Admisión a Estudios de Posgrado (EXADEP). The tests must be taken no later than February of the year of application. Applicants must also have a bachelor's degree from an accredited institution before enrolling.

The entering class is selected by converting the LSAT, the EXADEP, and the GPA into the student's admission index and making offers of admission to those with the 200 highest admission indexes. However, 7 percent of the new class is chosen from those with 201–260 indexes based on a complete profile of the applicant, taking into consideration his or her ability to study law, his or her past accomplishments, and his or her disadvantages in receiving a postsecondary education.

Applicants who cannot take the required aptitude tests because of disability are considered individually by the admission committee. The University of Puerto Rico does not discriminate against students on the basis of race, color, religion, gender, age, marital status, national origin, or disability.

■ Expenses and Financial Aid

Resident law students pay tuition and fees amounting to $127 per credit each semester. Nonresident students who are US citizens pay the same amount that would be required from Puerto Rican students if they were to study in the state from which the nonresidents come, thus establishing a reciprocity principle. Nonresident students who are not US citizens pay additional tuition and fees amounting approximately to $2,327.50 for eight or more credits for each semester.

All financial aid for the University of Puerto Rico School of Law is administered by the school's Office of Financial Aid. Each student is considered on his or her own merit and need. Awards are made only after an applicant has been admitted.

■ Alumni

Our student body is made up of graduates from public and private universities of Puerto Rico and the states, as well as foreign institutions. They come from a wide range of academic backgrounds and social experiences, providing a unique atmosphere in the classroom and outside. Our alumni are leaders in the legal field and in the public arena serving as governors, US ambassadors, partners in major law firms, Puerto Rico Supreme Court Justices, Attorneys General, presidents of the University of Puerto Rico, and chief executive officers in the banking industry.

■ Library and Physical Facilities

The School of Law's library is the largest law library in the Caribbean. Its collection encompasses both the Romano-Germanic civil law and Anglo-American common law traditions. Also, our library has been designated as a European Documentation Center by the European Union and a selective depository for US government documents. Our school is equipped with state-of-the-art technology, smart classrooms, courtroom-classrooms, and wireless connections for the students.

Applicant Profile

University of Puerto Rico School of Law
This grid includes only applicants who earned 120–180 LSAT scores under standard administrations.

LSAT Score	3.75 +		3.50–3.74		3.25–3.49		3.00–3.24		2.75–2.99		2.50–2.74		2.25–2.49		2.00–2.24		Below 2.00		No GPA		Total	
	Apps	Adm	Apps	Adm	Apps	Adm	Apps	Adm	Apps	Adm	Apps	Adm	Apps	Adm	Apps	Adm	Apps	Adm	Apps	Adm	Apps	Adm
175–180	0	0	0	0	0	0	0	0	0	0	0	0	0	0	0	0	0	0	0	0	0	0
170–174	0	0	0	0	0	0	0	0	0	0	0	0	0	0	0	0	0	0	0	0	0	0
165–169	0	0	0	0	0	0	0	0	0	0	0	0	0	0	0	0	0	0	0	0	0	0
160–164	0	0	1	1	2	2	1	1	0	0	0	0	0	0	0	0	0	0	0	0	4	4
155–159	2	1	3	3	9	8	1	1	3	2	0	0	0	0	0	0	0	0	0	0	18	15
150–154	6	5	12	11	4	4	12	11	2	2	0	0	2	1	0	0	0	0	1	1	39	35
145–149	15	15	17	12	12	10	17	13	7	2	6	2	3	0	2	0	0	0	2	0	81	54
140–144	27	23	39	25	35	18	30	6	13	0	15	0	4	0	3	0	1	1	5	2	172	75
135–139	22	15	25	6	36	3	24	0	16	0	17	0	2	0	3	0	0	0	5	0	150	24
130–134	14	1	21	1	30	1	14	0	32	0	7	0	7	0	1	0	1	0	6	0	133	3
125–129	5	0	5	0	15	0	2	0	8	0	4	0	3	0	3	0	0	0	5	0	50	0
120–124	0	0	4	0	1	0	1	0	1	0	0	0	2	0	0	0	0	0	3	0	12	0
Total	91	60	127	59	144	46	102	32	82	6	49	2	23	1	12	0	2	1	27	3	659	210

Apps = Number of Applicants
Adm = Number Admitted
Reflects 99% of the total applicant pool; average LSAT data reported.

Quinnipiac University School of Law

275 Mount Carmel Avenue
Hamden, CT 06518
Phone: 203.582.3400; Fax: 203.582.3339
E-mail: ladm@quinnipiac.edu; Website: http://law.quinnipiac.edu

ABA
Approved
Since
1992

The Basics

Type of school	Private
Term	Semester
Application deadline	3/1
Application fee	$40
Financial aid deadline	
Can first year start other than fall?	No
Student to faculty ratio	11.2 to 1
# of housing spaces available restricted to law students	
graduate housing for which law students are eligible	

Faculty and Administrators

	Total		Men		Women		Minorities	
	Spr	Fall	Spr	Fall	Spr	Fall	Spr	Fall
Full-time	26	27	15	15	11	12	2	2
Other full-time	5	5	4	4	1	1	0	0
Deans, librarians, & others who teach	3	3	2	2	1	1	0	0
Part-time	34	33	20	26	14	7	0	1
Total	68	68	41	47	27	21	2	3

Curriculum

	Full-Time	Part-Time
Typical first-year section size	75	58
Is there typically a "small section" of the first-year class, other than Legal Writing, taught by full-time faculty	Yes	Yes
If yes, typical size offered last year	37	29
# of classroom course titles beyond first-year curriculum	106	

# of upper division courses, excluding seminars, with an enrollment:		
Under 25	122	
25–49	15	
50–74	4	
75–99	1	
100+	0	

# of seminars	11	
# of seminar positions available	176	
# of seminar positions filled	37	52
# of positions available in simulation courses	283	
# of simulation positions filled	132	97
# of positions available in faculty supervised clinical courses	80	
# of faculty supervised clinical positions filled	50	5
# involved in field placements	100	0
# involved in law journals	41	19
# involved in moot court or trial competitions	12	5
# of credit hours required to graduate	86	

JD Enrollment and Ethnicity

	Men		Women		Full-Time		Part-Time		1st-Year		Total		JD Degs. Awd.
	#	%	#	%	#	%	#	%	#	%	#	%	
African Amer.	3	1.5	10	4.7	10	3.4	3	2.4	2	1.3	13	3.1	2
Amer. Indian	1	0.5	2	0.9	1	0.3	2	1.6	2	1.3	3	0.7	2
Asian Amer.	6	3.0	15	7.1	15	5.2	6	4.8	9	5.7	21	5.1	6
Mex. Amer.	0	0.0	0	0.0	0	0.0	0	0.0	0	0.0	0	0.0	0
Puerto Rican	0	0.0	0	0.0	0	0.0	0	0.0	0	0.0	0	0.0	0
Hispanic	4	2.0	12	5.7	9	3.1	7	5.6	7	4.4	16	3.9	7
Total Minority	14	6.9	39	18.4	35	12.0	18	14.5	20	12.7	53	12.8	17
For. Nation.	5	2.5	6	2.8	7	2.4	4	3.2	5	3.2	11	2.7	0
Caucasian	171	84.2	157	74.1	231	79.4	97	78.2	124	78.5	328	79.0	88
Unknown	13	6.4	10	4.7	18	6.2	5	4.0	9	5.7	23	5.5	8
Total	203	48.9	212	51.1	291	70.1	124	29.9	158	38.1	415		113

Transfers

Transfers in	4
Transfers out	10

Tuition and Fees

	Resident	Nonresident
Full-time	$40,780	$40,780
Part-time	$28,780	$28,780
Tuition Guarantee Program	N	

Living Expenses

Estimated living expenses for singles

Living on campus	Living off campus	Living at home
N/A	$19,756	$13,724

Quinnipiac University School of Law

ABA
Approved
Since
1992

GPA and LSAT Scores

	Total	Full-Time	Part-Time
# of apps	2,824	2,686	679
# of offers	1,178	1,093	85
# of matrics	160	113	47
75% GPA	3.60	3.63	3.51
Median GPA	3.31	3.32	3.29
25% GPA	3.09	3.10	3.01
75% LSAT	159	160	154
Median LSAT	157	158	153
25% LSAT	154	156	151

Grants and Scholarships (from prior year)

	Total		Full-Time		Part-Time	
	#	%	#	%	#	%
Total # of students	387		248		139	
Total # receiving grants	266	68.7	207	83.5	59	42.4
Less than 1/2 tuition	154	39.8	95	38.3	59	42.4
Half to full tuition	87	22.5	87	35.1	0	0.0
Full tuition	25	6.5	25	10.1	0	0.0
More than full tuition	0	0.0	0	0.0	0	0.0
Median grant amount			$20,000		$6,000	

Informational and Library Resources

Total amount spent on library materials	$1,056,853
Study seating capacity inside the library	350
# of full-time equivalent professional librarians	5
Hours per week library is open	93
# of open, wired connections available to students	264
# of networked computers available for use by students	103
Has wireless network?	Y
Require computer?	N

JD Attrition (from prior year)

	Academic	Other	Total	
	#	#	#	%
1st year	1	13	14	10.4
2nd year	1	0	1	0.9
3rd year	0	1	1	0.9
4th year	0	1	1	4.0

Employment (9 months after graduation)

	Total	Percentage
Employment status known	118	97.5
Employment status unknown	3	2.5
Employed	112	94.9
Pursuing graduate degrees	0	0.0
Unemployed (seeking, not seeking, or studying for the bar)	2	1.7
Type of Employment		
# employed in law firms	34	30.4
# employed in business and industry	28	25.0
# employed in government	23	20.5
# employed in public interest	2	1.8
# employed as judicial clerks	11	9.8
# employed in academia	1	0.9
Geographic Location		
# employed in state	71	63.4
# employed in foreign countries	0	0.0
# of states where employed	13	

Bar Passage Rates

First-time takers	120	Reporting %	85.00
Average school %	93.14	Average state %	88.28
Average pass difference	4.86		

Jurisdiction	Takers	Passers	Pass %	State %	Diff %
Connecticut	102	95	93.14	88.28	4.86

Quinnipiac University School of Law

275 Mount Carmel Avenue
Hamden, CT 06518
Phone: 203.582.3400; Fax: 203.582.3339
E-mail: ladm@quinnipiac.edu; Website: http://law.quinnipiac.edu

■ Introduction

Excellent law schools share many common traits—faculty renowned for their scholarship and commitment to teaching; academically rigorous courses; loyal, successful alumni; and motivated, focused students. All of these are essential components of Quinnipiac Law's identity. However, what sets Quinnipiac apart is its personal, student-centered approach to the law school experience. Contributing to this identity is a favorable 10:1 student-to-faculty ratio, the extraordinary accessibility of the faculty, and an environment that both challenges and supports its students as they prepare for careers in law.

Nestled among the hills, woods, and waterways of Connecticut on one of the most beautiful campuses in New England, yet just 75 miles from New York City, Quinnipiac's setting and location are ideal. The beautiful, state-of-the-art law center opened in 1995. Wireless computer access throughout provides students with a modern, relaxed, and safe environment for study.

■ Faculty

Our faculty's academic credentials span the nation's leading institutions from Harvard, Yale, and Berkeley to Chicago, Michigan, and Columbia. They combine excellence in scholarship and teaching with exceptional accessibility. The care with which faculty members demonstrate their interest in each student's progress and success is a distinguishing characteristic of Quinnipiac Law. Most faculty have an open-door policy and generously share their expertise, insight, and time. The low student-to-faculty ratio (10:1) allows students to work closely with faculty, and this translates into a different kind of law school experience.

■ Library and Physical Facilities

The 50,000-square-foot law library is at the center of the School of Law complex. With a collection of more than 425,000 volumes, it also provides comprehensive access to numerous electronic resources and databases such as LexisNexis, Westlaw/Dialog, JSTOR, and other Web-based services. Its interlibrary loan network makes it possible to obtain materials from any library in the world. The beautiful facility features spacious public areas, numerous reading rooms, and individual study carrels, providing a comfortable and relaxing environment for research and study.

■ Curriculum

The law school is fully approved by the ABA and is a member of AALS. Full-time day and part-time evening programs are offered beginning each fall. The academic program is designed to prepare students to be generalists or specialists. The program provides a dynamic blend of traditional classroom instruction and extensive experiential learning opportunities. Students who wish to focus on a specific area of study may choose from six different concentrations—**Civil Advocacy and Dispute Resolution, Criminal Law and Advocacy, Family Law, Health Law, Intellectual Property**,

and **Tax**. The law school also offers a joint JD/MBA degree (with a health care management track) and a summer study-abroad program with Trinity College in Dublin, Ireland.

■ Special Programs

Quinnipiac is recognized as having one of the premier clinical and externship programs in the country, and students often cite their experiences in these programs as one of the highlights of their law school career. These experiential learning opportunities allow students to bridge the gap between theory and practice. A total of 15 clinical and externship programs are available to students.

The six clinical programs include **Civil**, **Tax**, **Advanced**, **Evening** (for part-time students), **Defense Appellate**, and **Prosecution Appellate**. The nine externship programs are **Corporate Counsel**, **Criminal Justice**, **Family and Juvenile Law**, **Judicial**, **Legal Services**, **Legislative**, **Mediation**, **Public Interest**, and **Field Placement II**.

Quinnipiac has established two centers in specialized fields of law—the **Center for Health Law and Policy** and the **Center on Dispute Resolution**—both of which draw on the considerable academic strengths and resources within the law school community.

■ Admission

Admission is competitive and based upon a variety of factors: undergraduate academic record, LSAT scores, personal statement, letters of recommendation, résumé, and other evidence such as advanced degrees, life and work experience, and extracurricular activities. Applications are welcomed from students of color, nontraditional students, and all students who add to the diversity of the student body. A rolling admission system is employed; however, the priority application deadline for admission and scholarship consideration is March 1. *Candidates for the full-tuition Dean's Fellows awards must apply by February 1.*

■ Student Activities

Quinnipiac students often comment about the strong sense of community that permeates the law school. That sense of community is enhanced by the numerous and varied opportunities for students to participate in cocurricular activities, including a dynamic Student Bar Association, more than 25 different student organizations, a thriving Moot Court Society, a Mock Trial team, an active *Quinnipiac Law Review*, and two student journals—the *Health Law Journal* and the *Probate Law Journal*.

■ Expenses and Financial Aid

Approximately 90 percent of the student body receives some form of financial assistance. Every applicant is considered for merit-based scholarships that range from $3,000 to full tuition per year. March 1 is the application deadline for most merit awards. However, candidates for the full-tuition Dean's Fellows scholarships must submit applications by February 1.

Total institutional scholarships and grants for the 2009–2010 academic year totaled approximately $4.6 million.

■ Housing

Campus housing for graduate and professional students is not available. However, there is ample, affordable housing available near the campus and throughout New Haven county. The School of Law Admissions Office maintains a housing website and roommate locator online for its admitted students and also provides personal assistance in securing off-campus accommodations.

■ Career Services

The Office of Career Services provides students and graduates with the expert guidance necessary to make informed career decisions. It offers substantial support through individual counseling and workshops on topics such as writing résumés and interviewing techniques.

The office coordinates on- and off-campus recruitment programs. Students interview with employers for a variety of summer internships and permanent jobs in the private and public sector.

Over the past five years, more than 90 percent of our graduates have been employed within nine months of graduation. The graduating class of 2008 had a 95 percent placement rate and found employment as follows: 34 percent entered private practice, 28 percent took positions in business and industry, 23 percent chose government service work, 11 percent received judicial clerkships, 2 percent went into public interest work, and 1 percent were studying for advanced degrees. The remainder went into other fields of employment.

Applicant Profile

Quinnipiac University School of Law
This grid includes only applicants who earned 120–180 LSAT scores under standard administrations.

LSAT Score	3.75 +		3.50–3.74		3.25–3.49		3.00–3.24		2.75–2.99		2.50–2.74		Below 2.50		No GPA		Total	
	Apps	Adm	Apps	Adm	Apps	Adm	Apps	Adm	Apps	Adm	Apps	Adm	Apps	Adm	Apps	Adm	Apps	Adm
170–180	4	4	0	0	4	4	3	3	0	0	2	1	4	3	0	0	17	15
165–169	18	17	16	15	23	23	12	12	8	5	3	1	3	1	1	1	84	75
160–164	69	67	94	87	70	68	69	61	37	33	18	13	18	7	2	2	377	338
155–159	105	98	165	141	166	136	136	90	71	46	44	19	33	6	6	4	726	540
150–154	116	28	176	41	208	50	191	33	122	14	60	5	57	2	11	5	941	178
145–149	35	3	66	4	84	5	100	7	67	2	44	1	25	1	7	1	428	24
140–144	4	0	17	1	24	0	32	0	30	1	14	0	17	0	9	0	147	2
Below 140	1	0	9	0	18	0	11	0	24	0	12	0	19	0	6	0	100	0
Total	352	217	543	289	597	286	554	206	359	101	197	40	176	20	42	13	2820	1172

Apps = Number of Applicants
Adm = Number Admitted
Refects 99% of the total applicant pool; average LSAT data reported.

Regent University School of Law

1000 Regent University Drive, RH239
Virginia Beach, VA 23464
Phone: 757.352.4584; Fax: 757.352.4139
E-mail: lawschool@regent.edu; Website: www.regent.edu/law

ABA
Approved
Since
1989

The Basics

Type of school	Private
Term	Semester
Application deadline	6/1
Application fee	$50
Financial aid deadline	6/1
Can first year start other than fall?	No
Student to faculty ratio	16.2 to 1
# of housing spaces available restricted to law students graduate housing for which law students are eligible	860

Faculty and Administrators

	Total		Men		Women		Minorities	
	Spr	Fall	Spr	Fall	Spr	Fall	Spr	Fall
Full-time	20	21	13	14	7	7	4	3
Other full-time	5	4	5	3	0	1	0	1
Deans, librarians, & others who teach	11	11	8	8	3	3	1	1
Part-time	23	17	20	14	3	3	1	1
Total	59	53	46	39	13	14	6	6

Curriculum

	Full-Time	Part-Time
Typical first-year section size	72	72
Is there typically a "small section" of the first-year class, other than Legal Writing, taught by full-time faculty	Yes	Yes
If yes, typical size offered last year	36	36
# of classroom course titles beyond first-year curriculum	88	

# of upper division courses, excluding seminars, with an enrollment:		
Under 25	95	
25–49	16	
50–74	8	
75–99	9	
100+	0	

# of seminars	2	
# of seminar positions available	24	
# of seminar positions filled	11	0
# of positions available in simulation courses	451	
# of simulation positions filled	303	6
# of positions available in faculty supervised clinical courses	49	
# of faculty supervised clinical positions filled	32	0
# involved in field placements	49	1
# involved in law journals	65	1
# involved in moot court or trial competitions	51	0
# of credit hours required to graduate	90	

JD Enrollment and Ethnicity

	Men #	Men %	Women #	Women %	Full-Time #	Full-Time %	Part-Time #	Part-Time %	1st-Year #	1st-Year %	Total #	Total %	JD Degs. Awd.
African Amer.	9	4.2	19	9.4	25	6.3	3	13.0	11	6.8	28	6.7	6
Amer. Indian	4	1.9	2	1.0	6	1.5	0	0.0	2	1.2	6	1.4	1
Asian Amer.	8	3.7	12	5.9	20	5.1	0	0.0	5	3.1	20	4.8	5
Mex. Amer.	1	0.5	0	0.0	1	0.3	0	0.0	0	0.0	1	0.2	0
Puerto Rican	0	0.0	0	0.0	0	0.0	0	0.0	0	0.0	0	0.0	0
Hispanic	5	2.3	3	1.5	8	2.0	0	0.0	4	2.5	8	1.9	2
Total Minority	27	12.6	36	17.7	60	15.2	3	13.0	22	13.6	63	15.1	14
For. Nation.	1	0.5	3	1.5	4	1.0	0	0.0	0	0.0	4	1.0	0
Caucasian	179	83.6	156	76.8	316	80.2	19	82.6	134	82.7	335	80.3	121
Unknown	7	3.3	8	3.9	14	3.6	1	4.3	6	3.7	15	3.6	5
Total	214	51.3	203	48.7	394	94.5	23	5.5	162	38.8	417		140

Transfers

Transfers in	5
Transfers out	6

Tuition and Fees

	Resident	Nonresident
Full-time	$29,852	$29,852
Part-time	$23,027	$23,027
Tuition Guarantee Program	N	

Living Expenses

Estimated living expenses for singles

Living on campus	Living off campus	Living at home
$19,940	$19,940	$19,940

Regent University School of Law

ABA
Approved
Since
1989

GPA and LSAT Scores

	Total	Full-Time	Part-Time
# of apps	786	749	37
# of offers	368	351	17
# of matrics	162	152	10
75% GPA	3.71	3.71	3.67
Median GPA	3.37	3.36	3.44
25% GPA	3.00	3.00	2.96
75% LSAT	156	157	153
Median LSAT	152	153	150
25% LSAT	150	150	148

Grants and Scholarships (from prior year)

	Total		Full-Time		Part-Time	
	#	%	#	%	#	%
Total # of students	414		395		19	
Total # receiving grants	330	79.7	316	80.0	14	73.7
Less than 1/2 tuition	242	58.5	228	57.7	14	73.7
Half to full tuition	63	15.2	63	15.9	0	0.0
Full tuition	24	5.8	24	6.1	0	0.0
More than full tuition	1	0.2	1	0.3	0	0.0
Median grant amount			$6,000		$2,000	

Informational and Library Resources

Total amount spent on library materials	$746,349
Study seating capacity inside the library	324
# of full-time equivalent professional librarians	10
Hours per week library is open	109
# of open, wired connections available to students	241
# of networked computers available for use by students	70
Has wireless network?	Y
Require computer?	N

JD Attrition (from prior year)

	Academic	Other	Total	
	#	#	#	%
1st year	12	8	20	13.9
2nd year	0	2	2	1.6
3rd year	0	0	0	0.0
4th year	0	0	0	0.0

Employment (9 months after graduation)

	Total	Percentage
Employment status known	154	96.9
Employment status unknown	5	3.1
Employed	140	90.9
Pursuing graduate degrees	5	3.2
Unemployed (seeking, not seeking, or studying for the bar)	5	3.2
Type of Employment		
# employed in law firms	60	42.9
# employed in business and industry	16	11.4
# employed in government	27	19.3
# employed in public interest	12	8.6
# employed as judicial clerks	16	11.4
# employed in academia	7	5.0
Geographic Location		
# employed in state	62	44.3
# employed in foreign countries	1	0.7
# of states where employed	25	

Bar Passage Rates

First-time takers	161	Reporting %	74.53
Average school %	81.66	Average state %	84.35
Average pass difference –2.69			

Jurisdiction	Takers	Passers	Pass %	State %	Diff %
Virginia	71	52	73.24	82.70	–9.46
Georgia	7	7	100.00	89.27	10.73
North Carolina	7	7	100.00	82.61	17.39
Pennsylvania	6	6	100.00	86.69	13.31
Others (6)	29	26	89.66		

Regent University School of Law

1000 Regent University Drive, RH239
Virginia Beach, VA 23464
Phone: 757.352.4584; Fax: 757.352.4139
E-mail: lawschool@regent.edu; Website: www.regent.edu/law

■ Introduction

Regent University is distinctive among ABA-approved law schools because of its integration of Christian principles into the curriculum. It is this balance of professional legal training and affirmation of biblical principles that enables Regent graduates to provide excellent legal counsel to their clients while carrying forth the mission of the university—Christian Leadership to Change the World. Nearly 5,000 students are pursuing degrees at Regent University. The law school is composed of approximately 420 students. Regent University is situated on a stately, Georgian-style campus in Virginia Beach, minutes from the Atlantic Ocean, less than a two-hour drive from Richmond, and less than four hours from Washington, DC.

■ Christian Distinction

The foremost distinction of Regent Law School is its Christian perspective. The School of Law is unique in that its mission embraces a Christian world-view, while affirming the faith of individual students. This mission provides a strong basis for teaching the highest ethical standards for lawyers. The mission also helps make Regent a great overall experience for students. The Princeton Review consistently ranks Regent Law School in the top 10 for quality of student life.

■ Academic Program/Legal Skills

Regent Law School places great emphasis on developing practical lawyering skills through its Center for Advocacy. Courses have been designed to provide in-depth training and opportunities to develop these skills. Regent law students have enjoyed tremendous success in student competitions. Our recent national awards include 2009 National Pretrial Competition Overall Champions, including Best Brief and Best Oralist; 2008 ABA Regional Moot Court Champions; 2008 BLSA International Negotiation Competition Champions; 2007 ABA National Negotiation Champions; 2006 ABA Moot Court National Champions; and 2006 Best Brief in the National Appellate Advocacy Competition. The practical lawyering skills and strong ethical values of Regent graduates have enabled them to successfully obtain employment with top law firms, federal and state courts, business and technology companies, and national public interest law firms. Ten percent of our 2008 graduating class secured judicial clerkships.

■ Clinical Opportunities—Public Interest Law

Regent law students are noted for their commitment to public service, constitutional law, and equal justice. The School of Law provides opportunities for hands-on, student-client contact through our Civil Litigation Clinic. Additionally, the School of Law enjoys a special relationship with the American Center for Law and Justice (ACLJ), the nation's foremost public interest law firm defending religious liberties. Selected law students may obtain volunteer and paid positions to assist ACLJ staff attorneys involved in profamily and proliberty cases and may participate in a semester-in-DC program with ACLJ attorneys.

■ Full- and Part-Time Programs

The School of Law offers full- and part-time 90-semester-hour Juris Doctor programs, in-residence only. Students in the full-time program normally complete their degrees in three years; part-time students complete their degrees in four to five years.

■ Admission and the Bar

Applicants to the School of Law are required to submit a personal statement as part of the admission process. This personal statement is considered very carefully along with the applicant's LSAT score(s), undergraduate record, résumé, and letters of recommendation. The School of Law is committed to considering the entire application in the decision process, ultimately offering admission to prospective students who present a strong likelihood for success in law school. This commitment has resulted in a diverse student body. Applications from prospective students with LSAT scores of 150 and above and UGPAs above 3.0 are especially encouraged, as the School of Law has evidence that such students are very likely to succeed in law school and are also very likely to pass the bar exam on their first attempt. Regent's first-time bar passage rate for all 2008 graduates is as follows: for LSAT scores at or above 150, 91 percent; at or above 155, 92 percent; and at or above 160, 100 percent.

■ Academic Assistance

Regent Law School is on the cutting edge in offering academic assistance to its students. The School of Law employs two faculty members, a director and associate director of academic success, who oversee the three components of the school's Academic Success Program. Under the first component, the school invites selected first-year students to attend a two-week program as a condition for admission into the school. The program, which occurs in late summer right before orientation for all incoming students, helps students develop excellent law school study skills and introduces them to selected areas of the law in small sections taught by members of the full-time faculty. Under the second component, the school offers study skills workshops during the spring and fall semesters. As the third component, the associate director meets one-on-one with students to provide individualized counseling on how to improve their study strategies. The second and third components are available to all students. Student feedback on the school's Academic Success Program has been very positive.

■ The Law Library

Immediately adjacent to the School of Law and occupying the entire third floor of the library building, the newly renovated Law Library features 140 carrels in secluded study areas, as well as areas for group interaction, with both LAN and WiFi connections throughout for accessing essential legal research databases. With holdings of over 396,000 volumes and equivalents, the library's collection strengths are constitutional

law and history, legal history, jurisprudence, law and faith, philosophy of law, international human rights, and family law.

■ International Law and Summer-Abroad/ Exchange Programs

The School of Law has established the *Regent Journal of International Law* and has a very active International Law Society. The *Journal* is jointly edited by students from Regent Law School and our Korean sister school, Handong International Law School, making it truly an international journal. In addition, the law school hosts a summer program in Strasbourg, France, focusing on international law and human rights. A summer program in Haifa and Jerusalem, Israel focuses on issues of international law and the State of Israel, and provides a hermeneutical comparison of biblical and Qur'anic law. Regent also offers semester-abroad opportunities. Students may spend a semester studying international law at Handong International Law School in South Korea. The School of Law has created student-exchange programs with Spanish universities in Barcelona and Madrid. Students are able to spend a semester in Spain and take subjects such as civil law and international private law. The School of Law has also approved a study-abroad agreement with Shantou University in China. Under the agreement, Regent students will be able to study law in English at Shantou and Regent will welcome visiting students from Shantou.

■ Housing

Regent law students may choose from a variety of on- and off-campus housing options. Regent Village and Regent Commons offer convenient and quality housing within walking distance to the law school. Regent's on-campus housing provides a safe, friendly atmosphere and includes the following options: efficiency, quad, and one-, two-, and three-bedroom apartments. Housing applications are provided to admitted candidates only. Rates are comparable to or less than similar apartment complexes in the nearby vicinity.

■ Financial Aid

The School of Law is committed to helping students finance their legal education by awarding approximately $2.8 million in scholarships and grants, ranging from $500 to full tuition. In recent years, approximately 92 percent of law students received some type of financial aid; 70 percent received scholarships or grants. Typically, admitted candidates with LSAT scores greater than or equal to 160, UGPAs greater than or equal to 3.0, and personal goals evidencing a calling toward Christian leadership and service have been awarded academic merit scholarships ranging from 80 to 100 percent of tuition costs. Other scholarships are awarded on the basis of academic promise and other factors indicative of potential for law school success. Regent also provides grant assistance for qualified students who are called to serve minority communities upon graduation. Students not awarded financial assistance the first year of law school may qualify for assistance in future years based on academic performance. Residents of Virginia may also qualify for the Virginia Tuition Assistance Grant. Regent provides a student loan repayment assistance program (LRAP) for qualified graduates practicing in the area of public interest law. A variety of loan options, including Stafford and Graduate PLUS, are available to meet the tuition and living expenses related to law school.

■ Campus Visitations

Campus visitations: *www.regent.edu/lawvisitation*.
The Office of Admissions encourages prospective student visits. To RSVP for campus visitations or to arrange a visit to the law school, please e-mail *lawschool@regent.edu* or telephone 757.352.4584.

Applicant Profile

Regent University School of Law
This grid includes only applicants who earned 120–180 LSAT scores under standard administrations.

LSAT Score	GPA								
	3.75 +	3.50–3.74	3.25–3.49	3.00–3.24	2.75–2.99	2.50–2.74	2.25–2.49	2.00–2.24	Below 2.00
175–180									
170–174									
165–169									
160–164									
155–159									
150–154									
146–149									
120–145									

Strong Possibility   Possible   Unlikely

This grid is intended to provide prospective applicants a general sense of our admission standards, as based upon competition for entry into recent classes entering the law school. This grid does not adequately describe the numerous nonquantifiable factors that are considered by our Admission Committee. Prospective applicants are encouraged to review our admission materials for a fuller understanding of the admission review standards used by Regent University School of Law.

University of Richmond School of Law

28 Westhampton Way
University of Richmond, VA 23173
Phone: 804.289.8189; Fax: 804.287.6516
E-mail: lawadmissions@richmond.edu; Website: http://law.richmond.edu

The Basics

Type of school	Private
Term	Semester
Application deadline	2/15
Application fee	$35
Financial aid deadline	3/1
Can first year start other than fall?	Yes
Student to faculty ratio	15.9 to 1
# of housing spaces available restricted to law students	8
graduate housing for which law students are eligible	8

Faculty and Administrators

	Total		Men		Women		Minorities	
	Spr	Fall	Spr	Fall	Spr	Fall	Spr	Fall
Full-time	21	28	15	20	6	8	2	2
Other full-time	5	4	3	2	2	2	0	0
Deans, librarians, & others who teach	16	16	6	6	10	10	0	0
Part-time	56	53	36	36	19	17	1	2
Total	98	101	60	64	37	37	3	4

Curriculum

		Full-Time	Part-Time
Typical first-year section size		55	0
Is there typically a "small section" of the first-year class, other than Legal Writing, taught by full-time faculty		Yes	No
If yes, typical size offered last year		40	
# of classroom course titles beyond first-year curriculum		104	
# of upper division courses, excluding seminars, with an enrollment:	Under 25	103	
	25–49	25	
	50–74	8	
	75–99	5	
	100+	0	
# of seminars		18	
# of seminar positions available		321	
# of seminar positions filled		244	0
# of positions available in simulation courses		485	
# of simulation positions filled		418	0
# of positions available in faculty supervised clinical courses		58	
# of faculty supervised clinical positions filled	43	0
# involved in field placements		72	0
# involved in law journals		190	0
# involved in moot court or trial competitions	38	0
# of credit hours required to graduate		86	

JD Enrollment and Ethnicity

	Men		Women		Full-Time		Part-Time		1st-Year		Total		JD Degs. Awd.
	#	%	#	%	#	%	#	%	#	%	#	%	
African Amer.	21	8.6	21	9.5	42	9.0	0	0.0	14	9.3	42	9.0	18
Amer. Indian	3	1.2	1	0.5	4	0.9	0	0.0	1	0.7	4	0.9	0
Asian Amer.	10	4.1	18	8.1	28	6.0	0	0.0	9	6.0	28	6.0	2
Mex. Amer.	0	0.0	0	0.0	0	0.0	0	0.0	0	0.0	0	0.0	0
Puerto Rican	0	0.0	0	0.0	0	0.0	0	0.0	0	0.0	0	0.0	0
Hispanic	2	0.8	1	0.5	3	0.6	0	0.0	2	1.3	3	0.6	2
Total Minority	36	14.8	41	18.5	77	16.6	0	0.0	26	17.3	77	16.6	22
For. Nation.	3	1.2	0	0.0	3	0.6	0	0.0	0	0.0	3	0.6	0
Caucasian	204	84.0	181	81.5	385	82.8	0	0.0	124	82.7	385	82.8	131
Unknown	0	0.0	0	0.0	0	0.0	0	0.0	0	0.0	0	0.0	0
Total	243	52.3	222	47.7	465	100.0	0	0.0	150	32.3	465		153

Transfers

Transfers in	19
Transfers out	18

Tuition and Fees

	Resident	Nonresident
Full-time	$32,450	$32,450
Part-time		
Tuition Guarantee Program		N

Living Expenses

Estimated living expenses for singles

Living on campus	Living off campus	Living at home
$13,670	$15,270	$6,240

University of Richmond School of Law

ABA
Approved
Since
1928

GPA and LSAT Scores

	Total	Full-Time	Part-Time
# of apps	2,036	2,036	0
# of offers	584	584	0
# of matrics	149	149	0
75% GPA	3.63	3.63	0.00
Median GPA	3.48	3.48	0.00
25% GPA	3.19	3.19	0.00
75% LSAT	163	163	0
Median LSAT	161	161	0
25% LSAT	159	159	0

Grants and Scholarships (from prior year)

	Total #	Total %	Full-Time #	Full-Time %	Part-Time #	Part-Time %
Total # of students	482		477		5	
Total # receiving grants	344	71.4	344	72.1	0	0.0
Less than 1/2 tuition	317	65.8	317	66.5	0	0.0
Half to full tuition	27	5.6	27	5.7	0	0.0
Full tuition	0	0.0	0	0.0	0	0.0
More than full tuition	0	0.0	0	0.0	0	0.0
Median grant amount			$7,500		$0	

Informational and Library Resources

Total amount spent on library materials	$1,650,796
Study seating capacity inside the library	675
# of full-time equivalent professional librarians	6
Hours per week library is open	106
# of open, wired connections available to students	809
# of networked computers available for use by students	68
Has wireless network?	Y
Require computer?	Y

JD Attrition (from prior year)

	Academic #	Other #	Total #	Total %
1st year	0	22	22	13.6
2nd year	0	0	0	0.0
3rd year	0	0	0	0.0
4th year	0	0	0	0.0

Employment (9 months after graduation)

	Total	Percentage
Employment status known	164	96.5
Employment status unknown	6	3.5
Employed	143	87.2
Pursuing graduate degrees	7	4.3
Unemployed (seeking, not seeking, or studying for the bar)	11	6.7
Type of Employment		
# employed in law firms	76	53.1
# employed in business and industry	11	7.7
# employed in government	17	11.9
# employed in public interest	3	2.1
# employed as judicial clerks	25	17.5
# employed in academia	0	0.0
Geographic Location		
# employed in state	98	68.5
# employed in foreign countries	0	0.0
# of states where employed		19

Bar Passage Rates

First-time takers	170	Reporting %	74.71
Average school %	90.55	Average state %	82.70
Average pass difference	7.85		

Jurisdiction	Takers	Passers	Pass %	State %	Diff %
Virginia	127	115	90.55	82.70	7.85

University of Richmond School of Law

28 Westhampton Way
University of Richmond, VA 23173
Phone: 804.289.8189; Fax: 804.287.6516
E-mail: lawadmissions@richmond.edu; Website: http://law.richmond.edu

■ Introduction

The University of Richmond School of Law, founded in 1870, enjoys an established reputation for preparing its graduates for legal careers. Accredited by the ABA and a member of the AALS, its graduates are qualified to seek admission to the bar of all 50 states and the District of Columbia.

Situated on the university's 350-acre suburban campus, the school is only a 20-minute drive from downtown Richmond and its thriving legal community. In addition to being home to a number of international law firms, Richmond is the capital of the Commonwealth of Virginia, with numerous state and federal offices, and is the seat of both the Supreme Court of Virginia and the US Court of Appeals for the Fourth Circuit.

■ Library and Physical Facilities

The law school, located in a collegiate, gothic-style building, includes a moot courtroom that is the site of many classes, events, and mock trials, and where a panel of federal judges from the Fourth Circuit hears oral arguments once a year. The building has both wired and wireless connections, with almost 900 wired network connections. Every student has an individual study carrel, bearing his/her name, which functions as a personal office in the law library. The library offers a comprehensive collection of both electronic and print resources.

■ Curriculum

Courses in contracts, torts, criminal law, civil procedure, property, constitutional law, and a choice of one elective comprise the first-year curriculum. Required upper-level courses include professional responsibility and a third-year writing seminar. Elective courses in a variety of areas are available. In addition, all students complete a comprehensive, two-year program in legal reasoning, writing, research, and fundamental lawyering skills and values.

■ Academic Success Program and Bar Passage

Richmond Law has a comprehensive Academic Success Program geared toward assisting students to achieve at their highest possible academic level. The program also supports students in preparing for the bar exam, in whatever jurisdiction they choose to take it. Richmond Law consistently has one of the highest bar passage rates among first-time test takers in the Commonwealth of Virginia.

■ Special Programs

Several dual-degree programs allow students to earn the JD degree as well as a master's degree in a related discipline. Dual-degree programs are available in business administration, health administration, social work, urban studies and planning, public administration, as well as others.

The law school operates the Children's Law Center through which students may participate in the Delinquency Clinic, the Disability Clinic, the Juvenile Law and Policy Clinic, the Family Law Clinic, and the Advanced Children's Clinic.

Exciting clinical placements are arranged for academic credit in courts, law offices, corporations, and nonprofit agencies. Externships are available in civil, criminal, judicial, and business law.

The Intellectual Property Institute has developed a curriculum to enable students to obtain a certificate of concentration in Intellectual Property Law.

The National Center for Family Law fosters research, scholarship, reports, conferences, symposia, legislative testimony, and other public participation and discourse on issues related to Family Law.

The Robert R. Merhige Jr. Center for Environmental Studies engages in research, instruction, and public outreach on energy and environmental issues in the Mid-Atlantic region and beyond.

The Institute for Actual Innocence (IAI) works to identify, investigate, and exonerate wrongfully convicted individuals in the Commonwealth of Virginia. It joins a national community of innocence projects with similar goals. Students, with hands-on involvement by faculty and practicing lawyers, conduct reinvestigations of cases where credible evidence of actual innocence is present. Students learn the subtleties and pitfalls involved in interviewing witnesses, inmates, and other parties central to criminal cases. They learn to analyze a criminal trial or appellate record for new evidentiary perspectives. The IAI offers an environment for students to express their problem-solving, interpersonal, and analytical skills.

The "University of Richmond Downtown," a satellite campus in the heart of the city of Richmond, serves as a hub of community-based service, learning, research, and collaboration with nonprofit and government partners. UR Downtown aims to address pressing community needs through a combination of pro bono legal services provided by law students and attorneys, and community-based research and services provided by undergraduates and faculty.

■ International Programs

Richmond Law offers an extremely popular summer program at Emmanuel College in Cambridge, England, and an exchange program with the University of Paris, as well as with more than 20 universities worldwide, 9 of which have acclaimed law programs.

■ Student Activities

A student board publishes the *University of Richmond Law Review* on a quarterly basis. The *Richmond Journal of Law and Technology*, the first student-edited scholarly journal in the world to be published exclusively in electronic form, went online April 10, 1995. The *Richmond Journal of Law and the Public Interest* is a second online journal published by our students as an interdisciplinary journal dedicated to current and often controversial issues affecting the public. The *Richmond Journal of Global Law and Business* provides scholarly and practical insight into major legal and business issues affecting our global economy.

Richmond's moot court activities allow students to test their research, brief-writing, trial, negotiation, and appellate advocacy skills. Beginning in their 1L year, students

participate in intraschool tournaments that lead to membership on the Moot Court Board, the Trial Advocacy Board, and the Client Counseling and Negotiation Board. Moot Court, TAB, and CCNB teams represent the law school in regional, national, and international competitions.

■ Admission

Applications are reviewed as they become complete. All decisions are released by May 15. The admission committee considers the UGPA and LSAT as two important items, although extracurricular and community service activities and employment experience are also of interest. The law school provides an equal educational opportunity without regard to race, color, national origin, sex, disability, or religion.

We encourage class visits and, in keeping with our very personal approach to admission, we also encourage you to take advantage of meeting with a law student. Law students are available to give tours Monday through Saturday and may be reached at *LSAR@richmond.edu*.

■ Expenses and Financial Aid

Institutional aid in the form of grants and scholarships is available on the basis of need and merit. Financial Aid decisions are often made based on submission of the FAFSA and we recommend filing this form by February 25 to get the fullest consideration of all available aid. Parental income is not considered in determining financial aid for students who are considered to be independent by the law school.

John Marshall Scholars Program—The law school's most prestigious awards offer $10,000 annual stipends in addition to other merit aid, as well as other honors, and are renewable annually if criteria are met. The general application must be **completed** by February 1. If invited to compete for these

awards, a separate application must be submitted in mid-February. Committee consideration for these scholarships is based solely on merit and personal attributes. Some applicants may be able to demonstrate the required attributes by having successfully overcome serious disadvantages or obstacles. John Marshall Scholars will be awarded institutional grants and scholarships in addition to their JM Scholarship.

■ Housing

Limited on-campus housing is available on a first-come, first-served basis. Richmond offers an abundance of good, affordable housing in proximity to the law school. For information on housing, contact the Admissions Office.

■ Career Services

The Career Services Office works closely with law students and alumni in obtaining employment by helping to align their interests and talents with a desired career path, as well as assisting them with developing the skills and the knowledge necessary to conduct successful job searches. The office conducts a comprehensive, on-campus interview program which includes law firms and government and public interest employers, and it participates in a number of national job fairs. It also maintains an extensive employment database and organizes regular informational programs and networking opportunities for students.

Richmond has more types of courts than any city in the US outside of Washington, DC, or Boston, which provide a myriad of opportunities for externships and part-time employment while students are in their second and third years of study, thereby giving our students the benefit of gaining crucial legal experience and producing income for educational purposes.

Applicant Profile

University of Richmond School of Law
This grid includes only applicants who earned 120–180 LSAT scores under standard administrations.

LSAT Score	3.75 +		3.50–3.74		3.25–3.49		3.00–3.24		2.75–2.99		2.50–2.74		2.25–2.49		2.00–2.24		Below 2.00		No GPA		Total	
	Apps	Adm	Apps	Adm	Apps	Adm	Apps	Adm	Apps	Adm	Apps	Adm	Apps	Adm	Apps	Adm	Apps	Adm	Apps	Adm	Apps	Adm
175–180	0	0	0	0	0	0	0	0	0	0	0	0	0	0	0	0	0	0	0	0	0	0
170–174	1	0	0	0	2	1	3	1	4	1	1	0	2	0	0	0	0	0	0	0	13	3
165–169	11	4	16	10	22	13	11	6	11	6	9	4	2	1	0	0	0	0	1	0	83	44
160–164	64	55	88	77	118	99	71	41	37	16	18	3	2	1	5	1	1	0	0	0	404	293
155–159	87	26	177	80	164	31	103	19	56	6	35	7	15	0	4	1	1	0	3	0	645	170
150–154	65	8	113	16	109	14	86	10	51	7	25	0	8	1	4	2	0	0	8	1	469	59
145–149	17	1	40	0	33	1	50	3	41	2	14	0	15	0	1	0	3	0	2	0	216	7
140–144	4	0	18	0	25	0	26	0	19	0	20	0	5	0	2	0	1	0	5	0	125	0
135–139	1	0	6	0	9	0	7	0	8	0	11	0	7	0	3	0	2	0	2	0	56	0
130–134	0	0	0	0	6	0	0	0	11	0	0	0	1	0	3	0	0	0	3	0	24	0
125–129	0	0	0	0	0	0	0	0	1	0	1	0	0	0	1	0	0	0	1	0	4	0
120–124	0	0	0	0	0	0	0	0	0	0	0	0	0	0	0	0	0	0	0	0	0	0
Total	250	94	458	183	488	159	357	80	239	38	134	14	57	3	23	4	8	0	25	1	2039	576

Apps = Number of Applicants   Adm = Number Admitted   Reflects 99% of the total applicant pool; average LSAT data reported.

Roger Williams University School of Law

Ten Metacom Avenue
Bristol, RI 02809-5171
Phone: 401.254.4555 or 800.633.2727; Fax: 401.254.4516
E-mail: admissions@law.rwu.edu; Website: http://law.rwu.edu

ABA
Approved
Since
1995

The Basics

Type of school	Private
Term	Semester
Application deadline	3/15
Application fee	$60
Financial aid deadline	2/15
Can first year start other than fall?	No
Student to faculty ratio	16.7 to 1
# of housing spaces available restricted to law students	
graduate housing for which law students are eligible	72

Faculty and Administrators

	Total		Men		Women		Minorities	
	Spr	Fall	Spr	Fall	Spr	Fall	Spr	Fall
Full-time	27	27	18	16	9	11	3	4
Other full-time	1	2	0	0	1	2	0	0
Deans, librarians, & others who teach	10	10	4	4	6	6	0	0
Part-time	28	27	22	22	6	5	0	1
Total	66	66	44	42	22	24	3	5

JD Enrollment and Ethnicity

	Men		Women		Full-Time		Part-Time		1st-Year		Total		JD Degs. Awd.
	#	%	#	%	#	%	#	%	#	%	#	%	
African Amer.	7	2.6	6	2.1	13	2.4	0	0.0	4	1.8	13	2.4	5
Amer. Indian	2	0.7	1	0.4	3	0.5	0	0.0	0	0.0	3	0.5	1
Asian Amer.	5	1.9	8	2.9	13	2.4	0	0.0	6	2.7	13	2.4	8
Mex. Amer.	0	0.0	3	1.1	3	0.5	0	0.0	0	0.0	3	0.5	2
Puerto Rican	2	0.7	0	0.0	2	0.4	0	0.0	0	0.0	2	0.4	1
Hispanic	5	1.9	18	6.4	23	4.2	0	0.0	9	4.1	23	4.2	3
Total Minority	21	7.8	36	12.9	57	10.4	0	0.0	19	8.7	57	10.4	20
For. Nation.	2	0.7	3	1.1	5	0.9	0	0.0	2	0.9	5	0.9	1
Caucasian	212	78.5	215	76.8	427	77.6	0	0.0	174	79.5	427	77.6	136
Unknown	35	13.0	26	9.3	61	11.1	0	0.0	24	11.0	61	11.1	27
Total	270	49.1	280	50.9	550	100.0	0	0.0	219	39.8	550		184

Curriculum

	Full-Time	Part-Time
Typical first-year section size	60	0
Is there typically a "small section" of the first-year class, other than Legal Writing, taught by full-time faculty	No	No
If yes, typical size offered last year		
# of classroom course titles beyond first-year curriculum	110	

# of upper division courses, excluding seminars, with an enrollment:		
	Under 25	55
	25–49	16
	50–74	15
	75–99	7
	100+	1

# of seminars		47
# of seminar positions available		1,137
# of seminar positions filled	633	0
# of positions available in simulation courses		286
# of simulation positions filled	258	0
# of positions available in faculty supervised clinical courses		62
# of faculty supervised clinical positions filled	63	0
# involved in field placements	60	0
# involved in law journals	46	0
# involved in moot court or trial competitions	39	0
# of credit hours required to graduate		90

Transfers

Transfers in	6
Transfers out	12

Tuition and Fees

	Resident	Nonresident
Full-time	$35,570	$35,570
Part-time		
Tuition Guarantee Program		N

Living Expenses

Estimated living expenses for singles

Living on campus	Living off campus	Living at home
$19,368	$19,368	$19,368

Roger Williams University School of Law

ABA
Approved
Since
1995

GPA and LSAT Scores

	Total	Full-Time	Part-Time
# of apps	1,489	1,489	0
# of offers	871	871	0
# of matrics	420	210	0
75% GPA	3.49	3.49	0.00
Median GPA	3.26	3.26	0.00
25% GPA	2.99	2.99	0.00
75% LSAT	157	157	0
Median LSAT	152	152	0
25% LSAT	150	150	0

Grants and Scholarships (from prior year)

	Total		Full-Time		Part-Time	
	#	%	#	%	#	%
Total # of students	550		550		0	
Total # receiving grants	216	39.3	216	39.3	0	0.0
Less than 1/2 tuition	114	20.7	114	20.7	0	0.0
Half to full tuition	40	7.3	40	7.3	0	0.0
Full tuition	59	10.7	59	10.7	0	0.0
More than full tuition	3	0.5	3	0.5	0	0.0
Median grant amount			$12,500		$0	

Informational and Library Resources

Total amount spent on library materials	$945,649
Study seating capacity inside the library	403
# of full-time equivalent professional librarians	7
Hours per week library is open	110
# of open, wired connections available to students	196
# of networked computers available for use by students	83
Has wireless network?	Y
Require computer?	N

JD Attrition (from prior year)

	Academic	Other	Total	
	#	#	#	%
1st year	7	18	25	13.5
2nd year	1	2	3	1.7
3rd year	0	0	0	0.0
4th year	0	0	0	0.0

Employment (9 months after graduation)

	Total	Percentage
Employment status known	188	90.8
Employment status unknown	19	9.2
Employed	162	86.2
Pursuing graduate degrees	11	5.9
Unemployed (seeking, not seeking, or studying for the bar)	10	5.3
Type of Employment		
# employed in law firms	71	43.8
# employed in business and industry	34	21.0
# employed in government	21	13.0
# employed in public interest	13	8.0
# employed as judicial clerks	21	13.0
# employed in academia	1	0.6
Geographic Location		
# employed in state	70	43.2
# employed in foreign countries	2	1.2
# of states where employed	23	

Bar Passage Rates

First-time takers	207	Reporting %	116.43
Average school %	81.33	Average state %	86.60
Average pass difference	−5.27		

Jurisdiction	Takers	Passers	Pass %	State %	Diff %
Massachusetts	132	113	85.61	92.33	−6.72
Rhode Island	109	83	76.15	79.66	−3.51

Roger Williams University School of Law

Ten Metacom Avenue
Bristol, RI 02809-5171
Phone: 401.254.4555 or 800.633.2727; Fax: 401.254.4516
E-mail: admissions@law.rwu.edu; Website: http://law.rwu.edu

■ Introduction

Roger Williams University School of Law is located on a peninsula in the historic seacoast town of Bristol, Rhode Island. Providence, the state's capital and legal center, is 20 minutes away and offers extensive employment and externship opportunities. The resort town of Newport is located close by and is the hub of significant cultural, sporting, and recreational events. Boston is one hour to the north. The School of Law is the only law school in the state of Rhode Island. As a small school, the faculty is both accessible and approachable. While the academic environment is challenging, a collegial atmosphere exists.

■ Library and Physical Facilities

The School of Law is self-contained in a multimillion-dollar building designed exclusively for the study of law. The four-level facility contains class and seminar rooms and is equipped with state-of-the-art audiovisual and computer technology. The law library contains over 300,000 volumes and equivalents and provides wireless Internet access. The *WebCatalog* is available through the Internet, as are many library publications and resources. Access to the LexisNexis and Westlaw/Dialog services, the Internet, and CD-ROM publications is provided in three separate computer labs. Word processing and research-related and instructional programs are available to students in the labs.

■ Curriculum

The curriculum integrates intellectual theory, case analysis, and practical lawyering skills. The fundamental building blocks of effective lawyering constitute the first- and second-year curriculum. Students learn the skills of traditional legal analysis and the ability to elicit and convey information that every lawyer must master. The Legal Methods program and other required courses prepare students to become problem solvers; to comprehend, analyze, and synthesize complex material; and to communicate their positions effectively. In the latter years of their education, students gain expertise in legal specialties through clustering elective courses in particular fields of interest.

■ Joint-Degree Programs

Roger Williams University offers a JD/Master of Science in Criminal Justice. This program is designed to prepare graduates to formulate system policy and serve effectively as administrators to United States justice system agencies.

The School of Law also offers two joint-degree programs in conjunction with the University of Rhode Island. The JD/Master of Marine Affairs program is geared toward students interested in maritime, admiralty, and environmental law. The JD/Master of Science in Labor Relations and Human Resources program is designed for students interested in issues relating to employment and labor relations.

■ Special Programs

Marine Affairs Institute—The institute is recognized as a distinguished focal point for the exploration of legal, economic, and policy issues raised by the development of the oceans and coastal zone. Students take elective courses in traditional admiralty law and practice, pollution and environmental regulation, coastal zoning, fisheries, and the international law of the sea.

Feinstein Institute—The school believes that lawyers should serve the communities that support them. Introducing students to volunteerism and public service as part of their legal education, therefore, sets the stage for a lifetime of commitment. Thus, students are required to complete 50 hours of community service.

■ Honors Program

The Honors Program is a three-year program of seminars, clinics, and externships. Scholarships of half to full tuition are awarded to students selected for the Honors Program. The Admissions Committee selects students, evaluating them on their academic records, LSAT scores, and recommendations.

■ Practical Experience

The School of Law operates a Criminal Defense Clinic and an Immigration Clinic in Providence. These clinics provide a service to the community by helping indigent clients and at the same time provide an excellent opportunity for students to represent clients before courts and agencies under the supervision of a faculty member. The School of Law also operates a Mediation Clinic in Bristol. Law student-mediators assist people or groups in conflict resolution in a wide range of disputes or other community-sourced problems. As the only law school in Rhode Island, externship opportunities abound. Students may engage in a semester-long supervised clerkship in a judge's chambers or in a public interest or governmental law office for academic credit.

■ Study Abroad

The London Program on Comparative Advocacy internship program combines classroom learning at the Inner Temple (one of the four Inns of Court) with a unique and privileged opportunity for students to be trained in English common law trial techniques with a barrister or judge.

■ Admission

Admission is competitive and is based on the undergraduate grade-point average (UGPA) and the Law School Admission Test (LSAT) score, as well as other indicators of probable success in the study of law, such as graduate degree, work experience, undergraduate extracurricular activities, and community service. Applicants must register with LSAC Credential Assembly Service. A personal statement and the $60 fee must accompany all applications. One letter of recommendation is required.

■ Financial Aid

Merit-based scholarships of up to full tuition are available; no separate application is required. Federal and state governmental agencies, as well as private lenders, offer students loans at comparative rates and flexible repayment terms. Students must file the Free Application for Federal Student Aid (FAFSA) to be considered for federal loans.

■ Student Activities

Law Review—Membership on the *Roger Williams University Law Review* is considered one of the most valuable and prestigious student activities available. The *Law Review* is staffed and primarily administered by students who are selected based upon superior academic achievement and writing ability.

Moot Court Board—The Moot Court Board is composed of students possessing superior appellate advocacy and writing ability. This prestigious organization sponsors speakers and programs on appellate advocacy, organizes an intraschool competition, and sends moot court teams to interschool competitions.

Extracurricular Activities—Student organizations include, but are not limited to the Multicultural Law Students Association, Women's Law Association, the Alliance (LGBT), Black Law Students Association, Latino Law Students Association, Asian Pacific American Law Students Association, Older Wiser Law Students, Maritime Law Society, Sports and Entertainment Law Society, International Law Society, Association for Public Interest Law, and Association of Trial Lawyers of America.

■ Career Services

The Office of Career Services is dedicated to serving the needs of law students, alumni, and the legal community. The office features a welcoming suite for career research, on-campus interviews, and mock interviews. All of these tools help to prepare students to take advantage of the versatility of the Juris Doctor degree.

Applicant Profile

Roger Williams University School of Law

LSAT Score	GPA								
	3.75 +	3.50–3.74	3.25–3.49	3.00–3.24	2.75–2.99	2.50–2.74	2.25–2.49	2.00–2.24	Below 2.00
175–180									
170–174									
165–169									
160–164									
155–159									
150–154									
145–149									
140–144									
135–139									
130–134									
125–129									
120–124									

■ Good Possibility   ▨ Possible   □ Unlikely

This chart is to be used as a general guide only. Nonnumerical factors are strongly considered for all applicants.

Rutgers—The State University of New Jersey—School of Law—Camden

217 North Fifth Street
Camden, NJ 08102
Phone: 856.225.6102 or 800.466.7561; Fax: 856.969.7903
E-mail: admissions@camlaw.rutgers.edu; Website: www.camlaw.rutgers.edu

The Basics

Type of school	Public
Term	Semester
Application deadline	4/15 7/1
Application fee	$65
Financial aid deadline	7/15
Can first year start other than fall?	Yes
Student to faculty ratio	11.8 to 1
# of housing spaces available restricted to law students graduate housing for which law students are eligible 224	

Faculty and Administrators

	Total		Men		Women		Minorities	
	Spr	Fall	Spr	Fall	Spr	Fall	Spr	Fall
Full-time	50	50	34	33	16	17	6	6
Other full-time	4	4	2	2	2	2	1	1
Deans, librarians, & others who teach	15	15	6	6	9	9	1	1
Part-time	58	41	34	30	23	11	4	2
Total	127	110	76	71	50	39	12	10

Curriculum

		Full-Time	Part-Time
Typical first-year section size		56	40
Is there typically a "small section" of the first-year class, other than Legal Writing, taught by full-time faculty		No	No
If yes, typical size offered last year			
# of classroom course titles beyond first-year curriculum		139	
# of upper division courses, excluding seminars, with an enrollment:	Under 25	120	
	25–49	38	
	50–74	13	
	75–99	4	
	100+	0	
# of seminars		38	
# of seminar positions available		618	
# of seminar positions filled		252	128
# of positions available in simulation courses		617	
# of simulation positions filled		411	96
# of positions available in faculty supervised clinical courses		150	
# of faculty supervised clinical positions filled		102	18
# involved in field placements		101	9
# involved in law journals		156	15
# involved in moot court or trial competitions		23	0
# of credit hours required to graduate		84	

JD Enrollment and Ethnicity

	Men		Women		Full-Time		Part-Time		1st-Year		Total		JD Degs. Awd.
	#	%	#	%	#	%	#	%	#	%	#	%	
African Amer.	22	4.6	23	7.0	36	5.8	9	4.7	16	5.9	45	5.6	7
Amer. Indian	1	0.2	0	0.0	1	0.2	0	0.0	1	0.4	1	0.1	1
Asian Amer.	36	7.5	32	9.8	56	9.0	12	6.3	15	5.6	68	8.4	19
Mex. Amer.	1	0.2	2	0.6	3	0.5	0	0.0	0	0.0	3	0.4	3
Puerto Rican	6	1.2	5	1.5	9	1.5	2	1.0	4	1.5	11	1.4	2
Hispanic	12	2.5	13	4.0	23	3.7	2	1.0	8	3.0	25	3.1	12
Total Minority	78	16.2	75	22.9	128	20.7	25	13.1	44	16.3	153	18.9	44
For. Nation.	1	0.2	2	0.6	3	0.5	0	0.0	3	1.1	3	0.4	0
Caucasian	403	83.6	251	76.5	488	78.8	166	86.9	223	82.6	654	80.7	196
Unknown	0	0.0	0	0.0	0	0.0	0	0.0	0	0.0	0	0.0	0
Total	482	59.5	328	40.5	619	76.4	191	23.6	270	33.3	810		240

Transfers

Transfers in	47
Transfers out	10

Tuition and Fees

	Resident	Nonresident
Full-time	$23,860	$34,360
Part-time	$19,198	$27,938
Tuition Guarantee Program		N

Living Expenses

Estimated living expenses for singles

Living on campus	Living off campus	Living at home
$14,784	$19,044	$7,244

Rutgers—The State University of New Jersey—School of Law—Camden

ABA
Approved
Since
1950

GPA and LSAT Scores

	Total	Full-Time	Part-Time
# of apps	2,005	N/A	N/A
# of offers	619	N/A	N/A
# of matrics	268	227	41
75% GPA	3.70	3.70	3.70
Median GPA	3.46	3.53	3.41
25% GPA	3.18	3.21	3.05
75% LSAT	162	162	161
Median LSAT	161	161	160
25% LSAT	158	159	157

Grants and Scholarships (from prior year)

	Total #	Total %	Full-Time #	Full-Time %	Part-Time #	Part-Time %
Total # of students	747		545		202	
Total # receiving grants	201	26.9	186	34.1	15	7.4
Less than 1/2 tuition	191	25.6	176	32.3	15	7.4
Half to full tuition	9	1.2	9	1.7	0	0.0
Full tuition	1	0.1	1	0.2	0	0.0
More than full tuition	0	0.0	0	0.0	0	0.0
Median grant amount			$5,000		$2,250	

Informational and Library Resources

Total amount spent on library materials	$906,143
Study seating capacity inside the library	396
# of full-time equivalent professional librarians	7
Hours per week library is open	103
# of open, wired connections available to students	130
# of networked computers available for use by students	58
Has wireless network?	Y
Require computer?	Y

JD Attrition (from prior year)

	Academic #	Other #	Total #	Total %
1st year	0	22	22	10.1
2nd year	0	6	6	2.2
3rd year	0	0	0	0.0
4th year	0	0	0	0.0

Employment (9 months after graduation)

	Total	Percentage
Employment status known	265	95.0
Employment status unknown	14	5.0
Employed	244	92.1
Pursuing graduate degrees	0	0.0
Unemployed (seeking, not seeking, or studying for the bar)	17	6.4
Type of Employment		
# employed in law firms	99	40.6
# employed in business and industry	23	9.4
# employed in government	16	6.6
# employed in public interest	5	2.0
# employed as judicial clerks	97	39.8
# employed in academia	1	0.4
Geographic Location		
# employed in state	135	55.3
# employed in foreign countries	1	0.4
# of states where employed	18	

Bar Passage Rates

First-time takers	277	Reporting %	81.59
Average school %	84.51	Average state %	84.69
Average pass difference −0.18			

Jurisdiction	Takers	Passers	Pass %	State %	Diff %
New Jersey	226	191	84.51	84.69	−0.18

Rutgers—The State University of New Jersey—School of Law—Camden

217 North Fifth Street
Camden, NJ 08102
Phone: 856.225.6102 or 800.466.7561; Fax: 856.969.7903
E-mail: admissions@camlaw.rutgers.edu; Website: www.camlaw.rutgers.edu

■ Introduction

Chartered in 1766 by George III of Great Britain as the Queen's College, Rutgers—The State University of New Jersey is one of the oldest and largest state higher educational systems in the nation. The law school at the Camden campus is proud to continue this national reputation of excellence. With more than 100 faculty and staff members, the law school is a leading center of legal education. Noted for excellence in scholarship and rigor in training of new lawyers, the law school faculty is internationally recognized in fields as diverse as international law, health law, family and women's rights law, state constitutional law, and legal history.

Located at the base of the Benjamin Franklin Bridge, just minutes from the Liberty Bell and Independence Hall in Philadelphia, the law school is in one of the nation's largest legal markets. With its thriving, 25-acre, tree-lined urban campus in Camden, New Jersey, Rutgers is a handsome blend of converted Victorian buildings and newly constructed facilities. The Susquehanna Bank Center at the Waterfront, an indoor/outdoor concert venue; the Adventure Aquarium; the USS Battleship New Jersey; the renovated, historic Victor building with its upscale apartments; the new River LINE rail system; and Campbell's Field (the minor league baseball stadium), just a few blocks from the law school, are centerpieces for the ongoing development of Camden's waterfront. Camden, which is the county seat, has federal and local courts adjacent to the law school. A member of the Association of American Law Schools, the school is included on the list of approved schools of the American Bar Association.

■ Faculty

Faculty scholarship has been cited by numerous courts, including the United States Supreme Court, and faculty members have authored numerous casebooks and significant legal works. Faculty members testify regularly before Congress and serve as consultants and reporters for the American Bar Association, the American Law Institute, and several federal and state commissions, and act as counsel in important public interest litigation.

■ Library and Physical Facilities

The law school opened the doors to its new law building in 2008. A 2,300 square-foot courtroom and lobby with the new addition of 53,000 square feet almost doubles the size of the existing law building. The $40 million construction project has created state-of-the art classrooms, renovated two 100–150 seat lecture theaters and multiple seminar rooms, and expanded space for student organizations and social life at the law school. A magnificent two-story glass bridge and art display houses a student lounge and Law Café and welcomes visitors crossing the Benjamin Franklin Bridge from Philadelphia into New Jersey. A selective federal repository, the law library, with more than 445,000 bibliographic units, is one of the largest in the state. In addition to having access to traditional materials, students are trained on a number of computerized research systems, including a myriad of databases available on the Internet.

■ Curriculum and Special Programs

The first-year curriculum includes the traditional core legal courses. Central to the curriculum is the lawyering program that engages students in simulated lawyering activities and practical applications of the law. Upper-class students can typically choose from more than 100 exciting elective courses each year, including cyberlaw, trial advocacy, sports law, children's law, and international business transactions.

An outstanding Externship Program offers third-year students the opportunity to work with federal and state judges, public agencies, and public interest organizations. Other students participate in the Civil Practice Clinic and pro bono programs at the law school. Live client experiences include the Domestic Violence Project, the Pro Bono Bankruptcy Project, the Immigration Project, the Mediation Project, and the Elder Law Clinic, or representing clients in connection with the LEAP Charter School. Each of these programs constitutes a comprehensive initiative that reflects the law school's commitment to public service.

Students may pursue their legal studies in the full-time day program as well as the part-time program, available day or evening. Both programs are subject to the same rigorous admission and academic standards.

■ Joint-Degree Programs

Eight formal joint JD and master's or doctoral degree programs are available with the University of Medicine and Dentistry, Graduate School of Business, Bloustein School of Planning and Public Policy, School of Social Work, and Graduate School—Camden, including JD/MD, JD/DO, JD/MPA, JD/MBA, JD/MSW, and JD/MCRP. Upon approval of the faculty, students may also pursue self-designed joint-degree programs within Rutgers University or with other graduate institutions.

■ Admission

Although admission is highly competitive, the Committee on Admissions does consider each applicant's file individually, and special qualities may occasionally overcome lower numbers. Important factors to the committee include LSAT score, undergraduate and graduate grade-point average, undergraduate and graduate institutions, work experience, and letters of recommendation. Typically, half of the full-time entering class scores in the top quartile on the LSAT (160 or higher) with a median GPA of 3.5. The entering class size each fall is about 225 full- and part-time day and 45 part-time evening students. The law school draws from 30 states and 4 foreign countries. More than 250 colleges and universities are represented in the student body. Decisions are made on a rolling basis beginning in early December. The law school has rolling admission and will consider candidates who take the February and June LSAT. However, early applicants have an enhanced opportunity for admission. Applicants may also apply for advanced standing as transfer students but are only eligible upon completion of one year of law study. Students may request an application from the law school or apply online at *www.camlaw.rutgers.edu/*.

Rutgers—The State University of New Jersey—School of Law—Camden

■ Housing

Air-conditioned and carpeted law school apartments are located on campus; and nearby, the renovated, historic Victor building, with its spectacular views of the Philadelphia skyline, provides upscale apartment living. There are also abundant housing opportunities in the nearby suburbs and excellent public transportation systems. First-year admitted students are invited to utilize the law school's housing webpage and to attend the Dean's Law and Housing Day in the spring.

■ Financial Aid

In the 2008–2009 academic year, over $19 million was distributed to law students through fellowships, grants, loans, and employment. The average financial aid package was approximately $28,767, with 88 percent of the student body receiving some form of assistance. The William D. Ford Federal Direct Loan Program, the largest financial aid program, provided more than $17.2 million to over 666 students in the last academic year. For fall consideration, the FAFSA should be submitted by March 1. Merit-based scholarships are also available for outstanding academic performance.

■ Career Services

As a direct result of the quality of legal education at Rutgers, for the last five years the school has averaged an employment rate of over 92 percent in the legal profession within nine months of graduation. All major Philadelphia, New Jersey, and Delaware firms recruit from Rutgers, as do prestigious firms from New York City, California, and Washington, DC. The school's more than 8,100 alumni are leading members of the judiciary, government, and bar throughout this nation. The average salary of an associate who joins a private law firm is in excess of $98,000, with top students typically making in excess of $145,000. The school's placement rate is one of the best in the country (40 percent of last year's class) for highly desirable state and federal clerkships.

■ Student Activities

Among the numerous student organizations are the Latino Law Students Association, Asian/Pacific American Law Students Association, Association for Public Interest Law, Black Law Students Association, Christian Legal Society, Community Outreach Group, Cyberlaw, Environmental Law Students Association, Francis Deak International Law Society, OUTLAW Student Bar Association, Health Law Society, Italian-American Law Students Organization, Jewish Law Students Association, Law Journal (publishes the *Rutgers Law Journal*), *Journal of Law and Public Policy*, *Rutgers Journal of Law and Religion*, Phi Alpha Delta law fraternity, Pro Bono/Public Interest Steering Committee, and the Women's Law Caucus.

Applicant Profile

Rutgers—The State University of New Jersey—School of Law—Camden
This grid includes only applicants who earned 120–180 LSAT scores under standard administrations.

LSAT Score	GPA								
	3.75 +	3.50–3.74	3.25–3.49	3.00–3.24	2.75–2.99	2.50–2.74	2.25–2.49	2.00–2.24	Below 2.00
170–180									
165–169									
161–164									
158–160									
155–157									
150–154									
Below 150									

Very Likely   Likely   Possible   Unlikely*

*Special attributes may sometimes overcome lower scores/GPAs.
This chart is to be used as a general guide only. Nonnumerical factors are strongly considered for all applicants.

Rutgers University School of Law—Newark

Center for Law and Justice, 123 Washington Street
Newark, NJ 07102
Phone: 973.353.5554; Fax: 973.353.3459
E-mail: lawinfo@andromeda.rutgers.edu; Website: http://law.newark.rutgers.edu

ABA Approved Since 1941

The Basics

Type of school	Public
Term	Semester
Application deadline	3/15
Application fee	$65
Financial aid deadline	3/15
Can first year start other than fall?	No
Student to faculty ratio	17.6 to 1
# of housing spaces available restricted to law students	
graduate housing for which law students are eligible	110

Faculty and Administrators

	Total		Men		Women		Minorities	
	Spr	Fall	Spr	Fall	Spr	Fall	Spr	Fall
Full-time	36	34	22	22	14	12	13	12
Other full-time	2	1	1	1	1	0	1	0
Deans, librarians, & others who teach	15	14	8	7	7	7	5	5
Part-time	37	43	26	29	11	13	3	1
Total	90	92	57	59	33	32	22	18

Curriculum

	Full-Time	Part-Time
Typical first-year section size	60	65
Is there typically a "small section" of the first-year class, other than Legal Writing, taught by full-time faculty	Yes	Yes
If yes, typical size offered last year	33	34
# of classroom course titles beyond first-year curriculum	109	

# of upper division courses, excluding seminars, with an enrollment:		
Under 25	56	
25–49	43	
50–74	7	
75–99	4	
100+	4	

# of seminars	25	
# of seminar positions available	500	
# of seminar positions filled	252	65
# of positions available in simulation courses	325	
# of simulation positions filled	223	42
# of positions available in faculty supervised clinical courses	180	
# of faculty supervised clinical positions filled	152	20
# involved in field placements	86	4
# involved in law journals	183	30
# involved in moot court or trial competitions	70	11
# of credit hours required to graduate	84	

JD Enrollment and Ethnicity

	Men		Women		Full-Time		Part-Time		1st-Year		Total		JD Degs. Awd.
	#	%	#	%	#	%	#	%	#	%	#	%	
African Amer.	54	11.3	72	20.1	83	14.0	43	17.8	43	16.7	126	15.1	30
Amer. Indian	1	0.2	1	0.3	1	0.2	1	0.4	1	0.4	2	0.2	0
Asian Amer.	46	9.7	41	11.4	60	10.1	27	11.2	28	10.9	87	10.4	27
Mex. Amer.	5	1.1	5	1.4	8	1.3	2	0.8	0	0.0	10	1.2	2
Puerto Rican	12	2.5	10	2.8	17	2.9	5	2.1	7	2.7	22	2.6	5
Hispanic	34	7.1	26	7.2	41	6.9	19	7.9	20	7.8	60	7.2	17
Total Minority	152	31.9	155	43.2	210	35.4	97	40.1	99	38.5	307	36.8	81
For. Nation.	6	1.3	9	2.5	9	1.5	6	2.5	4	1.6	15	1.8	3
Caucasian	318	66.8	195	54.3	374	63.1	139	57.4	154	59.9	513	61.4	159
Unknown	0	0.0	0	0.0	0	0.0	0	0.0	0	0.0	0	0.0	0
Total	476	57.0	359	43.0	593	71.0	242	29.0	257	30.8	835		243

Transfers

Transfers in	18
Transfers out	9

Tuition and Fees

	Resident	Nonresident
Full-time	$23,676	$33,740
Part-time	$15,470	$22,174
Tuition Guarantee Program	N	

Living Expenses

Estimated living expenses for singles

Living on campus	Living off campus	Living at home
$16,064	$20,724	$8,324

Rutgers University School of Law—Newark

ABA
Approved
Since
1941

GPA and LSAT Scores

	Total	Full-Time	Part-Time
# of apps	3,465	2,761	704
# of offers	948	821	127
# of matrics	259	191	68
75% GPA	3.60	3.60	3.60
Median GPA	3.36	3.39	3.25
25% GPA	3.09	3.13	2.95
75% LSAT	161	161	159
Median LSAT	158	158	157
25% LSAT	155	155	154

Grants and Scholarships (from prior year)

	Total #	Total %	Full-Time #	Full-Time %	Part-Time #	Part-Time %
Total # of students	816		582		234	
Total # receiving grants	282	34.6	245	42.1	37	15.8
Less than 1/2 tuition	245	30.0	211	36.3	34	14.5
Half to full tuition	23	2.8	21	3.6	2	0.9
Full tuition	7	0.9	7	1.2	0	0.0
More than full tuition	7	0.9	6	1.0	1	0.4
Median grant amount			$6,000		$5,000	

Informational and Library Resources

Total amount spent on library materials	$705,246
Study seating capacity inside the library	532
# of full-time equivalent professional librarians	18
Hours per week library is open	95
# of open, wired connections available to students	570
# of networked computers available for use by students	180
Has wireless network?	Y
Require computer?	N

JD Attrition (from prior year)

	Academic #	Other #	Total #	Total %
1st year	0	18	18	7.0
2nd year	1	5	6	2.3
3rd year	0	1	1	0.4
4th year	0	0	0	0.0

Employment (9 months after graduation)

	Total	Percentage
Employment status known	243	98.0
Employment status unknown	5	2.0
Employed	226	93.0
Pursuing graduate degrees	5	2.1
Unemployed (seeking, not seeking, or studying for the bar)	7	2.9
Type of Employment		
# employed in law firms	104	46.0
# employed in business and industry	35	15.5
# employed in government	24	10.6
# employed in public interest	11	4.9
# employed as judicial clerks	49	21.7
# employed in academia	3	1.3
Geographic Location		
# employed in state	141	62.4
# employed in foreign countries	3	1.3
# of states where employed	15	

Bar Passage Rates

First-time takers		Reporting %	NA
Average school %	86.85	Average state %	84.69
Average pass difference	2.16		

Jurisdiction	Takers	Passers	Pass %	State %	Diff %
New Jersey	213	185	86.85	84.69	2.16

Rutgers University School of Law—Newark

Center for Law and Justice, 123 Washington Street
Newark, NJ 07102
Phone: 973.353.5554; Fax: 973.353.3459
E-mail: lawinfo@andromeda.rutgers.edu; Website: http://law.newark.rutgers.edu

■ Introduction

Rutgers University School of Law—Newark has been a pioneer in legal education for more than 100 years. Few law schools can match our contributions to the advancement of legal theory and practice, the diversity of our faculty and student body, the accomplishments of our public interest programs, and our reputation for outstanding academic quality and a progressive tradition. Our law professors are prominent scholars and experts in established and emerging areas of law who challenge students in an intense yet supportive environment. Our students come to us from around the world, bringing wide-ranging backgrounds and perspectives that enrich discourse in the classroom and throughout the law school community. Our clinical program offers invaluable hands-on instruction by noted litigators and teachers and the opportunity to provide service to the underserved. Our dual-degree program with several academic disciplines within the university and with the state's medical school enables students to add an interdisciplinary perspective to their study of law. The law school is located in the heart of New Jersey's largest city, which is home to leading law firms, courts, and government agencies, major cultural institutions, Fortune 100 companies, entrepreneurial ventures, and public interest groups that offer numerous learning, internship, and volunteer opportunities.

■ The Center for Law and Justice

The law school is housed in the Center for Law and Justice, one of the finest law school buildings in the country. Highlights include a light-filled library boasting over 570,000 volumes and volume-equivalents and five computer labs; lecture rooms with excellent acoustics, sight lines, and power lines at every seat; an attractive courtroom complex where the Appellate Division of the Superior Court regularly hears cases; and numerous lounge and study areas. Wireless Internet access is available throughout the building and in all classrooms. The center opens onto a pedestrian plaza and a garden terrace—favorite gathering spots for students and faculty.

■ Faculty

The faculty contribute to every aspect of the law school experience. Faculty members examine, shape, and resolve new and developing issues of law. Particular concentrations of academic strength lie in the fields of criminal law, constitutional law, legal history, and international law, with notable expertise as well in family law, race and the law, and labor and employment law. Faculty engage students through teaching styles that range from traditional Socratic method to interactive problem-solving. The faculty is diverse, ensuring the kind of intellectual inquiry that provides a rich foundation for a career in law.

■ Curriculum

The rigorous curriculum ensures the development of professional skills and values within a theoretical framework that promotes intellectual growth and a commitment to justice.

First-year students learn the essential conceptual, analytical, and research methods to be effective lawyers in complex environments. Upper-level students build on those skills through our extensive curriculum of over 200 class, clinic, and seminar options. The faculty review the curriculum regularly to ensure that the offerings prepare students for a rapidly changing legal environment.

An accredited semester of study abroad sends students to Leiden University in the Netherlands for an intensive program in international law, European Union law, comparative law, legal history, and law and international economics. The Rutgers Division of Global Affairs, located in our building, also serves as a nexus for students interested in the international dimension.

Joint-degree programs are available with the Rutgers Graduate Schools of Business, Planning and Public Policy, Criminal Justice, and Social Work, as well as with the University of Medicine and Dentistry of New Jersey. Students are encouraged to take advantage of the rich curriculum offerings throughout the university through cross-disciplinary registration. The Foreign Lawyer Program permits persons with foreign law degrees to earn a JD in two years.

Centers, institutes, and programs integrate faculty scholarship and activity, student interests and participation, and outreach to the larger university, legal, and other communities. As one example, the Center for Law, Science and Technology supports faculty and student interest in intellectual property law, as well as in the intersection of law and science more generally. Among other activities, the Center holds an annual conference on patent law involving leaders from the judiciary, practice, industry, and the academic community.

■ Clinics and Public Service

The 42-year-old clinical program offers students extensive opportunities for hands-on legal experience in real cases involving underrepresented clients, communities, or causes. Guided by talented and accomplished faculty with expertise in litigation, legislation, mediation, or transactional practice, our clinics are noted for their diversity, breadth, and comprehensiveness of experiences, as well as for their involvement in cases and projects of social and community impact. Clinical students provide corporate, transactional, and intellectual property legal services to nonprofit corporations and start-up, for-profit businesses; litigate important constitutional and international human rights issues; provide representation to low-income children and their families; assist low-income clients on tax matters; and participate in a wide range of community education and outreach efforts. Other opportunities include pro bono work, internships, fellowships, and summer placements. The Loan Repayment Assistance Program, one of the largest in the country, assists graduates pursuing careers in public service.

■ Students and Student Life

Rutgers enrolls students of extraordinary academic and professional promise who enrich the community with their intellectual strength and significant life and work experience.

Many students have earned advanced degrees while others provide a global perspective to the classroom.

Diversity of views enlivens the classroom and creates an inclusive environment. Our Minority Student Program reflects the faculty's long-standing commitment to preserve the diversity of the law school and to improve diversity in the legal profession. Student-run organizations reflect myriad interests, political positions, and backgrounds, from the Women's Law Forum to the Entertainment and Sports Law Society. Student publications include the *Rutgers Law Review*, *Rutgers Computer and Technology Law Journal*, *Women's Rights Law Reporter*, *Rutgers Race and the Law Review*, and the online *Rutgers Law Record*.

■ Admission

The faculty believe that diverse perspectives and backgrounds are essential to a complete understanding of the law and its relation to contemporary society. The law school seeks and attracts a talented student body with a breadth of experience and provides unparalleled opportunities for those who have been historically excluded from the legal profession.

The Admission Committee considers a broad range of factors, including, but not limited to, educational and employment experiences, community service, LSAT score, UGPA, race, ethnicity, socioeconomic background, and extraordinary family circumstances. Every applicant can choose to compete for admission with primary emphasis placed on numerical indicators (LSAT score and UGPA) or nonnumerical indicators (experiences and accomplishments).

In each entering class, 35–40 percent of our students are people of color. All regions of the country and more than two dozen foreign countries are represented.

■ Housing

On-campus graduate housing is located in close proximity to the law school. The recent addition of a new residence hall has increased the availability of on-campus housing for law students. Nearby suburban communities offer a variety of housing options. Public transportation is widely available.

■ Career Development

The Office of Career Development provides traditional and innovative services and programs, helping students and graduates develop career goals and conduct successful job searches. Individual counseling, skills training programs, panels, workshops, networking events, and on- and off-campus interview programs that attract many of the nation's leading law firms are a few of the myriad of services offered. The office also works closely with prospective employers to maximize recruitment opportunities.

Applicant Profile

Rutgers University School of Law—Newark

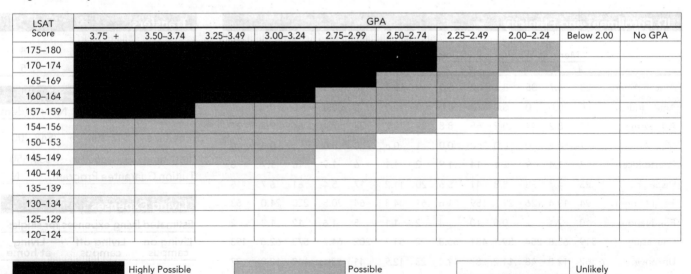

LSAT Score	GPA									
	3.75 +	3.50–3.74	3.25–3.49	3.00–3.24	2.75–2.99	2.50–2.74	2.25–2.49	2.00–2.24	Below 2.00	No GPA
175–180										
170–174										
165–169										
160–164										
157–159										
154–156										
150–153										
145–149										
140–144										
135–139										
130–134										
125–129										
120–124										

■ Highly Possible   ■ Possible   □ Unlikely

The information contained in this grid should be used as an approximate gauge as to the likelihood of admission. The Admissions Committee gives considerable weight to individual accomplishments and other nonnumerical factors in the admissions process. LSAT and UGPA are not the sole determinants for admission.

St. John's University School of Law

8000 Utopia Parkway
Queens, NY 11439
Phone: 718.990.6474; Fax: 718.990.2526
E-mail: lawinfo@stjohns.edu; Website: www.law.stjohns.edu

ABA
Approved
Since
1937

The Basics

Type of school	Private
Term	Semester
Application deadline	4/1
Application fee	$60
Financial aid deadline	4/1
Can first year start other than fall?	No
Student to faculty ratio	14.6 to 1
# of housing spaces available restricted to law students	84
graduate housing for which law students are eligible	84

Faculty and Administrators

	Total		Men		Women		Minorities	
	Spr	Fall	Spr	Fall	Spr	Fall	Spr	Fall
Full-time	49	47	27	26	22	21	9	10
Other full-time	3	3	0	1	3	2	1	1
Deans, librarians, & others who teach	5	5	3	3	2	2	0	0
Part-time	63	67	54	53	9	14	3	1
Total	120	122	84	83	36	39	13	12

Curriculum

		Full-Time	Part-Time
Typical first-year section size		85	65
Is there typically a "small section" of the first-year class, other than Legal Writing, taught by full-time faculty		No	No
If yes, typical size offered last year			
# of classroom course titles beyond first-year curriculum		184	
# of upper division courses, excluding seminars, with an enrollment:	Under 25	115	
	25–49	32	
	50–74	18	
	75–99	9	
	100+	2	
# of seminars		22	
# of seminar positions available		500	
# of seminar positions filled		321	51
# of positions available in simulation courses		430	
# of simulation positions filled		273	65
# of positions available in faculty supervised clinical courses		151	
# of faculty supervised clinical positions filled		142	9
# involved in field placements		243	32
# involved in law journals		92	1
# involved in moot court or trial competitions		51	3
# of credit hours required to graduate		86	

JD Enrollment and Ethnicity

	Men		Women		Full-Time		Part-Time		1st-Year		Total		JD Degs. Awd.
	#	%	#	%	#	%	#	%	#	%	#	%	
African Amer.	23	4.7	35	8.1	39	5.3	19	10.7	18	5.8	58	6.3	10
Amer. Indian	0	0.0	0	0.0	0	0.0	0	0.0	0	0.0	0	0.0	1
Asian Amer.	40	8.2	44	10.2	65	8.8	19	10.7	23	7.4	84	9.2	27
Mex. Amer.	1	0.2	0	0.0	0	0.0	1	0.6	0	0.0	1	0.1	0
Puerto Rican	7	1.4	9	2.1	14	1.9	2	1.1	6	1.9	16	1.7	0
Hispanic	23	4.7	38	8.8	41	5.6	20	11.2	17	5.4	61	6.7	15
Total Minority	94	19.4	126	29.3	159	21.6	61	34.3	64	20.5	220	24.0	53
For. Nation.	10	2.1	2	0.5	10	1.4	2	1.1	5	1.6	12	1.3	2
Caucasian	319	65.8	254	59.1	481	65.3	92	51.7	202	64.7	573	62.6	193
Unknown	62	12.8	48	11.2	87	11.8	23	12.9	41	13.1	110	12.0	37
Total	485	53.0	430	47.0	737	80.5	178	19.5	312	34.1	915		285

Transfers

Transfers in	8
Transfers out	5

Tuition and Fees

	Resident	Nonresident
Full-time	$42,200	$42,200
Part-time	$31,650	$31,650
Tuition Guarantee Program	N	

Living Expenses

Estimated living expenses for singles

Living on campus	Living off campus	Living at home
$22,217	$22,217	$9,140

St. John's University School of Law

ABA
Approved
Since
1937

GPA and LSAT Scores

	Total	Full-Time	Part-Time
# of apps	4,036	3,232	804
# of offers	1,479	1,260	219
# of matrics	315	231	84
75% GPA	3.73	3.70	3.77
Median GPA	3.53	3.48	3.62
25% GPA	3.16	3.16	3.12
75% LSAT	162	163	155
Median LSAT	160	161	153
25% LSAT	154	156	147

Grants and Scholarships (from prior year)

	Total #	Total %	Full-Time #	Full-Time %	Part-Time #	Part-Time %
Total # of students	901		719		182	
Total # receiving grants	336	37.3	316	43.9	20	11.0
Less than 1/2 tuition	160	17.8	144	20.0	16	8.8
Half to full tuition	65	7.2	65	9.0	0	0.0
Full tuition	101	11.2	97	13.5	4	2.2
More than full tuition	10	1.1	10	1.4	0	0.0
Median grant amount			$22,500		$7,500	

Informational and Library Resources

Total amount spent on library materials	$1,409,326
Study seating capacity inside the library	564
# of full-time equivalent professional librarians	10
Hours per week library is open	100
# of open, wired connections available to students	0
# of networked computers available for use by students	65
Has wireless network?	Y
Require computer?	N

JD Attrition (from prior year)

	Academic #	Other #	Total #	Total %
1st year	1	6	7	2.5
2nd year	6	10	16	5.2
3rd year	0	2	2	0.7
4th year	0	0	0	0.0

Employment (9 months after graduation)

	Total	Percentage
Employment status known	276	100.0
Employment status unknown	0	0.0
Employed	241	87.3
Pursuing graduate degrees	10	3.6
Unemployed (seeking, not seeking, or studying for the bar)	11	4.0
Type of Employment		
# employed in law firms	140	58.1
# employed in business and industry	36	14.9
# employed in government	40	16.6
# employed in public interest	8	3.3
# employed as judicial clerks	10	4.1
# employed in academia	7	2.9
Geographic Location		
# employed in state	217	90.0
# employed in foreign countries	0	0.0
# of states where employed	11	

Bar Passage Rates

First-time takers	277	Reporting %	100.00
Average school %	90.61	Average state %	88.98
Average pass difference	1.63		

Jurisdiction	Takers	Passers	Pass %	State %	Diff %
New York	277	251	90.61	88.98	1.63

St. John's University School of Law

8000 Utopia Parkway
Queens, NY 11439
Phone: 718.990.6474; Fax: 718.990.2526
E-mail: lawinfo@stjohns.edu; Website: www.law.stjohns.edu

■ Introduction

St. John's University School of Law is a forceful presence and an integral part of the New York metropolitan area. It imparts to its students training and competency in the basic skills and techniques of the legal profession, a grasp of the history and the system of common law, and a familiarity with important statutes and decisions in federal and state jurisdictions.

The law school is a state-of-the-art facility with a gross total square footage of 179,400, one of the highest space-per-student ratios in the country. Some highlights of the facility include a new high-tech clinical suite, alumni function areas, a student lounge, faculty offices, classrooms for teaching clinical and lawyering skills, and a state-of-the-art moot courtroom.

St. John's School of Law is approved by the ABA and is a member of the AALS.

■ Library and Physical Facilities

The showpiece of the law school building is its beautiful law library, which incorporates the most recent advances in law library science and technology. It contains a computer laboratory and several study rooms for student conferences. The library occupies approximately 50,000 square feet on five of the eight building levels. It has been designated a depository library for US government and UN documents.

The School of Law has recently completed a major renovation of its moot court, producing a beautiful, state-of-the-art facility that incorporates technologies that further the teaching and research missions of St. John's. In addition, the School of Law has completed renovations of first-year classrooms, clinic offices, the professional skills center, writing center, and the faculty library.

■ New York City

The School of Law is located on the Queens Campus of St. John's University. Situated on almost 100 rolling acres in a residential area, the campus boasts a spectacular view of the Manhattan skyline. The campus is easily accessible to Manhattan and all of New York City, and the location provides opportunities and access to the world's largest law firms, businesses, government agencies, and courts.

■ Clinical and Externship Programs

Elective clinical programs and externships are available to second- and third-year students.

Externships: Civil Externships, Criminal Justice Externships, Judicial Externships, International Human Rights Externships, Special Education Externship, Judicial/Matrimonial ADR Externship, Street Law Externship Program.

Clinics: Elder Law Clinic, Securities Arbitration Clinic, Child Advocacy Clinic, Domestic Violence Clinic, Prosecution Clinic, Refugee and Immigration Rights Clinic, Immigrant Tenant Advocacy Clinic, and the In the Bread and Life: Bridge to Justice Clinic in which students represent clients of St. John's Bread and Life Social Services who are dealing with immigration issues.

■ Special Diversity Admission Program

The School of Law sponsors a program for individuals who have faced the challenges of discrimination, chronic financial hardship, or other social, educational, or physical disadvantages to such an extent that their undergraduate performance or LSAT score would not otherwise warrant unconditional acceptance into the entering class. This Summer Institute program consists of a substantive course taught and graded according to the same qualitative standard applied to all first-year courses, as well as a legal writing course. The program enables individuals whose LSAT scores and GPAs are not reliable predictors of their success to demonstrate their ability to succeed in the study of law.

■ Vincentian Scholarship Program

The mission statement of St. John's University School of Law calls for the law school "to provide a superior legal education for a diverse population of students with special awareness for economic fairness and equal opportunity, consistent with and in fulfillment of the Vincentian tradition and mission." In furtherance of this Vincentian tradition and mission, the School of Law provides five full-tuition Vincentian scholarships each year in its ongoing effort to achieve a diverse student body.

■ Student Activities

Publications—*St. John's Law Review/St. Thomas More Institute for Research, Journal of Catholic Legal Studies, Journal of Civil Rights and Economic Development, New York International Law Review, American Bankruptcy Institute Law Review, N.Y. Litigator,* and *N.Y. Real Property Law Journal.*

Mock Trial and Appellate Activities—Moot Court Honor Society, Frank S. Polestino Trial Advocacy Institute. In the 2009 NITA Tournament of Champions, St. John's Law claimed the traveling trophy for the "best of the best" mock trial team in the country.

Specialized Legal Activities—Hugh L. Carey Center for Dispute Resolution, Ronald H. Brown Center, Student Bar Association, Admiralty Law Society, Women's Law Association, Bankruptcy Law Society, Environmental Law Club, Entertainment and Sports Club, International Law Society, Intellectual Property, Labor and Employment Club, Real Property Club, Black Law Students Association, South Asian Law Students Association, Asian Pacific American Law Students Association, Latino American Law Students Association, and Client Counseling Competition. The school also maintains chapters in two legal societies, Phi Delta Phi and Phi Alpha Delta.

■ Financial Aid and Housing

The School of Law provides extensive financial scholarship aid to students annually. There are new university housing facilities, and many students find other suitable living accommodations in the vicinity of the university. In addition, the Admission Office coordinates a housing network for students.

Academic Support

The Writing Center is a place where students can brainstorm about ideas, practice writing exam essays, edit scholarly pieces, submit papers to writing competitions, find publication sources for articles, polish briefs and memoranda for use as writing samples, practice proper citation form, hone grammar skills, or get help with any general writing problems. The Writing Center was recently renovated, is located on the first floor of the law school building, and is staffed by some of the law school's best writers.

Career Services

Career Services provides an array of services, including résumé and cover letter critiquing, mock interview coaching, job and judicial clerkship postings, newsletters, lists of prospective employers, interview programs, and career education panels. Recent graduates have obtained employment in many areas of the legal profession. Approximately 5 percent accept federal and state judicial clerkships. For the class of 2008, the employment rate (nine months after graduation) was 96 percent.

Alumni of the law school are currently practicing throughout the United States and its territories. Many have achieved positions of prominence in executive and legislative branches of the government, as members of the judiciary, and in both private and corporate practice. Two recent governors of New York, a congressman for New York, a recent governor of the US Virgin Islands, and a former governor of California were graduates of St. John's School of Law.

Bar Passage Rate

St. John's University School of Law's bar passage rate for first-time test takers was 92 percent on the July 2009 bar examination. St. John's has consistently placed among the top New York law schools in percentage of first-time test takers passing the bar exam.

Summer Study-Abroad Programs

Each summer, St. John's University offers two programs as a way to enjoy the experience of learning in a different setting. Students have the pleasure of learning and gaining credits toward graduation in Rome, Italy, in June and in Barcelona, Spain, in July. Courses in International or Comparative Law are traditionally offered in a four-week program (for up to six credits for each program). US and foreign law students are allowed to apply. They also have the opportunity to visit top Italian and Spanish legal institutions and develop networking connections for future reference. Limited externships are available after each program.

LLM in Bankruptcy and LLM in US Legal Studies

LLM in Bankruptcy—St. John's has the nation's first master's program in bankruptcy. It is designed to meet an important and special educational need in the field of bankruptcy law. Matriculating students will be required to complete 30 credits, including the preparation and defense of a major thesis on a current significant bankruptcy topic. Students may matriculate on a full- or part-time basis.

LLM in US Legal Studies—St. John's offers a new LLM Program (*Magister Legum* or Master of Law) tailored exclusively for foreign law school graduates. The program is one year in residence and requires the completion of 24 credits. Students may enroll on a full- or part-time basis.

Applicant Profile

St. John's University School of Law

Average LSAT data reported.

Saint Louis University School of Law

3700 Lindell Boulevard
St. Louis, MO 63108
Phone: 314.977.2800; Fax: 314.977.1464
E-mail: admissions@law.slu.edu; Website: http://law.slu.edu

ABA
Approved
Since
1924

The Basics

Type of school	Private
Term	Semester
Application deadline	3/1
Application fee	$55
Financial aid deadline	3/1
Can first year start other than fall?	No
Student to faculty ratio	17.1 to 1
# of housing spaces available restricted to law students	
graduate housing for which law students are eligible	

Faculty and Administrators

	Total		Men		Women		Minorities	
	Spr	Fall	Spr	Fall	Spr	Fall	Spr	Fall
Full-time	38	49	20	28	18	21	4	6
Other full-time	9	11	1	1	8	10	2	1
Deans, librarians, & others who teach	16	16	5	5	11	11	1	1
Part-time	57	41	38	29	19	12	10	9
Total	120	117	64	63	56	54	17	17

Curriculum

		Full-Time	Part-Time
Typical first-year section size		75	88
Is there typically a "small section" of the first-year class, other than Legal Writing, taught by full-time faculty		Yes	No
If yes, typical size offered last year		24	
# of classroom course titles beyond first-year curriculum		150	
# of upper division courses, excluding seminars, with an enrollment:	Under 25	183	
	25–49	36	
	50–74	20	
	75–99	12	
	100+	10	
# of seminars		35	
# of seminar positions available		425	
# of seminar positions filled		316	53
# of positions available in simulation courses		1,211	
# of simulation positions filled		833	230
# of positions available in faculty supervised clinical courses		103	
# of faculty supervised clinical positions filled		78	25
# involved in field placements		103	23
# involved in law journals		124	14
# involved in moot court or trial competitions		41	5
# of credit hours required to graduate		91	

JD Enrollment and Ethnicity

	Men		Women		Full-Time		Part-Time		1st-Year		Total		JD Degs. Awd.
	#	%	#	%	#	%	#	%	#	%	#	%	
African Amer.	21	4.1	46	10.1	54	7.0	13	6.6	21	6.4	67	6.9	14
Amer. Indian	3	0.6	3	0.7	5	0.6	1	0.5	2	0.6	6	0.6	1
Asian Amer.	20	3.9	30	6.6	41	5.3	9	4.6	20	6.1	50	5.2	13
Mex. Amer.	7	1.4	4	0.9	10	1.3	1	0.5	4	1.2	11	1.1	1
Puerto Rican	0	0.0	1	0.2	1	0.1	0	0.0	0	0.0	1	0.1	0
Hispanic	7	1.4	10	2.2	15	1.9	2	1.0	6	1.8	17	1.8	5
Total Minority	58	11.4	94	20.6	126	16.3	26	13.3	53	16.2	152	15.7	34
For. Nation.	1	0.2	2	0.4	2	0.3	1	0.5	0	0.0	3	0.3	1
Caucasian	418	81.8	332	72.8	600	77.8	150	76.5	250	76.5	750	77.6	254
Unknown	34	6.7	28	6.1	43	5.6	19	9.7	24	7.3	62	6.4	13
Total	511	52.8	456	47.2	771	79.7	196	20.3	327	33.8	967		302

Transfers

Transfers in	3
Transfers out	17

Tuition and Fees

	Resident	Nonresident
Full-time	$34,362	$34,362
Part-time	$25,047	$25,047
Tuition Guarantee Program		N

Living Expenses

Estimated living expenses for singles

Living on campus	Living off campus	Living at home
$22,604	$22,604	$22,604

Saint Louis University School of Law

ABA
Approved
Since
1924

GPA and LSAT Scores

	Total	Full-Time	Part-Time
# of apps	2,284	2,140	480
# of offers	1,195	1,024	171
# of matrics	331	243	88
75% GPA	3.61	3.64	3.45
Median GPA	3.37	3.41	3.25
25% GPA	3.16	3.21	3.02
75% LSAT	159	160	155
Median LSAT	156	157	153
25% LSAT	153	154	152

Grants and Scholarships (from prior year)

	Total		Full-Time		Part-Time	
	#	%	#	%	#	%
Total # of students	981		784		197	
Total # receiving grants	413	42.1	360	45.9	53	26.9
Less than 1/2 tuition	243	24.8	201	25.6	42	21.3
Half to full tuition	134	13.7	123	15.7	11	5.6
Full tuition	36	3.7	36	4.6	0	0.0
More than full tuition	0	0.0	0	0.0	0	0.0
Median grant amount			$17,740		$10,750	

Informational and Library Resources

Total amount spent on library materials	$995,400
Study seating capacity inside the library	505
# of full-time equivalent professional librarians	10
Hours per week library is open	106
# of open, wired connections available to students	594
# of networked computers available for use by students	76
Has wireless network?	Y
Require computer?	N

JD Attrition (from prior year)

	Academic	Other	Total	
	#	#	#	%
1st year	6	21	27	9.3
2nd year	1	7	8	2.4
3rd year	0	1	1	0.3
4th year	0	0	0	0.0

Employment (9 months after graduation)

	Total	Percentage
Employment status known	256	100.0
Employment status unknown	0	0.0
Employed	229	89.5
Pursuing graduate degrees	5	2.0
Unemployed (seeking, not seeking, or studying for the bar)	18	7.0
Type of Employment		
# employed in law firms	142	62.0
# employed in business and industry	38	16.6
# employed in government	17	7.4
# employed in public interest	24	10.5
# employed as judicial clerks	7	3.1
# employed in academia	1	0.4
Geographic Location		
# employed in state	142	62.0
# employed in foreign countries	0	0.0
# of states where employed		23

Bar Passage Rates

First-time takers	255	Reporting %	74.51
Average school %	94.21	Average state %	92.33
Average pass difference	1.88		

Jurisdiction	Takers	Passers	Pass %	State %	Diff %
Missouri	190	179	94.21	92.33	1.88

Saint Louis University School of Law

3700 Lindell Boulevard
St. Louis, MO 63108
Phone: 314.977.2800; Fax: 314.977.1464
E-mail: admissions@law.slu.edu; Website: http://law.slu.edu

■ Introduction

The mission of Saint Louis University School of Law (SLU Law) is to advance the understanding and development of law, and prepare students to achieve professional success and personal satisfaction through leadership and service to others. The school is guided by the Jesuit tradition of academic excellence, freedom of inquiry, and respect for individual differences.

Located in scenic midtown St. Louis, SLU Law is perfectly positioned to provide students with unparalleled exposure to the legal world. St. Louis boasts an impressive array of law firms, corporate offices, and governmental agencies, in addition to local, state, and federal courthouses throughout the city and surrounding counties, including the largest federal courthouse in the United States.

With an accomplished, accessible faculty and a diverse curriculum, SLU Law provides a challenging yet collegial environment designed to foster success for dedicated students. Whatever the interest—corporate and finance, criminal, health, international, intellectual property, tax, securities, real estate, labor and employment, or litigation—the school can help students achieve their desired career goals.

First-year, full-time law students benefit from the school's unique small-section program, where two of five classes have 25 or fewer students. This allows for individualized instruction and focused student interaction and, most importantly, builds a sense of community among classmates. The remaining classes are formed by combining different small sections to allow students to get to know others in their entering class.

For those who work full time and are unable to attend classes during the day, SLU Law offers a challenging **Part-Time Program**—the only program of its kind in the state of Missouri. Through this program, students can earn their law degree in four years with summer attendance or five years without summer attendance.

■ Special Academic Programs

Centers for Excellence—The school features one of the premier health law studies programs in the nation, along with specialized centers in employment law and international and comparative law.

- The **Center for Health Law Studies** boasts a nationally recognized faculty, an unparalleled curriculum, and some of the country's finest health law publications.
- The **Wefel Center for Employment Law** specializes in issues of labor disputes, benefits, hiring and discharging, and arbitration.
- The **Center for International and Comparative Law** offers a specialized program of study in areas such as public international law, international criminal law, and international corporate law. Students receive instruction from faculty who have experienced and studied foreign legal systems.

Concentrations—In addition to our three certificate programs through our Centers for Excellence, the School of Law offers concentrations in the following areas: Business Transactional Law; Civil Litigation Skills; Criminal Litigation Skills; Taxation; and Urban Development, Land Use, and Environmental Law. Students also have an opportunity to specialize in Intellectual Property.

Study Abroad and Exchange Programs—Through the Center for International and Comparative Law, students can study law at Saint Louis University's campus in **Madrid, Spain**, earning up to six credit hours of comparative law with foreign and American professors who have extensive experience in the fields of foreign and American criminal law, civil law, and global human rights. SLU Law also maintains cooperative agreements with the University College in Cork, Ireland; Université d'Orléans and Université de Paris-Dauphine in France; University of Georgia in Brussels, Belgium; and the Ruhr University in Bochum, Germany.

Dual-Degree Programs—The School of Law offers intensive dual-degree programs in cooperation with other university schools, including the Schools of Business, Public Health, and Public Policy. Candidates in a dual-degree program must complete the first-year law curriculum before beginning the dual program. The dual-degree programs available are JD/MBA, JD/MHA, JD/MA in Public Administration, JD/MA in Urban Affairs, JD/MPH, JD/MPH in Health Policy, JD/MSW, JD/MA in Sociology and Criminal Justice, and JD/PhD in Health Care Ethics.

■ Public Service

SLU Law has a strong commitment to public service and a faculty pro bono director. Starting with orientation and continuing throughout the year, SLU Law sponsors and participates in public service events and projects. Some of the programs include Make a Difference Day—Homeward Bound, Habitat for Humanity, Court Appointed Special Advocates, Stand Down for Homeless Veterans, and the Tax Assistance Project.

■ Professional Skills Training

Students participate in courses that focus on lawyering skills through simulated client situations or live client representation under the supervision of a faculty member. **Legal Clinics** allow students to represent clients in a variety of settings, from court appearances to appeals to real estate matters. Students in the judicial clerkship programs clerk for area judges. Externships allow students to work in outside placements ranging from government agencies to large health care systems. Simulated professional skills experiences include the **Trial Advocacy Program**, **Moot Court**, or **Appellate Advocacy Program**, as well as multiple drafting courses. Drafting courses are offered in a variety of specialized areas such as intellectual property, health law, real estate, and secured transactions. Courses such as Client Counseling and Negotiations provide students with the tools necessary for skillful client interaction and the art of effective negotiation in client representation. Many of the competitions and cocurricular activities also allow students to apply legal theory to simulated client representation.

■ Cocurricular Activities

SLU Law allows students to perfect their writing and editing skills by working on one of **three law journals**—*Saint Louis University Law Journal*, *Saint Louis University Public Law Review*, and the *Journal of Health Law and Policy*. Qualifying students are invited to write and edit the collections of scholarly work submitted by lawyers and law professors across the world. A broad spectrum of student competitions at the local, regional, and national levels allows students to further their skills. **Moot Court Competitions** hone a student's skills in the appellate phase of litigation, including research, analysis, writing, and oral argument before judges. SLU Law students regularly compete in the National Health Law Moot Court Competition, the ABA Moot Court Competition, the Jessup Moot Court Competition (International Law), the Intellectual Property Moot Court Competition, and the National Environmental Law Moot Court Competition. Numerous **Trial Advocacy Competitions** allow SLU Law students to practice the skills necessary for trying cases before a jury. Each year students participate in the Texas Young Lawyers Association Trial Advocacy Competition, the ABA Employment Law Trial Advocacy Competition, and the Thurgood Marshall Mock Trial Competition. Other competitions include the ABA's Client Counseling and Negotiations competitions.

■ Financial Aid/Scholarships

The Saint Louis University School of Law awards a substantial number of merit-based scholarships to a select group of highly qualified admitted students, including 10 full-tuition scholarships through the 1843 Scholars program. The school has a variety of ways to help students meet their financial goals. Contact the School of Law's Financial Aid Coordinator at *fin_aid@law.slu.edu*.

■ Library

The Omer Poos Law Library serves as the center for legal and interdisciplinary research. SLU Law's databases allow students to access a wide variety of legal materials at any time from anywhere. The library provides a state-of-the-art research environment with access to scores of electronic resources and a collection of over 600,000 volumes. Research librarians hold both law and library science degrees and are available during the day and evening to assist students with research. The SLU Law library faculty and staff take pride in providing personal attention and service to students.

■ Career Services

The Career Services Office, staffed by licensed attorneys and a licensed professional counselor, assists students in identifying their career goals. Students with differing backgrounds and career goals benefit from the personalized assistance that the office provides. Historically, graduating classes have outpaced the national employment average by approximately five percent each year. Across the nation, SLU Law alumni work at large and small firms, excel as CEOs and in-house counsel, and serve in national, state, and local government organizations.

Applicant Profile

Saint Louis University School of Law
This grid includes only applicants who earned 120–180 LSAT scores under standard administrations.

LSAT Score	3.75 + Apps	Adm	3.50–3.74 Apps	Adm	3.25–3.49 Apps	Adm	3.00–3.24 Apps	Adm	2.75–2.99 Apps	Adm	2.50–2.74 Apps	Adm	2.25–2.49 Apps	Adm	2.00–2.24 Apps	Adm	Below 2.00 Apps	Adm	No GPA Apps	Adm	Total Apps	Adm
175–180	1	1	0	0	0	0	0	0	0	0	0	0	0	0	0	0	0	0	0	0	1	1
170–174	1	1	3	3	5	5	0	0	4	3	0	0	0	0	0	0	0	0	0	0	13	12
165–169	31	30	13	11	8	8	10	10	4	3	3	1	2	0	1	0	0	0	1	0	73	63
160–164	72	72	66	62	63	60	44	42	14	11	12	3	5	1	4	0	0	0	5	3	285	254
155–159	102	99	138	130	139	121	83	64	34	21	28	11	12	4	8	1	2	0	7	5	553	456
150–154	108	51	149	73	182	75	137	60	76	23	38	6	15	3	1	0	0	0	24	4	730	295
145–149	27	5	58	12	84	21	67	10	50	5	52	5	17	1	5	0	5	0	8	0	373	59
140–144	9	1	13	0	26	4	26	3	17	1	22	1	10	0	3	0	0	0	7	0	133	10
135–139	4	0	5	0	8	0	10	0	8	0	16	2	6	0	3	0	0	0	2	1	62	3
130–134	0	0	1	0	1	0	3	0	4	0	5	0	1	0	1	0	1	0	3	0	20	0
125–129	0	0	0	0	0	0	2	0	1	0	1	0	1	0	1	0	0	0	0	0	6	0
120–124	0	0	0	0	0	0	0	0	1	0	0	0	0	0	1	0	0	0	0	0	2	0
Total	355	260	446	291	516	294	382	189	213	67	177	29	69	9	28	1	8	0	57	13	2251	1153

Apps = Number of Applicants
Adm = Number Admitted
Reflects 100% of the total applicant pool; average LSAT data reported.

St. Mary's University School of Law

One Camino Santa Maria
San Antonio, TX 78228-8601
Phone: 210.436.3523; Toll-free: 866.639.5831; Fax: 210.431.4202
E-mail: lawadmissions@stmarytx.edu; Website: http://law.stmarytx.edu

ABA Approved Since 1948

The Basics

Type of school	Private
Term	Semester
Application deadline	3/1
Application fee	$55
Financial aid deadline	3/31
Can first year start other than fall?	No
Student to faculty ratio	20.9 to 1
# of housing spaces available restricted to law students	
graduate housing for which law students are eligible	108

Faculty and Administrators

	Total Spr	Total Fall	Men Spr	Men Fall	Women Spr	Women Fall	Minorities Spr	Minorities Fall
Full-time	29	32	18	20	11	12	5	6
Other full-time	6	6	3	5	3	1	2	2
Deans, librarians, & others who teach	11	12	8	10	3	2	7	6
Part-time	51	47	28	28	23	19	7	6
Total	97	97	57	63	40	34	21	20

Curriculum

	Full-Time	Part-Time
Typical first-year section size	80	62
Is there typically a "small section" of the first-year class, other than Legal Writing, taught by full-time faculty	No	No
If yes, typical size offered last year		
# of classroom course titles beyond first-year curriculum	115	
# of upper division courses, excluding seminars, with an enrollment: Under 25	59	
25–49	26	
50–74	13	
75–99	17	
100+	8	
# of seminars	8	
# of seminar positions available	96	
# of seminar positions filled	81	4
# of positions available in simulation courses	255	
# of simulation positions filled	240	1
# of positions available in faculty supervised clinical courses	78	
# of faculty supervised clinical positions filled	78	0
# involved in field placements	33	2
# involved in law journals	89	2
# involved in moot court or trial competitions	45	0
# of credit hours required to graduate	90	

JD Enrollment and Ethnicity

	Men #	Men %	Women #	Women %	Full-Time #	Full-Time %	Part-Time #	Part-Time %	1st-Year #	1st-Year %	Total #	Total %	JD Degs. Awd.
African Amer.	9	1.8	22	6.0	23	3.4	8	4.4	9	2.5	31	3.6	5
Amer. Indian	3	0.6	5	1.4	5	0.7	3	1.6	5	1.4	8	0.9	2
Asian Amer.	19	3.8	21	5.7	30	4.4	10	5.5	19	5.2	40	4.6	8
Mex. Amer.	57	11.5	41	11.1	72	10.6	26	14.3	41	11.2	98	11.4	33
Puerto Rican	2	0.4	2	0.5	2	0.3	2	1.1	3	0.8	4	0.5	3
Hispanic	63	12.8	53	14.4	84	12.3	32	17.6	56	15.3	116	13.4	23
Total Minority	153	31.0	144	39.0	216	31.7	81	44.5	133	36.4	297	34.4	74
For. Nation.	1	0.2	0	0.0	1	0.1	0	0.0	1	0.3	1	0.1	0
Caucasian	340	68.8	225	61.0	464	68.1	101	55.5	232	63.6	565	65.5	133
Unknown	0	0.0	0	0.0	0	0.0	0	0.0	0	0.0	0	0.0	0
Total	494	57.2	369	42.8	681	78.9	182	21.1	365	42.3	863		207

Transfers

Transfers in	3
Transfers out	8

Tuition and Fees

	Resident	Nonresident
Full-time	$27,904	$27,904
Part-time	$18,864	$18,864
Tuition Guarantee Program		N

Living Expenses

Estimated living expenses for singles

Living on campus	Living off campus	Living at home
$15,444	$15,444	$15,444

St. Mary's University School of Law

ABA
Approved
Since
1948

GPA and LSAT Scores

	Total	Full-Time	Part-Time
# of apps	1,900	1,647	253
# of offers	806	712	94
# of matrics	292	231	61
75% GPA	3.49	3.50	3.44
Median GPA	3.18	3.21	3.00
25% GPA	2.82	2.88	2.67
75% LSAT	156	156	155
Median LSAT	154	154	153
25% LSAT	151	151	150

Grants and Scholarships (from prior year)

	Total		Full-Time		Part-Time	
	#	%	#	%	#	%
Total # of students	814		687		127	
Total # receiving grants	254	31.2	254	37.0	0	0.0
Less than 1/2 tuition	232	28.5	232	33.8	0	0.0
Half to full tuition	21	2.6	21	3.1	0	0.0
Full tuition	1	0.1	1	0.1	0	0.0
More than full tuition	0	0.0	0	0.0	0	0.0
Median grant amount			$1,824		$0	

Informational and Library Resources

Total amount spent on library materials	$1,055,484
Study seating capacity inside the library	390
# of full-time equivalent professional librarians	6
Hours per week library is open	108
# of open, wired connections available to students	604
# of networked computers available for use by students	77
Has wireless network?	Y
Require computer?	N

JD Attrition (from prior year)

	Academic	Other	Total	
	#	#	#	%
1st year	15	15	30	8.1
2nd year	0	11	11	4.7
3rd year	0	0	0	0.0
4th year	0	0	0	0.0

Employment (9 months after graduation)

	Total	Percentage
Employment status known	228	99.6
Employment status unknown	1	0.4
Employed	203	89.0
Pursuing graduate degrees	4	1.8
Unemployed (seeking, not seeking, or studying for the bar)	19	8.3
Type of Employment		
# employed in law firms	125	61.6
# employed in business and industry	22	10.8
# employed in government	37	18.2
# employed in public interest	4	2.0
# employed as judicial clerks	10	4.9
# employed in academia	5	2.5
Geographic Location		
# employed in state	180	88.7
# employed in foreign countries	0	0.0
# of states where employed		10

Bar Passage Rates

First-time takers	214	Reporting %	98.60
Average school %	87.20	Average state %	84.54
Average pass difference	2.66		

Jurisdiction	Takers	Passers	Pass %	State %	Diff %
Texas	211	184	87.20	84.54	2.66

St. Mary's University School of Law

One Camino Santa Maria
San Antonio, TX 78228-8601
Phone: 210.436.3523; Toll-free: 866.639.5831; Fax: 210.431.4202
E-mail: lawadmissions@stmarytx.edu; Website: http://law.stmarytx.edu

■ Introduction

St. Mary's University School of Law was founded in 1927 as part of the oldest and largest Catholic university in the Southwest. St. Mary's is located in the beautiful, unique, and legendary city of San Antonio. San Antonio combines a diverse blend of historic sites, natural beauty, charming vistas, and urban amenities. With its culturally rich population and environment, San Antonio is the perfect backdrop for the mission and goals of the School of Law. Enriched by the spirit of the Society of Mary (Marianists), the school imparts to its students the knowledge and attributes of mind and character essential to public service. St. Mary's is vigilant of the need to preserve a tradition of excellence in legal education with the development of new programs and methodologies for the changing world, and now offers a **part-time evening program** in addition to its traditional full-time day program.

■ Library and Physical Facilities

The Sarita Kenedy East Law Library is the largest legal information center in San Antonio and its surrounding area. The library is housed in a spacious, bright, and beautiful building. There is ample study-table seating and large private study carrels. Small conference rooms accommodate groups for discussion and collaboration. A federal depository library, the collection consists of print, microfilm, and multimedia items totaling over 400,000 volumes (or equivalent), which cover a wide range of subjects, including US federal and state laws, and foreign, comparative, and international law. The collection and resources are cataloged and searchable through an automated library information system. The library subscribes to LexisNexis, Westlaw, Loislaw, HeinOnline, LLMC-Digital, the Center for Computer-Assisted Legal Instruction (CALI), the Index to Legal Periodicals Full Text, Congressional Universe, AccessUN, the United Nations Treaty Series, and other information databases. Computers and Internet access, both wired and wireless, are available and supported throughout the library facilities. The library is staffed with eight degreed librarians and about eight paraprofessionals who provide friendly, quality service.

The Law Classroom Building contains four amphitheater-style classrooms with electronically retractable walls and a newly renovated and technologically advanced modern courtroom at its center. Electrical outlets and data ports are located at each student's seat, and the public lounges provide wireless access.

The law school's four primary buildings are located around an oak-shaded quadrangle, forming a central gathering spot. The recently completed Alumni Athletic and Convocation Center offers 135,000 square feet of wellness and fitness options. The center provides for ceremonial facilities as well as athletic endeavors.

■ Curriculum

Required full-time, first-year courses are Constitutional Law, Contracts, Criminal Law, Legal Research and Writing, Civil Procedure, Property, and Torts. All students must also take the required courses of Professional Responsibility, Evidence, and Texas Civil Procedure (only required of those planning to take the Texas bar examination), as well as a specified number of courses from a menu-style core curriculum. Students must also complete a research paper.

■ Clinical Legal Education

The Clinical Program at St. Mary's offers three clinical classes: Civil Justice, Criminal Justice, and Immigration/Human Rights. The clinics teach substantive law, lawyering skills, and responsibilities through the supervised representation of low-income clients and the development of community-based projects. The Civil Justice Clinic represents persons who are homeless; victims of violent crimes; persons who are undocumented, primarily in family law; social security claims; consumer issues; and tax controversies. The Criminal Justice Clinic accepts representation of individuals of any age in misdemeanor and low felony cases as well as some innocence claims. Immigration/Human Rights students represent indigent foreign nationals and refugees in Immigration Court and assist clients with applications for asylum, T and U (trafficking and violent crime victim) visas, and benefits under the Violence Against Women Act.

■ International Law

The St. Mary's Institute on World Legal Problems is conducted at the University of Innsbruck in Austria during July and August. The program is designed to provide law students with a broader understanding of global issues and the role law can play in their peaceful resolution.

Seven justices of the United States Supreme Court have participated in the program as distinguished visiting jurists—former Chief Justice William H. Rehnquist; current Chief Justice John G. Roberts, Jr.; Justice Antonin Scalia; Justice John Paul Stevens; Justice Samuel A. Alito, Jr.; Justice Ruth Bader Ginsburg; and former Justice Sandra Day O'Connor. The program draws students and faculty from all parts of the United States and abroad. It has included students from at least 100 American law schools as well as from Austria, Hungary, China, and Russia. More than 40 visiting professors from law schools in the United States and several foreign countries have also participated.

The Innsbruck Institute is part of the law school's program in international and comparative law, which also includes an LLM in international and comparative law in cooperation with Mexican law schools.

St. Mary's now houses a new **Center for Terrorism Law**, a nonpartisan, nonprofit institution dedicated to the study of legal issues associated with terrorism, with particular emphasis on cyberspace and information assurance technologies.

The **St. Mary's University School of Law Institute on Chinese Law and Business** is a new program of legal studies that prepares law students for the challenges of representing clients doing business with Chinese partners. This summer program is conducted with the cooperation of Beihang University in Beijing.

■ Judicial Internships

St. Mary's students may participate in a wide range of pregraduation judicial internships with outstanding state and federal courts. Students work under the supervision of a

judge or staff attorney, performing legal research and writing projects which often include the drafting of orders that will be used to decide pending cases, the composition of jury instructions, the researching of evidentiary questions, or attendance at settlement conferences.

■ Admission Standards

St. Mary's goal is to create an intellectually stimulating student body composed of persons with diverse backgrounds who share a desire for academic excellence and accomplishment in the practice of law. In addition to academic ability, St. Mary's seeks evidence of qualities such as leadership ability, maturity, community organization skills, knowledge of other languages and cultures, a history of overcoming disadvantage, public interest accomplishments, or success in a previous career. A faculty committee reviews all applications. No one is automatically rejected. All files are read.

■ Student Activities

St. Mary's has over 30 active student organizations. Student organizations are a key part of the collegial environment of the law school.

St. Mary's has two law reviews—the *St. Mary's Law Journal* and *The Scholar: St. Mary's Law Review on Minority Issues.* The reviews offer students excellent opportunities to develop advanced legal research and writing skills. The *Law Journal* has been cited as a persuasive authority in hundreds of court decisions.

St. Mary's students are active in moot court and mock trial competitions. During the spring semester, first-year students

participate in a school-wide moot court competition. Second- and third-year students can compete in on-campus tournaments and in St. Mary's External Advocacy Program (EAP). St. Mary's EAP students travel throughout the US to attend the ABA National Moot Court, National Mock Trial, ATLA Mock Trial, and negotiation competitions.

■ Career Services

The role of the Office of Career Services is to assist law students and graduates with their career searches by informing them of career options and job-search strategies and connecting them with potential employers. Career Services does so by sponsoring programs and job fairs designed to educate, facilitate, and connect students with potential employers during and after law school.

One-on-one confidential strategy sessions with the assistant dean provide a unique opportunity for students to develop a personal plan to assess and meet their career goals. The office maintains a job bank and a résumé bank. A Student Resource Center offers an extensive and up-to-date library of career resources and directories of attorneys, as well as computer terminals with Internet resources, to help students direct and begin their careers in legal and nontraditional positions. Students have extensive opportunities to interact with alumni, who assist with career programming and networking events throughout the year.

For the students in the class of 2009 who reported employment status, 89 percent are employed, with almost all of them working in the legal field.

Applicant Profile

St. Mary's University School of Law
This grid includes only applicants who earned 120–180 LSAT scores under standard administrations.

LSAT Score	3.75 +		3.50–3.74		3.25–3.49		3.00–3.24		2.75–2.99		2.50–2.74		2.25–2.49		2.00–2.24		Below 2.00		No GPA		Total	
	Apps	Adm	Apps	Adm	Apps	Adm	Apps	Adm	Apps	Adm	Apps	Adm	Apps	Adm	Apps	Adm	Apps	Adm	Apps	Adm	Apps	Adm
175–180	0	0	0	0	0	0	0	0	0	0	0	0	0	0	0	0	0	0	0	0	0	0
170–174	1	1	0	0	0	0	1	1	1	1	0	0	0	0	0	0	0	0	0	0	3	3
165–169	0	0	4	4	2	2	6	6	3	2	3	3	2	2	1	1	0	0	0	0	21	20
160–164	10	10	10	10	12	12	17	16	14	14	8	7	4	4	1	1	0	0	0	0	76	74
155–159	34	34	40	40	56	56	47	46	44	44	27	26	15	10	3	2	1	0	0	0	267	258
150–154	59	53	80	65	107	81	111	76	82	42	55	33	21	7	18	5	4	2	6	2	543	366
145–149	33	6	63	13	102	18	93	14	86	6	43	2	23	2	8	0	1	0	12	1	464	62
140–144	16	1	33	2	59	3	64	2	60	2	47	2	29	0	12	1	2	0	12	1	334	14
135–139	3	0	12	0	13	0	22	0	26	1	35	0	9	0	6	0	0	0	1	0	127	1
130–134	0	0	0	0	6	0	2	0	5	0	6	0	3	0	4	0	0	0	4	0	30	0
125–129	0	0	0	0	0	0	0	0	0	0	1	0	0	0	1	0	0	0	0	0	3	0
120–124	0	0	0	0	0	0	0	0	0	0	0	0	1	0	0	0	0	0	0	0	1	0
Total	156	105	242	134	357	172	363	161	321	112	225	73	107	25	54	10	9	2	35	4	1869	798

Apps = Number of Applicants
Adm = Number Admitted
Reflects 98% of the total applicant pool; average LSAT data reported.

University of St. Thomas School of Law—Minneapolis

1000 LaSalle Avenue
Minneapolis, MN 55403
Phone: 651.962.4895
E-mail: lawschool@stthomas.edu; Website: www.stthomas.edu/law

ABA
Approved
Since
2003

The Basics

Type of school	Private
Term	Semester
Application deadline	7/1
Application fee	
Financial aid deadline	7/1
Can first year start other than fall?	No
Student to faculty ratio	17.7 to 1
# of housing spaces available restricted to law students	
graduate housing for which law students are eligible	

Faculty and Administrators

	Total		Men		Women		Minorities	
	Spr	Fall	Spr	Fall	Spr	Fall	Spr	Fall
Full-time	22	21	14	13	8	8	3	4
Other full-time	3	2	1	1	2	1	1	1
Deans, librarians, & others who teach	13	13	5	5	8	8	1	1
Part-time	67	61	41	40	26	21	11	8
Total	105	97	61	59	44	38	16	14

Curriculum

	Full-Time	Part-Time
Typical first-year section size	75	0
Is there typically a "small section" of the first-year class, other than Legal Writing, taught by full-time faculty	Yes	No
If yes, typical size offered last year	37	
# of classroom course titles beyond first-year curriculum	76	
# of upper division courses, excluding seminars, with an enrollment: Under 25	123	
25–49	22	
50–74	9	
75–99	5	
100+	0	
# of seminars	18	
# of seminar positions available	387	
# of seminar positions filled	261	0
# of positions available in simulation courses	376	
# of simulation positions filled	369	0
# of positions available in faculty supervised clinical courses	78	
# of faculty supervised clinical positions filled	65	0
# involved in field placements	621	0
# involved in law journals	82	0
# involved in moot court or trial competitions	36	0
# of credit hours required to graduate	88	

JD Enrollment and Ethnicity

	Men		Women		Full-Time		Part-Time		1st-Year		Total		JD Degs. Awd.
	#	%	#	%	#	%	#	%	#	%	#	%	
African Amer.	9	3.6	10	4.8	19	4.2	0	0.0	7	4.1	19	4.1	8
Amer. Indian	0	0.0	1	0.5	1	0.2	0	0.0	1	0.6	1	0.2	2
Asian Amer.	11	4.4	18	8.7	29	6.3	0	0.0	14	8.2	29	6.3	3
Mex. Amer.	1	0.4	2	1.0	3	0.7	0	0.0	1	0.6	3	0.7	3
Puerto Rican	0	0.0	1	0.5	1	0.2	0	0.0	1	0.6	1	0.2	0
Hispanic	5	2.0	4	1.9	9	2.0	0	0.0	2	1.2	9	2.0	3
Total Minority	26	10.4	36	17.3	62	13.6	0	0.0	26	15.3	62	13.5	19
For. Nation.	0	0.0	0	0.0	0	0.0	0	0.0	0	0.0	0	0.0	0
Caucasian	197	78.5	149	71.6	344	75.3	2	100.0	130	76.5	346	75.4	111
Unknown	28	11.2	23	11.1	51	11.2	0	0.0	14	8.2	51	11.1	15
Total	251	54.7	208	45.3	457	99.6	2	0.4	170	37.0	459		145

Transfers

Transfers in	1
Transfers out	14

Tuition and Fees

	Resident	Nonresident
Full-time	$34,756	
Part-time		
Tuition Guarantee Program	N	

Living Expenses

Estimated living expenses for singles

Living on campus	Living off campus	Living at home
N/A	$18,178	$18,178

University of St. Thomas School of Law—Minneapolis

ABA
Approved
Since
2003

GPA and LSAT Scores

	Total	Full-Time	Part-Time
# of apps	1,551	1,551	0
# of offers	785	785	0
# of matrics	174	174	0
75% GPA	3.59	3.59	0.00
Median GPA	3.34	3.34	0.00
25% GPA	3.07	3.07	0.00
75% LSAT	161	161	0
Median LSAT	157	157	0
25% LSAT	153	153	0

Grants and Scholarships (from prior year)

	Total		Full-Time		Part-Time	
	#	%	#	%	#	%
Total # of students	451		451		0	
Total # receiving grants	269	59.6	269	59.6	0	0.0
Less than 1/2 tuition	110	24.4	110	24.4	0	0.0
Half to full tuition	65	14.4	65	14.4	0	0.0
Full tuition	94	20.8	94	20.8	0	0.0
More than full tuition	0	0.0	0	0.0	0	0.0
Median grant amount		$20,000			$0	

Informational and Library Resources

Total amount spent on library materials	$860,505
Study seating capacity inside the library	379
# of full-time equivalent professional librarians	6
Hours per week library is open	83
# of open, wired connections available to students	595
# of networked computers available for use by students	67
Has wireless network?	Y
Require computer?	N

JD Attrition (from prior year)

	Academic	Other	Total	
	#	#	#	%
1st year	1	14	15	9.9
2nd year	0	0	0	0.0
3rd year	0	0	0	0.0
4th year	0	0	0	0.0

Employment (9 months after graduation)

	Total	Percentage
Employment status known	146	100.0
Employment status unknown	0	0.0
Employed	127	87.0
Pursuing graduate degrees	3	2.1
Unemployed (seeking, not seeking, or studying for the bar)	13	8.9
Type of Employment		
# employed in law firms	56	44.1
# employed in business and industry	27	21.3
# employed in government	15	11.8
# employed in public interest	8	6.3
# employed as judicial clerks	18	14.2
# employed in academia	2	1.6
Geographic Location		
# employed in state	91	71.7
# employed in foreign countries	0	0.0
# of states where employed		17

Bar Passage Rates

First-time takers	142	Reporting %	89.44
Average school %	89.76	Average state %	91.15
Average pass difference	−1.39		

Jurisdiction	Takers	Passers	Pass %	State %	Diff %
Minnesota	116	104	89.66	91.09	−1.43
Wisconsin	11	10	90.91	91.79	−0.88

University of St. Thomas School of Law—Minneapolis

1000 LaSalle Avenue
Minneapolis, MN 55403
Phone: 651.962.4895
E-mail: lawschool@stthomas.edu; Website: www.stthomas.edu/law

■ Introduction

The University of St. Thomas integrates faith and reason in the search for truth through a focus on morality and social justice. The close-knit community, drawn together by this unique mission, shares a distinctive vision of what law and the legal profession can be. The School of Law attracts students from across the country who want to be servant leaders and who understand their responsibility to serve their clients, the community, and those who are most in need of, and least able to pay for, legal assistance.

■ Curriculum

The School of Law offers more than 85 advanced, elective courses in addition to 15 required courses.

The University of St. Thomas offers a unique, nationally recognized, structured mentor externship integrated into the curriculum that matches each student with an experienced lawyer or judge for each year of law school. Mentors introduce students to a range of lawyering tasks. In addition to gaining practical knowledge, students talk with their mentors about the intellectual, ethical, and moral challenges facing attorneys.

Students can also pursue one of five joint-degree programs, including Business Administration (JD/MBA), Catholic Studies (JD/MA), Public Policy (JD/MA), Professional Psychology (JD/MA), and Social Work (JD/MSW).

■ Special Programs

At the Interprofessional Center for Counseling and Legal Services (IPC), law students work side by side with students from graduate programs in social work and professional psychology. The IPC is among the first in the country to forge an equal partnership among the three disciplines. The IPC gives students experience working with actual clients on active cases.

The Holloran Center for Ethical Leadership unites leaders from a range of professions who work together to pursue practical solutions and create effective tools in confronting the challenge of creating ethical leaders. The center hosts an annual national professionals conference, business and law roundtables on ethical governance, and Trusted Adviser Seminars, in which servant leaders from the Twin Cities discuss issues with students in the professional schools.

The Terrence J. Murphy Institute for Catholic Thought, Law and Public Policy is a collaboration between the Center for Catholic Studies and the School of Law. The institute explores the various interactions between law and Catholic thought on topics ranging from workers' rights to criminal law to marriage and family.

■ The Area

The University of St. Thomas School of Law is located in downtown Minneapolis, the regional center for business and culture. Minneapolis and the nearby capital city of St. Paul make up the core of the Twin Cities metropolitan area—a metro area of more than 3.5 million residents. The Twin Cities are home to a vibrant business community that features 12 of Fortune 500's largest corporations. The Twin Cities are also home to a lively legal community that has embraced the School of Law through the mentor externship and summer employment opportunities.

The seemingly limitless recreational opportunities and distinctive beauty of the region add immeasurably to the quality of life. The Twin Cities boast 949 lakes in the metropolitan area. Outdoor enthusiasts have plenty of options from which to choose.

■ Admission

The School of Law seeks to identify students who show the potential to distinguish themselves academically and to integrate the fundamental characteristics of faith and values into their professional character and identity.

The Admissions Committee reviews applications with the goal of understanding the strengths, skills, and unique perspectives of each applicant. While the committee examines quantitative criteria such as LSAT scores and undergraduate transcripts, it also focuses on qualitative factors, such as writing skills, leadership experience, motivation, public service orientation, and commitment to our mission of exploring the integration of faith and reason.

The committee carefully examines all materials submitted to determine whether the School of Law and the student are a good fit. A student's personal statement, letters of recommendation, and other subjective information play an important role in assisting the committee with its goal.

■ Faculty

The faculty are a distinguished group of scholars with an impressive mixture of skills, expertise, and experience. Faculty members are nationally recognized for their professional and scholarly proficiency; all have experience as teachers and as practicing lawyers or expert witnesses, and 16 have advanced degrees in other disciplines.

Of equal importance, faculty members have demonstrated a commitment to service and leadership. All have developed reputations as caring, accessible mentors for students, and each has an inspiring record of service to the community. Faculty members share a strong commitment to our mission and a dedication to assisting each student in his or her formation as an accomplished servant leader.

Each academic year, the full-time faculty is supplemented by over 75 practicing attorneys and judges who serve as adjunct professors.

■ Enrollment/Student Body

The student body is diverse. In the fall 2009 entering class, students represented 20 states and 76 undergraduate institutions. While many students come to the School of Law directly from undergraduate institutions, others have earned postgraduate degrees or have work experience.

■ Library and Physical Facilities

The School of Law occupies a new building, of over 150,000 square feet, in downtown Minneapolis, near the federal

University of St. Thomas School of Law—Minneapolis

courthouse and major laws firms and businesses. The building has several defining features that make it "quite simply breathtaking," as described by an ABA site-evaluation team. These include the dramatic four-story Schultz Grand Atrium, used for lectures, conferences, and social gatherings; the Frey Moot Courtroom, which provides a striking setting in which to learn lawyering skills or hear moot court arguments; and the beautiful Chapel of St. Thomas More.

Modern technology enhances the classrooms, library, groups study areas, moot courtroom, and private offices. A computer lab and a computer training center accommodate student research needs.

The library, with its ample seating, 12 group study rooms, and 3 AV viewing rooms, provides an attractive, functional environment for group or individual study. The library's strong electronic collection provides convenient access to many resources from both on and off campus.

■ Financial Aid

St. Thomas is committed to making high-quality legal education available to students by offering scholarships, grants, employment, and loans. The School of Law administers two scholarship programs that acknowledge applicants who have outstanding academic records, who contribute to our dedicated diversity effort, or who are particularly likely to contribute to the school's mission. All incoming students are automatically considered for scholarship awards.

The UST Loan Repayment Assistance Program (UST-LRAP) provides up to $6,000 in annual assistance for up to 10 years for qualifying applicants. In general, graduates with financial need who undertake public service jobs benefiting the poor and underserved will be eligible to receive assistance with repaying loans for law school tuition.

■ Career Services

Alumni and students work with federal and state judges; international, national, and local public interest organizations; corporations; banks; and law firms of all sizes.

The Office of Career and Professional Development supports students and alumni wherever they are in their career paths and encourages them to consider how their career choices complement their spiritual and ethical beliefs. Available resources include résumé and cover letter writing workshops and individual review, interviewing skills seminars, mock interviews, an online job center, a resource center, practice area panel discussions with local attorneys, networking events, career fairs, and on-campus interviewing.

■ Student Activities

Students are encouraged to form and join student organizations that help them integrate their faith or passion for social justice with their image of themselves as lawyers. Students have created several unique student organizations dedicated to integrating faith and reason in the search for truth with an emphasis on social justice.

The University of St. Thomas Law Journal gives students the opportunity to contribute to the development of legal scholarship and further hone their research, analytical, and writing abilities. The Board of Advocates oversees interscholastic competitions in moot court, trial advocacy, client counseling, and negotiation.

All students are required to perform 50 hours of community service work, exploring a variety of ways in which their interests, skills, and talents can best serve the public. The Public Service Board administers the School of Law's public service requirement, and maintains and distributes information about public service opportunities.

Applicant Profile

University of St. Thomas School of Law—Minneapolis
This grid includes only applicants who earned 120–180 LSAT scores under standard administrations.

LSAT Score	3.75 +		3.50–3.74		3.25–3.49		3.00–3.24		2.75–2.99		2.50–2.74		2.25–2.49		2.00–2.24		Below 2.00		No GPA		Total	
	Apps	Adm	Apps	Adm	Apps	Adm	Apps	Adm	Apps	Adm	Apps	Adm	Apps	Adm	Apps	Adm	Apps	Adm	Apps	Adm	Apps	Adm
175–180	0	0	1	1	0	0	0	0	0	0	0	0	0	0	0	0	0	0	0	0	1	1
170–174	1	1	3	2	1	1	1	1	1	1	0	0	0	0	0	0	0	0	0	0	7	6
165–169	8	8	9	9	8	8	6	6	5	5	2	2	1	1	2	0	0	0	0	0	41	39
160–164	36	36	42	41	30	30	33	32	15	13	5	5	6	4	1	1	1	0	2	2	171	164
155–159	49	45	78	75	68	63	55	50	29	27	12	8	7	4	2	1	2	2	1	1	303	276
150–154	66	48	82	57	96	63	83	46	49	14	30	3	13	3	3	0	1	0	6	2	429	236
145–149	27	11	50	14	77	15	65	13	41	4	28	1	14	0	5	0	0	0	5	0	312	58
140–144	10	0	14	1	38	0	43	0	27	0	17	0	9	0	4	0	0	0	5	0	167	1
135–139	3	1	2	0	5	0	8	0	10	0	11	0	6	0	6	0	0	0	7	0	58	1
130–134	2	0	2	0	3	0	3	0	4	0	5	0	8	0	4	0	2	0	6	0	39	0
125–129	0	0	0	0	0	0	0	0	0	0	2	0	2	0	1	0	1	0	2	0	9	0
120–124	0	0	0	0	0	0	0	0	0	0	0	0	0	0	0	0	0	0	0	0	0	0
Total	202	150	283	200	326	180	297	148	182	64	112	19	66	12	28	2	7	2	34	5	1537	782

Apps = Number of Applicants   Adm = Number Admitted   Reflects 99% of the total applicant pool; average LSAT data reported.

St. Thomas University School of Law

16401 NW 37th Avenue
Miami Gardens, FL 33054
Phone: 800.245.4569, 305.623.2310; Fax: 305.623.2357
E-mail: admitme@stu.edu; Website: www.stu.edu/lawschool

ABA
Approved
Since
1988

Section of Legal Education
and Admissions to the Bar

The Basics

Type of school	Private
Term	Semester
Application deadline	5/1 11/15
Application fee	$60
Financial aid deadline	4/1
Can first year start other than fall?	Yes
Student to faculty ratio	21.1 to 1
# of housing spaces available restricted to law students	
graduate housing for which law students are eligible	100

Faculty and Administrators

	Total		Men		Women		Minorities	
	Spr	Fall	Spr	Fall	Spr	Fall	Spr	Fall
Full-time	26	25	15	14	11	11	4	4
Other full-time	3	3	0	0	2	2	1	1
Deans, librarians, & others who teach	12	12	8	8	4	4	3	3
Part-time	36	29	25	17	10	12	6	7
Total	77	69	48	39	27	29	14	15

Curriculum

		Full-Time	Part-Time
Typical first-year section size		58	0
Is there typically a "small section" of the first-year class, other than Legal Writing, taught by full-time faculty		No	No
If yes, typical size offered last year			
# of classroom course titles beyond first-year curriculum		108	
# of upper division courses, excluding seminars, with an enrollment:	Under 25	157	
	25–49	36	
	50–74	13	
	75–99	9	
	100+	0	
# of seminars		13	
# of seminar positions available		208	
# of seminar positions filled	167		0
# of positions available in simulation courses		268	
# of simulation positions filled	235		0
# of positions available in faculty supervised clinical courses		73	
# of faculty supervised clinical positions filled	73		0
# involved in field placements	194		0
# involved in law journals	123		0
# involved in moot court or trial competitions	65		0
# of credit hours required to graduate		90	

JD Enrollment and Ethnicity

	Men		Women		Full-Time		Part-Time		1st-Year		Total		JD Degs. Awd.
	#	%	#	%	#	%	#	%	#	%	#	%	
African Amer.	19	5.2	34	10.7	53	7.8	0	0.0	15	6.3	53	7.8	14
Amer. Indian	2	0.5	0	0.0	2	0.3	0	0.0	1	0.4	2	0.3	0
Asian Amer.	13	3.6	11	3.5	24	3.5	0	0.0	8	3.3	24	3.5	5
Mex. Amer.	4	1.1	1	0.3	5	0.7	0	0.0	3	1.3	5	0.7	1
Puerto Rican	2	0.5	5	1.6	7	1.0	0	0.0	5	2.1	7	1.0	4
Hispanic	96	26.4	119	37.4	215	31.5	0	0.0	61	25.5	215	31.5	53
Total Minority	136	37.4	170	53.5	306	44.9	0	0.0	93	38.9	306	44.9	77
For. Nation.	6	1.6	11	3.5	17	2.5	0	0.0	5	2.1	17	2.5	6
Caucasian	208	57.1	122	38.4	330	48.4	0	0.0	133	55.6	330	48.4	92
Unknown	14	3.8	15	4.7	29	4.3	0	0.0	8	3.3	29	4.3	4
Total	364	53.4	318	46.6	682	100.0	0	0.0	239	35.0	682		179

Transfers

Transfers in	6
Transfers out	18

Tuition and Fees

	Resident	Nonresident
Full-time	$31,616	$31,616
Part-time		
Tuition Guarantee Program	N	

Living Expenses

Estimated living expenses for singles

Living on campus	Living off campus	Living at home
$22,002	$22,076	N/A

St. Thomas University School of Law

ABA
Approved
Since
1988

GPA and LSAT Scores

	Total	Full-Time	Part-Time
# of apps	2,352	2,352	0
# of offers	1,071	1,071	0
# of matrics	263	263	0
75% GPA	3.19	3.19	0.00
Median GPA	2.90	2.90	0.00
25% GPA	2.90	2.90	0.00
75% LSAT	153	153	0
Median LSAT	150	150	0
25% LSAT	150	150	0

Grants and Scholarships (from prior year)

	Total		Full-Time		Part-Time	
	#	%	#	%	#	%
Total # of students	639		639		0	
Total # receiving grants	229	35.8	229	35.8	0	0.0
Less than 1/2 tuition	172	26.9	172	26.9	0	0.0
Half to full tuition	56	8.8	56	8.8	0	0.0
Full tuition	1	0.2	1	0.2	0	0.0
More than full tuition	0	0.0	0	0.0	0	0.0
Median grant amount			$15,110		$0	

Informational and Library Resources

Total amount spent on library materials	$680,406
Study seating capacity inside the library	480
# of full-time equivalent professional librarians	6
Hours per week library is open	106
# of open, wired connections available to students	70
# of networked computers available for use by students	36
Has wireless network?	Y
Require computer?	N

JD Attrition (from prior year)

	Academic	Other	Total	
	#	#	#	%
1st year	28	26	54	22.6
2nd year	3	1	4	1.8
3rd year	3	0	3	1.7
4th year	0	0	0	0.0

Employment (9 months after graduation)

	Total	Percentage
Employment status known	208	100.0
Employment status unknown	0	0.0
Employed	142	68.3
Pursuing graduate degrees	10	4.8
Unemployed (seeking, not seeking, or studying for the bar)	56	26.9
Type of Employment		
# employed in law firms	69	48.6
# employed in business and industry	37	26.1
# employed in government	17	12.0
# employed in public interest	11	7.7
# employed as judicial clerks	2	1.4
# employed in academia	2	1.4
Geographic Location		
# employed in state	106	74.6
# employed in foreign countries	1	0.7
# of states where employed	13	

Bar Passage Rates

First-time takers	200	Reporting %	82.50
Average school %	78.79	Average state %	80.76
Average pass difference	−1.97		

Jurisdiction	Takers	Passers	Pass %	State %	Diff %
Florida	165	130	78.79	80.76	−1.97

St. Thomas University School of Law

16401 NW 37th Avenue
Miami Gardens, FL 33054
Phone: 800.245.4569, 305.623.2310; Fax: 305.623.2357
E-mail: admitme@stu.edu; Website: www.stu.edu/lawschool

■ Introduction

St. Thomas University School of Law, a fully accredited law school by the American Bar Association and the prestigious Association of American Law Schools, was founded in 1984 and is one of the most culturally diverse and technologically advanced law schools in the country. St. Thomas emphasizes professional ethics throughout its programs, provides intensive academic support on an individual and small-group basis, and offers a broad curriculum, including an array of clinical experiences.

St. Thomas University is located on a 140-acre campus several miles northwest of Miami. Fifteen miles southeast, in downtown Miami, stands the federal courthouse, the location of the United States District Court for the Southern District of Florida. State trial and appellate courts are several blocks away. Approximately 20 miles to the north of the law school is the city of Ft. Lauderdale, another venue for state and appellate courts.

■ Library and Physical Facilities

The St. Thomas University Law Library furnishes students with an online catalog to assist them in locating both digital content and traditional materials. The library meets the needs of students in the twenty-first century by providing them with a wide array of online databases to assist with their research and allow them to pursue their interests in scholarship. Moreover, the library has a large microform collection to provide added collection depth. A wireless network enables students, through their laptops or one of 30 library workstations, to access digital information resources from anywhere on campus. Students may also access most of the databases from home through the school's proxy server. A professional reference staff provides instruction in performing online and traditional research. Reference services are also available to assist students in the evenings and on weekends.

■ Clinical Legal Education Programs

St. Thomas University School of Law requires six credits of professional skills courses to graduate. Students are eligible to participate in any of the law school's 10 clinical offerings in an effort to meet that requirement.

Bankruptcy Clinic—The Bankruptcy Clinic offers a comprehensive set of legal services focused on assisting and empowering low-income individuals in their interaction with the bankruptcy system.

Family Court Clinic—This clinic allows third-year students an opportunity to represent clients in both Family Court and the Domestic Violence Court. The Family Court Clinic is a two-semester, two-track, four-credits-per-semester course. The family division track allows students to learn about family law matters, including the dissolution of marriage, paternity, custody, and adoption cases. In the domestic violence division, students are given the opportunity to provide in-court representation to victims of domestic violence in civil permanent injunction hearings.

Appellate Litigation Clinic—This is a year-long clinical program open to third-year students that provides experience in handling criminal cases in state appellate courts. Each student will have primary responsibility for at least two cases from inception through record preparation, all relevant motions, and the writing of briefs and oral arguments. The program also features a weekly seminar in the appellate process.

Immigration Clinic—Third-year law students will represent asylum seekers, battered spouses and children who have fled their native country, and other noncitizens seeking immigration relief in Immigration Court before the Board of Immigration Appeals and the Department of Homeland Security (formerly the INS).

Judicial Internship—Judicial internships provide an opportunity for students to hear arguments, discuss cases with judges, and apply research and writing skills to real facts. Interns will work closely with supervising staff attorneys and judges.

Tax Clinic—The Tax Clinic, offered to second- and third-year students, is one of the components of the law school's skills training program. The student represents clients before the Internal Revenue Service (IRS), the District Counsel, and the United States Tax Court. In addition, the student is expected to attend conferences with the IRS, job fairs in the community, and Tax Court sessions.

Civil Practice Clinic—This course can be taken full time or part time in one semester and is available to second- and third-year students. Those students whose placement requires they be a Certified Legal Intern must be in their third year. Typical placements include Legal Aid, City Attorney, County Attorney, Attorney General, or other public sector agencies handling civil matters.

Criminal Practice Clinic—This course can be taken full time or part time in one semester and is only available to incoming third-year students. Typical placements include the offices of the State Attorney, US Attorney, and Public Defender. The externship also contains a classroom component in which students discuss their cases and review relevant law.

Students learn through a combination of actual trial practice and classroom work. Under the supervision of an assistant state attorney, the students engage in plea bargain negotiations and try cases.

Placement in the Public Defender's office provides students with the opportunity to defend indigent adults and minors charged with felonies and misdemeanor crimes.

Elder Law Clinic—This course covers the growing legal needs of the elderly. Students will work with the Probate Division of the Circuit Court and members of the Elder Law Bar on case management issues and strategies to deal with a continually aging population.

Florida Supreme Court—For one semester, the intern will function as a law clerk to an individual justice or as a central staff law clerk working for all of the justices.

■ Graduate-Degree Programs

The **LLM/MA in Intercultural Human Rights** offers in-depth instruction on a critical issue of our time: the protection of human dignity across political, cultural, and religious lines. The faculty of global distinction includes top-level United Nations experts, outstanding scholars, judges, and practitioners in the field.

The **JSD Program in Intercultural Human Rights** provides a premier opportunity for budding human rights scholars to make a lasting contribution to this dynamic and action-oriented field.

■ Special Programs

- **Summer-in-Spain Program**—Law students have the opportunity to take six credits at the Royal College University Escorial María Cristina, a part of the University of Madrid. The program is designed to prepare participants for practicing law in the globalized twenty-first century.
- **Summer Conditional Program**—Applicants who may not have strong academic credentials, but nonetheless possess the abilities necessary to succeed in a rigorous program of legal study, may be invited to participate in a summer conditional program. Students who successfully complete the summer conditional program are offered admission to the fall entering class. This program is usually offered each year but, under special circumstances, may not be available.
- **Joint-Degree Programs**—The law school offers four joint-degree programs in cooperation with other graduate divisions of the university. A JD/MBA in Accounting couples lawyering skills with those traditionally in great demand in the corporate, tax, and accounting worlds. The joint JD/MBA in International Business opens the burgeoning field of international transactional law to the new attorney. The JD/MS in Marriage and Family Counseling, one of the only programs of its kind in the country, fills a serious need in the family lawyer's repertory of skills. A joint JD/MS in Sports Administration prepares participants for a diverse set of positions in the world of sports.
- **Academic Support Program**—The law school is committed to the success of its students and offers a comprehensive support system, including Dean's Fellows, tutors, practice examinations, lectures, a director for academic support, and a program to assist graduates with the bar examination.

■ Career Services

The Office of Career Services is dedicated to assisting students in identifying and attaining their professional goals. It offers a range of traditional and innovative services, including a career services resource center, on-campus interviews with major law firms and government agencies, and speakers drawn from various areas of legal practice.

■ Student Activities

The *St. Thomas Law Review* is a student-operated scholarly journal, publishing articles submitted by law faculty and members of the bench and bar nationwide. Membership is determined on the basis of academic excellence and demonstrated writing ability.

The Student Bar Association sponsors various social and educational programs for the student body and otherwise represents student interests. In the student-run Moot Court Program, teams of student advocates compete in interscholastic tournaments across the country, preparing written briefs and presenting oral arguments in simulated appellate cases presided over by members of the bench and bar. Numerous student organizations are active on campus.

■ Housing

Law students can reserve on-campus housing at the University Inn or Villanova Hall, which offer private rooms with private baths and a choice of meal plans.

For law students desiring to live off campus, numerous apartment complexes are located within minutes of the law school.

Applicant Profile

St. Thomas University School of Law
This grid includes only applicants who earned 120–180 LSAT scores under standard administrations.

LSAT Score	3.75 +		3.50–3.74		3.25–3.49		3.00–3.24		2.75–2.99		2.50–2.74		2.25–2.49		2.00–2.24		Below 2.00		No GPA		Total	
	Apps	Adm	Apps	Adm	Apps	Adm	Apps	Adm	Apps	Adm	Apps	Adm	Apps	Adm	Apps	Adm	Apps	Adm	Apps	Adm	Apps	Adm
175–180	0	0	0	0	0	0	0	0	0	0	0	0	0	0	0	0	0	0	0	0	0	0
170–174	0	0	0	0	0	0	0	0	0	0	0	0	0	0	0	0	0	0	0	0	0	0
165–169	1	1	1	1	1	1	1	1	0	0	1	1	1	1	0	0	0	0	0	0	6	6
160–164	4	3	1	1	2	2	5	4	4	4	4	4	1	1	1	1	0	0	0	0	22	20
155–159	12	10	17	15	15	15	18	16	17	17	19	18	14	14	3	2	1	1	1	1	117	109
150–154	17	17	49	48	55	54	80	76	71	66	48	46	37	31	16	14	2	1	4	4	379	357
145–149	22	18	76	62	138	101	151	96	143	76	108	50	53	17	10	4	3	2	18	5	722	431
140–144	16	3	56	14	98	14	121	11	131	11	92	4	42	3	23	2	5	0	22	6	606	68
135–139	7	0	11	0	33	0	41	1	51	0	35	1	36	0	10	0	4	0	14	5	242	7
130–134	1	0	3	0	4	0	15	0	15	0	14	0	11	0	7	0	2	0	7	2	79	2
125–129	0	0	0	0	0	0	0	0	2	0	5	0	0	0	1	0	0	0	0	0	8	0
120–124	0	0	0	0	0	0	0	0	0	0	0	0	0	0	1	0	0	0	1	0	2	0
Total	80	52	214	141	346	187	432	205	434	174	326	124	195	67	72	23	17	4	67	23	2183	1000

Apps = Number of Applicants   Adm = Number Admitted   Reflects 99% of the total applicant pool; average LSAT data reported.

Samford University, Cumberland School of Law

800 Lakeshore Drive
Birmingham, AL 35229
Phone: 800.888.7213; Fax: 205.726.2057
E-mail: lawadm@samford.edu; Website: www.cumberland.samford.edu

ABA
Approved
Since
1949

ABA American Bar Association
Section of Legal Education
and Admissions to the Bar

The Basics

Type of school	Private
Term	Semester
Application deadline	12/31 2/28
Application fee	$50
Financial aid deadline	3/1
Can first year start other than fall?	No
Student to faculty ratio	18.0 to 1
# of housing spaces available restricted to law students	
graduate housing for which law students are eligible	

Faculty and Administrators

	Total		Men		Women		Minorities	
	Spr	Fall	Spr	Fall	Spr	Fall	Spr	Fall
Full-time	23	22	16	15	7	7	3	4
Other full-time	0	0	0	0	0	0	0	0
Deans, librarians, & others who teach	11	11	5	5	6	6	2	2
Part-time	34	21	28	14	6	7	1	1
Total	68	54	49	34	19	20	6	7

JD Enrollment and Ethnicity

	Men		Women		Full-Time		Part-Time		1st-Year		Total		JD Degs. Awd.
	#	%	#	%	#	%	#	%	#	%	#	%	
African Amer.	5	1.9	21	9.4	26	5.3	0	0.0	6	3.4	26	5.3	10
Amer. Indian	2	0.7	3	1.3	5	1.0	0	0.0	3	1.7	5	1.0	1
Asian Amer.	1	0.4	3	1.3	4	0.8	0	0.0	4	2.2	4	0.8	2
Mex. Amer.	0	0.0	0	0.0	0	0.0	0	0.0	0	0.0	0	0.0	0
Puerto Rican	1	0.4	0	0.0	1	0.2	0	0.0	0	0.0	1	0.2	0
Hispanic	2	0.7	1	0.4	3	0.6	0	0.0	2	1.1	3	0.6	1
Total Minority	11	4.1	28	12.6	39	7.9	0	0.0	15	8.4	39	7.9	14
For. Nation.	1	0.4	2	0.9	3	0.6	0	0.0	3	1.7	3	0.6	0
Caucasian	206	76.3	167	74.9	373	75.7	0	0.0	139	77.7	373	75.7	138
Unknown	52	19.3	26	11.7	78	15.8	0	0.0	22	12.3	78	15.8	11
Total	270	54.8	223	45.2	493	100.0	0	0.0	179	36.3	493		163

Curriculum

	Full-Time	Part-Time
Typical first-year section size	55	0
Is there typically a "small section" of the first-year class, other than Legal Writing, taught by full-time faculty	No	No
If yes, typical size offered last year		
# of classroom course titles beyond first-year curriculum	105	
# of upper division courses, excluding seminars, with an enrollment: Under 25	70	
25–49	37	
50–74	17	
75–99	1	
100+	0	
# of seminars	18	
# of seminar positions available	269	
# of seminar positions filled	214	0
# of positions available in simulation courses	418	
# of simulation positions filled	366	0
# of positions available in faculty supervised clinical courses	0	
# of faculty supervised clinical positions filled	0	0
# involved in field placements	63	0
# involved in law journals	96	0
# involved in moot court or trial competitions	51	0
# of credit hours required to graduate	90	

Transfers

Transfers in	4
Transfers out	11

Tuition and Fees

	Resident	Nonresident
Full-time	$31,698	$31,698
Part-time	$18,814	$18,814
Tuition Guarantee Program		N

Living Expenses

Estimated living expenses for singles

Living on campus	Living off campus	Living at home
N/A	$21,950	$21,950

Samford University, Cumberland School of Law

 ABA
Approved
Since
1949

GPA and LSAT Scores

	Total	Full-Time	Part-Time
# of apps	980	980	0
# of offers	506	506	0
# of matrics	178	178	0
75% GPA	3.59	3.59	0.00
Median GPA	3.31	3.31	0.00
25% GPA	3.01	3.01	0.00
75% LSAT	157	157	0
Median LSAT	155	155	0
25% LSAT	153	153	0

Grants and Scholarships (from prior year)

	Total		Full-Time		Part-Time	
	#	%	#	%	#	%
Total # of students	494		494		0	
Total # receiving grants	166	33.6	166	33.6	0	0.0
Less than 1/2 tuition	60	12.1	60	12.1	0	0.0
Half to full tuition	37	7.5	37	7.5	0	0.0
Full tuition	43	8.7	43	8.7	0	0.0
More than full tuition	26	5.3	26	5.3	0	0.0
Median grant amount			$20,000		$0	

Informational and Library Resources

Total amount spent on library materials	$919,016
Study seating capacity inside the library	474
# of full-time equivalent professional librarians	8
Hours per week library is open	105
# of open, wired connections available to students	200
# of networked computers available for use by students	71
Has wireless network?	Y
Require computer?	N

JD Attrition (from prior year)

	Academic	Other	Total	
	#	#	#	%
1st year	1	14	15	8.8
2nd year	1	2	3	1.9
3rd year	0	0	0	0.0
4th year	0	0	0	0.0

Employment (9 months after graduation)

	Total	Percentage
Employment status known	159	100.0
Employment status unknown	0	0.0
Employed	133	83.6
Pursuing graduate degrees	15	9.4
Unemployed (seeking, not seeking, or studying for the bar)	10	6.3
Type of Employment		
# employed in law firms	97	72.9
# employed in business and industry	15	11.3
# employed in government	14	10.5
# employed in public interest	0	0.0
# employed as judicial clerks	4	3.0
# employed in academia	3	2.3
Geographic Location		
# employed in state	77	57.9
# employed in foreign countries	1	0.8
# of states where employed		17

Bar Passage Rates

First-time takers	156	Reporting %	73.08
Average school %	94.73	Average state %	89.07
Average pass difference	5.66		

Jurisdiction	Takers	Passers	Pass %	State %	Diff %
Alabama	92	88	95.65	89.02	6.63
Georgia	22	20	90.91	89.27	1.64

Samford University, Cumberland School of Law

800 Lakeshore Drive
Birmingham, AL 35229
Phone: 800.888.7213; Fax: 205.726.2057
E-mail: lawadm@samford.edu; Website: www.cumberland.samford.edu

■ Introduction

The Cumberland School of Law, established in 1847 as a part of Cumberland University in Lebanon, Tennessee, is one of the oldest law schools in the country. The law school was acquired by Samford University in 1961. Today, Samford University is the largest privately supported and fully accredited institution of higher learning in Alabama. Samford's beautiful 300 acre campus is located in a suburban area of Birmingham, the state's largest industrial, business, and cultural center. The Cumberland School of Law has been a member of the Association of American Law Schools (AALS) since 1952 and has been accredited by the American Bar Association (ABA) since 1949.

■ Advocacy and Skills Training

Cumberland's emphasis on teaching students the art and science of courtroom advocacy begins in the first-year curriculum. Lawyering and Legal Reasoning is a six-credit, two-semester course that provides students with hands-on, practical instruction in pretigation skills, such as client interviewing, counseling, memorandum preparation, and negotiation; pretrial skills, including summary judgment motions and making compelling oral arguments; and appellate litigation skills. This intensive course prepares students to work effectively in their first summer clerkships, where they may be expected to research cases and write briefs.

The state-of-the-art Advanced Trial Advocacy Courtroom provides students with access to the modern technology found in most courtrooms across the country. In Cumberland's Advanced Trial Advocacy course, students learn how to reproduce evidence with three-dimensional digital presenters, video, and DVD reenactments. By mastering this technology and completing the hands-on training in the Advanced Trial Advocacy course, students will be equipped for success in any courtroom.

Cumberland has an exceptional record of recent trial advocacy competition victories. It won the 2008 American Association for Justice National Championship (finishing as a runner-up in 2009) and both the ABA and Association of Trial Lawyers of America national championships (including several national second- and third-place awards). Cumberland has also won 37 regional championships; and the coveted American College of Trial Lawyers' Emil Gumpert Award for Excellence in Teaching Trial Advocacy. The law school also offers a Certificate in Trial Advocacy to recognize students' achievements. Cumberland students have the chance to get class credit and professional experience working for Birmingham's major law firms, judges' offices, and corporate legal departments. The clinical curriculum offers second- and third-year students judicial and corporate externships, as well as externships in the offices of the IRS, US Attorney, and organizations that serve underrepresented or economically disadvantaged groups. In addition, the Alabama Third-Year Practice Rule gives third-year students a chance to practice law under the supervision of a licensed attorney.

■ Library and Physical Facilities

The Lucille Stewart Beeson Law Library, a freestanding Georgian structure, is visually stunning, as well as superbly functional. The building's design is intended to make all facilities easily accessible to students with disabilities. All study carrels and conference rooms are wired for data transmission. In addition, law students have full access to the university's four campus libraries, as well as six computer labs. Wireless Internet access is available here and in many areas around campus.

■ Center for Biotechnology, Law, and Ethics (CBLE)

As the only one of its kind in the United States, the CBLE is dedicated to furthering practical training in the legal disciplines critical to biotechnology. Cumberland's unique program builds on a base of intellectual property, health care, environmental, tort, and natural resources law. The CBLE highlights issues related to the medical, pharmaceutical, and agricultural sectors, and offers students research opportunities. In addition, the CBLE hosts an annual symposium during which experts from around the world speak on such topics.

■ Center for Community Mediation and Public Interest Law Project

The Cumberland Community Mediation Center (CCMC) emphasizes a commitment to public service, an important attribute of the education received at Cumberland. The CCMC provides free and confidential mediation services to the Birmingham community. Students completing the Mediator Practice course are eligible to volunteer as mediators. The mission of the Public Interest Law Project is to promote, encourage, and complete community service and legal public interest projects in the Birmingham community. Recently, Cumberland partnered with the Alabama State Bar and held a number of legal clinics throughout the state to help senior citizens and the underprivileged.

■ Joint-Degree Programs

To broaden their perspective and prepare them for careers in special fields, Cumberland students may pursue seven different joint degrees: JD/Master of Accountancy, JD/MBA, JD/MPH, JD/MPA, JD/Master of Divinity, JD/Master of Theological Studies, and JD/MS in Environmental Management. Some of these joint-degree programs can be completed in three years.

■ Admission

The law school seeks a diverse student body that will make a contribution to the law school and the legal profession. To that end, every applicant's file is thoroughly reviewed for admission. In addition to the LSAT and GPA, difficulty of major, personal challenges overcome, graduate work completed, scholarly achievements, and volunteer and work experience are also considered. Applications are evaluated on a rolling basis, so it

is important to apply early. Applications for fall admission are accepted from September 1 to February 28.

■ Flex-Time Option

Cumberland's flex-time option allows students a maximum of five years to complete their studies. Flex students are required to take a minimum of eight credit hours each semester. Flex students attend classes during the day and pay an hourly tuition rate.

■ Scholarships

Generous merit-based scholarship assistance is awarded to Cumberland's entering and current law students annually. In addition, numerous other scholarships are provided to those students who distinguish themselves academically, make outstanding contributions through leadership in the law school, or demonstrate financial need.

■ Student Activities

The Student Bar Association functions as the first professional organization of a law student's career. In addition to the nearly two dozen outstanding organizations, students may also be invited to join one of three national legal fraternities and be inducted into two honorary societies, Order of the Barrister and Curia Honoris. Student-run publications include *Cumberland Law Review* and *American Journal of Trial Advocacy*.

■ International Law

Cumberland conducts an ABA-approved international summer program that is offered at Sidney Sussex College, Cambridge, England. The graduate degree of Master of Comparative Law is offered to international law school graduates.

■ Career Services

The Office of Career Services provides the training, resources, and guidance to enable Cumberland students and alumni to make well-informed career choices, secure employment as quickly and efficiently as possible, and forge rewarding careers. To help students and graduates achieve these goals, the office provides career counseling, résumé editing, practice interviews, on-campus interview programs, job fairs, job listings, instructional handouts, a resource library, and extensive educational programming. In addition to educational programs on résumé drafting, interviewing skills, networking, and job searching, Career Services also presents a "Lunch with a Lawyer" series, in which Cumberland alumni and other law school graduates come to campus to discuss the practical aspects of their work in various traditional and nontraditional legal jobs. All programs are taught by the attorneys on the Career Services staff and by Cumberland alumni and other attorneys.

Applicant Profile

Samford University, Cumberland School of Law

LSAT Score	GPA								
	3.75 +	3.50–3.74	3.25–3.49	3.00–3.24	2.75–2.99	2.50–2.74	2.25–2.49	2.00–2.24	Below 2.00
175–180									
170–174									
165–169									
160–164									
155–159									
150–154									
145–149									
140–144									
135–139									
130–134									
125–129									
120–124									

■ Good Possibility   □ Possible   ▨ Unlikely

Average LSAT data reported.

University of San Diego—School of Law

Warren Hall Room 203, 5998 Alcalá Park
San Diego, CA 92110-2492
Phone: 619.260.4528; Fax: 619.260.2218
E-mail: jdinfo@sandiego.edu; Website: www.law.sandiego.edu

ABA
Approved
Since
1961

The Basics

Type of school	Private
Term	Semester
Application deadline	2/1
Application fee	$50
Financial aid deadline	2/1
Can first year start other than fall?	No
Student to faculty ratio	14.3 to 1
# of housing spaces available restricted to law students	
graduate housing for which law students are eligible	92

Faculty and Administrators

	Total		Men		Women		Minorities	
	Spr	Fall	Spr	Fall	Spr	Fall	Spr	Fall
Full-time	56	51	42	36	14	15	5	3
Other full-time	6	8	1	1	5	7	1	1
Deans, librarians, & others who teach	11	10	5	5	6	5	1	1
Part-time	43	49	33	34	10	15	4	5
Total	116	118	81	76	35	42	11	10

Curriculum

	Full-Time	Part-Time
Typical first-year section size	80	80
Is there typically a "small section" of the first-year class, other than Legal Writing, taught by full-time faculty	Yes	Yes
If yes, typical size offered last year	40	40
# of classroom course titles beyond first-year curriculum	133	
# of upper division courses, excluding seminars, with an enrollment: Under 25	192	
25–49	33	
50–74	17	
75–99	22	
100+	1	
# of seminars	34	
# of seminar positions available	579	
# of seminar positions filled	372	103
# of positions available in simulation courses	825	
# of simulation positions filled	525	156
# of positions available in faculty supervised clinical courses	218	
# of faculty supervised clinical positions filled	188	53
# involved in field placements	192	28
# involved in law journals	144	33
# involved in moot court or trial competitions	128	16
# of credit hours required to graduate	85	

JD Enrollment and Ethnicity

	Men #	Men %	Women #	Women %	Full-Time #	Full-Time %	Part-Time #	Part-Time %	1st-Year #	1st-Year %	Total #	Total %	JD Degs. Awd.
African Amer.	5	0.9	10	2.2	12	1.5	3	1.6	6	1.9	15	1.5	10
Amer. Indian	5	0.9	6	1.3	8	1.0	3	1.6	2	0.6	11	1.1	2
Asian Amer.	83	15.2	85	18.7	136	16.7	32	17.4	61	18.9	168	16.8	60
Mex. Amer.	24	4.4	22	4.8	38	4.7	8	4.3	12	3.7	46	4.6	17
Puerto Rican	2	0.4	0	0.0	1	0.1	1	0.5	1	0.3	2	0.2	1
Hispanic	17	3.1	15	3.3	22	2.7	10	5.4	12	3.7	32	3.2	6
Total Minority	136	25.0	138	30.3	217	26.6	57	31.0	94	29.1	274	27.4	96
For. Nation.	1	0.2	3	0.7	4	0.5	0	0.0	1	0.3	4	0.4	0
Caucasian	406	74.5	311	68.4	591	72.4	126	68.5	227	70.3	717	71.7	231
Unknown	2	0.4	3	0.7	4	0.5	1	0.5	1	0.3	5	0.5	0
Total	545	54.5	455	45.5	816	81.6	184	18.4	323	32.3	1000		327

Transfers

Transfers in	14
Transfers out	14

Tuition and Fees

	Resident	Nonresident
Full-time	$40,014	$40,014
Part-time	$28,904	$28,904
Tuition Guarantee Program		N

Living Expenses

Estimated living expenses for singles

Living on campus	Living off campus	Living at home
$20,600	$20,600	$10,677

University of San Diego—School of Law

ABA
Approved
Since
1961

GPA and LSAT Scores

	Total	Full-Time	Part-Time
# of apps	4,404	4,010	394
# of offers	1,504	1,416	88
# of matrics	321	281	40
75% GPA	3.59	3.60	3.56
Median GPA	3.44	3.46	3.25
25% GPA	3.22	3.24	3.10
75% LSAT	162	162	160
Median LSAT	160	160	158
25% LSAT	158	158	156

Grants and Scholarships (from prior year)

	Total		Full-Time		Part-Time	
	#	%	#	%	#	%
Total # of students	1,025		795		230	
Total # receiving grants	433	42.2	354	44.5	79	34.3
Less than 1/2 tuition	186	18.1	149	18.7	37	16.1
Half to full tuition	185	18.0	152	19.1	33	14.3
Full tuition	29	2.8	20	2.5	9	3.9
More than full tuition	33	3.2	33	4.2	0	0.0
Median grant amount			$21,000		$15,000	

Informational and Library Resources

Total amount spent on library materials	$1,359,422
Study seating capacity inside the library	590
# of full-time equivalent professional librarians	9
Hours per week library is open	112
# of open, wired connections available to students	240
# of networked computers available for use by students	64
Has wireless network?	Y
Require computer?	N

JD Attrition (from prior year)

	Academic	Other	Total	
	#	#	#	%
1st year	11	28	39	11.6
2nd year	0	4	4	1.2
3rd year	0	3	3	0.9
4th year	0	0	0	0.0

Employment (9 months after graduation)

	Total	Percentage
Employment status known	327	100.0
Employment status unknown	0	0.0
Employed	296	90.5
Pursuing graduate degrees	13	4.0
Unemployed (seeking, not seeking, or studying for the bar)	5	1.5
Type of Employment		
# employed in law firms	164	55.4
# employed in business and industry	54	18.2
# employed in government	39	13.2
# employed in public interest	19	6.4
# employed as judicial clerks	12	4.1
# employed in academia	6	2.0
Geographic Location		
# employed in state	260	87.8
# employed in foreign countries	0	0.0
# of states where employed	17	

Bar Passage Rates

First-time takers	306	Reporting %	100.00
Average school %	80.72	Average state %	78.51
Average pass difference	2.21		

Jurisdiction	Takers	Passers	Pass %	State %	Diff %
California	280	221	78.93	78.07	0.86
New York	6	6	100.00	88.98	11.02
Washington	4	4	100.00	74.40	25.60
Arizona	3	3	100.00	84.03	15.97
Others (7)	13	13	100.00		

University of San Diego—School of Law

Warren Hall Room 203, 5998 Alcalá Park
San Diego, CA 92110-2492
Phone: 619.260.4528; Fax: 619.260.2218
E-mail: jdinfo@sandiego.edu; Website: www.law.sandiego.edu

■ Introduction

As one of the most selective law schools in the country, the University of San Diego (USD) School of Law is a leading center of academic excellence. The school's internationally regarded faculty of scholars and expert practitioners create a demanding, yet welcoming, environment that emphasizes individualized legal education. The school is also known as a leader in creating programs and courses to prepare future lawyers to practice in a rapidly changing world marked by globalization and dramatic advancements in technology. Founded in 1954, the law school is part of the University of San Diego, a private, nonprofit, independent Roman Catholic university. The university is located on a 182-acre campus overlooking Mission Bay and the Pacific Ocean, featuring Spanish Renaissance architecture and well-maintained, garden-like grounds.

■ Admission

USD School of Law strives to draw talented students from all regions of the country and from different ethnic and social backgrounds. The university is committed to advancing academic excellence, expanding legal and professional knowledge, creating a diverse and inclusive community, and preparing leaders dedicated to ethical conduct and compassionate service.

■ Accreditation and Membership

Accredited—American Bar Association (ABA), Committee of Bar Examiners—State of California.
   Membership—Association of American Law Schools (AALS), Order of the Coif.

■ Legal Research Center (LRC)

The Pardee Legal Research Center offers a full range of traditional printed and state-of-the-art electronic services. Computer legal research systems include those of BNA, CCH, HeinOnline, LegalTrac, LexisNexis, and Westlaw. Among all law libraries at ABA-accredited schools, USD is in the top one third in collection size with over half a million volumes, and is number 20 in the nation based on title count.

■ Special Programs

Summer Law Study Abroad Program—USD School of Law, in cooperation with foreign universities, conducts summer law study programs in England, France, Ireland, Italy, Russia, and Spain. The programs introduce American law students to foreign law and legal institutions and provide intensive study during four- to five-week sessions. Classes abroad sensitize students to the cultural differences that influence effective international dealing and expose students to the perspectives of foreign experts.
   Clinical Education Program—This program is recognized as one of the most extensive and successful in the nation, including extensive client-based clinics and placement clinics as well as an externship/internship program. In the legal clinics, which close about 600 cases each year, students represent low-income clients in eight areas of law under the supervision of a clinical professor who is a licensed attorney specializing in that area.
   Research and Advocacy Institutes—In 2008–2009, the school launched two new research institutes: the Center for Corporate and Securities Law and the Center for Intellectual Property Law and Markets. USD also houses the Center for Public Interest Law, Children's Advocacy Institute, Institute for Law and Philosophy, Center for the Study of Constitutional Originalism, Energy Policy Initiatives Center, and Center for Education Policy and Law.
   Concurrent Degrees—Students desiring to concentrate in business or international relations may concurrently pursue the JD/MBA, JD/International MBA, or JD/MA in International Relations.
   Lawyering Skills—Students receive extensive training in a variety of legal skills, including first-year legal writing and research, interviewing, counseling, discovery, trial advocacy, and alternative dispute resolution.
   Oral Advocacy—USD's National Moot Court and National Mock Trial teams consistently rank among the finest teams in the nation. The Mock Trial team has taken first place in the prestigious American Inns of Court's National Tournament of Champions. The Mock Trial team has won the Western Regional Championship of the Association of Trial Lawyers of America nine times and has been selected as the best team in the Ninth Circuit for seven of the last nine years.

■ Campus Highlights

The law school buildings sit directly across from the new Student Life Pavilion, a 62,000-square-foot expansion of the Hahn University Center (UC), the nexus of the USD campus. The UC now offers 134,000 square feet of office space for student organizations and multiuse areas, including a bakery, deli, grill, mini-grocery store, pizza parlor, and the university's main dining hall.

■ Student Activities

With more than 40 different groups available, student organizations not only serve the various interests of our students but also develop a sense of community among their members. The active groups promote leadership, conduct orientation programs, provide study assistance, represent group concerns, sponsor speaker programs, and promote community relations. The school's four law journals, the *San Diego International Law Journal*, the *Journal of Contemporary Legal Issues*, the *San Diego Law Review*, and the *San Diego Journal of Climate and Energy Law*, each offer opportunities to be on the inside of developing legal scholarship.

■ Financial Aid

The School of Law is committed to providing all possible financial assistance to eligible students whose personal resources are insufficient to meet their educational expenses. Sources of financial aid include over 410 need/merit-, merit-, and diversity-based scholarships; federal plans, such as work-study programs; the Perkins, Stafford, and Graduate

PLUS federal loan programs; and institutional loans. Private loan programs are also available to assist law students with supplemental financing.

■ Career Services

USD Law's Career Services office is committed to supporting all students in achieving their diverse career objectives. Throughout their law school years, students are offered opportunities to explore career options with private law firms, government agencies, and public interest organizations, and to obtain internships, fellowships, and clerkships with federal and state courts nationwide. Traditionally, more than 300 interviewers each year interview USD students on and off campus as part of an extensive recruiting process.

USD's law graduates practice in 50 states, the District of Columbia, and at least 60 foreign countries. For the graduating class of 2008, within nine months of graduation, approximately 98 percent were employed or enrolled in a full-time degree program. For the Class of 2008, approximately 55 percent accepted positions with law firms and 24 percent began their careers in public service, including local, state, and federal government; federal courts; and public interest agencies. Others pursued careers in a range of business and corporate positions. Those in private practice had an average salary of $96,500. Those working in public sectors had an average salary of $60,600.

■ Housing

The USD Department of Residential Life and the School of Law Office of Admissions assist in providing information and resources in locating on- and off-campus accommodations.

Applicant Profile

University of San Diego—School of Law
(Note: This chart is to be used as a general guide only. Nonnumerical factors are also considered.)

LSAT Score	GPA								
	3.75 +	3.50–3.74	3.25–3.49	3.00–3.24	2.75–2.99	2.50–2.74	2.25–2.49	2.00–2.24	Below 2.00
175–180									
170–174									
165–169									
160–164									
155–159									
150–154									
145–149									
140–144									
135–139									
130–134									
125–129									
120–124									

■ Very Likely   ■ Possible   □ Unlikely

University of San Francisco School of Law

USF School of Law, 2130 Fulton Street
San Francisco, CA 94117-1080
Phone: 415.422.6586; Fax: 415.422.5442
E-mail: lawadmissions@usfca.edu; Website: www.law.usfca.edu

ABA
Approved
Since
1935

The Basics

Type of school	Private
Term	Semester
Application deadline	2/1
Application fee	$60
Financial aid deadline	2/15
Can first year start other than fall?	No
Student to faculty ratio	15.2 to 1
# of housing spaces available restricted to law students graduate housing for which law students are eligible	25

Faculty and Administrators

	Total		Men		Women		Minorities	
	Spr	Fall	Spr	Fall	Spr	Fall	Spr	Fall
Full-time	34	37	17	20	17	17	13	14
Other full-time	0	0	0	0	0	0	0	0
Deans, librarians, & others who teach	6	5	3	3	3	2	0	0
Part-time	41	44	30	32	11	12	9	11
Total	81	86	50	55	31	31	22	25

Curriculum

	Full-Time	Part-Time
Typical first-year section size	97	51
Is there typically a "small section" of the first-year class, other than Legal Writing, taught by full-time faculty	No	No
If yes, typical size offered last year		
# of classroom course titles beyond first-year curriculum	101	
# of upper division courses, excluding seminars, with an enrollment: Under 25	81	
25–49	38	
50–74	14	
75–99	2	
100+	0	
# of seminars	13	
# of seminar positions available	255	
# of seminar positions filled	187	16
# of positions available in simulation courses	330	
# of simulation positions filled	222	34
# of positions available in faculty supervised clinical courses	120	
# of faculty supervised clinical positions filled	92	11
# involved in field placements	125	11
# involved in law journals	77	8
# involved in moot court or trial competitions	90	4
# of credit hours required to graduate	86	

JD Enrollment and Ethnicity

	Men		Women		Full-Time		Part-Time		1st-Year		Total		JD Degs. Awd.
	#	%	#	%	#	%	#	%	#	%	#	%	
African Amer.	19	6.0	35	9.0	32	5.6	22	16.7	21	7.8	54	7.6	7
Amer. Indian	0	0.0	7	1.8	4	0.7	3	2.3	1	0.4	7	1.0	1
Asian Amer.	43	13.5	72	18.6	93	16.2	22	16.7	41	15.3	115	16.3	41
Mex. Amer.	14	4.4	22	5.7	30	5.2	6	4.5	12	4.5	36	5.1	16
Puerto Rican	1	0.3	1	0.3	1	0.2	1	0.8	1	0.4	2	0.3	1
Hispanic	22	6.9	12	3.1	29	5.1	5	3.8	13	4.9	34	4.8	6
Total Minority	99	31.0	149	38.5	189	32.9	59	44.7	89	33.2	248	35.1	72
For. Nation.	4	1.3	10	2.6	13	2.3	1	0.8	7	2.6	14	2.0	2
Caucasian	146	45.8	174	45.0	265	46.2	55	41.7	123	45.9	320	45.3	91
Unknown	70	21.9	54	14.0	107	18.6	17	12.9	49	18.3	124	17.6	31
Total	319	45.2	387	54.8	574	81.3	132	18.7	268	38.0	706		196

Transfers

Transfers in	1
Transfers out	11

Tuition and Fees

	Resident	Nonresident
Full-time	$37,310	$37,310
Part-time	$26,645	$26,645
Tuition Guarantee Program		N

Living Expenses

Estimated living expenses for singles

Living on campus	Living off campus	Living at home
$21,324	$20,660	$10,060

University of San Francisco School of Law

ABA
Approved
Since
1935

GPA and LSAT Scores

	Total	Full-Time	Part-Time
# of apps	3,876	3,391	485
# of offers	1,351	1,247	104
# of matrics	272	227	45
75% GPA	3.57	3.57	3.61
Median GPA	3.41	3.41	3.47
25% GPA	3.12	3.15	2.96
75% LSAT	160	160	160
Median LSAT	158	158	156
25% LSAT	155	156	153

Grants and Scholarships (from prior year)

	Total		Full-Time		Part-Time	
	#	%	#	%	#	%
Total # of students	669		521		148	
Total # receiving grants	282	42.2	224	43.0	58	39.2
Less than 1/2 tuition	157	23.5	111	21.3	46	31.1
Half to full tuition	125	18.7	113	21.7	12	8.1
Full tuition	0	0.0	0	0.0	0	0.0
More than full tuition	0	0.0	0	0.0	0	0.0
Median grant amount			$18,000		$6,500	

Informational and Library Resources

Total amount spent on library materials	$1,434,219
Study seating capacity inside the library	419
# of full-time equivalent professional librarians	6
Hours per week library is open	98
# of open, wired connections available to students	300
# of networked computers available for use by students	59
Has wireless network?	Y
Require computer?	N

JD Attrition (from prior year)

	Academic	Other	Total	
	#	#	#	%
1st year	18	14	32	13.3
2nd year	2	1	3	1.6
3rd year	1	1	2	0.9
4th year	0	0	0	0.0

Employment (9 months after graduation)

	Total	Percentage
Employment status known	215	94.3
Employment status unknown	13	5.7
Employed	206	95.8
Pursuing graduate degrees	1	0.5
Unemployed (seeking, not seeking, or studying for the bar)	6	2.8
Type of Employment		
# employed in law firms	101	49.0
# employed in business and industry	49	23.8
# employed in government	20	9.7
# employed in public interest	21	10.2
# employed as judicial clerks	3	1.5
# employed in academia	2	1.0
Geographic Location		
# employed in state	176	85.4
# employed in foreign countries	1	0.5
# of states where employed	9	

Bar Passage Rates

First-time takers	222	Reporting %	96.40
Average school %	85.98	Average state %	78.07
Average pass difference	7.91		

Jurisdiction	Takers	Passers	Pass %	State %	Diff %
California	214	184	85.98	78.07	7.91

University of San Francisco School of Law

USF School of Law, 2130 Fulton Street
San Francisco, CA 94117-1080
Phone: 415.422.6586; Fax: 415.422.5442
E-mail: lawadmissions@usfca.edu; Website: www.law.usfca.edu

■ Introduction

Founded in 1912, the University of San Francisco (USF) School of Law is located on a hilltop campus in a quiet residential neighborhood overlooking Golden Gate Park, the Pacific Ocean, and downtown San Francisco.

The San Francisco Bay Area is an extension of the campus and plays a vital role in the educational experience. The law school is located minutes away from the Civic Center, home to federal, state, and local government agencies, as well as federal and state courts, including the California Supreme Court. The city and its surrounding communities provide unsurpassed learning, practice, placement, and service opportunities to complement the academic program. Students represent clients in law school clinics, intern year-round in the city's many major national and international law firms, clerk for judges, and work in public interest organizations.

The USF School of Law is fully accredited by the American Bar Association and is a member of the Association of American Law Schools.

■ Educating for Justice

The USF School of Law offers a rigorous education with a global perspective in a diverse, supportive community. Our graduates are skilled, ethical professionals prepared for any legal career, with a commitment to social justice as their enduring foundation. Our inclusive Jesuit mission of educating minds and hearts to change the world integrates humanity and ethical conduct into the practice of law. Evidence of this mission in action includes our extensive list of programs dedicated to serving communities throughout the United States and around the globe and our unique curriculum focused on ethics and professional responsibility.

■ Degree Programs

The USF School of Law offers full- and part-time Juris Doctor (JD) programs that empower students to develop their analytical abilities, master legal writing and research skills, acquire a firm foundation of basic law, explore an array of specialties, and refine their skills in practical settings. The full-time program requires three years of study, while the part-time program can be completed in four years. Students entering the part-time program may accelerate their studies and complete the degree in seven semesters or they may convert to the full-time program after the first year and graduate in three years. In conjunction with the USF School of Business and Management, the law school offers a four-year, full-time concurrent JD/MBA degree program. The law school also offers a Master of Laws (LLM) in International Transactions and Comparative Law for foreign lawyers and a Master of Laws in Intellectual Property and Technology Law for foreign and US lawyers.

■ Facilities

The USF School of Law is housed in the Koret Law Center and comprises Kendrick Hall, where classrooms and faculty offices are located, and the Dorraine Zief Law Library. Kendrick Hall, built in the 1960s and recently renovated, features a rotunda skylight, spiral stairways, and circular configurations that enhance natural light and offer informal gathering spaces for students and faculty. Students prepare for trial practice in a new, 70-seat moot courtroom. Classrooms offer power and wireless connections at every seat. Administrative offices are located in Kendrick Hall to provide easy access to services and staff. Office space for student organizations and clinical programs, a student lounge, and a café are all found here as well.

Linked to Kendrick Hall by a soaring glass atrium, the Dorraine Zief Law Library, which opened in 2000, is a modern, technologically advanced study environment. It houses an extensive collection and connects to countless online resources. The library also features individual and group study rooms equipped with audiovisual equipment, computer classrooms, and research rooms.

By being part of a larger campus community, USF law students benefit from the amenities and facilities one expects to find at a major urban university, including the outstanding recreational and fitness facilities of USF's award-winning Koret Health and Recreation Center. The university's 55-acre campus also features a main library, bookstore, student center, and dining facilities.

■ The Curriculum

The core curriculum, concentrated in the first year of the full-time program and the first and second years of the part-time program, includes courses essential to a solid understanding of dominant legal concepts. The core curriculum is complemented by a rich offering of courses and programs providing almost unlimited opportunities for specialized study and practical experience. Elective courses are constantly updated to reflect changes in the law, to meet the pace of technological change, and to match student interest.

JD certificate programs and elective clusters offer concentrated study for students who wish to pursue particular career objectives or develop specialized skills. Notable among these are courses in international and comparative law, public interest law, advocacy and alternative dispute resolution, business law, and intellectual property and cyberspace law. There are also opportunities for participation in unique clinical programs, including a Mediation Clinic, an Investor Justice Clinic, a Criminal and Juvenile Justice Law Clinic, a Child Advocacy Clinic, an Internet and Intellectual Property Justice Clinic, and an International Human Rights Law Clinic.

■ International Programs

Our extensive menu of international programs provides exceptional opportunities to study and intern abroad. Traditional summer study-abroad programs are offered in Dublin and Prague, and internship and service opportunities are offered in India, Vietnam, Spain, China, Cambodia, and the Dominican Republic, among other countries. USF's innovative Frank C. Newman International Human Rights Law Clinic affords many students the opportunity to personally present their research and policy proposals to the United Nations Commission on Human Rights in Geneva or the Commission on the Status of Women in New York. The

Center for Law and Global Justice acquaints students with differing legal traditions and provides opportunities for international internships and service learning. The center is a resource for international programming and courses, and creates opportunities for students to conduct research on critical human rights issues.

■ Student Activities

Much of a USF law student's education takes place outside the classroom. Students expand their scholarship interests by writing, editing, and publishing several law journals, including the *USF Law Review*, the *USF Maritime Law Journal*, and the *Intellectual Property Law Bulletin*. Opportunities to hone advocacy and leadership skills abound. Students participate in the annual Advocate of the Year Competition and compete in interschool moot court and trial advocacy competitions.

The representative student government, the Student Bar Association (SBA), oversees more than 40 student organizations that reflect the diversity and varied interests of USF law students. The USF Public Interest Law Foundation's annual gala auction, which raises funds for students working in unpaid summer internships in the public interest and public sector, is one example of the many student-sponsored events held each year.

Frequent panels, guest speakers, special programs, and symposia provide students with regular opportunities for informal interchange with faculty, alumni, members of the bench and bar, and visiting dignitaries. Examples of recent symposia topics include Internet neutrality, the domestic response to global climate change, California's prison crisis, and human trafficking.

The Pro Bono Project and the Law in Motion Service Program offer opportunities for service, sponsoring a variety of legal and nonlegal community outreach projects.

■ Faculty

USF School of Law professors bring to the classroom the highest educational credentials, substantial practical experience, and an underlying dedication to teaching, scholarship, and service. They are respected authors, researchers, and legal theorists who write books, casebooks, practice guides, law review articles, and book reviews. Faculty members have achieved numerous scholastic accomplishments, graduating from the most elite law schools, earning honors, and serving as editors of prestigious law journals. Almost all have substantial practical experience and continue to be involved in service to the community and the profession. Their zeal for teaching comes to life in the classroom, in clinics, and in informal conversations with students. They create an intellectually challenging but supportive atmosphere in which each student thrives.

The full-time faculty is complemented by approximately 60 adjunct professors, including federal and state court judges, attorneys from many public agencies, and other distinguished members of the bar in private practice. Our location in the dynamic San Francisco Bay Area legal community allows the law school to expand its curriculum with specialized courses and provides students access to a wealth of practical expertise.

Applicant Profile

University of San Francisco School of Law
This grid includes only applicants who earned 120–180 LSAT scores under standard administrations.

LSAT Score	3.75 +		3.50–3.74		3.25–3.49		3.00–3.24		2.75–2.99		2.50–2.74		2.25–2.49		2.00–2.24		Below 2.00		No GPA		Total	
	Apps	Adm	Apps	Adm	Apps	Adm	Apps	Adm	Apps	Adm	Apps	Adm	Apps	Adm	Apps	Adm	Apps	Adm	Apps	Adm	Apps	Adm
175–180	0	0	0	0	0	0	0	0	2	2	0	0	0	0	0	0	0	0	0	0	2	2
170–174	3	3	3	2	4	4	2	2	1	1	1	0	1	1	0	0	1	0	0	0	16	13
165–169	11	11	25	25	18	16	19	17	17	17	6	2	7	4	0	0	0	0	2	2	105	94
160–164	57	56	109	107	109	106	75	69	49	43	38	25	15	8	5	1	2	0	7	5	466	420
155–159	92	88	227	209	284	175	186	72	97	27	55	8	22	2	13	0	3	0	14	7	993	588
150–154	74	22	186	73	264	39	276	26	153	8	76	3	40	2	11	0	6	0	19	2	1105	175
145–149	39	5	105	15	147	12	149	8	117	3	58	0	44	0	12	0	3	0	12	0	686	43
140–144	10	0	27	2	59	0	84	1	64	0	42	1	27	0	13	0	3	0	12	0	341	4
135–139	1	0	7	0	16	0	20	0	14	0	17	0	10	0	3	0	3	0	5	0	96	0
130–134	0	0	2	0	2	0	5	0	2	0	6	0	4	0	4	0	0	0	3	0	28	0
125–129	0	0	0	0	1	0	1	0	1	0	2	0	0	0	1	0	0	0	1	0	7	0
120–124	0	0	0	0	0	0	0	0	0	0	0	0	0	0	0	0	0	0	1	0	1	0
Total	287	185	691	433	904	352	817	195	517	101	301	39	170	17	62	1	21	0	76	16	3846	1339

Apps = Number of Applicants
Adm = Number Admitted
Reflects 99% of the total applicant pool; average LSAT data reported.

Santa Clara University School of Law

500 El Camino Real
Santa Clara, CA 95053
Phone: 408.554.5048; Fax: 408.554.7897
E-mail: LawAdmissions@scu.edu; Website: http://law.scu.edu

ABA
Approved
Since
1937

AMERICAN BAR ASSOCIATION
Section of Legal Education
and Admissions to the Bar

The Basics

Type of school	Private
Term	Semester
Application deadline	2/1
Application fee	$75
Financial aid deadline	3/1
Can first year start other than fall?	No
Student to faculty ratio	17.9 to 1
# of housing spaces available restricted to law students	
graduate housing for which law students are eligible	68

Faculty and Administrators

	Total		Men		Women		Minorities	
	Spr	Fall	Spr	Fall	Spr	Fall	Spr	Fall
Full-time	40	42	20	22	20	20	10	10
Other full-time	11	10	5	4	6	6	1	1
Deans, librarians, & others who teach	16	18	5	6	11	12	3	5
Part-time	55	35	35	20	20	15	4	6
Total	122	105	65	52	57	53	18	22

Curriculum

	Full-Time	Part-Time
Typical first-year section size	73	72
Is there typically a "small section" of the first-year class, other than Legal Writing, taught by full-time faculty	Yes	Yes
If yes, typical size offered last year	38	36
# of classroom course titles beyond first-year curriculum	179	

# of upper division courses, excluding seminars, with an enrollment:		
	Under 25	139
	25–49	39
	50–74	20
	75–99	13
	100+	1

# of seminars	96	
# of seminar positions available	1,572	
# of seminar positions filled	1,316	0
# of positions available in simulation courses	305	
# of simulation positions filled	249	0
# of positions available in faculty supervised clinical courses	247	
# of faculty supervised clinical positions filled	195	0
# involved in field placements	233	0
# involved in law journals	108	0
# involved in moot court or trial competitions	34	0
# of credit hours required to graduate	86	

JD Enrollment and Ethnicity

	Men		Women		Full-Time		Part-Time		1st-Year		Total		JD Degs. Awd.
	#	%	#	%	#	%	#	%	#	%	#	%	
African Amer.	19	3.4	10	2.2	21	2.8	8	3.2	7	2.2	29	2.9	18
Amer. Indian	8	1.4	8	1.8	11	1.5	5	2.0	6	1.9	16	1.6	1
Asian Amer.	147	26.6	153	34.2	211	28.2	89	35.3	112	35.1	300	30.0	67
Mex. Amer.	0	0.0	0	0.0	0	0.0	0	0.0	0	0.0	0	0.0	0
Puerto Rican	0	0.0	0	0.0	0	0.0	0	0.0	0	0.0	0	0.0	0
Hispanic	52	9.4	34	7.6	68	9.1	18	7.1	26	8.2	86	8.6	19
Total Minority	226	40.9	205	45.8	311	41.5	120	47.6	151	47.3	431	43.1	105
For. Nation.	0	0.0	0	0.0	0	0.0	0	0.0	0	0.0	0	0.0	0
Caucasian	326	59.0	243	54.2	437	58.3	132	52.4	168	52.7	569	56.8	156
Unknown	1	0.2	0	0.0	1	0.1	0	0.0	0	0.0	1	0.1	0
Total	553	55.2	448	44.8	749	74.8	252	25.2	319	31.9	1001		261

Transfers

Transfers in	23
Transfers out	12

Tuition and Fees

	Resident	Nonresident
Full-time	$38,040	$38,040
Part-time	$26,628	$26,628
Tuition Guarantee Program	N	

Living Expenses

Estimated living expenses for singles

Living on campus	Living off campus	Living at home
$21,794	$21,794	$21,794

Santa Clara University School of Law

ABA
Approved
Since
1937

GPA and LSAT Scores

	Total	Full-Time	Part-Time
# of apps	4,580	4,099	481
# of offers	1,955	1,826	129
# of matrics	311	235	76
75% GPA	3.59	3.61	3.41
Median GPA	3.35	3.39	3.21
25% GPA	3.03	3.11	2.88
75% LSAT	161	161	159
Median LSAT	159	160	157
25% LSAT	157	157	156

Grants and Scholarships (from prior year)

	Total		Full-Time		Part-Time	
	#	%	#	%	#	%
Total # of students	963		732		231	
Total # receiving grants	330	34.3	246	33.6	84	36.4
Less than 1/2 tuition	250	26.0	193	26.4	57	24.7
Half to full tuition	52	5.4	35	4.8	17	7.4
Full tuition	28	2.9	18	2.5	10	4.3
More than full tuition	0	0.0	0	0.0	0	0.0
Median grant amount			$12,500		$10,000	

Informational and Library Resources

Total amount spent on library materials	$1,203,888
Study seating capacity inside the library	452
# of full-time equivalent professional librarians	9
Hours per week library is open	106
# of open, wired connections available to students	870
# of networked computers available for use by students	57
Has wireless network?	Y
Require computer?	N

JD Attrition (from prior year)

	Academic	Other	Total	
	#	#	#	%
1st year	19	25	44	14.5
2nd year	0	1	1	0.3
3rd year	0	0	0	0.0
4th year	1	0	1	3.6

Employment (9 months after graduation)

	Total	Percentage
Employment status known	296	99.7
Employment status unknown	1	0.3
Employed	242	81.8
Pursuing graduate degrees	4	1.4
Unemployed (seeking, not seeking, or studying for the bar)	19	6.4
Type of Employment		
# employed in law firms	137	56.6
# employed in business and industry	64	26.4
# employed in government	22	9.1
# employed in public interest	9	3.7
# employed as judicial clerks	4	1.7
# employed in academia	3	1.2
Geographic Location		
# employed in state	216	89.3
# employed in foreign countries	0	0.0
# of states where employed		13

Bar Passage Rates

First-time takers	285	Reporting %	97.89
Average school %	78.49	Average state %	78.07
Average pass difference	0.42		

Jurisdiction	Takers	Passers	Pass %	State %	Diff %
California	279	219	78.49	78.07	0.42

Santa Clara University School of Law

500 El Camino Real
Santa Clara, CA 95053
Phone: 408.554.5048; Fax: 408.554.7897
E-mail: LawAdmissions@scu.edu; Website: http://law.scu.edu

■ Introduction

Santa Clara Law, just 40 miles south of San Francisco, is located on the lush, historic, 105-acre campus of Santa Clara University, California's oldest operating institution of higher learning. The university was founded by the Jesuits in 1851 on the site of the Mission Santa Clara de Asis, one of California's original 21 missions. Established in 1911, Santa Clara Law has fostered an exceptional academic program based on the Jesuit tradition for nearly a century. Approved by the ABA, Santa Clara Law is a member of the Order of the Coif and the AALS.

Santa Clara Law students are committed to excellence, ethics, and social justice. The school strives to prepare its students to serve as lawyers who lead in any field, and offers students ample opportunities to apply their skills in internships, clinics, field placements, and community involvement.

■ Location

Santa Clara Law is located in the heart of Silicon Valley, one of the most vibrant and exciting economies in the world, and home to leading national and international law firms as well as companies such as Google, Apple, eBay, Intel, and Yahoo!.

Our location enhances the curriculum, including the nationally acclaimed high tech and intellectual property program, which features experienced Silicon Valley executives and attorneys who share their experience in courses, workshops, and lectures. In addition, students benefit from the location through internship and job opportunities, lectures, and networking events.

The San Francisco Bay Area is one of the most beautiful regions in the US, and the Mediterranean climate boasts sun more than 300 days a year. North of Santa Clara are the world-class cities of Berkeley, Oakland, and San Francisco. Southwest are the coastal towns of Santa Cruz, Monterey, Carmel, and Big Sur.

■ Diversity

Santa Clara Law is one of the most diverse law schools in the country, and the school offers an array of programs that encourage and support diversity. Santa Clara Law students learn with students from all 50 states and numerous foreign countries, and they are taught by a diverse and talented group of faculty members who are committed to an inclusive learning experience. More than 57 percent of applicants for fall 2009 were from outside California, and the 2009 entering class included 48 percent minorities and 46 percent women.

■ Library and Physical Facilities

Towering palm trees, spacious lawns, and vibrant flower gardens surround the Heafey Law Library. A traditional moot courtroom provides the setting for advocacy training and activities of the Edwin A. Heafey Jr. Center for Trial and Appellate Advocacy. Other facilities include the Bergin Hall faculty office building and Bannan Hall, where our law career services, Academic Success Program, and many other programs are located. Students also have access to the full array of campus facilities, including computer labs; the Cowell

Student Health Center; Benson Memorial Center; and the Pat Malley Fitness Center, which includes a well-equipped weight room, fitness classes, an outdoor pool, locker rooms with steam rooms and saunas, and courts for basketball, volleyball, and racquetball.

■ Curriculum

Santa Clara Law offers full-time and part-time programs (with day and evening classes), extensive diversity outreach programs, and an Academic Success Program. More than 200 courses are available, and 86 semester units are required to graduate. The degrees available include JD, JD/MBA, JD/MSIS, LLM in International Law, LLM in US Law for Foreign Attorneys, and LLM in Intellectual Property. An academic orientation introduces first-year students to the study of law. The first-year curriculum is prescribed.

The JD/MBA and the JD/MSIS combined-degree programs are a powerful union of Santa Clara's nationally recognized School of Law and Leavey School of Business. Students earn both degrees in a full-time program lasting three and one-half to four years.

■ International Law Certificate

The International Law Program sponsors summer law study programs in more locations than any other American law school, including programs in: Munich, Germany; Strasbourg, France; Geneva, Switzerland; Oxford, England; Hong Kong; Singapore; Shanghai, China; The Hague, the Netherlands; Istanbul, Turkey; San Jose, Costa Rica; Tokyo, Japan; Vienna; Bratislava; Budapest; and Sydney and Perth, Australia. Nearly all programs offer internships with law offices, corporations, or groups particularly suited to allow students on-site observation and participation in areas of international law. Students may earn a certificate in International Law.

■ Computer and High Technology Law Certificate

With its central Silicon Valley location, **Santa Clara Law is one of the top places in the country to study intellectual property and high tech law** for good reasons. Students learn from a dozen full-time faculty members with expertise in every aspect of IP and high tech law plus two dozen part-time faculty members working in IP and high tech law at leading Silicon Valley firms and companies. Students have unparalleled internship opportunities with leading high tech companies and law firms. The IP and high tech curricula is one of the largest in the country, and students can create a highly personalized course of study, including a certificate in High Tech Law or International High Tech Law.

■ Public Interest and Social Justice Law Certificate

The Santa Clara Law community has a true commitment to social justice, and students serve the poor and the marginalized in many ways while in law school, including work for the Center for Social Justice and Public Service, which

offers an array of resources for students who want to focus on this area during their legal education and in practice. Santa Clara Law takes seriously the charge of graduating lawyers who lead with a commitment to a more humane and just world, and many students choose to earn a certificate in Public Interest.

■ Clinical Programs

At Santa Clara Law's Katharine and George Alexander Community Law Center, experienced attorneys mentor students as they participate in all phases of a case from the initial client interview through the trial. Students can earn credit for work as law clerks with public agencies such as the district attorney or public defender, with legal aid offices, or with private law offices. Students may also work as judges' clerks in appellate courts, including the California Supreme Court, or trial courts, including the United States District Court and local superior court. Another clinical opportunity is the Northern California Innocence Project (NCIP), in which students work under the supervision of experienced legal and forensic staff to evaluate case histories and work with prisoners, crime and evidence labs, law enforcement, defense attorneys, and prosecutors to help prove claims of innocence.

■ Student Activities

Santa Clara Law has 35 student groups, including an extensive array of minority student organizations and national and international moot court teams. The school's quarterly, *Santa Clara Law Review*, is published by a student editorial board. The *Computer and High Technology Law Journal* provides a practical resource for the high tech industry and legal community. The *Journal of International Law* is a respected, peer-reviewed scholarly journal. Through the Student Bar Association and student-faculty committees, students participate in the decision processes of the school.

■ Admission

A faculty committee reviews all applications. No one is automatically accepted or rejected. When the LSAT is repeated, the highest score received is used.

Santa Clara Law has a policy for special admission, and applicants may request special consideration because of race, disadvantaged background, or other factors.

Applicants are encouraged to visit Santa Clara Law. Arrangements can be made through the Admissions Office to tour the campus, attend a class, or meet with an admission counselor.

■ Career Services

Law Career Services offers several workshops, presentations, and services to help students launch a career; these include on-campus interviewing, job fairs, mock interviews, diversity receptions, and speed networking. Each year, a number of law firms, companies, and public and government agencies interview on campus or request résumés from our students. A high percentage of our graduates are employed within nine months of graduation in positions throughout the United States.

Applicant Profile

Santa Clara University School of Law
This grid includes only applicants who earned 120–180 LSAT scores under standard administrations.

LSAT Score	GPA																				
	3.75 +		3.50–3.74		3.25–3.49		3.00–3.24		2.75–2.99		2.50–2.74		2.25–2.49		2.00–2.24		Below 2.00		No GPA		Total	
	Apps	Adm	Apps	Adm	Apps	Adm	Apps	Adm	Apps	Adm	Apps	Adm	Apps	Adm	Apps	Adm	Apps	Adm	Apps	Adm	Apps	Adm
175–180	0	0	2	2	1	1	0	0	1	1	2	2	0	0	0	0	0	0	0	0	6	6
170–174	19	19	11	11	11	10	10	10	0	0	1	1	3	3	0	0	0	0	1	1	56	55
165–169	73	73	72	70	57	55	44	44	27	23	10	8	5	3	1	1	0	0	1	1	290	278
160–164	185	184	278	275	189	180	144	120	72	41	45	20	14	5	9	4	3	0	15	14	954	843
155–159	154	128	295	221	360	158	241	73	121	21	46	4	23	3	11	1	3	0	40	21	1294	630
150–154	109	24	222	38	288	34	268	24	122	3	55	7	24	0	9	0	2	0	42	12	1141	142
145–149	33	2	65	2	107	2	114	0	90	0	37	0	20	0	7	0	0	0	18	0	491	6
140–144	8	0	24	0	40	0	58	0	47	0	28	0	16	0	6	0	1	0	16	0	244	0
135–139	1	0	8	0	11	0	20	0	12	0	10	0	6	0	3	0	1	0	3	0	75	0
130–134	0	0	2	0	2	0	3	0	3	0	5	0	2	0	2	0	0	0	3	0	22	0
125–129	0	0	0	0	1	0	2	0	0	0	2	0	1	0	1	0	0	0	0	0	7	0
120–124	0	0	0	0	0	0	0	0	0	0	0	0	0	0	0	0	0	0	1	0	1	0
Total	582	430	979	619	1067	440	904	271	495	89	241	42	114	14	49	6	10	0	140	49	4581	1960

Apps = Number of Applicants
Adm = Number Admitted
Reflects 99% of the total applicant pool; average LSAT data reported.

Seattle University School of Law

901 12th Avenue, Sullivan Hall
Seattle, WA 98122-1090
Phone: 206.398.4200; Fax: 206.398.4058
E-mail: lawadmis@seattleu.edu; Website: www.law.seattleu.edu

ABA Approved Since 1994

AMERICAN BAR ASSOCIATION
Section of Legal Education
and Admissions to the Bar

The Basics

Type of school	Private
Term	Semester
Application deadline	3/1
Application fee	$60
Financial aid deadline	
Can first year start other than fall?	Yes
Student to faculty ratio	12.3 to 1
# of housing spaces available restricted to law students	
graduate housing for which law students are eligible	

Faculty and Administrators

	Total		Men		Women		Minorities	
	Spr	Fall	Spr	Fall	Spr	Fall	Spr	Fall
Full-time	64	63	38	37	26	26	13	18
Other full-time	1	2	1	2	0	0	1	1
Deans, librarians, & others who teach	10	11	3	4	7	7	2	2
Part-time	44	43	30	27	14	16	9	2
Total	119	119	72	70	47	49	25	23

Curriculum

	Full-Time	Part-Time
Typical first-year section size	85	60
Is there typically a "small section" of the first-year class, other than Legal Writing, taught by full-time faculty	No	No
If yes, typical size offered last year		
# of classroom course titles beyond first-year curriculum	160	

# of upper division courses, excluding seminars, with an enrollment:		
Under 25	128	
25–49	51	
50–74	16	
75–99	12	
100+	1	

	Full-Time	Part-Time
# of seminars	38	
# of seminar positions available	703	
# of seminar positions filled	429	51
# of positions available in simulation courses	655	
# of simulation positions filled	349	179
# of positions available in faculty supervised clinical courses	140	
# of faculty supervised clinical positions filled	93	35
# involved in field placements	134	8
# involved in law journals	99	10
# involved in moot court or trial competitions	31	1
# of credit hours required to graduate	90	

JD Enrollment and Ethnicity

	Men		Women		Full-Time		Part-Time		1st-Year		Total		JD Degs. Awd.
	#	%	#	%	#	%	#	%	#	%	#	%	
African Amer.	19	3.7	26	4.9	34	4.2	11	4.8	12	3.6	45	4.3	10
Amer. Indian	3	0.6	8	1.5	9	1.1	2	0.9	6	1.8	11	1.1	3
Asian Amer.	76	14.9	75	14.2	122	15.1	29	12.7	43	13.0	151	14.6	47
Mex. Amer.	14	2.8	14	2.7	26	3.2	2	0.9	11	3.3	28	2.7	12
Puerto Rican	1	0.2	3	0.6	2	0.2	2	0.9	2	0.6	4	0.4	3
Hispanic	10	2.0	12	2.3	16	2.0	6	2.6	2	0.6	22	2.1	4
Total Minority	123	24.2	138	26.2	209	25.9	52	22.8	76	23.0	261	25.2	79
For. Nation.	4	0.8	4	0.8	8	1.0	0	0.0	0	0.0	8	0.8	5
Caucasian	356	69.9	370	70.2	561	69.4	165	72.4	239	72.4	726	70.1	238
Unknown	26	5.1	15	2.8	30	3.7	11	4.8	15	4.5	41	4.0	15
Total	509	49.1	527	50.9	808	78.0	228	22.0	330	31.9	1036		337

Transfers

Transfers in	19
Transfers out	6

Tuition and Fees

	Resident	Nonresident
Full-time	$35,406	$35,406
Part-time	$29,494	$29,494
Tuition Guarantee Program	N	

Living Expenses

Estimated living expenses for singles

Living on campus	Living off campus	Living at home
$17,843	$17,843	$9,887

Seattle University School of Law

ABA
Approved
Since
1994

GPA and LSAT Scores

	Total	Full-Time	Part-Time
# of apps	2,626	2,374	252
# of offers	998	895	103
# of matrics	332	268	64
75% GPA	3.63	3.63	3.55
Median GPA	3.35	3.37	3.26
25% GPA	3.15	3.16	2.99
75% LSAT	160	160	159
Median LSAT	157	158	156
25% LSAT	155	155	153

Grants and Scholarships (from prior year)

	Total		Full-Time		Part-Time	
	#	%	#	%	#	%
Total # of students	1,043		812		231	
Total # receiving grants	513	49.2	429	52.8	84	36.4
Less than 1/2 tuition	497	47.7	417	51.4	80	34.6
Half to full tuition	9	0.9	5	0.6	4	1.7
Full tuition	7	0.7	7	0.9	0	0.0
More than full tuition	0	0.0	0	0.0	0	0.0
Median grant amount			$9,000		$7,000	

Informational and Library Resources

Total amount spent on library materials	$1,249,465
Study seating capacity inside the library	429
# of full-time equivalent professional librarians	9
Hours per week library is open	119
# of open, wired connections available to students	2,116
# of networked computers available for use by students	16
Has wireless network?	Y
Require computer?	Y

JD Attrition (from prior year)

	Academic	Other	Total	
	#	#	#	%
1st year	2	22	24	7.4
2nd year	0	2	2	0.6
3rd year	0	1	1	0.3
4th year	0	0	0	0.0

Employment (9 months after graduation)

	Total	Percentage
Employment status known	362	100.0
Employment status unknown	0	0.0
Employed	332	91.7
Pursuing graduate degrees	9	2.5
Unemployed (seeking, not seeking, or studying for the bar)	12	3.3
Type of Employment		
# employed in law firms	150	45.2
# employed in business and industry	103	31.0
# employed in government	39	11.7
# employed in public interest	15	4.5
# employed as judicial clerks	22	6.6
# employed in academia	3	0.9
Geographic Location		
# employed in state	280	84.3
# employed in foreign countries	1	0.3
# of states where employed	20	

Bar Passage Rates

First-time takers	326	Reporting %	88.96
Average school %	78.97	Average state %	74.40
Average pass difference	4.57		

Jurisdiction	Takers	Passers	Pass %	State %	Diff %
Washington	290	229	78.97	74.40	4.57

Seattle University School of Law

901 12th Avenue, Sullivan Hall
Seattle, WA 98122-1090
Phone: 206.398.4200; Fax: 206.398.4058
E-mail: lawadmis@seattleu.edu; Website: www.law.seattleu.edu

■ Introduction

Seattle University School of Law, the largest and most diverse law school in the Pacific Northwest, is dedicated to the twin goals of academic excellence and education for justice.

The School of Law is home to leading academic programs, including the country's top-ranked legal writing program and the Ronald A. Peterson Law Clinic, as well as distinguished centers and institutes. These programs and a superb faculty support the law school's mission to educate outstanding lawyers to be leaders for a just and humane world.

The school enrolls more than 1,000 students representing more than 250 undergraduate schools and drawn from the top third of the national law school applicant pool. We serve an impressive body of students, whose diversity encompasses age, life experience, and cultural heritage. The law school is recognized nationally for its diverse faculty and welcoming environment. It is the only Washington law school with a part-time program geared to meet the needs of working professionals.

The law school is accredited by the ABA and holds membership in the AALS. Students may pursue a Juris Doctor or one of many joint degrees.

■ Location

Located in the heart of dynamic Seattle, the law school is a vital part of the community. It is located on the beautiful urban campus of Seattle University in the lively Capitol Hill neighborhood just steps from downtown Seattle. The area offers a mix of exciting, professional, cultural, and recreational opportunities.

One of the most beautiful and livable cities in the United States, Seattle is a legal, business, technological, and cultural hub that provides law students access to summer and school-year employment with major players in the economy, multinational law firms, and public agencies.

Sullivan Hall, home to the law school, is an award-winning, state-of-the-art facility with the latest technology throughout its impressive library, classrooms, courtroom, and study and activity areas.

■ Focus Area Curriculum

After completion of rigorous first-year studies that emphasize sound legal analytical skills, the curriculum allows students to select a primary area of interest and supports that interest with enrollment in a prescribed range of courses. Students may focus their upper-division legal studies in one of 14 substantive areas, including Civil Advocacy, Criminal Practice, Environmental Law, Health Law, Labor and Employment, or Real Estate Law.

■ Faculty

Seattle University School of Law is home to an outstanding faculty of committed teacher-scholars. Our professors do not choose between scholarship and teaching, but rather are experts in their fields who are drawn to share their knowledge with students.

A primary mission that drives the academic program is the faculty's desire to prepare students to practice the law with competence, honor, and commitment to public service. Our talented faculty members teach students to analyze problems and construct policy arguments, as well as train them to write and speak with clarity and precision.

The teaching is both demanding and humane. It blends legal theory, doctrinal analysis, and comprehensive practical-skills training. Reflecting the Jesuit tradition of open inquiry, social responsibility, and concern for personal growth, the law school values freedom of conscience, thought, and speech.

Since 2000, law school faculty members have authored or coauthored 117 books, 130 book chapters, and more than 901 articles that have appeared in prestigious law reviews and specialized journals. Articles by our faculty are among the most read on Social Sciences Research Network (SSRN).

■ Academic Enrichment Programs

Access to Justice Institute (ATJI)—The mission of ATJI is to inspire all law students toward a lifelong commitment to equal justice. The institute connects students to public interest opportunities that fulfill unmet legal needs, facilitates advocacy and legal skills training, hosts social justice forums and events, counsels students in public interest career exploration, and collaborates with local, state, and national efforts to promote equal justice.

Center for Law and Equality—The Fred T. Korematsu Center for Law and Equality aims to advance social justice by fostering critical thinking about discrimination in US society and through targeted advocacy to promote equality and freedom. The center's work is divided into three units: research, advocacy, and education projects.

International Initiatives—Seattle University School of Law is a leader in global legal education and has expanded its international reach to offer students and faculty a greater world view. Among the many compelling programs are the International and Comparative Law Program, the Center for Global Justice, and international study and externship opportunities.

Adolf A. Berle Center—The Berle Center conducts and promotes interdisciplinary scholarship while serving as a platform for sustained discussion among academics, legal practitioners, business leaders, activists, policy makers, and community members on the complex and important relationships between enterprises and their many stakeholders.

■ Admission and Financial Aid

In admission decisions, the law school places equal emphasis on three factors: (1) LSAT performance; (2) the undergraduate academic record; and (3) personal achievements, especially talents or factors that contribute to our law school community in special and significant ways.

We also admit a limited group of applicants annually through our **Access Admission Program**, which addresses those cases in which traditional admission criteria are inadequate predictors of success in law school and in the practice of law. Members of historically disadvantaged, underrepresented, or physically challenged groups are

among those individuals considered for this program (limited to no more than 10 percent of the entering class).

The law school's **Scholarship Program** is among the most ambitious in the region, awarding over $3 million per year to approximately 350 students. Its objectives are twofold: to offer to all students—regardless of economic or social background—the advantages of a private legal education, and to recognize and reward—regardless of financial need—the achievements and outstanding potential of the most highly qualified students in the applicant pool. Upon admission, all entering students are automatically considered for scholarships. The School of Law offers a **Loan Repayment Assistance Program** to support graduates who choose full-time public interest legal careers as licensed attorneys doing law-related, public interest work. It offers two annual full-tuition **Scholars for Justice Awards** to outstanding students committed to social justice work, a full-tuition **Native American Scholarship** to an enrolled member of a federally recognized tribe, and the **Adolf A. Berle Scholarship** to a student committed to studying corporate governance.

Applicant Profile

Seattle University School of Law
This grid includes only applicants who earned 120–180 LSAT scores under standard administrations.

LSAT Score	3.75 +		3.50–3.74		3.25–3.49		3.00–3.24		2.75–2.99		2.50–2.74		2.25–2.49		2.00–2.24		Below 2.00		No GPA		Total	
	Apps	Adm	Apps	Adm	Apps	Adm	Apps	Adm	Apps	Adm	Apps	Adm	Apps	Adm	Apps	Adm	Apps	Adm	Apps	Adm	Apps	Adm
175–180	0	0	0	0	1	0	0	0	0	0	0	0	0	0	0	0	0	0	0	0	1	0
170–174	3	2	1	1	3	3	3	2	1	0	1	1	1	0	0	0	0	0	0	0	13	9
165–169	18	18	20	18	27	27	15	14	9	7	6	1	0	0	0	0	0	0	0	0	95	85
160–164	57	52	112	97	69	60	64	46	29	20	19	7	7	1	3	2	1	0	4	2	365	287
155–159	87	70	195	137	181	106	131	65	61	14	35	7	15	2	2	0	2	0	10	5	719	406
150–154	69	25	152	46	201	47	175	22	79	9	39	4	17	3	3	1	1	0	27	8	763	165
145–149	25	1	68	7	82	8	89	5	51	8	27	2	17	3	7	0	2	1	9	1	377	36
140–144	13	1	25	3	28	2	39	1	31	0	25	0	10	0	11	0	1	0	6	0	189	7
135–139	4	0	5	0	13	0	11	0	12	0	11	0	4	0	4	0	3	0	9	0	76	0
130–134	0	0	2	0	1	0	2	0	4	0	1	0	2	0	1	0	1	0	4	0	18	0
125–129	0	0	0	0	2	0	0	0	2	0	1	0	0	0	0	0	0	0	1	0	6	0
120–124	0	0	0	0	0	0	0	0	0	0	1	0	1	0	0	0	0	0	0	0	2	0
Total	276	169	580	309	608	253	529	155	279	58	166	22	74	9	31	3	11	1	70	16	2624	995

Apps = Number of Applicants
Adm = Number Admitted
Reflects 99% of the total applicant pool; average LSAT data reported.

Seton Hall University School of Law

Office of Admissions, One Newark Center
Newark, NJ 07102-5210
Phone: 888.415.7271, 973.642.8747; Fax: 973.642.8876
E-mail: admitme@shu.edu; Website: http://law.shu.edu

ABA
Approved
Since
1951
AMERICAN BAR ASSOCIATION
Section of Legal Education
and Admissions to the Bar

The Basics

Type of school	Private
Term	Semester
Application deadline	4/1
Application fee	$65
Financial aid deadline	4/1
Can first year start other than fall?	No
Student to faculty ratio	15.4 to 1
# of housing spaces available restricted to law students graduate housing for which law students are eligible	

Faculty and Administrators

	Total		Men		Women		Minorities	
	Spr	Fall	Spr	Fall	Spr	Fall	Spr	Fall
Full-time	51	52	28	28	23	23	9	9
Other full-time	1	3	1	1	0	2	0	1
Deans, librarians, & others who teach	17	18	5	5	12	12	4	4
Part-time	93	84	60	48	33	36	8	6
Total	162	157	94	82	68	73	21	20

Curriculum

	Full-Time	Part-Time
Typical first-year section size	70	75
Is there typically a "small section" of the first-year class, other than Legal Writing, taught by full-time faculty	No	No
If yes, typical size offered last year		
# of classroom course titles beyond first-year curriculum	138	
# of upper division courses, excluding seminars, with an enrollment: Under 25	192	
25–49	43	
50–74	27	
75–99	7	
100+	1	
# of seminars	20	
# of seminar positions available	326	
# of seminar positions filled	177	106
# of positions available in simulation courses	1,359	
# of simulation positions filled	773	415
# of positions available in faculty supervised clinical courses	109	
# of faculty supervised clinical positions filled	103	4
# involved in field placements	117	45
# involved in law journals	173	8
# involved in moot court or trial competitions	36	2
# of credit hours required to graduate	88	

JD Enrollment and Ethnicity

	Men		Women		Full-Time		Part-Time		1st-Year		Total		JD Degs. Awd.
	#	%	#	%	#	%	#	%	#	%	#	%	
African Amer.	14	2.4	22	4.4	15	2.1	21	5.7	15	4.2	36	3.3	7
Amer. Indian	1	0.2	0	0.0	0	0.0	1	0.3	0	0.0	1	0.1	0
Asian Amer.	41	6.9	38	7.6	42	5.8	37	10.1	25	7.0	79	7.2	27
Mex. Amer.	0	0.0	0	0.0	0	0.0	0	0.0	0	0.0	0	0.0	0
Puerto Rican	9	1.5	8	1.6	7	1.0	10	2.7	4	1.1	17	1.6	0
Hispanic	22	3.7	14	2.8	20	2.8	16	4.4	20	5.6	36	3.3	10
Total Minority	87	14.7	82	16.5	84	11.6	85	23.2	64	18.0	169	15.5	44
For. Nation.	6	1.0	6	1.2	5	0.7	7	1.9	2	0.6	12	1.1	9
Caucasian	497	83.8	403	81.1	631	87.3	269	73.3	290	81.5	900	82.6	255
Unknown	3	0.5	6	1.2	3	0.4	6	1.6	0	0.0	9	0.8	0
Total	593	54.4	497	45.6	723	66.3	367	33.7	356	32.7	1090		308

Transfers

Transfers in	8
Transfers out	15

Tuition and Fees

	Resident	Nonresident
Full-time	$42,980	$42,980
Part-time	$32,430	$32,430
Tuition Guarantee Program		N

Living Expenses

Estimated living expenses for singles

Living on campus	Living off campus	Living at home
N/A	$19,605	$9,435

Seton Hall University School of Law

ABA
Approved
Since
1951

GPA and LSAT Scores

	Total	Full-Time	Part-Time
# of apps	3,392	2,804	588
# of offers	1,679	1,453	226
# of matrics	357	240	117
75% GPA	3.64	3.68	3.47
Median GPA	3.40	3.48	3.24
25% GPA	3.13	3.21	3.00
75% LSAT	160	161	156
Median LSAT	158	160	153
25% LSAT	154	158	150

Grants and Scholarships (from prior year)

	Total #	Total %	Full-Time #	Full-Time %	Part-Time #	Part-Time %
Total # of students	1,099		717		382	
Total # receiving grants	415	37.8	359	50.1	56	14.7
Less than 1/2 tuition	231	21.0	186	25.9	45	11.8
Half to full tuition	184	16.7	173	24.1	11	2.9
Full tuition	0	0.0	0	0.0	0	0.0
More than full tuition	0	0.0	0	0.0	0	0.0
Median grant amount			$20,000		$5,425	

Informational and Library Resources

Total amount spent on library materials	$1,460,944
Study seating capacity inside the library	533
# of full-time equivalent professional librarians	8
Hours per week library is open	81
# of open, wired connections available to students	54
# of networked computers available for use by students	165
Has wireless network?	Y
Require computer?	Y

JD Attrition (from prior year)

	Academic #	Other #	Total #	Total %
1st year	25	4	29	7.7
2nd year	7	17	24	7.1
3rd year	0	1	1	0.3
4th year	0	0	0	0.0

Employment (9 months after graduation)

	Total	Percentage
Employment status known	304	100.0
Employment status unknown	0	0.0
Employed	288	94.7
Pursuing graduate degrees	2	0.7
Unemployed (seeking, not seeking, or studying for the bar)	10	3.3
Type of Employment		
# employed in law firms	115	39.9
# employed in business and industry	36	12.5
# employed in government	16	5.6
# employed in public interest	3	1.0
# employed as judicial clerks	113	39.2
# employed in academia	3	1.0
Geographic Location		
# employed in state	203	70.5
# employed in foreign countries	0	0.0
# of states where employed	13	

Bar Passage Rates

First-time takers	278	Reporting %	97.12
Average school %	90.37	Average state %	84.69
Average pass difference	5.68		

Jurisdiction	Takers	Passers	Pass %	State %	Diff %
New Jersey	270	244	90.37	84.69	5.68

Seton Hall University School of Law

Office of Admissions, One Newark Center
Newark, NJ 07102-5210
Phone: 888.415.7271, 973.642.8747; Fax: 973.642.8876
E-mail: admitme@shu.edu; Website: http://law.shu.edu

■ Introduction

Founded in 1951, Seton Hall University School of Law is the only private law school in the state of New Jersey. While it values its Catholic identity, the law school is a pluralistic community representing a diversity of racial, cultural, religious, and socioeconomic backgrounds. The school is consistently recognized for its outstanding teaching and high level of student satisfaction.

■ One Newark Center, Our Home

Rich in history and culture, Newark is a city to explore. Whatever your interest, you'll find it here—the performing and visual arts, sports, great food, and captivating architecture are within easy reach. The law school is a block from Newark's Penn Station, from which a 20-minute train ride takes students to Manhattan and the world's largest law firms. Students can walk to Newark's major law firms, government agencies, and the federal and state courthouses. Housing options are extensive. Students enjoy living in nearby historic buildings and, with its expansive network of train lines, Newark is within easy reach of New York City, Hoboken, Jersey City, and many suburban communities. The law school's open, welcoming design is a reflection of the faculty and administration's commitment to students. Offices, classrooms, moot courtrooms, and the library are interconnected by balconies overlooking a striking five-story, glass-encased atrium. The entire law school complex is saturated with Wi-Fi Internet connectivity, including access to wireless printing. The building has unusually large student space, including newly renovated student journal and organization offices, lounges, meeting rooms, a chapel, and a cafeteria. The Peter W. Rodino Jr. Law Library is located on three floors and accommodates 600 students and 100 terminals for student use. The Law Library's collection contains more than 425,000 volumes covering a wide array of law and law-related subjects. Health Law and Intellectual Property Law are areas of particular strength. The Rodino Library is a depository for US government documents and for New Jersey state documents.

■ Curriculum

The JD requires 88 credits to graduate and may be completed as a full-time or a part-time program. The school offers both a day and an evening program following a semester calendar. The program emphasizes humanistic principles and encourages their synthesis with knowledge of the law and professional responsibility. The law school is committed to in-depth training in legal writing and research.

In addition to the core required courses, more than 200 courses are offered in a wide range of areas grouped as follows: Constitutional Law, Corporate Law, Criminal Law and Procedure, Health and Drug Law, Intellectual Property and Entertainment Law, International Legal Studies, Labor and Employment Law, Personal and Family Law, Property and Estates Law, Public Interest, and Taxation. Externships, journals, pro bono, and moot court programs are also included in the school's offerings.

Master of Laws (LLM) and a Master of Science in Jurisprudence (MSJ) are also offered in the areas of health, science, and technology law.

■ Public Interest

Seton Hall School of Law is committed to public interest and clinical education. Through the Seton Hall Law Center for Social Justice, students are provided with one of the most comprehensive clinical and pro bono programs offered by any New York area law school. The school's clinics presently represent more than 3,000 disadvantaged and underrepresented clients each year in a wide range of litigation such as civil litigation, family law, impact litigation, immigration and human rights, immigrant workers rights, and juvenile justice. Clinical projects include International Human Rights/Rule of Law and Urban Revitalization. The Center for Social Justice provides services in the public's interest while training and mentoring future attorneys whose careers will be dedicated in whole or in part to public interest work. Students can take part in various programs geared toward public interest beginning as early as their first year, including clinical programs, externships, and pro bono assignments. Scholarship and other financial assistance are available through the Distinguished Public Interest Scholarship, Summer Public Interest Law Fellowship, and Public Interest Loan Repayment Assistance Program.

■ Special Programs

Internships—The law school offers judicial internships with justices of the New Jersey Supreme Court, judges of the New Jersey Appellate Division, Chancery and Law Courts, the Third Circuit Court of Appeals, the US District Courts, and the US Bankruptcy Courts. There are myriad internship programs with nonprofit and government agencies.

Externships—Externship offerings include environmental law, health law, entertainment law, international organizations, the European Court of Justice or Court of First Instance, the Federal Public Defender, Securities and Exchange Commission, New York Stock Exchange, Internal Revenue Service, National Labor Relations Board, and US Attorney.

Concentrations—The law school offers concentrations in Health Law and Intellectual Property Law that allow students to study a specialized curriculum developed by faculty in consultation with attorneys and government officials working in the field. The breadth and depth of both curricula is unparalleled. In addition to coursework, students have the opportunity to participate in externships and take part in frequent symposia and colloquia.

Joint-Degree Programs—JD/MBA—a four-year program with Seton Hall University Stillman School of Business, **JD/MADIR**—a four-year program with Seton Hall University School of Diplomacy and International Relations, **JD/MD**—a six-year program with the Robert Wood Johnson Medical School of the University of Medicine and Dentistry of New Jersey, **MSJ/MD**—a five-year program with the Robert Wood Johnson Medical School of the University of Medicine and Dentistry of New Jersey.

Journals—The law school offers students an opportunity to advance legal scholarship through four student journals—the *Seton Hall Law Review, Seton Hall Legislative Journal, Circuit Review*, and the *Journal of Sports and Entertainment Law*.

International Study—The law school offers a summer program for the study of law in the Middle East at the American University of Cairo in Egypt and a program in Geneva, Switzerland, focusing on intellectual property. Seton Hall's Zanzibar program is the only ABA-approved winter-intersession program focusing on modern day slavery and human trafficking.

LLM and MSJ Degrees—Seton Hall offers LLM degrees in Health Law and Intellectual Property. Seton Hall also offers a Master of Science in Jurisprudence (MSJ) degree in Health Law, Science, and Technology, which provides professionals with a solid foundation in legal aspects of health care and intellectual property regulation. Such a concentrated exposure to health law issues can be vital to medical directors, regulatory and contract compliance officers, risk and case managers, employee benefits personnel, lobbyists, and pharmaceutical employees. Full- and part-time programs are available for both the LLM and MSJ degrees.

Moot Court Program—Students represent the law school in the National Moot Court competition as well as in 10 interschool competitions focusing on specific areas of law.

LEO Institute—The Monsignor Thomas Fahy Legal Education Opportunities Institute provides an intense summer classroom experience for educationally disadvantaged students. Applicants from disadvantaged groups, regardless of race, religion, age, sex, sexual orientation, or national origin, may wish to inquire about this program.

■ Student Activities

There are over 35 student organizations at Seton Hall Law, representing various personal and professional interests. The Student Bar Association (SBA) and other student organizations sponsor a variety of practical, social, and educational events. The SBA plays a major role in orientation, and sponsors a holiday party each November in Newark and a Barristers' Ball in the spring. Organizations sponsor career seminars focused on different areas of the law, host symposiums and panel discussions that focus on current legal and societal issues, and plan annual banquets and networking receptions during the year.

■ Committed to Your Success

At Seton Hall you will find a school committed to your success. The majority of our students participate in hands-on clinical training or externships, and 95 percent of our students are employed within nine months of graduation. Seton Hall Law maintains a proactive Career Services Office staffed by full-time counselors who assist students in defining their career objectives and goals and establishing contact with employers. Each fall and spring, law firms, accounting firms, and public interest and governmental employers conduct interviews through the school's On-Campus Interview Program. Alumni are practicing nationwide.

Applicant Profile

Seton Hall University School of Law
This grid includes only applicants who earned 120–180 LSAT scores under standard administrations.

LSAT Score	3.75 +		3.50–3.74		3.25–3.49		3.00–3.24		2.75–2.99		2.50–2.74		2.25–2.49		2.00–2.24		Below 2.00		No GPA		Total	
	Apps	Adm	Apps	Adm	Apps	Adm	Apps	Adm	Apps	Adm	Apps	Adm	Apps	Adm	Apps	Adm	Apps	Adm	Apps	Adm	Apps	Adm
170–180	9	9	3	3	5	5	5	4	2	2	2	1	3	2	0	0	0	0	0	0	29	26
165–169	29	26	17	16	28	28	18	17	8	8	6	5	5	5	2	1	0	0	0	0	113	106
160–164	108	101	143	131	156	138	118	107	69	54	34	21	22	15	9	3	2	0	6	6	667	576
155–159	122	105	224	197	210	148	164	96	110	48	51	17	30	9	13	3	4	1	18	7	946	631
150–154	84	44	141	53	212	48	179	35	100	12	60	8	25	2	13	0	1	0	21	4	836	206
145–149	25	2	76	10	106	11	125	7	96	5	53	2	23	0	4	0	2	0	6	0	516	37
140–144	12	3	29	2	55	6	63	2	58	2	32	0	19	1	9	0	5	0	8	0	290	16
Below 140	2	0	17	0	22	1	37	0	30	0	33	0	22	0	13	0	5	0	20	1	201	2
Total	391	290	650	412	794	385	709	268	473	131	271	54	149	34	63	7	19	1	79	18	3598	1600

Apps = Number of Applicants
Adm = Number Admitted
Reflects 99% of the total applicant pool, average LSAT data reported.

SMU Dedman School of Law

Office of Admissions, PO Box 750110
Dallas, TX 75275-0110
Phone: 214.768.2550, 888.768.5291; Fax: 214.768.2549
E-mail: lawadmit@smu.edu; Website: www.law.smu.edu

ABA Approved Since 1927

The Basics

Type of school	Private
Term	Semester
Application deadline	12/1 2/15
Application fee	$75
Financial aid deadline	12/1 2/15
Can first year start other than fall?	No
Student to faculty ratio	15.0 to 1
# of housing spaces available restricted to law students	
graduate housing for which law students are eligible	

Faculty and Administrators

	Total Spr	Total Fall	Men Spr	Men Fall	Women Spr	Women Fall	Minorities Spr	Minorities Fall
Full-time	42	44	26	29	16	15	9	9
Other full-time	4	5	4	3	0	2	1	1
Deans, librarians, & others who teach	8	7	6	5	2	2	0	0
Part-time	42	27	36	22	5	5	7	1
Total	96	83	72	59	23	24	17	11

Curriculum

	Full-Time	Part-Time
Typical first-year section size	82	96
Is there typically a "small section" of the first-year class, other than Legal Writing, taught by full-time faculty	No	No
If yes, typical size offered last year		
# of classroom course titles beyond first-year curriculum	134	

# of upper division courses, excluding seminars, with an enrollment:		
Under 25	71	
25–49	37	
50–74	24	
75–99	13	
100+	3	

# of seminars	23	
# of seminar positions available	460	
# of seminar positions filled	328	69
# of positions available in simulation courses	1,040	
# of simulation positions filled	858	137
# of positions available in faculty supervised clinical courses	206	
# of faculty supervised clinical positions filled	171	35
# involved in field placements	52	10
# involved in law journals	185	43
# involved in moot court or trial competitions	47	1
# of credit hours required to graduate	87	

JD Enrollment and Ethnicity

	Men #	Men %	Women #	Women %	Full-Time #	Full-Time %	Part-Time #	Part-Time %	1st-Year #	1st-Year %	Total #	Total %	JD Degs. Awd.
African Amer.	15	3.1	31	7.3	22	4.2	24	6.3	9	3.6	46	5.1	8
Amer. Indian	8	1.7	5	1.2	6	1.1	7	1.8	3	1.2	13	1.4	1
Asian Amer.	32	6.7	37	8.7	38	7.3	31	8.2	18	7.1	69	7.6	27
Mex. Amer.	2	0.4	1	0.2	1	0.2	2	0.5	1	0.4	3	0.3	0
Puerto Rican	1	0.2	0	0.0	0	0.0	1	0.3	1	0.4	1	0.1	0
Hispanic	35	7.3	48	11.3	48	9.2	35	9.2	27	10.7	83	9.2	19
Total Minority	93	19.4	122	28.8	115	21.9	100	26.4	59	23.3	215	23.8	55
For. Nation.	3	0.6	1	0.2	3	0.6	1	0.3	1	0.4	4	0.4	0
Caucasian	351	73.1	277	65.5	375	71.6	253	66.8	171	67.6	628	69.5	243
Unknown	33	6.9	23	5.4	31	5.9	25	6.6	22	8.7	56	6.2	7
Total	480	53.2	423	46.8	524	58.0	379	42.0	253	28.0	903		305

Transfers

Transfers in	28
Transfers out	4

Tuition and Fees

	Resident	Nonresident
Full-time	$38,406	$38,406
Part-time	$28,805	$28,805
Tuition Guarantee Program	N	

Living Expenses

Estimated living expenses for singles

Living on campus	Living off campus	Living at home
$18,400	$18,400	$18,400

SMU Dedman School of Law

*ABA
Approved
Since
1927*

GPA and LSAT Scores

	Total	Full-Time	Part-Time
# of apps	2,275	2,056	699
# of offers	608	465	143
# of matrics	256	178	78
75% GPA	3.84	3.87	3.76
Median GPA	3.66	3.76	3.60
25% GPA	3.24	3.30	3.17
75% LSAT	165	165	160
Median LSAT	162	164	159
25% LSAT	155	158	153

Grants and Scholarships (from prior year)

	Total		Full-Time		Part-Time	
	#	%	#	%	#	%
Total # of students	953		527		426	
Total # receiving grants	909	95.4	670	127.1	239	56.1
Less than 1/2 tuition	609	63.9	388	73.6	221	51.9
Half to full tuition	261	27.4	243	46.1	18	4.2
Full tuition	0	0.0	0	0.0	0	0.0
More than full tuition	39	4.1	39	7.4	0	0.0
Median grant amount			$10,000		$5,000	

Informational and Library Resources

Total amount spent on library materials	$1,414,054
Study seating capacity inside the library	724
# of full-time equivalent professional librarians	6
Hours per week library is open	104
# of open, wired connections available to students	0
# of networked computers available for use by students	109
Has wireless network?	Y
Require computer?	N

JD Attrition (from prior year)

	Academic	Other	Total	
	#	#	#	%
1st year	0	0	0	0.0
2nd year	0	11	11	4.0
3rd year	3	6	9	2.9
4th year	1	2	3	2.6

Employment (9 months after graduation)

	Total	Percentage
Employment status known	294	100.0
Employment status unknown	0	0.0
Employed	269	91.5
Pursuing graduate degrees	5	1.7
Unemployed (seeking, not seeking, or studying for the bar)	4	1.4
Type of Employment		
# employed in law firms	177	65.8
# employed in business and industry	61	22.7
# employed in government	14	5.2
# employed in public interest	4	1.5
# employed as judicial clerks	6	2.2
# employed in academia	7	2.6
Geographic Location		
# employed in state	253	94.1
# employed in foreign countries	0	0.0
# of states where employed	12	

Bar Passage Rates

First-time takers	286	Reporting %	94.76
Average school %	93.73	Average state %	84.54
Average pass difference	9.19		

Jurisdiction	Takers	Passers	Pass %	State %	Diff %
Texas	271	254	93.73	84.54	9.19

SMU Dedman School of Law

Office of Admissions, PO Box 750110
Dallas, TX 75275-0110
Phone: 214.768.2550, 888.768.5291; Fax: 214.768.2549
E-mail: lawadmit@smu.edu; Website: www.law.smu.edu

■ Introduction

Founded in 1925, SMU Dedman School of Law is located on a magnificent tree-lined campus in a beautiful residential neighborhood just five miles north of downtown Dallas. SMU offers an intimate learning community within a vibrant urban center.

With a relatively small entering class size, an outstanding teaching faculty, and distinguished guest lecturers, SMU offers a scholarly community with fantastic opportunities both inside and outside the classroom. SMU also has a well-rounded, diverse student body from approximately 200 colleges and universities, 30 states, and 20 countries.

■ Law School Campus

SMU offers a beautiful setting in which to pursue legal studies. The Law School Quadrangle, a six-acre, self-contained corner of the campus, offers students convenient access to all law school facilities. The larger SMU campus offers students a variety of housing options, a childcare facility, a health center, and a new fitness/wellness center.

SMU recently completed a multimillion-dollar renovation of all of the law school classrooms. A four-story parking garage with 500 spaces is available exclusively for law student parking, and a new dining hall opened in 2005.

■ Curriculum

SMU offers seven degree programs: JD (full-time day or part-time evening), JD/MBA, JD/MA in Economics, LLM (General), LLM (Taxation), LLM (for foreign attorneys), and SJD.

Students find a sophisticated curriculum that complements SMU's wide breadth of class offerings with extensive depth of focus. The JD curriculum is designed to achieve the goal of producing lawyers who are capable and responsible professionals through its emphasis on providing substantive knowledge, ethical and moral training, and practical skills to serve clients in local, national, and global communities.

Each JD student must complete 87 credit hours. Thirty-one of these hours comprise the mandatory first-year curriculum. After the first year, students must complete a course in professional responsibility and two upper-level writing courses (including an edited writing seminar in which an extensive scholarly, expository writing project is reviewed and critiqued by the professor).

SMU offers many small classes in which students will get to know their classmates and professors. Each entering class is divided into three sections (two full-time day and one part-time evening) of approximately 90 students each. Each semester, first-year students are assigned to a legal research, writing, and advocacy class of approximately 25 students. Over one-half of SMU's upper-division courses have fewer than 25 students, and approximately three-quarters have fewer than 50 students.

SMU's rich upper-division curricular offerings, with over 165 upper-division courses per year, provide students with a wide range of courses and the freedom to tailor a program of study that furthers their professional and personal goals. With traditional strengths in business, litigation, tax, and international law, the curriculum extends to many areas, including intellectual property, health care, environmental, and family law.

SMU's LLM programs are intended to enhance careers in the private practice of law, teaching, and public service by providing the opportunity for students who already have their basic law degree to increase their understanding of legal theory and policies. The LLM program for foreign attorneys is the largest graduate program, enrolling approximately 40 students from about 20 countries each year. SMU has over 1,400 international alumni from over 70 countries, including many who hold significant positions in major international corporations, in the highest courts of their nations, and in other key government and private entities.

■ Student Activities and Law Reviews

Students are able to enhance their legal education by participating in numerous programs and conferences sponsored by various faculty and student groups and centers. Selected law students serve on five major journals for which they receive academic credit. Law students are able to expand their legal education experience by participating in over 20 moot court, trial advocacy, client counseling, and negotiation competitions held at the local, regional, national, and international level, and by becoming active members in over 30 student organizations.

■ Externships and Clinics

Externships offer students the opportunity to work at a government agency for up to two hours of course credit. Popular externships include those with the US Attorney, the SEC, and the EPA.

Clinics offer students an opportunity to engage in the practice of law for up to six hours of course credit. Currently SMU has eight clinical opportunities: civil litigation, criminal defense, criminal prosecution, death penalty, federal taxation, small business, consumer law, and child advocacy.

■ Public Service

All students are required to perform 30 hours of public service before graduating. This model public service program not only allows the student to learn in a hands-on setting, but also provides an early exposure to pro bono practice, which is integral to the US legal system. SMU professors voluntarily hold themselves to this same requirement.

■ Overseas Study

SMU offers students an opportunity to study law for six weeks at University College at Oxford University in England.

■ Career Services and Bar Passage

SMU provides students with job placement assistance throughout their legal careers. The Career Services Office helps students develop their job search and career

development skills, and partners with students in locating summer and permanent job opportunities.

SMU graduates fare very well in the legal market. Within nine months of graduation, approximately 99 percent of the class of 2008 was employed. They had an average starting salary of over $115,000 in the private sector and an average starting salary of over $101,000 overall.

In July 2008, 93.97 percent of SMU first-time test takers passed the Texas bar exam, ranking first among all Texas law schools.

■ Admission

SMU looks for excellent, well-rounded students with strong academic backgrounds, life experiences, and perspectives that will enrich its educational community. Each application is considered in its entirety: LSAT score, undergraduate performance, graduate studies, work experience, activities, personal statement, and letters of recommendation are all read and evaluated. Applications can be downloaded from the Web.

■ Scholarships

SMU provides approximately 50 percent of its entering class with scholarship assistance. SMU law scholarships, including several full-tuition Hutchison scholarships, are awarded on the basis of the admission application, including the applicant's answer to an optional question. In addition, two private foundations, the Hatton W. Sumners Foundation and the Dallas Bar Foundation, fund and select five to nine additional full-tuition scholarships per entering class. Both foundations require a separate scholarship application, available from the SMU Admissions Office. The Sarah T. Hughes Scholarships, sponsored by the Dallas Bar Foundation, are awarded to outstanding minority applicants. The Sumners Scholars are selected from a competitive pool of applicants with strong academics and extracurricular activities. Both foundations require that the SMU application, the respective scholarship application, and all supporting documents be submitted by February 15.

Applicant Profile

SMU Dedman School of Law
This grid includes only applicants who earned 120–180 LSAT scores under standard administrations.

LSAT Score	3.75 +		3.50–3.74		3.25–3.49		3.00–3.24		2.75–2.99		2.50–2.74		2.25–2.49		2.00–2.24		Below 2.00		No GPA		Total	
	Apps	Adm	Apps	Adm	Apps	Adm	Apps	Adm	Apps	Adm	Apps	Adm	Apps	Adm	Apps	Adm	Apps	Adm	Apps	Adm	Apps	Adm
175–180	1	1	1	1	1	1	0	0	0	0	0	0	0	0	1	0	0	0	0	0	4	3
170–174	10	9	3	3	7	7	4	3	0	0	1	1	1	0	0	0	0	0	0	0	26	23
165–169	45	44	43	42	28	27	25	22	8	6	9	8	7	5	1	1	0	0	0	0	166	155
160–164	125	98	108	45	88	35	66	24	36	13	14	6	4	3	1	0	0	0	9	2	451	226
155–159	109	60	165	26	134	18	101	10	46	4	25	3	14	3	5	0	2	0	13	2	614	126
150–154	82	43	122	15	109	3	108	12	66	6	35	2	14	2	2	0	1	0	16	0	555	83
145–149	26	14	40	5	73	0	63	3	43	0	29	0	10	0	5	0	2	0	5	0	296	22
140–144	6	2	14	1	26	0	27	0	15	0	14	0	13	0	6	0	0	0	2	0	123	3
135–139	0	0	7	0	7	0	13	0	10	0	6	0	5	0	5	0	0	0	2	0	55	0
130–134	1	0	1	0	3	0	3	0	4	0	4	0	2	0	2	0	0	0	5	0	25	0
125–129	0	0	0	0	0	0	2	0	1	0	2	0	1	0	0	0	2	0	1	0	9	0
120–124	0	0	0	0	1	0	0	0	0	0	0	0	0	0	1	0	0	0	0	0	2	0
Total	405	271	504	138	477	91	412	74	229	29	139	20	71	13	29	1	7	0	53	4	2326	641

Apps = Number of Applicants
Adm = Number Admitted
Reflects 93% of the total applicant pool; average LSAT data reported.

University of South Carolina School of Law

701 South Main Street
Columbia, SC 29208
Phone: 803.777.6605; Fax: 803.777.2847
E-mail: usclaw@law.sc.edu; Website: www.law.sc.edu

ABA
Approved
Since
1925

The Basics

Type of school	Public
Term	Semester
Application deadline	3/1
Application fee	$60
Financial aid deadline	3/1
Can first year start other than fall?	No
Student to faculty ratio	14.9 to 1
# of housing spaces available restricted to law students graduate housing for which law students are eligible	429

Faculty and Administrators

	Total		Men		Women		Minorities	
	Spr	Fall	Spr	Fall	Spr	Fall	Spr	Fall
Full-time	38	38	24	23	14	15	5	5
Other full-time	1	1	1	1	0	0	0	0
Deans, librarians, & others who teach	13	12	5	5	8	7	0	0
Part-time	19	10	15	7	4	3	0	0
Total	71	61	45	36	26	25	5	5

Curriculum

	Full-Time	Part-Time
Typical first-year section size	82	0
Is there typically a "small section" of the first-year class, other than Legal Writing, taught by full-time faculty	No	No
If yes, typical size offered last year		
# of classroom course titles beyond first-year curriculum	116	
# of upper division courses, excluding seminars with an enrollment: Under 25	62	
25–49	30	
50–74	22	
75–99	7	
100+	1	
# of seminars	17	
# of seminar positions available	335	
# of seminar positions filled	313	0
# of positions available in simulation courses	553	
# of simulation positions filled	514	0
# of positions available in faculty supervised clinical courses	67	
# of faculty supervised clinical positions filled	67	0
# involved in field placements	0	0
# involved in law journals	206	0
# involved in moot court or trial competitions	52	0
# of credit hours required to graduate	90	

JD Enrollment and Ethnicity

	Men		Women		Full-Time		Part-Time		1st-Year		Total		JD Degs. Awd.
	#	%	#	%	#	%	#	%	#	%	#	%	
African Amer.	18	4.5	40	14.0	58	8.5	0	0.0	20	8.4	58	8.5	19
Amer. Indian	1	0.3	0	0.0	1	0.1	0	0.0	0	0.0	1	0.1	1
Asian Amer.	7	1.8	6	2.1	13	1.9	0	0.0	5	2.1	13	1.9	3
Mex. Amer.	0	0.0	0	0.0	0	0.0	0	0.0	0	0.0	0	0.0	0
Puerto Rican	0	0.0	0	0.0	0	0.0	0	0.0	0	0.0	0	0.0	0
Hispanic	5	1.3	4	1.4	9	1.3	0	0.0	0	0.0	9	1.3	7
Total Minority	31	7.8	50	17.5	81	11.8	0	0.0	25	10.5	81	11.8	30
For. Nation.	0	0.0	0	0.0	0	0.0	0	0.0	0	0.0	0	0.0	2
Caucasian	321	80.3	219	76.8	540	78.8	0	0.0	178	74.5	540	78.8	211
Unknown	48	12.0	16	5.6	64	9.3	0	0.0	36	15.1	64	9.3	2
Total	400	58.4	285	41.6	685	100.0	0	0.0	239	34.9	685		245

Transfers

Transfers in	21
Transfers out	6

Tuition and Fees

	Resident	Nonresident
Full-time	$19,034	$38,014
Part-time		
Tuition Guarantee Program		N

Living Expenses

Estimated living expenses for singles

Living on campus	Living off campus	Living at home
$16,667	$16,667	$8,833

University of South Carolina School of Law

ABA
Approved
Since
1925

GPA and LSAT Scores

	Total	Full-Time	Part-Time
# of apps	1,973	1,973	0
# of offers	730	730	0
# of matrics	240	240	0
75% GPA	3.70	3.70	0.00
Median GPA	3.46	3.46	0.00
25% GPA	3.14	3.14	0.00
75% LSAT	160	160	0
Median LSAT	158	158	0
25% LSAT	156	156	0

Grants and Scholarships (from prior year)

	Total		Full-Time		Part-Time	
	#	%	#	%	#	%
Total # of students	683		682		1	
Total # receiving grants	342	50.1	342	50.1	0	0.0
Less than 1/2 tuition	258	37.8	258	37.8	0	0.0
Half to full tuition	72	10.5	72	10.6	0	0.0
Full tuition	8	1.2	8	1.2	0	0.0
More than full tuition	4	0.6	4	0.6	0	0.0
Median grant amount			$8,912		$0	

Informational and Library Resources

Total amount spent on library materials	$906,565
Study seating capacity inside the library	504
# of full-time equivalent professional librarians	9
Hours per week library is open	99
# of open, wired connections available to students	42
# of networked computers available for use by students	42
Has wireless network?	Y
Require computer?	Y

JD Attrition (from prior year)

	Academic	Other	Total	
	#	#	#	%
1st year	2	9	11	4.9
2nd year	0	10	10	4.7
3rd year	2	2	4	1.6
4th year	0	0	0	0.0

Employment (9 months after graduation)

	Total	Percentage
Employment status known	201	93.9
Employment status unknown	13	6.1
Employed	183	91.0
Pursuing graduate degrees	9	4.5
Unemployed (seeking, not seeking, or studying for the bar)	9	4.5
Type of Employment		
# employed in law firms	94	51.4
# employed in business and industry	17	9.3
# employed in government	27	14.8
# employed in public interest	8	4.4
# employed as judicial clerks	35	19.1
# employed in academia	2	1.1
Geographic Location		
# employed in state	133	72.7
# employed in foreign countries	1	0.5
# of states where employed	13	

Bar Passage Rates

First-time takers	212	Reporting %	73.11
Average school %	90.97	Average state %	81.83
Average pass difference	9.14		

Jurisdiction	Takers	Passers	Pass %	State %	Diff %
South Carolina	155	141	90.97	81.83	9.14

University of South Carolina School of Law

701 South Main Street
Columbia, SC 29208
Phone: 803.777.6605; Fax: 803.777.2847
E-mail: usclaw@law.sc.edu; Website: www.law.sc.edu

■ Introduction

The University of South Carolina School of Law, established in 1867, is located in Columbia, South Carolina. With a metropolitan population approaching 700,000, Columbia combines the advantages of a progressive, growing area with the pace of a smaller city. The School of Law is located two blocks from the state capitol building. As the seat of state government, Columbia is home to the South Carolina Supreme Court, Court of Appeals, federal district court, criminal and civil courts, and courts of special jurisdiction. There are also numerous law firms in proximity to the law school. Columbia residents enjoy easy access to the mountains and the beautiful South Carolina low country and coastal region. The School of Law is accredited by the American Bar Association. The School of Law has been a member of the Association of American Law Schools since 1924.

■ Library and Academic Programs

Since its founding, the School of Law has provided outstanding preparation for law students. The curriculum combines traditional teaching methods and courses with modern, state-of-the-art instruction. The School of Law houses a major research library with a collection of more than 500,000 volumes and extensive computer-assisted research capabilities, including LexisNexis, Westlaw, Loislaw, HeinOnline, BNA, SSRN, and the online catalog. The library also includes the South Carolina Legal History Collection. Law students and faculty have access to the collection of the main university library, the Thomas Cooper Library. A highly skilled staff of librarians provides assistance and instruction in research and reference techniques. The library is open approximately 100 hours per week and for extended hours during the examination period. The computer lab and an electronic learning facility are also located within the library. Individual closed study carrels are available for assignment to students, and larger study rooms and open carrels are also available. A wireless computer network is available throughout the building and the law center.

The School of Law offers a full-time-only day program leading to the Juris Doctor degree. In order to earn the JD, a student must successfully complete 90 semester hours of coursework. In each semester, a student must register for a minimum of 12 credit hours. The School of Law offers one seven-week summer session each year.

In addition to all first-year courses, students are required to take Constitutional Law II, Criminal Procedure, Professional Responsibility, and a perspective course, and to satisfy an upper-level writing requirement. The School of Law offers advanced courses that allow detailed study in corporate and commercial law, tax and estate planning, and litigation. The peer-assistance tutoring program provides academic support to first-year students, and numerous resources are available to assist students in succeeding academically.

■ Dual-Degree Programs

The School of Law, in cooperation with other graduate programs at USC, currently offers dual JD and master's degrees in the following: Law and International Business Administration, Law and Human Resources, Law and Accountancy, Law and Economics, Law and Public Administration, Law and Criminology and Criminal Justice, Law and Social Work, Law and Earth and Environmental Resources Management, and Law and Health Administration. The USC School of Law and Vermont Law School offer a dual degree in environmental law. Students may earn a JD from USC and a Master of Studies in Environmental Law degree from Vermont Law School in only three years.

■ Clinics, Public Service, and Special Programs

The School of Law recognizes that experiential learning in the area of professional skills is essential to a well-rounded legal education. Under special court rule, third-year law students in South Carolina may represent clients and appear in court when enrolled in a clinical legal education course. The clinical education program offers courses designed to develop critical lawyering skills. The program offers training in trial advocacy, interviewing, counseling, negotiation, alternative dispute resolution, and legal drafting. Clinics include criminal practice, veterans' rights, bankruptcy, federal litigation, and nonprofit organizations. Externships are available in childrens' law and foreign practice.

The Pro Bono Program, one of the longest operating programs of its type, has an outstanding national and local reputation. Under the leadership of a full-time director and a student board, the program offers students opportunities to work with a wide range of public interest organizations, including CASA, the environmental law monitoring project, the Homeless Legal Clinic, juvenile arbitration, the Greater Columbia Literacy Project, Project Ayuda, the Legal Justice Center, the public defenders' office, the South Carolina Department of Consumer Affairs, the South Carolina Department of Indigent Defense, and volunteer income tax assistance, among others.

The Law School's Children's Law Center provides training to professionals who work with children in the juvenile and family courts. The Nelson Mullins Riley and Scarborough Center on Professionalism at the Law School provides a professionalism series for first-year students and is a national leader in the development of mentoring programs to assist in the transition from law school to law practice. The National Advocacy Center and the National College of District Attorneys are located on the USC campus. The Advocacy Center, operated by the US Department of Justice, provides intensive training to approximately 15,000 federal prosecutors and attorneys from across the country. The National College of District Attorneys provides training to nearly 2,000 prosecutors.

■ Admission

The School of Law seeks to enroll qualified students who will enhance and embrace the school's rigorous educational environment and, as graduates, make positive societal contributions to South Carolina, the region, and the nation. In making decisions, the Faculty Committee on Admissions employs a holistic approach, taking into account all

information available about each candidate. No single factor is conclusive. While undergraduate grades and the Law School Admission Test (LSAT) are important, the committee's decision is also influenced by other factors, including the applicant's personal statement, graduate study, military service, leadership and community service, employment or other life experience, residency, letters of recommendation, and contribution to a diverse educational environment.

■ Student Activities

The School of Law publishes the *South Carolina Law Review*; the *ABA Real Property, Trust and Estate Law Journal*; the *Southeastern Environmental Law Journal*; the *Journal of Law and Education*; and the *South Carolina Journal of International Law and Business*. Moot court and mock trial teams are sponsored in national, international, ABA, and various other competitions. Students who have obtained high academic achievement are eligible for membership in the Order of the Coif, a national legal honorary society, and the Order of the Wig and Robe, a local scholastic organization founded in 1935. The Peer Mentoring Program pairs each first-year student with upper-class students to help with the transition to law school. Student organizations include the Student Bar Association; Black Law Students Association; Women in Law; SALSA, the Hispanic Law Students Association; APALSA, the Asian Pacific Law Students Association; Christian Legal Society; Environmental Law Society; Children's Advocacy Law Society; Federalist Society; Health Law Society; Intellectual Property Law Society; James L. Petigru Public Interest Law Society; Just Democracy; International Law Society; OutLaw; Sports and Entertainment Law Society; Law School Democrats; Law School Republicans; national law fraternities Phi Alpha Delta and Phi Delta Phi;

Service Members and Veterans in Law; and the American Constitution Society, among others.

■ Scholarships and Financial Aid

While many students depend on federal and private student loans to help finance their legal education, the School of Law does offer scholarship assistance based both on merit and on financial need. Merit-based scholarships may range from $1,000 to full tuition. Awards are made on a rolling basis, typically beginning in March of each year. Candidates who want priority consideration for merit-based scholarships should make sure that the completed application and all supporting materials are received in the Office of Admissions no later than February 1. There is no separate application for merit-based scholarships. Applicants who wish to be considered for need-based scholarships or loans should submit the FAFSA.

■ Office of Career Services

The Office of Career Services serves as liaison between students and legal employers and offers services to equip students with the skills and information necessary for a successful employment search. The Office of Career Services uses eAttorney and OCI+. Services available include individual counseling, résumé writing and interviewing seminars, on-campus interviews, and participation in job fairs. The School of Law regularly participates in the Southeastern Law Placement Consortium in Atlanta; the Mid-Atlantic Legal Recruiting Conference in Washington, DC; the Southeastern Minority Job Fair; the Patent Law Interview Program in Chicago; the Atlanta Legal Hiring Conference; and the National Public Interest Career Fair.

Applicant Profile

University of South Carolina School of Law
This grid includes only applicants who earned 120–180 LSAT scores under standard administrations.

LSAT Score	3.75 +		3.50–3.74		3.25–3.49		3.00–3.24		2.75–2.99		2.50–2.74		2.25–2.49		2.00–2.24		Below 2.00		No GPA		Total	
	Apps	Adm	Apps	Adm	Apps	Adm	Apps	Adm	Apps	Adm	Apps	Adm	Apps	Adm	Apps	Adm	Apps	Adm	Apps	Adm	Apps	Adm
175–180	0	0	0	0	0	0	0	0	1	1	0	0	0	0	0	0	0	0	0	0	1	1
170–174	3	3	3	3	2	2	1	1	2	2	0	0	0	0	1	0	0	0	0	0	12	11
165–169	15	15	13	12	10	10	8	8	8	8	3	3	4	3	1	0	0	0	0	0	62	59
160–164	67	66	81	78	36	33	42	39	19	16	13	9	4	0	3	3	1	1	0	0	266	245
155–159	77	66	130	94	140	65	107	47	56	17	26	6	7	2	2	1	0	0	2	0	547	298
150–154	70	21	124	36	135	14	109	14	63	4	31	2	21	1	3	1	0	0	9	0	565	93
145–149	27	6	43	2	64	6	68	2	29	0	24	2	11	1	2	0	3	0	2	0	273	19
140–144	5	0	26	2	30	2	40	1	32	0	23	0	6	0	2	0	0	0	3	0	167	5
135–139	2	0	3	0	8	0	17	0	8	0	7	0	3	0	2	0	0	0	1	1	51	1
130–134	1	0	3	0	2	0	2	0	6	0	1	0	2	0	3	0	0	0	2	0	22	0
125–129	0	0	1	0	1	0	0	0	1	0	2	0	1	0	1	0	0	0	0	0	7	0
120–124	0	0	0	0	0	0	0	0	2	0	1	0	0	0	0	0	0	0	0	0	3	0
Total	267	177	427	227	428	132	394	112	227	48	131	22	59	7	20	5	4	1	19	1	1976	732

Apps = Number of Applicants
Adm = Number Admitted
Reflects 99% of the total applicant pool; average LSAT data reported.

The University of South Dakota School of Law

414 E. Clark
Vermillion, SD 57069-2390
Phone: 605.677.5443; Fax: 605.677.5417
E-mail: law@usd.edu; Website: www.usd.edu/law

ABA
Approved
Since
1923

The Basics

Type of school	Public
Term	Semester
Application deadline	3/1
Application fee	$35
Financial aid deadline	3/15
Can first year start other than fall?	No
Student to faculty ratio	12.3 to 1
# of housing spaces available restricted to law students	
graduate housing for which law students are eligible	188

Faculty and Administrators

	Total		Men		Women		Minorities	
	Spr	Fall	Spr	Fall	Spr	Fall	Spr	Fall
Full-time	14	13	9	9	5	4	1	0
Other full-time	2	2	2	2	0	0	0	0
Deans, librarians, & others who teach	2	2	2	2	0	0	0	0
Part-time	6	3	4	2	2	1	0	0
Total	24	20	17	15	7	5	1	0

JD Enrollment and Ethnicity

	Men		Women		Full-Time		Part-Time		1st-Year		Total		JD Degs. Awd.
	#	%	#	%	#	%	#	%	#	%	#	%	
African Amer.	0	0.0	3	2.9	3	1.5	0	0.0	0	0.0	3	1.5	0
Amer. Indian	4	4.0	4	3.9	8	4.0	0	0.0	6	7.5	8	3.9	1
Asian Amer.	1	1.0	0	0.0	1	0.5	0	0.0	1	1.3	1	0.5	0
Mex. Amer.	0	0.0	1	1.0	1	0.5	0	0.0	0	0.0	1	0.5	0
Puerto Rican	0	0.0	0	0.0	0	0.0	0	0.0	0	0.0	0	0.0	0
Hispanic	2	2.0	0	0.0	2	1.0	0	0.0	1	1.3	2	1.0	0
Total Minority	7	6.9	8	7.8	15	7.4	0	0.0	8	10.0	15	7.4	1
For. Nation.	0	0.0	0	0.0	0	0.0	0	0.0	0	0.0	0	0.0	0
Caucasian	94	93.1	95	92.2	187	92.6	2	100.0	72	90.0	189	92.6	72
Unknown	0	0.0	0	0.0	0	0.0	0	0.0	0	0.0	0	0.0	0
Total	101	49.5	103	50.5	202	99.0	2	1.0	80	39.2	204		73

Curriculum

	Full-Time	Part-Time
Typical first-year section size	61	0
Is there typically a "small section" of the first-year class, other than Legal Writing, taught by full-time faculty	Yes	No
If yes, typical size offered last year	31	
# of classroom course titles beyond first-year curriculum		52
# of upper division courses, excluding seminars, with an enrollment: Under 25		37
25–49		12
50–74		5
75–99		1
100+		0
# of seminars		0
# of seminar positions available		0
# of seminar positions filled	0	0
# of positions available in simulation courses		150
# of simulation positions filled	145	0
# of positions available in faculty supervised clinical courses		0
# of faculty supervised clinical positions filled	0	0
# involved in field placements	13	0
# involved in law journals	25	0
# involved in moot court or trial competitions	32	0
# of credit hours required to graduate		90

Transfers

Transfers in	0
Transfers out	1

Tuition and Fees

	Resident	Nonresident
Full-time	$10,695	$20,575
Part-time	$5,508	$10,607
Tuition Guarantee Program		N

Living Expenses

Estimated living expenses for singles

Living on campus	Living off campus	Living at home
$10,089	$12,776	N/A

The University of South Dakota School of Law

ABA
Approved
Since
1923

GPA and LSAT Scores

	Total	Full-Time	Part-Time
# of apps	382	382	0
# of offers	217	217	0
# of matrics	79	78	1
75% GPA	3.65	3.65	0.00
Median GPA	3.44	3.44	0.00
25% GPA	3.13	3.13	0.00
75% LSAT	155	155	0
Median LSAT	151	152	0
25% LSAT	149	149	0

Grants and Scholarships (from prior year)

	Total #	Total %	Full-Time #	Full-Time %	Part-Time #	Part-Time %
Total # of students	199		197		2	
Total # receiving grants	85	42.7	85	43.1	0	0.0
Less than 1/2 tuition	80	40.2	80	40.6	0	0.0
Half to full tuition	4	2.0	4	2.0	0	0.0
Full tuition	0	0.0	0	0.0	0	0.0
More than full tuition	1	0.5	1	0.5	0	0.0
Median grant amount			$1,305		$0	

Informational and Library Resources

Total amount spent on library materials	$522,965
Study seating capacity inside the library	227
# of full-time equivalent professional librarians	5
Hours per week library is open	168
# of open, wired connections available to students	452
# of networked computers available for use by students	37
Has wireless network?	Y
Require computer?	N

JD Attrition (from prior year)

	Academic #	Other #	Total #	Total %
1st year	0	3	3	4.8
2nd year	0	1	1	1.5
3rd year	0	0	0	0.0
4th year	0	0	0	0.0

Employment (9 months after graduation)

	Total	Percentage
Employment status known	85	98.8
Employment status unknown	1	1.2
Employed	78	91.8
Pursuing graduate degrees	1	1.2
Unemployed (seeking, not seeking, or studying for the bar)	4	4.7
Type of Employment		
# employed in law firms	25	32.1
# employed in business and industry	11	14.1
# employed in government	17	21.8
# employed in public interest	6	7.7
# employed as judicial clerks	14	17.9
# employed in academia	3	3.8
Geographic Location		
# employed in state	50	64.1
# employed in foreign countries	0	0.0
# of states where employed	13	

Bar Passage Rates

First-time takers	77	Reporting %	76.62
Average school %	94.92	Average state %	95.18
Average pass difference	−0.26		

Jurisdiction	Takers	Passers	Pass %	State %	Diff %
South Dakota	59	56	94.92	95.18	−0.26

The University of South Dakota School of Law

414 E. Clark
Vermillion, SD 57069-2390
Phone: 605.677.5443; Fax: 605.677.5417
E-mail: law@usd.edu; Website: www.usd.edu/law

■ Introduction

The University of South Dakota School of Law (USD Law), located on the University of South Dakota campus in Vermillion, is noted for its contributions in training distinguished leaders for the bench, the bar, and the lawmaking bodies of the state and region. Established in 1901, USD Law is approved by the ABA and is a member of the AALS. The law school offers a strong American Indian Law Program, and the Legal Writing Program is designed to soon become among the best in the nation. The city of Vermillion, with a population of about 11,000 and located in the southeastern corner of South Dakota along the Missouri National Recreational River, provides a small-town atmosphere. The professional community setting at USD Law provides students with opportunities for individual attention by professors. USD Law offers an extraordinary experience in legal education at a remarkably reasonable tuition rate for both residents and nonresidents.

■ Library and Physical Facilities

The three-story McKusick Law Library is equipped to meet the research needs of students, faculty, and members of the bar. Students, staff, and faculty have access to the law school facility 7 days a week, 24 hours a day through swipe-card access. It is South Dakota's largest and most complete law library, providing essential research services to the courts, legislature, government agencies, lawyers, private citizens, and students conducting interdisciplinary research. The book and microform collections include court reports, statutes, and other legal authorities.

The School of Law building, completed in 1981, has received national recognition for its design. The law school's balconied courtroom, situated in the middle of the building, is the architectural focal point. The courtroom is fully equipped with state-of-the-art videoconferencing technologies and has an adjoining audiovisual control room and judges' chambers. The building also contains two large classrooms; two smaller classrooms; a seminar room; a computer laboratory; a student lounge and locker area; and suites of offices for faculty, administration, and student organizations. The law school building is equipped for wireless network connectivity. The student organization suites contain study carrels for member use. The law library has 227 study seats, including 166 carrels assigned to members of the student body.

■ Curriculum

Ninety semester credits are required for the JD degree. The first-year curriculum is required of all students. In the second and third years, electives are available in addition to required courses. During the summer, an externship program is offered for six credit hours. Externs learn by doing under the close supervision of an attorney and the externship director. Skills training is also available to second- and third-year students in the trial techniques course, negotiations, and other courses, each of which utilizes to the fullest extent the technological capabilities of the law school.

■ Special Programs

- Joint-Degree Programs—There are nine programs with other graduate departments, with master's degrees available in professional accountancy, business administration, history, English, psychology, education administration, political science, public administration, and administrative studies. Students may transfer nine hours of approved interdisciplinary coursework for JD credit and must complete both programs in three years to receive maximum credit.
- Interdisciplinary Study—For upper-division students not in a joint-degree program, up to six graduate credits in other university divisions may be taken and applied toward the hours required for the JD degree. This allows a law student to broaden his or her education by the pursuit of new disciplines.
- Areas of Curricular Emphases—The American Indian Law Program provides students with the knowledge, skills, and experiences necessary to meet the challenges and opportunities facing today's Indian peoples. Nationally recognized professors direct a unique and extensive curriculum with a concentration in the study of American Indian law. Nine American Indian reservations are located within the borders of South Dakota. The law school hosts the longest running biennial Indian Law Symposium in the US, supports the Native American Law Student Association (NALSA), and works closely on the USD campus with the American Indian Studies Department and the Institute of American Indian Studies, directed by a law professor.
- The USD School of Law and Vermont Law School offer a dual degree in environmental law. Students earn a JD from USD and a Master of Science in Environmental Law (MSEL) from Vermont Law School.

■ Admission Options

- Flex-Time Program—This program permits certain well-qualified students to take less than the normal load of credits each semester and obtain a JD in five years instead of three. The program admits a limited number of students who could not attend law school on a full-time basis. The law school does not offer evening or weekend courses.
- Accelerated Admission—An applicant may apply for accelerated admission, and be admitted to and enroll in law school without final completion of the requirements for the applicant's undergraduate degree. The undergraduate degree must be attained by the applicant prior to graduation from law school.
- Law Honors Scholars Program—High school seniors who are accepted as USD undergraduate Honors Scholars may apply for and receive provisional (automatic) admission to the law school upon successful completion of their undergraduate degree in four years with a 3.5 GPA, fulfillment of the University Honors Program requirements, and completion of the LSAT for statistical purposes only.
- Law Screening Program—Applicants who are not regularly admitted may be invited to participate in the Law Screening Program. The summer program consists of two courses offered in five weeks of lectures and finals during the sixth week. Participants are admitted or denied

admission on the basis of their performance on final exams, which are graded anonymously.

■ Student Activities

The *South Dakota Law Review* publishes articles by legal scholars, lawyers, jurists, and students three times a year. The *Sustainable Development Law Journal* publishes articles on a variety of law topics, including environmental law and natural resources. Other cocurricular activities include a Moot Court Board, Client Counseling and Negotiations Board, and Trial Advocacy teams. Boards successfully compete at the intramural, regional, and national levels. The school is active in the Law Student Division of the ABA. Other organizations include Student Bar Association, Women in Law, Black Law Students Association, Christian Legal Society, Environmental Law Society, Law School Democrats, Federalist Society, American Constitution Society, Delta Theta Phi, Phi Alpha Delta, Phi Delta Phi, Trial Advocacy Group, Military and Veterans Law Society, and Corporate and Business Law Association. The Native American Law Student Association USD chapter is represented nationally and scheduled to host the national NALSA Moot Court Tournament in spring 2010.

SD Supreme Court—Each spring, USD Law hosts the three-day March term of the Supreme Court of South Dakota, which provides an extraordinary opportunity for law and undergraduate students, faculty, and the public to observe oral arguments before the state's highest appeals court. The law school also works closely with Access to Justice, the pro bono office of the State Bar of South Dakota.

Pro bono Opportunities—The Law School provides substantial pro bono experiences for students assisting people with their legal needs by working closely with Access to Justice and AmeriCorps, the South Dakota Bar's pro bono office, as well as an Elder Law Program, R.D. Hurd Volunteer Society, area legal services offices, South Dakota Innocence Project, Equal Justice Works, Volunteer Income Tax Assistance (VITA) program, and the Domestic Violence Legal Program, among others.

■ Career Services

The placement opportunities for third-year law students are excellent in South Dakota, the surrounding areas, and throughout the United States. Approximately 20 percent of the graduates are placed in judicial clerkships, and one-third are employed outside South Dakota. The law school has an active program to place first- and second-year students in summer internship programs with law firms.

Applicant Profile

The University of South Dakota School of Law

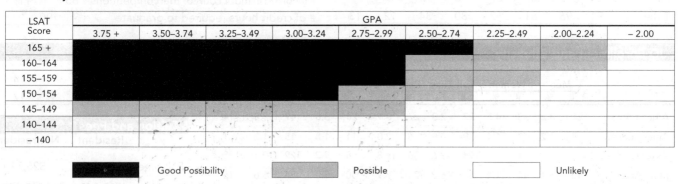

LSAT Score	GPA								
	3.75 +	3.50–3.74	3.25–3.49	3.00–3.24	2.75–2.99	2.50–2.74	2.25–2.49	2.00–2.24	– 2.00
165 +									
160–164									
155–159									
150–154									
145–149									
140–144									
– 140									

■ Good Possibility ■ Possible □ Unlikely

USD School of Law considers many factors beyond LSAT score and GPA. This chart should be used only as a general rule.

For fall 2009:

Applicants:	388	
Completed applications:	382	
Standard full-time admits:	202	
Accepted from Law Screening or PLSI:	15	
Total admitted:	217	
Matriculated full-time:	78	

Stats for the 202 standard admits:

	LSAT	GPA
75th:	155	3.68
Median:	153	3.47
25th:	151	3.16

South Texas College of Law

1303 San Jacinto Street
Houston, TX 77002-7006
Phone: 713.659.8040; Fax: 713.646.2906
E-mail: admissions@stcl.edu; Website: www.stcl.edu

The Basics

Type of school	Private
Term	Semester
Application deadline	2/15 10/1
Application fee	$55
Financial aid deadline	5/1 10/1
Can first year start other than fall?	Yes
Student to faculty ratio	20.0 to 1
# of housing spaces available restricted to law students	
graduate housing for which law students are eligible	

Faculty and Administrators

	Total		Men		Women		Minorities	
	Spr	Fall	Spr	Fall	Spr	Fall	Spr	Fall
Full-time	47	49	31	32	16	17	4	5
Other full-time	0	0	0	0	0	0	0	0
Deans, librarians, & others who teach	5	5	3	3	2	2	1	1
Part-time	39	42	27	27	12	15	7	7
Total	91	96	61	62	30	34	12	13

JD Enrollment and Ethnicity

	Men		Women		Full-Time		Part-Time		1st-Year		Total		JD Degs. Awd.
	#	%	#	%	#	%	#	%	#	%	#	%	
African Amer.	21	3.2	28	4.5	22	2.3	27	8.9	24	3.8	49	3.8	14
Amer. Indian	8	1.2	7	1.1	9	0.9	6	2.0	11	1.8	15	1.2	1
Asian Amer.	48	7.3	81	13.1	93	9.6	36	11.8	58	9.2	129	10.1	38
Mex. Amer.	40	6.1	44	7.1	60	6.2	24	7.9	50	8.0	84	6.6	16
Puerto Rican	0	0.0	2	0.3	2	0.2	0	0.0	0	0.0	2	0.2	1
Hispanic	22	3.3	31	5.0	40	4.1	13	4.3	31	4.9	53	4.1	11
Total Minority	139	21.1	193	31.2	226	23.2	106	34.8	174	27.7	332	26.0	81
For. Nation.	2	0.3	1	0.2	3	0.3	0	0.0	1	0.2	3	0.2	0
Caucasian	518	78.6	425	68.7	744	76.5	199	65.2	453	72.1	943	73.8	290
Unknown	0	0.0	0	0.0	0	0.0	0	0.0	0	0.0	0	0.0	0
Total	659	51.6	619	48.4	973	76.1	305	23.9	628	49.1	1278		371

Curriculum

	Full-Time	Part-Time
Typical first-year section size	95	70
Is there typically a "small section" of the first-year class, other than Legal Writing, taught by full-time faculty	No	No
If yes, typical size offered last year		
# of classroom course titles beyond first-year curriculum	163	

# of upper division courses, excluding seminars, with an enrollment:		
	Under 25	161
	25–49	47
	50–74	22
	75–99	20
	100+	0

# of seminars	25
# of seminar positions available	496
# of seminar positions filled	212 115
# of positions available in simulation courses	1,192
# of simulation positions filled	633 253
# of positions available in faculty supervised clinical courses	198
# of faculty supervised clinical positions filled	44 31
# involved in field placements	64 49
# involved in law journals	228 64
# involved in moot court or trial competitions	65 11
# of credit hours required to graduate	90

Transfers

Transfers in	4
Transfers out	17

Tuition and Fees

	Resident	Nonresident
Full-time	$25,710	$25,710
Part-time	$17,340	$17,340
Tuition Guarantee Program		N

Living Expenses

Estimated living expenses for singles

Living on campus	Living off campus	Living at home
N/A	$18,700	$18,700

South Texas College of Law

ABA
Approved
Since
1959

GPA and LSAT Scores

	Total	Full-Time	Part-Time
# of apps	2,377	2,076	301
# of offers	1,118	989	129
# of matrics	434	350	84
75% GPA	3.51	3.56	3.26
Median GPA	3.25	3.30	3.02
25% GPA	2.99	3.04	2.70
75% LSAT	156	156	155
Median LSAT	153	153	152
25% LSAT	151	151	150

Grants and Scholarships (from prior year)

	Total		Full-Time		Part-Time	
	#	%	#	%	#	%
Total # of students	1,267		953		314	
Total # receiving grants	429	33.9	357	37.5	72	22.9
Less than 1/2 tuition	422	33.3	351	36.8	71	22.6
Half to full tuition	5	0.4	4	0.4	1	0.3
Full tuition	1	0.1	1	0.1	0	0.0
More than full tuition	1	0.1	1	0.1	0	0.0
Median grant amount			$3,400		$1,900	

Informational and Library Resources

Total amount spent on library materials	$1,571,680
Study seating capacity inside the library	877
# of full-time equivalent professional librarians	11
Hours per week library is open	106
# of open, wired connections available to students	1,150
# of networked computers available for use by students	92
Has wireless network?	Y
Require computer?	N

JD Attrition (from prior year)

	Academic	Other	Total	
	#	#	#	%
1st year	16	18	34	5.3
2nd year	3	5	8	2.4
3rd year	1	0	1	0.4
4th year	0	0	0	0.0

Employment (9 months after graduation)

	Total	Percentage
Employment status known	303	89.1
Employment status unknown	37	10.9
Employed	273	90.1
Pursuing graduate degrees	2	0.7
Unemployed (seeking, not seeking, or studying for the bar)	22	7.3
Type of Employment		
# employed in law firms	170	62.3
# employed in business and industry	46	16.8
# employed in government	34	12.5
# employed in public interest	7	2.6
# employed as judicial clerks	13	4.8
# employed in academia	3	1.1
Geographic Location		
# employed in state	253	92.7
# employed in foreign countries	0	0.0
# of states where employed	8	

Bar Passage Rates

First-time takers	330	Reporting %	95.45
Average school %	89.21	Average state %	84.54
Average pass difference	4.67		

Jurisdiction	Takers	Passers	Pass %	State %	Diff %
Texas	315	281	89.21	84.54	4.67

South Texas College of Law

1303 San Jacinto Street
Houston, TX 77002-7006
Phone: 713.659.8040; Fax: 713.646.2906
E-mail: admissions@stcl.edu; Website: www.stcl.edu

■ Introduction

South Texas College of Law, situated at the very core of Houston's vibrant downtown legal and financial centers, is a private, nonprofit, independent law school founded in 1923. South Texas is the oldest law school in Houston, one of the largest in the nation, is accredited by the American Bar Association, and is a member of the AALS. The college offers full- and part-time programs leading to the Doctor of Jurisprudence degree.

■ Admission

Full- and part-time students are admitted to South Texas in the fall semester, while only full-time students are admitted in the spring. Admission application deadlines are February 15 for fall consideration and October 1 for spring. Early application is encouraged. A bachelor's degree is required. Applicants must also take the LSAT and register with LSAC's Credential Assembly Service.

Students are admitted primarily on the basis of their LSAT score and undergraduate GPA. However, a significant percentage of each incoming class is selected on the basis of additional factors. Every attempt is made to evaluate each applicant as an individual, a prospective student, and a future professional.

■ Curriculum

The curriculum at South Texas combines traditional classroom instruction with a broad range of innovative simulated and clinical courses. The college offers a class scheduling system whereby students may select convenient class times rather than have to choose between day and evening divisions. To accommodate part-time working students, a complete curriculum of classes is scheduled after 5:30 PM, with a few classes also scheduled on Saturdays.

For students interested in the increased globalization of law, South Texas offers a variety of study-abroad programs throughout the year. Two ABA-approved cooperative exchange programs allow students to study for a semester in the Netherlands or Denmark. Summer programs are offered in Malta, Turkey, Ireland, England, Chile, and the Czech Republic.

■ JD/MBA Cooperative Program

Through a special cooperative program, students in the JD program at South Texas College of Law are eligible to apply for admission to the MBA program at Mays Business School, Texas A&M University. Upon acceptance into the MBA program, students are granted a leave of absence after their second year of law studies to attain their MBA and then return to South Texas to complete their JD degree.

■ Special Programs

Development of strong legal and advocacy skills is important at South Texas, as evidenced by its four Centers of Excellence and its skills and clinical programs.

Since 1980, the **Advocacy Program** has outperformed all other law school teams in the nation by winning an array of state, regional, and national championship victories. The **Frank Evans Center for Conflict Resolution** allows students to learn from and interact with practicing attorneys who specialize in mediation and arbitration. The **Corporate Compliance Center** involves students who are interested in working as in-house counsel, corporate counsel, outside counsel, and business lawyers. The center explores issues such as how companies promote policies and procedures that ensure legal and ethical behavior and how companies detect and deter wrongdoing. The **Transactional Practice Center** is designed to teach students the fundamental elements of completing a business transaction such as purchasing or developing real estate, buying or selling a corporation, or creating a partnership.

South Texas offers off-site clinics that place students in the real world of lawyering, including state and federal trial and appellate court chambers, prosecutors' and defenders' offices, public interest legal service providers, and state and federal government agencies. In the **International Process Clinic**, students work with defenders involved with the United Nations' ad hoc International Criminal Tribunal for the former Yugoslavia. In the **Direct Representation Clinics**, students work in an on-site clinic while providing direct representation for clients in a variety of administrative and state court settings.

Academic Assistance and Counseling. Students are encouraged to participate in the varied programs and services offered, which are designed to help them reach their full academic potential.

The **Langdell Scholar Program**, conducted by course-proficient upperclassmen, continues to benefit students in mastering the framework of legal analysis, while garnering a proficiency in effective outlining, study skills, and exam-taking techniques. Students attend these valuable sessions voluntarily or are selected into the program based on their LSAT performance, undergraduate GPA, and academic assistance diagnostic test.

■ Student Activities

Students at South Texas have the opportunity to become members of approximately 40 active student organizations representing a wide range of interests.

■ Scholarly Publications

South Texas College of Law students participate in journals on the basis of outstanding scholarship and writing ability. Our students edit and publish a variety of scholarly publications, including the *South Texas Law Review*, *Currents: International Trade Law Journal*, and the *Corporate Counsel Review*; and coedit the *Construction Law Journal* and *Texas Business Journal* in conjunction with each journal's respective state bar section.

■ Library and Physical Facilities

Recent additions to the South Texas campus ensure that students have access to and are trained with state-of-the-art

tools now used in the legal profession. The T. Gerald Treece Courtroom houses a nine-seat judges' bench and boasts the very latest courtroom technology available to trial attorneys. The courtroom is heavily used by the school's nationally recognized advocacy program for practice and competitions. It is also available to the members of Houston's legal community, including the judiciary.

The Fred Parks Law Library encompasses more than 72,000 square feet. Each of the 870-plus seats in the six-story facility is wired for data and power and is also internet accessible through wireless connectivity. The building is crowned with a conference center and rooftop terrace that is perfect for congregating students as well as for campus events.

The college is also the home of the First and Fourteenth Texas Courts of Appeals, distinguishing South Texas as one of only two American law schools housing appellate courts on a permanent basis.

■ Financial Assistance

South Texas offers an extensive financial aid program, in terms of both scholarships and outside funding options. Depending on their qualifications, Texas residents are eligible for state and federal tuition assistance grants, which have amounted to as much as several thousand dollars in prior years. In addition, the Office of Scholarships and Financial Aid administers financial assistance through the Federal

Work-Study Program, federal and private loans, and a variety of scholarship offerings. Incoming students are considered for merit scholarships based on UGPA, LSAT, and financial need. Continuing students are eligible for both merit- and need-based scholarships. Contact the Office of Scholarships and Financial Aid for eligibility and documentation requirements at 713.646.1820.

■ Career Services

In light of today's competitive job market, the Career Resources Center (CRC) continues to provide South Texas students and graduates with a full range of services to assist in their employment search, while at the same time being responsive to the changes in hiring trends and patterns. The office serves as a counseling and resource center for students seeking employment on either a full- or part-time basis and assists graduates pursuing permanent employment. In addition to on-campus recruiting, the CRC also offers an array of professional development programs and career panels designed to assist students in their job-search preparation and networking. The objective of the CRC staff is to aid students in exploring career options, while helping them build valuable job-search skills utilizing their strengths and abilities. By taking advantage of the many programs and services offered by the CRC, students are better equipped to maximize their career-planning opportunities.

Applicant Profile

South Texas College of Law
This grid includes only applicants who earned 120–180 LSAT scores under standard administrations.

LSAT Score	GPA																			
	3.75 +		3.50–3.74		3.25–3.49		3.00–3.24		2.75–2.99		2.50–2.74		2.25–2.49		2.00–2.24		Below 2.00		No GPA		Total
	Apps	Adm	Apps	Adm	Apps	Adm	Apps	Adm	Apps	Adm	Apps	Adm	Apps	Adm	Apps	Adm	Apps	Adm	Apps	Adm	Apps Adm
170–180	0	0	0	0	0	0	2	2	0	0	0	0	1	1	0	0	0	0	0	0	3 3
165–169	1	1	4	3	3	3	9	8	4	3	2	1	1	0	1	0	0	0	0	0	25 19
160–164	15	15	20	20	22	19	24	23	16	16	14	9	4	2	2	0	0	0	0	0	117 104
155–159	34	33	62	59	52	49	50	46	42	34	22	13	10	6	2	1	1	0	4	1	279 242
150–154	46	43	92	86	123	114	115	100	89	48	66	19	22	2	12	1	1	0	5	4	571 417
145–149	40	20	62	28	98	36	128	39	83	11	61	4	25	0	8	0	1	0	14	4	520 142
140–144	12	0	31	1	65	9	78	2	60	2	39	2	32	0	14	0	2	0	10	0	343 16
Below 140	3	0	10	0	22	0	29	0	27	0	30	0	11	0	16	0	2	0	9	0	159 0
Total	151	112	281	197	385	230	435	220	321	114	234	48	106	11	55	2	7	0	42	9	2017 943

Apps = Number of Applicants
Adm = Number Admitted
Reflects 99% of the total applicant pool; average LSAT data reported.

University of Southern California, Gould School of Law

699 Exposition Boulevard
Los Angeles, CA 90089-0074
Phone: 213.740.2523; Fax: 213.740.4570
E-mail: admissions@law.usc.edu; Website: www.law.usc.edu

ABA Approved Since 1924

The Basics

Type of school	Private
Term	Semester
Application deadline	2/1
Application fee	$75
Financial aid deadline	3/2
Can first year start other than fall?	No
Student to faculty ratio	12.4 to 1
# of housing spaces available restricted to law students	
graduate housing for which law students are eligible	46

Faculty and Administrators

	Total		Men		Women		Minorities	
	Spr	Fall	Spr	Fall	Spr	Fall	Spr	Fall
Full-time	43	40	25	26	18	14	8	6
Other full-time	1	1	0	0	1	1	0	0
Deans, librarians, & others who teach	16	17	7	6	9	11	3	5
Part-time	71	53	44	33	27	20	11	14
Total	131	111	76	65	55	46	22	25

Curriculum

		Full-Time	Part-Time
Typical first-year section size		70	0
Is there typically a "small section" of the first-year class, other than Legal Writing, taught by full-time faculty		No	No
If yes, typical size offered last year			
# of classroom course titles beyond first-year curriculum		107	
# of upper division courses, excluding seminars, with an enrollment:	Under 25	97	
	25–49	30	
	50–74	10	
	75–99	4	
	100+	4	
# of seminars		19	
# of seminar positions available		392	
# of seminar positions filled		157	0
# of positions available in simulation courses		509	
# of simulation positions filled		394	0
# of positions available in faculty supervised clinical courses		86	
# of faculty supervised clinical positions filled		77	0
# involved in field placements		127	0
# involved in law journals		156	0
# involved in moot court or trial competitions		43	0
# of credit hours required to graduate		88	

JD Enrollment and Ethnicity

	Men		Women		Full-Time		Part-Time		1st-Year		Total		JD Degs. Awd.
	#	%	#	%	#	%	#	%	#	%	#	%	
African Amer.	15	4.9	29	9.3	44	7.1	0	0.0	13	6.1	44	7.1	13
Amer. Indian	4	1.3	0	0.0	4	0.6	0	0.0	0	0.0	4	0.6	0
Asian Amer.	49	16.0	78	25.1	127	20.6	0	0.0	48	22.6	127	20.6	38
Mex. Amer.	21	6.8	17	5.5	38	6.1	0	0.0	12	5.7	38	6.1	23
Puerto Rican	1	0.3	2	0.6	3	0.5	0	0.0	0	0.0	3	0.5	1
Hispanic	19	6.2	8	2.6	27	4.4	0	0.0	6	2.8	27	4.4	8
Total Minority	109	35.5	134	43.1	243	39.3	0	0.0	79	37.3	243	39.3	83
For. Nation.	3	1.0	8	2.6	11	1.8	0	0.0	2	0.9	11	1.8	4
Caucasian	144	46.9	129	41.5	273	44.2	0	0.0	91	42.9	273	44.2	99
Unknown	51	16.6	40	12.9	91	14.7	0	0.0	40	18.9	91	14.7	23
Total	307	49.7	311	50.3	618	100.0	0	0.0	212	34.3	618		209

Transfers

Transfers in	19
Transfers out	4

Tuition and Fees

	Resident	Nonresident
Full-time	$46,264	$46,264
Part-time		
Tuition Guarantee Program	N	

Living Expenses

Estimated living expenses for singles

Living on campus	Living off campus	Living at home
$21,584	$21,584	$10,784

University of Southern California, Gould School of Law

ABA Approved Since 1924

GPA and LSAT Scores

	Total	Full-Time	Part-Time
# of apps	6,024	6,024	0
# of offers	1,322	1,322	0
# of matrics	215	215	0
75% GPA	3.71	3.71	0.00
Median GPA	3.60	3.60	0.00
25% GPA	3.47	3.47	0.00
75% LSAT	167	167	0
Median LSAT	167	167	0
25% LSAT	165	165	0

Grants and Scholarships (from prior year)

	Total #	Total %	Full-Time #	Full-Time %	Part-Time #	Part-Time %
Total # of students	605		605		0	
Total # receiving grants	412	68.1	412	68.1	0	0.0
Less than 1/2 tuition	357	59.0	357	59.0	0	0.0
Half to full tuition	36	6.0	36	6.0	0	0.0
Full tuition	13	2.1	13	2.1	0	0.0
More than full tuition	6	1.0	6	1.0	0	0.0
Median grant amount			$12,000		$0	

Informational and Library Resources

Total amount spent on library materials	$1,091,009
Study seating capacity inside the library	230
# of full-time equivalent professional librarians	9
Hours per week library is open	100
# of open, wired connections available to students	42
# of networked computers available for use by students	110
Has wireless network?	Y
Require computer?	N

JD Attrition (from prior year)

	Academic #	Other #	Total #	Total %
1st year	0	7	7	3.5
2nd year	0	1	1	0.5
3rd year	0	0	0	0.0
4th year	0	0	0	0.0

Employment (9 months after graduation)

	Total	Percentage
Employment status known	206	98.1
Employment status unknown	4	1.9
Employed	201	97.6
Pursuing graduate degrees	2	1.0
Unemployed (seeking, not seeking, or studying for the bar)	3	1.5
Type of Employment		
# employed in law firms	152	75.6
# employed in business and industry	13	6.5
# employed in government	8	4.0
# employed in public interest	11	5.5
# employed as judicial clerks	10	5.0
# employed in academia	6	3.0
Geographic Location		
# employed in state	172	85.6
# employed in foreign countries	0	0.0
# of states where employed	13	

Bar Passage Rates

First-time takers	207	Reporting %	87.92
Average school %	89.56	Average state %	78.07
Average pass difference	11.49		

Jurisdiction	Takers	Passers	Pass %	State %	Diff %
California	182	163	89.56	78.07	11.49

University of Southern California, Gould School of Law

699 Exposition Boulevard
Los Angeles, CA 90089-0074
Phone: 213.740.2523; Fax: 213.740.4570
E-mail: admissions@law.usc.edu; Website: www.law.usc.edu

■ Introduction

The University of Southern California, Gould School of Law is a private, highly selective national law school with over a 105-year history and a reputation for academic excellence. Under the leadership of a stellar, energetic faculty, the school's rigorous, interdisciplinary program focuses on the law as an expression of social values and an instrument for implementing social goals. USC is known for its diverse student body, its leadership in clinical education, and its tight-knit alumni network composed of national leaders in the legal profession, business, and the public sector. With 210 entering students in each class, the school is small, informal, and collegial.

USC Law School is located on the beautiful 226-acre main campus of the University of Southern California, just south of downtown Los Angeles and in the heart of the city's exciting Arts and Entertainment Corridor. The campus offers a lush, park-like atmosphere within a bustling urban setting. A dynamic laboratory for legal training, Los Angeles is a center of state, national, and international commerce and government, and the city's legal market is among the most extensive in the world. The law school is housed in a five-level, technologically advanced facility that provides a superb setting for professional training and sophisticated legal research.

■ Curriculum

USC's curriculum is comprehensive, uniquely interdisciplinary, and designed to challenge. Courses provide a solid foundation in all substantive areas of law as well as extensive opportunities to explore specializations in traditional and emerging fields. Many faculty members have expertise in both law and other disciplines, such as economics, communication, public policy, medicine, history, psychology, and philosophy. The first-year curriculum consists of courses that examine the foundation of the legal system. The second and third years of study allow students to pursue individual interests in areas such as international law, intellectual property, corporations and business-government relationships, taxation, bioethics, civil rights and liberties, and judicial administration.

■ Special Programs

Dual Degrees: The law school offers 16 dual-degree programs in coordination with USC graduate and professional schools and the California Institute of Technology. These programs enable qualified students to earn a law degree and a master's degree in the following fields: Business Administration, Business Taxation, Economics, Communications Management, Gerontology, International Relations, Philosophy, Political Science, Public Administration, Public Policy, Real Estate Development, and Social Work. A JD/PhD program in Political Science, a JD/PharmD program, and a JD/PhD program in Social Science with the California Institute of Technology are also offered. In addition, the law school offers an LLM in taxation.

Legal Clinics: The nationally recognized Post-Conviction Justice Project, the Employer Legal Advice Clinic, the Small Business Clinic, and the Immigration Clinic enable students to gain valuable advocacy and lawyering skills by representing real clients under faculty supervision. Students in the Intellectual Property and Technology Law Clinic review technology contracts, engage in patent evaluation and application, assist with litigation, and perform film clearance work.

Public Service Programs: The Office of Public Service provides comprehensive opportunities and coordination for all external service learning and community service. These opportunities include more than 60 clinical field placements, allowing students to earn academic credit while engaging in service learning at government and public interest agencies and with federal and state judges, as well as pro bono and community service in the surrounding Los Angeles neighborhoods.

International Programs: USC offers students several opportunities to study abroad. Students can participate in the law school's semester abroad exchange program with the University of Hong Kong, which is designed for individuals interested in international business or comparative law. The law school also offers a dual-degree program (JD/LLM) with the London School of Economics. Moreover, students may participate in programs offered around the world by other ABA-approved law schools.

Research Centers: Law students participate in the scholarly activities of several interdisciplinary research centers: the Pacific Center for Health Policy and Ethics; the Center in Law, Economics, and Organization; the USC-Caltech Center for the Study of Law and Politics; the Center for Law, History, and Culture; and the Center for Law and Philosophy.

Continuing Legal Education: Students help coordinate the law school's practice-oriented programs and serve as research assistants for the Institute on Entertainment Law and Business and the Intellectual Property Institute.

■ Student Activities and Cocurricular Programs

Academic life is exciting and fast paced, and students are often engaged in numerous scholarly pursuits and cocurricular programs. The *Southern California Law Review* has one of the largest circulations in the country. Students also publish the *Southern California Interdisciplinary Law Journal* and the *Southern California Review of Law and Social Justice*. The Moot Court Honors Program sends participants to national and state competitions.

Public service activities abound. The Public Interest Law Foundation is one of the largest in the country, providing summer grants for public service employment as well as the Irmas Fellowship for public interest law, which awards a year's salary to a third-year student committed to postgraduate work in public interest.

The diversity of USC Law School's student population is reflected in nearly 40 political, religious, social, cultural, and ethnic organizations. Our students play an active and valued role in the day-to-day operation of the law school including service on faculty committees. Students are given a wide range of opportunities to create and implement ideas for activities and are encouraged to pursue their interests by

University of Southern California, Gould School of Law

forming new student organizations or planning social or academic events. Asian, African American, Muslim, Middle Eastern, Jewish, and Latino law students are represented by associations. Other student organizations include international and entertainment law societies, Women's Law Association, OUTLaw, Legal Aid Alternative Breaks Project, Christian Legal Society, Health Law and Bioethics Society, Intellectual Property and Technology Law Society, Street Law, Sports Law, Trial Lawyers, and chapters of the ACLU and the Federalist Society.

■ Professional Careers

USC graduates accept job offers in all regions of the country, with New York and Washington, DC, being the most popular placement locations outside the West Coast. A number of graduates begin their professional careers as judicial law clerks to federal and state judges. Each year, several hundred private firms, government agencies, public interest organizations, and corporations from throughout the country come to USC to recruit students for summer and permanent employment. An off-campus recruiting program helps coordinate interviews with East Coast employers. The school's enthusiastic network of alumni is a valuable tool in the job-search process. The Alumni Mentor Lunch provides first-year students with the opportunity to meet graduates who practice in the student's field of interest, and other programs bring alumni from a range of fields to campus to discuss career opportunities. Overall placement statistics are consistently strong; historically, more than 97 percent of each graduating class finds employment within nine months of graduation. Average starting salaries are among the highest in the nation.

■ Housing

Graduate law housing is available in an apartment-style residence located within easy walking distance of the law school for a limited number of incoming students. The two-bedroom apartments are fully furnished and equipped with Internet. A roommate referral service is available to help incoming students arrange shared housing in various Los Angeles neighborhoods.

■ Admission and Financial Aid

Admission decisions are made on the basis of the student's academic record, LSAT score and writing sample, personal statement, letters of recommendation, résumé, extra-curricular activities, and other information in the file. The Admissions Committee gives primary consideration to outstanding academic and professional promise and to qualities that will enhance the diversity of the student body or enrich the law school educational environment. Two letters of recommendation are required; applicants are strongly urged to submit at least one academic recommendation letter. The law school operates on a semester basis and admits only full-time students. USC is committed to helping students successfully finance their legal education. In addition to various loan programs, the law school offers substantial scholarship awards to a large percentage of the incoming class. Most scholarships are based on merit as evidenced by strong academic credentials and test scores. In addition, the school offers a Loan Repayment Assistance Program which assists graduates who accept employment with governmental agencies and public interest organizations that traditionally offer lower pay than private firms.

Applicant Profile

University of Southern California, Gould School of Law
This grid includes only applicants who earned 120–180 LSAT scores under standard administrations.

LSAT Score	GPA														
	3.75 +		3.50–3.74		3.25–3.49		3.00–3.24		2.75–2.99		Below 2.75		No GPA		Total	
	Apps	Adm	Apps	Adm	Apps	Adm	Apps	Adm	Apps	Adm	Apps	Adm	Apps	Adm	Apps	Adm
175–180	33	29	18	15	14	8	7	0	2	1	4	0	0	0	78	53
170–174	127	117	113	91	83	25	33	5	12	0	9	1	7	1	384	240
165–169	456	352	513	307	261	64	127	8	43	0	21	1	20	1	1441	733
160–164	410	85	542	89	374	30	188	12	54	1	29	0	37	0	1634	217
155–159	202	12	347	26	278	18	183	6	78	0	33	0	34	0	1155	62
150–154	67	3	164	2	164	1	144	0	66	0	41	0	17	0	663	6
Below 150	38	0	90	0	136	0	136	0	96	0	105	0	21	0	622	0
Total	1333	598	1787	530	1310	146	818	31	351	2	242	2	136	2	5977	1311

Apps = Number of Applicants
Adm = Number Admitted
Reflects 99% of the total applicant pool; average LSAT data reported.

Southern Illinois University School of Law

Office of Admissions and Financial Aid, SOL Welcome Center, 1209 W. Chautauqua, Mailcode 6811
Carbondale, IL 62901
Phone: 800.739.9187 or 618.453.8858; Fax: 618.453.8921
E-mail: lawadmit@siu.edu; Website: www.law.siu.edu

ABA Approved Since 1974

The Basics

Type of school	Public
Term	Semester
Application deadline	3/1
Application fee	$50
Financial aid deadline	4/1
Can first year start other than fall?	No
Student to faculty ratio	11.7 to 1
# of housing spaces available restricted to law students graduate housing for which law students are eligible	360

Faculty and Administrators

	Total Spr	Total Fall	Men Spr	Men Fall	Women Spr	Women Fall	Minorities Spr	Minorities Fall
Full-time	25	27	14	14	11	13	1	2
Other full-time	0	0	0	0	0	0	0	0
Deans, librarians, & others who teach	10	8	7	6	3	2	2	1
Part-time	8	10	4	7	4	3	0	1
Total	43	45	25	27	18	18	3	4

Curriculum

	Full-Time	Part-Time
Typical first-year section size	56	0
Is there typically a "small section" of the first-year class, other than Legal Writing, taught by full-time faculty	No	No
If yes, typical size offered last year		
# of classroom course titles beyond first-year curriculum	70	
# of upper division courses, excluding seminars, with an enrollment: Under 25	79	
25–49	20	
50–74	12	
75–99	2	
100+	0	
# of seminars	9	
# of seminar positions available	111	
# of seminar positions filled	96	0
# of positions available in simulation courses	453	
# of simulation positions filled	329	0
# of positions available in faculty supervised clinical courses	57	
# of faculty supervised clinical positions filled	38	0
# involved in field placements	36	0
# involved in law journals	53	0
# involved in moot court or trial competitions	28	0
# of credit hours required to graduate	90	

JD Enrollment and Ethnicity

	Men #	Men %	Women #	Women %	Full-Time #	Full-Time %	Part-Time #	Part-Time %	1st-Year #	1st-Year %	Total #	Total %	JD Degs. Awd.
African Amer.	5	2.1	8	5.6	13	3.4	0	0.0	6	4.4	13	3.4	7
Amer. Indian	0	0.0	2	1.4	2	0.5	0	0.0	1	0.7	2	0.5	0
Asian Amer.	5	2.1	4	2.8	9	2.4	0	0.0	3	2.2	9	2.3	1
Mex. Amer.	2	0.8	1	0.7	3	0.8	0	0.0	1	0.7	3	0.8	1
Puerto Rican	0	0.0	0	0.0	0	0.0	0	0.0	0	0.0	0	0.0	1
Hispanic	4	1.7	1	0.7	4	1.0	1	100.0	0	0.0	5	1.3	2
Total Minority	16	6.7	16	11.1	31	8.1	1	100.0	11	8.1	32	8.4	12
For. Nation.	0	0.0	1	0.7	1	0.3	0	0.0	0	0.0	1	0.3	0
Caucasian	202	84.5	116	80.6	318	83.2	0	0.0	114	84.4	318	83.0	94
Unknown	21	8.8	11	7.6	32	8.4	0	0.0	10	7.4	32	8.4	10
Total	239	62.4	144	37.6	382	99.7	1	0.3	135	35.2	383		116

Transfers

Transfers in	11
Transfers out	4

Tuition and Fees

	Resident	Nonresident
Full-time	$14,137	$33,040
Part-time		
Tuition Guarantee Program	N	

Living Expenses

Estimated living expenses for singles

Living on campus	Living off campus	Living at home
$14,128	$14,128	$5,170

Southern Illinois University School of Law

ABA
Approved
Since
1974

GPA and LSAT Scores

	Total	Full-Time	Part-Time
# of apps	753	753	0
# of offers	362	362	0
# of matrics	137	137	0
75% GPA	3.52	3.52	0.00
Median GPA	3.25	3.25	0.00
25% GPA	3.01	3.01	0.00
75% LSAT	157	157	0
Median LSAT	153	153	0
25% LSAT	151	151	0

Grants and Scholarships (from prior year)

	Total		Full-Time		Part-Time	
	#	%	#	%	#	%
Total # of students	361		361		0	
Total # receiving grants	176	48.8	176	48.8	0	0.0
Less than 1/2 tuition	92	25.5	92	25.5	0	0.0
Half to full tuition	58	16.1	58	16.1	0	0.0
Full tuition	10	2.8	10	2.8	0	0.0
More than full tuition	16	4.4	16	4.4	0	0.0
Median grant amount			$5,000		$0	

Informational and Library Resources

Total amount spent on library materials	$817,638
Study seating capacity inside the library	349
# of full-time equivalent professional librarians	5
Hours per week library is open	78
# of open, wired connections available to students	12
# of networked computers available for use by students	53
Has wireless network?	Y
Require computer?	N

JD Attrition (from prior year)

	Academic	Other	Total	
	#	#	#	%
1st year	1	13	14	13.0
2nd year	1	3	4	2.8
3rd year	0	0	0	0.0
4th year	0	0	0	0.0

Employment (9 months after graduation)

	Total	Percentage
Employment status known	107	100.0
Employment status unknown	0	0.0
Employed	86	80.4
Pursuing graduate degrees	4	3.7
Unemployed (seeking, not seeking, or studying for the bar)	16	15.0
Type of Employment		
# employed in law firms	40	46.5
# employed in business and industry	12	14.0
# employed in government	23	26.7
# employed in public interest	6	7.0
# employed as judicial clerks	2	2.3
# employed in academia	3	3.5
Geographic Location		
# employed in state	58	67.4
# employed in foreign countries	0	0.0
# of states where employed	14	

Bar Passage Rates

First-time takers	103	Reporting %	84.47
Average school %	95.40	Average state %	91.11
Average pass difference	4.29		

Jurisdiction	Takers	Passers	Pass %	State %	Diff %
Illinois	76	72	94.74	90.94	3.80
Missouri	11	11	100.00	92.33	7.67

Southern Illinois University School of Law

Office of Admissions and Financial Aid, SOL Welcome Center, 1209 W. Chautauqua, Mailcode 6811
Carbondale, IL 62901
Phone: 800.739.9187 or 618.453.8858; Fax: 618.453.8921
E-mail: lawadmit@siu.edu; Website: www.law.siu.edu

■ Introduction

The School of Law is located on the campus of Southern Illinois University Carbondale, a 141-year-old university with a tradition of excellence as well as a diverse, multicultural student body of 21,000. Carbondale, a community of 27,000 people, is one of the most scenic areas of Illinois. National forests, state parks, historic sites, campgrounds, theaters, festivals, and cultural events make Carbondale's quality of life among the highest in small cities in Illinois. The 12:1 student-to-faculty ratio at the School of Law is among the best in the nation. The School of Law is fully accredited by the ABA and the AALS.

■ Curriculum

All students have a uniform first-year curriculum. A broad range of courses and seminars are offered in the second and third years. Throughout the curriculum, the faculty emphasizes professional skills such as writing, oral argumentation, drafting documents, interviewing, negotiating, and counseling.

An innovative and nationally recognized first-year Lawyering Skills Program gives students a strong foundation in basic lawyering skills, including legal research and writing, oral advocacy, client interviewing and counseling, and negotiation.

The school has a strong health law curriculum and is the site for the National Health Law Moot Court Competition as well as a Center for Health Law and Policy. The school also has groups of courses in trial/litigation skills, intellectual property, and criminal, labor, corporate, family, international, and environmental law.

The School of Law has partnered with the University of Missouri—Kansas City to offer students a four-week study-abroad program in Ireland. The program allows students to receive six elective credit hours, and the chance to study at some of Ireland's preeminent institutions.

■ Special Programs

Clinical programs enable senior law students to represent clients under the supervision of licensed attorneys. The Civil Practice/Elder Clinic provides direct legal assistance to persons 60 years of age and older in the 13 southernmost counties of Illinois. Students may participate in the Externship Program and obtain academic credit while working at nonprofit, local, state, or federal legal offices. The Domestic Violence Clinic provides legal assistance to victims of domestic violence. Students can also gain valuable experience through work in the award-winning Self Help Legal Center.

Two **semester away programs** allow second- and third-year students the opportunity to spend a semester living and working in different locations. The **Law and Government program**, located in the Illinois state capital of Springfield, focuses on state and local government. The second program, located in southeast Missouri, provides hands-on experience with the Missouri Public Defender System.

The school provides a comprehensive **trial and appellate moot court program** with teams that have successfully competed in the McGee National Civil Rights Moot Court, ABA Moot Court, and Darras Disability Law Moot Court competitions. The school also holds an annual intramural Appellate Moot Court Competition.

All entering law students are assigned to a study group and an upper-level law student tutor as part of the Academic Success Program.

The School of Law sponsors two annual **lecture series**: the Hiram H. Lesar Distinguished Lecture Series and the Dr. Arthur Grayson Distinguished Lecture Series. Past speakers include Morris Dees, David Kessler, Nadine Strossen, Governor Douglas Wilder, Kerry Kennedy Cuomo, and Hans Blix. In addition, the school cosponsors an annual health law symposium, the Health Policy Institute, that brings experts in health law policy from across the country to Carbondale.

Students participate in the Professional Development Workshop Series, which received the 2004 E. Smythe Gambrell Professionalism Award from the American Bar Association.

A variety of **concurrent JD/master's degree programs** in accountancy, business administration, education, electrical and computer engineering, public administration, and social work are offered in conjunction with the graduate school. A concurrent PhD program is available in political science. A six-year program offered in cooperation with the School of Medicine permits students to concurrently obtain JD and MD degrees. A Master of Legal Studies program and Master of Laws program are also available.

■ Library and Physical Facilities

Southern Illinois University School of Law's primary facility is the Lesar Law Building housing the classrooms, courtroom, auditorium, faculty offices, and law library. Because the number of activities and services has expanded since the main building was completed in 1981, some offices are located in two nearby buildings. The Office of Admissions and Financial Aid and the law journal offices are housed in the Welcome Center, and the clinical programs and emeritus faculty offices are located in Kaplan Hall. Both additional facilities are in immediate proximity to the Lesar Law Building, creating an informal law school campus within the broader university grounds. An additional small classroom in Kaplan Hall overlooks the campus lake. All together, the facilities offer over 100,000 square feet of space.

Law students enjoy 24-hour access to the law library, which has ample study space. The law library's collection of over 400,000 volumes of legal and nonlegal materials provides students with all the research materials needed to succeed in law school as well as in the practice of law. In addition to a rich print and microform collection, the law library has evolved to meet the changing nature of legal research and user expectations by providing wireless access to a wide array of electronic legal materials. Law students also have virtual as well as physical access to the university's Morris Library, which houses a major research collection and is located within walking distance of the law school. The law library employs a friendly and welcoming staff who interacts on a first-name basis with law students. The law librarians are committed to teaching law students the fundamentals of legal research formally, by coteaching the Lawyering Skills first-year course, and informally, through their interactions at the reference desk. Additionally, the law librarians offer an advanced legal research course for upper-level students.

■ Student Activities

The school publishes the *SIU Law Journal*, which provides editorial and writing experience for a number of upper-class students. Students with a particular interest in health law can also publish articles in the *Journal of Legal Medicine*.

All students belong to the Student Bar Association. The SBA schedules lectures and social affairs, provides services to its members, and serves as a channel of communication between students and faculty. Students play an active role in law school governance, serving on most faculty committees. Past and current student organizations include Equal Justice Works, Phi Alpha Delta, International Law Society, Women's Law Forum, Environmental Law Society, Parents as Law Students, Animal Legal Defense Fund, Business Law Society, Black Law Student Association, Federalist Society, Law School Democrats, Law School Republicans, Media Law Society, Lesbian and Gay Law Students and Supporters, Sports Law Society, Phi Delta Phi, Law and Medicine Society, Christian Legal Society, Decalogue Society, Employment and Labor Law Association, Justinian Society, Military Law Society, Hispanic Law Student Association, Asian American Law Student Association, Alternative Dispute Resolution Student Society, J. Reuben Clark Law Society, and law student divisions of the Illinois State Bar Association and the American Bar Association.

■ Career Services

School of Law graduates find employment nationwide, with alumni in 49 states and several foreign countries, including Austria, Belgium, Canada, Hong Kong, Japan, Puerto Rico, Ukraine, and the Virgin Islands. School of Law graduates continue to excel with bar passage rates at or above the state and national averages. The Office of Career Services provides services for both enrolled students and alumni, including individual career counseling, on-campus interviews, career workshops, subscriptions to a variety of job newsletters, an in-house job-vacancy bulletin, and job-bulletin exchanges with other law schools. Special presentations that cover a variety of career and employment topics are offered throughout the year, and students have the opportunity to participate in a variety of regional and national job fairs and career conferences. The Career Library contains diverse career materials, including national and international directories, judicial clerkship information, and government and public interest job information. Students can contact the Office of Career Services at 618.453.8707 or by e-mail at *lawjobs@siu.edu.*

■ Expenses, Scholarships, and Financial Aid

Due to a generous program of scholarships for both incoming and current students, graduates of the SIU School of Law enjoy an average debt load that is below the national law school average. Students can qualify for the in-state resident tuition rate after they have been an Illinois resident for six consecutive months. Student loans, work-study opportunities, and most other forms of financial aid are administered by the university's Financial Aid Office. Information concerning in-state resident applications, loans, and financial aid procedures may be obtained from the Office of Admissions and Financial Aid at 618.453.8858 or by e-mail at *lawadmit@siu.edu.*

■ Admission

Admission decisions are based on a number of factors. Although the LSAT score and undergraduate GPA are important, nonnumerical factors are considered as well. The highest LSAT score is used for repeat test takers. Other factors considered by the Admission Committee include trends in academic performance, writing ability, leadership and maturity, letters of recommendation, work experience, community and public service, and obstacles imposed by religious, ethnic, gender, or disability discrimination.

Applicant Profile

Southern Illinois University School of Law
This grid includes only applicants who earned 120–180 LSAT scores under standard administrations.

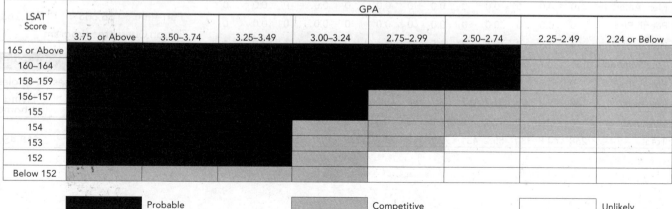

LSAT Score	GPA							
	3.75 or Above	3.50–3.74	3.25–3.49	3.00–3.24	2.75–2.99	2.50–2.74	2.25–2.49	2.24 or Below
165 or Above								
160–164								
158–159								
156–157								
155								
154								
153								
152								
Below 152								

■ Probable   ■ Competitive   □ Unlikely

This grid reflects the highest LSAT score of the applicant.

Southern University Law Center

Admission Office, PO Box 9294
Baton Rouge, LA 70813
Phone: 225.771.4976 or 800.537.1135; Fax: 225.771.2121
E-mail: admission@sulc.edu; Website: www.sulc.edu

ABA Approved Since 1953

The Basics

Type of school	Public
Term	Semester
Application deadline	2/28 5/1
Application fee	$25
Financial aid deadline	4/15
Can first year start other than fall?	No
Student to faculty ratio	12.4 to 1
# of housing spaces available restricted to law students graduate housing for which law students are eligible	5

Faculty and Administrators

	Total		Men		Women		Minorities	
	Spr	Fall	Spr	Fall	Spr	Fall	Spr	Fall
Full-time	35	35	16	16	19	19	21	21
Other full-time	0	0	0	0	0	0	0	0
Deans, librarians, & others who teach	5	5	4	4	1	1	5	5
Part-time	17	10	13	6	3	4	11	7
Total	57	50	33	26	23	24	37	33

JD Enrollment and Ethnicity

	Men		Women		Full-Time		Part-Time		1st-Year		Total		JD Degs. Awd.
	#	%	#	%	#	%	#	%	#	%	#	%	
African Amer.	129	48.1	222	67.3	259	60.1	92	55.1	141	59.0	351	58.7	68
Amer. Indian	0	0.0	0	0.0	0	0.0	0	0.0	0	0.0	0	0.0	0
Asian Amer.	3	1.1	3	0.9	3	0.7	3	1.8	0	0.0	6	1.0	1
Mex. Amer.	0	0.0	0	0.0	0	0.0	0	0.0	0	0.0	0	0.0	0
Puerto Rican	0	0.0	0	0.0	0	0.0	0	0.0	0	0.0	0	0.0	0
Hispanic	4	1.5	2	0.6	2	0.5	4	2.4	2	0.8	6	1.0	1
Total Minority	136	50.7	227	68.8	264	61.3	99	59.3	143	59.8	363	60.7	70
For. Nation.	0	0.0	0	0.0	0	0.0	0	0.0	0	0.0	0	0.0	0
Caucasian	132	49.3	103	31.2	167	38.7	68	40.7	96	40.2	235	39.3	58
Unknown	0	0.0	0	0.0	0	0.0	0	0.0	0	0.0	0	0.0	0
Total	268	44.8	330	55.2	431	72.1	167	27.9	239	40.0	598		128

Curriculum

	Full-Time	Part-Time
Typical first-year section size	55	75
Is there typically a "small section" of the first-year class, other than Legal Writing, taught by full-time faculty	No	No
If yes, typical size offered last year		
# of classroom course titles beyond first-year curriculum		73
# of upper division courses, excluding seminars, with an enrollment:	Under 25	52
	25–49	57
	50–74	5
	75–99	0
	100+	0
# of seminars		14
# of seminar positions available		210
# of seminar positions filled	0	0
# of positions available in simulation courses		163
# of simulation positions filled	125	38
# of positions available in faculty supervised clinical courses		202
# of faculty supervised clinical positions filled	132	70
# involved in field placements	114	61
# involved in law journals	37	5
# involved in moot court or trial competitions	8	0
# of credit hours required to graduate		96

Transfers

Transfers in	1
Transfers out	4

Tuition and Fees

	Resident	Nonresident
Full-time	$7,978	$12,580
Part-time	$6,668	$11,268
Tuition Guarantee Program		Y

Living Expenses

Estimated living expenses for singles

Living on campus	Living off campus	Living at home
$18,450	$18,450	$18,450

Southern University Law Center

ABA Approved Since 1953

GPA and LSAT Scores

	Total	Full-Time	Part-Time
# of apps	1,125	849	276
# of offers	461	369	92
# of matrics	239	156	83
75% GPA	3.21	3.31	3.10
Median GPA	2.84	2.86	2.72
25% GPA	2.55	2.60	2.41
75% LSAT	148	149	148
Median LSAT	145	146	144
25% LSAT	143	143	142

Grants and Scholarships (from prior year)

	Total		Full-Time		Part-Time	
	#	%	#	%	#	%
Total # of students	525		396		129	
Total # receiving grants	162	30.9	162	40.9	0	0.0
Less than 1/2 tuition	98	18.7	98	24.7	0	0.0
Half to full tuition	48	9.1	48	12.1	0	0.0
Full tuition	0	0.0	0	0.0	0	0.0
More than full tuition	16	3.0	16	4.0	0	0.0
Median grant amount			$1,864		$0	

Informational and Library Resources

Total amount spent on library materials	$1,178,038
Study seating capacity inside the library	284
# of full-time equivalent professional librarians	4
Hours per week library is open	99
# of open, wired connections available to students	565
# of networked computers available for use by students	56
Has wireless network?	Y
Require computer?	N

JD Attrition (from prior year)

	Academic	Other	Total	
	#	#	#	%
1st year	30	10	40	18.7
2nd year	2	0	2	1.4
3rd year	0	0	0	0.0
4th year	0	0	0	0.0

Employment (9 months after graduation)

	Total	Percentage
Employment status known	121	98.4
Employment status unknown	2	1.6
Employed	99	81.8
Pursuing graduate degrees	2	1.7
Unemployed (seeking, not seeking, or studying for the bar)	20	16.5
Type of Employment		
# employed in law firms	56	56.6
# employed in business and industry	9	9.1
# employed in government	16	16.2
# employed in public interest	3	3.0
# employed as judicial clerks	8	8.1
# employed in academia	7	7.1
Geographic Location		
# employed in state	87	87.9
# employed in foreign countries	0	0.0
# of states where employed	8	

Bar Passage Rates

First-time takers	95	Reporting %	NA
Average school %	NA	Average state %	NA
Average pass difference	NA		

Jurisdiction	Takers	Passers	Pass %	State %	Diff %

Southern University Law Center

Admission Office, PO Box 9294
Baton Rouge, LA 70813
Phone: 225.771.4976 or 800.537.1135; Fax: 225.771.2121
E-mail: admission@sulc.edu; Website: www.sulc.edu

■ Introduction

In September 1947, the Southern University school of law was officially opened, and it was redesignated as a law center in 1985. Accredited by the American Bar Association, the Supreme Court of Louisiana, and the Southern Association of Colleges and Secondary Schools, the Law Center maintains a high standard of professional education. It is fully approved by the Veterans Administration for the training of eligible veterans. The Southern University Law Center adheres to the principle of equal opportunity without regard to ethnicity, gender, creed, national origin, age, disability, or marital status.

The Law Center is located in Baton Rouge, the capital of Louisiana. With a population of over 600,000, this seat of state government includes state agencies and courts. As a hub of legal activity, Baton Rouge offers law students many opportunities to participate in state government through interaction with the legislature, state agencies, and private law firms.

■ Library

The law library contains more than 450,000 volumes, 1,000,000 microfiche, 40,000 rolls of microfilm, and 800 law reviews. The library offers research assistance and reference services to students, faculty, and the public. Its collection adequately supports the curriculum and conforms to the standards of the American Bar Association. Both federal and Louisiana state governments have designated Southern University Law Center Library as an official depository for government documents. A complete collection of Louisiana legal materials, including continuing legal education materials of the Louisiana Bar Association, is provided in the library. Although library acquisitions reflect the civil law tradition of Louisiana, sufficient materials for research in the common law and a substantial number of basic legal reference works are available. Media equipment in the library includes copying machines for printed materials and microform.

The library occupies a 30,000-square-foot area, which includes computer and multimedia law learning labs. Cooperative arrangements with the Louisiana State University Law Center Library provide access to one of the largest Anglo-American and civil law resource collections in the southern region. Interlibrary loans from other libraries can be made through the Southern University Law Library.

■ Curriculum

The program of study is designed to give students a comprehensive knowledge of both the civil law and the common law. While emphasis is given to the substantive and procedural law of Louisiana with its French and Spanish origins, Anglo-American law is strongly integrated into the curriculum. Fundamental differences in method and approach, and the results reached in the two systems, are analyzed.

The civil law system of Louisiana offers the law student a unique educational opportunity. The program of instruction examines the historical background of the Anglo-American setting. Students are trained in the art of advocacy, legal research, and the sources and social purposes of legal principles. Techniques to discipline the students' minds in legal reasoning are an integral part of the educational objectives of the Law Center. Students are instructed in the ethics of the legal profession and the professional responsibility of the lawyer to society.

The Juris Doctor (JD) degree is offered at the Southern University Law Center through a full-time and a part-time day/evening program. The JD program has a three-year curriculum requiring 96 hours of academic credits. The part-time program requires enrollment in at least eight credit hours each semester and can be completed in four years. A JD and Master of Public Administration (JD/MPA) joint degree is also offered by the Law Center and the Southern University Nelson Mandela School of Public Policy and Urban Affairs. The JD/MPA joint-degree program requires 123 hours of academic credit and can be completed in four years.

■ Admission

The Law Center does not prescribe any prelegal courses but strongly recommends a foundation in such courses as English, speech, political science, history, economics, psychology, logic, mathematics, analytical courses, and science.

Students beginning the study of law are admitted only in the fall semester. Applicants are advised to take the LSAT prior to the February test date of the expected year of enrollment. Under no circumstances will a score received on a test administered more than three years prior to the anticipated date of acceptance be considered. All applications for admission are reviewed by a special committee. Many variables are taken into consideration for admission, including, but not limited to, the undergraduate grade-point average and the LSAT. Work experience and past pursuits are also reviewed.

Completed application forms, in addition to two letters of recommendation and one copy of an official transcript showing degree earned, should be filed with the admission office during the fall semester prior to the year in which admission is sought.

■ Student Activities

Third-year law students are eligible to enroll in the Clinical Education Program, which allows students to handle cases under the direct supervision of a full-time faculty member of the Law Center.

The *Southern University Law Review* is a scholarly periodical published under the auspices of the Southern University Law Center. Editorial administration and managerial responsibilities are handled by the student members of the *Law Review* staff with guidance from a faculty advisor. Students who complete the first year with at least 29 credit hours and are ranked in the top 7 percent of their class at the end of the spring semester shall be invited to membership. Students who complete the first year with at least 29 credit hours and a cumulative undergraduate grade-point average of 3.0 may participate in the "write-on" competition.

Law Review membership provides eligible students with a wealth of experience in legal research and writing.

The Student Bar Association (SBA), an affiliate of the American Law Student Association, is a self-governing organization that receives full cooperation of the Law Center faculty. Any student in good standing enrolled at the Law Center is eligible for membership.

The purpose of the Student Bar Association is to promote the general welfare of the Law Center, encourage among its members high scholarship, and cultivate rapport and cooperation among the students, faculty, and members of the legal profession.

■ Housing

Limited dormitory accommodations are available for law students. All students desiring to live in campus housing are required to submit an application to the Housing Office, in addition to a security deposit of $50. Applications should be made to the Director of Housing, Southern University, as early as possible.

■ Other Student Organizations

Other student organizations include the Moot Court Board; Law Student Division, ABA; Black Law Students Association;

Delta Theta Phi Law Fraternity International; Phi Alpha Delta Law Fraternity, International; Women in Law; Environmental Law Society; Sports and Entertainment Legal Association; Louisiana Trial Lawyers Association; Christians at Law Society; International Law Students Association; Southern Student Association of Criminal Defense Lawyers; Public Interest Law Society; Phi Delta Phi International Legal Fraternity; Business Entrepreneurship Leadership Association; and the Thurgood Marshall Club.

■ Career Services

The Office of Career Counseling and Development assists students and alumni in obtaining meaningful employment opportunities. Information on part-time employment before graduation is available through this office. The office maintains a resource center directed toward résumé and cover letter writing, interview skills, and legal career opportunities. The Law Center is a member of the National Association for Legal Career Professionals (formerly National Association for Law Placement) and subscribes to its standards for promoting career planning and development activities.

Applicant Profile Not Available

Southwestern Law School

3050 Wilshire Boulevard
Los Angeles, CA 90010-1106
Phone: 213.738.6717; Fax: 213.383.1688
E-mail: admissions@swlaw.edu; Website: www.swlaw.edu

ABA
Approved
Since
1970

The Basics

Type of school	Private
Term	Semester
Application deadline	4/1
Application fee	$60
Financial aid deadline	6/1
Can first year start other than fall?	No
Student to faculty ratio	14.3 to 1
# of housing spaces available restricted to law students	
graduate housing for which law students are eligible	

Faculty and Administrators

	Total		Men		Women		Minorities	
	Spr	Fall	Spr	Fall	Spr	Fall	Spr	Fall
Full-time	53	53	30	32	23	21	12	11
Other full-time	4	3	3	2	1	1	0	0
Deans, librarians, & others who teach	7	7	4	4	3	3	0	0
Part-time	47	24	29	18	18	6	10	5
Total	111	87	66	56	45	31	22	16

Curriculum

		Full-Time	Part-Time
Typical first-year section size		76	79
Is there typically a "small section" of the first-year class, other than Legal Writing, taught by full-time faculty		No	No
If yes, typical size offered last year			
# of classroom course titles beyond first-year curriculum		151	
# of upper division	Under 25	133	
courses, excluding	25–49	42	
seminars, with	50–74	32	
an enrollment:	75–99	8	
	100+	0	
# of seminars		15	
# of seminar positions available		308	
# of seminar positions filled		170	42
# of positions available in simulation courses		941	
# of simulation positions filled		538	171
# of positions available in faculty supervised clinical courses		38	
# of faculty supervised clinical positions filled	34	2	
# involved in field placements	269	41	
# involved in law journals	81	20	
# involved in moot court or trial competitions	87	15	
# of credit hours required to graduate		87	

JD Enrollment and Ethnicity

	Men		Women		Full-Time		Part-Time		1st-Year		Total		JD Degs. Awd.
	#	%	#	%	#	%	#	%	#	%	#	%	
African Amer.	27	5.6	44	7.8	40	5.5	31	9.6	20	5.2	71	6.7	7
Amer. Indian	2	0.4	5	0.9	6	0.8	1	0.3	2	0.5	7	0.7	1
Asian Amer.	61	12.6	98	17.3	113	15.5	46	14.2	63	16.2	159	15.1	51
Mex. Amer.	32	6.6	39	6.9	46	6.3	25	7.7	27	7.0	71	6.7	21
Puerto Rican	1	0.2	2	0.4	3	0.4	0	0.0	3	0.8	3	0.3	0
Hispanic	23	4.7	44	7.8	50	6.9	17	5.3	25	6.4	67	6.4	17
Total Minority	146	30.1	232	40.9	258	35.4	120	37.2	140	36.1	378	35.9	97
For. Nation.	0	0.0	2	0.4	2	0.3	0	0.0	2	0.5	2	0.2	2
Caucasian	244	50.3	238	42.0	334	45.8	148	45.8	197	50.8	482	45.8	159
Unknown	95	19.6	95	16.8	135	18.5	55	17.0	49	12.6	190	18.1	31
Total	485	46.1	567	53.9	729	69.3	323	30.7	388	36.9	1052		289

Transfers

Transfers in	5
Transfers out	26

Tuition and Fees

	Resident	Nonresident
Full-time	$36,950	$36,950
Part-time	$22,250	$22,250
Tuition Guarantee Program		N

Living Expenses

Estimated living expenses for singles

Living on campus	Living off campus	Living at home
N/A	$26,819	$13,094

Southwestern Law School

ABA
Approved
Since
1970

GPA and LSAT Scores

	Total	Full-Time	Part-Time
# of apps	3,494	2,994	500
# of offers	1,105	926	179
# of matrics	395	284	111
75% GPA	3.51	3.56	3.41
Median GPA	3.26	3.29	3.18
25% GPA	3.06	3.10	2.89
75% LSAT	156	157	155
Median LSAT	154	155	153
25% LSAT	152	153	151

Grants and Scholarships (from prior year)

	Total		Full-Time		Part-Time	
	#	%	#	%	#	%
Total # of students	1,011		699		312	
Total # receiving grants	327	32.3	257	36.8	70	22.4
Less than 1/2 tuition	171	16.9	129	18.5	42	13.5
Half to full tuition	114	11.3	97	13.9	17	5.4
Full tuition	5	0.5	4	0.6	1	0.3
More than full tuition	37	3.7	27	3.9	10	3.2
Median grant amount			$15,000		$8,000	

Informational and Library Resources

Total amount spent on library materials	$1,667,974
Study seating capacity inside the library	610
# of full-time equivalent professional librarians	9
Hours per week library is open	108
# of open, wired connections available to students	326
# of networked computers available for use by students	134
Has wireless network?	Y
Require computer?	N

JD Attrition (from prior year)

	Academic #	Other #	Total #	Total %
1st year	10	10	20	5.6
2nd year	5	25	30	10.3
3rd year	0	3	3	1.0
4th year	0	0	0	0.0

Employment (9 months after graduation)

	Total	Percentage
Employment status known	274	96.1
Employment status unknown	11	3.9
Employed	257	93.8
Pursuing graduate degrees	2	0.7
Unemployed (seeking, not seeking, or studying for the bar)	4	1.5
Type of Employment		
# employed in law firms	154	59.9
# employed in business and industry	49	19.1
# employed in government	23	8.9
# employed in public interest	9	3.5
# employed as judicial clerks	5	1.9
# employed in academia	7	2.7
Geographic Location		
# employed in state	235	91.4
# employed in foreign countries	0	0.0
# of states where employed	8	

Bar Passage Rates

First-time takers	285	Reporting %	96.14
Average school %	69.71	Average state %	78.07
Average pass difference	−8.36		

Jurisdiction	Takers	Passers	Pass %	State %	Diff %
California	274	191	69.71	78.07	−8.36

Southwestern Law School

3050 Wilshire Boulevard
Los Angeles, CA 90010-1106
Phone: 213.738.6717; Fax: 213.383.1688
E-mail: admissions@swlaw.edu; Website: www.swlaw.edu

■ Introduction

With a long-standing emphasis on diversity, public service, innovative programs, and a mid-city campus featuring a world-renowned Art Deco landmark, Southwestern Law School reflects the vibrancy of Los Angeles and provides an ideal setting for law study. Founded in 1911 as an independent, nonprofit, nonsectarian institution, Southwestern is fully approved by the ABA and is a member of the AALS. It is the only law school to offer four JD courses of study that differ in scheduling and instructional approach, including traditional full- and part-time programs, as well as a unique two-year alternative curriculum. Southwestern's 10,000 alumni include prominent public officials—from members of Congress to mayors, and over 200 judges—as well as founders of major law firms and general counsels of multinational corporations. The law school has strong ties to the legal, business, and civic sectors, and its Biederman Entertainment and Media Law Institute is closely linked to the entertainment industry in Hollywood and internationally.

■ Diverse and Talented Student Body

There is a strong sense of community among the students who come to Southwestern from virtually every state and a dozen foreign countries, and represent over 250 undergraduate institutions. About two thirds have prior work experience or have already completed advanced degrees in diverse disciplines from accounting to urban planning. In the most recent entering class, women represent 55 percent, while minorities make up 38 percent, and students report fluency in over 20 foreign languages. The average age is 26, with a range from 21 to 60.

■ Distinguished Faculty

Southwestern's faculty focus on enhancing the classroom experience and providing personal attention to each student. The full-time faculty include internationally recognized experts in alternative dispute resolution, antitrust, civil rights, criminal justice, entertainment and media, environmental, ethics, human rights, intellectual property, international, and urban development, among other areas of the law. The adjunct faculty of distinguished judges and attorneys are known for their expertise in specialized practices and enjoy sharing their real-world knowledge with students in stimulating elective courses.

■ Award-Winning Campus Facilities

In 2004, Southwestern completed a $29 million campus expansion. Now encompassing nearly two city blocks, the campus includes the extraordinary Bullocks Wilshire Building, which is listed on the National Register of Historic Places. The award-winning facilities feature state-of-the-art multimedia technology in the classrooms, courtrooms, and clinics; wireless Internet access; spacious dining facilities and student lounges in restored historic areas; large terraces with panoramic city views; tranquil student commons and promenade plazas; as well as a 10,000-square-foot,

spa-quality fitness center. At over 83,000 square feet, Southwestern's Taylor Law Library is the second largest academic law library facility in California. The law school's Julian C. Dixon Courtroom and Advocacy Center is the most technologically sophisticated center of its kind.

■ Two-, Three-, and Four-Year JD Programs

Four JD programs are offered: a three-year, full-time day program; a four-year, part-time evening program; PLEAS—a four-year, part-time day program for students with child or elder-care responsibilities; and SCALE—an accelerated two-year, full-time program featuring small classes, practical skills training, and real-world experience. Southwestern has also established exciting new dual-degree affiliations with the Drucker Graduate School of Management of Claremont Graduate University for a JD/MBA and JD/MA in Management, as well as California State University, Dominguez Hills, for a unique JD/MA in Negotiation, Conflict Resolution, and Peacebuilding. LLM programs are offered in individualized law studies and in entertainment and media law.

■ Comprehensive Curriculum

Recently recognized by the Carnegie Foundation for innovation, Southwestern's cutting-edge, first-year curriculum provides a unique opportunity for students to choose one of three tracks in their legal research and writing course—appellate, negotiation, or trial advocacy—and to take an elective as early as their second semester. Recent upper-division enhancements include a January intersession, capstone courses, and special "mini-term" courses taught by international legal experts. The required traditional curriculum includes 17 courses, while nearly 200 elective courses, more than 150 externship placements, and three clinical programs allow students to design a broad-based legal education or emphasize an area of law. Southwestern's location, faculty expertise, alumni presence in the profession, and history have enabled the law school to develop a reputation as a leader, particularly in entertainment and media law, international law, criminal law, and trial advocacy/litigation. Southwestern sponsors summer law programs in Argentina, Canada, England, and Mexico. The Diversity Affairs Office and the Student Resource Center offer a wide array of academic support programs and a Writing Center to ensure student success.

■ Entertainment and Media Law Institute

Southwestern's internationally recognized Biederman Entertainment and Media Law Institute features the largest contingent of full-time entertainment and media law faculty of any law school, and benefits from an extensive network of alumni and adjunct faculty who hold prominent positions in these industries. The institute sponsors over 40 courses, 50 externships, the Biederman Scholars program, a special law firm practicum, a scholarly journal, and summer programs in Los Angeles and London, in addition to lectures and symposia with industry leaders. Southwestern also established the first LLM program in Entertainment and Media Law.

■ Student Activities

Southwestern's interscholastic Moot Court Honors Program, Negotiation Honors Program, Trial Advocacy Honors Program, and client counseling teams consistently earn top awards in competitions around the country. Students demonstrate their outstanding research, writing, and editing skills through service on the *Southwestern Law Review* and the *Southwestern Journal of International Law*, as well as the *Journal of International Media and Entertainment Law* published in conjunction with the ABA Forums on Communications Law and the Entertainment and Sports Industries. The Student Bar Association sponsors award-winning student welfare and community outreach programs and oversees over 35 student organizations, including three legal fraternities; minority, cultural, political, and religious groups; and societies focused on specific areas of law.

■ Public Interest Opportunities

Southwestern encourages, recognizes, and rewards students' public interest involvement through its Public Service Policy and a variety of programs: the Children's Rights, Immigration Law, and Street Law clinics; special scholarship funds; the Public Interest Service Award; the Silbert Public Interest Fellowship Program; Public Interest Summer Grants for students working with public service agencies; extensive student volunteer work with local schools and community organizations; and a large selection of externships. During the annual Public Interest Law Week, the entire law school community rallies to raise awareness and funds supporting public interest activities.

■ Career Services and Alumni Network

The Career Services Office offers individualized career counseling and coordinates a full calendar of workshops, networking events, mock interviews, and panel presentations, as well as the Alumni Resource Network to help students prepare for and secure legal employment. The office sponsors intensive on- and off-campus interview programs and provides Web-based access to extensive job listings and on-campus interview opportunities through Symplicity. Although the majority of Southwestern graduates choose to practice in California, alumni can be found in 47 states and 17 foreign countries.

■ Admission Criteria

Admission to Southwestern is highly selective, with an average acceptance rate over the past five years of under 30 percent. While emphasis is placed on undergraduate GPA and LSAT scores earned within the past three years, community involvement, work experience, motivation, recommendations, and diversity are also major factors. Transfer applications are considered from students who have successfully completed at least one year at another ABA-approved law school.

■ Financial Aid/Scholarships

About 90 percent of Southwestern's students receive some form of financial aid that may include scholarships, grants, loans, and work-study funds. Among the more than 50 institutional scholarship funds is the Wildman/Schumacher Scholarship Program, which provides up to full-tuition renewable scholarships to members of the first-year entering class who demonstrate exceptional academic and leadership potential.

Applicant Profile

Southwestern Law School
Prospects for Admission

GPA	LSAT Score						
	120–144	145–149	150–154	155–159	160–164	165–169	170 +
3.75 +							
3.50–3.74							
3.25–3.49							
3.00–3.24							
2.75–2.99							
2.50–2.74							
2.25–2.49							
2.00–2.24							

Unlikely   Possible   Likely

Note: This chart is to be used as a general guide only in determining chances for admittance. Nonnumerical factors are seriously considered for all applicants.

Stanford University Law School

Office of Admissions, 559 Nathan Abbott Way
Stanford, CA 94305-8610
Phone: 650.723.4985; Fax: 650.723.0838
E-mail: Admissions@law.stanford.edu; Website: www.law.stanford.edu

ABA
Approved
Since
1923

AMERICAN BAR ASSOCIATION
Section of Legal Education
and Admissions to the Bar

The Basics

Type of school	Private
Term	Quarter
Application deadline	2/1
Application fee	$75
Financial aid deadline	3/15
Can first year start other than fall?	No
Student to faculty ratio	8.0 to 1
# of housing spaces available restricted to law students	
graduate housing for which law students are eligible	595

Faculty and Administrators

	Total Spr	Total Fall	Men Spr	Men Fall	Women Spr	Women Fall	Minorities Spr	Minorities Fall
Full-time	57	58	37	39	20	19	8	10
Other full-time	10	12	4	6	6	6	5	5
Deans, librarians, & others who teach	18	17	11	11	7	6	4	4
Part-time	45	29	25	15	20	14	5	3
Total	130	116	77	71	53	45	22	22

Curriculum

	Full-Time	Part-Time
Typical first-year section size	60	0
Is there typically a "small section" of the first-year class, other than Legal Writing, taught by full-time faculty	Yes	No
If yes, typical size offered last year	30	
# of classroom course titles beyond first-year curriculum	160	

# of upper division courses, excluding seminars, with an enrollment:	
Under 25	145
25–49	25
50–74	7
75–99	2
100+	1

	Full-Time	Part-Time
# of seminars	57	
# of seminar positions available	1,040	
# of seminar positions filled	657	0
# of positions available in simulation courses	439	
# of simulation positions filled	401	0
# of positions available in faculty supervised clinical courses	227	
# of faculty supervised clinical positions filled	198	0
# involved in field placements	34	0
# involved in law journals	389	0
# involved in moot court or trial competitions	44	0
# of credit hours required to graduate	111	

JD Enrollment and Ethnicity

	Men #	Men %	Women #	Women %	Full-Time #	Full-Time %	Part-Time #	Part-Time %	1st-Year #	1st-Year %	Total #	Total %	JD Degs. Awd.
African Amer.	25	8.5	35	13.3	60	10.8	0	0.0	21	11.7	60	10.8	15
Amer. Indian	8	2.7	4	1.5	12	2.2	0	0.0	4	2.2	12	2.2	5
Asian Amer.	34	11.6	36	13.7	70	12.6	0	0.0	15	8.3	70	12.6	22
Mex. Amer.	25	8.5	23	8.7	48	8.6	0	0.0	15	8.3	48	8.6	15
Puerto Rican	2	0.7	3	1.1	5	0.9	0	0.0	1	0.6	5	0.9	2
Hispanic	3	1.0	1	0.4	4	0.7	0	0.0	3	1.7	4	0.7	2
Total Minority	97	33.0	102	38.8	199	35.7	0	0.0	59	32.8	199	35.7	61
For. Nation.	4	1.4	7	2.7	11	2.0	0	0.0	5	2.8	11	2.0	3
Caucasian	176	59.9	137	52.1	313	56.2	0	0.0	102	56.7	313	56.2	95
Unknown	17	5.8	17	6.5	34	6.1	0	0.0	14	7.8	34	6.1	22
Total	294	52.8	263	47.2	557	100.0	0	0.0	180	32.3	557		181

Transfers

Transfers in	16
Transfers out	1

Tuition and Fees

	Resident	Nonresident
Full-time	$44,121	$44,121
Part-time		
Tuition Guarantee Program	N	

Living Expenses

Estimated living expenses for singles

Living on campus	Living off campus	Living at home
$23,739	$25,917	N/A

Stanford University Law School

ABA
Approved
Since
1923

GPA and LSAT Scores

	Total	Full-Time	Part-Time
# of apps	4,082	4,082	0
# of offers	373	373	0
# of matrics	180	180	0
75% GPA	3.97	3.97	0.00
Median GPA	3.88	3.88	0.00
25% GPA	3.77	3.77	0.00
75% LSAT	172	172	0
Median LSAT	170	170	0
25% LSAT	167	167	0

Grants and Scholarships (from prior year)

	Total		Full-Time		Part-Time	
	#	%	#	%	#	%
Total # of students	539		539		0	
Total # receiving grants	270	50.1	270	50.1	0	0.0
Less than 1/2 tuition	119	22.1	119	22.1	0	0.0
Half to full tuition	138	25.6	138	25.6	0	0.0
Full tuition	9	1.7	9	1.7	0	0.0
More than full tuition	4	0.7	4	0.7	0	0.0
Median grant amount			$22,178		$0	

Informational and Library Resources

Total amount spent on library materials	$1,087,587
Study seating capacity inside the library	508
# of full-time equivalent professional librarians	10
Hours per week library is open	103
# of open, wired connections available to students	250
# of networked computers available for use by students	59
Has wireless network?	Y
Require computer?	Y

JD Attrition (from prior year)

	Academic	Other	Total	
	#	#	#	%
1st year	0	0	0	0.0
2nd year	0	3	3	1.7
3rd year	0	1	1	0.5
4th year	0	0	0	0.0

Employment (9 months after graduation)

	Total	Percentage
Employment status known	175	99.4
Employment status unknown	1	0.6
Employed	172	98.3
Pursuing graduate degrees	1	0.6
Unemployed (seeking, not seeking, or studying for the bar)	2	1.1
Type of Employment		
# employed in law firms	105	61.0
# employed in business and industry	8	4.7
# employed in government	6	3.5
# employed in public interest	11	6.4
# employed as judicial clerks	40	23.3
# employed in academia	2	1.2
Geographic Location		
# employed in state	75	43.6
# employed in foreign countries	3	1.7
# of states where employed	22	

Bar Passage Rates

First-time takers	160	Reporting %	95.00
Average school %	97.37	Average state %	81.44
Average pass difference	15.93		

Jurisdiction	Takers	Passers	Pass %	State %	Diff %
California	105	101	96.19	78.07	18.12
New York	47	47	100.00	88.98	11.02

Stanford University Law School

Office of Admissions, 559 Nathan Abbott Way
Stanford, CA 94305-8610
Phone: 650.723.4985; Fax: 650.723.0838
E-mail: Admissions@law.stanford.edu; Website: www.law.stanford.edu

■ Introduction

Stanford Law School is part of one of the world's leading research institutions, providing plentiful opportunities for interdisciplinary cooperation. Stanford University is a private university located in the heart of Silicon Valley, just 35 miles south of San Francisco. The university's 8,180 acres stretch between the foothills of the Santa Cruz Mountains and the cities of Palo Alto and Menlo Park, in a part of the country that offers an ideal, Mediterranean climate of dry, warm summers and wet, but temperate winters.

Current enrollment at the university is approximately 15,000 students, of whom about 8,000 are graduate students. The law school is small, with about 557 JD students, 38 LLM and JSM students, and more than 45 permanent faculty members. The school has teaching and research ties with schools and departments across campus. Law School courses are taught in 16 multimedia classrooms with full wireless Internet connectivity.

Stanford Law School offers a unique combination of the classic and cutting edge in legal education. The school is preparing its students for a rich and varied professional life in an era of great excitement and rapid change—much of it generated by the remarkable innovations in information technology pioneered in Silicon Valley—and for careers in an increasingly global community.

■ Faculty

Stanford Law School's faculty is distinguished not only for its scholarship, but also for its commitment to teaching and curricular innovation. The school's unusually low student/faculty ratio of 7.9 to 1 creates an intimate, collegial environment that fosters students' intellectual and professional development both in and out of the classroom. Students have many opportunities to work closely with faculty members as research assistants on scholarly projects, and the faculty encourages interested students to develop their own scholarship for future academic careers. The relationships formed between Stanford Law faculty and students often last a lifetime.

Instruction at Stanford Law takes place primarily in small classes and seminars and through individually directed research. It also takes place via a diverse range of legal clinics, which offer students experience with real cases and clients and personalized feedback.

The faculty is continually engaged in developing new teaching methods to complement curricular innovations. Case studies, similar to those of business schools, challenge students to consider the interaction of legal and nonlegal factors involved in a given situation. Numerous interdisciplinary opportunities allow faculty and students from the law school and other parts of the university, joined by practitioners and policymakers, to engage in applied research.

■ Library and Physical Facilities

Housed within Crown Quadrangle is the Robert Crown Law Library, which holds an excellent collection of print materials and a vast collection of online resources. Popular with the law students are the library's spacious reading rooms. An entire floor of the library, with its comfortable reading room and technology-enabled meeting rooms and classroom, is available 24 hours a day, 7 days a week. The 27 friendly and service-minded staff members are dedicated to helping students, faculty, and staff with all their research needs.

■ Special Programs

Joint-Degree Programs—Stanford Law School is actively expanding its joint-degree programs, leveraging the highly rated graduate schools and academic programs across Stanford University. To facilitate interdisciplinary study and scholarship, and simplify the pursuit of joint degrees, Stanford Law has adapted the law school calendar to be compatible with that of the wider university. The school now offers 20 formal joint-degree programs in such areas as Bioengineering, Business, Computer Science, Economics, Education, Electrical Engineering, Environment and Resources, Health Research and Policy, History, International and Comparative Area Studies, International Policy Studies, Management Science and Engineering, Philosophy, Political Science, Psychology, Public Policy, and Sociology. Joint-degree programs are also offered with Princeton's Woodrow Wilson School of Public and International Affairs and Johns Hopkins' School of Advanced International Studies. For students with specialized career aspirations, opportunities to customize a joint degree are limitless.

Programs and Centers—Stanford Law School's 20 innovative academic programs and centers give students the opportunity for concentrated study and close interaction with faculty. Students may engage in graduate-level research and policy-oriented study through centers and programs such as the Stanford Constitutional Law Center; the Stanford Criminal Justice Center; the Environmental and Natural Resources Law and Policy Program; the Stanford Center on International Conflict and Negotiation; the Rule of Law Program; the Stanford Program in International Law; the Arthur and Toni Rembe Rock Center for Corporate Governance; the John M. Olin Program in Law and Economics; the Stanford Program in Law, Science and Technology; the Center for E-Commerce; the Center for Internet and Society; the Center for Law and the BioSciences; the Transatlantic Technology Law Forum; CodeX: Stanford Center for Computers and Law; the Stanford Center on the Legal Profession; the Martin Daniel Gould Center for Conflict Resolution; the Gould Negotiation and Mediation Program; and the John and Terry Levin Center for Public Service and Public Interest Law.

Team-Taught Courses and Concentration—Stanford Law now offers 12 team-oriented, problem-solving courses, many of which are cotaught by law school faculty and faculty from Stanford's other top-rated schools and departments. Classes are open to students from a variety of disciplines.

Clinical Program—Stanford Law is a leader in the development of clinical teaching and has expanded its clinical program to include 10 clinics that offer students the opportunity to undertake, under the close supervision of experienced practitioners, the roles and responsibilities of practicing lawyers. Students engage in witness examination, depositions, discovery, negotiations, drafting pleadings and memos, oral arguments, and analysis of tactical and ethical problems. Clinics include the Criminal Defense Clinic, the Criminal Prosecution Clinic,

the Cyberlaw Clinic, the Environmental Law Clinic, the Immigrants' Rights Clinic, the International Human Rights Clinic, the Organizations and Transactions Clinic, the Stanford Community Law Clinic, the Supreme Court Litigation Clinic, and the Youth and Education Law Project.

■ Housing

Stanford provides a variety of housing options for law students. Students may choose from furnished single rooms to four bedroom apartments equipped with full kitchens. A new residence built specifically for law students and other graduate students from around campus—and adjacent to the law school—intensifies the interdisciplinary learning experience. The university also lists off-campus housing opportunities. More information about housing is available at the Housing Assignment Services website: www.stanford.edu/dept/hds/has/.

■ Student Activities

Sixty-one student organizations enrich the law school experience. Opportunities for scholarly work are provided through the *Stanford Law Review; Stanford Journal of Civil Rights and Civil Liberties; Stanford Journal of International Law; Stanford Journal of Law, Business and Finance; Stanford Law and Policy Review; Stanford Technology Law Review; Stanford Environmental Law Journal; Stanford Journal of Animal Law and Policy;* and *Stanford Journal of Law, Science, and Policy.* Advocacy skills are developed in moot court and mock trial.

Students who are female, Asian, African American, Latino, Native American, Christian, or LGBT will all find groups that share their particular concerns. Other organizations focus on environmental law, international law, law and technology, and public interest law. Local affiliates of the Federalist Society, the American Constitution Society, and the National Lawyers Guild are present.

■ Expenses and Financial Aid

Estimated expenses are as follows: for 2009–2010, full-time tuition is $42,420, with additional expenses including housing estimated at $25,440 for single students living on campus and $27,618 for single students living off campus. Scholarships are awarded on the basis of financial need. The purpose of financial aid is to assist students who would otherwise be unable to pursue a legal education at Stanford. Approximately 80 percent of the student body receives tuition fellowship or loan assistance.

Stanford law students planning public service careers may apply for Public Service Fellowships for their second and third years of school. The school also offers funding to students who dedicate a law school summer to qualified public service work. And for graduates who take low-paying public interest jobs and have substantial educational debt, the school has an excellent loan repayment assistance program—the Miles and Nancy Rubin Loan Repayment Assistance Program.

■ Career Services

The Office of Career Services, together with the John and Terry Levin Center for Public Service and Public Interest Law, helps students find employment. Approximately 250 employers representing over 500 offices worldwide participate in the spring and fall on-campus interview programs. The office also offers counseling and information on traditional and nontraditional careers and employers. The school encourages students to consider public interest and public sector employment and assists students to secure such positions.

A survey of students graduating in the class of 2008 shows the following employment patterns: law firm associates, 61 percent; judicial clerks, 23 percent; business (legal and nonlegal), 5 percent; public interest, government, or law teaching, 11 percent.

Applicant Profile

Our admission process takes into consideration many factors besides the undergraduate GPA and LSAT score. A statistical grid, as is typically provided here, only takes into consideration these two factors. We have chosen not to provide applicants with such a grid because our admission process would not be accurately portrayed.

Stetson University College of Law

1401 61st Street South
Gulfport, FL 33707
Phone: 727.562.7802; Fax: 727.343.0136
E-mail: lawadmit@law.stetson.edu; Website: www.law.stetson.edu

ABA Approved Since 1930

The Basics

Type of school	Private
Term	Semester
Application deadline	3/15
Application fee	$55
Financial aid deadline	8/22
Can first year start other than fall?	No
Student to faculty ratio	15.8 to 1
# of housing spaces available restricted to law students	214
graduate housing for which law students are eligible	

Faculty and Administrators

	Total		Men		Women		Minorities	
	Spr	Fall	Spr	Fall	Spr	Fall	Spr	Fall
Full-time	53	49	28	26	25	23	8	7
Other full-time	5	6	5	6	0	0	0	0
Deans, librarians, & others who teach	5	5	2	2	3	3	0	0
Part-time	47	57	34	39	13	18	7	4
Total	110	117	69	73	41	44	15	11

JD Enrollment and Ethnicity

	Men		Women		Full-Time		Part-Time		1st-Year		Total		JD Degs. Awd.
	#	%	#	%	#	%	#	%	#	%	#	%	
African Amer.	25	4.9	49	8.6	63	7.2	11	5.3	24	6.1	74	6.8	21
Amer. Indian	1	0.2	8	1.4	6	0.7	3	1.4	3	0.8	9	0.8	3
Asian Amer.	11	2.1	25	4.4	30	3.4	6	2.9	16	4.1	36	3.3	12
Mex. Amer.	3	0.6	1	0.2	4	0.5	0	0.0	3	0.8	4	0.4	2
Puerto Rican	8	1.6	8	1.4	15	1.7	1	0.5	7	1.8	16	1.5	6
Hispanic	36	7.0	38	6.7	60	6.8	14	6.7	28	7.1	74	6.8	22
Total Minority	84	16.3	129	22.6	178	20.3	35	16.8	81	20.5	213	19.6	66
For. Nation.	1	0.2	4	0.7	5	0.6	0	0.0	1	0.3	5	0.5	3
Caucasian	377	73.3	391	68.6	607	69.3	161	77.4	285	72.2	768	70.8	245
Unknown	52	10.1	46	8.1	86	9.8	12	5.8	28	7.1	98	9.0	8
Total	514	47.4	570	52.6	876	80.8	208	19.2	395	36.4	1084		322

Curriculum

	Full-Time	Part-Time
Typical first-year section size	70	60
Is there typically a "small section" of the first-year class, other than Legal Writing, taught by full-time faculty	No	No
If yes, typical size offered last year		
# of classroom course titles beyond first-year curriculum	172	
# of upper division courses, excluding seminars, with an enrollment: Under 25	240	
25–49	45	
50–74	30	
75–99	6	
100+	0	
# of seminars	25	
# of seminar positions available	416	
# of seminar positions filled	287	29
# of positions available in simulation courses	974	
# of simulation positions filled	761	113
# of positions available in faculty supervised clinical courses	175	
# of faculty supervised clinical positions filled	105	10
# involved in field placements	234	18
# involved in law journals	83	10
# involved in moot court or trial competitions	81	6
# of credit hours required to graduate	88	

Transfers

Transfers in	22
Transfers out	9

Tuition and Fees

	Resident	Nonresident
Full-time	$31,640	$31,640
Part-time	$21,920	$21,920
Tuition Guarantee Program		N

Living Expenses

Estimated living expenses for singles

Living on campus	Living off campus	Living at home
$21,706	$21,706	$21,706

Stetson University College of Law

ABA
Approved
Since
1930

GPA and LSAT Scores

	Total	Full-Time	Part-Time
# of apps	3,053	2,845	621
# of offers	1,233	1,099	134
# of matrics	395	335	60
75% GPA	3.65	3.65	3.59
Median GPA	3.44	3.46	3.39
25% GPA	3.19	3.21	3.12
75% LSAT	158	158	156
Median LSAT	156	156	153
25% LSAT	153	153	151

Grants and Scholarships (from prior year)

	Total		Full-Time		Part-Time	
	#	%	#	%	#	%
Total # of students	1,027		791		236	
Total # receiving grants	208	20.3	179	22.6	29	12.3
Less than 1/2 tuition	95	9.3	75	9.5	20	8.5
Half to full tuition	42	4.1	37	4.7	5	2.1
Full tuition	37	3.6	33	4.2	4	1.7
More than full tuition	34	3.3	34	4.3	0	0.0
Median grant amount			$15,250		$5,000	

Informational and Library Resources

Total amount spent on library materials	$1,872,380
Study seating capacity inside the library	680
# of full-time equivalent professional librarians	10
Hours per week library is open	93
# of open, wired connections available to students	1,595
# of networked computers available for use by students	117
Has wireless network?	Y
Require computer?	Y

JD Attrition (from prior year)

	Academic	Other	Total	
	#	#	#	%
1st year	0	16	16	4.6
2nd year	1	16	17	5.5
3rd year	0	0	0	0.0
4th year	0	0	0	0.0

Employment (9 months after graduation)

	Total	Percentage
Employment status known	294	98.0
Employment status unknown	6	2.0
Employed	275	93.5
Pursuing graduate degrees	7	2.4
Unemployed (seeking, not seeking, or studying for the bar)	10	3.4
Type of Employment		
# employed in law firms	167	60.7
# employed in business and industry	30	10.9
# employed in government	30	10.9
# employed in public interest	18	6.5
# employed as judicial clerks	9	3.3
# employed in academia	9	3.3
Geographic Location		
# employed in state	222	80.7
# employed in foreign countries	1	0.4
# of states where employed	19	

Bar Passage Rates

First-time takers	283	Reporting %	92.23
Average school %	81.99	Average state %	80.76
Average pass difference	1.23		

Jurisdiction	Takers	Passers	Pass %	State %	Diff %
Florida	261	214	81.99	80.76	1.23

Stetson University College of Law

1401 61st Street South
Gulfport, FL 33707
Phone: 727.562.7802; Fax: 727.343.0136
E-mail: lawadmit@law.stetson.edu; Website: www.law.stetson.edu

■ Introduction

Founded in 1900, Stetson University College of Law is Florida's first law school. The College's main campus is in Gulfport, a suburb of St. Petersburg. Located in a former resort hotel, the campus provides an outstanding environment in which to study law. A satellite campus in downtown Tampa hosts some classes in our part-time and full-time JD programs and houses judges on Florida's Second District Court of Appeal. Stetson is fully accredited by the American Bar Association and has been an Association of American Law Schools member since 1931. The college is an equal opportunity educational institution. For additional information, visit *www.law.stetson.edu.*

■ Library and Physical Facilities

Stetson's amazing facilities boast seven courtrooms—including the nation's first elder-friendly courtroom—and modern classrooms designed to enhance the learning experience. The Student Center features organizational offices, interviewing rooms, a gym, a pool, and nearby athletic fields. Stetson's Gulfport Law Library and Tampa Law Center satellite library form one of the Southeast's most advanced research and communications technology centers. Housing more than 420,000 volumes and providing 50 group-study rooms, this library system offers 24/7 swipe card access, wireless access to many online databases, and outstanding professional legal reference assistance. There is a laptop requirement for all students.

■ Admission

Last year, Stetson received 3,599 applications, offered admission to 1,233 applicants, and enrolled 395 first-year students: 335 full-time and 60 part-time. The 2009 entering class included 21 percent minority students and 50 percent women; 142 undergraduate institutions, 33 states, and 3 countries were represented within the group of new students. These numbers represent the spring and fall full-time and part-time 2009 entering classes. We no longer offer a spring JD start date. The student body consists of approximately 867 full-time and 209 part-time JD students, 19 students in the International Law LLM program (from 7 countries), and 40 Elder Law LLM students (online program). Our students, faculty, and staff work together toward one common goal: preparing our students to be the best lawyers and leaders possible.

■ Faculty

The intellectual exchange among students and faculty is continuous, both inside and outside the classroom. The 55 full-time professors are engaged in projects that bring them regional, national, and international prominence, but make teaching and working with students their top priority. Each semester, the full-time faculty is supplemented by approximately 50 practicing attorneys and judges who serve as adjunct professors in specialized areas.

■ Curriculum

Academic Success Programs: Stetson offers many programs, including academic advising, an academic orientation, bar exam preparation, a semester-long academic skills workshop, and a writing clinic, designed to assist all students in achieving their academic potential.

Lawyering Skills: Stetson's academic program focuses on the lawyering process. Stetson is a pioneer and a national leader in advocacy and clinical training.

Public Service: All JD students must complete a pro bono graduation requirement. Each year, all students participate in a Legal Community in Action Day to learn more about the profession and serve the community.

Additional Academic Offerings: Stetson offers a part-time JD program that allows a student to earn a law degree in four years by taking classes in the evenings; part-time students must take classes at both the Gulfport and Tampa campuses. Qualified foreign attorneys may receive advanced standing to complete the JD program in two years. Stetson offers three joint-degree programs (JD/MBA, JD/MD, and JD/MPH). Study-abroad opportunities are available in Argentina, China, The Netherlands, Spain, Switzerland, and the Cayman Islands. A rotating one-week study-abroad experience is also available; the 2010 trip is to Ireland. A semester-abroad program in London is offered each fall. A new dual-degree program is available with a Spanish law school. Stetson has Centers for Excellence in Advocacy, Elder Law, Higher Education Law and Policy, and International Law. The school also hosts the National Clearinghouse for Science, Technology and the Law; the Institute for Biodiversity Law and Policy; and the Institute for Caribbean Law and Policy. Students may participate in a Civil Rights Bus Tour in the summer.

■ Expenses and Financial Aid

Full-time tuition for 2009–2010 (fall/spring) was $31,420, and part-time tuition for 2009–2010 (fall/spring/summer) was $27,320. Partial- and full-merit and diversity scholarships are offered on a competitive basis. Need and merit scholarships are offered for continuing students. There is no financial aid deadline. Stetson offers a public service scholarship for third-year students.

■ Special Programs

Advocacy: Stetson is recognized as one of the best law schools for advocacy. Stetson's teams routinely win international, national, regional, and state mock trial, moot court, and alternative dispute resolution competitions.

Clinics and Internships: Stetson offers upper-level students a wide variety of opportunities to work closely with attorneys and judges, and, in some cases, actually represent clients and try cases. Clinical opportunities include Immigration, Civil Poverty Law, Elder Law, Local Government, Prosecution, and Public Defender. Internships include American/Caribbean Law, Bankruptcy Judicial, Elder Law, Employment Discrimination, Environmental Law, EEOC, Family Law, Federal and State Judicial (Tampa Bay/Tallahassee), In-House Counsel, Intellectual Property, Labor Law, State and Federal Litigation,

and the US Court of Appeals for Veterans Claims (DC). Stetson also offers a summer Law and Policy internship program in Washington, DC.

Certificates of Concentration: Students can apply to a certificate program in which they focus their elective credits on advocacy, elder law, or international law. The joint JD/MBA offers a concentration in Eco-Asset Management.

Law Review: The *Stetson Law Review* publishes three issues each year. Stetson also publishes the *Journal of International Aging Law and Policy* in cooperation with AARP and the *Journal of International Wildlife Law and Policy*.

Honors Program: Full-time students who rank in the top 15 percent of their entering class after their first or second semester and part-time students who rank in the top 15 percent of their entering class after their first or second year are invited to join the Honors Program, which features a special colloquium and seminar. Honors students also are invited to attend a wide variety of faculty colloquia and other special events.

Continuing Legal Education and High-Profile Speakers: Students are encouraged to attend the numerous seminars and conferences sponsored by the College of Law for practicing attorneys, judges, and other professionals. Recent featured speakers include US Supreme Court Justices Antonin Scalia and Clarence Thomas, former US Attorney General Janet Reno, Innocence Project founder Barry Scheck, and civil rights icon Representative John Lewis.

■ Residential Life

Stetson offers a variety of housing opportunities on and near campus including 49 dorm rooms, some of which are designated for special needs students. The university also owns 42 single-family homes and a 32-unit apartment complex, all located within a few blocks of the campus. A wait-list is maintained for these spaces. Once a seat confirmation fee is submitted, students must e-mail *housing@law.stetson.edu* to be placed on the wait-list for Stetson housing. The Office of Residential Life also maintains a roommates-wanted list and a general listing of other rental opportunities in the local area, although these rentals are not formally affiliated with Stetson.

■ Career Development

Stetson's commitment to helping students achieve their goals is reflected in its strong career development program. The Office of Career Development assists students and alumni in securing all types of legal and law-related employment and provides group seminars and individual counseling on subjects ranging from interviewing techniques to résumé writing. More than 96 percent of the 2008 graduating class reported that they found employment within nine months of graduation. Approximately 81 percent of recent Stetson graduates practice within Florida; however, alumni are located in 48 states and 22 countries.

■ Office of Student Life

The Office of Student Life offers student activities that support Stetson's academic mission and enrich the law school experience, such as cultural programs, experiential education trips, pro bono service opportunities, and monthly leadership luncheons. Stetson has more than 40 diverse and active student organizations. The Student Bar Association is the umbrella organization under which all others are coordinated. The Stetson Chapter of the American Bar Association (ABA) Law Student Division has been recognized regionally and nationally as one of the largest and best, and the Student Leadership Development Program was recently awarded the ABA's prestigious E. Smythe Gambrell Award for excellence in professionalism programming. A strong Office of Student Life presence on campus allows students many opportunities to hone their leadership and communication skills, network socially with their peers and legal professionals, and grow interpersonally as strong future members of the legal profession.

Applicant Profile

Stetson University College of Law
This grid includes only applicants who earned 120–180 LSAT scores under standard administrations.

LSAT Score	3.75 + Apps	3.75 + Adm	3.50–3.74 Apps	3.50–3.74 Adm	3.25–3.49 Apps	3.25–3.49 Adm	3.00–3.24 Apps	3.00–3.24 Adm	2.75–2.99 Apps	2.75–2.99 Adm	2.50–2.74 Apps	2.50–2.74 Adm	2.25–2.49 Apps	2.25–2.49 Adm	2.00–2.24 Apps	2.00–2.24 Adm	Below 2.00 Apps	Below 2.00 Adm	No GPA Apps	No GPA Adm	Total Apps	Total Adm
175–180	1	1	0	0	0	0	0	0	0	0	0	0	0	0	0	0	0	0	0	0	1	1
170–174	1	1	2	2	1	1	2	2	0	0	1	1	1	0	0	0	0	0	0	0	8	7
165–169	7	7	8	7	8	8	7	7	2	2	4	2	2	1	2	0	0	0	0	0	40	34
160–164	44	44	33	33	37	33	30	26	23	18	13	5	4	0	3	0	1	0	2	2	190	161
155–159	83	81	142	134	147	131	126	94	64	32	38	9	21	3	7	0	0	0	2	1	630	485
150–154	90	69	184	100	227	86	210	45	119	12	55	2	30	1	9	0	4	0	14	3	942	318
145–149	45	13	124	16	126	11	143	9	91	2	71	0	32	1	9	0	6	0	13	1	660	53
140–144	20	1	54	3	59	1	79	0	58	0	39	0	16	0	8	0	4	0	10	0	347	5
135–139	3	0	13	0	23	1	14	0	21	0	15	0	18	0	3	0	1	0	5	0	116	1
130–134	0	0	1	0	3	0	6	0	7	0	6	0	4	0	4	0	0	0	3	0	34	0
125–129	0	0	0	0	0	0	1	0	2	0	1	0	0	0	0	0	0	0	1	0	5	0
120–124	0	0	0	0	0	0	0	0	0	0	0	0	0	0	0	0	0	0	0	0	0	0
Total	294	217	561	295	631	272	618	183	387	66	243	19	128	6	45	0	16	0	50	7	2973	1065

Apps = Number of Applicants   Adm = Number Admitted   Reflects 99% of the total applicant pool; average LSAT data reported.

Suffolk University Law School

David J. Sargent Hall, 120 Tremont Street
Boston, MA 02108-4977
Phone: 617.573.8144; Fax: 617.523.1367
E-mail: lawadm@suffolk.edu; Website: www.law.suffolk.edu

ABA
Approved
Since
1953

The Basics

Type of school	Private
Term	Semester
Application deadline	3/1
Application fee	
Financial aid deadline	3/1
Can first year start other than fall?	No
Student to faculty ratio	16.6 to 1
# of housing spaces available restricted to law students	
graduate housing for which law students are eligible	

Faculty and Administrators

	Total		Men		Women		Minorities	
	Spr	Fall	Spr	Fall	Spr	Fall	Spr	Fall
Full-time	66	78	42	47	24	31	12	12
Other full-time	2	1	0	1	2	0	0	0
Deans, librarians, & others who teach	13	14	8	8	5	6	0	0
Part-time	69	62	48	48	21	14	3	3
Total	150	155	98	104	52	51	15	15

JD Enrollment and Ethnicity

	Men		Women		Full-Time		Part-Time		1st-Year		Total		JD Degs. Awd.
	#	%	#	%	#	%	#	%	#	%	#	%	
African Amer.	13	1.5	29	3.6	29	2.7	13	2.2	17	3.2	42	2.5	13
Amer. Indian	4	0.5	3	0.4	4	0.4	3	0.5	3	0.6	7	0.4	3
Asian Amer.	38	4.3	81	10.2	88	8.2	31	5.1	41	7.6	119	7.1	27
Mex. Amer.	0	0.0	0	0.0	0	0.0	0	0.0	0	0.0	0	0.0	0
Puerto Rican	0	0.0	0	0.0	0	0.0	0	0.0	0	0.0	0	0.0	0
Hispanic	30	3.4	39	4.9	48	4.4	21	3.5	28	5.2	69	4.1	17
Total Minority	85	9.6	152	19.1	169	15.7	68	11.3	89	16.6	237	14.1	60
For. Nation.	16	1.8	15	1.9	17	1.6	14	2.3	5	0.9	31	1.8	4
Caucasian	710	80.1	550	69.1	798	74.0	462	76.6	396	73.7	1260	74.9	353
Unknown	75	8.5	79	9.9	95	8.8	59	9.8	47	8.8	154	9.2	57
Total	886	52.7	796	47.3	1079	64.1	603	35.9	537	31.9	1682		474

Curriculum

	Full-Time	Part-Time
Typical first-year section size	89	98
Is there typically a "small section" of the first-year class, other than Legal Writing, taught by full-time faculty	Yes	No
If yes, typical size offered last year	45	
# of classroom course titles beyond first-year curriculum	281	

# of upper division courses, excluding seminars, with an enrollment:	Under 25	114
	25–49	55
	50–74	27
	75–99	18
	100+	14

# of seminars	53	
# of seminar positions available	994	
# of seminar positions filled	540	260
# of positions available in simulation courses	1,200	
# of simulation positions filled	733	379
# of positions available in faculty supervised clinical courses	96	
# of faculty supervised clinical positions filled	86	10
# involved in field placements	81	9
# involved in law journals	151	21
# involved in moot court or trial competitions	108	17
# of credit hours required to graduate	84	

Transfers

Transfers in	14
Transfers out	18

Tuition and Fees

	Resident	Nonresident
Full-time	$39,670	$39,670
Part-time	$29,754	$29,754
Tuition Guarantee Program		N

Living Expenses

Estimated living expenses for singles

Living on campus	Living off campus	Living at home
N/A	$21,782	$15,338

Suffolk University Law School

ABA
Approved
Since
1953

GPA and LSAT Scores

	Total	Full-Time	Part-Time
# of apps	3,261	2,630	631
# of offers	1,696	1,333	363
# of matrics	531	339	192
75% GPA	3.50	3.60	3.50
Median GPA	3.30	3.30	3.20
25% GPA	3.00	3.30	2.90
75% LSAT	158	159	156
Median LSAT	156	157	153
25% LSAT	153	154	151

Grants and Scholarships (from prior year)

	Total		Full-Time		Part-Time	
	#	%	#	%	#	%
Total # of students	1,652		1,031		621	
Total # receiving grants	678	41.0	550	53.3	128	20.6
Less than 1/2 tuition	554	33.5	445	43.2	109	17.6
Half to full tuition	111	6.7	93	9.0	18	2.9
Full tuition	11	0.7	11	1.1	0	0.0
More than full tuition	2	0.1	1	0.1	1	0.2
Median grant amount			$10,000		$5,550	

Informational and Library Resources

Total amount spent on library materials	$1,978,215
Study seating capacity inside the library	880
# of full-time equivalent professional librarians	13
Hours per week library is open	103
# of open, wired connections available to students	3,700
# of networked computers available for use by students	278
Has wireless network?	Y
Require computer?	N

JD Attrition (from prior year)

	Academic	Other	Total	
	#	#	#	%
1st year	15	17	32	5.8
2nd year	0	15	15	3.1
3rd year	0	1	1	0.2
4th year	0	0	0	0.0

Employment (9 months after graduation)

	Total	Percentage
Employment status known	466	98.9
Employment status unknown	5	1.1
Employed	403	86.5
Pursuing graduate degrees	13	2.8
Unemployed (seeking, not seeking, or studying for the bar)	44	9.4
Type of Employment		
# employed in law firms	162	40.2
# employed in business and industry	114	28.3
# employed in government	53	13.2
# employed in public interest	13	3.2
# employed as judicial clerks	45	11.2
# employed in academia	12	3.0
Geographic Location		
# employed in state	326	80.9
# employed in foreign countries	1	0.2
# of states where employed	22	

Bar Passage Rates

First-time takers	413	Reporting %	87.65
Average school %	92.82	Average state %	92.33
Average pass difference	0.49		

Jurisdiction	Takers	Passers	Pass %	State %	Diff %
Massachusetts	362	336	92.82	92.33	0.49

Suffolk University Law School

David J. Sargent Hall, 120 Tremont Street
Boston, MA 02108-4977
Phone: 617.573.8144; Fax: 617.523.1367
E-mail: lawadm@suffolk.edu; Website: www.law.suffolk.edu

■ Introduction

Suffolk University Law School has produced some of the nation's most distinguished legal professionals. Suffolk Law's curriculum combines a strong academic foundation with expertise in an array of specialty areas, and a nationally known faculty provides superior preparation for practice. Through clinical, internship, and public service opportunities, students earn credit while experiencing how the law works in the real world. Suffolk Law is an unmatched place to launch a successful career in the law.

■ Technology and Physical Facilities

Every seat in Sargent Hall's classrooms, library, and common areas has direct access to a high-speed network. Sargent Hall is wireless accessible throughout and all classrooms contain multimedia capabilities. A central media control room provides the ability to conduct videoconferencing and webcasting from any of the Law School's classrooms.

■ Concentrations and Joint-Degree Programs

Students may enroll in one of five concentrations: Business Law and Financial Services, Civil Litigation, Health and Biomedical Law, Intellectual Property (which includes a specialization in Patent Law), or International Law. Suffolk Law offers five, four-year, joint-degree programs that combine a Juris Doctor with a Master of Business Administration, Public Administration, International Economics, Finance, or Criminal Justice, as well as a three-year JD/MBA program.

■ Clinical and Internship Programs

Students are encouraged to enroll in one of our clinical programs. Suffolk Law's clinics include the Battered Women's Advocacy Program, Education Advocacy, Evening Landlord-Tenant, Family Advocacy, Housing, International Suffolk-Haifa Clinical Legal Exchange Program, Immigration, Juvenile Defenders, Suffolk Defenders, and Suffolk Prosecutors. Additionally, students can participate in the Civil and Judicial Internship Program, interning in a variety of legal settings, including state and federal courts; federal, state, and local government agencies; legal aid organizations; public defenders' offices; and private law firms and companies.

■ Foreign and Graduate Programs

Suffolk Law, in conjunction with the University of Lund, offers a summer study-abroad program held in Lund, Sweden. The program combines the strengths of our international law curriculum with the expertise offered by the University of Lund law faculty and the Swedish Bar and Judiciary.

Suffolk Law has an exclusive agreement with the Center for International Legal Studies (CILS) in Salzburg, Austria, to offer internships to US law students and externships to graduates with law degrees. International internships are available to JD students, and international externships are offered to LLM students and other postgraduates with law degrees.

Internships are available at law firms, businesses, and nonprofit organizations in almost every country of the world.

Suffolk Law offers two LLM degree programs. One is in Global Law and Technology, which offers specializations in Intellectual Property and Information Technology Law, Biomedicine and Health Law, International Law and Business, and US Law and Legal Methods, and is held in Boston, Massachusetts. The second program offers an LLM in US and Global Business Law exclusively to lawyers from international jurisdictions and is administered at law schools abroad only.

■ Academic Support Programs

The goal of the Academic Support Program (ASP) is to help students make the most of their abilities. To accomplish this goal, the faculty conducts weekly classes on such diverse topics as legal analysis and writing, course outlining, and time management. These optional classes are open to all first-year students. In addition, ASP professors are always available to meet with individual or small groups of students in order to address specific questions or issues. The ASP also has a lending library containing study aids and material on substantive legal topics. Additionally, the ASP library contains exercises on grammar, legal writing, and analysis. All students are encouraged to stop by and take advantage of these resources.

■ Scholarships and Loans

Suffolk Law participates in student financial aid programs to assist students in financing the cost of their legal education. Both need-based and merit-based aid is available. Financial aid awards (scholarships, grants, loans, and employment awards) are made to assist students in financing educational costs when their personal and family resources may not be sufficient. Merit-based scholarships are awarded by the law school's Admissions Committee at the time a candidate is admitted. These awards are made to students based on outstanding academic achievement.

In addition to the need-based grant and merit-based scholarship programs, Suffolk Law offers Sargent Scholarships ranging from $20,000 to full tuition to entering students with significant financial need and exceptional academic strength. All admitted students who apply for need-based financial aid are considered for an award.

Suffolk Law also has a Loan Repayment Assistance Program for students who, upon graduation, pursue low-income, public service, law-related employment.

■ Student Activities, Publications, and Opportunities

Students have a number of opportunities to develop legal skills outside of the classroom through participation in the *Suffolk University Law Review*, the *Suffolk Transnational Law Review*, the *Journal of High Technology Law* (www.jhtl.org), and the *Suffolk Journal of Health and Biomedical Law*. Students can also participate in the Moot Court Board (which also publishes the *Suffolk Journal of Trial and Appellate Advocacy*) as well as on moot court competition teams such as the National Trial Competition Team, ATLA Trial Team,

Constitutional Law Team, Information Technology and Privacy Law Team, Intellectual Property Law Team, Jessup International Law Team, National Invitational Trial Tournament of Champions, National Moot Court Team, Securities Law Team, Sports Law Team, and Tax Law Team. Students can also join one of more than 40 student organizations or participate in the Student Bar Association.

■ Career Development Office

Suffolk University Law School is committed to preparing students to serve diverse clients and communities. Suffolk Law graduates can be found in private practice; corporations; public interest organizations; the military; the executive, judicial, and legislative branches of government; and in rewarding careers outside the legal realm. The Career Development Office coordinates on- and off-campus recruitment programs and résumé collections throughout the academic year, and also maintains an extensive online job database, a resource library, and employment websites. The Career Development Office offers career counseling, résumé and cover letter critiques, mock interviews, and innovative programs, panels, workshops, and information sessions for students. Staff conduct employer visits and related job cultivation nationwide. The Career Development Office prides itself on connecting with students through personal outreach and technology and makes sure all students are supported in their job searches and career development endeavors.

■ Peer Mentoring Program

This program helps nontraditional students achieve their full potential as law students. Suffolk Law defines nontraditional students as those who have been historically excluded or marginalized from the law school community based on any of the following factors: (1) race, (2) ethnicity, (3) socioeconomic disadvantage, or (4) history of low performance on standardized tests.

The program starts with a two-week summer session that begins two weeks before orientation. Participating students attend classes on criminal law and contracts and receive extensive training in case briefing, legal analysis, outlining, exam preparation, and exam writing. Students also receive feedback on case briefs and practice exams and, at the end of each class, an upper-class student mentor leads a small group discussion regarding the class material.

Building on the summer session, the program holds weekly seminars during the academic year to help students master the skills to perform well on both multiple-choice and essay exams. Students have the opportunity to meet individually on an ongoing basis with both an upper-class student mentor and the program director. The purpose of both the weekly seminars and the individual meetings is to help students develop and adhere to sound time management practices, effective study habits, and critical thinking skills.

■ Rappaport Center for Law and Public Service

The Rappaport Center for Law and Public Service was established in 2006, with the generous support of Jerry and Phyllis Rappaport and the Rappaport Charitable Foundation. Leveraging Suffolk Law School's ideal downtown location, and rich tradition of public service, the Rappaport Center brings together elected officials, senior policymakers, community advocates, private sector leaders, faculty, and students to engage in dialogue around important public policy issues. The center also provides career advising to students interested in public service, administers the law school's pro bono program, and is home to the highly competitive Rappaport Fellows Program in Law and Public Policy. For more information about the Rappaport Center, please visit www.rappaportcenter.org.

Applicant Profile

Suffolk University Law School

LSAT Score	GPA								
	3.75 +	3.50–3.74	3.25–3.49	3.00–3.24	2.75–2.99	2.50–2.74	2.25–2.49	2.00–2.24	Below 2.00
175–180									
170–174									
165–169									
160–164									
155–159									
150–154									
145–149									
140–144									
135–139									
130–134									
125–129									
120–124									

■ Very Likely   □ Possible   ▨ Unlikely

Syracuse University College of Law

Office of Admissions and Financial Aid, Suite 340
Syracuse, NY 13244-1030
Phone: 315.443.1962; Fax: 315.443.9568
E-mail: admissions@law.syr.edu; Website: www.law.syr.edu

ABA Approved Since 1923

The Basics

Type of school	Private
Term	Semester
Application deadline	4/1
Application fee	$70
Financial aid deadline	2/15
Can first year start other than fall?	No
Student to faculty ratio	10.9 to 1
# of housing spaces available restricted to law students	8
graduate housing for which law students are eligible	134

Faculty and Administrators

	Total		Men		Women		Minorities	
	Spr	Fall	Spr	Fall	Spr	Fall	Spr	Fall
Full-time	45	49	28	32	17	17	9	11
Other full-time	17	15	8	6	9	9	3	3
Deans, librarians, & others who teach	7	6	2	2	5	4	1	1
Part-time	26	17	21	13	5	4	10	3
Total	95	87	59	53	36	34	23	18

Curriculum

	Full-Time	Part-Time
Typical first-year section size	68	0
Is there typically a "small section" of the first-year class, other than Legal Writing, taught by full-time faculty	Yes	No
If yes, typical size offered last year	46	
# of classroom course titles beyond first-year curriculum	129	
# of upper division courses, excluding seminars, with an enrollment: Under 25	118	
25–49	24	
50–74	15	
75–99	5	
100+	0	
# of seminars	11	
# of seminar positions available	195	
# of seminar positions filled	142	0
# of positions available in simulation courses	583	
# of simulation positions filled	399	0
# of positions available in faculty supervised clinical courses	137	
# of faculty supervised clinical positions filled	135	0
# involved in field placements	124	0
# involved in law journals	107	0
# involved in moot court or trial competitions	54	0
# of credit hours required to graduate	87	

JD Enrollment and Ethnicity

	Men #	Men %	Women #	Women %	Full-Time #	Full-Time %	Part-Time #	Part-Time %	1st-Year #	1st-Year %	Total #	Total %	JD Degs. Awd.
African Amer.	11	3.1	11	4.4	22	3.7	0	0.0	10	4.5	22	3.6	9
Amer. Indian	0	0.0	3	1.2	3	0.5	0	0.0	2	0.9	3	0.5	2
Asian Amer.	37	10.5	35	14.0	71	11.9	1	20.0	29	13.2	72	11.9	24
Mex. Amer.	4	1.1	3	1.2	7	1.2	0	0.0	1	0.5	7	1.2	0
Puerto Rican	1	0.3	2	0.8	3	0.5	0	0.0	1	0.5	3	0.5	0
Hispanic	9	2.5	10	4.0	19	3.2	0	0.0	5	2.3	19	3.2	6
Total Minority	62	17.6	64	25.6	125	20.9	1	20.0	48	21.8	126	20.9	41
For. Nation.	14	4.0	12	4.8	25	4.2	1	20.0	5	2.3	26	4.3	0
Caucasian	200	56.7	127	50.8	324	54.2	3	60.0	132	60.0	327	54.2	125
Unknown	77	21.8	47	18.8	124	20.7	0	0.0	35	15.9	124	20.6	51
Total	353	58.5	250	41.5	598	99.2	5	0.8	220	36.5	603		217

Transfers

Transfers in	3
Transfers out	25

Tuition and Fees

	Resident	Nonresident
Full-time	$44,856	$44,856
Part-time	$39,088	$39,088
Tuition Guarantee Program		Y

Living Expenses

Estimated living expenses for singles

Living on campus	Living off campus	Living at home
$18,524	$18,524	$18,524

Syracuse University College of Law

ABA Approved Since 1923

GPA and LSAT Scores

	Total	Full-Time	Part-Time
# of apps	2,518	2,518	0
# of offers	960	960	0
# of matrics	223	223	0
75% GPA	3.51	3.51	0.00
Median GPA	3.32	3.32	0.00
25% GPA	3.13	3.13	0.00
75% LSAT	157	157	0
Median LSAT	155	155	0
25% LSAT	153	153	0

Grants and Scholarships (from prior year)

	Total #	Total %	Full-Time #	Full-Time %	Part-Time #	Part-Time %
Total # of students	640		634		6	
Total # receiving grants	475	74.2	468	73.8	7	116.7
Less than 1/2 tuition	409	63.9	403	63.6	6	100.0
Half to full tuition	63	9.8	62	9.8	1	16.7
Full tuition	1	0.2	1	0.2	0	0.0
More than full tuition	2	0.3	2	0.3	0	0.0
Median grant amount			$6,500		$5,250	

Informational and Library Resources

Total amount spent on library materials	$1,409,503
Study seating capacity inside the library	402
# of full-time equivalent professional librarians	10
Hours per week library is open	106
# of open, wired connections available to students	19
# of networked computers available for use by students	90
Has wireless network?	Y
Require computer?	Y

JD Attrition (from prior year)

	Academic #	Other #	Total #	Total %
1st year	5	26	31	13.6
2nd year	1	14	15	8.2
3rd year	0	0	0	0.0
4th year	0	0	0	0.0

Employment (9 months after graduation)

	Total	Percentage
Employment status known	216	96.4
Employment status unknown	8	3.6
Employed	193	89.4
Pursuing graduate degrees	11	5.1
Unemployed (seeking, not seeking, or studying for the bar)	4	1.9
Type of Employment		
# employed in law firms	90	46.6
# employed in business and industry	47	24.4
# employed in government	27	14.0
# employed in public interest	11	5.7
# employed as judicial clerks	17	8.8
# employed in academia	1	0.5
Geographic Location		
# employed in state	77	39.9
# employed in foreign countries	2	1.0
# of states where employed	26	

Bar Passage Rates

First-time takers	224	Reporting %	100.00
Average school %	84.84	Average state %	87.56
Average pass difference	−2.72		

Jurisdiction	Takers	Passers	Pass %	State %	Diff %
New York	132	111	84.09	88.98	−4.89
Pennsylvania	16	15	93.75	86.69	7.06
California	16	8	50.00	78.07	−28.07
Illinois	10	10	100.00	90.94	9.06
Others (19)	50	46	92.00		

Syracuse University College of Law

Office of Admissions and Financial Aid, Suite 340
Syracuse, NY 13244-1030
Phone: 315.443.1962; Fax: 315.443.9568
E-mail: admissions@law.syr.edu; Website: www.law.syr.edu

■ Introduction

Syracuse University College of Law was established in 1895. The College is a charter member of the AALS and is fully approved by the ABA. Embedded in a dynamic teaching and research university, the College of Law is one of the oldest of the 11 schools and colleges comprising Syracuse University. The College of Law complex is located on the 200-acre SU main campus overlooking scenic Central New York and the city of Syracuse.

■ Curriculum

Syracuse University College of Law's mission is guided by the philosophy that the best way to educate lawyers to practice in today's world is to engage them in a process of interdisciplinary learning while teaching them to apply what they learn in the classroom to real legal issues, problems, and clients. Beginning in the first year and continuing throughout the curriculum, students are exposed to educational settings that integrate opportunities to acquire a better understanding of legal theory and doctrine, develop professional skills, and gain exposure to the values and ethics of the legal profession. As a result, Syracuse students are better prepared for the practice of law.

■ Interdisciplinary Learning Opportunities

- **Disability Law and Policy Program**—Students may pursue a joint degree in law and disability studies and certificate programs in disability law and policy. Coursework, internships, and the Disability Rights Clinic push the boundaries of a traditional legal education and engage students in hands-on learning for the public good.
- **Institute for National Security and Counterterrorism (INSCT)**—The institute, a joint enterprise of the College of Law and the Maxwell School of Citizenship and Public Affairs, is dedicated to interdisciplinary teaching, research, and public service focused on important national and global problems of security and terrorism. INSCT students pursuing professional and doctoral degrees engage in advanced coursework toward specialty certificates in security and terrorism studies. The institute's research portfolio is broad and deep, ranging from faculty-supervised student working papers and research reports, to significant articles and books for academic journals and presses, to sponsorship of major workshops and conferences designed to further a research agenda in security or terrorism. While all INSCT research advances knowledge in the field, many projects are conducted on behalf of or in consultation with agencies, municipalities, and other public entities, thus providing direct public service.
- **Technology Commercialization Law Program**—The program is a course concentration within the law curriculum that provides an interdisciplinary and applied approach to the study of commercial development of new technologies. The program combines classroom courses, case study problem-solving, negotiation and drafting exercises, and applied research projects.
- **Family Law and Social Policy Center**—The center prepares students for a career in family law by engaging them in interdisciplinary research, providing them with applied learning experiences, and connecting them with the community to provide services that benefit families and children. The center offers opportunities that blend interdisciplinary theory and practice in the field of family law in challenging and rewarding ways. These combined experiences allow students to emerge from the program with the professional skills and experiences necessary to launch successful and satisfying careers in family law.
- **Center for Global Law and Practice**—The center provides students with specialized foreign, comparative, and international courses as well as cocurricular offerings. Students are exposed to the myriad ways in which the process of globalization increasingly impacts trade and commerce; the environment; national, regional, and local governments; individual rights and welfare; and even the legal profession itself. A summer-abroad program is offered in London.
- **Center for Indigenous Law, Governance, and Citizenship**—The center is a research-based law and policy institute focused on indigenous nations, their development, and their interaction with the US and Canadian governments.
- **Institute for the Study of the Judiciary, Politics, and the Media (IJPM)**—The institute is a collaborative effort between Syracuse University's College of Law, Maxwell School of Citizenship and Public Affairs, and the S. I. Newhouse School of Public Communications. The institute is devoted to the study of issues at the intersection of law, politics, and the media. The institute sponsors lectures, conferences, and symposia designed to foster discussion and debate between legal scholars, sitting judges, and working journalists.
- **Center on Property, Citizenship, and Social Entrepreneurism**—The center brings together experts from a variety of fields and institutions to discuss and explore issues related to modern real estate transactions and finance; community development and housing; global property law systems; and access to ownership for inclusion of the elderly, the poor, and persons with disabilities.
- **Burton Blatt Institute (BBI) Centers of Innovation on Disability**—Through research and scholarship in action, the institute will advance the civic, economic, and social participation of persons with disabilities in a global society. The institute seeks to create a collaborative environment —with entrepreneurial innovation and best business practices—to foster public-private dialogue, and create the capacity to transform policy, systems, and people through inclusive education, the workforce, and communities.

■ Other Opportunities for Specialization

- **Clinical Programs**—Legal concepts learned in the classroom come to life for students who participate in the in-house clinics and externship program. Students work with lawyers in law offices, becoming immersed in the actual practice of law through their work on real cases affecting real clients. Students provide much-needed legal services to our community, as many of our clients are unable to afford private counsel. Diverse clinical

opportunities at the College of Law include the Criminal Defense Law Clinic, the Community Development Law Clinic, the Children's Rights and Family Law Clinic, the Disability Rights Clinic, the Elder Law Clinic, the Low Income Taxpayer Law Clinic, and the Securities Arbitration Clinic/Consumer Law Clinic. In addition, the externship program provides opportunities for students to work in government offices, judges' chambers, university-based programs, and public interest organizations.

- **Joint-Degree Programs**—Students who desire a greater degree of specialization may select from a number of joint-degree opportunities. Formal joint-degree programs exist in public administration, international relations, business administration or accounting, communications, environmental law, education (disability studies), social work, and engineering. Joint degrees may also be designed to fit special career objectives.
- **Advocacy Skills**—Syracuse Law is recognized for its exceptional advocacy programs. Students are actively involved and have been highly successful in national and regional moot court competitions. Syracuse students participate in intraschool programs throughout the year in trial and appellate competitions covering a wide variety of areas.

■ Library

The law library's four spacious levels within the College of Law complex house more than 473,000 volumes in print and microform; 2,200 serials; and extensive audio, video, and electronic holdings—all accessible through the university-wide online library catalog. On the main floor, the circulation and reference desks offer conveniently located services and research support in close proximity to the Electronic Research Center. The library adds approximately 2,500 new titles to its catalog each year, including a growing number of licensed electronic databases.

■ Admission

History reveals that undergraduate grades and LSAT scores are reliable measures, in most cases, for predicting probable success in law study. Thus, an index combining grades and test scores becomes a factor in most admission decisions. However, recognizing that numerical indicators are not always the best predictors of success in law school—even when considered in combination with other factors—the college admits a limited number of students each year through its Legal Education Opportunity (LEO) Program. The program's dual objectives are to recruit and admit persons who may have been deprived of equal education opportunities for reasons of race, gender, poverty, or other factors beyond their control; and persons with unusual accomplishments, backgrounds, and experiences that suggest traditional admission criteria may be inadequate predictors of likely success in law study.

■ Financial Aid

The college is committed to assisting students in financing their legal education through a comprehensive financial aid program. Awards are made from a variety of sources, including merit-based scholarships; need-based tuition grants; and from federal sources, including the work-study program and the Perkins and Direct Loan programs.

■ Professional and Career Development

The Office of Professional and Career Development provides a full range of career-oriented services to students, including a broad mix of innovative and traditional support. Programming is designed to prepare students for leadership, service, and professionalism, while developing their ability to deal with lifelong career planning. The program offers a variety of services including individual career counseling and job-search strategies.

Applicant Profile

Syracuse University College of Law
This grid includes only applicants who earned 120–180 LSAT scores under standard administrations.

LSAT Score	3.75 +		3.50–3.74		3.25–3.49		3.00–3.24		2.75–2.99		2.50–2.74		2.25–2.49		2.00–2.24		Below 2.00		No GPA		Total	
	Apps	Adm	Apps	Adm	Apps	Adm	Apps	Adm	Apps	Adm	Apps	Adm	Apps	Adm	Apps	Adm	Apps	Adm	Apps	Adm	Apps	Adm
170–180	0	0	0	0	0	0	0	0	0	0	0	0	1	0	0	0	0	0	0	0	1	0
165–169	3	2	4	3	4	4	5	5	2	2	4	1	2	1	1	0	0	0	0	0	25	18
160–164	12	12	20	19	24	24	18	15	24	13	14	6	6	0	1	0	2	0	1	0	122	89
155–159	40	40	85	85	120	117	104	93	61	30	39	6	15	0	8	0	0	0	9	6	481	377
150–154	74	46	160	96	241	128	189	88	124	27	64	1	14	0	8	0	2	0	15	2	891	388
145–149	48	5	87	13	142	26	142	17	93	7	49	1	21	0	4	0	1	0	9	0	596	69
120–144	12	1	40	0	72	2	65	0	75	0	66	0	28	0	13	0	2	0	17	0	390	3
Total	189	106	396	216	603	301	523	218	379	79	236	15	87	1	35	0	7	0	51	8	2506	944

Apps = Number of Applicants   Adm = Number Admitted   Reflects 99% of the total applicant pool; average LSAT data reported.

This chart is provided as a general guide in assessing an applicant's possibility of admission based solely on quantitative factors. It should be noted that nonquantitative factors are also considered in all admission decisions.

Temple University—James E. Beasley School of Law

1719 North Broad Street
Philadelphia, PA 19122
Phone: 800.560.1428; Fax: 215.204.9319
E-mail: lawadmis@temple.edu; Website: www.law.temple.edu

ABA
Approved
Since
1933

The Basics

Type of school	Public
Term	Semester
Application deadline	3/1
Application fee	$60
Financial aid deadline	3/1
Can first year start other than fall?	No
Student to faculty ratio	13.0 to 1
# of housing spaces available restricted to law students graduate housing for which law students are eligible	

Faculty and Administrators

	Total		Men		Women		Minorities	
	Spr	Fall	Spr	Fall	Spr	Fall	Spr	Fall
Full-time	58	56	32	33	26	23	15	13
Other full-time	1	1	1	1	0	0	1	1
Deans, librarians, & others who teach	14	14	6	6	8	8	3	3
Part-time	125	91	87	51	38	40	15	14
Total	198	162	126	91	72	71	34	31

JD Enrollment and Ethnicity

	Men		Women		Full-Time		Part-Time		1st-Year		Total		JD Degs. Awd.
	#	%	#	%	#	%	#	%	#	%	#	%	
African Amer.	25	4.8	44	9.8	59	7.5	10	5.2	26	8.6	69	7.1	20
Amer. Indian	6	1.1	3	0.7	8	1.0	1	0.5	5	1.6	9	0.9	3
Asian Amer.	40	7.6	54	12.0	74	9.4	20	10.4	24	7.9	94	9.6	20
Mex. Amer.	3	0.6	2	0.4	5	0.6	0	0.0	3	1.0	5	0.5	2
Puerto Rican	2	0.4	8	1.8	8	1.0	2	1.0	3	1.0	10	1.0	2
Hispanic	16	3.0	18	4.0	28	3.6	6	3.1	15	4.9	34	3.5	7
Total Minority	92	17.5	129	28.6	182	23.2	39	20.3	76	25.0	221	22.6	54
For. Nation.	1	0.2	7	1.6	7	0.9	1	0.5	3	1.0	8	0.8	2
Caucasian	424	80.8	307	68.1	582	74.2	149	77.6	222	73.0	731	74.9	225
Unknown	8	1.5	8	1.8	13	1.7	3	1.6	3	1.0	16	1.6	4
Total	525	53.8	451	46.2	784	80.3	192	19.7	304	31.1	976		285

Curriculum

	Full-Time	Part-Time
Typical first-year section size	60	60
Is there typically a "small section" of the first-year class, other than Legal Writing, taught by full-time faculty	No	No
If yes, typical size offered last year		

# of classroom course titles beyond first-year curriculum		185
# of upper division courses, excluding seminars, with an enrollment:	Under 25	191
	25–49	52
	50–74	20
	75–99	8
	100+	3
# of seminars		57
# of seminar positions available		885
# of seminar positions filled	574	106
# of positions available in simulation courses	1,156	
# of simulation positions filled	799	122
# of positions available in faculty supervised clinical courses		90
# of faculty supervised clinical positions filled	62	3
# involved in field placements	189	10
# involved in law journals	168	12
# involved in moot court or trial competitions	32	5
# of credit hours required to graduate		87

Transfers

Transfers in	8
Transfers out	7

Tuition and Fees

	Resident	Nonresident
Full-time	$17,226	$29,516
Part-time	$13,908	$23,744
Tuition Guarantee Program		N

Living Expenses

Estimated living expenses for singles

Living on campus	Living off campus	Living at home
$20,054	$20,054	$14,820

Temple University—James E. Beasley School of Law

ABA
Approved
Since
1933

GPA and LSAT Scores

	Total	Full-Time	Part-Time
# of apps	4,651	4,194	457
# of offers	1,869	1,737	132
# of matrics	303	239	64
75% GPA	3.61	3.60	3.65
Median GPA	3.41	3.43	3.28
25% GPA	3.11	3.14	2.89
75% LSAT	163	163	161
Median LSAT	161	161	159
25% LSAT	159	160	156

Grants and Scholarships (from prior year)

	Total		Full-Time		Part-Time	
	#	%	#	%	#	%
Total # of students	974		773		201	
Total # receiving grants	450	46.2	416	53.8	34	16.9
Less than 1/2 tuition	315	32.3	282	36.5	33	16.4
Half to full tuition	59	6.1	59	7.6	0	0.0
Full tuition	76	7.8	75	9.7	1	0.5
More than full tuition	0	0.0	0	0.0	0	0.0
Median grant amount			$7,500		$3,750	

Informational and Library Resources

Total amount spent on library materials	$1,458,497
Study seating capacity inside the library	664
# of full-time equivalent professional librarians	19
Hours per week library is open	96
# of open, wired connections available to students	425
# of networked computers available for use by students	127
Has wireless network?	Y
Require computer?	N

JD Attrition (from prior year)

	Academic	Other	Total	
	#	#	#	%
1st year	0	6	6	1.8
2nd year	1	11	12	3.9
3rd year	0	2	2	0.7
4th year	0	0	0	0.0

Employment (9 months after graduation)

	Total	Percentage
Employment status known	298	98.0
Employment status unknown	6	2.0
Employed	265	88.9
Pursuing graduate degrees	4	1.3
Unemployed (seeking, not seeking, or studying for the bar)	21	7.0
Type of Employment		
# employed in law firms	121	45.7
# employed in business and industry	39	14.7
# employed in government	37	14.0
# employed in public interest	18	6.8
# employed as judicial clerks	43	16.2
# employed in academia	7	2.6
Geographic Location		
# employed in state	184	69.4
# employed in foreign countries	2	0.8
# of states where employed		20

Bar Passage Rates

First-time takers	304	Reporting %	81.58
Average school %	89.11	Average state %	86.69
Average pass difference	2.42		

Jurisdiction	Takers	Passers	Pass %	State %	Diff %
Pennsylvania	248	221	89.11	86.69	2.42

Temple University—James E. Beasley School of Law

1719 North Broad Street
Philadelphia, PA 19122
Phone: 800.560.1428; Fax: 215.204.9319
E-mail: lawadmis@temple.edu; Website: www.law.temple.edu

■ Introduction

Temple Law School is recognized both nationally and internationally as a leader in legal education. We offer both day and evening programs, and students may enroll on either a full- or part-time basis. Our innovative student-centered curriculum integrates both critical thinking and practical legal skills and has been developed in response to new realities and new challenges, such as globalization, technology, and interdisciplinary studies. Students at Temple build lawyering skills both in the classroom and in the law firms, courts, public service agencies, and financial institutions of Philadelphia, a major legal, commercial, and cultural center. Our students, faculty, and alumni are shaping the law at every level and are making an impact in Philadelphia, the United States, and around the world.

Temple students are bright, dynamic, and diverse. They come from a variety of backgrounds and disciplines. Many have traveled and lived in other countries, and their real-life experiences vitalize classroom discussion. A recent entering class hailed from 129 colleges and universities, and from 32 states and foreign countries. Thirteen percent had earned advanced degrees, and over 75 percent had at least one year of work experience before entering law school.

The faculty is an extraordinary group who are recognized throughout the world as legal experts, scholars, and policy makers. Their breadth of experience in virtually every area of practice brings a rich and distinctive quality to classroom discussions. While their accomplishments are many, it is their commitment to teaching that many students note as their greatest achievement.

■ The Study of Law at Temple

Trial skills enhance every lawyer's abilities in areas that intersect all aspects of practice, and Temple students benefit from one of the most advanced **trial advocacy** programs in the nation. Experienced faculty, innovative teaching methods, and extensive clinical offerings set Temple's program above the rest. The trial advocacy curriculum includes the innovative Integrated Program, which combines the teaching of trial advocacy, evidence, and civil procedure in a year-long course. Temple's record in law school trial competitions is unmatched, having won an unparalleled 21 consecutive regional National Trial Competition championships, 5 national championships, and 14 invitational tournaments. Consistently recognized for its prizewinning trial advocacy programs, Temple has the distinction of being the only two-time winner of the American College of Trial Lawyers' Emil Gumpert Award for Excellence in Teaching Trial Advocacy.

Temple students have access to an extensive array of programs to prepare them to practice law in an increasingly global society. Temple's strength in **international law** includes opportunities for summer study in Rome, Italy; semester-abroad programs in Tokyo, Japan; Beijing, China; Cork, Ireland; Tel Aviv, Israel; and Utrecht, the Netherlands; a Master of Laws program for international students holding foreign law degrees; and active student organizations, such as an international law journal, the International Law Society, and the Jessup International Moot Court team. Temple's

strong reputation in international law has been enhanced by the JD/LLM in Transnational Law for American law students; an LLM program in Beijing, China, in which Chinese lawyers study American law; and the creation of the Institute for International Law and Public Policy. Students may also design individualized study-abroad options at law schools around the world.

Temple is a pioneer in **intellectual property and technology law**, preparing students to learn and succeed in the virtual world. Temple has expanded the boundaries of traditional intellectual property law by integrating bodies of law that focus on the rapid expansion of the Internet, electronic commerce, biotechnologies, and other newly emerging legal issues. With faculty members who are experts in the field, and through hands-on activities outside the classroom, such as writing for a journal specializing in technology law or participating on the Intellectual Property Law Moot Court Team, students learn how to meet the challenges of practicing law in a world without borders.

Temple offers superior training in **business and tax law**, including a creative program that combines the teaching of professional responsibility, substantive law courses, and business skills, such as interviewing, negotiating, and drafting. Prospective business lawyers can also pursue a JD/LLM in Taxation or, in conjunction with the Fox School of Business and Management, pursue a dual JD/MBA degree, or earn a certificate in business law.

Public service is a Temple tradition. The Office of Public Interest Programs is the focal point for public interest activities at the law school. Students provide legal services in the Philadelphia area through the extensive clinical program, the Temple Legal Aid Office, and various volunteer and community outreach programs. Public interest careers are supported by the Student Public Interest Network, which provides grants for summer internships; the Public Interest Scholars Program, which provides scholarships to entering students with a demonstrated commitment to public service; and the Barrack Public Interest Fellowships, a loan repayment assistance program for graduates in public interest jobs.

The curriculum is anchored by the first-year **legal research and writing program**. Instruction in law schools is founded on the notion of teaching each student to think like an attorney. Temple's legal research and writing program is a year-long course of study that teaches the basics of writing and speaking like a lawyer. Students learn basic legal research techniques and the fundamentals of legal writing. It is one of the most intensive and advanced programs of its kind in the country and is rated as one of the best in the nation.

■ Technology and Facilities

Located in the heart of a thriving, urban university, the law school complex consists of three recently renovated buildings designed to provide students with a state-of-the-art educational environment. "Smart" classrooms equipped with cutting-edge technology, including video, audio, and Internet access, allow faculty to use technology in all of the classrooms. The law school's "anytime, anywhere" computer access program includes a combination of wired and wireless network access, wired study carrels, and state-of-the-art

computer labs. The faculty and administration regularly communicate with students via e-mail, and the law school uses a sophisticated course management system that allows the faculty to post assignments, syllabi, announcements, and links to a variety of additional resources for each class.

■ Student Activities

Students are an integral part of policy making and governance at the law school. The Student Bar Association is the governing organization that oversees the more than 30 student groups that flourish at Temple, including the Black Law Students Association, the Latino Law Students Association, the Asian/Pacific Islander American Law Student Association, the Women's Law Caucus, and OUTLaw. Student publications include the *Temple Law Review;* the *Temple Journal of Science, Technology, and Environmental Law;* the *Temple International and Comparative Law Journal;* and the *Temple Political and Civil Rights Law Review.* Students who excel in advocacy may participate in the National Trial Team or the Moot Court Honor Society.

■ Career Planning

Temple students are poised and ready to succeed in every sector of the legal job market, having acquired unique practical training that other schools don't offer. As graduates, they carry a strong reputation for being able to hit the ground running, confident and prepared to practice law in the field of their choice. The Career Planning Office assists students with the development of strategies for securing employment and provides the resources necessary to

supplement each student's individualized job search. Through the school's online career planning manager, students can search job postings, participate in various recruiting programs, and apply for jobs. In addition, one-on-one career counseling is available, and workshops and programs are offered to assist students in sharpening their job-search skills, including résumé writing, networking, and interviewing. Temple alumni are working in all 50 states and around the world and in a variety of legal fields.

■ Admission and Financial Aid

Temple's highly competitive admission process is designed to look at the whole person. The faculty Admissions Committee carefully evaluates each application and is committed to admitting the very best from a pool of talented applicants. In keeping with Temple's commitment to diversity and its mission of offering opportunities to students who might otherwise be precluded from pursuing a high-quality legal education, the committee may consider an application under its discretionary admission process, the Sp.A.C.E. program. Under this program, the committee carefully selects applicants who have outstanding performance records and exceptional aptitudes for the study and practice of law that are not necessarily reflected by grades and LSAT scores alone.

The financial aid program supports the admission process with a combination of loans and both need- and merit-based scholarships, including the Beasley Scholars program, Conwell Law Scholarships, Law Faculty Scholarships, the Rubin-Presser Public Interest Scholars program, and First Year Scholar Awards.

Applicant Profile

Temple University—James E. Beasley School of Law
This grid includes only applicants who earned 120–180 LSAT scores under standard administrations.

LSAT Score	3.75 +		3.50–3.74		3.25–3.49		3.00–3.24		2.75–2.99		2.50–2.74		2.25–2.49		2.00–2.24		Below 2.00		No GPA		Total	
	Apps	Adm	Apps	Adm	Apps	Adm	Apps	Adm	Apps	Adm	Apps	Adm	Apps	Adm	Apps	Adm	Apps	Adm	Apps	Adm	Apps	Adm
170–180	24	24	22	22	19	19	15	15	6	5	3	3	0	0	0	0	0	0	0	0	89	88
165–169	88	85	98	95	81	81	63	59	25	22	4	3	5	3	0	0	0	0	1	1	365	349
160–164	249	215	336	266	359	258	205	133	64	40	34	20	9	3	2	1	0	0	10	7	1268	943
155–159	166	67	326	130	299	76	212	64	101	34	42	8	15	3	4	1	1	1	14	3	1180	387
150–154	91	6	161	17	220	28	185	21	95	13	44	3	26	1	5	0	0	0	15	3	842	92
145–149	33	1	88	1	100	2	102	3	67	0	42	0	20	0	7	0	3	0	9	0	471	7
140–144	11	0	39	0	41	0	53	0	44	0	32	0	14	0	4	0	1	0	8	0	247	0
Below 140	1	0	9	0	28	0	30	0	46	0	41	0	15	0	8	0	1	0	24	0	203	0
Total	663	398	1079	531	1147	464	865	295	448	114	242	37	104	10	30	2	6	1	81	14	4665	1866

Apps = Number of Applicants
Adm = Number Admitted
Reflects 99% of the total applicant pool; average LSAT data reported.

University of Tennessee College of Law

Admissions Office, 1505 W. Cumberland Avenue, Suite 161
Knoxville, TN 37996-1810
Phone: 865.974.4131; Fax: 865.974.1572
E-mail: lawadmit@utk.edu; Website: www.law.utk.edu

ABA
Approved
Since
1925

The Basics

Type of school	Public
Term	Semester
Application deadline	2/15
Application fee	$15
Financial aid deadline	3/1
Can first year start other than fall?	No
Student to faculty ratio	13.8 to 1
# of housing spaces available restricted to law students	
graduate housing for which law students are eligible	

Faculty and Administrators

	Total		Men		Women		Minorities	
	Spr	Fall	Spr	Fall	Spr	Fall	Spr	Fall
Full-time	30	26	19	19	11	7	3	2
Other full-time	0	1	0	1	0	0	0	0
Deans, librarians, & others who teach	16	16	6	6	10	10	1	1
Part-time	39	38	27	22	12	16	0	0
Total	85	81	52	48	33	33	4	3

Curriculum

		Full-Time	Part-Time
Typical first-year section size		55	0
Is there typically a "small section" of the first-year class, other than Legal Writing, taught by full-time faculty		No	No
If yes, typical size offered last year			
# of classroom course titles beyond first-year curriculum		130	
# of upper division courses, excluding seminars, with an enrollment:	Under 25	86	
	25–49	24	
	50–74	10	
	75–99	3	
	100+	0	
# of seminars		25	
# of seminar positions available		449	
# of seminar positions filled		365	0
# of positions available in simulation courses		583	
# of simulation positions filled		577	0
# of positions available in faculty supervised clinical courses		115	
# of faculty supervised clinical positions filled		111	0
# involved in field placements		37	0
# involved in law journals		295	0
# involved in moot court or trial competitions		156	0
# of credit hours required to graduate		89	

JD Enrollment and Ethnicity

	Men		Women		Full-Time		Part-Time		1st-Year		Total		JD Degs. Awd.
	#	%	#	%	#	%	#	%	#	%	#	%	
African Amer.	21	8.4	35	15.8	56	11.9	0	0.0	18	11.4	56	11.9	18
Amer. Indian	1	0.4	3	1.4	4	0.8	0	0.0	1	0.6	4	0.8	0
Asian Amer.	7	2.8	13	5.9	20	4.2	0	0.0	8	5.1	20	4.2	1
Mex. Amer.	2	0.8	4	1.8	6	1.3	0	0.0	1	0.6	6	1.3	0
Puerto Rican	1	0.4	1	0.5	2	0.4	0	0.0	1	0.6	2	0.4	0
Hispanic	4	1.6	4	1.8	8	1.7	0	0.0	1	0.6	8	1.7	1
Total Minority	36	14.5	60	27.0	96	20.4	0	0.0	30	19.0	96	20.4	20
For. Nation.	1	0.4	3	1.4	4	0.8	0	0.0	0	0.0	4	0.8	0
Caucasian	203	81.5	155	69.8	358	76.0	0	0.0	123	77.8	358	76.0	117
Unknown	9	3.6	4	1.8	13	2.8	0	0.0	4	2.5	13	2.8	3
Total	249	52.9	222	47.1	471	100.0	0	0.0	158	33.5	471		140

Transfers

Transfers in	2
Transfers out	5

Tuition and Fees

	Resident	Nonresident
Full-time	$13,118	$31,862
Part-time		
Tuition Guarantee Program		N

Living Expenses

Estimated living expenses for singles

Living on campus	Living off campus	Living at home
$17,392	$17,392	$12,746

University of Tennessee College of Law

ABA Approved Since 1925

GPA and LSAT Scores

	Total	Full-Time	Part-Time
# of apps	1,468	1,468	0
# of offers	398	398	0
# of matrics	158	158	0
75% GPA	3.77	3.77	0.00
Median GPA	3.55	3.55	0.00
25% GPA	3.28	3.28	0.00
75% LSAT	161	161	0
Median LSAT	160	160	0
25% LSAT	157	157	0

Grants and Scholarships (from prior year)

	Total		Full-Time		Part-Time	
	#	%	#	%	#	%
Total # of students	468		468		0	
Total # receiving grants	294	62.8	294	62.8	0	0.0
Less than 1/2 tuition	208	44.4	208	44.4	0	0.0
Half to full tuition	56	12.0	56	12.0	0	0.0
Full tuition	9	1.9	9	1.9	0	0.0
More than full tuition	21	4.5	21	4.5	0	0.0
Median grant amount			$4,000		$0	

Informational and Library Resources

Total amount spent on library materials	$950,890
Study seating capacity inside the library	437
# of full-time equivalent professional librarians	17
Hours per week library is open	96
# of open, wired connections available to students	77
# of networked computers available for use by students	77
Has wireless network?	Y
Require computer?	N

JD Attrition (from prior year)

	Academic	Other	Total	
	#	#	#	%
1st year	0	2	2	1.3
2nd year	0	7	7	4.2
3rd year	1	0	1	0.7
4th year	0	0	0	0.0

Employment (9 months after graduation)

	Total	Percentage
Employment status known	138	96.5
Employment status unknown	5	3.5
Employed	126	91.3
Pursuing graduate degrees	3	2.2
Unemployed (seeking, not seeking, or studying for the bar)	3	2.2
Type of Employment		
# employed in law firms	74	58.7
# employed in business and industry	8	6.3
# employed in government	20	15.9
# employed in public interest	5	4.0
# employed as judicial clerks	16	12.7
# employed in academia	3	2.4
Geographic Location		
# employed in state	86	68.3
# employed in foreign countries	1	0.8
# of states where employed	17	

Bar Passage Rates

First-time takers	137	Reporting %	84.67
Average school %	89.66	Average state %	88.10
Average pass difference	1.56		

Jurisdiction	Takers	Passers	Pass %	State %	Diff %
Tennessee	116	104	89.66	88.10	1.56

University of Tennessee College of Law

Admissions Office, 1505 W. Cumberland Avenue, Suite 161
Knoxville, TN 37996-1810
Phone: 865.974.4131; Fax: 865.974.1572
E-mail: lawadmit@utk.edu; Website: www.law.utk.edu

■ Introduction

For more than a century, the University of Tennessee College of Law has offered a strong combination of practical and theoretical legal training. Established in 1890, the College of Law is a charter member of the AALS and is ABA approved.

■ Enrollment/Student Body

The College of Law enrolls a small, selective, and diverse class each August. The 2009 entering class was composed of 158 students, of which 49 percent were women, 51 percent were men, and 19 percent were students of color. Entering students were graduates of 77 colleges and universities across the nation and around the world, and were residents of 23 states. Although many members of each entering class are pursuing a law degree directly from undergraduate school, a number of law students have advanced degrees and have had careers in fields as diverse as engineering, teaching, medicine, journalism, and business.

■ Faculty

The quality of our faculty is evidenced by their legal training at some of the finest law schools in the US, the significance of their scholarly writings, their activity in professional associations, and their involvement with public service. Current students at UT tell potential candidates for admission that they find the faculty to be excellent teachers, accessible, and caring.

■ College of Law, Library, and Physical Facilities

The law center at the University of Tennessee—a melding of the old with the new—is an exceptional setting for education in the twenty-first century. The 110,000-square-foot facility was completed in 1997 and is located on Cumberland Avenue, just across from the University Center, in the heart of the campus. The law center includes the Joel A. Katz Law Library, dedicated to a distinguished corporate and entertainment lawyer and alumnus.

■ Location

The College of Law is located on the main campus of the University of Tennessee. Knoxville is the largest city in eastern Tennessee and the third largest in the state. More than 28,000 students attend UTK. Knoxville has the natural advantage of being located in the foothills of the Great Smoky Mountains, making hiking, biking, golf, and fishing popular and accessible activities. Knoxville is close to major legal markets in the Southeast, including Atlanta, Nashville, Birmingham, and Charlotte.

■ Curriculum

First-year students begin law school with a week-long introductory period; a series of minicourses introduce students to the study of law. Second- and third-year students may choose from over 80 elective courses. Two dual-degree programs are offered—the JD/MBA and the JD/MPA (Master of Public Administration).

The College of Law offers two optional concentrations for students. The **James L. Clayton Center for Entrepreneurial Law** offers integrated upper-division courses that expose students to facets of law that affect business deals and provide hands-on experience in negotiating and documenting transactions with insight into the needs and concerns of the business community. A **Business Clinic** is offered for students seeking practical experience working with business clients.

The **Center for Advocacy and Dispute Resolution** allows interested students to focus their second- and third-year experience toward a career in advocacy (commonly known as litigation or trial practice) with an expanded emphasis on alternative forms of dispute resolution. UT was recognized by the American College of Trial Lawyers for the 1996 Emil Gumpert Award for Excellence in Teaching Trial Advocacy.

The **Charles H. Miller Legal Clinic** is the site for UT's clinical programs in advocacy and mediation. Established in 1947, this is one of the oldest continually operating clinical programs in the United States and is nationally recognized for excellence in teaching. UT also offers a Mediation Clinic, in which students work in teams to mediate real civil and misdemeanor cases in the lower courts. Other clinical programs focus on Business, Domestic Violence, and Environmental issues.

UT offers three **Externships**—judicial, prosecutorial, and public defender. The Prosecutorial Externship Program enables students to prosecute real cases on behalf of the state under the supervision of experienced district attorneys in Knox County.

■ Student Activities and Programs

Students can choose from a variety of student programs, activities, publications, and organizations. A complete listing is available on our website.

UT moot court teams have distinguished themselves in national competitions. Tennessee has won three Jerome Prince Evidence Moot Court national championships and was the first team in the history of that competition to win back-to-back titles in 2000 and 2001.

The *Tennessee Law Review* offers participants an excellent opportunity to conduct legal research and produce writings of a scholarly and practical nature. The *Transactions Business Journal* provides an opportunity for students to write about topical issues and legal developments of interest to the business bar. Students participating in the *Tennessee Journal of Law and Policy* analyze the latest developments in law and public decision making. The Student Bar Association and various other student organizations offer numerous programs, services, and special events. The national honor society, Order of the Coif, and two leading professional fraternities, Phi Delta Phi and Phi Alpha Delta, have local chapters here.

UT Pro Bono is a student-directed, community service organization. Working with local attorneys and legal aid organizations, UT Pro Bono serves as a resource by providing law students for research, educational, and investigatory assistance. UT Pro Bono currently operates programs working with the homeless and low income populations, immigrant assistance, animal law, and volunteer income tax assistance projects.

■ Admission

The College of Law strives to craft a class of diverse individuals, whose life experiences will enrich the law school community. Admission to the College of Law is competitive. The Admissions Committee places substantial emphasis on traditional indicators of performance—UGPA and LSAT score. The committee also considers factors such as improvement in undergraduate grades and graduate school performance, strength of undergraduate institution and major course of study, extracurricular activities, community service, and employment and professional experience. Also considered are circumstances that may have affected an applicant's grades or LSAT score; economic, social, or cultural background; and success in overcoming social or economic disadvantage. Applicants are required to submit two letters of recommendation and write a personal statement and an essay.

The College of Law recognizes its obligation to assure legal education to qualified applicants who are members of historically underrepresented groups in the legal profession and encourages applications from such students.

Successful completion of the CLEO Summer Institute may also be considered by the Admissions Committee.

■ Expenses, Financial Aid, and Housing

The College of Law offers a number of scholarships for entering students. Scholarships may be based on academic credentials (LSAT score and UGPA), records of leadership and community service, or other factors as established by the scholarship donor. Several scholarships may be awarded for which financial need, as established by the university after the FAFSA process is complete, is a primary criterion. Candidates for admission should complete the FAFSA process as soon as possible after the first of the year to be considered for scholarships in which financial need is a factor. Candidates for admission will automatically be considered for all scholarships for which they are eligible. Please check our website or our Applicant Guide for more information and application guidelines. Campus apartment housing is open to law students. Knoxville also offers ample private apartment housing at a reasonable cost within walking distance or a short drive from the law school.

■ Career Center

Recruiting and hiring practices in the legal job market suggest that making career decisions should be an ongoing, developmental process that begins in the first year of law school and continues through and after graduation. UT students acquire the skills and knowledge necessary to research, select, and seek the right career path for them and gain necessary information about the professional areas in which a law degree can be used.

The staff of the Bettye B. Lewis Career Center offers a comprehensive menu of services for employers who seek to recruit Tennessee students through formal and informal recruitment methods, off-campus job fairs, and recruiting consortia. First-year students are introduced to career development and job-search strategies through individual counseling and small group resource training sessions called the IL Career Integration Program. Students are coached in the development of individual job-search strategy plans throughout their law school careers.

These efforts have contributed to a consistently high employment rate for UT graduates that is well above the national average. Most graduates choose to stay in the southeastern United States, but graduates accept positions across the country. For detailed information, please see the College of Law website at *www.law.utk.edu*.

Applicant Profile

University of Tennessee College of Law
This grid includes only applicants who earned 120–180 LSAT scores under standard administrations.

LSAT Score	3.75 + Apps	3.75 + Adm	3.50–3.74 Apps	3.50–3.74 Adm	3.25–3.49 Apps	3.25–3.49 Adm	3.00–3.24 Apps	3.00–3.24 Adm	2.75–2.99 Apps	2.75–2.99 Adm	2.50–2.74 Apps	2.50–2.74 Adm	2.25–2.49 Apps	2.25–2.49 Adm	2.00–2.24 Apps	2.00–2.24 Adm	Below 2.00 Apps	Below 2.00 Adm	No GPA Apps	No GPA Adm	Total Apps	Total Adm
175–180	0	0	0	0	0	0	0	0	0	0	0	0	0	0	0	0	0	0	0	0	0	0
170–174	4	4	2	2	1	1	1	1	0	0	0	0	1	0	1	0	1	0	0	0	11	8
165–169	16	15	7	6	7	6	10	9	7	6	3	2	0	0	0	0	0	0	1	1	51	45
160–164	51	50	48	40	34	28	36	26	9	3	13	5	2	2	0	0	1	0	2	0	196	154
155–159	84	44	113	40	98	24	81	13	36	4	12	2	8	1	2	1	1	0	4	1	439	130
150–154	56	11	93	16	83	6	56	9	37	2	17	0	13	1	4	0	0	0	6	1	365	46
145–149	25	4	38	8	49	4	41	6	23	1	15	3	10	0	1	0	1	0	3	0	206	26
140–144	5	0	15	0	21	2	33	1	10	0	13	0	7	0	5	0	0	0	2	0	111	3
135–139	0	0	6	0	5	0	12	0	10	0	12	0	2	0	1	0	1	0	2	0	51	0
130–134	0	0	1	0	2	0	5	0	7	0	5	0	5	0	1	0	1	0	0	0	27	0
125–129	0	0	0	0	1	0	0	0	2	0	1	0	1	0	0	0	0	0	0	0	5	0
120–124	0	0	0	0	0	0	0	0	0	0	0	0	0	0	0	0	0	0	1	0	1	0
Total	241	128	323	112	301	71	275	65	141	16	91	12	49	4	15	1	6	0	21	3	1463	412

Apps = Number of Applicants   Adm = Number Admitted   Reflects 99% of the total applicant pool; average LSAT data reported.

The University of Texas School of Law

727 East Dean Keeton Street
Austin, TX 78705
Phone: 512.232.1200; Fax: 512.471.2765
E-mail: admissions@law.utexas.edu; Website: www.utexas.edu/law/

ABA
Approved
Since
1923

The Basics

Type of school	Public
Term	Semester
Application deadline	11/1 2/1
Application fee	$70
Financial aid deadline	3/31
Can first year start other than fall?	No
Student to faculty ratio	11.3 to 1
# of housing spaces available restricted to law students	
graduate housing for which law students are eligible	

Faculty and Administrators

	Total		Men		Women		Minorities	
	Spr	Fall	Spr	Fall	Spr	Fall	Spr	Fall
Full-time	84	88	52	54	32	34	10	11
Other full-time	24	19	14	10	10	9	2	1
Deans, librarians, & others who teach	6	6	2	2	4	4	1	1
Part-time	72	55	56	41	16	14	8	9
Total	186	168	124	107	62	61	21	22

JD Enrollment and Ethnicity

	Men		Women		Full-Time		Part-Time		1st-Year		Total		JD Degs. Awd.
	#	%	#	%	#	%	#	%	#	%	#	%	
African Amer.	29	4.4	42	8.0	71	6.0	0	0.0	23	6.0	71	6.0	25
Amer. Indian	4	0.6	3	0.6	7	0.6	0	0.0	3	0.8	7	0.6	1
Asian Amer.	39	6.0	41	7.8	80	6.8	0	0.0	21	5.5	80	6.8	26
Mex. Amer.	91	13.9	77	14.6	168	14.2	0	0.0	56	14.6	168	14.2	67
Puerto Rican	0	0.0	0	0.0	0	0.0	0	0.0	0	0.0	0	0.0	0
Hispanic	9	1.4	8	1.5	17	1.4	0	0.0	6	1.6	17	1.4	6
Total Minority	172	26.3	171	32.4	343	29.0	0	0.0	109	28.4	343	29.0	125
For. Nation.	4	0.6	3	0.6	7	0.6	0	0.0	3	0.8	7	0.6	0
Caucasian	383	58.5	296	56.2	679	57.4	0	0.0	221	57.6	679	57.4	269
Unknown	96	14.7	57	10.8	153	12.9	0	0.0	51	13.3	153	12.9	39
Total	655	55.4	527	44.6	1182	100.0	0	0.0	384	32.5	1182		433

Curriculum

	Full-Time	Part-Time
Typical first-year section size	99	0
Is there typically a "small section" of the first-year class, other than Legal Writing, taught by full-time faculty	Yes	No
If yes, typical size offered last year	25	
# of classroom course titles beyond first-year curriculum	158	
# of upper division courses, excluding seminars, with an enrollment: Under 25	198	
25–49	57	
50–74	12	
75–99	7	
100+	14	
# of seminars	71	
# of seminar positions available	934	
# of seminar positions filled	701	0
# of positions available in simulation courses	503	
# of simulation positions filled	421	0
# of positions available in faculty supervised clinical courses	319	
# of faculty supervised clinical positions filled	248	0
# involved in field placements	192	0
# involved in law journals	620	0
# involved in moot court or trial competitions	100	0
# of credit hours required to graduate	86	

Transfers

Transfers in	13
Transfers out	9

Tuition and Fees

	Resident	Nonresident
Full-time	$27,177	$42,814
Part-time		
Tuition Guarantee Program	N	

Living Expenses

Estimated living expenses for singles

Living on campus	Living off campus	Living at home
$14,698	$15,076	$7,246

The University of Texas School of Law

ABA
Approved
Since
1923

GPA and LSAT Scores

	Total	Full-Time	Part-Time
# of apps	5,275	5,275	0
# of offers	1,224	1,224	0
# of matrics	379	379	0
75% GPA	3.87	3.87	0.00
Median GPA	3.71	3.71	0.00
25% GPA	3.54	3.54	0.00
75% LSAT	168	168	0
Median LSAT	167	167	0
25% LSAT	164	164	0

Grants and Scholarships (from prior year)

	Total #	Total %	Full-Time #	Full-Time %	Part-Time #	Part-Time %
Total # of students	1,233		1,233		0	
Total # receiving grants	951	77.1	951	77.1	0	0.0
Less than 1/2 tuition	795	64.5	795	64.5	0	0.0
Half to full tuition	133	10.8	133	10.8	0	0.0
Full tuition	2	0.2	2	0.2	0	0.0
More than full tuition	21	1.7	21	1.7	0	0.0
Median grant amount			$8,320		$0	

Informational and Library Resources

Total amount spent on library materials	$1,410,726
Study seating capacity inside the library	1,039
# of full-time equivalent professional librarians	14
Hours per week library is open	99
# of open, wired connections available to students	310
# of networked computers available for use by students	164
Has wireless network?	Y
Require computer?	N

JD Attrition (from prior year)

	Academic #	Other #	Total #	Total %
1st year	0	4	4	1.0
2nd year	0	14	14	3.5
3rd year	0	1	1	0.2
4th year	0	0	0	0.0

Employment (9 months after graduation)

	Total	Percentage
Employment status known	441	100.0
Employment status unknown	0	0.0
Employed	417	94.6
Pursuing graduate degrees	2	0.5
Unemployed (seeking, not seeking, or studying for the bar)	8	1.8
Type of Employment		
# employed in law firms	262	62.8
# employed in business and industry	40	9.6
# employed in government	43	10.3
# employed in public interest	13	3.1
# employed as judicial clerks	54	12.9
# employed in academia	3	0.7
Geographic Location		
# employed in state	278	66.7
# employed in foreign countries	5	1.2
# of states where employed	24	

Bar Passage Rates

First-time takers	416	Reporting %	75.96
Average school %	88.92	Average state %	84.54
Average pass difference	4.38		

Jurisdiction	Takers	Passers	Pass %	State %	Diff %
Texas	316	281	88.92	84.54	4.38

The University of Texas School of Law

727 East Dean Keeton Street
Austin, TX 78705
Phone: 512.232.1200; Fax: 512.471.2765
E-mail: admissions@law.utexas.edu; Website: www.utexas.edu/law/

■ Introduction

The School of Law is located at The University of Texas at Austin. This location in the heart of the capital city provides ready access to the state legislature, the Supreme Court of Texas, the federal trial and appellate court, the offices of state and federal agencies, and the libraries and other main campus facilities. Recognized for its distinguished faculty and rich academic program, the law school has been a member of the AALS since 1907, was approved by the ABA in 1923, and is fully accredited.

Situated on the banks of the Colorado River, Austin is an eclectic city noted for its politics, scholars, rolling hills, film industry, and live music and restaurant scene. The University of Texas plays an important role in this metropolitan area of over one million people, and many entertainment and cultural activities cater to the student population.

■ Library and Physical Facilities

The Tarlton Law Library of the Joseph D. Jamail Center for Legal Research, with over one million volumes, is the eighth largest academic law library in the United States and the finest legal research center in the Southwest. It houses working collections from many other countries, with special strength in primary legal materials from Latin American and Western European nations, as well as a full depository for European Union documents. A suite of rooms in the law library houses rare books, manuscripts, law school archives, and special collections of materials ranging from a fifteenth century Roman law codex to the papers of former Supreme Court Justice Tom C. Clark. The Hyder Collection, a 4,000-item collection of law-related artifacts, makes the library an unusually welcoming place for study.

■ Faculty

The University of Texas School of Law has long had one of the most outstanding faculties in the nation, both in terms of scholarly distinction of the faculty members and their success in the classroom. More than one-third of the faculty is elected to the American Law Institute, one of the highest percentage memberships in the nation. Texas is also one of nine schools with four faculty elected to the American Academy of Arts and Sciences, the nation's most prestigious learned society. The law school has consistently hired the best and brightest young scholars, including eight former clerks for justices of the United States Supreme Court.

Texas enjoys a leadership position in many areas of legal study. The breadth and depth of offerings in several areas—constitutional law, environmental law, wills and estates, admiralty and maritime law, torts and product liability, labor law, jurisprudence, and philosophy—is matched by few schools in the country. With one of the largest faculties in the country, Texas is able to offer students coverage of all fields of law and exposure to truly diverse scholarly perspectives on legal questions.

■ Enrollment/Student Body

As a Texas public institution, the School of Law's nonresident enrollment is limited by the Texas Legislature to 35 percent of the population. We currently have over 126 undergraduate institutions and 28 states represented in our student body. Please refer to the statistical information for details regarding the strength of the student body and the competition for admission.

■ Special Programs

The school offers clinical education courses for credit in such fields as actual innocence, community development, capital punishment, children's rights, criminal defense, domestic violence, environmental law, housing, immigration, juvenile justice, mediation, mental health, national security and human rights, supreme court, and transnational workers' rights. Internships are available to qualified students with the Texas Supreme Court, the Texas Court of Criminal Appeals, and the Third Court of Appeals. A limited number of externships are available for credit in the public service area. The law school also has an extensive trial-advocacy program boasting several national championships. There are a number of joint-degree programs—JD/MPAff; JD/MBA; JD/Master of Arts in Latin American Studies; JD/Master of Science in Community and Regional Planning; JD/Master of Arts in Russian, East European, and Eurasian Studies; JD/MS in Social Work; JD/Master of Arts in Middle Eastern Studies; and JD/Master of Global Policy Studies—in addition to several combined programs with a PhD.

■ Curriculum

All first-year students are required to take a full courseload, averaging 15 hours per week, in contracts, property, torts, civil procedure, criminal law, constitutional law, brief writing and oral advocacy, and legal research and writing. After the first year, the only required courses are professional responsibility, advanced constitutional law, a writing and research seminar, and a skills class. A student may design his or her course of study from an array of course offerings in many fields of law. These offerings include interdisciplinary and advanced public and private law courses.

■ Student-Edited Journals

The School of Law offers many student-administered, cocurricular activities that enhance the law students' regular studies. Student-edited journals include the *American Journal of Criminal Law*; *Texas Environmental Law Journal*; *Texas Journal on Civil Liberties and Civil Rights*; *Texas Hispanic Journal of Law and Policy*; *Texas Intellectual Property Law Journal*; *Texas International Law Journal*; *Texas Journal of Oil, Gas, and Energy Law*; *Texas Journal of Women and the Law*; *Texas Law Review*; *Texas Review of Entertainment and Sports Law*; *Texas Review of Law and Politics*; and the *Review of Litigation*.

Admission

Admission to the JD program at UT Law is competitive. For the entering class of 2009, approximately 5,275 applicants competed for 400 available seats. As a general rule, there are no presumptive numbers. Every application completed and submitted is reviewed in its entirety. Each applicant must take the LSAT and have earned a baccalaureate degree from an accredited college or university with a minimum grade-point average of 2.2 as calculated by the Law School Admission Council (LSAC), or have completed the equivalent of six semesters and expect to graduate during the current academic year. Each candidate must complete all application forms and fulfill all mandatory attachments as described in the application.

Financial Aid

A limited number of scholarships are available for first-year students on the basis of merit and financial need. The prestigious Townes-Rice Scholarship is offered to eight outstanding law students with full tuition and fees plus a $5,000 stipend for all three years of law school. The law school also offers an Equal Justice Scholarship for an entering student interested in a career in public interest. Scholarships and research assistantships are available for second- and third-year students. The law school administers several short-term and long-term loan funds for students with financial need, and the university offers substantial federally funded loan programs.

Housing

Approximately 95 percent of all law students live off campus. The Division of Housing and Food Services (PO Box 7666, University Station, Austin, TX 78713; telephone: 512.471.3136) has information regarding on-campus living. Other sources of information are classified ads in the student newspaper, the Daily Texan; apartment management services; rental agencies; and current students.

Career Services

Each year, nearly 500 employers participate in career services programs and recruit our students for summer and full-time positions through on-campus interviews, recruit-by-mail opportunities, and off-campus job fairs. Over 50 percent of on-campus employers are from outside the state of Texas. For the past three years, more than 98 percent of graduates who were actively seeking employment have secured it within nine months of graduation.

Applicant Profile

The University of Texas School of Law
This grid includes only applicants who earned 120–180 LSAT scores under standard administrations.

LSAT Score	3.75 +		3.50–3.74		3.25–3.49		3.00–3.24		2.75–2.99		2.50–2.74		2.25–2.49		2.00–2.24		Below 2.00		No GPA		Total	
	Apps	Adm	Apps	Adm	Apps	Adm	Apps	Adm	Apps	Adm	Apps	Adm	Apps	Adm	Apps	Adm	Apps	Adm	Apps	Adm	Apps	Adm
175–180	48	47	15	13	11	3	13	1	4	0	3	0	1	0	0	0	0	0	0	0	95	64
170–174	136	135	103	94	82	18	31	3	10	0	6	0	0	0	0	0	0	0	3	2	371	252
165–169	418	348	382	190	219	41	94	5	36	0	13	0	11	0	0	0	0	0	15	9	1188	593
160–164	465	122	455	73	312	20	158	8	49	0	23	1	3	0	4	0	1	0	38	0	1508	224
155–159	217	16	263	22	217	20	127	2	63	1	26	0	12	0	2	0	2	0	28	0	957	61
150–154	96	2	159	5	140	3	104	0	54	1	30	0	9	0	8	0	0	0	10	0	610	11
145–149	31	1	50	0	69	0	55	0	36	0	20	0	7	0	6	0	2	0	10	0	286	1
140–144	11	0	25	0	25	0	35	0	14	0	12	0	9	0	3	0	0	0	5	0	139	0
135–139	0	0	5	0	11	0	8	0	8	0	13	0	1	0	4	0	0	0	2	0	52	0
130–134	0	0	0	0	0	0	3	0	4	0	4	0	1	0	1	0	0	0	1	0	14	0
125–129	0	0	0	0	0	0	2	0	1	0	0	0	0	0	0	0	0	0	1	0	4	0
120–124	0	0	0	0	0	0	0	0	0	0	0	0	0	0	1	0	0	0	0	0	1	0
Total	1422	671	1457	397	1086	105	630	19	279	2	150	1	54	0	29	0	5	0	113	11	5225	1206

Apps = Number of Applicants
Adm = Number Admitted
Reflects 99% of the total applicant pool; average LSAT data reported.

Texas Southern University—Thurgood Marshall School of Law

Office of Admissions, 3100 Cleburne
Houston, TX 77004
Phone: 713.313.7114 or 713.313.7115; Fax: 713.313.7297
E-mail: erene@tmslaw.tsu.edu; Website: www.tsulaw.edu

*ABA
Approved
Since
1949*

The Basics

Type of school	Public
Term	Semester
Application deadline	4/1
Application fee	$55
Financial aid deadline	4/1
Can first year start other than fall?	No
Student to faculty ratio	13.0 to 1
# of housing spaces available restricted to law students	
graduate housing for which law students are eligible	

Faculty and Administrators

	Total		Men		Women		Minorities	
	Spr	Fall	Spr	Fall	Spr	Fall	Spr	Fall
Full-time	33	34	13	13	20	21	25	27
Other full-time	1	1	1	1	0	0	0	0
Deans, librarians, & others who teach	16	15	10	9	6	6	15	14
Part-time	23	12	17	6	6	6	18	9
Total	73	62	41	29	32	33	58	50

Curriculum

	Full-Time	Part-Time
Typical first-year section size	60	0
Is there typically a "small section" of the first-year class, other than Legal Writing, taught by full-time faculty	No	No
If yes, typical size offered last year		
# of classroom course titles beyond first-year curriculum		74
# of upper division courses, excluding seminars, with an enrollment: Under 25		93
25–49		33
50–74		14
75–99		2
100+		1
# of seminars		23
# of seminar positions available		688
# of seminar positions filled	383	0
# of positions available in simulation courses		240
# of simulation positions filled	145	0
# of positions available in faculty supervised clinical courses		128
# of faculty supervised clinical positions filled	128	0
# involved in field placements	59	0
# involved in law journals	43	0
# involved in moot court or trial competitions	30	0
# of credit hours required to graduate		90

JD Enrollment and Ethnicity

	Men		Women		Full-Time		Part-Time		1st-Year		Total		JD Degs. Awd.
	#	%	#	%	#	%	#	%	#	%	#	%	
African Amer.	103	39.9	169	59.5	272	50.2	0	0.0	109	47.0	272	50.2	91
Amer. Indian	1	0.4	1	0.4	2	0.4	0	0.0	0	0.0	2	0.4	0
Asian Amer.	21	8.1	14	4.9	35	6.5	0	0.0	16	6.9	35	6.5	12
Mex. Amer.	70	27.1	59	20.8	129	23.8	0	0.0	64	27.6	129	23.8	49
Puerto Rican	0	0.0	0	0.0	0	0.0	0	0.0	0	0.0	0	0.0	0
Hispanic	0	0.0	0	0.0	0	0.0	0	0.0	0	0.0	0	0.0	0
Total Minority	195	75.6	243	85.6	438	80.8	0	0.0	189	81.5	438	80.8	152
For. Nation.	5	1.9	8	2.8	13	2.4	0	0.0	4	1.7	13	2.4	6
Caucasian	57	22.1	33	11.6	90	16.6	0	0.0	38	16.4	90	16.6	34
Unknown	1	0.4	0	0.0	1	0.2	0	0.0	1	0.4	1	0.2	0
Total	258	47.6	284	52.4	542	100.0	0	0.0	232	42.8	542		192

Transfers

Transfers in	3
Transfers out	7

Tuition and Fees

	Resident	Nonresident
Full-time	$13,235	$16,985
Part-time		
Tuition Guarantee Program		N

Living Expenses

Estimated living expenses for singles

Living on campus	Living off campus	Living at home
$18,692	$18,692	$18,692

Texas Southern University—Thurgood Marshall School of Law

ABA
Approved
Since
1949

GPA and LSAT Scores

	Total	Full-Time	Part-Time
# of apps	2,003	2,003	0
# of offers	684	684	0
# of matrics	219	219	0
75% GPA	3.21	3.21	0.00
Median GPA	2.98	2.98	0.00
25% GPA	2.66	2.66	0.00
75% LSAT	148	148	0
Median LSAT	146	146	0
25% LSAT	144	144	0

Grants and Scholarships (from prior year)

	Total #	Total %	Full-Time #	Full-Time %	Part-Time #	Part-Time %
Total # of students	550		550		0	
Total # receiving grants	235	42.7	235	42.7	0	0.0
Less than 1/2 tuition	185	33.6	185	33.6	0	0.0
Half to full tuition	15	2.7	15	2.7	0	0.0
Full tuition	35	6.4	35	6.4	0	0.0
More than full tuition	0	0.0	0	0.0	0	0.0
Median grant amount			$3,000		$0	

Informational and Library Resources

Total amount spent on library materials	$1,116,330
Study seating capacity inside the library	378
# of full-time equivalent professional librarians	9
Hours per week library is open	108
# of open, wired connections available to students	955
# of networked computers available for use by students	80
Has wireless network?	Y
Require computer?	N

JD Attrition (from prior year)

	Academic #	Other #	Total #	Total %
1st year	26	6	32	15.8
2nd year	1	0	1	0.6
3rd year	0	1	1	0.5
4th year	0	0	0	0.0

Employment (9 months after graduation)

	Total	Percentage
Employment status known	190	95.0
Employment status unknown	10	5.0
Employed	135	71.1
Pursuing graduate degrees	5	2.6
Unemployed (seeking, not seeking, or studying for the bar)	21	11.1
Type of Employment		
# employed in law firms	77	57.0
# employed in business and industry	32	23.7
# employed in government	13	9.6
# employed in public interest	1	0.7
# employed as judicial clerks	2	1.5
# employed in academia	4	3.0
Geographic Location		
# employed in state	87	64.4
# employed in foreign countries	1	0.7
# of states where employed	15	

Bar Passage Rates

First-time takers	192	Reporting %	86.46
Average school %	59.64	Average state %	84.54
Average pass difference	−24.90		

Jurisdiction	Takers	Passers	Pass %	State %	Diff %
Texas	166	99	59.64	84.54	−24.90

Texas Southern University—Thurgood Marshall School of Law

Office of Admissions, 3100 Cleburne
Houston, TX 77004
Phone: 713.313.7114 or 713.313.7115; Fax: 713.313.7297
E-mail: erene@tmslaw.tsu.edu; Website: www.tsulaw.edu

■ Enrollment/Student Body

A majority of the students are from Texas, but all parts of the country are represented. Approximately 49 percent of the students are black, 23 percent Chicano, 17 percent Caucasian, and 6 percent Asian and Native American. The median age range is about 26 to 36 years.

■ Introduction

The Thurgood Marshall School of Law, a state institution founded in 1947, seeks to provide a legal education and an opportunity to excel to students from a wide range of backgrounds, including those who otherwise would not have an opportunity for legal training. The law school is accredited by the ABA. The student body is truly multiethnic and multicultural. The law school is housed in a trilevel structure that is located just outside of downtown Houston. Near-campus housing is available in the form of modern apartments for single and married students. The school makes extensive use of legal facilities in Houston through its clinical programs.

■ Library and Physical Facilities

Students receive individual or group orientation and intensive training in the use of the library. The law school has undergone approximately $16 million in renovations, expanding the available space from 103,000 to 108,000 square feet.

■ Curriculum

Upon entry to the School of Law, all students in the first-year class are required to attend a week-long orientation program. Attention is given to examinations, briefing cases, outlining, and an overview of law school life and expectations.

The law school offers a three-year, full-time JD program. The minimum courseload is 12 hours. Required courses for the first year are Lawyering Process I and II, Civil Procedure, Property, Contracts, Torts, and Criminal Law. Second-year students must take Constitutional Law, Evidence, Criminal Procedure, Trial Simulation, Business Associations, Commercial Law, Professional Responsibility, and Wills and Trusts. Second- or third-year students are required to take Federal Jurisdiction and Procedure, a seminar/independent research project, and Basic Federal Taxation. Third-year students are required to take Consumer Rights and Texas Practice. The remaining hours required to complete the degree may be selected from a number of areas of interest.

The law school operates a full-time, in-house clinic in which students work under the supervision of faculty and adjunct faculty members. Internships are available with the Harris County District Attorney's Office, the Federal Magistrates, Gulf Coast Legal Foundation, the US Bankruptcy Court, the Harris County Attorney's Office, the Internal Revenue Service, and the US District Court. The school operates a number of clinics, including advanced skills, basic skills, civil and criminal externships, environmental justice, family law, and housing law. A judicial externship with state and federal judges is available to academically outstanding third-year students.

■ Admission

The admission decision is based primarily on the applicant's motivation and intellectual capacity as demonstrated by his or her undergraduate records, and on his or her aptitude for the study of law as measured by the LSAT. Leadership ability, prior community service, work experience, the student's background, extracurricular activities, and graduate study in another discipline are all considered.

No particular undergraduate major is preferred, but the school looks for applicants with broad backgrounds in the social sciences, natural sciences, humanities, and business sciences. Newly admitted students must send two seat deposits ($150 upon acceptance and $100 in June), which are refundable upon matriculation. The law school's student body represents one of the most culturally and ethnically diverse student bodies in the country. Transfer applications are accepted; students must submit a transcript and letter from the dean of his/her former law school stating that they are in good standing. All newly admitted students must submit an official transcript from the baccalaureate degree-granting institution as well as all law schools attended. No application will be evaluated by the admission committee until the LSAC Law School Report has been received.

In order to ensure complete review, applications must be received by the Office of Admissions no later than April 1, although earlier submission is encouraged. Entering students are admitted only in August (fall semester). Students are notified of acceptance after the admission committee has reviewed the complete file. Admission decisions are made on a rolling basis.

■ Student Activities

Numerous law school organizations are active on campus. A student board edits the *Thurgood Marshall Law Review*. Moot court competitions are held in trial and appellate work, labor law, and client counseling.

■ Expenses and Financial Aid

About 90 percent of the students receive some form of aid. The law school administers its own scholarship program, which is competitive. Scholarships are awarded on the basis of both need and merit, and may range up to full tuition. The university also offers additional scholarship aid, and the law school and the university offer loan assistance. Between 10 and 15 percent of the students hold assistantships. The aid application deadline is April 1.

The scholarship program makes several awards (approximately 60) each year. The awards have enabled out-of-state residents to qualify for resident tuition rates. In addition, a number of law students each year qualify for the federal work-study and loan programs. Additional limited scholarship aid is available to students after they have completed a year of law study. An applicant in need of other financial assistance should make arrangements for financial aid through the law school financial aid counselor by either calling 713.313.7243 or e-mailing *kepercival@tmslaw.tsu.edu*.

Texas Southern University—Thurgood Marshall School of Law

■ Career Development

The law school employs a full-time career development officer. Graduates are placed primarily with law firms, federal and state agencies, legal services, judges, and businesses. The Career Development Office also conducts a major national effort to encourage legal employers in every major city in the United States to recruit Texas Southern University—Thurgood Marshall School of Law graduates.

Applicant Profile

Texas Southern University—Thurgood Marshall School of Law
This grid includes only applicants who earned 120–180 LSAT scores under standard administrations.

LSAT Score	3.75 +		3.50–3.74		3.25–3.49		3.00–3.24		2.75–2.99		2.50–2.74		2.25–2.49		2.00–2.24		Below 2.00		No GPA		Total	
	Apps	Adm	Apps	Adm	Apps	Adm	Apps	Adm	Apps	Adm	Apps	Adm	Apps	Adm	Apps	Adm	Apps	Adm	Apps	Adm	Apps	Adm
175–180	0	0	0	0	0	0	0	0	0	0	0	0	0	0	0	0	0	0	0	0	0	0
170–174	0	0	0	0	0	0	1	1	0	0	0	0	0	0	0	0	0	0	0	0	1	1
165–169	0	0	0	0	0	0	0	0	0	0	0	0	0	0	0	0	0	0	0	0	0	0
160–164	0	0	0	0	2	2	0	0	4	4	0	0	1	1	3	1	0	0	0	0	10	8
155–159	3	2	4	3	2	2	9	8	8	7	10	6	7	5	3	2	1	0	1	0	48	35
150–154	14	10	24	22	24	19	36	25	35	24	36	24	17	4	13	4	2	2	2	0	203	134
145–149	15	12	40	30	84	58	113	72	103	47	75	29	36	8	25	6	5	2	13	3	509	267
140–144	15	8	61	24	96	31	119	30	128	26	94	15	74	5	26	2	8	0	24	0	645	141
135–139	7	1	15	0	52	1	67	2	68	2	65	3	47	1	26	1	6	1	10	0	363	12
130–134	2	0	8	0	12	0	26	0	19	0	25	0	21	0	8	1	2	0	11	0	134	1
125–129	0	0	0	0	2	0	4	0	4	0	5	0	3	0	5	0	2	0	3	0	28	0
120–124	0	0	0	0	1	0	0	0	0	0	0	0	2	0	0	0	0	0	1	0	4	0
Total	56	33	152	79	275	113	375	138	369	110	310	77	208	24	109	17	26	5	65	3	1945	599

Apps = Number of Applicants
Adm = Number Admitted
Reflects 98% of the total applicant pool; average LSAT data reported.

Texas Tech University School of Law

1802 Hartford Avenue
Lubbock, TX 79409
Phone: 806.742.3990; Fax: 806.742.4617
E-mail: admissions.law@ttu.edu; Website: www.law.ttu.edu

*ABA
Approved
Since
1969*

The Basics

Type of school	Public
Term	Semester
Application deadline	11/1 2/1 3/15
Application fee	
Financial aid deadline	3/15
Can first year start other than fall?	No
Student to faculty ratio	15.3 to 1
# of housing spaces available restricted to law students	
graduate housing for which law students are eligible	

Faculty and Administrators

	Total		Men		Women		Minorities	
	Spr	Fall	Spr	Fall	Spr	Fall	Spr	Fall
Full-time	36	34	22	21	14	13	8	5
Other full-time	0	0	0	0	0	0	0	0
Deans, librarians, & others who teach	6	7	4	5	2	2	2	2
Part-time	13	16	12	12	1	4	3	2
Total	55	57	38	38	17	19	13	9

Curriculum

	Full-Time	Part-Time
Typical first-year section size	51	0
Is there typically a "small section" of the first-year class, other than Legal Writing, taught by full-time faculty	No	No
If yes, typical size offered last year		
# of classroom course titles beyond first-year curriculum	95	

# of upper division courses, excluding seminars, with an enrollment:		
Under 25	67	
25–49	17	
50–74	16	
75–99	5	
100+	6	

# of seminars	30	
# of seminar positions available	480	
# of seminar positions filled	388	0
# of positions available in simulation courses	222	
# of simulation positions filled	185	0
# of positions available in faculty supervised clinical courses	145	
# of faculty supervised clinical positions filled	140	0
# involved in field placements	122	0
# involved in law journals	138	0
# involved in moot court or trial competitions	63	0
# of credit hours required to graduate	90	

JD Enrollment and Ethnicity

	Men		Women		Full-Time		Part-Time		1st-Year		Total		JD Degs. Awd.
	#	%	#	%	#	%	#	%	#	%	#	%	
African Amer.	10	2.7	14	5.3	24	3.8	0	0.0	10	4.4	24	3.8	9
Amer. Indian	2	0.5	4	1.5	6	0.9	0	0.0	3	1.3	6	0.9	2
Asian Amer.	17	4.6	11	4.1	28	4.4	0	0.0	11	4.8	28	4.4	6
Mex. Amer.	56	15.1	42	15.8	98	15.4	0	0.0	35	15.4	98	15.4	24
Puerto Rican	1	0.3	1	0.4	2	0.3	0	0.0	0	0.0	2	0.3	1
Hispanic	0	0.0	1	0.4	1	0.2	0	0.0	1	0.4	1	0.2	0
Total Minority	86	23.2	73	27.4	159	25.0	0	0.0	60	26.4	159	25.0	42
For. Nation.	0	0.0	0	0.0	0	0.0	0	0.0	0	0.0	0	0.0	0
Caucasian	285	76.8	193	72.6	478	75.0	0	0.0	168	74.0	478	75.0	164
Unknown	0	0.0	0	0.0	0	0.0	0	0.0	0	0.0	0	0.0	0
Total	371	58.2	266	41.8	637	100.0	0	0.0	228	35.6	637		206

Transfers

Transfers in	10
Transfers out	1

Tuition and Fees

	Resident	Nonresident
Full-time	$15,194	$22,110
Part-time		
Tuition Guarantee Program		N

Living Expenses

Estimated living expenses for singles

Living on campus	Living off campus	Living at home
$13,476	$13,476	N/A

Texas Tech University School of Law

ABA
Approved
Since
1969

GPA and LSAT Scores

	Total	Full-Time	Part-Time
# of apps	1,768	1,768	0
# of offers	652	652	0
# of matrics	213	213	0
75% GPA	3.62	3.75	0.00
Median GPA	3.43	3.57	0.00
25% GPA	3.13	3.34	0.00
75% LSAT	158	157	0
Median LSAT	156	154	0
25% LSAT	153	151	0

Grants and Scholarships (from prior year)

	Total		Full-Time		Part-Time	
	#	%	#	%	#	%
Total # of students	647		647		0	
Total # receiving grants	342	52.9	342	52.9	0	0.0
Less than 1/2 tuition	176	27.2	176	27.2	0	0.0
Half to full tuition	38	5.9	38	5.9	0	0.0
Full tuition	0	0.0	0	0.0	0	0.0
More than full tuition	128	19.8	128	19.8	0	0.0
Median grant amount			$7,000		$0	

Informational and Library Resources

Total amount spent on library materials	$1,110,292
Study seating capacity inside the library	578
# of full-time equivalent professional librarians	8
Hours per week library is open	168
# of open, wired connections available to students	1,118
# of networked computers available for use by students	110
Has wireless network?	Y
Require computer?	N

JD Attrition (from prior year)

	Academic	Other	Total	
	#	#	#	%
1st year	1	6	7	3.3
2nd year	2	0	2	0.9
3rd year	0	0	0	0.0
4th year	0	0	0	0.0

Employment (9 months after graduation)

	Total	Percentage
Employment status known	220	91.7
Employment status unknown	20	8.3
Employed	199	90.5
Pursuing graduate degrees	5	2.3
Unemployed (seeking, not seeking, or studying for the bar)	14	6.4

Type of Employment

	Total	Percentage
# employed in law firms	108	54.3
# employed in business and industry	34	17.1
# employed in government	41	20.6
# employed in public interest	5	2.5
# employed as judicial clerks	9	4.5
# employed in academia	1	0.5

Geographic Location

	Total	Percentage
# employed in state	164	82.4
# employed in foreign countries	2	1.0
# of states where employed	5	

Bar Passage Rates

First-time takers	209	Reporting %	100.00
Average school %	86.60	Average state %	84.54
Average pass difference	2.06		

Jurisdiction	Takers	Passers	Pass %	State %	Diff %
Texas	209	181	86.60	84.54	2.06

Texas Tech University School of Law

1802 Hartford Avenue
Lubbock, TX 79409
Phone: 806.742.3990; Fax: 806.742.4617
E-mail: admissions.law@ttu.edu; Website: www.law.ttu.edu

■ Introduction

The school, which accepted its first class in 1967, is located on the main campus of Texas Tech University in Lubbock. It is fully accredited with the Supreme Court of Texas and the ABA and is a member of the AALS. Its graduates are eligible to take the bar examination in any state in the nation. In 1974, a chapter of the Order of the Coif was established, a distinction accorded to only one third of American law schools. The faculty embraces an open-door policy, enabling students to engage in continuing dialogue beyond formal class hours.

■ Library and Physical Facilities

The school is designed to meet the needs of a contemporary legal education. The law library supports the research and academic needs of the students and faculty, as evinced by superb computer resources and wireless Internet access, complementing a substantial collection of printed materials. All students have 24/7 access to the library and assigned library carrels that serve as small office-like work spaces. All classrooms are equipped with multimedia technology. The 34,000-square-foot Lanier Professional Development Center houses the Office of Academic Success Programs, the Career Services Center, a state-of-the-art courtroom designed to support technology-driven advocacy training, and ample space for student meetings.

■ Programs of Study

The school offers several dual-degree programs: the JD/MBA; the JD/MPA; the JD/MD; the JD/MS in Agriculture and Applied Economics; the JD/MS in Accounting (Taxation); the JD/Master of Environmental Toxicology; the JD/Master of Biotechnology; the JD/MS in Crop Science; JD/MS in Soil Science; JD/MS in Horticultural and Turfgrass Sciences; JD/MS in Entomology; JD/MS in Engineering; and the JD/MS in Personal Financial Planning, which qualifies students to sit for the Certified Financial Planning exam. The school also offers certificate programs in Business Law, Health Law, and Law and Science with a specialization in IP Law, Environmental Law, Biodefense Law, Energy Law, and Water Law.

■ Curriculum

The program of study equips students to practice law as advocates, counselors, judges, or law teachers, and the school recognizes that legal education is also a stepping-stone to careers in government, politics, or business. The required curriculum provides a broad-based legal education. Elective courses afford students the opportunity to create an area of concentration, ranging from business law to emerging areas such as health law, natural resources law, and national security law. The School of Law offers an Academic Success Program to assist students in developing the skills to succeed in the study and practice of law.

■ Legal Publication and Research Opportunities

Texas Tech has several publications that allow students to hone their research and writing skills. The *Texas Tech Law Review* publishes articles written by students and leading jurists, practitioners, and academics.

The State Bar of Texas selected the school to publish the *Texas Tech Administrative Law Journal*. The *Estate Planning and Community Property Law Journal* is the only legal journal of its kind committed to community property law, and only the second in the nation devoted to estate planning. The *Texas Bank Lawyer* publishes articles about banking and commercial law.

The school is home to the Center for Water Law and Policy, the Center for Military Law and Policy, and the Center for Biodefense Law and Policy, which all provide research and scholarship opportunities.

Students take the lead in writing and producing the school's alumni magazine, the *Texas Tech Lawyer*.

■ Admission

The school uses a rolling admission policy. The Admissions Committee admits applicants from a wide range of backgrounds and experiences. While an applicant's LSAT and GPA figure significantly in the admission process, the committee also considers other factors, including extracurricular activities, public interest service, previous employment, and leadership qualities. A bachelor's degree from an accredited college or university is required.

The school offers a binding Early Decision Program with an application deadline of November 1. The deadline for regular decision applicants is February 1. Some students may be admitted through a Summer Entry Program.

Anyone filing an application after February 1 will be at a disadvantage. Those applicants accepted in the Early Decision Program will be required to pay a nonrefundable deposit of $750, and those accepted in the regular admission process must pay a deposit of $300 to hold their places.

■ Clinical Program

The school boasts a recently remodeled clinic facility that includes a state-of-the-art multimedia teleconference room. Students have the opportunity to represent clients and participate in real cases through several clinical courses taught by full-time, tenure-track faculty. Students enrolled in the Civil Practice Clinic represent clients in a wide range of civil matters. The Criminal Justice Clinic provides a unique opportunity for third-year law students to represent actual clients in state and federal criminal courts. In the Tax Clinic, students represent taxpayers in disputes with the IRS. The Alternative Dispute Resolution Clinic and Health Care and Bioethics Mediation Clinic focus on resolving legal issues without litigation. The Innocence Project Clinic considers claims by prisoners of actual innocence. The school also offers a wide array of externship opportunities.

■ Advocacy Program

Students gain advocacy experience in simulated practice settings through intraschool and interschool competitions. The school boasts multiple championships and top finishes in the country's most prestigious advocacy competitions, including two consecutive state championships at the Texas State Moot Court Competition, dual regional championships and the national best brief at the 2009 ABA National Appellate Advocacy Competition, two straight national championships at the National Latino/a Law Student Association Moot Court Competition, and a national championship at the 2008 ABA Arbitration Competition. In the spring of 2008, the school opened a state-of-the-art technological courtroom and professional development center for advocacy training.

■ Student Activities

The Student Bar Association is the focal point for many student activities. The school has approximately 50 student organizations and three legal fraternities.

■ Study-Abroad Programs

Texas Tech is a consortium partner in the Summer Law Institute, a cooperative teaching program with the historic University of Guanajuato, Mexico. The Summer Law Institute offers an introduction to Mexican law, international law, and legal subjects of interest to both US and Mexican lawyers, such as NAFTA. See www.law.ttu.edu for additional information.

French-fluent students are offered legal study for credit through a cooperative program with the University of Lyon in France. The law school has a second cooperative exchange program with La Trobe University in Melbourne, Australia.

■ Financial Aid and Scholarships

The School of Law offers numerous scholarships to entering students. In-state Tuition Scholarships are awarded to many nonresident applicants. Additional scholarships are available for second- and third-year students.

Grants and educational loan funds are available for students who qualify. Please visit www.law.ttu.edu/prospective/financialaid/ for more information.

■ Career Services

The School of Law is a member of NALP and participates in on- and off-campus interviewing programs. Ninety-one percent of 2008 graduates were employed within nine months of graduation.

Please visit www.law.ttu.edu or call 806.742.3990, extension 277, for additional information.

■ Housing

Information about campus housing may be obtained from the Housing Office at www.law.ttu.edu/studentlife/housing.

Applicant Profile

Texas Tech University School of Law
This grid includes only applicants who earned 120–180 LSAT scores under standard administrations.

LSAT Score	3.75 +		3.50–3.74		3.25–3.49		3.00–3.24		2.75–2.99		2.50–2.74		2.25–2.49		2.00–2.24		Below 2.00		No GPA		Total	
	Apps	Adm	Apps	Adm	Apps	Adm	Apps	Adm	Apps	Adm	Apps	Adm	Apps	Adm	Apps	Adm	Apps	Adm	Apps	Adm	Apps	Adm
175–180	0	0	0	0	0	0	0	0	0	0	0	0	0	0	0	0	0	0	0	0	0	0
170–174	0	0	0	0	0	0	0	0	1	0	0	0	0	0	0	0	0	0	0	0	1	0
165–169	6	6	6	6	7	6	8	8	1	1	1	0	2	0	0	0	0	0	0	0	31	27
160–164	30	29	28	26	33	30	29	25	14	11	5	3	1	0	1	0	0	0	0	0	141	124
155–159	55	52	80	73	109	91	60	46	40	20	23	6	13	4	6	1	0	0	1	1	387	294
150–154	84	42	130	53	152	28	122	25	73	5	35	0	20	0	4	0	1	0	6	3	627	156
145–149	43	5	75	15	88	7	79	8	54	2	30	1	10	0	8	0	1	0	2	0	390	38
140–144	15	0	29	1	35	3	46	4	27	0	24	0	14	0	6	0	0	0	4	0	200	8
135–139	0	0	4	0	9	0	12	0	9	0	9	0	6	0	1	0	0	0	1	0	51	0
130–134	0	0	0	0	3	0	3	0	2	0	2	0	0	0	1	0	0	0	3	0	14	0
125–129	0	0	0	0	0	0	1	0	1	0	1	0	0	0	0	0	0	0	0	0	3	0
120–124	0	0	0	0	0	0	0	0	1	0	0	0	0	0	0	0	0	0	0	0	1	0
Total	233	134	352	174	436	165	360	116	223	39	130	10	66	4	27	1	2	0	17	4	1846	647

Apps = Number of Applicants
Adm = Number Admitted
Reflects 99% of the total applicant pool; average LSAT data reported.

Texas Wesleyan University School of Law

1515 Commerce Street, Office of Admissions
Fort Worth, TX 76102
Phone: 817.212.4040, 800.733.9529; Fax: 817.212.4141
E-mail: lawadmissions@law.txwes.edu; Website: www.law.txwes.edu

ABA Approved Since 1994

Section of Legal Education and Admissions to the Bar

The Basics

Type of school	Private
Term	Semester
Application deadline	3/31
Application fee	$55
Financial aid deadline	3/15
Can first year start other than fall?	No
Student to faculty ratio	24.3 to 1
# of housing spaces available restricted to law students	
graduate housing for which law students are eligible	

Faculty and Administrators

	Total		Men		Women		Minorities	
	Spr	Fall	Spr	Fall	Spr	Fall	Spr	Fall
Full-time	25	23	14	14	11	9	4	3
Other full-time	6	6	6	6	0	0	0	0
Deans, librarians, & others who teach	8	8	5	5	3	3	3	3
Part-time	15	15	10	10	5	5	1	1
Total	54	52	35	35	19	17	8	7

Curriculum

	Full-Time	Part-Time
Typical first-year section size	95	65
Is there typically a "small section" of the first-year class, other than Legal Writing, taught by full-time faculty	No	No
If yes, typical size offered last year		
# of classroom course titles beyond first-year curriculum		94
# of upper division courses, excluding seminars, with an enrollment: Under 25		90
25–49		27
50–74		16
75–99		12
100+		3
# of seminars		14
# of seminar positions available		224
# of seminar positions filled	72	65
# of positions available in simulation courses		273
# of simulation positions filled	102	123
# of positions available in faculty supervised clinical courses		171
# of faculty supervised clinical positions filled	54	80
# involved in field placements	33	33
# involved in law journals	57	37
# involved in moot court or trial competitions	29	36
# of credit hours required to graduate		90

JD Enrollment and Ethnicity

	Men		Women		Full-Time		Part-Time		1st-Year		Total		JD Degs. Awd.
	#	%	#	%	#	%	#	%	#	%	#	%	
African Amer.	15	3.8	35	8.7	27	5.2	23	8.5	26	6.3	50	6.3	9
Amer. Indian	6	1.5	6	1.5	8	1.5	4	1.5	5	1.2	12	1.5	3
Asian Amer.	23	5.9	32	8.0	31	5.9	24	8.9	26	6.3	55	6.9	10
Mex. Amer.	0	0.0	0	0.0	0	0.0	0	0.0	0	0.0	0	0.0	0
Puerto Rican	0	0.0	0	0.0	0	0.0	0	0.0	0	0.0	0	0.0	0
Hispanic	43	11.0	36	9.0	45	8.6	34	12.5	41	9.9	79	10.0	11
Total Minority	87	22.2	109	27.2	111	21.3	85	31.4	98	23.7	196	24.7	33
For. Nation.	0	0.0	0	0.0	0	0.0	0	0.0	0	0.0	0	0.0	0
Caucasian	295	75.3	280	69.8	395	75.7	180	66.4	307	74.3	575	72.5	164
Unknown	10	2.6	12	3.0	16	3.1	6	2.2	8	1.9	22	2.8	10
Total	392	49.4	401	50.6	522	65.8	271	34.2	413	52.1	793		207

Transfers

Transfers in	2
Transfers out	9

Tuition and Fees

	Resident	Nonresident
Full-time	$26,000	$26,000
Part-time	$18,650	$18,650
Tuition Guarantee Program		N

Living Expenses

Estimated living expenses for singles

Living on campus	Living off campus	Living at home
$11,304	$15,525	$15,525

Texas Wesleyan University School of Law

ABA
Approved
Since
1994

GPA and LSAT Scores

	Total	Full-Time	Part-Time
# of apps	1,977	1,606	371
# of offers	872	757	115
# of matrics	233	170	63
75% GPA	3.44	3.46	3.33
Median GPA	3.17	3.21	3.03
25% GPA	2.88	2.93	2.73
75% LSAT	155	156	154
Median LSAT	153	153	152
25% LSAT	151	151	151

Grants and Scholarships (from prior year)

	Total		Full-Time		Part-Time	
	#	%	#	%	#	%
Total # of students	812		521		291	
Total # receiving grants	359	44.2	243	46.6	116	39.9
Less than 1/2 tuition	252	31.0	165	31.7	87	29.9
Half to full tuition	100	12.3	76	14.6	24	8.2
Full tuition	7	0.9	2	0.4	5	1.7
More than full tuition	0	0.0	0	0.0	0	0.0
Median grant amount			$7,500		$5,000	

Informational and Library Resources

Total amount spent on library materials	$1,705,255
Study seating capacity inside the library	383
# of full-time equivalent professional librarians	8
Hours per week library is open	112
# of open, wired connections available to students	0
# of networked computers available for use by students	60
Has wireless network?	Y
Require computer?	N

JD Attrition (from prior year)

	Academic	Other	Total	
	#	#	#	%
1st year	10	21	31	6.7
2nd year	0	0	0	0.0
3rd year	0	0	0	0.0
4th year	0	0	0	0.0

Employment (9 months after graduation)

	Total	Percentage
Employment status known	161	87.5
Employment status unknown	23	12.5
Employed	124	77.0
Pursuing graduate degrees	4	2.5
Unemployed (seeking, not seeking, or studying for the bar)	25	15.5
Type of Employment		
# employed in law firms	72	58.1
# employed in business and industry	36	29.0
# employed in government	13	10.5
# employed in public interest	1	0.8
# employed as judicial clerks	2	1.6
# employed in academia	0	0.0
Geographic Location		
# employed in state	101	81.5
# employed in foreign countries	0	0.0
# of states where employed	9	

Bar Passage Rates

First-time takers	180	Reporting %	100.00
Average school %	77.78	Average state %	84.54
Average pass difference	−6.76		

Jurisdiction	Takers	Passers	Pass %	State %	Diff %
Texas	180	140	77.78	84.54	−6.76

Texas Wesleyan University School of Law

1515 Commerce Street, Office of Admissions
Fort Worth, TX 76102
Phone: 817.212.4040, 800.733.9529; Fax: 817.212.4141
E-mail: lawadmissions@law.txwes.edu; Website: www.law.txwes.edu

■ Introduction

Established in 1989, the law school became part of Texas
Wesleyan University in 1992 with a mission to provide excellence
in legal education. The program emphasizes service to our
diverse student body, our profession, and our community
through outstanding teaching and scholarship, the development
of innovative academic programs, and a commitment to public
service, as well as by promoting the highest ethical standards in
the practice of law.

The law school is fully approved by the ABA and offers both
full-time and part-time programs leading to the Juris Doctor
degree. The law school is located in downtown Fort Worth,
Texas, in close proximity to the legal and judicial communities.
The Fort Worth/Dallas Metroplex, with approximately 5.8 million
residents, has rapidly grown to become one of the largest and
most diverse metropolitan areas in the country, offering a
relatively low cost of living, a growing economy, and extensive
opportunities for professional advancement.

■ Student Body

Texas Wesleyan Law is committed to educating students of
diverse backgrounds, varied life experiences, and differing
educational perspectives. In its short but dynamic 20-year
history, Texas Wesleyan School of Law has provided
excellence in legal education to traditional full-time students
as well as to accomplished nontraditional part-time students.
The increasing rise in the quality of students is a reflection of
our continued emphasis on service to a diverse student body,
the profession, and the community. Over the past several
years, applications have increased and median LSAT scores,
as well as median undergraduate GPAs, have risen.

■ Faculty

Texas Wesleyan Law has a highly qualified, energetic,
accessible faculty. The members of the faculty hold degrees
from the top law schools across the country and have diverse
professional backgrounds and experience. They have served
in a variety of high-level governmental positions, in the
judiciary and state legislatures, and in law firms. Faculty
members are talented and active scholars and have published
numerous books and articles. The student-to-faculty ratio
ensures that students have the attention they need, both
inside and outside of the classroom.

■ Library and Physical Facilities

The law school boasts first-rate facilities, including spacious
classrooms, well-designed courtrooms, an in-house law clinic,
and an impressive library. Texas Wesleyan's law library contains
over 250,000 volumes and equivalents. The law library's
mission is to support the educational, instructional, curricular,
and research needs of the faculty, students, and staff. In
addition to its law book collection, the law library subscribes to
major online electronic legal information services, including
LexisNexis, Westlaw, and legal research Internet sites.

Complementing the library's book and electronic sources,
an extensive collection of US Congressional documents,
including full transcripts of all congressional hearings since
1970, is available on microfiche. The law library has 8 full-time
librarians and a staff of 14 and is open 112 hours per week,
89 of which have reference services available.

■ Curriculum

Ninety (90) hours of academic course credit are required for
completion of the Juris Doctor degree. Students may choose
between full-time day, part-time day, or part-time evening
courseloads. The part-time program and Wesleyan's flexible
scheduling make it possible for those with continuing business
and family responsibilities to meet their obligations while
obtaining a legal education. The law school offers over 115
courses divided among traditional law courses and advanced
courses that provide training in a variety of specialized law
areas. Students are required to complete a minimum of 30
hours of pro bono legal service before graduation.

■ Skills Training

To help students develop necessary practical lawyering skills,
Texas Wesleyan has developed a series of courses in its Juris
Doctor curriculum—each called a practicum—in some
substantive areas as well as in particular skills areas. The term
practicum identifies courses involving the supervised practical
application of previously studied theory.

The law school offers a variety of externships with trial and
appellate courts, government agencies, nonprofit
organizations, and law firms. For academic credit, students
perform legal tasks and apply their academic studies to
real-client cases, gaining valuable insight into the operation
of legal institutions. Texas Wesleyan also has an in-house
legal clinic that functions as an actual law office where
students represent indigent clients in court under the
direction of a faculty supervisor. All skills programs are
coordinated by a full-time professor, ensuring significant legal
experience in interviewing, negotiating, client counseling, or
alternative dispute resolution.

The law school also prides itself on its ability to help students
apply lessons learned in the classroom to real-world legal
problems through the Equal Justice Program, a mandatory
30-hour community-related pro bono requirement that must
be completed by every student before graduation. Texas
Wesleyan School of Law is proud to be one of only a handful of
ABA-accredited schools that have such a requirement.
Students can fulfill this requirement in many ways, such as by
volunteering with a public service agency or with a private
attorney doing pro bono work. In addition, the school is
committed to serving the community through a variety of
programs, such as National Adoption Day, Street Law, and
High School Law Day, in which students can gain legal
experience while helping to address community legal needs.

■ Student Life

Texas Wesleyan Law's student organizations provide a broad
spectrum of opportunities for student involvement. Our
enthusiastic law students engage in competitions and leadership
activities at the state, regional, and national levels. Students

have won numerous competitions in negotiations, mock trial, and recently, the national moot court championships in entertainment law and information technology and privacy law. Through membership in law student organizations, participants reap the benefits of professional contacts, social activities, and exposure to legal specialties. Our student organizations provide opportunities for students to engage in professional bar associations, legal specialties, networking opportunities, and public service projects. In addition, the *Texas Wesleyan Law Review* encourages legal scholarship on issues of interest to academicians, practitioners, and law students. The *Law Review* is published by student editors with a faculty advisor. Participation is limited to those who meet academic requirements and those who are selected through a writing competition.

■ Career Services

The Texas Wesleyan University School of Law Office of Career Services assists students, graduates, and employers in their mutual efforts to link those seeking legal positions with those providing legal employment opportunities. Career Services also supports students in securing part-time or temporary employment while attending law school. A range of services, such as one-on-one career counseling, résumé and cover letter review, career seminars, on-campus interviews, off-campus job fairs, and an online job bank, are available to students and graduates. The Office of Career Services also provides numerous online and hard copy career resources in the career planning library. The school is a member of NALP, the Association for Legal Career Professionals.

■ Expenses and Financial Aid

Texas Wesleyan Law offers a highly competitive and low private tuition cost. Tuition and general costs vary by courseload. For 2009–2010, annual tuition for full-time students was $25,250; for part-time students, $17,900. Fees were an additional $375 per semester. The law school works with individual students to provide the best financial aid package the student is eligible to receive. The financial aid package may include several types of assistance for financing a law school education, including scholarships, grants, employment opportunities, and loan programs. A majority of law students receive some form of financial assistance.

■ Admission

To be considered for admission, an applicant to Texas Wesleyan School of Law must hold a baccalaureate degree from a regionally accredited college or university prior to matriculation. A Law School Admission Test (LSAT) score is also required. The law school offers full-time and part-time programs, and new students are admitted only in the fall. The final deadline for applying is March 31; however, the School of Law reviews applications and awards scholarships on a rolling basis, so applicants are encouraged to apply early.

The admission committee will endeavor to determine the academic and professional promise of each applicant. Accordingly, the admission committee evaluates all factors relevant to an applicant's potential to be successful in meeting the academic standards of the Juris Doctor program, as well as his or her potential for success on the bar examination and in other professional endeavors. Traditional criteria, such as undergraduate academic achievement, LSAT performance, graduate studies, work experience, life experience, activities, honors, the personal statement, recommendation letters, and other experiences, are used in the admission evaluation process.

Applicant Profile

Texas Wesleyan University School of Law
This grid includes only applicants who earned 120–180 LSAT scores under standard administrations.

LSAT Score	3.75 +		3.50–3.74		3.25–3.49		3.00–3.24		2.75–2.99		2.50–2.74		Below 2.50		No GPA		Total	
	Apps	Adm	Apps	Adm	Apps	Adm	Apps	Adm	Apps	Adm	Apps	Adm	Apps	Adm	Apps	Adm	Apps	Adm
170–180	0	0	0	0	0	0	1	1	1	1	0	0	0	0	0	0	2	2
165–169	1	1	2	2	2	2	3	3	2	2	2	2	2	0	0	0	14	12
160–164	16	15	11	11	12	12	20	20	15	15	9	7	5	0	0	0	88	80
155–159	26	26	40	40	63	62	48	46	33	33	19	15	28	12	2	1	259	235
150–154	52	51	82	73	111	99	104	95	79	66	60	34	48	6	6	1	542	425
145–149	33	6	65	18	113	24	107	31	98	19	64	6	49	2	5	1	534	107
140–144	15	0	24	0	62	3	68	0	59	0	50	0	49	0	4	1	331	4
Below 140	2	0	11	0	18	0	37	0	32	0	51	0	44	0	9	0	204	0
Total	145	99	235	144	381	202	388	196	319	136	255	64	225	20	26	4	1974	865

Apps = Number of Applicants
Adm = Number Admitted
Reflects 99% of the total applicant pool; average LSAT data reported.

The Thomas M. Cooley Law School

PO Box 13038, 300 S. Capitol Avenue
Lansing, MI 48901
Phone: 517.371.5140, ext. 2244; Fax: 517.334.5718
E-mail: admissions@cooley.edu; Website: www.cooley.edu

ABA
Approved
Since
1975

The Basics

Type of school	Private
Term	Semester
Application deadline	9/1 1/1 5/1
Application fee	$0
Financial aid deadline	5/1 8/18 12/17
Can first year start other than fall?	Yes
Student to faculty ratio	23.5 to 1
# of housing spaces available restricted to law students	
graduate housing for which law students are eligible	20

Faculty and Administrators

	Total		Men		Women		Minorities	
	Spr	Fall	Spr	Fall	Spr	Fall	Spr	Fall
Full-time	86	97	53	58	33	39	14	16
Other full-time	3	2	2	1	1	1	2	1
Deans, librarians, & others who teach	25	25	10	10	15	15	4	4
Part-time	176	162	120	108	56	54	8	8
Total	290	286	185	177	105	109	28	29

Curriculum

	Full-Time	Part-Time
Typical first-year section size	54	54
Is there typically a "small section" of the first-year class, other than Legal Writing, taught by full-time faculty	No	No
If yes, typical size offered last year		
# of classroom course titles beyond first-year curriculum	223	

# of upper division courses, excluding seminars, with an enrollment:		
	Under 25	452
	25–49	139
	50–74	93
	75–99	60
	100+	11

# of seminars		373
# of seminar positions available		7,742
# of seminar positions filled	848	4,413
# of positions available in simulation courses		5,601
# of simulation positions filled	616	3,208
# of positions available in faculty supervised clinical courses		347
# of faculty supervised clinical positions filled	39	203
# involved in field placements	122	637
# involved in law journals	63	328
# involved in moot court or trial competitions	12	60
# of credit hours required to graduate		90

JD Enrollment and Ethnicity

	Men		Women		Full-Time		Part-Time		1st-Year		Total		JD Degs. Awd.
	#	%	#	%	#	%	#	%	#	%	#	%	
African Amer.	136	7.0	309	17.4	50	8.5	395	12.6	271	13.9	445	11.9	81
Amer. Indian	8	0.4	8	0.5	2	0.3	14	0.4	10	0.5	16	0.4	5
Asian Amer.	98	5.0	98	5.5	32	5.5	164	5.2	116	5.9	196	5.3	53
Mex. Amer.	29	1.5	40	2.3	10	1.7	59	1.9	39	2.0	69	1.9	22
Puerto Rican	8	0.4	13	0.7	1	0.2	20	0.6	18	0.9	21	0.6	3
Hispanic	54	2.8	57	3.2	17	2.9	94	3.0	59	3.0	111	3.0	20
Total Minority	333	17.0	525	29.6	112	19.1	746	23.8	513	26.3	858	23.0	184
For. Nation.	77	3.9	72	4.1	28	4.8	121	3.9	87	4.5	149	4.0	36
Caucasian	1405	71.9	1072	60.5	404	68.9	2073	66.0	1226	62.7	2477	66.5	699
Unknown	139	7.1	104	5.9	42	7.2	201	6.4	128	6.6	243	6.5	34
Total	1954	52.4	1773	47.6	586	15.7	3141	84.3	1954	52.4	3727		953

Transfers

Transfers in	7
Transfers out	188

Tuition and Fees

	Resident	Nonresident
Full-time	$28,740	$28,740
Part-time	$18,490	$18,490
Tuition Guarantee Program	N	

Living Expenses

Estimated living expenses for singles

Living on campus	Living off campus	Living at home
N/A	$13,800	$13,800

The Thomas M. Cooley Law School

ABA
Approved
Since
1975

GPA and LSAT Scores

	Total	Full-Time	Part-Time
# of apps	5,775	4,986	789
# of offers	4,570	3,622	948
# of matrics	1,510	221	1,289
75% GPA	3.35	3.42	3.34
Median GPA	2.99	3.06	2.97
25% GPA	2.62	2.80	2.58
75% LSAT	150	152	149
Median LSAT	146	148	145
25% LSAT	144	146	143

Grants and Scholarships (from prior year)

	Total		Full-Time		Part-Time	
	#	%	#	%	#	%
Total # of students	3678		439		3239	
Total # receiving grants	1851	50.3	470	107.1	1381	42.6
Less than 1/2 tuition	1130	30.7	285	64.9	845	26.1
Half to full tuition	600	16.3	148	33.7	452	14.0
Full tuition	121	3.3	37	8.4	84	2.6
More than full tuition	0	0.0	0	0.0	0	0.0
Median grant amount			$7,704		$5,742	

Informational and Library Resources

Total amount spent on library materials	$2,637,051
Study seating capacity inside the library	1,058
# of full-time equivalent professional librarians	25
Hours per week library is open	124
# of open, wired connections available to students	48
# of networked computers available for use by students	251
Has wireless network?	Y
Require computer?	N

JD Attrition (from prior year)

	Academic	Other	Total	
	#	#	#	%
1st year	207	220	427	22.4
2nd year	65	68	133	14.5
3rd year	14	0	14	1.6
4th year	0	0	0	0.0

Employment (9 months after graduation)

	Total	Percentage
Employment status known	741	87.8
Employment status unknown	103	12.2
Employed	584	78.8
Pursuing graduate degrees	27	3.6
Unemployed (seeking, not seeking, or studying for the bar)	103	13.9
Type of Employment		
# employed in law firms	312	53.4
# employed in business and industry	98	16.8
# employed in government	89	15.2
# employed in public interest	24	4.1
# employed as judicial clerks	26	4.5
# employed in academia	21	3.6
Geographic Location		
# employed in state	194	33.2
# employed in foreign countries	6	1.0
# of states where employed	39	

Bar Passage Rates

First-time takers	718	Reporting %	72.42
Average school %	70.58	Average state %	84.47
Average pass difference −13.89			

Jurisdiction	Takers	Passers	Pass %	State %	Diff %
Michigan	278	224	80.58	82.13	−1.55
New York	71	43	60.56	88.98	−28.42
Illinois	66	48	72.73	90.94	−18.21
California	29	10	34.48	78.07	−43.59
Others (3)	76	42	55.26		

The Thomas M. Cooley Law School

PO Box 13038, 300 S. Capitol Avenue
Lansing, MI 48901
Phone: 517.371.5140, ext. 2244; Fax: 517.334.5718
E-mail: admissions@cooley.edu; Website: www.cooley.edu

■ President's Welcome

The Thomas M. Cooley Law School has earned the reputation for providing graduates with the practical skills necessary for a seamless transition from academia to the real world. Cooley's emphasis on sound academic knowledge, practice skills, and professionalism prepares our graduates for roles of leadership. Cooley was established to provide an opportunity to those who share the dream of becoming a lawyer. Our stated mission is to provide access to the legal profession.

Choosing a law school is a daunting task, particularly with so much misinformation, subjectivity, and bias confronting the potential law student. When you are researching law schools, please look at the three essential attributes of every successful law school—high-quality people, an excellent legal education program, and first-class facilities. These attributes are what should guide your law school selection.

Cooley pioneered practice-based legal education, and has provided law students with the knowledge, skills, and ethics needed for successful practice for the past 37 years. You are invited to learn more about why the people of Cooley are its greatest asset, how our program is a model of modern legal education theory and practice, and how Cooley's facilities are unmatched in size, scope, functionality, and beauty.

■ People—Our Greatest Asset

Cooley is the largest law school in the nation. We have the largest full-time faculty in the country, nearly all of whom are former practicing lawyers or judges. Their highest priority is helping students become competent lawyers, and they are accessible and supportive of student activities. **A Global Community**—Our students come from all 50 states, we lead all law schools in minority enrollment and foreign national students, and our graduates are found in every state and in numerous foreign countries. Our size and diversity allow our students to practice legal skills as they would in the real world—as a global community.

■ Knowledge, Skills, and Ethics

Broad Knowledge—Cooley's 90 credit-hour curriculum provides all students with the substantive knowledge, legal skills, and ethics needed for bar examinations, law practice, and further graduate study. Students complete 63 hours of required substantive and skills-based courses, and have the option of focusing their electives in one of seven practice area concentrations. **Practical Skills and Clinics**—All Cooley students gain extensive experience in the actual practice of law through simulation courses, competitions, and clinics. Practice skills are woven into substantive courses throughout the curriculum. Competitions in client counseling, negotiation, trial, and appellate skills allow students to compete against others from across the country. Cooley's expansive clinical programs immerse students in hands-on learning. Students can choose from one of Cooley's eight clinics or from more than 2,100 externship sites around the globe. **World Leader in Plain English Writing**—Recognized as a world leader in training students in the use of plain language, Cooley has the preeminent research and writing

program and an innovative curriculum. **Lifelong Ethics**—Beginning with the application process, Cooley fosters a culture of professionalism. At each step of the law school journey, students are challenged to adopt professionalism as a way of life.

■ Facilities—Unmatched in Size and Beauty

Four Campus Locations in Michigan: Lansing, Auburn Hills, Grand Rapids, and Ann Arbor—Cooley's four distinct campuses are unmatched in size and functionality. Each campus has a full complement of faculty, staff, libraries, and services. Our buildings and technology were designed to meet the academic and research needs of today's legal community. High-tech courtrooms and classrooms are equipped with the latest technology to enhance the educational experience. Cooley's library facilities are among the nation's largest and finest. The 600,000+ volume collection includes research materials from all 50 states as well as federal and international materials.

■ Accessible, Affordable Legal Education

The Juris Doctor curriculum is offered at each of Cooley's locations. Cooley operates a rolling admissions process with the option of starting classes in January, May, or September. Study full- or part-time. Complete the JD degree in two to five years by choosing from flexible scheduling options. Classes are offered mornings, afternoons, evenings, and on weekends.

Cooley uses a straightforward, objective formula to determine eligibility (UGPA x 15 + Highest LSAT = Admission Index). Admission to Cooley is also contingent on meeting character and fitness standards. There is no application fee.

Scholarships—Thanks in part to a generous scholarship program, Cooley is among the nation's most affordable independent law schools. Prospective students can determine the scholarship amount before applying. Students can earn up to 100 percent of tuition in two ways:

1. Admission Index levels:

Index	Honors Scholarship
215+	100%
210–214	75%
205–209	50%
195–204	25%

2. Student's highest LSAT score:

LSAT	Honors Scholarship
163+	100%
158–162	75%
153–157	50%
149–152	25%

Michigan residents who qualify for an entering LSAT Honors Scholarship are eligible for an additional 10 percent scholarship. Qualified **Canadian students** may be eligible to attend Cooley at a reduced cost. **Transfer students** are eligible for scholarships. Nonscholarship financial aid is available. Please refer to www.cooley.edu for the most current information.

Expenses—Tuition: $1,025 per credit hour in 2009–2010. **Fees:** $20 per term. See Cooley's online tuition calculator to compare tuition costs.

■ An Active, Engaged Academic Community

Scholarly Publications—Cooley's premier scholarly journal, *Thomas M. Cooley Law Review*, provides students opportunities to edit and publish traditional in-depth scholarship. The student editors of the *Journal of Practical and Clinical Law* work with lawyers and professors to address more practice-oriented issues. Cooley's newest publication is the *Art and Museum Law Journal*. **Symposia** bring together scholars from around the world to discuss timely topics. **Centers** in Ethics and Responsibility, Forensic Science and the Law, and Indian Law foster discussion and research. **Collaborations** with major research institutions open opportunities for dual-degree programs, including Juris Doctor/Master of Public Administration and Juris Doctor/Master of Business Administration programs with Oakland University and Western Michigan University. **Service**—Cooley strives to foster the highest caliber of relationships with surrounding communities. The Cooley Volunteer Corps matches organizations with students seeking substantive volunteer experiences. All students are members of the Student Bar Association, and there are more than 50 clubs and organizations in which students can become involved.

■ Commitment to Academic Success

Students receive support and enrichment at the Academic Resource Center (ARC). The ARC's professional staff provides ongoing assistance through the Introduction to Law class, seminars, one-on-one coaching, and other programs to help students refine skills critical to a successful legal career. Cooley provides students with institutional support to prepare them for state bar examinations, including practice bar exams, prebar courses, and individual counseling.

Computer-assisted legal instruction, assistance for students requiring disability accommodations, and other support services are all free to students.

■ A Culture of Professionalism

National Professionalism Award—Cooley was awarded American Bar Association's *E. Smythe Gambrell Professionalism Award* in 2006 for its innovative Professionalism Plan. Professional development at Cooley combines classroom experience, volunteering, public service, pro bono work, clinical experience, employment, and mentoring. **Faculty and Career and Professional Development** staff assist students in developing professionalism portfolios that prepare them for their chosen careers. Students can take advantage of résumé review services, mock interview programs, online job bulletins, and workshops.

■ Graduate and International Studies

LLM—Cooley offers graduate law degrees in Tax, Intellectual Property, Corporate Law and Finance, Insurance Law, US Law for Foreign Lawyers, and Self-Directed Legal Studies. Dual JD/LLM degree programs are available. **International Studies**—Cooley students study law around the world. Each January, Cooley's 13-week program in Australia and New Zealand beckons students "down under." In the summer, Cooley invites students to Toronto, Canada. Cooley also cooperates with other law schools to provide students with options extending around the globe.

Applicant Profile

Typically, schools include a statistical table showing the likelihood of admission to their program. Cooley instead uses a straightforward, fair, objective, and transparent formula to determine eligibility for admission. Please visit our website at *www.cooley.edu* for the several ways to qualify for admission.

Thomas Jefferson School of Law

2121 San Diego Avenue
San Diego, CA 92110
Phone: 619.297.9700; 800.956.5070; Fax: 619.294.4713
E-mail: admissions@tjsl.edu; Website: www.tjsl.edu

ABA Approved Since 1996

The Basics

Type of school	Private
Term	Semester
Application deadline	8/10 12/18
Application fee	$50
Financial aid deadline	4/30
Can first year start other than fall?	Yes
Student to faculty ratio	18.0 to 1
# of housing spaces available restricted to law students graduate housing for which law students are eligible	

Faculty and Administrators

	Total		Men		Women		Minorities	
	Spr	Fall	Spr	Fall	Spr	Fall	Spr	Fall
Full-time	35	36	17	16	18	20	9	8
Other full-time	1	1	1	1	0	0	0	0
Deans, librarians, & others who teach	5	5	4	4	1	1	0	0
Part-time	40	27	25	19	15	8	1	1
Total	81	69	47	40	34	29	10	9

Curriculum

	Full-Time	Part-Time
Typical first-year section size	85	50
Is there typically a "small section" of the first-year class, other than Legal Writing, taught by full-time faculty	No	No
If yes, typical size offered last year		
# of classroom course titles beyond first-year curriculum	95	

# of upper division courses, excluding seminars, with an enrollment:		
	Under 25	90
	25–49	21
	50–74	7
	75–99	9
	100+	1

# of seminars	22	
# of seminar positions available	441	
# of seminar positions filled	145	77
# of positions available in simulation courses	352	
# of simulation positions filled	166	115
# of positions available in faculty supervised clinical courses	54	
# of faculty supervised clinical positions filled	26	5
# involved in field placements	233	60
# involved in law journals	79	14
# involved in moot court or trial competitions	74	16
# of credit hours required to graduate	88	

JD Enrollment and Ethnicity

	Men		Women		Full-Time		Part-Time		1st-Year		Total		JD Degs. Awd.
	#	%	#	%	#	%	#	%	#	%	#	%	
African Amer.	29	6.0	31	7.7	45	6.9	15	6.2	19	6.2	60	6.7	20
Amer. Indian	6	1.2	3	0.7	5	0.8	4	1.7	4	1.3	9	1.0	0
Asian Amer.	50	10.3	52	12.9	71	11.0	31	12.9	37	12.1	102	11.5	20
Mex. Amer.	33	6.8	38	9.4	49	7.6	22	9.1	19	6.2	71	8.0	14
Puerto Rican	2	0.4	3	0.7	2	0.3	3	1.2	0	0.0	5	0.6	5
Hispanic	22	4.5	24	5.9	34	5.2	12	5.0	10	3.3	46	5.2	13
Total Minority	142	29.3	151	37.4	206	31.8	87	36.1	89	29.1	293	33.0	72
For. Nation.	3	0.6	4	1.0	7	1.1	0	0.0	5	1.6	7	0.8	0
Caucasian	340	70.1	249	61.6	435	67.1	154	63.9	212	69.3	589	66.3	148
Unknown	0	0.0	0	0.0	0	0.0	0	0.0	0	0.0	0	0.0	0
Total	485	54.6	404	45.4	648	72.9	241	27.1	306	34.4	889		220

Transfers

Transfers in	0
Transfers out	26

Tuition and Fees

	Resident	Nonresident
Full-time	$36,300	$36,300
Part-time	$24,000	$24,000
Tuition Guarantee Program		N

Living Expenses

Estimated living expenses for singles

Living on campus	Living off campus	Living at home
$28,860	$28,860	$28,860

Thomas Jefferson School of Law

ABA
Approved
Since
1996

GPA and LSAT Scores

	Total	Full-Time	Part-Time
# of apps	2,979	2,587	395
# of offers	1,533	1,339	194
# of matrics	395	305	90
75% GPA	3.19	3.22	3.10
Median GPA	2.96	3.00	2.86
25% GPA	2.70	2.71	2.63
75% LSAT	153	153	152
Median LSAT	151	151	149
25% LSAT	148	149	147

Grants and Scholarships (from prior year)

	Total		Full-Time		Part-Time	
	#	%	#	%	#	%
Total # of students	792		608		184	
Total # receiving grants	347	43.8	272	44.7	75	40.8
Less than 1/2 tuition	222	28.0	183	30.1	39	21.2
Half to full tuition	115	14.5	84	13.8	31	16.8
Full tuition	9	1.1	5	0.8	4	2.2
More than full tuition	1	0.1	0	0.0	1	0.5
Median grant amount			$12,500		$8,000	

Informational and Library Resources

Total amount spent on library materials	$999,400
Study seating capacity inside the library	266
# of full-time equivalent professional librarians	10
Hours per week library is open	115
# of open, wired connections available to students	12
# of networked computers available for use by students	17
Has wireless network?	Y
Require computer?	Y

JD Attrition (from prior year)

	Academic	Other	Total	
	#	#	#	%
1st year	24	31	55	22.0
2nd year	7	5	12	4.2
3rd year	0	0	0	0.0
4th year	0	0	0	0.0

Employment (9 months after graduation)

	Total	Percentage
Employment status known	220	96.9
Employment status unknown	7	3.1
Employed	190	86.4
Pursuing graduate degrees	9	4.1
Unemployed (seeking, not seeking, or studying for the bar)	12	5.5
Type of Employment		
# employed in law firms	90	47.4
# employed in business and industry	42	22.1
# employed in government	17	8.9
# employed in public interest	6	3.2
# employed as judicial clerks	11	5.8
# employed in academia	5	2.6
Geographic Location		
# employed in state	135	71.1
# employed in foreign countries	2	1.1
# of states where employed		18

Bar Passage Rates

First-time takers	221	Reporting %	100.00
Average school %	75.08	Average state %	79.77
Average pass difference	−4.69		

Jurisdiction	Takers	Passers	Pass %	State %	Diff %
California	165	116	70.30	78.07	−7.77
Illinois	11	11	100.00	90.94	9.06
Nevada	8	8	100.00	76.94	23.06
Texas	6	6	100.00	84.54	15.46
Others (17)	31	25	80.65		

Thomas Jefferson School of Law

2121 San Diego Avenue
San Diego, CA 92110
Phone: 619.297.9700; 800.956.5070; Fax: 619.294.4713
E-mail: admissions@tjsl.edu; Website: www.tjsl.edu

■ Introduction

Thomas Jefferson School of Law (TJSL) is a private, nonprofit, and independent law school. Accredited by the ABA and AALS, the law school emphasizes an individualized approach to learning by integrating the cognitive sciences and learning theory into its curriculum.

The flexible curriculum allows students to commence their studies in either August or January. Also, students can pursue a law degree in a full- or part-time (day or evening) program and accelerate graduation by attending classes in the summer. This multitrack approach, traceable to the school's roots as a long-time supporter of military personnel and working adults, gives students the option of pursuing a law degree full or part time while continuing their employment.

■ New Campus Opening in 2010–2011

The law school is currently located in Old Town San Diego, but will be moving to a $70 million, eight-story, high-rise building in Downtown San Diego in January 2011. The brand new campus will feature a state-of-the-art library, in-house legal clinics, and a café. The location will place students within walking distance from many law firms, major businesses, and the state and federal courts.

■ Vibrant and Diverse Student Community

The mission of the Thomas Jefferson School of Law is to provide an outstanding legal education for a nationally based, diverse student body in a collegial and supportive environment. The TJSL campus truly reflects its commitment to diversity: the student body is gender-balanced, 20 percent of the students are the first in their family to attend law school, students of color comprise 33 percent of the student body, many students are openly GLBT, 23 percent are multilingual, and they represent more than 23 countries.

■ Location, Location, Location!

San Diego's mild Mediterranean climate promises nearly 265 days of sunshine annually and moderate temperatures throughout the year. The city is uniquely situated to offer law students ample opportunity for both professional development and personal fulfillment. As the border city to Tijuana, Mexico, and just 120 miles south of Los Angeles, San Diego is a training ground for everything from international law to entertainment law. Also, as the second largest city in California and the eighth largest city in the United States, it is a vibrant social and economic center.

■ Internationally Renowned Faculty

TJSL is proud to have a first-rate faculty consisting of distinguished practitioners and scholars. Our professors have structured business transactions at both the international and the domestic levels and litigated before the World Court at The Hague, the US Supreme Court, and federal and state trial and appellate courts. Their clients have ranged from the largest multinational corporations to the most impoverished members of society.

All 42 members of our faculty pride themselves on providing quality instruction and being accessible to students outside the classroom. First-year students are assigned faculty advisors, but all members of the faculty emphasize being available to students outside of class.

■ Cutting-Edge Legal Skills Programs

Our academic resources consist of a writing lab, student organization-led study sessions, and individual feedback from professors. However, the anchor of our academic resources is the highly effective academic success program, the **SUMMIT Series**, which is a part of the first-year curriculum and continues until preparation for the bar exam. The series brings scientific principles in psychology, neuroscience, and cognitive science to the study of law and equips students with a personal and succinct methodology for acquiring the fundamental skills to succeed in law school and on the bar exam. Our **Bar Secrets** course is a continuation of these principles and is a proven means of preparing for the California bar exam.

■ Progressive and Practical Curriculum

The academic program at Thomas Jefferson School of Law has been carefully designed to ensure a balanced and comprehensive curriculum that will prepare students to practice in any area of the law. During their first semester, entering students have the opportunity, in all their courses, to receive feedback from the faculty on their written legal analytical skills in order to enhance their understanding of the course material and hone their performance prior to final exams.

Academic Centers. A growing faculty has allowed the school to acquire special strengths in the areas of law that most reflect our changing world; that is, those relating to technological change, globalization, and the transformation of our social order. To provide an institutional framework for the study of these embryonic areas of law, the school has established three Academic Centers.

1. *The Center for Law, Technology, and Communications* prepares students for careers related to high technology and communications.

2. *The Center for Global Legal Studies* prepares students for the transborder aspects of contemporary legal practice and offers a wide variety of courses in international law.

3. *The Center for Law and Social Justice* prepares students for practice geared toward the preservation of the values of liberty and equality in an ever-changing world.

4. *The Externship Program* offers a large number of courses that train students in professional skills, supplemented by a variety of field-placement programs. Our externship coordinator works with students to place them in an endless number and type of for-credit legal positions. Past placements consist of public legal agencies, private law firms, corporations, and sports teams.

JD/MBA Program

Students can earn in eight semesters a Juris Doctor degree from Thomas Jefferson School of Law and a Master of Business Administration degree from San Diego State University (SDSU). The objective of the concurrent degree program is to prepare students who are competent in both law and business for advanced practice in areas where the fields converge.

Classes will be taken at both campuses. Applicants must conform to the application procedures for each institution, including taking both the LSAT and GMAT. Because the sequence for the program is for students first to attend TJSL for two semesters, the expectation is that students will be admitted to TJSL and then apply to SDSU during their first year at TJSL.

International Law Programs

Thomas Jefferson offers several study-abroad opportunities for students to gain experience in a broad array of international law subjects, focusing on business and social justice issues. The locations include **Hangzhou, China**; **Nice, France**; **Dijon, France**; and **Kingston, Ontario, Canada**.

LLM Programs

Thomas Jefferson School of Law offers three LLM (Master of Laws) programs, two of which will give students expertise in important areas of international law, and one of which will allow foreign students to obtain a US law degree. Specifically, the programs offered are LLM in International Tax and Financial Services—a completely online program—LLM in International Trade and Investment, and LLM in American Legal Studies for Foreign Law Graduates. The latter two programs are residential.

Student Activities

Thomas Jefferson students manage and edit the *Thomas Jefferson Law Review*. Cocurricular programs include the Moot Court, Mock Trial, and Alternative Dispute Resolution teams. Some student organizations are formed as a result of heightened student interest in substantive areas of law practice, such as the International Law Society, the Entertainment and the Sports Law Societies, and the Public Interest Law Foundation. Many student organizations provide a source of mutual support for various groups of students, including the Student Bar Association, Black Law Students Association, La Raza Students Association, and the Asian Pacific American Law Students Association.

Career Services

The Career Services Office assists students and alumni in finding temporary and permanent law-related employment. The office maintains listings of employment opportunities and schedules on-campus interviewing. Also, through the Judicial Internship Program, students may gain academic credit by working with local, federal, and state judges. The Career Services Office has developed an alumni mentoring program, which matches current students with one of the law school's more than 5,600 alumni.

Admission

Thomas Jefferson conducts a rolling admission process under which applicants are considered when their applications are complete. Applications are accepted through July for the fall term and through December for the spring term. Although there is no deadline for either the fall or spring term, due to the large applicant pool, early applications are encouraged. Decisions are made and sent out on a rolling basis.

In addition to the LSAT score, the Admissions Committee considers the applicant's undergraduate record, extracurricular activities, work ethic and experience, and demonstrated ability to overcoming adversity.

Expenses and Financial Aid

Thomas Jefferson offers need- and merit-based scholarships and uses its funds for both recruitment as well as retention. Because of the broad array of scholarship criteria, applicants need not submit a separate scholarship application. Awards are based on information already accessible to the law school in your application. Should you have significant financial need that you would like us to consider, you can submit a brief but detailed written statement as a part of the application for admission.

Scholarship offers are made on a rolling basis as quickly after admission as possible. All scholarship recipients receive a detailed offer letter containing the terms of the award and any criteria for renewal.

Students can seek loans to finance their education. Also, students interested in work-study can secure jobs on campus. The school works with students seeking work-study on an individual basis upon matriculation.

Applicant Profile Not Available

The University of Toledo College of Law

2801 West Bancroft Street
Toledo, OH 43606-3390
Phone: 419.530.4131; Fax: 419.530.4345
E-mail: law.admissions@utoledo.edu; Website: www.utlaw.edu

ABA
Approved
Since
1939

The Basics

Type of school	Public
Term	Semester
Application deadline	8/1
Application fee	$0
Financial aid deadline	4/1
Can first year start other than fall?	No
Student to faculty ratio	13.4 to 1
# of housing spaces available restricted to law students	
graduate housing for which law students are eligible	

Faculty and Administrators

	Total		Men		Women		Minorities	
	Spr	Fall	Spr	Fall	Spr	Fall	Spr	Fall
Full-time	27	28	15	16	12	12	2	2
Other full-time	1	1	0	0	1	1	0	0
Deans, librarians, & others who teach	4	4	3	3	1	1	0	0
Part-time	24	18	16	13	8	5	0	2
Total	56	51	34	32	22	19	2	4

Curriculum

	Full-Time	Part-Time
Typical first-year section size	55	36
Is there typically a "small section" of the first-year class, other than Legal Writing, taught by full-time faculty	No	No
If yes, typical size offered last year		
# of classroom course titles beyond first-year curriculum	88	
# of upper division courses, excluding seminars, with an enrollment: Under 25	86	
25–49	24	
50–74	11	
75–99	4	
100+	0	
# of seminars	5	
# of seminar positions available	100	
# of seminar positions filled	35	3
# of positions available in simulation courses	410	
# of simulation positions filled	250	40
# of positions available in faculty supervised clinical courses	86	
# of faculty supervised clinical positions filled	48	5
# involved in field placements	104	4
# involved in law journals	45	1
# involved in moot court or trial competitions	45	1
# of credit hours required to graduate	89	

JD Enrollment and Ethnicity

	Men		Women		Full-Time		Part-Time		1st-Year		Total		JD Degs. Awd.
	#	%	#	%	#	%	#	%	#	%	#	%	
African Amer.	9	3.1	10	5.1	8	2.3	11	7.5	8	3.7	19	3.9	4
Amer. Indian	0	0.0	0	0.0	0	0.0	0	0.0	0	0.0	0	0.0	0
Asian Amer.	9	3.1	6	3.0	9	2.6	6	4.1	8	3.7	15	3.0	1
Mex. Amer.	0	0.0	0	0.0	0	0.0	0	0.0	0	0.0	0	0.0	0
Puerto Rican	0	0.0	0	0.0	0	0.0	0	0.0	0	0.0	0	0.0	0
Hispanic	6	2.0	8	4.0	9	2.6	5	3.4	6	2.8	14	2.8	8
Total Minority	24	8.1	24	12.1	26	7.5	22	15.0	22	10.1	48	9.7	13
For. Nation.	6	2.0	4	2.0	9	2.6	1	0.7	4	1.8	10	2.0	1
Caucasian	193	65.4	131	66.2	221	63.9	103	70.1	145	66.5	324	65.7	99
Unknown	72	24.4	39	19.7	90	26.0	21	14.3	38	17.4	111	22.5	42
Total	295	59.8	198	40.2	346	70.2	147	29.8	218	44.2	493		155

Transfers

Transfers in	4
Transfers out	11

Tuition and Fees

	Resident	Nonresident
Full-time	$19,137	$29,553
Part-time	$14,343	$22,155
Tuition Guarantee Program	N	

Living Expenses

Estimated living expenses for singles

Living on campus	Living off campus	Living at home
$13,780	$15,412	$7,546

The University of Toledo College of Law

ABA
Approved
Since
1939

GPA and LSAT Scores

	Total	Full-Time	Part-Time
# of apps	868	639	229
# of offers	521	367	154
# of matrics	181	99	82
75% GPA	3.54	3.59	3.36
Median GPA	3.23	3.35	2.98
25% GPA	2.92	3.07	2.60
75% LSAT	156	158	152
Median LSAT	153	155	150
25% LSAT	150	152	149

Grants and Scholarships (from prior year)

	Total		Full-Time		Part-Time	
	#	%	#	%	#	%
Total # of students	494		342		152	
Total # receiving grants	228	46.2	217	63.5	11	7.2
Less than 1/2 tuition	59	11.9	52	15.2	7	4.6
Half to full tuition	58	11.7	57	16.7	1	0.7
Full tuition	47	9.5	46	13.5	1	0.7
More than full tuition	64	13.0	62	18.1	2	1.3
Median grant amount			$15,216		$2,742	

Informational and Library Resources

Total amount spent on library materials	$671,680
Study seating capacity inside the library	449
# of full-time equivalent professional librarians	5
Hours per week library is open	109
# of open, wired connections available to students	34
# of networked computers available for use by students	31
Has wireless network?	Y
Require computer?	N

JD Attrition (from prior year)

	Academic	Other	Total	
	#	#	#	%
1st year	7	10	17	9.3
2nd year	3	10	13	7.6
3rd year	0	11	11	9.2
4th year	0	0	0	0.0

Employment (9 months after graduation)

	Total	Percentage
Employment status known	140	97.9
Employment status unknown	3	2.1
Employed	133	95.0
Pursuing graduate degrees	3	2.1
Unemployed (seeking, not seeking, or studying for the bar)	3	2.1
Type of Employment		
# employed in law firms	57	42.9
# employed in business and industry	18	13.5
# employed in government	33	24.8
# employed in public interest	11	8.3
# employed as judicial clerks	5	3.8
# employed in academia	6	4.5
Geographic Location		
# employed in state	82	61.7
# employed in foreign countries	1	0.8
# of states where employed	18	

Bar Passage Rates

First-time takers	139	Reporting %	70.50
Average school %	88.78	Average state %	87.12
Average pass difference	1.66		

Jurisdiction	Takers	Passers	Pass %	State %	Diff %
Ohio	82	72	87.80	88.09	−0.29
Michigan	16	15	93.75	82.13	11.62

The University of Toledo College of Law

2801 West Bancroft Street
Toledo, OH 43606-3390
Phone: 419.530.4131; Fax: 419.530.4345
E-mail: law.admissions@utoledo.edu; Website: www.utlaw.edu

■ Introduction

The University of Toledo is a state university of more than 22,000 students, conveniently located on the western edge of Toledo, Ohio, in one of the city's nicest residential areas.

The College of Law, located on the main campus of the University of Toledo, is accredited by the ABA and is a member of the AALS and the League of Ohio Law Schools. It has been training lawyers since 1906 and, in 1984, was awarded a chapter of the Order of the Coif. The College of Law provides a quality legal education with a personal touch at an affordable price. The nationally recognized faculty emphasizes classroom teaching and student accessibility as its primary function. The College of Law is committed to its open-door policy that provides total student support.

■ Student Body

The College of Law seeks a diverse student body. Nearly two-thirds of the students hail from outside the local area. More than 200 undergraduate institutions are represented. This diversity exposes students to an interesting, stimulating, and creative atmosphere where insights and ideas flourish. Diversity is reflected in student groups and activities, representing a broad spectrum of social, political, ethnic, and religious perspectives.

■ Faculty

The full-time faculty earned law degrees from some of the most outstanding universities in the country. Many have advanced degrees.

While many faculty members have national reputations for scholarship, the faculty places a high priority on effective teaching and accessibility to students.

■ Library and Physical Facilities

The spacious, newly renovated Law Center includes tiered classrooms, a striking student lounge, a state-of-the-art moot courtroom, and an amphitheater-style auditorium. The entire building affords wireless access.

Occupying four levels within the Law Center, the library contains group-study rooms, videotaping facilities, and a modern computer lab available for use by law students. Students are trained in the use of two vast electronic law libraries—LexisNexis and Westlaw.

■ Curriculum

The College of Law requires the successful completion of 89 semester hours for graduation. The curriculum in the first year of the full-time program and the first two years of the part-time program consists of required courses. An extensive and ever-growing curriculum covers traditional subjects as well as cutting-edge environmental law, intellectual property law, and international law subjects, and incorporates the development of professional legal skills and values.

Our academic success program provides teaching assistants for students in all basic required courses and offers tutors for any student who requests academic support. Students can graduate with certificates in criminal, environmental, intellectual property, international, and labor/employment law.

The College of Law has joint-degree programs with the Colleges of Engineering, Business, and Arts and Sciences, leading to a Master of Science in Engineering, PhD in Engineering, Master of Business Administration, Master of Public Administration, or Master of Criminal Justice. Students may also design individual joint-degree programs.

■ Special Programs

Legal Clinics—A pioneer in clinical legal education, the College of Law provides an atmosphere for learning basic lawyering techniques and allows students the opportunity to further sharpen their skills in live client settings. Under close supervision, students appear in court in both civil and criminal cases.

Through the Dispute Resolution Clinic, mediation experience is available in a variety of matters, including unruly child complaints, and custody and visitation issues in parentage cases in juvenile court. Students in the Public Service Externship Clinic are assigned to public service legal entities, such as the judiciary, legal services offices, pro bono programs, public defender offices, legislative bodies, government agencies, and public interest organizations.

Legal Institute of the Great Lakes—The institute supports research and sponsors conferences on the legal, economic, and social issues of importance to the Great Lakes region of the United States and Canada. The highlight of this program is an annual symposium on the national and international water crisis and the need for fresh water.

■ Admission

A bachelor's degree from an accredited institution is required. Grades and LSAT scores are the most important determinants of admission. However, the Admission Committee carefully considers each application on its full merits. Letters of recommendation are important.

Prospective students are encouraged to visit the law school, talk to our students and faculty, and sit in on a class. Appointments can be made through the Admission Office.

■ Student Activities

The *University of Toledo Law Review* is published four times a year by students selected on the basis of academic performance and a writing competition. Training and practice in brief writing and oral argument beyond the required appellate advocacy course are obtained through the Moot Court Program, in the Charles Fornoff Intramural Moot Court Competition, and in several national and regional competitions.

The Student Bar Association, American Constitution Society, Black Law Students Association, Business Law Society, Christian Legal Society, Criminal Justice Society, Environmental Law Society, Federalist Society, Health Law Association, Hispanic Law Students Association, International Law Society, Jewish Law Students Association, Labor and Employment Law Association, OUTLaw, Sports Law

The University of Toledo College of Law

Association, and Women Law Students Association are among many active organizations.

■ Financial Aid

The College of Law strives to provide a quality legal education at an affordable cost. Every effort is made to ensure that students graduate without large financial obligations that may take years to repay. The College of Law awards scholarships totaling in excess of $1.5 million each year. Residents of the following Michigan counties are treated as in-state residents for tuition purposes: Hillsdale, Lenawee, Monroe, Oakland, Washtenaw, and Wayne. The goal of the financial aid program is to ensure that graduates have the greatest freedom to choose their careers without regard to financial obligations.

■ Career Services

The College of Law places top priority on providing comprehensive career planning and placement for its students and graduates. The Law Career Services Office assists students through workshops and counseling, and provides guest speakers on legal career options.

As a result of both on- and off-campus interviews, second- and third-year students accept summer or attorney positions in all major cities of Ohio and Michigan, as well as locations throughout the United States.

The college's Judicial Clerkship Program places graduates as clerks with federal and state courts around the country. Graduates are successfully practicing in major law firms, government offices, the judiciary, and in public interest positions in nearly every state. Graduates also can be found in Asia, Europe, and Africa.

Graduates are a valuable resource for current students as they pursue employment opportunities nationwide.

Applicant Profile

The University of Toledo College of Law

GPA	\multicolumn{9}{c}{LSAT (10) Percentile Intervals}
	0–20	21–30	31–40	41–50	51–60	61–70	71–80	81–90	91–99
3.75 Above									
3.74 3.50									
3.49 3.25									
3.24 3.00									
2.99 2.75									
2.74 2.50									
2.49 2.25									
2.24 2.00									
Below 2.00									

■ Highly Likely   ■ Possible   □ Unlikely

Touro College—Jacob D. Fuchsberg Law Center

225 Eastview Drive
Central Islip, NY 11722
Phone: 631.761.7010; Fax: 631.761.7019
E-mail: admissions@tourolaw.edu; Website: www.tourolaw.edu

ABA
Approved
Since
1983

The Basics

Type of school	Private
Term	Semester
Application deadline	8/1
Application fee	$60
Financial aid deadline	4/15
Can first year start other than fall?	No
Student to faculty ratio	15.9 to 1
# of housing spaces available restricted to law students	
graduate housing for which law students are eligible	

Faculty and Administrators

	Total		Men		Women		Minorities	
	Spr	Fall	Spr	Fall	Spr	Fall	Spr	Fall
Full-time	33	36	19	19	14	16	3	4
Other full-time	2	3	1	1	1	2	1	0
Deans, librarians, & others who teach	10	11	3	3	7	8	1	1
Part-time	26	25	22	18	4	7	1	4
Total	71	75	45	41	26	33	6	9

Curriculum

	Full-Time	Part-Time
Typical first-year section size	70	61
Is there typically a "small section" of the first-year class, other than Legal Writing, taught by full-time faculty	No	No
If yes, typical size offered last year		
# of classroom course titles beyond first-year curriculum		91
# of upper division courses, excluding seminars, with an enrollment: Under 25		94
25–49		38
50–74		12
75–99		4
100+		2
# of seminars		16
# of seminar positions available		288
# of seminar positions filled	133	64
# of positions available in simulation courses		420
# of simulation positions filled	164	116
# of positions available in faculty supervised clinical courses		90
# of faculty supervised clinical positions filled	48	20
# involved in field placements	138	25
# involved in law journals	32	9
# involved in moot court or trial competitions	51	17
# of credit hours required to graduate		88

JD Enrollment and Ethnicity

	Men #	Men %	Women #	Women %	Full-Time #	Full-Time %	Part-Time #	Part-Time %	1st-Year #	1st-Year %	Total #	Total %	JD Degs. Awd.
African Amer.	28	6.9	42	11.1	38	6.9	32	13.7	33	10.6	70	8.9	20
Amer. Indian	2	0.5	0	0.0	2	0.4	0	0.0	1	0.3	2	0.3	0
Asian Amer.	24	5.9	25	6.6	38	6.9	11	4.7	22	7.1	49	6.2	12
Mex. Amer.	3	0.7	1	0.3	3	0.5	1	0.4	0	0.0	4	0.5	0
Puerto Rican	4	1.0	5	1.3	4	0.7	5	2.1	5	1.6	9	1.1	0
Hispanic	18	4.4	18	4.8	23	4.2	13	5.6	19	6.1	36	4.6	7
Total Minority	79	19.4	91	24.1	108	19.5	62	26.6	80	25.7	170	21.6	39
For. Nation.	9	2.2	5	1.3	14	2.5	0	0.0	4	1.3	14	1.8	9
Caucasian	305	74.8	261	69.0	408	73.8	158	67.8	214	68.8	566	72.0	146
Unknown	15	3.7	21	5.6	23	4.2	13	5.6	13	4.2	36	4.6	7
Total	408	51.9	378	48.1	553	70.4	233	29.6	311	39.6	786		201

Transfers

Transfers in	18
Transfers out	33

Tuition and Fees

	Resident	Nonresident
Full-time	$39,130	$39,130
Part-time	$29,330	$29,330
Tuition Guarantee Program		N

Living Expenses

Estimated living expenses for singles

Living on campus	Living off campus	Living at home
$23,560	$23,560	$11,560

Touro College—Jacob D. Fuchsberg Law Center

ABA
Approved
Since
1983

GPA and LSAT Scores

	Total	Full-Time	Part-Time
# of apps	2,095	1,610	485
# of offers	962	793	169
# of matrics	315	234	81
75% GPA	3.39	3.41	3.33
Median GPA	3.14	3.17	3.09
25% GPA	2.86	2.88	2.81
75% LSAT	153	153	152
Median LSAT	151	151	150
25% LSAT	149	149	149

Grants and Scholarships (from prior year)

	Total		Full-Time		Part-Time	
	#	%	#	%	#	%
Total # of students	729		498		231	
Total # receiving grants	481	66.0	349	70.1	132	57.1
Less than 1/2 tuition	450	61.7	326	65.5	124	53.7
Half to full tuition	26	3.6	19	3.8	7	3.0
Full tuition	4	0.5	3	0.6	1	0.4
More than full tuition	1	0.1	1	0.2	0	0.0
Median grant amount			$4,000		$2,420	

Informational and Library Resources

Total amount spent on library materials	$1,077,306
Study seating capacity inside the library	476
# of full-time equivalent professional librarians	10
Hours per week library is open	86
# of open, wired connections available to students	0
# of networked computers available for use by students	48
Has wireless network?	Y
Require computer?	N

JD Attrition (from prior year)

	Academic	Other	Total	
	#	#	#	%
1st year	19	33	52	19.4
2nd year	5	3	8	3.8
3rd year	0	0	0	0.0
4th year	0	0	0	0.0

Employment (9 months after graduation)

	Total	Percentage
Employment status known	188	94.0
Employment status unknown	12	6.0
Employed	135	71.8
Pursuing graduate degrees	0	0.0
Unemployed (seeking, not seeking, or studying for the bar)	44	23.4
Type of Employment		
# employed in law firms	78	57.8
# employed in business and industry	19	14.1
# employed in government	26	19.3
# employed in public interest	4	3.0
# employed as judicial clerks	7	5.2
# employed in academia	1	0.7
Geographic Location		
# employed in state	122	90.4
# employed in foreign countries	0	0.0
# of states where employed	5	

Bar Passage Rates

First-time takers	212	Reporting %	100.00
Average school %	77.37	Average state %	88.64
Average pass difference	−11.27		

Jurisdiction	Takers	Passers	Pass %	State %	Diff %
New York	186	145	77.96	88.98	−11.02
New Jersey	15	10	66.67	84.69	−18.02
Connecticut	11	9	81.82	88.28	−6.46

Touro College—Jacob D. Fuchsberg Law Center

225 Eastview Drive
Central Islip, NY 11722
Phone: 631.761.7010; Fax: 631.761.7019
E-mail: admissions@tourolaw.edu; Website: www.tourolaw.edu

■ New Building and New Location

Established in 1980, Touro Law Center is fully accredited by the American Bar Association and is a member of the Association of American Law Schools. The Law Center occupies a new 185,000-square-foot state-of-the-art building in Central Islip on the south shore of Long Island. Touro is at the center of what is arguably the nation's first integrated "law campus," comprising a United States courthouse and federal building and a New York State court center, with supreme, family, and district courts.

Located about one hour by car or train from New York City, Central Islip boasts a wide variety of affordable housing options. Students may also use the Office of Admissions' Housing Information Network, which provides current listings of accommodations, as well as information regarding car pools and shared living arrangements. On-campus parking is free of charge.

■ New Curriculum: Courtrooms as Classrooms

Touro is a leader in bridging the gap between law school and law practice, between the classroom and the courtroom. Taking advantage of its unique location as part of a law campus, adjacent to and working with both a federal courthouse and a state courthouse, Touro's innovative Court Observation Program enables students to experience the workings of the judicial system from the very first days of their legal education. Beginning in their first semester, students are exposed to the challenges of law practice through simulations in both litigation and nonlitigation settings and through faculty-supervised small-group visits to courts in session, court-related agencies, and court administration. In an effort to facilitate experiential learning, students not only observe live proceedings, but also discuss with the participants (judges, attorneys, and sometimes the parties themselves) their perspectives on law in action.

Practice Modules: A central feature of the upper-level curriculum is the linkage of substantive law with practice modules in Business Organizations, Criminal Procedure, Family Law, and Trusts and Estates. Using the rules they have learned in the classroom, students solve practical problems, such as helping investors select an appropriate business entity, drawing up a criminal indictment, structuring a marital separation agreement, or drafting a will that satisfies an individual's personal and financial interests.

Clinics: Touro offers six in-house clinics where clients bring real cases to on-campus offices: Civil Rights Litigation, Elder Law, Family Law, Mortgage Foreclosure and Bankruptcy, Not-for-Profit Corporation Law, and Veterans and Servicemembers' Rights. Some clinics are arranged to accommodate the scheduling needs of part-time evening students.

Field Placement Externships: There are five field placement externships in which students work off campus: Business, Law, and Technology (Internet and high-tech companies, corporate law departments, and law firms); Civil Practice (law firms, corporations, and private and public agencies); Criminal Law (District Attorneys' and Legal Aid/Public Defenders' offices); Judicial Clerkship (state and federal judges' chambers); and US Attorney's Office Rotation (Eastern District of New York).

Public Advocacy Center (PAC) and Public Service Projects: In a unique concept, Touro's William Randolph Hearst Public Advocacy Center (PAC) houses 14 independent public interest agencies at the law school where students can gain practical experience in Immigration Law, Housing Law, Employment Law, Rights of Children, Education Law, Constitutional Law, and Poverty Law. The Center is also the focal point for student pro bono activities including the Student Disaster Relief Network, Street Law, Foreclosure Project, Domestic Violence Project, and tax assistance program. Students can work for academic credit, for financial compensation, or on pro bono basis for these agencies. Touro also provides an unlimited selection of externship placements in private law firms, corporate law departments, government agencies, the courts, and public interest organizations.

Institutes: Touro hosts the Institute for Business, Law, and Technology; the Jewish Law Institute; and the Institute for International Human Rights and the Holocaust.

Summer Programs: In addition to the Law Center's on-site summer program, which features special programs on New York law, there are opportunities for work and study abroad in China, Croatia, Germany, India, and Israel. Touro also offers summer internships in law firms, courts, and government offices in Europe and Israel.

■ Students and Faculty

The Law Center's students, coming from diverse backgrounds and experiences, represent over 112 undergraduate institutions and a broad mix of majors. Women make up 48 percent of the total enrollment; minorities, 25 percent.

Touro is proud to offer two honor societies: the *Touro Law Review* and the Moot Court Board. There are also over 30 student organizations devoted to specialized professional and social concerns.

Of Touro's 50 full-time faculty members, many have advanced degrees in other disciplines, including medicine, philosophy, business, and finance. Almost all have extensive practice backgrounds, ranging from the judicial bench, major law firms, criminal prosecution and defense, government agencies, and public interest organizations.

The faculty shares one common characteristic: accessibility to students. Every entering student is assigned a faculty advisor, matched by background or interest area, for discussions on any aspect of the law school experience, including study strategy, course selection, and career goals. With an open-door policy and a student-to-faculty ratio of 16:1, everyone reaps the benefits of a personal and dynamic educational experience.

■ Academic Programs

Juris Doctor (JD): Touro offers the JD degree full time, part time in the day (Monday–Friday), and part time in the evening (Monday–Thursday). Students wishing to accelerate may graduate within two and one-half years (full time) and three and one-half years (part time), by attending summer sessions.

Dual Degrees: The JD may be combined with a Master of Business Administration (MBA), a Master of Public Administration (MPA) in Health Care, or a Master of Social Work (MSW), allowing students to complete the two degrees with significant time and cost savings.

Master of Laws (LLM): The Law Center also offers a 24-credit general LLM, full time or part time, and a 27-credit LLM in US Legal Studies (for foreign law graduates), full time or part time.

■ Academic Support and Enrichment

The Law Center provides a unique program of outside-the-classroom assistance. Teaching assistants (TAs) review material covered in class and conduct small-group sessions on effective study methods and test-taking techniques. The Writing Center offers students an opportunity for intensive, individual work to develop their professional writing skills. Assistance is available in all facets of writing—from reviewing the basics to polishing an article for publication. In addition, the Legal Education Access Program (LEAP) enhances the experience of students of color through a four-week summer program for new students and mentoring during the academic year.

The Touro Law Center Honors Program offers approximately 20 to 25 exceptional students per class year an enriched, comprehensive law school experience. Students in the Honors Program will participate in enhanced academic, experiential, and social opportunities as part of a community of student scholars.

■ Career Services

The Career Services Office offers students and graduates valuable hands-on assistance in their search for part-time, full-time, and summer employment. In addition to placing students in national, regional, and local law firms, there are opportunities in federal, state, and local courts and government agencies, and in the legal departments of corporations and municipalities.

■ Admission and Financial Aid

Touro Law Center does not provide an Applicant Profile Grid for its entering class because such data fail to reflect the complexity of the selection process.

At no point on a purely objective scale is an applicant assured of a particular decision. Among the most important criteria are the LSAT score and UGPA. However, evaluation is based on a variety of factors that may be indicative of potential for success—college major and course selection, graduate study, work experience, community involvement, and character.

In order to finance law school, Touro provides access to federal loans and work study, New York State loan and assistance programs, and need-based Touro Grants.

■ Scholarships

Most students receive some form of financial aid, and about 60 percent of entering students receive scholarships. Institutional aid is available to entering students (based on LSAT/UGPA) and to continuing law students (based on law school academic performance). Assistance includes dean's fellowships (full-tuition remission), merit scholarships (up to 90 percent tuition remission), and incentive awards (up to $8,800 per year). In addition, the Law Center offers stipends for Public Interest Law Fellowships, judicial clerkships, and federal work-study placements during the summer.

Applicant Profile

Please refer to section on Admission and Financial Aid.

Tulane University Law School

John Giffen Weinmann Hall, 6329 Freret Street
New Orleans, LA 70118
Phone: 504.865.5930; Fax: 504.865.6710
E-mail: admissions@law.tulane.edu; Website: www.law.tulane.edu

ABA Approved Since 1925

American Bar Association
Section of Legal Education
and Admissions to the Bar

The Basics

Type of school	Private
Term	Semester
Application deadline	3/15
Application fee	$60
Financial aid deadline	2/15
Can first year start other than fall?	No
Student to faculty ratio	14.1 to 1
# of housing spaces available restricted to law students	
graduate housing for which law students are eligible	166

Faculty and Administrators

	Total		Men		Women		Minorities	
	Spr	Fall	Spr	Fall	Spr	Fall	Spr	Fall
Full-time	44	45	27	30	17	15	3	5
Other full-time	9	9	2	2	7	7	0	0
Deans, librarians, & others who teach	7	7	4	4	3	3	0	0
Part-time	40	28	33	25	7	3	0	2
Total	100	89	66	61	34	28	3	7

JD Enrollment and Ethnicity

	Men		Women		Full-Time		Part-Time		1st-Year		Total		JD Degs. Awd.
	#	%	#	%	#	%	#	%	#	%	#	%	
African Amer.	25	5.4	31	9.9	56	7.3	0	0.0	21	7.4	56	7.2	18
Amer. Indian	4	0.9	7	2.2	11	1.4	0	0.0	4	1.4	11	1.4	1
Asian Amer.	9	2.0	10	3.2	19	2.5	0	0.0	7	2.5	19	2.5	12
Mex. Amer.	1	0.2	0	0.0	1	0.1	0	0.0	0	0.0	1	0.1	1
Puerto Rican	4	0.9	3	1.0	7	0.9	0	0.0	3	1.1	7	0.9	2
Hispanic	21	4.6	11	3.5	32	4.2	0	0.0	12	4.2	32	4.1	8
Total Minority	64	13.9	62	19.7	126	16.3	0	0.0	47	16.6	126	16.3	42
For. Nation.	9	2.0	8	2.5	15	1.9	2	66.7	5	1.8	17	2.2	3
Caucasian	353	76.7	226	72.0	578	75.0	1	33.3	220	77.7	579	74.8	197
Unknown	34	7.4	18	5.7	52	6.7	0	0.0	11	3.9	52	6.7	15
Total	460	59.4	314	40.6	771	99.6	3	0.4	283	36.6	774		257

Curriculum

	Full-Time	Part-Time
Typical first-year section size	83	0
Is there typically a "small section" of the first-year class, other than Legal Writing, taught by full-time faculty	No	No
If yes, typical size offered last year		
# of classroom course titles beyond first-year curriculum	193	

# of upper division courses, excluding seminars, with an enrollment:		
	Under 25	106
	25–49	57
	50–74	11
	75–99	6
	100+	5

# of seminars		24
# of seminar positions available		406
# of seminar positions filled	408	0
# of positions available in simulation courses	382	
# of simulation positions filled	334	0
# of positions available in faculty supervised clinical courses	104	
# of faculty supervised clinical positions filled	102	0
# involved in field placements	57	0
# involved in law journals	235	0
# involved in moot court or trial competitions	167	0
# of credit hours required to graduate	88	

Transfers

Transfers in	19
Transfers out	9

Tuition and Fees

	Resident	Nonresident
Full-time	$40,644	$40,644
Part-time		
Tuition Guarantee Program	N	

Living Expenses

Estimated living expenses for singles

Living on campus	Living off campus	Living at home
$19,370	$19,370	$9,850

Tulane University Law School

ABA
Approved
Since
1925

GPA and LSAT Scores

	Total	Full-Time	Part-Time
# of apps	2,990	2,990	0
# of offers	894	894	0
# of matrics	284	284	0
75% GPA	3.75	3.75	0.00
Median GPA	3.60	3.60	0.00
25% GPA	3.34	3.34	0.00
75% LSAT	164	164	0
Median LSAT	162	162	0
25% LSAT	160	160	0

Grants and Scholarships (from prior year)

	Total		Full-Time		Part-Time	
	#	%	#	%	#	%
Total # of students	746		746		0	
Total # receiving grants	461	61.8	461	61.8	0	0.0
Less than 1/2 tuition	260	34.9	260	34.9	0	0.0
Half to full tuition	201	26.9	201	26.9	0	0.0
Full tuition	0	0.0	0	0.0	0	0.0
More than full tuition	0	0.0	0	0.0	0	0.0
Median grant amount			$15,000		$0	

Informational and Library Resources

Total amount spent on library materials	$1,047,018
Study seating capacity inside the library	553
# of full-time equivalent professional librarians	7
Hours per week library is open	113
# of open, wired connections available to students	293
# of networked computers available for use by students	98
Has wireless network?	Y
Require computer?	N

JD Attrition (from prior year)

	Academic	Other	Total	
	#	#	#	%
1st year	1	22	23	9.6
2nd year	2	4	6	2.4
3rd year	2	2	4	1.5
4th year	0	0	0	0.0

Employment (9 months after graduation)

	Total	Percentage
Employment status known	236	97.5
Employment status unknown	6	2.5
Employed	213	90.3
Pursuing graduate degrees	6	2.5
Unemployed (seeking, not seeking, or studying for the bar)	17	7.2
Type of Employment		
# employed in law firms	122	57.3
# employed in business and industry	21	9.9
# employed in government	21	9.9
# employed in public interest	19	8.9
# employed as judicial clerks	26	12.2
# employed in academia	4	1.9
Geographic Location		
# employed in state	80	37.6
# employed in foreign countries	5	2.3
# of states where employed	32	

Bar Passage Rates

First-time takers	231	Reporting %	77.92
Average school %	79.45	Average state %	76.82
Average pass difference	2.63		

Jurisdiction	Takers	Passers	Pass %	State %	Diff %
Louisiana	83	63	75.90	67.32	8.58
New York	47	43	91.49	88.98	2.51
California	26	16	61.54	78.07	–16.53
Texas	24	21	87.50	84.54	2.96

Tulane University Law School

John Giffen Weinmann Hall, 6329 Freret Street
New Orleans, LA 70118
Phone: 504.865.5930; Fax: 504.865.6710
E-mail: admissions@law.tulane.edu; Website: www.law.tulane.edu

■ Introduction

The opportunity to attend law school in New Orleans, perhaps the most dynamic city in the United States today, can transform an ordinary law school experience into an extraordinary one. Tulane Law School, established in 1847, is the 12th oldest law school in the United States. The Law School is centrally located on the main university campus in uptown New Orleans, in a picturesque neighborhood of residences, both large and small, as well as restaurants, bookstores, and other commercial establishments.

■ New Orleans

New Orleans offers extensive legal resources, including the US Court of Appeals for the Fifth Circuit, US District Court, the Louisiana Supreme Court, and all of the lower state civil, criminal, and specialized courts. Within the legal community, students have the opportunity to work with both prosecutors and public defenders, in the private sector, the public sector, and in the public interest. Life outside of the law is rich, too. New Orleans is justly renowned for its music and its food. In addition to numerous events at Tulane University, students enjoy the advantages of city life and the variety within New Orleans culture. Concerts, festivals, and innumerable citywide events take place throughout the year.

■ Facilities

The Law School is housed in the 160,000-square-foot John Giffen Weinmann Hall. Designed to integrate classrooms, other student spaces, faculty offices, and a library containing both national and international collections, the building is centrally located on Tulane University's campus. Immediately adjacent to Weinmann Hall is the Law School's Career Development Office. Within minutes of the Law School building are the university's Howard-Tilton Memorial Library, housing over one million volumes; the Lavin-Bernick Center for University Life; various university dining facilities; the university bookstore; the Reily Student Recreation Center; the Freeman School of Business; the Newcomb Art Gallery; and various auditoriums and performance venues.

■ The Academic Program

The Law School curriculum offers a full range of common law and federal subjects. In addition, Tulane offers electives in the civil law, with the result that students have the opportunity to pursue comparative education in the world's two major legal systems. The breadth and depth of the curriculum permit students to survey a broad range of subject areas or to concentrate in one or more. The background, enthusiasm, and scholarship of the nationally and internationally known faculty further enrich the educational experience.

Six semesters in residence, completion of 88 credits with at least a C average, fulfillment of an upper-level writing requirement, and a 30-hour pro bono obligation are required for graduation from the JD degree program. The first-year curriculum comprises eight required courses, including Legal Research and Writing.

After the first year, all courses are elective, except for the required Legal Profession course. All first-year and many upper-level courses are taught in multiple sections to allow for smaller classes. The upper-level curriculum includes introductory as well as advanced courses in a broad range of subject areas, including international and comparative law, business and corporate law, environmental law, maritime law, criminal law, intellectual property, taxation, and litigation and procedure, among others.

At the graduate level, the Law School offers a general LLM program and an SJD program, as well as specialized LLM programs in Admiralty, Energy and Environmental Law, American Business Law, and International and Comparative Law.

■ Special Programs

The school offers optional concentration programs that allow JD students to receive one certificate of completion of successful studies in (a) European Legal Studies, (b) Environmental Law, (c) Maritime Law, (d) Sports Law, (e) Civil Law, or (f) International and Comparative Law. Tulane's Eason-Weinmann Center for Comparative Law, the Payson Center for International Development and Technology Transfer, the Maritime Law Center, and the Institute for Water Law and Policy add depth to the curriculum. Tulane also offers strong curricula in intellectual property law and constitutional law, as well as business, corporate, and commercial law.

Tulane conducts an annual summer school in New Orleans and offers summer-study programs abroad in England, the Netherlands, France, Italy, Germany, and Greece. It also offers semester-long exchange programs with select law schools in a number of countries throughout the world.

The school was the first in the country to institute a pro bono program requiring that each student complete 30 hours of community service work prior to graduation.

■ Clinical Programs

The school offers the following live-client clinical programs: civil litigation, criminal defense, juvenile litigation, domestic violence, environmental law, and legislative and administrative advocacy. A new mediation clinic was initiated in spring 2008. In addition, there is a trial advocacy program, and third-year students may engage in externships with federal and state judges, with a variety of public interest organizations, with a local death penalty project, or with certain administrative agencies.

■ Joint-Degree Programs

Joint-degree programs are offered in conjunction with Tulane's Freeman School of Business (JD/MBA and JD/MACCT), School of Public Health and Tropical Medicine (JD/MHA and JD/MPH), School of Social Work (JD/MSW), and several of the academic departments of the university. The JD/MS in International Development is offered in cooperation with the Law School's Payson Center for International Development and Technology Transfer, and the JD/MA in Latin American Studies is offered in cooperation

with the Stone Center for Latin American Studies. Proposals for additional programs are considered on an ad hoc basis.

■ Admission and Financial Aid

Our admission process is based on a complete review of all of the information in each candidate's file. This naturally includes the LSAT score and the undergraduate academic record. In the case of multiple LSAT scores, the school sees all scores but will give more weight to the higher score based on the candidate's explanation. Tulane looks closely at subjective factors such as grade trends, courseload, undergraduate school, nonacademic activities, the student's background and experience, barriers overcome, and the personal statement. The Law School processes applications for admission beginning September 1 and starts to announce decisions after December 1. All candidates receive consideration for merit-based scholarship awards. Need-based and credit-based loans require submission of the FAFSA. A loan repayment assistance program is available to graduates working full time in eligible public interest employment.

■ Student Life

Journals published or edited at Tulane Law School include the *Tulane Law Review, Tulane Maritime Law Journal, Tulane Environmental Law Journal, Law and Sexuality, Tulane European and Civil Law Forum, Tulane Journal of International and Comparative Law, Tulane Journal of Technology and Intellectual Property*, and *Sports Lawyers Journal*. An active moot court program holds trial and appellate competitions within the school and fields teams for a variety of interschool competitions, including alternative dispute resolution methods.

The Law School has a chapter of the Order of the Coif.

The Student Bar Association functions as the student government and recommends students for appointment to faculty committees. Over 40 student organizations exist at Tulane, including the International Law Society, Black Law Students Association, La Alianza del Derecho, Asian-Pacific-American Law Students Association, Business Law Society, and Sports Law Society, among others. The Tulane Public Interest Law Foundation raises funds, matched by the Law School, to support as many as 30 students each summer in public interest fellowships with a variety of organizations. The Environmental Law Society hosts a major science and the public interest conference each spring.

Most students live in a variety of off-campus neighborhoods throughout the New Orleans metropolitan area, often within walking or biking distance of the Law School.

■ Career Services

The Law School Career Development Office assists both students and alumni in their job searches. Each student is assigned a career counselor as a first-year student and thereafter has access to a full range of career counseling services from the entire staff as well as to programs on job-search skills and practice areas. A large career-services library is available, including extensive online resources. Tulane organizes both on- and off-campus interview programs for its students. Career Development staff members also engage in employer development activities on a national basis. The office takes a proactive stance in assisting students with their job searches, with the result that Tulane graduates find law-related employment throughout the United States.

Applicant Profile

Tulane University Law School

LSAT Score	GPA									
	3.75 +	3.50–3.74	3.25–3.49	3.00–3.24	2.75–2.99	2.50–2.74	2.25–2.49	2.00–2.24	Below 2.00	No GPA
175–180										
170–174										
165–169										
160–164										
155–159										
150–154										
145–149										
140–144										
135–139										
130–134										
125–129										
120–124										

Excellent   Good   Possible   Unlikely

Reflects 99% of the total applicant pool; average LSAT data reported.

The University of Tulsa College of Law

3120 East Fourth Place
Tulsa, OK 74104-3189
Phone: 918.631.2406; Fax: 918.631.3630
E-mail: lawadmissions@utulsa.edu; Website: www.law.utulsa.edu/admissions/

ABA
Approved
Since
1950

The Basics

Type of school	Private
Term	Semester
Application deadline	2/1
Application fee	$30
Financial aid deadline	2/1
Can first year start other than fall?	No
Student to faculty ratio	12.0 to 1
# of housing spaces available restricted to law students graduate housing for which law students are eligible	256

Faculty and Administrators

	Total		Men		Women		Minorities	
	Spr	Fall	Spr	Fall	Spr	Fall	Spr	Fall
Full-time	28	29	16	15	12	14	4	5
Other full-time	0	0	0	0	0	0	0	0
Deans, librarians, & others who teach	5	3	2	2	3	1	1	0
Part-time	23	24	18	16	5	8	0	2
Total	56	56	36	33	20	23	5	7

JD Enrollment and Ethnicity

	Men		Women		Full-Time		Part-Time		1st-Year		Total		JD Degs. Awd.
	#	%	#	%	#	%	#	%	#	%	#	%	
African Amer.	1	0.4	3	1.8	4	1.0	0	0.0	0	0.0	4	0.9	1
Amer. Indian	22	8.5	18	11.0	34	8.9	6	15.0	11	8.0	40	9.5	9
Asian Amer.	7	2.7	5	3.0	10	2.6	2	5.0	4	2.9	12	2.8	1
Mex. Amer.	6	2.3	6	3.7	11	2.9	1	2.5	4	2.9	12	2.8	2
Puerto Rican	0	0.0	0	0.0	0	0.0	0	0.0	0	0.0	0	0.0	0
Hispanic	0	0.0	0	0.0	0	0.0	0	0.0	0	0.0	0	0.0	0
Total Minority	36	14.0	32	19.5	59	15.4	9	22.5	19	13.8	68	16.1	13
For. Nation.	1	0.4	0	0.0	1	0.3	0	0.0	0	0.0	1	0.2	1
Caucasian	186	72.1	110	67.1	270	70.7	26	65.0	100	72.5	296	70.1	127
Unknown	35	13.6	22	13.4	52	13.6	5	12.5	19	13.8	57	13.5	21
Total	258	61.1	164	38.9	382	90.5	40	9.5	138	32.7	422		162

Curriculum

	Full-Time	Part-Time
Typical first-year section size	45	0
Is there typically a "small section" of the first-year class, other than Legal Writing, taught by full-time faculty	No	No
If yes, typical size offered last year		
# of classroom course titles beyond first-year curriculum	132	
# of upper division courses, excluding seminars, with an enrollment: Under 25	88	
25–49	24	
50–74	9	
75–99	0	
100+	0	
# of seminars	11	
# of seminar positions available	165	
# of seminar positions filled	108	0
# of positions available in simulation courses	608	
# of simulation positions filled	459	0
# of positions available in faculty supervised clinical courses	32	
# of faculty supervised clinical positions filled	32	0
# involved in field placements	44	0
# involved in law journals	150	0
# involved in moot court or trial competitions	41	0
# of credit hours required to graduate	88	

Transfers

Transfers in	3
Transfers out	7

Tuition and Fees

	Resident	Nonresident
Full-time	$29,040	$29,040
Part-time		
Tuition Guarantee Program	N	

Living Expenses

Estimated living expenses for singles

Living on campus	Living off campus	Living at home
$15,310	$18,726	$8,466

The University of Tulsa College of Law

ABA
Approved
Since
1950

GPA and LSAT Scores

	Total	Full-Time	Part-Time
# of apps	1,304	1,304	0
# of offers	659	659	0
# of matrics	140	140	0
75% GPA	3.55	3.55	0.00
Median GPA	3.22	3.22	0.00
25% GPA	2.83	2.83	0.00
75% LSAT	157	157	0
Median LSAT	155	155	0
25% LSAT	152	152	0

Grants and Scholarships (from prior year)

	Total #	Total %	Full-Time #	Full-Time %	Part-Time #	Part-Time %
Total # of students	460		415		45	
Total # receiving grants	214	46.5	191	46.0	23	51.1
Less than 1/2 tuition	117	25.4	103	24.8	14	31.1
Half to full tuition	76	16.5	67	16.1	9	20.0
Full tuition	11	2.4	11	2.7	0	0.0
More than full tuition	10	2.2	10	2.4	0	0.0
Median grant amount			$12,000		$11,500	

Informational and Library Resources

Total amount spent on library materials	$1,010,054
Study seating capacity inside the library	718
# of full-time equivalent professional librarians	8
Hours per week library is open	113
# of open, wired connections available to students	376
# of networked computers available for use by students	98
Has wireless network?	Y
Require computer?	N

JD Attrition (from prior year)

	Academic #	Other #	Total #	Total %
1st year	5	5	10	7.2
2nd year	4	9	13	8.9
3rd year	0	0	0	0.0
4th year	0	0	0	0.0

Employment (9 months after graduation)

	Total	Percentage
Employment status known	154	92.2
Employment status unknown	13	7.8
Employed	143	92.9
Pursuing graduate degrees	6	3.9
Unemployed (seeking, not seeking, or studying for the bar)	3	1.9
Type of Employment		
# employed in law firms	84	58.7
# employed in business and industry	30	21.0
# employed in government	16	11.2
# employed in public interest	7	4.9
# employed as judicial clerks	2	1.4
# employed in academia	4	2.8
Geographic Location		
# employed in state	81	56.6
# employed in foreign countries	1	0.7
# of states where employed	21	

Bar Passage Rates

First-time takers	166	Reporting %	78.31
Average school %	92.30	Average state %	91.41
Average pass difference	0.89		

Jurisdiction	Takers	Passers	Pass %	State %	Diff %
Oklahoma	108	100	92.59	92.80	–0.21
Texas	22	20	90.91	84.54	6.37

The University of Tulsa College of Law

3120 East Fourth Place
Tulsa, OK 74104-3189
Phone: 918.631.2406; Fax: 918.631.3630
E-mail: lawadmissions@utulsa.edu; Website: www.law.utulsa.edu/admissions/

■ Introduction

Expect an exceptional legal education from the University of Tulsa. The faculty and staff at TU prove daily that it is possible for friendliness, challenge, respect, and excellence to coexist in law school. Housed in technologically advanced John Rogers Hall on the University of Tulsa campus, and fully accredited by the ABA, the law school presents a forum for study and exploration of legal issues enhanced by professors with exemplary credentials. A true open-door policy and faculty mentoring program invite students to expand their legal education from the classroom to one-on-one accessibility and interaction with the TU Law faculty. We also honor student talent with scholarships ranging up to full tuition. Approximately 60 percent of an entering class receives merit- or need-based assistance. With most students coming to Tulsa from states other than Oklahoma, a rich fabric of diversity expands the learning experience of every student. Located in the beautiful, culturally diverse, and extraordinarily friendly city of Tulsa, law students can enjoy award-winning theater, national touring concerts, world-class museums, gorgeous parks, and vibrant neighborhood shopping areas. The city also boasts an internationally recognized burgeoning environment for high-tech industry and commerce.

■ Library and Physical Facilities

Recently cited by the *National Jurist* as one of the top 12 libraries in the US, the impressive Mabee Legal Information Center (MLIC) is much more than a library. The center was designed for students. Enter the center and you will feel the warmth of Southwestern colors used throughout the MLIC, such as burnished mahogany, bayberry, and sienna. It would be very difficult to find a more attractive, pleasant place to spend your hours of study, research, and, yes, even relaxation. While the MLIC is proud of its technological innovations and numerous electronic resources, the center also pays homage to the traditional uses and print publications many students appreciate in a library. The center is additional proof that meeting the varied needs and uses of our students is our highest priority at Tulsa.

For students, the MLIC is an ideal locale for collaborating, preparing for class or exams, working on journal scholarship, conducting extensive research, conferring with reference librarians, or preparing for a moot court competition. Over 60 computers are available for use throughout the information center, including several laptops that are available for checkout. To better accommodate the needs of our students, a rededication of space in 2006 dramatically doubled the number of popular group collaborative study rooms available throughout the MLIC. Student staffing offices for the Board of Advocates, the *Tulsa Law Review*, the *Energy Law Journal*, and the *Tulsa Journal of Comparative and International Law* provide generous working space for these important enterprises at the College of Law. In 2009 the MLIC provided additional office space to several other important student organizations that are active within the college. Jobs are secured for summer or permanent employment in the comfortable interview rooms also located in the MLIC. Specialized classrooms include a laptop lab and the

Alternative Dispute Resolution Center where negotiation exercises are possible within a variety of simulation configurations. The Utsey Family Native American Law Center and the Frank M. Rowell Jr. Comparative and International Law Center offer inviting forums for study, research, and the exchange of ideas, with impressive artwork providing a showcase for these two exceptional programs. In October 2009, the John F. Hicks and John Rogers Archives Room was opened to preserve the rich history of the college and to provide the means to collect important documents, photographs, and artifacts for the many significant achievements of the College of Law now and in the future.

If quiet study is for you, the two main reading rooms reflect quiet, inviting, wide-open spaces with natural lighting. With over 700 seats available and seven miles of shelving space, there is plenty of space for students, alumni, and books. Nearly 300 study carrels, many of which can be reserved a semester at a time, provide private work space.

Professional librarians, most with law degrees, are ready to help with legal research in the 410,000 volume collection. An impressive array of electronic resources are accessible to students on-site or from home.

The College of Law has wireless access throughout the building. Classrooms provide access for instruction from a variety of computerized configurations, including smart podiums, large-screen projection, and Internet feeds. Faculty are readily accessible for consultation with the students and most of their offices are conveniently located across the hallway from the classrooms. Both faculty and students appreciate the original Native American artwork throughout the school. The Boesche Legal Clinic and the modern Price-Turpen model courtroom bring the same state-of-the-art capacities to the study and training for trial and appellate advocacy. They are outstanding facilities in which the best in preparation is available for Tulsa law students as they prepare for future legal practice and train for many regional and national moot court competitions.

■ Curriculum and Specialization

Full-time and reduced schedule options are available, as well as summer classes. Students may choose either general legal study, covering a broad expanse of expertise, or specialization. Areas of curricular focus include Comparative and International Law; Resources, Energy, and Environmental Law; Native American Law; and Health Law. Additional areas of concentrated study include Public Policy and Regulation, Lawyering Skills, and Entrepreneurial Law.

Summer- and semester-abroad programs ensure that Tulsa students will have the opportunity to become immersed in the excitement of broadening international horizons for legal training and personal exploration. The University of Tulsa International Law Program is augmented by exciting opportunities to study abroad during the summer in Dublin (Ireland), Geneva (Switzerland), Tianjin (China), and Buenos Aires (Argentina), plus the opportunity for a fall semester of study in London.

Students at Tulsa have a great variety of career choices available to them, including interdisciplinary study. The following joint-degree programs are available: JD/MBA,

JD/MA in Anthropology, JD/MA in History, JD/MA in Industrial/Organizational Psychology, JD/MA in English, JD/MS in Computer Science, JD/MS in Biological Sciences, JD/MA in Clinical Psychology, JD/MS in Geosciences, JD/MS in Finance, and JD/MS in Taxation.

■ Professors

Knowledge and experience, matched by the passion for teaching, typifies the character of the professors at the University of Tulsa. Recognized nationally and internationally for their expertise, Tulsa professors are always accessible to their students. Specializations and strong experiential expertise in areas as diverse as international trade, energy regulation, family and juvenile law, sports law, Native American tribal jurisdiction, trial advocacy, and bioethics confirm the rich learning experience available to Tulsa law students. The ability to develop strong relationships with professors will strengthen Tulsa students' law school experience and their future legal practice in remarkable ways.

■ Housing

Law students at Tulsa may choose to live on or off campus. On-campus housing includes well-maintained and modern apartments built exclusively for law and graduate students. Located within an easy walking distance from the law school, each apartment unit includes computer connections and large, spacious floor plans. With a very attractive low cost of living, the city of Tulsa offers a great variety of affordable housing opportunities. Information about housing may be obtained by calling 918.631.5249 or by contacting the Office of Law Admissions at 918.631.2406.

■ Office of Professional Development

Students at Tulsa gain significant personalized assistance in career counseling. On-campus interview coordination, résumé/dossier preparation services, informative seminar offerings, and summer and permanent job placement make the Office of Professional Development an invaluable resource for future success. Tulsa graduates practicing in all 50 states, and internationally, make networking a vital resource in the enhancement of employment potential for students and alumni. Utilizing a high tech content management system called Simplicity, the Office of Professional Development takes a proactive role in coordinating employment postings for both students and alumni. Currently, 93 percent of our graduates report being employed within nine months of graduation.

■ Practical Experience

Tulsa law students gain first-hand training beyond the classroom. The Boesche Legal Clinic is housed in a beautiful, spacious facility conveniently located across the street from John Rogers Hall. The Legal Clinic offers programs such as the Immigrant Rights Project and the Social Enterprise and Economic Development (SEED) Law Project. Federal and state judicial internships are available, as well as the Legal Internship Program, which enables a student to represent clients in criminal and civil cases, subject to rules authorized by the Oklahoma Supreme Court. The TU Law Pro Bono Program allows students to assist with cases going to trial, assist with civil legal matters, participate in interviewing clients and witnesses, and perform research.

Applicant Profile

The University of Tulsa College of Law
This chart is to be used as a guide only. Nonnumerical factors are strongly considered for all applicants.

LSAT Score	GPA								Totals
	3.75 +	3.50–3.74	3.25–3.49	3.00–3.24	2.75–2.99	2.50–2.74	2.25–2.49	Below 2.25	
175–180	0	0	0	0	0	0	0	0	0
170–174	1	2	1	0	0	0	0	0	4
165–169	7	6	5	1	0	0	0	0	19
160–164	14	16	16	9	10	6	2	2	75
155–159	31	45	48	44	37	18	18	8	249
150–154	41	56	67	65	32	18	10	2	291
145–149	3	4	1	0	0	0	0	0	8
140–144	0	0	0	0	0	0	0	0	0
Below 140	0	0	0	0	0	0	0	0	0
Total	97	129	138	119	79	42	30	12	646

University of Utah S.J. Quinney College of Law

332 South 1400 East, Room 101
Salt Lake City, UT 84112-0730
Phone: 801.581.6833; Fax: 801.820.9154
E-mail: admissions@law.utah.edu; Website: www.law.utah.edu

*ABA
Approved
Since
1927*

The Basics

Type of school	Public
Term	Semester
Application deadline	2/1
Application fee	
Financial aid deadline	4/15
Can first year start other than fall?	No
Student to faculty ratio	8.1 to 1
# of housing spaces available restricted to law students	4
graduate housing for which law students are eligible	286

Faculty and Administrators

	Total		Men		Women		Minorities	
	Spr	Fall	Spr	Fall	Spr	Fall	Spr	Fall
Full-time	38	40	26	29	12	11	4	6
Other full-time	0	0	0	0	0	0	0	0
Deans, librarians, & others who teach	9	10	5	5	4	5	0	0
Part-time	28	22	22	13	6	9	0	0
Total	75	72	53	47	22	25	4	6

Curriculum

	Full-Time	Part-Time
Typical first-year section size	39	0
Is there typically a "small section" of the first-year class, other than Legal Writing, taught by full-time faculty	Yes	No
If yes, typical size offered last year	20	
# of classroom course titles beyond first-year curriculum	120	

# of upper division courses, excluding seminars, with an enrollment:		
	Under 25	83
	25–49	16
	50–74	7
	75–99	1
	100+	0

# of seminars	13	
# of seminar positions available	156	
# of seminar positions filled	137	0
# of positions available in simulation courses	601	
# of simulation positions filled	319	0
# of positions available in faculty supervised clinical courses	0	
# of faculty supervised clinical positions filled	0	0
# involved in field placements	221	0
# involved in law journals	92	0
# involved in moot court or trial competitions	28	0
# of credit hours required to graduate	88	

JD Enrollment and Ethnicity

	Men		Women		Full-Time		Part-Time		1st-Year		Total		JD Degs. Awd.
	#	%	#	%	#	%	#	%	#	%	#	%	
African Amer.	2	0.8	5	3.0	7	1.8	0	0.0	2	1.6	7	1.8	0
Amer. Indian	5	2.1	3	1.8	8	2.1	0	0.0	1	0.8	8	2.0	0
Asian Amer.	7	3.0	7	4.3	14	3.7	0	0.0	6	4.7	14	3.5	8
Mex. Amer.	0	0.0	3	1.8	3	0.8	0	0.0	2	1.6	3	0.8	0
Puerto Rican	0	0.0	0	0.0	0	0.0	0	0.0	0	0.0	0	0.0	0
Hispanic	10	4.2	11	6.7	19	5.0	2	10.5	6	4.7	21	5.3	2
Total Minority	24	10.2	29	17.7	51	13.4	2	10.5	17	13.4	53	13.3	10
For. Nation.	0	0.0	0	0.0	0	0.0	0	0.0	0	0.0	0	0.0	0
Caucasian	185	78.4	116	70.7	285	74.8	16	84.2	100	78.7	301	75.3	102
Unknown	27	11.4	19	11.6	45	11.8	1	5.3	10	7.9	46	11.5	19
Total	236	59.0	164	41.0	381	95.3	19	4.8	127	31.8	400		131

Transfers

Transfers in	17
Transfers out	3

Tuition and Fees

	Resident	Nonresident
Full-time	$16,666	$33,084
Part-time		
Tuition Guarantee Program		N

Living Expenses

Estimated living expenses for singles

Living on campus	Living off campus	Living at home
$17,638	$17,638	$9,985

University of Utah S.J. Quinney College of Law

ABA
Approved
Since
1927

GPA and LSAT Scores

	Total	Full-Time	Part-Time
# of apps	1,277	1,277	0
# of offers	375	375	0
# of matrics	129	129	0
75% GPA	3.76	3.76	0.00
Median GPA	3.60	3.60	0.00
25% GPA	3.41	3.41	0.00
75% LSAT	163	163	0
Median LSAT	160	160	0
25% LSAT	156	156	0

Grants and Scholarships (from prior year)

	Total		Full-Time		Part-Time	
	#	%	#	%	#	%
Total # of students	385		385		0	
Total # receiving grants	197	51.2	197	51.2	0	0.0
Less than 1/2 tuition	126	32.7	126	32.7	0	0.0
Half to full tuition	55	14.3	55	14.3	0	0.0
Full tuition	0	0.0	0	0.0	0	0.0
More than full tuition	16	4.2	16	4.2	0	0.0
Median grant amount			$5,406		$0	

Informational and Library Resources

Total amount spent on library materials	$875,178
Study seating capacity inside the library	665
# of full-time equivalent professional librarians	8
Hours per week library is open	79
# of open, wired connections available to students	300
# of networked computers available for use by students	34
Has wireless network?	Y
Require computer?	Y

JD Attrition (from prior year)

	Academic	Other	Total	
	#	#	#	%
1st year	2	7	9	7.4
2nd year	0	1	1	0.8
3rd year	0	0	0	0.0
4th year	0	0	0	0.0

Employment (9 months after graduation)

	Total	Percentage
Employment status known	131	100.0
Employment status unknown	0	0.0
Employed	129	98.5
Pursuing graduate degrees	1	0.8
Unemployed (seeking, not seeking, or studying for the bar)	0	0.0
Type of Employment		
# employed in law firms	77	59.7
# employed in business and industry	9	7.0
# employed in government	19	14.7
# employed in public interest	7	5.4
# employed as judicial clerks	13	10.1
# employed in academia	4	3.1
Geographic Location		
# employed in state	100	77.5
# employed in foreign countries	1	0.8
# of states where employed	13	

Bar Passage Rates

First-time takers	149	Reporting %	74.50
Average school %	86.49	Average state %	87.29
Average pass difference	−0.80		

Jurisdiction	Takers	Passers	Pass %	State %	Diff %
Utah	111	96	86.49	87.29	−0.80

University of Utah S.J. Quinney College of Law

332 South 1400 East, Room 101
Salt Lake City, UT 84112-0730
Phone: 801.581.6833; Fax: 801.820.9154
E-mail: admissions@law.utah.edu; Website: www.law.utah.edu

■ Introduction

Established in 1913, the University of Utah S.J. Quinney College of Law is nationally recognized for its outstanding academic reputation, stellar faculty, intimate learning environment, innovative curriculum, excellent faculty-to-student ratio, and stunning location. The College of Law is a vibrant learning community with both well-established expertise and exciting new projects on the critical issues of our time: climate change, conflict and security, health justice, the new frontier of family law, technology commercialization, conservation, addiction, innocence, victims' rights, global mediation, and many others. We have also launched four innovative, crosscutting initiatives in leadership, cross-disciplinary training, smart technology, and global legal education. These creative intellectual investments have generated astounding results for each class of 125 entering students.

Among the students, there is a prevailing sense of community fostered by an open and service-oriented faculty and administration. The law school is less than a 10-minute drive or light rail ride from downtown Salt Lake City—the seat of federal, state, and local governmental bodies. Salt Lake City is the economic center of the region and is regularly voted one of America's most livable cities. This location provides ample professional opportunities for our students, as well as superb outdoor recreational access and a strong cultural scene.

■ Library and Physical Facilities

The S.J. Quinney law library and the law building are wireless environments. First-year students are provided with their own study hall furnished with group-study tables and carrels. Advanced students are provided carrels which also have wireless network access in the adjacent Quinney law library—a modern, spacious facility with the latest technological equipment and library research services.

The library holds more than 340,000 volumes of law and law-related material and serves as a depository for US government documents. CD-ROM and web-based databases provide access to primary legal materials, journal indexes, directories, and other law-related information. There is a computer lab with 29 workstations located in the library. Eight librarians (six with law degrees) teach the research component of the Legal Methods course.

■ Curriculum

The Quinney law school's innovative academic programs blend theory and practice skills that prepare graduates to tackle the major questions of our time and practice law in any jurisdiction. The curriculum is designed to allow more efficient and rational sequencing of legal education that responds to the evolving legal, social, and ethical needs of our society.

The entering students are first offered an intensive four-day Introduction to Law course before they begin the required first-year curriculum. The first-year doctrinal courses include a small section in which enrollment is limited to no more than 25 students. Second-year students select from a variety of foundational courses. In the third year, students may take year-long intensive courses that provide the opportunity for in-depth study, research, and a practicum in a focused area of law.

Additionally, outside the formal classroom, clinical and cocurricular opportunities ensure that students learn the most critical professional and intellectual lessons in simulated competitions and real-world settings. We have several award-winning moot court teams, three first-rate journals, and a series of new student think tanks working on the major issues of our time (including the global justice think tank, which is working on its third Oxford University Press book and a $10.4 million grant to provide law and policy advice to the Iraqi government). Through our think tanks, clinics (over 200 placements each year) and award-winning pro bono initiative (with 125 placements each semester), our students contributed over 30,000 hours of public service in just one year.

■ Special Programs

The Wallace Stegner Center for Land, Resources, and the Environment provides opportunities for students to engage in academic courses and related law activities focusing on public lands, environmental and natural resources law, and energy law. A Certificate in Environmental and Natural Resources Law is awarded to students who complete a sequence of approved courses with a specified GPA. The law school also offers an LLM degree in natural resources and environmental law.

The Utah Criminal Justice Center is an interdisciplinary partnership between the University of Utah and state government. The center supports collaborative work among academic units at the university in partnership with the Utah Commission on Criminal and Juvenile Justice. The interdisciplinary character and the potential benefits for policymaking and employment make the Utah Criminal Justice Center unique in American higher education and a model for productive collaboration between academia and government.

The clinical programs offer both live and simulated opportunities for students to assume the lawyering role. In the Civil Clinic and the Criminal Clinic, students represent clients, investigate cases, and appear in court. In the Judicial Clinic, students act as clerks to judges, researching issues and drafting opinions in pending cases. The Judicial Extern Program allows students to spend a semester away from school working as full-time clerks for certain courts. Other clinical opportunities are available in our Environmental, Health Law, Legislative, and Mediation clinics.

The Pro Bono Initiative is a voluntary program offered to emphasize the centrality of public service to the legal profession. The College of Law encourages students to perform at least 50 hours of law-related volunteer work during their time in law school. The Pro Bono Initiative facilitates this opportunity by providing students with a broad spectrum of developed volunteer placements.

Through the London Law Consortium, students engage in the law school's study-abroad program during spring semester.

The College of Law maintains three formal joint-degree programs. Students may earn joint degrees in the areas of business (JD/MBA), public administration (JD/MPA), or public policy (JD/MPP). A fourth program in the area of social work (JD/MSW) is expected to be approved in 2010.

The Academic Support Program provides assistance to students whose backgrounds and experiences before law school indicate a need for such assistance. Students apply to participate in the program after admission to the College of Law.

■ Admission Standards

No applicant is accepted or rejected without members of the Admission Committee having first fully considered the entire application. The personal statement should expand on the applicant's biographic and academic background and motivations for seeking a legal education. The College of Law makes a special effort to attract students from diverse cultural, educational, economic, ethnic, racial, and nontraditional backgrounds. Each applicant is evaluated for the contribution that person can make to the student body or the legal profession, in addition to evidence of demonstrated high academic ability.

■ Student Activities

The *Utah Law Review*, the *Journal of Law and Family Studies*, and the *Journal of Land, Resources, and Environmental Law* are professional journals edited and published by students. The *Utah Law Review* selects staff members on the basis of academic achievement and a writing competition. The other journals select staff members based on a writing competition.

Student organizations include the Student Bar Association, the Women's Law Caucus, Natural Resources Law Forum, the Minority Law Caucus, the International Legal Issues Society, Business Law Society, American Constitution Society, the Federalist Society, Outlaws, Native American Law Student Association, the Public Interest Law Organization, Utah Criminal Justice Society, Phi Delta Phi, LDS Law Student Association, the Jackie Chiles Law Society, J. Reuben Clark Society, the Sports Law Club, and the Student Intellectual Property Law Association.

■ Financial Aid

The College of Law provides an effective financial aid program that includes generous scholarships. The University of Utah participates in Federal Perkins, Stafford, and Graduate PLUS loan programs. More information on these student loan programs, is available at: *www.law.utah.edu/prospective/financial-aid/*. Merit scholarships are awarded to selected candidates based on the information contained in their application materials. Need-based scholarships are awarded to students based on information provided through the Free Application for Federal Student Aid and a separate application provided to all admitted candidates. The law school also has a Loan Forgiveness Program for qualified graduates who practice in the public sector or the public interest field.

■ Career Services

College of Law students and graduates have access to one of the most advanced legal career services programs in the US. The office, known as the Professional Development Office (PDO), transmits information to prospective employers, both on and off campus and coordinates the on-campus interview process. PDO also conducts personal career counseling and assists students with the development of their résumés and other material used in the employment search. PDO maintains a resource library and sponsors numerous seminars throughout the year.

Applicant Profile

University of Utah S.J. Quinney College of Law
This grid includes only applicants who earned 120–180 LSAT scores under standard administrations.

LSAT Score	3.75 +		3.50–3.74		3.25–3.49		3.00–3.24		2.75–2.99		2.50–2.74		2.25–2.49		2.00–2.24		Below 2.00		No GPA		Total	
	Apps	Adm	Apps	Adm	Apps	Adm	Apps	Adm	Apps	Adm	Apps	Adm	Apps	Adm	Apps	Adm	Apps	Adm	Apps	Adm	Apps	Adm
175–180	0	0	0	0	1	1	0	0	0	0	0	0	0	0	0	0	0	0	0	0	1	1
170–174	10	9	2	2	2	0	4	3	3	1	0	0	0	0	0	0	0	0	0	0	21	15
165–169	23	23	19	19	13	11	11	8	1	0	3	1	3	0	0	0	0	0	1	0	74	62
160–164	77	71	71	54	48	33	30	13	13	5	9	0	2	1	1	0	0	0	1	0	252	177
155–159	64	42	117	46	81	26	48	8	18	0	11	1	5	0	1	0	1	0	3	0	349	123
150–154	49	17	66	21	78	10	46	9	22	3	8	0	6	0	3	0	0	0	3	0	281	60
145–149	13	1	31	6	39	3	38	3	22	0	9	0	10	0	1	0	1	0	5	0	169	13
140–144	3	0	8	1	22	3	13	0	12	0	7	1	4	0	1	0	0	0	2	0	72	5
135–139	0	0	3	0	7	0	9	0	5	0	2	0	3	0	3	0	1	0	2	0	35	0
130–134	0	0	3	0	0	0	2	0	2	0	3	0	4	0	0	0	0	0	2	0	16	0
125–129	0	0	0	0	0	0	0	0	2	0	0	0	0	0	0	0	0	0	1	0	3	0
120–124	0	0	0	0	0	0	0	0	0	0	0	0	0	0	0	0	0	0	0	0	0	0
Total	239	163	320	149	291	87	201	44	100	9	52	3	37	1	10	0	3	0	20	0	1273	456

Apps = Number of Applicants   Adm = Number Admitted   Reflects 99% of the total applicant pool; average LSAT data reported.

Note: This chart is to be used as a general guide only. Nonnumerical factors are strongly considered for all applicants.

Valparaiso University School of Law

656 S. Greenwich, Wesemann Hall
Valparaiso, IN 46383-4945
Phone: 219.465.7821; Fax: 219.465.7975
E-mail: law.admissions@valpo.edu; Website: www.valpo.edu/law/

*ABA
Approved
Since
1929*

The Basics

Type of school	Private
Term	Semester
Application deadline	6/1
Application fee	$60
Financial aid deadline	3/1
Can first year start other than fall?	No
Student to faculty ratio	16.4 to 1
# of housing spaces available restricted to law students	
graduate housing for which law students are eligible	

Faculty and Administrators

	Total		Men		Women		Minorities	
	Spr	Fall	Spr	Fall	Spr	Fall	Spr	Fall
Full-time	27	30	18	19	9	11	2	3
Other full-time	3	3	3	3	0	0	1	1
Deans, librarians, & others who teach	12	11	5	5	7	6	1	0
Part-time	28	27	19	17	8	10	3	3
Total	70	71	45	44	24	27	7	7

Curriculum

		Full-Time	Part-Time
Typical first-year section size		72	0
Is there typically a "small section" of the first-year class, other than Legal Writing, taught by full-time faculty		No	No
If yes, typical size offered last year			
# of classroom course titles beyond first-year curriculum		100	
# of upper division courses, excluding seminars, with an enrollment:	Under 25	82	
	25–49	27	
	50–74	9	
	75–99	3	
	100+	4	
# of seminars		16	
# of seminar positions available		232	
# of seminar positions filled		158	4
# of positions available in simulation courses		731	
# of simulation positions filled		545	26
# of positions available in faculty supervised clinical courses		132	
# of faculty supervised clinical positions filled		110	2
# involved in field placements		197	1
# involved in law journals		48	0
# involved in moot court or trial competitions		98	0
# of credit hours required to graduate		90	

JD Enrollment and Ethnicity

	Men		Women		Full-Time		Part-Time		1st-Year		Total		JD Degs. Awd.
	#	%	#	%	#	%	#	%	#	%	#	%	
African Amer.	13	4.3	30	10.8	39	7.2	4	9.8	24	11.3	43	7.4	8
Amer. Indian	2	0.7	2	0.7	4	0.7	0	0.0	2	0.9	4	0.7	0
Asian Amer.	8	2.6	8	2.9	14	2.6	2	4.9	9	4.2	16	2.7	3
Mex. Amer.	5	1.6	8	2.9	13	2.4	0	0.0	6	2.8	13	2.2	1
Puerto Rican	0	0.0	0	0.0	0	0.0	0	0.0	0	0.0	0	0.0	1
Hispanic	12	3.9	7	2.5	19	3.5	0	0.0	11	5.2	19	3.3	9
Total Minority	40	13.1	55	19.9	89	16.5	6	14.6	52	24.4	95	16.3	22
For. Nation.	2	0.7	5	1.8	6	1.1	1	2.4	1	0.5	7	1.2	1
Caucasian	242	79.3	194	70.0	412	76.2	24	58.5	140	65.7	436	74.9	124
Unknown	21	6.9	23	8.3	34	6.3	10	24.4	20	9.4	44	7.6	17
Total	305	52.4	277	47.6	541	93.0	41	7.0	213	36.6	582		164

Transfers

Transfers in	4
Transfers out	23

Tuition and Fees

	Resident	Nonresident
Full-time	$35,230	$35,230
Part-time	$22,010	$22,010
Tuition Guarantee Program	N	

Living Expenses

Estimated living expenses for singles

Living on campus	Living off campus	Living at home
N/A	$12,760	$5,960

Valparaiso University School of Law

ABA
Approved
Since
1929

GPA and LSAT Scores

	Total	Full-Time	Part-Time
# of apps	1,575	1,440	135
# of offers	934	889	45
# of matrics	203	191	12
75% GPA	3.59	3.59	3.22
Median GPA	3.34	3.34	2.95
25% GPA	3.08	3.08	2.82
75% LSAT	152	152	151
Median LSAT	150	150	149
25% LSAT	148	148	147

Grants and Scholarships (from prior year)

	Total		Full-Time		Part-Time	
	#	%	#	%	#	%
Total # of students	575		519		56	
Total # receiving grants	145	25.2	138	26.6	7	12.5
Less than 1/2 tuition	65	11.3	58	11.2	7	12.5
Half to full tuition	22	3.8	22	4.2	0	0.0
Full tuition	35	6.1	35	6.7	0	0.0
More than full tuition	23	4.0	23	4.4	0	0.0
Median grant amount			$16,250		$0	

Informational and Library Resources

Total amount spent on library materials	$926,113
Study seating capacity inside the library	386
# of full-time equivalent professional librarians	7
Hours per week library is open	111
# of open, wired connections available to students	46
# of networked computers available for use by students	37
Has wireless network?	Y
Require computer?	N

JD Attrition (from prior year)

	Academic	Other	Total	
	#	#	#	%
1st year	2	27	29	13.4
2nd year	0	0	0	0.0
3rd year	1	0	1	0.6
4th year	0	0	0	0.0

Employment (9 months after graduation)

	Total	Percentage
Employment status known	133	100.0
Employment status unknown	0	0.0
Employed	111	83.5
Pursuing graduate degrees	1	0.8
Unemployed (seeking, not seeking, or studying for the bar)	14	10.5
Type of Employment		
# employed in law firms	67	60.4
# employed in business and industry	14	12.6
# employed in government	13	11.7
# employed in public interest	0	0.0
# employed as judicial clerks	13	11.7
# employed in academia	4	3.6
Geographic Location		
# employed in state	50	45.0
# employed in foreign countries	0	0.0
# of states where employed		23

Bar Passage Rates

First-time takers	124	Reporting %	75.81
Average school %	77.66	Average state %	86.56
Average pass difference	−8.90		

Jurisdiction	Takers	Passers	Pass %	State %	Diff %
Indiana	52	43	82.69	84.39	−1.70
Illinois	26	16	61.54	90.94	−29.40
Michigan	4	2	50.00	82.13	−32.13
Utah	3	3	100.00	87.29	12.71
Others (4)	9	9	100.00		

Valparaiso University School of Law

656 S. Greenwich, Wesemann Hall
Valparaiso, IN 46383-4945
Phone: 219.465.7821; Fax: 219.465.7975
E-mail: law.admissions@valpo.edu; Website: www.valpo.edu/law/

■ Introduction

The School of Law at Valparaiso University was founded in 1879. Throughout its 130-year history our law school has been recognized for the following four traits:

Exceptional Legal Research and Writing: According to a survey by the American Bar Foundation, hiring partners at law firms ranked research and writing skills as the most important skill set a new lawyer can bring to the job. It is common for law schools to have one year of legal writing as part of the first-year curriculum. We offer three years of required research and writing.

Enduring Core Competencies: No matter how much the world and laws change, no matter how often attorneys change their practice, there are certain constants: the ability to engage in critical, analytical, and creative thinking, and the ability to communicate clearly and concisely. These core competencies comprise the cornerstone of a Valparaiso Law education.

Truly Personal Manner of Teaching and Learning: The teaching and learning style of Valparaiso Law is highly collaborative and integrated. Our students interact with faculty both in and out of the classroom. We know our students and strive to provide a legal education that is tailored to their individual aspirations. Every pedagogical component is designed to help the individual student succeed as a professional.

Law as a Calling: We are a community dedicated to imparting not just skills and knowledge, but also values, a sense of self, and a commitment to service. Our graduates are not just solid lawyers, but great people; not just influential leaders, but ones who use their influence for the highest service and the greater good.

■ Curriculum

The School of Law provides a comprehensive and intensive study of the foundations of law, an introduction to the substantive areas of law, and an opportunity for advanced study in specific areas. The curriculum provides a grounding in legal analysis, legal writing and research, practical skills training, perspectives on the law, and ethics. The curriculum focuses on six key areas: **general practice**, **business law**, **public interest representation**, **property**, **litigation**, and **taxation**. To learn more, visit *www.valpo.edu/law/academics/curriculum.php*.

Upon completing the required first-year curriculum, students are given the opportunity to explore various avenues of study. During the second year, students begin to take electives. By the third year, most required courses have been completed and students select courses for general legal competency and focus on areas of interest.

The School of Law is committed to the highest standards of professional ethics and encourages vigorous inquiry into the values upon which legal theories are founded. Students are expected to view the legal system as dynamic and thereby actively engage with it through ethical and intellectual analysis.

Students are encouraged to participate in externships and internships and to enhance their skills in one of our eight legal practice clinics. Valparaiso Law requires 40 hours of pro bono work for graduation.

■ Degree Programs

We offer the JD degree as a three year full-time day, a five year part-time day, or a two and one-half year accelerated day program. In addition, students may begin an MBA or one of six master's degree programs at Valparaiso University after their first year in the JD program, completing both degrees in four years of full-time study. The School of Law also offers a one to one and one-half year full-time day LLM program for international students who have already obtained a law degree.

■ Special Programs

Clinical Law Program—Students enrolled in the live-client law clinic represent indigent clients and participate in all stages of representation. The clinic practice areas are civil, criminal, domestic violence, juvenile, mediation, sports law, tax, and wrongful conviction.

Professional Representation—Students work with faculty on selected current cases.

Externships—The School of Law offers over 70 externships throughout the United States and at international sites.

International Summer Programs—Valparaiso Law offers a comparative law program in London and Cambridge, England, and a program in international human rights in Chile and Argentina.

Honors Program—First-year students are selected for this unique learning community based on academic performance and demonstrated leadership.

Public Interest—Scholarships are awarded to students who choose to work without pay in the public sector during the summer. The Loan Repayment Assistance Program is designed to offer financial assistance to graduates who incurred debt from education loans and chose to go into public service employment. The assistance is in the form of grants that range from $1,000 to $6,000 each year.

Academic Success Program—The Academic Success Program is available to students who seek assistance with the transition from college or the workforce to law school. There is a 10-day summer program prior to law school orientation and a nine-session program held in the fall semester.

■ Career Planning

Our service mission is to assist all students and graduates in planning career paths, preparing for the job market, and identifying and creating professional opportunities. We work closely with employers, including our several thousand alumni, in developing career-related networks for all our law students. In 2008, 83 percent of our graduates were employed within nine months of graduation. About 60 percent are employed in law firms and 40 percent in judicial clerkships, government, public interest work, business, and academia. Our bar passage rate averages 88 percent.

■ Faculty

Our professors have been Fulbright scholars, clerks to federal appellate and state supreme court judges, and have served in government. They bring to their teaching practical experience

in public and private sectors. Their scholarship spans a wide range of legal theory. Visit *www.valpo.edu/law/faculty*.

■ Library and Physical Facilities

The law library is the largest legal research facility in northwest Indiana. Individual and group study carrels are available for student use. A computer lab provides facilities for word processing and Web access, and offers access to LexisNexis, Westlaw, CALI, HeinOnline, LexisNexis Congressional, LegalTrac, and LLMC-Digital, among other databases. A wireless network is available for students' use throughout the campus. Wireless printing is also available. The School of Law occupies two buildings that house classrooms, the law library, a state-of-the-art courtroom and jury room, the law clinic, and administration and faculty offices.

■ Student Activities

The *Valparaiso University Law Review* is a scholarly journal published three times a year. Because of Valparaiso's emphasis on research and writing, membership for the *Law Review* is based on academic achievement as well as excellence in legal writing. Students interested in enhancing their advocacy skills may participate on the Trial Advocacy team, the Moot Court Society, and the International Moot Court Society.

Valparaiso Law has over 25 student organizations that are academic, service, and culturally focused. Just as the students represent a wide cross section of society so, too, do the organizations on campus. Visit *www.valpo.edu/law/students/organizations/*.

■ Student Body Profile

Our student body is composed of individuals committed to fostering a culture of respect, integrity, and inclusiveness. We actively recruit students of all races, ethnicities, ages, socioeconomic statuses, abilities, national origins, sexual identities, religions, and veteran statuses. Our 2009 first-year class represents our commitment to diversity: 26 percent are from racial and ethnic groups underrepresented in the law, 53 percent are males, and 47 percent are females. Close to a third of our new students are age 25 and older. Collectively, our students represent 37 states and 11 foreign countries.

■ Expenses and Financial Aid

The School of Law is committed to helping students meet the cost of attendance. Approximately one-third of our JD students receive scholarships and/or grants. Eighty-five percent of all law students receive assistance through loan programs.

Applicant Profile

Admission to Valparaiso School of Law is competitive. The selection process involves a holistic application review that considers motivation, professionalism, maturity, and service to others as well as academic achievement.

Vanderbilt University Law School

131 21st Avenue South
Nashville, TN 37203
Phone: 615.322.6452; Fax: 615.322.1531
E-mail: admissions@law.vanderbilt.edu; Website: www.law.vanderbilt.edu

ABA
Approved
Since
1925

The Basics

Type of school	Private
Term	Semester
Application deadline	3/15
Application fee	$50
Financial aid deadline	2/15
Can first year start other than fall?	No
Student to faculty ratio	14.4 to 1
# of housing spaces available restricted to law students	25
graduate housing for which law students are eligible	

Faculty and Administrators

	Total		Men		Women		Minorities	
	Spr	Fall	Spr	Fall	Spr	Fall	Spr	Fall
Full-time	36	32	23	19	13	13	5	4
Other full-time	0	0	0	0	0	0	0	0
Deans, librarians, & others who teach	8	11	5	7	3	4	0	0
Part-time	60	34	38	20	22	14	2	4
Total	104	77	66	46	38	31	7	8

Curriculum

		Full-Time	Part-Time
Typical first-year section size		97	0
Is there typically a "small section" of the first-year class, other than Legal Writing, taught by full-time faculty		Yes	No
If yes, typical size offered last year		48	
# of classroom course titles beyond first-year curriculum		151	
# of upper division	Under 25	93	
courses, excluding	25–49	38	
seminars, with	50–74	8	
an enrollment:	75–99	4	
	100+	3	
# of seminars		21	
# of seminar positions available		365	
# of seminar positions filled		277	0
# of positions available in simulation courses		345	
# of simulation positions filled		312	0
# of positions available in faculty supervised clinical courses		75	
# of faculty supervised clinical positions filled		75	0
# involved in field placements		122	0
# involved in law journals		181	0
# involved in moot court or trial competitions		13	0
# of credit hours required to graduate		88	

JD Enrollment and Ethnicity

	Men		Women		Full-Time		Part-Time		1st-Year		Total		JD Degs. Awd.
	#	%	#	%	#	%	#	%	#	%	#	%	
African Amer.	16	5.2	38	13.2	54	9.1	0	0.0	18	9.2	54	9.1	16
Amer. Indian	2	0.7	1	0.3	3	0.5	0	0.0	1	0.5	3	0.5	1
Asian Amer.	9	2.9	12	4.2	21	3.5	0	0.0	7	3.6	21	3.5	5
Mex. Amer.	0	0.0	0	0.0	0	0.0	0	0.0	0	0.0	0	0.0	0
Puerto Rican	0	0.0	0	0.0	0	0.0	0	0.0	0	0.0	0	0.0	0
Hispanic	8	2.6	15	5.2	23	3.9	0	0.0	6	3.1	23	3.9	5
Total Minority	35	11.4	66	22.9	101	17.0	0	0.0	32	16.3	101	17.0	27
For. Nation.	9	2.9	8	2.8	17	2.9	0	0.0	6	3.1	17	2.9	6
Caucasian	196	64.1	154	53.5	350	58.9	0	0.0	115	58.7	350	58.9	121
Unknown	66	21.6	60	20.8	126	21.2	0	0.0	43	21.9	126	21.2	34
Total	306	51.5	288	48.5	594	100.0	0	0.0	196	33.0	594		188

Transfers

Transfers in	14
Transfers out	4

Tuition and Fees

	Resident	Nonresident
Full-time	$44,074	$44,074
Part-time		
Tuition Guarantee Program		N

Living Expenses

Estimated living expenses for singles

Living on campus	Living off campus	Living at home
$21,948	$21,948	$21,948

Vanderbilt University Law School

ABA
Approved
Since
1925

GPA and LSAT Scores

	Total	Full-Time	Part-Time
# of apps	4,850	4,850	0
# of offers	1,181	1,181	0
# of matrics	195	195	0
75% GPA	3.86	3.86	0.00
Median GPA	3.71	3.71	0.00
25% GPA	3.50	3.50	0.00
75% LSAT	169	169	0
Median LSAT	168	168	0
25% LSAT	164	164	0

Grants and Scholarships (from prior year)

	Total		Full-Time		Part-Time	
	#	%	#	%	#	%
Total # of students	578		578		0	
Total # receiving grants	407	70.4	407	70.4	0	0.0
Less than 1/2 tuition	305	52.8	305	52.8	0	0.0
Half to full tuition	86	14.9	86	14.9	0	0.0
Full tuition	3	0.5	3	0.5	0	0.0
More than full tuition	13	2.2	13	2.2	0	0.0
Median grant amount			$15,000		$0	

Informational and Library Resources

Total amount spent on library materials	$1,637,363
Study seating capacity inside the library	278
# of full-time equivalent professional librarians	6
Hours per week library is open	111
# of open, wired connections available to students	250
# of networked computers available for use by students	40
Has wireless network?	Y
Require computer?	N

JD Attrition (from prior year)

	Academic	Other	Total	
	#	#	#	%
1st year	0	4	4	2.1
2nd year	0	1	1	0.5
3rd year	0	0	0	0.0
4th year	0	0	0	0.0

Employment (9 months after graduation)

	Total	Percentage
Employment status known	220	99.1
Employment status unknown	2	0.9
Employed	210	95.5
Pursuing graduate degrees	7	3.2
Unemployed (seeking, not seeking, or studying for the bar)	2	0.9
Type of Employment		
# employed in law firms	155	73.8
# employed in business and industry	6	2.9
# employed in government	13	6.2
# employed in public interest	4	1.9
# employed as judicial clerks	31	14.8
# employed in academia	1	0.5
Geographic Location		
# employed in state	38	18.1
# employed in foreign countries	3	1.4
# of states where employed	32	

Bar Passage Rates

First-time takers	213	Reporting %	70.89
Average school %	96.69	Average state %	86.83
Average pass difference	9.86		

Jurisdiction	Takers	Passers	Pass %	State %	Diff %
Tennessee	46	44	95.65	88.10	7.55
New York	33	31	93.94	88.98	4.96
Georgia	21	21	100.00	89.27	10.73
Texas	16	16	100.00	84.54	15.46
Others (3)	35	34	97.14		

Vanderbilt University Law School

131 21st Avenue South
Nashville, TN 37203
Phone: 615.322.6452; Fax: 615.322.1531
E-mail: admissions@law.vanderbilt.edu; Website: www.law.vanderbilt.edu

■ Welcome to a New Way of Thinking

Among the nation's leading law schools, Vanderbilt is recognized for its distinguished faculty, its talented students drawn from across the nation and around the world, and its rigorous curriculum with an array of joint-degree, specialized, and interdisciplinary programs. Building on this tradition of excellence, Vanderbilt has established itself as a leader in designing innovative programs that connect outstanding theoretical training to real-world information and experiences relevant to twenty-first century law practice. A legal education that links the best scholarly research to effective lawyering provides immediate advantages to Vanderbilt graduates.

With about 195 students in each entering JD class, Vanderbilt fosters a tradition of challenging intellectual inquiry in an atmosphere of mutual respect. This small-school sense of collegiality combined with a distinguished and accessible faculty creates an exceptional environment to prepare for leadership in private practice, public service, business, or government. With state-of-the-art facilities situated on a beautiful and vibrant university campus in a sophisticated and livable city, Vanderbilt offers a first-rate legal education in a setting that promotes a great quality of life.

■ A Distinguished and Accessible Faculty

Widely respected for their scholarly impact, the faculty includes leading experts in an array of fields, including corporate and business law, constitutional law, litigation, criminal law, negotiation, international law, law and human behavior, dispute resolution, and intellectual property. Professors draw on their cutting-edge research to create engaging educational experiences that not only train students "to think like lawyers," but also to use their training effectively in practice. Faculty members take an open-door, student-centered approach, extending their availability to students well beyond class times.

■ A Rigorous and Relevant Curriculum

An outstanding foundational curriculum reinforced by innovative and interdisciplinary approaches to advanced training are the hallmarks of a Vanderbilt legal education. The first-year curriculum provides an intellectual framework on which to build a legal education tailored to individual needs and interests in the second and third years. Entering students begin their studies with the "Life of the Law," a one-credit course designed to distill the core ideas on which legal education is based, providing tools and information helpful to understanding first-year courses as fully as possible. First-year courses in torts, constitutional law, contracts, criminal law, civil procedure, property, the regulatory state, and legal writing set the stage for continued studies.

Upper-level courses are almost entirely elective, allowing students to choose from a broad curriculum, combining courses, seminars, clinics, externships, independent studies, and Vanderbilt courses outside the law school. Students may also participate in programs that focus on particular areas of law. The Law and Business Program is designed to produce lawyers who understand the complex corporate finance and

regulatory environments that corporate managers face. The Cecil D. Branstetter Litigation and Dispute Resolution Program is directed at connecting scholarly research on litigation and court systems to practice-based skills and strategies used to settle disputes. The International Legal Studies Program offers a unique International Law Practice Lab in which students undertake specific projects for real-world clients such as the Iraqi Special Tribunal and the International Criminal Court. The Regulatory Program is dedicated to the study of how government regulations and agencies influence public and private behavior in areas such as environmental protection, international trade, labor, health, tax, immigration, corporations, copyright, and securities. Vanderbilt also offers opportunities to focus on constitutional law and theory, law and human behavior, technology and entertainment law, and social justice.

■ International Study, Special Programs, Clinics, and Joint Degrees

Vanderbilt in Venice allows students to study abroad in the rich cultural center of Venice, Italy. Taught by Vanderbilt Law and University of Venice faculty, courses cover topics in international law with intensive classwork augmented by outside experiences. The six-week program concludes in early July, allowing students to work or intern during the remainder of the summer.

The law and economics movement has been an important influence in legal scholarship, and Vanderbilt's PhD in Law and Economics provides the next generation of training in this field: a combination of professional and academic degrees that train scholars for academic positions, law practice, policy making, and public interest work. Students either have a JD upon entry to the PhD program, or obtain a PhD and JD concurrently at Vanderbilt.

Students earn academic credit while serving the public in real practice settings through the Law School's clinical programs. Clinical offerings include international law, appellate litigation, civil practice, criminal practice, domestic violence, community and economic development, and intellectual property and the arts. Students also can gain valuable experience in nonprofits, government agencies, and other organizations around the world through various externship and summer stipend opportunities including the Legal Aid Society and Public Interest Stipend Fund.

Joint-degree programs make it possible to combine the JD with an MBA, MD, MDiv, MTS, MPP, MA, or PhD in conjunction with the university's various graduate and professional schools. The law school also offers an LLM program for international lawyers and the LLM/MA in Latin American Studies.

■ Law School Building and Library

The Law School facilities are among the best designed in the nation, featuring a central open courtyard with adjacent cafe, comfortable lounges, and abundant natural light. Situated on a park-like campus that is designated a national arboretum, the building is designed for twenty-first century legal studies and research with wireless connectivity, state-of-the-art

classrooms and trial courtroom, and on-site and remote access to a host of electronic resources. The law library provides a variety of study spaces, including two reading rooms and nearly 200 carrels. The service-oriented library staff oversees a collection of over 605,000 volumes and more than 250 electronic databases, and all other Vanderbilt libraries, containing more than 3.3 million volumes, are also available to law students.

■ Student Life, Journals, and Law School Environs

One of the reasons that students choose Vanderbilt is the congenial, collaborative atmosphere on campus. Spirited competition in an atmosphere of mutual respect creates an intellectual vibrancy and a sense of community that are rare. A busy schedule of visiting speakers, symposia, and conferences is augmented by the activities of more than 50 student organizations. Four student publications provide opportunities to strengthen legal research and writing skills—*Vanderbilt Law Review*, *Vanderbilt Journal of Entertainment and Technology Law*, *Vanderbilt Journal of Transnational Law*, and *Environmental Law and Policy Annual Review* in conjunction with the Environmental Law Institute (ELI) in Washington, DC.

Vanderbilt is an internationally recognized university with strong partnerships among its 10 schools, neighboring institutions, and the Nashville community. In the natural beauty of Tennessee, Vanderbilt's hometown has emerged as a vibrant and progressive city that offers numerous professional opportunities, wide-ranging cultural and recreational options, and a great quality of life. Among the nation's most livable cities, Nashville is the state capital with a metropolitan area population of 1.5 million, and Vanderbilt is ideally situated in this major center for legal activity, allowing students an array of opportunities in law firms, state and federal courts and government, public agencies, nonprofits, and corporations.

■ Career Services

Legal employers across the nation are familiar with the qualities of Vanderbilt graduates and regularly come to campus to recruit students for summer and permanent employment and solicit students' résumés throughout the year. For the JD Classes of 2006 through 2009, 18 percent of graduates took employment in Tennessee, and 82 percent fanned out broadly over 39 other states, DC, and abroad with the largest numbers taking employment in New York (10.3 percent); Atlanta (8.4 percent); Washington, DC (7.9 percent); Texas (6.3 percent); Chicago (5.8 percent); California (5.4 percent); North Carolina (4.4 percent); and Florida (3.4 percent), with an additional 3.3 percent taking employment abroad. In all, the Law School's alumni network covers 49 states; Washington, DC; 3 US territories; and 26 foreign nations. About 70 percent of recent graduates have chosen employment with law firms, 8 percent in government or public service, and 4 percent in corporate positions. About 10 to 15 percent of graduating classes enter judicial clerkships each year, the great majority with federal judges.

■ Scholarships and Loan Repayment Assistance

Vanderbilt provides generous financial assistance through need- and merit-based scholarships. All admitted applicants are considered for merit scholarships, and several Law Scholar Merit Awards of full tuition plus stipend are given each year through a supplemental application process. Vanderbilt's Loan Repayment Assistance Program provides financial support to graduates who choose low-paying public service employment upon graduation.

Applicant Profile

Admission to Vanderbilt is competitive, and the selection process reflects our belief that the quality of the educational environment at the Law School benefits from considering a range of information about each prospective student that is far broader than GPA and LSAT. Each file is reviewed in its entirety for indicators of academic excellence, intellectual curiosity, hard work, interest in others' welfare, obstacles overcome, professionalism, and other characteristics of successful law students. We believe that talented students with a mix of backgrounds, perspectives, and goals promote a vibrant and beneficial educational environment and that full-file review in the admission process is central to that objective. We do not provide a two-factor applicant profile grid to describe a multifactor selection process in which decisions are based on experienced judgment applied to individual cases.

Vermont Law School

164 Chelsea Street, PO Box 96
South Royalton, VT 05068
Phone: 888.277.5985 (toll-free) or 802.831.1239; Fax: 802.831.1174
E-mail: admiss@vermontlaw.edu; Website: www.vermontlaw.edu

ABA
Approved
Since
1975

The Basics

Type of school	Private
Term	Semester
Application deadline	3/1
Application fee	$60
Financial aid deadline	3/1
Can first year start other than fall?	No
Student to faculty ratio	13.5 to 1
# of housing spaces available restricted to law students	
graduate housing for which law students are eligible	

Faculty and Administrators

	Total		Men		Women		Minorities	
	Spr	Fall	Spr	Fall	Spr	Fall	Spr	Fall
Full-time	34	34	21	21	13	13	2	4
Other full-time	14	12	6	6	8	6	1	0
Deans, librarians, & others who teach	12	13	5	6	7	7	2	3
Part-time	26	14	18	8	8	6	0	1
Total	86	73	50	41	36	32	5	8

Curriculum

	Full-Time	Part-Time
Typical first-year section size	65	0
Is there typically a "small section" of the first-year class, other than Legal Writing, taught by full-time faculty	Yes	No
If yes, typical size offered last year	30	
# of classroom course titles beyond first-year curriculum	128	

# of upper division courses, excluding seminars, with an enrollment:		
	Under 25	79
	25–49	42
	50–74	8
	75–99	2
	100+	0

# of seminars	34	
# of seminar positions available	570	
# of seminar positions filled	367	0
# of positions available in simulation courses	554	
# of simulation positions filled	442	0
# of positions available in faculty supervised clinical courses	72	
# of faculty supervised clinical positions filled	65	0
# involved in field placements	157	0
# involved in law journals	109	0
# involved in moot court or trial competitions	35	0
# of credit hours required to graduate	87	

JD Enrollment and Ethnicity

	Men		Women		Full-Time		Part-Time		1st-Year		Total		JD Degs. Awd.
	#	%	#	%	#	%	#	%	#	%	#	%	
African Amer.	5	1.8	11	3.9	16	2.8	0	0.0	7	3.0	16	2.8	20
Amer. Indian	1	0.4	1	0.4	2	0.4	0	0.0	0	0.0	2	0.4	4
Asian Amer.	4	1.4	12	4.2	16	2.8	0	0.0	3	1.3	16	2.8	6
Mex. Amer.	2	0.7	2	0.7	4	0.7	0	0.0	0	0.0	4	0.7	1
Puerto Rican	1	0.4	2	0.7	3	0.5	0	0.0	2	0.9	3	0.5	1
Hispanic	7	2.5	1	0.4	8	1.4	0	0.0	4	1.7	8	1.4	1
Total Minority	20	7.1	29	10.2	49	8.6	0	0.0	16	6.9	49	8.6	33
For. Nation.	3	1.1	3	1.1	6	1.1	0	0.0	2	0.9	6	1.1	3
Caucasian	228	80.6	225	79.2	453	79.9	0	0.0	189	81.5	453	79.9	137
Unknown	32	11.3	27	9.5	59	10.4	0	0.0	25	10.8	59	10.4	18
Total	283	49.9	284	50.1	567	100.0	0	0.0	232	40.9	567		191

Transfers

Transfers in	0
Transfers out	7

Tuition and Fees

	Resident	Nonresident
Full-time	$40,420	$40,420
Part-time		
Tuition Guarantee Program		N

Living Expenses

Estimated living expenses for singles

Living on campus	Living off campus	Living at home
N/A	$16,440	$16,440

Vermont Law School

ABA
Approved
Since
1975

GPA and LSAT Scores

	Total	Full-Time	Part-Time
# of apps	884	884	0
# of offers	590	590	0
# of matrics	233	233	0
75% GPA	3.57	3.57	0.00
Median GPA	3.32	3.32	0.00
25% GPA	3.05	3.05	0.00
75% LSAT	158	158	0
Median LSAT	155	155	0
25% LSAT	152	152	0

Grants and Scholarships (from prior year)

	Total		Full-Time		Part-Time	
	#	%	#	%	#	%
Total # of students	539		537		2	
Total # receiving grants	369	68.5	369	68.7	0	0.0
Less than 1/2 tuition	346	64.2	346	64.4	0	0.0
Half to full tuition	19	3.5	19	3.5	0	0.0
Full tuition	4	0.7	4	0.7	0	0.0
More than full tuition	0	0.0	0	0.0	0	0.0
Median grant amount			$8,000		$0	

Informational and Library Resources

Total amount spent on library materials	$807,576
Study seating capacity inside the library	382
# of full-time equivalent professional librarians	6
Hours per week library is open	110
# of open, wired connections available to students	110
# of networked computers available for use by students	105
Has wireless network?	Y
Require computer?	N

JD Attrition (from prior year)

	Academic	Other	Total	
	#	#	#	%
1st year	1	7	8	4.2
2nd year	1	0	1	0.6
3rd year	0	0	0	0.0
4th year	0	0	0	0.0

Employment (9 months after graduation)

	Total	Percentage
Employment status known	171	100.0
Employment status unknown	0	0.0
Employed	144	84.2
Pursuing graduate degrees	13	7.6
Unemployed (seeking, not seeking, or studying for the bar)	8	4.7
Type of Employment		
# employed in law firms	50	34.7
# employed in business and industry	27	18.7
# employed in government	23	16.0
# employed in public interest	22	15.3
# employed as judicial clerks	21	14.6
# employed in academia	1	0.7
Geographic Location		
# employed in state	21	14.6
# employed in foreign countries	0	0.0
# of states where employed	29	

Bar Passage Rates

First-time takers	146	Reporting %	71.23
Average school %	90.40	Average state %	86.85
Average pass difference	3.55		

Jurisdiction	Takers	Passers	Pass %	State %	Diff %
New York	30	25	83.33	88.98	−5.65
Vermont	25	23	92.00	84.38	7.62
Massachusetts	17	17	100.00	92.33	7.67
New Hampshire	13	13	100.00	88.27	11.73
Others (2)	19	16	84.21		

Vermont Law School

164 Chelsea Street, PO Box 96
South Royalton, VT 05068
Phone: 888.277.5985 (toll-free) or 802.831.1239; Fax: 802.831.1174
E-mail: admiss@vermontlaw.edu; Website: www.vermontlaw.edu

■ Introduction

Vermont Law School (VLS) operates from the belief that lawyers and legal scholars should advocate for the common good and help protect the natural world, and that legal education in service to those objectives should be both rigorous and practical. The school's legal scholars, practitioners, and staff guide and prepare students to impact fields affecting the public interest, public policy, and social justice. Graduates work for nonprofit organizations, private firms, government agencies, and educational institutions.

As an international leader in environmental law, VLS is active in broadening the array of social justice, energy policy, and climate crisis issues to be addressed by legal scholarship and in legal education. The school features distinctive programs in international law and dual JD/master's degree programs in business administration, environmental management, environmental policy, philosophy, and other fields.

Vermont Law School also works with advocacy organizations, domestic and international governments, and other educational institutions that share its commitment to make substantial, positive change in their communities and countries. The experiential education VLS provides prepares its graduates to engage in the critical issues of our time.

■ Faculty

The stimulating environment at Vermont Law School has attracted scholars and practitioners of national and international renown. In their teaching VLS faculty strike a balance between scholarship and application, between rigorous research and a realistic approach to problem-solving. They understand the nuanced analytic and political abilities needed in advocacy work, while also recognizing the portfolio of core skills graduates will need in their first jobs and throughout their legal careers.

As legal experts, VLS faculty are frequently sought out by national and international law firms, educational institutions, government agencies, and advocacy organizations. VLS faculty members regularly work on important cases in environmental law, international and comparative law, human rights, national security law, business law, and constitutional law, providing frequent opportunities for students to engage in related independent study and research projects. Because VLS is slightly smaller than many law schools, close relationships between students and faculty tend to last a lifetime.

■ Curriculum and Experiential Programs

The fundamentals of law are rigorously addressed in the required general curriculum, in addition to which VLS students can customize their educations to build skill sets in practice areas on the leading edge of the law and social change.

At VLS, in-depth scholarship is balanced with experiential opportunities that highlight what lawyers are actually called upon to do in the field. VLS students are able to take advantage of many clinics and experiential programs that provide hands-on training and involve students in real cases and legal issues including:

- The **Semester in Practice** program, which matches self-directed students with mentors, who are legal professionals in a range of fields, for independent projects.
- The **South Royalton Legal Clinic**, which serves low-income area residents who need assistance in matters involving family law, housing, welfare and unemployment, health care, immigration, Social Security, children's rights, consumer protection, bankruptcy, contracts, wills, and civil rights. Guided by experienced attorneys, students represent clients in state court, federal court, and administrative hearings.
- The **Environmental and Natural Resource Law Clinic**, where qualified students work alongside legal experts to advance environmental protection goals while developing their research, advocacy, and litigation skills.
- The **Legislative Clinic**, which takes advantage of VLS's proximity to the state capital through internships with the Vermont General Assembly.
- The **Mediation Clinic**, which trains students to mediate civil disputes in Vermont Superior Court, Small Claims Court, and the Environmental Court. Students also mediate conflicts in which the parties choose to avoid court or postpone filing a court action until attempting mediation.
- **Judicial externships**, which are programs structured to provide students with both academic background on judicial issues and hands-on experience working in judges' chambers.
- **JD, MELP (Master of Environmental Law and Policy)**, and **LLM internships** in which students gain real-world experience in general and environmental law and policy in a wide variety of settings both locally and worldwide.
- The **General Practice Program (GPP)**, which simulates a professional law firm with professors as partners overseeing student associates who are expected to perform a range of legal activities and handle client cases. The GPP received the 2007 E. Smythe Gambrell Professionalism Award from the American Bar Association.

■ Joint and Dual Degrees and Specialized Program Offerings

In addition to the general JD program, VLS offers:
- A unique, one-year master's degree in environmental law and policy and specialized programs in land use, energy, climate change, and international environmental law.
- Dual JD/master's degree programs in business administration, environmental management, environmental policy, philosophy, and other fields through partnerships with Yale, Dartmouth, Northeastern, Cambridge, Cergy-Pontoise, Seville, Thunderbird, and the University of Vermont.
- Semester exchange programs with five US law schools as well as McGill and Trento.
- The largest number and most extensive environmental law courses in the country, taught by some of the top scholars in the field.
- Extensive summer programs that attract legal, energy, industry, and environmental experts from around the country and the world who teach courses and lead seminars on a range of pressing topics.

Student Community

Recent VLS students have come from every state and from countries including Guam, Brazil, Canada, Italy, Japan, Russia, and Spain. The undergraduate institutions they attended span the geographic spectrum of the country and range in size and type from Yale to the University of Colorado to Western Washington University. In a typical year, the entering class will represent over 40 states and at least 150 undergraduate institutions. Men and women are equally represented in both the student and faculty populations. And while some students come to VLS soon after graduating from college, others have spent years in a wide variety of professions including engineering, teaching, lobbying, corporate management, and nonprofit programming. This important mix of backgrounds allows VLS to enjoy a diversity of perspectives on campus and in the classroom.

VLS's size and emphasis on collaboration fosters an environment where students are valued for the contributions they make and the initiative they take within the VLS community. Whether through independent collaboration with faculty, engagement with one of the many active student organizations, or through the Student Government Association, students help shape academic and cocurricular coursework and campus policies.

Admission

Successful candidates demonstrate substantial academic ability and motivation and will bring diverse perspectives and interests, as well as strong talents, to the community. The two admission criteria that are weighed most heavily are academic records and two required personal essays. In addition, the school responds favorably to candidates who have been active in their communities and engaged with student organizations or professional endeavors. VLS is committed to supporting individuals traditionally underrepresented in the legal profession. Applications are reviewed on a rolling basis, beginning on the first of December.

Tuition and Financial Aid

At Vermont Law School, a combination of merit scholarships, loans, tuition grants, and work-study opportunities are employed to address the financial needs of law school candidates. On average, 90 percent of the student body receives some form of financial assistance, and approximately 40 percent of enrolling students receive VLS merit- or need-based aid. In addition to counseling students on loan repayment strategies—including the new federal income-based loan repayment and loan forgiveness program—VLS offers a Loan Repayment Assistance Program, which is designed to support graduates pursuing public interest careers in repaying educational debts.

Career Services

In addition to the network of staff, peers, and faculty advocates who serve as ready resources to every VLS student and graduate, the Office of Career Services operates as a clearinghouse for information on professional and experiential opportunities for students throughout their law school years. The office also provides tools for résumé and interview preparation, assists students in researching and applying for internships and summer jobs, and helps them explore a range of postgraduate placements.

Applicant Profile

Vermont Law School
This grid includes only applicants who earned 120–180 LSAT scores under standard administrations.

LSAT Score	GPA																	
	3.75 +		3.50–3.74		3.25–3.49		3.00–3.24		2.75–2.99		2.50–2.74		Below 2.50		No GPA		Total	
	Apps	Adm	Apps	Adm	Apps	Adm	Apps	Adm	Apps	Adm	Apps	Adm	Apps	Adm	Apps	Adm	Apps	Adm
170–180	3	3	3	3	1	1	0	0	1	1	0	0	0	0	0	0	8	8
165–169	7	7	13	13	5	5	1	1	3	2	0	0	0	0	2	1	31	29
160–164	18	18	17	16	24	22	22	22	14	12	1	1	4	3	1	1	101	95
155–159	36	35	34	33	30	28	33	32	13	13	12	11	7	3	3	2	168	157
150–154	27	25	47	46	63	60	66	58	39	25	19	11	14	7	7	4	282	236
145–149	11	4	27	10	41	16	43	17	16	2	13	2	14	1	5	1	170	53
140–144	5	1	12	2	6	2	23	0	20	1	10	1	10	0	1	0	87	7
Below 140	1	0	2	1	4	0	4	0	3	0	11	0	8	0	2	0	35	1
Total	108	93	155	124	174	134	192	130	109	56	66	26	57	14	21	9	882	586

Apps = Number of Applicants
Adm = Number Admitted
Reflects 99% of the total applicant pool; average LSAT data reported.

Vermont Law School does not use cutoff LSAT scores or GPAs.

Villanova University School of Law

299 North Spring Mill Road
Villanova, PA 19085
Phone: 610.519.7010; Fax: 610.519.6291
E-mail: admissions@law.villanova.edu; Website: www.law.villanova.edu

ABA
Approved
Since
1954

AMERICAN BAR ASSOCIATION
Section of Legal Education
and Admissions to the Bar

The Basics

Type of school	Private
Term	Semester
Application deadline	3/1
Application fee	$75
Financial aid deadline	
Can first year start other than fall?	No
Student to faculty ratio	17.3 to 1
# of housing spaces available restricted to law students	
graduate housing for which law students are eligible	

Faculty and Administrators

	Total		Men		Women		Minorities	
	Spr	Fall	Spr	Fall	Spr	Fall	Spr	Fall
Full-time	36	36	21	22	15	14	4	4
Other full-time	8	9	2	3	6	6	0	0
Deans, librarians, & others who teach	13	13	5	5	8	8	4	4
Part-time	65	48	51	36	13	10	9	6
Total	122	106	79	66	42	38	17	14

Curriculum

		Full-Time	Part-Time
Typical first-year section size		85	0
Is there typically a "small section" of the first-year class, other than Legal Writing, taught by full-time faculty		Yes	No
If yes, typical size offered last year		43	
# of classroom course titles beyond first-year curriculum		117	
# of upper division courses, excluding seminars, with an enrollment:	Under 25	91	
	25–49	29	
	50–74	16	
	75–99	10	
	100+	2	
# of seminars		22	
# of seminar positions available		341	
# of seminar positions filled		279	0
# of positions available in simulation courses		696	
# of simulation positions filled		681	0
# of positions available in faculty supervised clinical courses		72	
# of faculty supervised clinical positions filled		72	0
# involved in field placements		170	0
# involved in law journals		169	0
# involved in moot court or trial competitions		54	0
# of credit hours required to graduate		88	

JD Enrollment and Ethnicity

	Men		Women		Full-Time		Part-Time		1st-Year		Total		JD Degs. Awd.
	#	%	#	%	#	%	#	%	#	%	#	%	
African Amer.	6	1.4	9	2.7	15	2.0	0	0.0	6	2.3	15	2.0	11
Amer. Indian	1	0.2	2	0.6	3	0.4	0	0.0	0	0.0	3	0.4	1
Asian Amer.	28	6.6	37	11.1	65	8.6	0	0.0	20	7.8	65	8.6	19
Mex. Amer.	0	0.0	0	0.0	0	0.0	0	0.0	0	0.0	0	0.0	0
Puerto Rican	0	0.0	0	0.0	0	0.0	0	0.0	0	0.0	0	0.0	0
Hispanic	29	6.9	18	5.4	47	6.2	0	0.0	26	10.1	47	6.2	8
Total Minority	64	15.2	66	19.9	130	17.2	0	0.0	52	20.2	130	17.2	39
For. Nation.	4	0.9	2	0.6	6	0.8	0	0.0	1	0.4	6	0.8	0
Caucasian	354	83.9	264	79.5	618	82.0	0	0.0	205	79.5	618	82.0	196
Unknown	0	0.0	0	0.0	0	0.0	0	0.0	0	0.0	0	0.0	0
Total	422	56.0	332	44.0	754	100.0	0	0.0	258	34.2	754		235

Transfers

Transfers in	9
Transfers out	5

Tuition and Fees

	Resident	Nonresident
Full-time	$35,250	$35,250
Part-time		
Tuition Guarantee Program	N	

Living Expenses

Estimated living expenses for singles

Living on campus	Living off campus	Living at home
N/A	$19,695	$6,915

Villanova University School of Law

ABA
Approved
Since
1954

GPA and LSAT Scores

	Total	Full-Time	Part-Time
# of apps	3,254	3,254	0
# of offers	1,401	1,401	0
# of matrics	255	255	0
75% GPA	3.63	3.63	0.00
Median GPA	3.44	3.44	0.00
25% GPA	3.17	3.17	0.00
75% LSAT	163	163	0
Median LSAT	162	162	0
25% LSAT	160	160	0

Grants and Scholarships (from prior year)

	Total		Full-Time		Part-Time	
	#	%	#	%	#	%
Total # of students	744		744		0	
Total # receiving grants	156	21.0	156	21.0	0	0.0
Less than 1/2 tuition	108	14.5	108	14.5	0	0.0
Half to full tuition	39	5.2	39	5.2	0	0.0
Full tuition	9	1.2	9	1.2	0	0.0
More than full tuition	0	0.0	0	0.0	0	0.0
Median grant amount			$15,000		$0	

Informational and Library Resources

Total amount spent on library materials	$1,335,729
Study seating capacity inside the library	445
# of full-time equivalent professional librarians	11
Hours per week library is open	168
# of open, wired connections available to students	27
# of networked computers available for use by students	27
Has wireless network?	Y
Require computer?	N

JD Attrition (from prior year)

	Academic	Other	Total	
	#	#	#	%
1st year	0	11	11	4.3
2nd year	0	1	1	0.4
3rd year	1	1	2	0.9
4th year	0	0	0	0.0

Employment (9 months after graduation)

	Total	Percentage
Employment status known	225	99.6
Employment status unknown	1	0.4
Employed	203	90.2
Pursuing graduate degrees	4	1.8
Unemployed (seeking, not seeking, or studying for the bar)	12	5.3
Type of Employment		
# employed in law firms	113	55.7
# employed in business and industry	35	17.2
# employed in government	12	5.9
# employed in public interest	13	6.4
# employed as judicial clerks	30	14.8
# employed in academia	0	0.0
Geographic Location		
# employed in state	122	60.1
# employed in foreign countries	1	0.5
# of states where employed	15	

Bar Passage Rates

First-time takers	224	Reporting %	78.13
Average school %	93.14	Average state %	86.43
Average pass difference	6.71		

Jurisdiction	Takers	Passers	Pass %	State %	Diff %
Pennsylvania	152	142	93.42	86.69	6.73
New Jersey	23	21	91.30	84.69	6.61

Villanova University School of Law

299 North Spring Mill Road
Villanova, PA 19085
Phone: 610.519.7010; Fax: 610.519.6291
E-mail: admissions@law.villanova.edu; Website: www.law.villanova.edu

■ Introduction

Today, as never before, there is a need for law schools to teach far more than the letter of the law. They must give future lawyers a sense of the importance of their role in the larger society, and they must prepare lawyers to work in an environment of burgeoning technology with issues of global importance.

With its Catholic roots, Villanova offers a legal education designed to teach the rules of law and their application; to demonstrate how lawyers analyze legal issues and express arguments and conclusions; to inculcate the skills of the counselor, advocate, and decision maker; and to explore the ethical and moral dimensions of law practice and professional conduct. The school is also providing leadership in information technology, public interest, taxation, and international law, among other fields.

Few law schools are located in a more beautiful and tranquil environment. Adjacent to the university campus is Philadelphia's Main Line. The school is at the approximate midpoint of east coast legal centers in New York and Washington, DC, and only 20 minutes by commuter rail from the center of Philadelphia.

Opened in 1953, the school is approved by the American Bar Association and is a member of the Association of American Law Schools. Students are graduates of well over 100 colleges and universities; many have significant work experience outside of the law. The atmosphere of the school is noted for its collegiality.

■ Faculty

While Villanova faculty members are recognized nationally and internationally for their legal scholarship and for their contributions to the study and practice of law, they are also deeply committed to teaching. The student-to-faculty ratio is 17 to 1.

■ Library and Physical Facilities

The spectacular new building opened its doors in July 2009, providing almost twice as much usable space as the law school's former home.

A soaring commons anchors the main floor and provides a breathtaking public space and comfortable casual seating for students, faculty, and staff. Bright, comfortable classrooms are tailored to the size and nature of the classes being taught and are equipped with state-of-the-art technology. The stunning Ceremonial Courtroom provides an inspiring venue for trial and advocacy events. Faculty offices are located adjacent to the classrooms to ensure that the give and take of the classroom continues after class.

The building's hallmark is its student-centeredness. The most beautiful, comfortable and spacious places are the student areas. For example, the library reading rooms are elegantly appointed, comfortably equipped, and bathed in natural light by their three floor-to-ceiling window walls. The student lounge overlooks the quad on the first floor, again boasting floor to ceiling windows. The dining room and the coffee bar emphasize our commitment to the importance of quality of life for students who are working long hours.

The library in the new building occupies almost an entire wing and anchors one of the main entrances. Highly functional, comfortable, beautifully appointed, and equipped with the latest technology, the library's open spaces, glass walls, and high ceilings draw users.

■ Joint JD/MBA Program

Offered in collaboration with Villanova's top ranked School of Business, the joint JD/MBA program is designed to provide careful integration of the two disciplines and to allow students to earn both degrees in far less time than it would take to obtain them separately. Students in this program typically begin their MBA studies after the first year of law school and often finish both degrees in three to four years.

■ Joint JD/LLM in International Studies

Joint programs offered with the University of Edinburgh, Scotland; Leiden University, the Netherlands; the University of London; and the University of Singapore allow students to earn both a JD and an international LLM in three years. Students spend the first two years at Villanova, completing their JD courses. They then study abroad during the third year, completing the LLM. Each school accepts credits from the other, allowing students who qualify for this highly selective program to finish both degrees in the time it would normally take to finish the JD.

■ Joint JD/LLM in Taxation and LLM in Taxation

Students in the JD/LLM in Taxation program earn both the JD and the graduate law degree in taxation in less time and at a reduced cost than earning the degrees separately. Beginning in their second year of law school, JD students enroll in a series of tax courses that, taken together, qualify for both degrees. Following the award of the JD degree, a student can complete the remaining LLM requirements in one additional academic semester.

The interdisciplinary LLM program is conducted under the auspices of the School of Law and the Villanova School of Business. The program enriches the tax curriculum available to JD candidates, who are able to enroll in LLM courses.

■ Special Programs

Beyond the skills of written and oral expression developed in the first-year writing program and the required upper-level moot court program, drafting, and seminar courses, Villanova students acquire the fundamental skills of the practicing lawyer—including counseling, negotiation, advocacy, mediation, dispute resolution, conciliation, and mature judgment. Hands-on clinical opportunities allow students to apply classroom experiences to real-world client representation, often while performing public service. Clinical programs include Federal Tax; Civil Justice; Asylum, Refugee, and Emigrant Services; and Farmworkers Legal Aid.

■ Student Activities

The *Villanova Law Review* is a scholarly journal prepared and edited by law students. Members are selected on the basis of academic rank or through an open writing competition.

The *Villanova Environmental Law Journal* publishes both student and outside articles dealing with environmental issues. Students are selected for membership by an open writing competition.

The *Villanova Sports and Entertainment Law Journal* contains articles prepared by practitioners and professors in sports and entertainment law as well as by students. Membership is earned by selection through an open writing competition.

Each year, second- and third-year students have the opportunity to practice lawyering skills through the Client Interviewing and Counseling Competition, the Reimel Moot Court Competition, and several outside moot court competitions.

Student organizations include Asian Pacific American Law Students, Black Law Students Association, Corporate Law Society, Criminal Law Society, Environmental and Energy Law Society, Health Law Society, Intellectual Property Society, International Law Society, Islamic Law Forum, Jewish Law Students Association, Latin American Law Students Association, Justinian Society, OUTlaw, Phi Delta Phi, Pro Bono Society, St. Thomas More Society, Sports and Entertainment Law Society, Student Animal Defense League, Tax Law Society, and Women's Caucus.

■ Career Strategy and Advancement

The mission of the Career Strategy and Advancement Office is to provide career planning education, recruitment programs, and individual counseling as the foundation for future career development and satisfaction of our students. Distinctive features and programs include three attorney-advisors, including a public service/pro bono specialist; an open-door policy, including a daily "on call" advisor for walk-ins and "quick questions"; small group workshops for 1Ls; dozens of career workshops and panel programs on topics ranging from interviews, résumés, and networking, to public interest careers, judicial clerkships, and a multitude of practice specialty areas; "Day in the Law," a program designed to expose 1Ls to the practice of law by matching them with a graduate for a day over winter break; recruitment programs throughout the year, including a diverse array of employers in private practice (large and small firms), government, nonprofits, the judiciary, and corporations; special recruitment programs designed to enhance diversity in the profession; job fairs targeting unique geographic or practice preferences; and job-search coaching for new graduates on the job market. Pro bono programs, such as "Lawyering Together" and other projects, provide students with the opportunity to serve the disadvantaged while developing skills and positive relationships with practicing attorneys.

Applicant Profile

Villanova has chosen not to provide prospective students with an admission profile based on individual undergraduate GPAs and LSAT scores. The Admissions Committee seeks to create a diverse community by adhering to a comprehensive evaluation of a candidate's file that includes academic performance as well as professional promise. Each candidate's background, interests, accomplishments, and goals are considered before a decision is made.

University of Virginia School of Law

Office of Admissions, 580 Massie Road
Charlottesville, VA 22903-1738
Phone: 434.924.7351; Fax: 434.982.2128
E-mail: lawadmit@virginia.edu; Website: www.law.virginia.edu

ABA
Approved
Since
1923

The Basics

Type of school	Public
Term	Semester
Application deadline	3/1
Application fee	$75
Financial aid deadline	3/1
Can first year start other than fall?	No
Student to faculty ratio	12.6 to 1
# of housing spaces available restricted to law students	
graduate housing for which law students are eligible	779

Faculty and Administrators

	Total		Men		Women		Minorities	
	Spr	Fall	Spr	Fall	Spr	Fall	Spr	Fall
Full-time	75	76	54	54	21	22	7	7
Other full-time	0	0	0	0	0	0	0	0
Deans, librarians, & others who teach	6	6	4	3	2	3	1	1
Part-time	109	88	85	72	24	16	5	5
Total	190	170	143	129	47	41	13	13

Curriculum

	Full-Time	Part-Time
Typical first-year section size	72	0
Is there typically a "small section" of the first-year class, other than Legal Writing, taught by full-time faculty	Yes	No
If yes, typical size offered last year	31	
# of classroom course titles beyond first-year curriculum	233	
# of upper division courses, excluding seminars, with an enrollment: Under 25	121	
25–49	37	
50–74	27	
75–99	16	
100+	9	
# of seminars	84	
# of seminar positions available	1,353	
# of seminar positions filled	1,171	0
# of positions available in simulation courses	981	
# of simulation positions filled	888	0
# of positions available in faculty supervised clinical courses	68	
# of faculty supervised clinical positions filled	52	0
# involved in field placements	138	0
# involved in law journals	551	0
# involved in moot court or trial competitions	88	0
# of credit hours required to graduate	86	

JD Enrollment and Ethnicity

	Men		Women		Full-Time		Part-Time		1st-Year		Total		JD Degs. Awd.
	#	%	#	%	#	%	#	%	#	%	#	%	
African Amer.	19	3.0	41	8.3	60	5.3	0	0.0	23	6.3	60	5.3	37
Amer. Indian	8	1.3	8	1.6	16	1.4	0	0.0	6	1.6	16	1.4	5
Asian Amer.	42	6.7	52	10.5	94	8.4	0	0.0	43	11.8	94	8.4	29
Mex. Amer.	0	0.0	0	0.0	0	0.0	0	0.0	0	0.0	0	0.0	0
Puerto Rican	0	0.0	0	0.0	0	0.0	0	0.0	0	0.0	0	0.0	0
Hispanic	31	4.9	20	4.0	51	4.5	0	0.0	24	6.6	51	4.5	8
Total Minority	100	15.9	121	24.4	221	19.7	0	0.0	96	26.3	221	19.7	79
For. Nation.	6	1.0	4	0.8	10	0.9	0	0.0	3	0.8	10	0.9	4
Caucasian	394	62.8	274	55.4	668	59.5	0	0.0	233	63.8	668	59.5	227
Unknown	127	20.3	96	19.4	223	19.9	0	0.0	33	9.0	223	19.9	95
Total	627	55.9	495	44.1	1122	100.0	0	0.0	365	32.5	1122		405

Transfers

Transfers in	13
Transfers out	7

Tuition and Fees

	Resident	Nonresident
Full-time	$38,800	$43,800
Part-time		
Tuition Guarantee Program	N	

Living Expenses

Estimated living expenses for singles

Living on campus	Living off campus	Living at home
$19,200	$19,200	$19,200

University of Virginia School of Law

ABA
Approved
Since
1923

GPA and LSAT Scores

	Total	Full-Time	Part-Time
# of apps	7,880	7,880	0
# of offers	1,166	1,166	0
# of matrics	368	368	0
75% GPA	3.92	3.92	0.00
Median GPA	3.85	3.85	0.00
25% GPA	3.54	3.54	0.00
75% LSAT	171	171	0
Median LSAT	170	170	0
25% LSAT	165	165	0

Grants and Scholarships (from prior year)

	Total		Full-Time		Part-Time	
	#	%	#	%	#	%
Total # of students	1,156		1,155		1	
Total # receiving grants	665	57.5	665	57.6	0	0.0
Less than 1/2 tuition	570	49.3	570	49.4	0	0.0
Half to full tuition	85	7.4	85	7.4	0	0.0
Full tuition	8	0.7	8	0.7	0	0.0
More than full tuition	2	0.2	2	0.2	0	0.0
Median grant amount			$15,000		$0	

Informational and Library Resources

Total amount spent on library materials	$1,627,609
Study seating capacity inside the library	798
# of full-time equivalent professional librarians	14
Hours per week library is open	112
# of open, wired connections available to students	84
# of networked computers available for use by students	46
Has wireless network?	Y
Require computer?	Y

JD Attrition (from prior year)

	Academic	Other	Total	
	#	#	#	%
1st year	0	9	9	2.4
2nd year	0	3	3	0.8
3rd year	1	1	2	0.5
4th year	0	0	0	0.0

Employment (9 months after graduation)

	Total	Percentage
Employment status known	403	100.0
Employment status unknown	0	0.0
Employed	398	98.8
Pursuing graduate degrees	3	0.7
Unemployed (seeking, not seeking, or studying for the bar)	2	0.5
Type of Employment		
# employed in law firms	305	76.6
# employed in business and industry	5	1.3
# employed in government	18	4.5
# employed in public interest	15	3.8
# employed as judicial clerks	54	13.6
# employed in academia	1	0.3
Geographic Location		
# employed in state	45	11.3
# employed in foreign countries	8	2.0
# of states where employed	34	

Bar Passage Rates

First-time takers	382	Reporting %	94.24
Average school %	98.06	Average state %	85.30
Average pass difference	12.76		

Jurisdiction	Takers	Passers	Pass %	State %	Diff %
New York	106	103	97.17	88.98	8.19
Virginia	97	95	97.94	82.70	15.24
California	37	37	100.00	78.07	21.93
Texas	23	21	91.30	84.54	6.76
Others (12)	97	97	100.00		

University of Virginia School of Law

Office of Admissions, 580 Massie Road
Charlottesville, VA 22903-1738
Phone: 434.924.7351; Fax: 434.982.2128
E-mail: lawadmit@virginia.edu; Website: www.law.virginia.edu

■ Introduction

Founded by Thomas Jefferson in 1819, the University of Virginia School of Law is a world-renowned training ground for distinguished lawyers and public servants. Located in Charlottesville, Virginia, just two hours southwest of Washington, DC, the Law School offers students a unique environment in which to study law.

The Law School is dedicated to upholding Thomas Jefferson's conviction that lawyers must serve the public interest. The school provides special career counseling and placement assistance, operates pro bono programs, and administers a loan forgiveness program.

At Virginia, law students share their experiences in a cooperative spirit, both in and out of the classroom, and build a network that lasts well beyond their three years here. Faculty build intellectual and personal relationships with students. They are leaders in the academic life of the community, organizing and speaking at lectures and other events, working with student organizations, volunteering for pro bono service, and building new curricular programs.

■ Curriculum and Degrees

Virginia offers more than 200 courses and seminars each year, including 20 clinics and other opportunities for hands-on training. Students pursuing interdisciplinary ideas benefit from an environment where nearly half of all law faculty hold advanced degrees in fields such as psychology, economics, philosophy, history, medicine, and theology. Each first-year student takes one *small-section* class of 30 students during the first semester, which helps bond classmates from the start.

Virginia's curriculum is enhanced by several academic programs, including those in international law, human rights, environmental law, legal and constitutional history, race and law, intellectual property, health law, and immigration law. The Law and Business Program offers students courses that integrate business and legal analysis in the law school classroom. Foundational courses in accounting and finance allow students in the program to take more advanced instruction in real-life corporate law problems.

Students may enroll in several joint-degree programs. The JD/MBA program is a four-year program in conjunction with the Darden School of Business. Other combined-degree programs include a JD/MA in English, government and foreign affairs, history, philosophy, or sociology; a JD/MS in accounting; a JD/MUEP in planning; and a JD/MPH in public health. In addition, students may combine a law degree from Virginia with the MPA from Princeton, MALD from the Fletcher School at Tufts, or the MA in international relations and international economics from Johns Hopkins.

■ Facilities

The Law Grounds offers an expansive and attractive setting reflecting Jefferson's position that an intellectual community in a beautiful environment fosters learning and personal growth. The library, with more than 890,000 volumes, is one of the largest law libraries in the country. Virginia offers numerous study spaces, offices for student organizations and journals, and a large dining facility.

■ Admission

Each year, many highly qualified college graduates apply for the necessarily limited number of places in the first-year class. Our admission process aims to select from the applicant pool an entering class of students who will contribute to this academic community during their three years of residency and, ultimately, to society and the legal profession. To that end, we consider many factors. These include not only intellectual aptitude and academic achievement, but also individual accomplishments and experiences—such as dedication or a constructive response to adversity—that predict success, as well as geographic, racial, ethnic, economic, and ideological diversity.

Rigid standards based simply on a combination of an LSAT score and cumulative undergraduate grade-point average cannot be the only criteria for selecting an entering class. We assess each applicant as an individual. This assessment takes into account not only LSAT scores and undergraduate grades, but also the strength of an applicant's undergraduate or graduate curriculum, trends in grades, the maturing effect of experiences since college, the nature and quality of any work experience, significant achievement in extracurricular activities in college, service in the military, contributions to campus or community through service and leadership, and personal qualities displayed. An applicant's experiences surmounting economic, social, or educational difficulties with grace and courage, demonstrating the capacity to grow in response to challenge, and showing compassion for the welfare of others can play a role in the admission decision.

If the University of Virginia is your first choice for law school, you may apply under the Early Decision option. Early Decision applicants commit to enrolling if admitted and must withdraw all applications to other law schools once notified of Early Decision admission.

While individual interviews are not a part of the admission process, prospective students are encouraged to visit the School of Law. When classes are in session, student-led tours are available and classes are open to visitors. On most Friday afternoons throughout the summer and during the school year, the School of Law also holds admission information sessions and student life panels for prospective students. Check our website at *www.law.virginia.edu/admissions* for details.

■ Financial Aid

The Law School helps students finance their legal education through a variety of resources, including scholarships, federally sponsored loan and work-study programs, and private-sector educational loans. While the primary responsibility for financing a legal education rests with students and their families, the Financial Aid Office works with students to identify sources of financial support and develop realistic budgets to meet their educational and professional goals.

Career Services

After law school, Virginia graduates join the nation's leading law firms, clerk for federal and state courts, and serve in and even establish nationally recognized public interest organizations. Our alumni are leaders in their fields: Virginia is third among national law schools in the number of graduates who are law firm chairpersons and managing partners, according to a 2004 survey of 850 US law firms. During the 2009–2010 court term, only Virginia, Harvard, and Yale had four or more graduates clerking for the US Supreme Court. Five graduates in the past three years received Skadden Fellowships, the nation's most prestigious public service grant.

Public Service

Virginia upholds Thomas Jefferson's conviction that lawyers have a special obligation to serve the public interest. Many students at Virginia volunteer their legal services, work in public service jobs over the summer, and pursue public interest careers after graduating. Virginia supports these students through the Virginia Loan Forgiveness Program, the Mortimer Caplin Public Service Center, the Pro Bono Project, and fellowships.

The Virginia Loan Forgiveness Program assists graduates with annual law school loan payments. The program has three key features: annual loan forgiveness, no income cap, and no asset test.

The Mortimer Caplin Public Service Center provides individual counseling and sponsors events focused on educating students about working in the public sector.

The Pro Bono Project is a voluntary program encouraging all students to complete at least 75 hours of pro bono service during their three years of law school. Opportunities are available locally and nationwide. The center also organizes pro bono projects that focus on areas such as child advocacy, immigration law, and veterans' disability claims.

Each year the Law School provides more than $300,000 to students working in public service over the summer. Virginia also offers a two-year, salaried fellowship to a graduating student who plans to work in public service.

Student Life

Nine academic journals and 70 student organizations—from social clubs to groups dedicated to the community's legal needs—ensure that students explore the world outside law school and expand their legal experiences while leading well-rounded lives.

Charlottesville is a picturesque and thriving metropolitan area of more than 135,000. Area restaurants are featured in publications such as *Gourmet* magazine and the *New York Times*. Each year the city hosts the nationally acclaimed Virginia Film Festival and gathers literary luminaries for the Virginia Festival of the Book. Students enjoy going to sporting events and concerts in one of the country's finest college arenas.

Applicant Profile

The University of Virginia School of Law has elected not to provide an applicant profile based only on GPA and LSAT, as these numbers cannot be the sole criteria for selecting an entering class. Each applicant is assessed as an individual, taking into account not only LSAT scores and undergraduate grades, but also the strength of an applicant's undergraduate or graduate curriculum, trends in grades, the maturing effect of experiences since college, the nature and quality of any work experience, significant achievement in extracurricular activities, service in the military, contributions to campus or community through service and leadership, and personal qualities.

Wake Forest University School of Law

Box 7206
Winston-Salem, NC 27109
Phone: 336.758.5437; Fax: 336.758.3930
E-mail: admissions@law.wfu.edu; Website: www.law.wfu.edu

ABA
Approved
Since
1936

The Basics

Type of school	Private
Term	Semester
Application deadline	3/1
Application fee	$60
Financial aid deadline	5/1
Can first year start other than fall?	No
Student to faculty ratio	9.8 to 1
# of housing spaces available restricted to law students graduate housing for which law students are eligible	

Faculty and Administrators

	Total		Men		Women		Minorities	
	Spr	Fall	Spr	Fall	Spr	Fall	Spr	Fall
Full-time	41	39	25	23	16	16	5	5
Other full-time	2	2	0	0	2	2	1	1
Deans, librarians, & others who teach	8	8	3	3	5	5	1	1
Part-time	21	18	13	15	8	3	1	0
Total	72	67	41	41	31	26	8	7

JD Enrollment and Ethnicity

	Men		Women		Full-Time		Part-Time		1st-Year		Total		JD Degs. Awd.
	#	%	#	%	#	%	#	%	#	%	#	%	
African Amer.	14	5.1	28	14.1	41	8.9	1	7.7	14	9.3	42	8.8	7
Amer. Indian	3	1.1	1	0.5	4	0.9	0	0.0	4	2.6	4	0.8	0
Asian Amer.	9	3.2	7	3.5	16	3.5	0	0.0	4	2.6	16	3.4	6
Mex. Amer.	0	0.0	0	0.0	0	0.0	0	0.0	0	0.0	0	0.0	0
Puerto Rican	0	0.0	0	0.0	0	0.0	0	0.0	0	0.0	0	0.0	0
Hispanic	11	4.0	8	4.0	19	4.1	0	0.0	9	6.0	19	4.0	1
Total Minority	37	13.4	44	22.1	80	17.3	1	7.7	31	20.5	81	17.0	14
For. Nation.	0	0.0	1	0.5	1	0.2	0	0.0	0	0.0	1	0.2	0
Caucasian	210	75.8	145	72.9	344	74.3	11	84.6	100	66.2	355	74.6	121
Unknown	30	10.8	9	4.5	38	8.2	1	7.7	20	13.2	39	8.2	17
Total	277	58.2	199	41.8	463	97.3	13	2.7	151	31.7	476		152

Curriculum

	Full-Time	Part-Time
Typical first-year section size	38	0
Is there typically a "small section" of the first-year class, other than Legal Writing, taught by full-time faculty	No	No
If yes, typical size offered last year		
# of classroom course titles beyond first-year curriculum	108	

# of upper division courses, excluding seminars, with an enrollment:		
Under 25	61	
25–49	33	
50–74	15	
75–99	1	
100+	0	

# of seminars	45	
# of seminar positions available	724	
# of seminar positions filled	613	0
# of positions available in simulation courses	266	
# of simulation positions filled	255	0
# of positions available in faculty supervised clinical courses	103	
# of faculty supervised clinical positions filled	90	0
# involved in field placements	20	0
# involved in law journals	127	0
# involved in moot court or trial competitions	69	0
# of credit hours required to graduate	90	

Transfers

Transfers in	13
Transfers out	4

Tuition and Fees

	Resident	Nonresident
Full-time	$36,166	$36,166
Part-time		
Tuition Guarantee Program		N

Living Expenses

Estimated living expenses for singles

Living on campus	Living off campus	Living at home
N/A	$17,050	N/A

Wake Forest University School of Law

ABA
Approved
Since
1936

GPA and LSAT Scores

	Total	Full-Time	Part-Time
# of apps	2,775	2,775	0
# of offers	905	905	0
# of matrics	154	154	0
75% GPA	3.70	3.70	0.00
Median GPA	3.60	3.60	0.00
25% GPA	3.20	3.20	0.00
75% LSAT	164	164	0
Median LSAT	162	162	0
25% LSAT	160	160	0

Grants and Scholarships (from prior year)

	Total		Full-Time		Part-Time	
	#	%	#	%	#	%
Total # of students	470		463		7	
Total # receiving grants	240	51.1	240	51.8	0	0.0
Less than 1/2 tuition	127	27.0	127	27.4	0	0.0
Half to full tuition	40	8.5	40	8.6	0	0.0
Full tuition	62	13.2	62	13.4	0	0.0
More than full tuition	11	2.3	11	2.4	0	0.0
Median grant amount			$12,000		$0	

Informational and Library Resources

Total amount spent on library materials	$1,455,039
Study seating capacity inside the library	576
# of full-time equivalent professional librarians	7
Hours per week library is open	106
# of open, wired connections available to students	0
# of networked computers available for use by students	24
Has wireless network?	Y
Require computer?	Y

JD Attrition (from prior year)

	Academic	Other	Total	
	#	#	#	%
1st year	0	1	1	0.7
2nd year	0	6	6	3.5
3rd year	0	3	3	2.0
4th year	0	0	0	0.0

Employment (9 months after graduation)

	Total	Percentage
Employment status known	146	98.0
Employment status unknown	3	2.0
Employed	141	96.6
Pursuing graduate degrees	1	0.7
Unemployed (seeking, not seeking, or studying for the bar)	4	2.7
Type of Employment		
# employed in law firms	98	69.5
# employed in business and industry	9	6.4
# employed in government	12	8.5
# employed in public interest	0	0.0
# employed as judicial clerks	13	9.2
# employed in academia	5	3.5
Geographic Location		
# employed in state	78	55.3
# employed in foreign countries	0	0.0
# of states where employed	20	

Bar Passage Rates

First-time takers	163	Reporting %	72.39
Average school %	97.46	Average state %	83.37
Average pass difference	14.09		

Jurisdiction	Takers	Passers	Pass %	State %	Diff %
North Carolina	81	78	96.30	82.61	13.69
New York	15	15	100.00	88.98	11.02
Virginia	13	13	100.00	82.70	17.30
South Carolina	9	9	100.00	81.83	18.17

Wake Forest University School of Law

Box 7206
Winston-Salem, NC 27109
Phone: 336.758.5437; Fax: 336.758.3930
E-mail: admissions@law.wfu.edu; Website: www.law.wfu.edu

■ Introduction

Wake Forest University School of Law, established in 1894, is located in Winston-Salem, North Carolina. It is a member of the AALS and is ABA-approved. In 1998, the law school was awarded a chapter of the Order of the Coif, a national honorary society.

Wake Forest offers students a solid and personalized legal education. Class sizes are smaller than in virtually any other law school in the nation, with approximately 40 students in each first-year section and about 20 students in first-year legal writing sections.

Faculty members are nationally renowned teachers and scholars. The director of trial advocacy was awarded the Roscoe Pound Foundation's Richard S. Jacobson Award for Excellence in Teaching Trial Advocacy, and Wake Forest has also received the prestigious Emil Gumpert Award from the American College of Trial Lawyers for its outstanding trial advocacy program. Faculty chairs are held by six of the nation's most respected authorities in the areas of administrative law, commercial law, sports and entertainment law, constitutional law, torts and product liability, and health care law and policy.

Wake Forest law school embraces seven principal commitments: (1) to maintain a school of the right size that begins with a first-year class of approximately 160 students composed of four sections of about 40 students each; (2) to develop and retain a faculty strong in teaching, experience, and current scholarly writing; (3) to assure that students are taught substantive law, legal research, and writing through the maximum use of leading-edge technology; (4) to continue the school's emphasis on dispute resolution and litigation skills through instruction, competition, and clinical practice; (5) to build a bridge between law and management communities through an enhanced curriculum, the sharing of resources, and collaborative instruction; (6) to seek to provide career opportunities for our students and graduates that match their potential; and (7) to teach the transcendence of ethics and to inculcate in graduates the importance of doing good while doing well throughout their professional lives.

■ Admission

Requirements: Bachelor's degree from accredited college or university, application and a dean's certification before matriculation, academic recommendation, LSAT and LSAC Credential Assembly Service, application fee—$60, application deadline—March 1.

First-year students are admitted only in the fall semester for full-time study. The law school has an Early Decision program. This choice is not for all candidates and a rolling admission program is used for applicants not choosing Early Decision. Completed files are individually reviewed to select a diverse group of students who are likely to succeed in law school and contribute to the legal profession. The LSAT and undergraduate GPA, as well as a number of subjective factors are considered. This includes personal talents, work experience, community service, leadership potential, graduate study, and a history of overcoming social or economic hardship—indicating intellectual capacity, character, motivation, and maturity. For multiple LSAT scores, the higher test score will be used. Early application is encouraged as scholarship offers begin in late January. The applicant's file must be complete for consideration.

A $300 nonrefundable deposit is due by April 15 (except for Early Decision candidates), and a tuition deposit must be paid by June 15. (Both fees are applicable toward tuition.) Personal interviews are not required; however, we encourage all applicants to visit the law school.

Transfer students meeting the admission requirements are accepted on a space-available basis after the successful completion of one year at an AALS- or ABA-approved law school.

■ Expenses and Financial Aid

Tuition/fees: $35,450; estimated living expenses: $10,000–$15,000.

Merit, need-based, and diversity scholarships are available. The FAFSA is due April 1.

■ Clinical Programs

Five exceptional clinical programs allow students to gain hands-on legal experience. In the Litigation Clinic, students are placed in offices such as the US attorney's office, the district attorney's office, the public defender's office, legal aid, the National Labor Relations Board, private law firms, and corporate counsel. While receiving classroom instruction and skills training in interviewing, counseling, negotiation, and discovery, students represent clients under the supervision of an experienced attorney.

The Elder Law Clinic is an in-house clinic representing low- to moderate-income clients over the age of 60. Located at the Wake Forest University Baptist Medical Center, the clinic features a classroom component that is jointly taught by members of the law and medical school faculties. Students draft essential documents, such as wills, and handle administrative representation and state court litigation with a clinic professor/attorney.

The Community Law and Business Clinic provides a legal resource for low-income entrepreneurs and nonprofit organizations working to improve the quality of life in low-wealth communities. Students will assist in various stages of the business development process and gain experience in a transactional practice setting.

The Innocence and Justice Clinic allows law students to work with defense attorneys, prosecutors, and law enforcement officers to identify cases that qualify for DNA testing for prisoners who might benefit from this testing to demonstrate their innocence. This arrangement, combining the efforts of law students, prosecutors, defense attorneys, and law enforcement officers, makes this a unique educational experience.

The Appellate Advocacy Clinic represents low-income clients in all sorts of appeals, both civil and criminal, and in a variety of appellate courts, including the Fourth Circuit and Seventh Circuit. Working in pairs, students handle an actual appeal from start to finish, with advice and assistance from their professor, who is counsel of record. Students also travel to Washington, DC, to observe arguments at the United States Supreme Court.

■ Technology

Wake Forest prepares students to embrace the rapidly changing technological environment of the legal profession. Classrooms feature multimedia theaters allowing technology to augment classroom teaching. Many professors routinely use Web pages to distribute essential course information and provide online discussion forums outside of the classroom.

Each student is required to have a laptop. The law school wireless network gives students instant access to e-mail, essential legal research systems, the Internet, and a variety of other resources. A university-wide network allows students to register for courses, receive grades, obtain transcripts, and interact with university offices.

■ Joint-Degree Programs

The law school currently offers the following joint degrees: JD/MBA program with the Babcock Graduate School of Management, JD/MA in Religion, JD/MDiv with the Divinity School, a JD/MA in Bioethics with the Medical School. Admission and scholarship decisions are made independently at each school. The law school also offers an LLM in American Law for graduates of foreign law schools. A separate (LLM) application is required and may be obtained at *http:/law.wfu/edu/llm* or by writing the director of the LLM program.

■ Foreign Study

Students in good standing may participate in a four-week program offered each summer at the Worrell House, the university's residential center near Regent's Park in London, England; at Casa Artom on the Grand Canal in Venice, Italy; and at the University of Vienna in Vienna, Austria. Students participating in this program can earn up to six hours of academic credit.

■ Career Services

The Career Services Office aggressively seeks opportunities for students in both summer and permanent legal positions. Knowledgeable staff members personally counsel students to assist them in developing solid career portfolios. The office also conducts workshops in résumé preparation, interviewing, and career planning. Faculty and staff expand career opportunities by visiting law firms, corporations, and agencies throughout the country to acquaint them with the exceptional Wake Forest program. A large number of employers interview students on campus each year or request that résumés be forwarded by the Career Services Office. Wake Forest law graduates are located throughout the country.

Applicant Profile

Wake Forest University School of Law
This grid includes only applicants who earned 120–180 LSAT scores under standard administrations.

LSAT Score	3.75 +		3.50–3.74		3.25–3.49		3.00–3.24		2.75–2.99		2.50–2.74		2.25–2.49		2.00–2.24		Below 2.00		No GPA		Total	
	Apps	Adm	Apps	Adm	Apps	Adm	Apps	Adm	Apps	Adm	Apps	Adm	Apps	Adm	Apps	Adm	Apps	Adm	Apps	Adm	Apps	Adm
175–180	3	3	2	2	1	1	1	1	1	1	0	0	0	0	1	0	0	0	0	0	9	8
170–174	11	11	11	11	7	7	10	10	5	3	1	1	0	0	0	0	1	0	0	0	46	43
165–169	72	71	51	50	47	46	40	37	13	8	12	7	7	4	2	1	0	0	1	1	245	225
160–164	159	141	201	126	178	66	124	42	42	13	15	7	9	2	4	1	0	0	7	0	739	398
155–159	142	59	214	31	199	22	151	15	66	4	22	0	10	0	2	0	0	0	4	0	810	131
150–154	68	12	119	18	132	15	113	18	43	2	15	1	5	0	2	0	0	0	7	0	504	66
145–149	17	5	40	4	70	6	57	5	26	0	13	0	10	0	2	0	0	0	5	0	240	20
140–144	2	0	16	0	24	0	19	0	22	0	11	0	8	0	0	0	0	0	4	0	106	0
135–139	1	0	4	0	9	0	9	0	6	0	4	0	1	0	0	0	1	0	3	0	38	0
130–134	0	0	2	0	3	0	3	0	3	0	3	0	3	0	1	0	0	0	2	0	20	0
125–129	0	0	0	0	0	0	0	0	0	0	0	0	0	0	0	0	0	0	0	0	0	0
120–124	0	0	0	0	0	0	0	0	0	0	0	0	0	0	0	0	0	0	0	0	0	0
Total	475	302	660	242	670	163	527	128	227	31	96	16	53	6	14	2	2	0	33	1	2757	891

Apps = Number of Applicants
Adm = Number Admitted
Reflects 99% of the total applicant pool; average LSAT data reported.

Washburn University School of Law

1700 SW College Avenue
Topeka, KS 66621-0001
Phone: 800.WASHLAW or 800.927.4529; Fax: 785.670.1120
E-mail: admissions@washburnlaw.edu; Website: http://washburnlaw.edu

ABA
Approved
Since
1923

The Basics

Type of school	Public
Term	Semester
Application deadline	4/1 11/1
Application fee	$40
Financial aid deadline	7/1
Can first year start other than fall?	Yes
Student to faculty ratio	12.9 to 1
# of housing spaces available restricted to law students	
graduate housing for which law students are eligible	192

Faculty and Administrators

	Total		Men		Women		Minorities	
	Spr	Fall	Spr	Fall	Spr	Fall	Spr	Fall
Full-time	28	27	17	15	11	12	5	4
Other full-time	1	1	1	1	0	0	0	0
Deans, librarians, & others who teach	5	7	4	5	1	2	2	2
Part-time	30	28	20	16	10	12	0	0
Total	64	63	42	37	22	26	7	6

Curriculum

	Full-Time	Part-Time
Typical first-year section size	76	0
Is there typically a "small section" of the first-year class, other than Legal Writing, taught by full-time faculty	Yes	No
If yes, typical size offered last year	38	
# of classroom course titles beyond first-year curriculum		97

# of upper division courses, excluding seminars, with an enrollment:		
	Under 25	66
	25–49	19
	50–74	13
	75–99	2
	100+	0

# of seminars		24
# of seminar positions available		459
# of seminar positions filled	313	0
# of positions available in simulation courses		514
# of simulation positions filled	334	0
# of positions available in faculty supervised clinical courses		105
# of faculty supervised clinical positions filled	96	0
# involved in field placements	85	0
# involved in law journals	68	0
# involved in moot court or trial competitions	47	0
# of credit hours required to graduate		90

JD Enrollment and Ethnicity

	Men		Women		Full-Time		Part-Time		1st-Year		Total		JD Degs. Awd.
	#	%	#	%	#	%	#	%	#	%	#	%	
African Amer.	5	1.9	13	7.3	18	4.1	0	0.0	7	4.3	18	4.1	3
Amer. Indian	5	1.9	1	0.6	6	1.4	0	0.0	1	0.6	6	1.4	3
Asian Amer.	4	1.5	9	5.0	13	2.9	0	0.0	4	2.5	13	2.9	2
Mex. Amer.	6	2.3	4	2.2	10	2.3	0	0.0	2	1.2	10	2.3	3
Puerto Rican	1	0.4	1	0.6	2	0.5	0	0.0	0	0.0	2	0.5	1
Hispanic	4	1.5	4	2.2	8	1.8	0	0.0	2	1.2	8	1.8	2
Total Minority	25	9.5	32	17.9	57	12.9	0	0.0	16	9.8	57	12.9	14
For. Nation.	1	0.4	1	0.6	2	0.5	0	0.0	1	0.6	2	0.5	0
Caucasian	228	87.0	145	81.0	373	84.6	0	0.0	142	87.1	373	84.6	121
Unknown	8	3.1	1	0.6	9	2.0	0	0.0	4	2.5	9	2.0	2
Total	262	59.4	179	40.6	441	100.0	0	0.0	163	37.0	441		137

Transfers

Transfers in	7
Transfers out	8

Tuition and Fees

	Resident	Nonresident
Full-time	$16,150	$25,150
Part-time		
Tuition Guarantee Program		N

Living Expenses

Estimated living expenses for singles

Living on campus	Living off campus	Living at home
$15,991	$15,991	$15,991

Washburn University School of Law

ABA
Approved
Since
1923

GPA and LSAT Scores

	Total	Full-Time	Part-Time
# of apps	957	957	0
# of offers	453	453	0
# of matrics	159	159	0
75% GPA	3.68	3.68	0.00
Median GPA	3.31	3.31	0.00
25% GPA	2.95	2.95	0.00
75% LSAT	157	157	0
Median LSAT	154	154	0
25% LSAT	152	152	0

Grants and Scholarships (from prior year)

	Total		Full-Time		Part-Time	
	#	%	#	%	#	%
Total # of students	429		429		0	
Total # receiving grants	202	47.1	202	47.1	0	0.0
Less than 1/2 tuition	122	28.4	122	28.4	0	0.0
Half to full tuition	55	12.8	55	12.8	0	0.0
Full tuition	0	0.0	0	0.0	0	0.0
More than full tuition	25	5.8	25	5.8	0	0.0
Median grant amount			$7,500		$0	

Informational and Library Resources

Total amount spent on library materials	$1,263,758
Study seating capacity inside the library	384
# of full-time equivalent professional librarians	9
Hours per week library is open	96
# of open, wired connections available to students	26
# of networked computers available for use by students	58
Has wireless network?	Y
Require computer?	N

JD Attrition (from prior year)

	Academic	Other	Total	
	#	#	#	%
1st year	1	19	20	13.0
2nd year	0	2	2	1.5
3rd year	0	0	0	0.0
4th year	0	0	0	0.0

Employment (9 months after graduation)

	Total	Percentage
Employment status known	141	95.3
Employment status unknown	7	4.7
Employed	127	90.1
Pursuing graduate degrees	5	3.5
Unemployed (seeking, not seeking, or studying for the bar)	4	2.8
Type of Employment		
# employed in law firms	54	42.5
# employed in business and industry	16	12.6
# employed in government	30	23.6
# employed in public interest	12	9.4
# employed as judicial clerks	12	9.4
# employed in academia	1	0.8
Geographic Location		
# employed in state	83	65.4
# employed in foreign countries	0	0.0
# of states where employed	15	

Bar Passage Rates

First-time takers	140	Reporting %	71.43
Average school %	88.00	Average state %	89.78
Average pass difference	−1.78		

Jurisdiction	Takers	Passers	Pass %	State %	Diff %
Kansas	85	76	89.41	89.33	0.08
Missouri	15	12	80.00	92.33	−12.33

Washburn University School of Law

1700 SW College Avenue
Topeka, KS 66621-0001
Phone: 800.WASHLAW or 800.927.4529; Fax: 785.670.1120
E-mail: admissions@washburnlaw.edu; Website: http://washburnlaw.edu

■ Introduction

Washburn University School of Law was founded in 1903, became a member of the AALS in 1905, and appeared on the initial list of ABA-approved schools in 1923. The essence of Washburn Law is the commitment of the law school community at every level—from the dean's office to facilities staff—to the success of our students. In addition, the law school endeavors to impart to its students the value of treating others with respect, dignity, and a sense of caring. Its network of more than 6,600 alumni located in all 50 states and many foreign countries includes nationally recognized lawyers, state and federal judges, politicians, journalists, and senior executives of Fortune 500 companies.

■ Curriculum

All entering students participate in the law school's Ex-L program, which begins during an elaborate and rigorous "first week" program designed to teach students the learning strategies they need to succeed in law school. Ex-L includes a structured study-group program in which groups of 4–6 students meet twice per week to apply cooperative learning strategies to their law school experience under the supervision of carefully trained and supervised upper-division students. Second- and third-year students satisfy advanced writing and oral presentation requirements and take one or more classes from a group of Perspectives on Law courses, and one or more classes from a group of Skills courses.

■ Centers for Excellence

Four centers for excellence complement Washburn's tradition of excellence in teaching. Students may add an element of concentration by participating in one of the school's seven certificate programs, most of which are administered through the centers.

Business and Transactional Law Center—The center provides students with additional educational opportunities in business law while developing the essential skills of transactional lawyers. The hands-on involvement of alumni actively engaged in business and transactional law also allows the center to accomplish a major subsidiary goal: making the law school experience more realistic, and relevant, by providing additional opportunities to bridge the gap between theory and practice.

Center for Excellence in Advocacy—The center trains law students in the persuasive and skilled use of advocacy techniques. Students hone their advocacy skills in Washburn's live-client law clinic and in a variety of advocacy skills courses. The center coordinates student participation in trial advocacy, negotiation, and client counseling; sponsors national and regional advocacy conferences; and hosts a practitioner in residence each year.

Center for Law and Government—Washburn Law is ideally situated to offer law students unique and varied opportunities to learn about lawmaking, judicial decision-making, administrative law, and the regulatory process, given its proximity to the state capitol, judicial center, federal courthouse, and state agencies. As its primary focus, the center provides superior legal education to prepare highly qualified public servants for a broad range of careers associated with local, state, and federal government.

Children and Family Law Center—Washburn houses the American Bar Association's *Family Law Quarterly*. Students working in the center have the opportunity to take a range of courses related to children and families and to participate in the Washburn Law Clinic representing clients in divorce, children in need of care, and other family law cases.

■ Certificate Programs

Washburn Law offers certificates of specialization in Advocacy, Business and Transactional Law, Estate Planning, Family Law, International and Comparative Law, Natural Resources Law, and Tax Law. The certificate programs allow students to fully develop their legal interests in these fields. Students who earn certificates graduate with a highly developed working knowledge of the practice area.

■ Law Clinic

In 1970, Washburn Law Clinic was one of the nation's first in-house clinics. From its inception, faculty members teaching in the clinic have been on a tenure track, placing our clinic at the forefront of legal education. Faculty-supervised students provide a full range of legal services to live clients in six clinics—Children and Family Law Clinic, Criminal Defense Clinic, State Tribal Court Practice Clinic, Civil Litigation Clinic, Criminal Appellate Advocacy Clinic, and Small Business and Transactional Law Clinic.

■ International Programs

Currently, Washburn expands students' understandings of different legal systems through its summer program at the University of the West Indies, in Barbados, and its semester-long program at Maastricht University, in the Netherlands.

■ Externships

Washburn Law's externship program allows students to earn course credit through placement in legal settings outside the law school. Students can experience the practice of law in a wide variety of settings tailored to their specific interests and needs. Students are closely supervised by an attorney and by the externship director.

■ Accelerated Degree Program

This program allows students to complete law school in two years by taking courses during both summers.

■ Facilities and Technology

For 25 years, the Washburn Law Library has been at the top of all law school libraries for new titles added, its extensive collection, and its innovative use of technology. WashLaw has been a premier legal research portal since its creation in the early 1990s, and it is nationally acclaimed as a comprehensive

Washburn University School of Law

source for legal information on the Internet. Students have wireless access throughout the building. Classrooms include enhanced audio, video, and computer technologies. The state-of-the-art Robinson Courtroom/Bianchino Technology Center offers students the opportunity to practice their skills in a high-tech environment.

■ Admission

While an applicant's LSAT score and GPA are significant factors, there is no bright-line cutoff. The Admissions Committee uses the high LSAT for multiple-test takers. It carefully considers other factors, including a determination of whether the individual would be an asset for the class as a whole based on gender, ethnicity, geographic diversity, international experience, and undergraduate institution.

■ Student Activities

More than 30 active student organizations, including Black, Hispanic, Asian, and Native American law student associations, accommodate the wide and diverse interests students bring to the law school and add to the cultural and intellectual life of the law school community.

Students may be selected to serve on the board of editors of the *Washburn Law Journal* or the student editorial board of the ABA's peer-reviewed *Family Law Quarterly*, which has been located at Washburn since 1992, enhancing the Children and Family Law Center.

■ Expenses and Financial Aid

Scholarships are awarded based on academic performance. Contribution to diversity is also considered in making scholarship awards. Resident status for tuition purposes can be established with a primary Kansas residence after six months. Topeka is one of the most affordable housing markets in the country. Most students live in the residential areas surrounding the campus.

■ Professional Development

The Professional Development Office offers programs that emphasize assessment of career goals, exploration of varied applications of a legal education, and support for the transition into the professional marketplace. The office makes available extensive resources regarding local, regional, national, and international legal employment in the public and private sectors, graduate and foreign study, and judicial clerkships.

Washburn Law graduates enjoy great success in seeking employment. Washburn Law alumni reside in every state in the nation, the District of Columbia, and many foreign countries.

■ Writing Program

During the past several years, Washburn Law has made a major commitment of resources to its Legal Analysis, Research, and Writing program, resulting in national recognition. All first-year students must complete six hours of graded legal analysis, research, and writing. An upper-level writing course is also required. The class sizes are small and are taught by tenure-track professors dedicated to legal writing as their chosen profession.

■ Spring Start Program

Students may start law school in January through the Spring Start Program, which provides an alternative to those who do not want to wait for the traditional fall start.

■ Pro Bono Program

Students are encouraged to embrace their future professional obligation to provide legal services to individuals of limited means. Through the Washburn Law Pro Bono Program, they participate in a pro bono initiative that rewards pro bono work with recognition at graduation.

Applicant Profile

Washburn University School of Law
This grid includes only applicants who earned 120–180 LSAT scores under standard administrations.

LSAT Score	GPA																	
	3.75 +		3.50–3.74		3.25–3.49		3.00–3.24		2.75–2.99		2.50–2.74		2.25–2.49		Below 2.25		No GPA		Total	
	Apps	Adm	Apps	Adm	Apps	Adm	Apps	Adm	Apps	Adm	Apps	Adm	Apps	Adm	Apps	Adm	Apps	Adm	Apps	Adm
175–180	0	0	0	0	0	0	0	0	0	0	0	0	0	0	0	0	0	0	0	0
170–174	0	0	1	1	0	0	0	0	0	0	0	0	0	0	0	0	0	0	1	1
165–169	3	3	2	2	2	2	0	0	1	1	3	3	0	0	0	0	0	0	11	11
160–164	14	14	5	5	5	5	3	3	2	1	4	4	2	2	1	1	2	2	38	37
155–159	22	22	24	24	21	19	24	23	6	6	15	13	9	9	2	1	1	1	124	118
150–154	37	34	39	29	57	45	54	42	38	22	30	18	9	5	10	4	4	3	278	202
145–149	18	8	41	11	58	9	44	7	29	6	22	3	9	1	8	0	5	2	234	47
140–144	6	2	26	4	25	2	22	2	28	2	11	0	9	0	4	0	1	0	132	12
Below 140	2	0	4	0	13	0	14	0	17	0	19	0	9	0	8	0	1	0	87	0
Total	102	83	142	76	181	82	161	77	121	38	104	41	47	17	33	6	14	8	905	428

Apps = Number of Applicants   Adm = Number Admitted   Reflects 100% of the total applicant pool; average LSAT data reported.

University of Washington School of Law

William H. Gates Hall, Box 35-3020
Seattle, WA 98195-3020
Phone: 206.543.4078
E-mail: lawadm@u.washington.edu; Website: www.law.washington.edu

ABA
Approved
Since
1924

The Basics

Type of school	Public
Term	Quarter
Application deadline	1/15
Application fee	$50
Financial aid deadline	2/28
Can first year start other than fall?	No
Student to faculty ratio	10.1 to 1
# of housing spaces available restricted to law students	
graduate housing for which law students are eligible	500

Faculty and Administrators

	Total		Men		Women		Minorities	
	Spr	Fall	Spr	Fall	Spr	Fall	Spr	Fall
Full-time	42	46	25	26	17	20	7	7
Other full-time	9	8	6	5	3	3	2	2
Deans, librarians, & others who teach	4	4	2	2	2	2	1	1
Part-time	72	46	45	31	24	15	17	5
Total	127	104	78	64	46	40	27	15

Curriculum

	Full-Time	Part-Time
Typical first-year section size	52	0
Is there typically a "small section" of the first-year class, other than Legal Writing, taught by full-time faculty	Yes	No
If yes, typical size offered last year	26	
# of classroom course titles beyond first-year curriculum	126	

# of upper division courses, excluding seminars, with an enrollment:		
Under 25	78	
25–49	54	
50–74	21	
75–99	5	
100+	0	

# of seminars	41	
# of seminar positions available	615	
# of seminar positions filled	511	0
# of positions available in simulation courses	223	
# of simulation positions filled	223	0
# of positions available in faculty supervised clinical courses	128	
# of faculty supervised clinical positions filled	128	0
# involved in field placements	147	0
# involved in law journals	123	0
# involved in moot court or trial competitions	59	0
# of credit hours required to graduate	135	

JD Enrollment and Ethnicity

	Men		Women		Full-Time		Part-Time		1st-Year		Total		JD Degs. Awd.
	#	%	#	%	#	%	#	%	#	%	#	%	
African Amer.	4	1.7	7	2.4	11	2.1	0	0.0	1	0.6	11	2.1	2
Amer. Indian	7	2.9	7	2.4	14	2.6	0	0.0	3	1.7	14	2.6	5
Asian Amer.	27	11.3	43	14.8	70	13.2	0	0.0	26	14.4	70	13.2	18
Mex. Amer.	5	2.1	6	2.1	11	2.1	0	0.0	4	2.2	11	2.1	0
Puerto Rican	0	0.0	0	0.0	0	0.0	0	0.0	0	0.0	0	0.0	0
Hispanic	4	1.7	7	2.4	11	2.1	0	0.0	5	2.8	11	2.1	2
Total Minority	47	19.7	70	24.1	117	22.1	0	0.0	39	21.5	117	22.1	27
For. Nation.	7	2.9	9	3.1	16	3.0	0	0.0	8	4.4	16	3.0	5
Caucasian	180	75.3	210	72.2	390	73.6	0	0.0	132	72.9	390	73.6	135
Unknown	5	2.1	2	0.7	7	1.3	0	0.0	2	1.1	7	1.3	6
Total	239	45.1	291	54.9	530	100.0	0	0.0	181	34.2	530		173

Transfers

Transfers in	5
Transfers out	4

Tuition and Fees

	Resident	Nonresident
Full-time	$22,267	$32,777
Part-time		
Tuition Guarantee Program		N

Living Expenses

Estimated living expenses for singles

Living on campus	Living off campus	Living at home
$17,871	$17,871	$8,031

University of Washington School of Law

ABA
Approved
Since
1924

GPA and LSAT Scores

	Total	Full-Time	Part-Time
# of apps	2,448	2,448	0
# of offers	622	622	0
# of matrics	181	181	0
75% GPA	3.80	3.80	0.00
Median GPA	3.66	3.66	0.00
25% GPA	3.47	3.47	0.00
75% LSAT	166	166	0
Median LSAT	163	163	0
25% LSAT	160	160	0

Grants and Scholarships (from prior year)

	Total		Full-Time		Part-Time	
	#	%	#	%	#	%
Total # of students	534		534		0	
Total # receiving grants	258	48.3	258	48.3	0	0.0
Less than 1/2 tuition	170	31.8	170	31.8	0	0.0
Half to full tuition	51	9.6	51	9.6	0	0.0
Full tuition	2	0.4	2	0.4	0	0.0
More than full tuition	35	6.6	35	6.6	0	0.0
Median grant amount			$6,000		$0	

Informational and Library Resources

Total amount spent on library materials	$1,369,254
Study seating capacity inside the library	391
# of full-time equivalent professional librarians	7
Hours per week library is open	89
# of open, wired connections available to students	0
# of networked computers available for use by students	67
Has wireless network?	Y
Require computer?	N

JD Attrition (from prior year)

	Academic	Other	Total	
	#	#	#	%
1st year	0	4	4	2.1
2nd year	0	0	0	0.0
3rd year	0	0	0	0.0
4th year	0	0	0	0.0

Employment (9 months after graduation)

	Total	Percentage
Employment status known	173	100.0
Employment status unknown	0	0.0
Employed	162	93.6
Pursuing graduate degrees	5	2.9
Unemployed (seeking, not seeking, or studying for the bar)	3	1.7
Type of Employment		
# employed in law firms	87	53.7
# employed in business and industry	12	7.4
# employed in government	22	13.6
# employed in public interest	13	8.0
# employed as judicial clerks	26	16.0
# employed in academia	2	1.2
Geographic Location		
# employed in state	101	62.3
# employed in foreign countries	3	1.9
# of states where employed	16	

Bar Passage Rates

First-time takers	159	Reporting %	77.99
Average school %	84.68	Average state %	74.40
Average pass difference	10.28		

Jurisdiction	Takers	Passers	Pass %	State %	Diff %
Washington	124	105	84.68	74.40	10.28

University of Washington School of Law

William H. Gates Hall, Box 35-3020
Seattle, WA 98195-3020
Phone: 206.543.4078
E-mail: lawadm@u.washington.edu; Website: www.law.washington.edu

■ Introduction

Established in 1899, the School of Law is part of the main campus of the University of Washington, approximately four miles from downtown Seattle. The university, the largest single-campus institution in the western United States, with an enrollment of 48,022 students, offers nearly every discipline for study. The School of Law has 66 full-time faculty members and about 530 JD students. Because of the favorable student-to-faculty ratio, classes are generally small, with frequent opportunities for student-teacher contact. Each first-year student is usually in at least one class of 30 or fewer students, in addition to the Basic Legal Skills course. The school is a member of the AALS, is approved by the ABA, and has a chapter of the Order of the Coif.

■ Curriculum

The first-year curriculum is prescribed. After that, except for an advanced writing requirement and a class in professional responsibility, all courses in the second and third years are elective. In addition to traditional courses and seminars, advanced students may participate in one of 12 clinics—Innocence Project Northwest, Berman Environmental Law, Mediation, Child Advocacy, Children and Youth Legislative Advocacy, Unemployment Compensation, Street Law, Tribal Court Criminal Defense, Immigration Law, Refugee and Immigrant Advocacy, Entrepreneurial Law, or Federal Tax—or in courses in trial advocacy. Judicial, legislative, agency, and public interest externships are available. Students must also perform 60 hours of public service legal work.

Students are encouraged to rely on their initiative and to develop their own powers of perception. Classroom discussion, in which students participate fully, is one means used to assist this development. Independent research projects, either in the context of a seminar or through individualized study under faculty supervision, are also emphasized. Although it is a state law school, Washington's state law is not emphasized unduly. Graduates of the school are prepared to practice law anywhere in the United States or in other common law countries.

■ Special Programs

Concentration tracks are available in Asian law, dispute resolution, public service, environmental law, health law, intellectual property, and international and comparative law.

There are centers for Advanced Study and Research on Intellectual Property (CASRIP); Indian Law; and Law, Commerce, and Technology.

JD students may take courses in any of the LLM programs during their second and third years of study. Additionally, JD students may enroll in graduate-level courses from other disciplines offered at the UW and count a limited number of those credits toward their JD. Students may pursue the JD concurrently with any graduate degree program to which they have been admitted. The UW also offers a master's degree in Law Librarianship.

■ Admission Standards

In selecting the entering class, the law school does not make all of its admission decisions solely on the basis of predicted academic performance. Important academic objectives are furthered by classes composed of students having talents and skills derived from diverse backgrounds believed to be relevant to a rich and effective study of law.

■ Gates Public Service Law Scholars Program

Five Gates Public Service Law (PSL) Scholars are selected annually from among the first-year students entering the UW School of Law JD program. Each Gates PSL Scholar award will cover tuition, books, other normal fees imposed for university and UW School of Law enrollment, costs of room and board, and incidental expenses. Acceptance of a Gates PSL scholarship represents a commitment on the part of each recipient to work in public service for at least five years following graduation. More information about the program, including the application it requires, may be found at *www.law.washington.edu/GatesScholar/*.

■ Student Activities

The *Washington Law Review*, *Pacific Rim Law and Policy Journal*, and *Shidler Journal of Law, Commerce and Technology* are edited and published by students. The University of Washington is consistently among the top scoring moot court teams in the nation.

Through the Student Bar Association and student/faculty committees, students participate in the decision processes of the law school. Student organizations include the American Bar Association/Law Student Division; American Constitution Society; American Civil Liberties Union; Asian/Pacific American Law Student Association; Black Law Students Association; Center for Human Rights and Justice; Center for Labor and Employment Justice; Chinese American Law Students Association; Christian Legal Society; Disability Law Alliance; Federalist Society; GreenLaw; Immigrant Families Advocacy Project; Innocence Project Northwest; International Law Society; Jewish Legal Society; Korean American Law Student Association; Latino/Latina Law Students Association; Law and Alternative Dispute Resolution; Law Students for Reproductive Justice; Law Women's Caucus; Military Law Students Association; Minority Law Students Association; Moot Court Honor Board; National Lawyers Guild; Native American Law Student Association; Nontraditional Law Students; Outlaws (LBGT Student Group); PALS: Parents Attending Law School; Public Interest Law Association; Society for Small Business Development; Sports and Entertainment Law Club; Street Youth Legal Advocates of Washington; Student Animal Legal Defense Fund; Student Bar Association; Student Health Law Organization; and Technology Law Society.

■ Career Services

The Career Services Office serves as a liaison between students and prospective employers. Firms, agencies, and

University of Washington School of Law

other potential employers are invited to interview at the school and to list job openings in the regularly published placement bulletin. About 62 percent of graduates choose to remain in Washington State.

■ William H. Gates Hall

The law school moved into its $80 million new facility in September 2003. The building is named for one of its most distinguished graduates, and it features the latest technology, including wireless access, to educate lawyers for the twenty-first century.

■ Visitation

The law school invites prospective students to visit a large-section, first-year class. The schedule can be found at *www.law.washington.edu/admissions/Visit/Default.aspx*.

Applicant Profile

University of Washington School of Law
This grid includes only applicants who earned 120–180 LSAT scores under standard administrations.

LSAT Score	3.75 +		3.50–3.74		3.25–3.49		3.00–3.24		2.75–2.99		2.50–2.74		2.25–2.49		2.00–2.24		Below 2.00		No GPA		Total	
	Apps	Adm	Apps	Adm	Apps	Adm	Apps	Adm	Apps	Adm	Apps	Adm	Apps	Adm	Apps	Adm	Apps	Adm	Apps	Adm	Apps	Adm
175–180	5	4	4	4	5	4	2	2	2	1	3	0	0	0	0	0	0	0	0	0	21	15
170–174	34	31	20	18	15	11	15	7	4	2	3	2	0	0	0	0	0	0	1	1	92	72
165–169	93	84	136	92	92	42	30	7	11	1	5	1	3	0	0	0	0	0	4	3	374	230
160–164	206	105	264	69	164	29	83	8	25	0	19	1	3	0	0	0	0	0	19	7	783	219
155–159	129	26	225	29	131	6	65	0	17	0	14	1	8	0	1	0	0	0	26	3	616	65
150–154	57	8	95	9	83	1	63	1	19	0	8	0	3	0	0	0	0	0	18	1	346	20
145–149	16	1	23	0	31	0	21	0	10	0	6	0	3	0	3	0	0	0	3	0	116	1
140–144	2	0	9	0	9	0	11	0	12	0	6	0	3	0	1	0	1	0	6	0	60	0
135–139	2	0	1	0	3	0	3	0	3	0	1	0	2	0	1	0	0	0	2	0	18	0
130–134	0	0	0	0	1	0	4	0	2	0	1	0	2	0	0	0	0	0	1	0	11	0
125–129	0	0	0	0	0	0	0	0	1	0	0	0	0	0	0	0	0	0	0	0	1	0
120–124	0	0	0	0	0	0	0	0	0	0	0	0	0	0	0	0	0	0	0	0	0	0
Total	544	259	777	221	534	93	297	25	106	4	66	5	27	0	6	0	1	0	80	15	2438	622

Apps = Number of Applicants
Adm = Number Admitted
Reflects 100% of the total applicant pool; average LSAT data reported.

Washington and Lee University School of Law

Office of Admissions, Sydney Lewis Hall
Lexington, VA 24450
Phone: 540.458.8503; Fax: 540.458.8586
E-mail: LawAdm@wlu.edu; Website: www.law.wlu.edu

ABA
Approved
Since
1923

The Basics

Type of school	Private
Term	Semester
Application deadline	2/1
Application fee	$0
Financial aid deadline	3/15
Can first year start other than fall?	No
Student to faculty ratio	9.4 to 1
# of housing spaces available	
restricted to law students	56
graduate housing for which law students are eligible	56

Faculty and Administrators

	Total		Men		Women		Minorities	
	Spr	Fall	Spr	Fall	Spr	Fall	Spr	Fall
Full-time	35	35	26	25	9	10	5	6
Other full-time	6	2	5	2	1	0	3	1
Deans, librarians, & others who teach	6	6	3	3	3	3	0	0
Part-time	18	21	16	21	2	0	0	0
Total	65	64	50	51	15	13	8	7

Curriculum

	Full-Time	Part-Time
Typical first-year section size	51	0
Is there typically a "small section" of the first-year class, other than Legal Writing, taught by full-time faculty	Yes	No
If yes, typical size offered last year	21	

# of classroom course titles beyond first-year curriculum		81
# of upper division courses, excluding seminars, with an enrollment:	Under 25	79
	25–49	19
	50–74	6
	75–99	2
	100+	1

# of seminars		14
# of seminar positions available		187
# of seminar positions filled	163	0
# of positions available in simulation courses		431
# of simulation positions filled	348	0
# of positions available in faculty supervised clinical courses		68
# of faculty supervised clinical positions filled	68	0
# involved in field placements	59	0
# involved in law journals	113	0
# involved in moot court or trial competitions	123	0
# of credit hours required to graduate		85

JD Enrollment and Ethnicity

	Men		Women		Full-Time		Part-Time		1st-Year		Total		JD Degs. Awd.
	#	%	#	%	#	%	#	%	#	%	#	%	
African Amer.	14	6.3	17	10.1	31	7.9	0	0.0	11	8.2	31	7.9	3
Amer. Indian	3	1.4	3	1.8	6	1.5	0	0.0	0	0.0	6	1.5	2
Asian Amer.	10	4.5	11	6.5	21	5.4	0	0.0	4	3.0	21	5.4	15
Mex. Amer.	1	0.5	0	0.0	1	0.3	0	0.0	1	0.7	1	0.3	1
Puerto Rican	0	0.0	0	0.0	0	0.0	0	0.0	0	0.0	0	0.0	0
Hispanic	7	3.2	7	4.2	14	3.6	0	0.0	5	3.7	14	3.6	2
Total Minority	35	15.8	38	22.6	73	18.7	0	0.0	21	15.7	73	18.7	23
For. Nation.	5	2.3	4	2.4	9	2.3	0	0.0	1	0.7	9	2.3	3
Caucasian	181	81.5	125	74.4	306	78.5	0	0.0	111	82.8	306	78.5	112
Unknown	1	0.5	1	0.6	2	0.5	0	0.0	1	0.7	2	0.5	0
Total	222	56.9	168	43.1	390	100.0	0	0.0	134	34.4	390		138

Transfers

Transfers in	11
Transfers out	9

Tuition and Fees

	Resident	Nonresident
Full-time	$38,062	$38,062
Part-time		
Tuition Guarantee Program	N	

Living Expenses

Estimated living expenses for singles

Living on campus	Living off campus	Living at home
$19,043	$19,043	$2,000

Washington and Lee University School of Law

ABA
Approved
Since
1923

GPA and LSAT Scores

	Total	Full-Time	Part-Time
# of apps	3,416	3,416	0
# of offers	873	873	0
# of matrics	135	135	0
75% GPA	3.78	3.78	0.00
Median GPA	3.53	3.53	0.00
25% GPA	3.28	3.28	0.00
75% LSAT	167	167	0
Median LSAT	166	166	0
25% LSAT	160	160	0

Grants and Scholarships (from prior year)

	Total		Full-Time		Part-Time	
	#	%	#	%	#	%
Total # of students	391		391		0	
Total # receiving grants	245	62.7	245	62.7	0	0.0
Less than 1/2 tuition	153	39.1	153	39.1	0	0.0
Half to full tuition	83	21.2	83	21.2	0	0.0
Full tuition	8	2.0	8	2.0	0	0.0
More than full tuition	1	0.3	1	0.3	0	0.0
Median grant amount			$15,000		$0	

Informational and Library Resources

Total amount spent on library materials	$1,095,312
Study seating capacity inside the library	517
# of full-time equivalent professional librarians	8
Hours per week library is open	168
# of open, wired connections available to students	325
# of networked computers available for use by students	68
Has wireless network?	Y
Require computer?	N

JD Attrition (from prior year)

	Academic	Other	Total	
	#	#	#	%
1st year	0	1	1	0.8
2nd year	0	10	10	7.9
3rd year	0	1	1	0.7
4th year	0	0	0	0.0

Employment (9 months after graduation)

	Total	Percentage
Employment status known	138	97.9
Employment status unknown	3	2.1
Employed	124	89.9
Pursuing graduate degrees	1	0.7
Unemployed (seeking, not seeking, or studying for the bar)	13	9.4
Type of Employment		
# employed in law firms	71	57.3
# employed in business and industry	9	7.3
# employed in government	11	8.9
# employed in public interest	7	5.6
# employed as judicial clerks	25	20.2
# employed in academia	1	0.8
Geographic Location		
# employed in state	34	27.4
# employed in foreign countries	2	1.6
# of states where employed	23	

Bar Passage Rates

First-time takers	138	Reporting %	70.29
Average school %	85.55	Average state %	84.40
Average pass difference	1.15		

Jurisdiction	Takers	Passers	Pass %	State %	Diff %
Virginia	43	36	83.72	82.70	1.02
New York	16	14	87.50	88.98	-1.48
California	13	10	76.92	78.07	-1.15
Pennsylvania	10	10	100.00	86.69	13.31
Others (3)	15	13	86.67		

Washington and Lee University School of Law

Office of Admissions, Sydney Lewis Hall
Lexington, VA 24450
Phone: 540.458.8503; Fax: 540.458.8586
E-mail: LawAdm@wlu.edu; Website: www.law.wlu.edu

■ Introduction

Washington and Lee University School of Law, founded in 1849, is located in Lexington, Virginia, a three-hour interstate highway drive from Washington, DC. The School of Law is fully accredited by the ABA and is a member of the AALS. Washington and Lee is known for providing its students with an academically rigorous and professionally challenging legal education in an environment characterized by a commitment to students, small classes, a generous student-to-faculty ratio, and a collegial community.

■ The Honor System

The W&L community is governed by an Honor System that is the foundation for academic and student life at the university. The Honor System is an integral part of a professional education that fosters a sensitivity to the ethical imperatives of the legal profession. The Honor System means that the library is always open, exams are unproctored, the exam schedule for upper-class students is flexible, and professors are free to give take-home examinations. The Honor System contributes significantly to a law school environment characterized by mutual respect, trust, and collegiality.

■ Curriculum

All first-year classes are required; in their second year, students augment several required classes with elective courses. The third year blends classic academic and professional values with a view toward deliberately preparing students for the transition to law practice, and integrates cognitive learning, practical skills, and development of professional identity. Each semester begins with intensive preparatory instruction and a year-long course on professionalism is required. The intensive preparatory course is followed by elective offerings in the full range of traditional subject matter, as well as clinical or extern experiences. In realistic settings that simulate actual client experiences, students will be required to exercise professional judgment, work in teams, solve problems, counsel clients, negotiate solutions, and serve as advocates and counselors—the full complement of professional skills required to apply legal theory and legal doctrines to real-world issues and serve clients ethically and honorably within the highest traditions of the profession. Students can expect rigorous intellectual content, intense evaluation, thoughtful guidance, and meaningful feedback. For additional details about the third-year curriculum, visit www.law.wlu.edu/thirdyear.

Offerings in corporate and business law, international law, health law, and civil and criminal litigation are particularly strong. A wide variety of clinical programs and externships provide opportunities for hands-on experience as part of the academic program. Clinics include the Virginia Capital Case Clearinghouse, established to assist attorneys representing clients charged with or convicted of capital crimes; the Black Lung Legal Clinic, in which students represent coal miners seeking disability benefits under federal law; the Community Legal Practice Center, which provides a range of legal services to qualified area residents; the Tax Clinic, in which students represent low-income taxpayers in controversies with the Internal Revenue Service; the Public Prosecutors Program, in which students assist federal and state prosecutors with investigations, trial preparation, pretrial and trial practice, and appeals; the Criminal Justice Clinic, in which students defend area residents accused of misdemeanors; the Community Law Clinic at Oliver Hill House in Roanoke, VA, through which students assist in legal representation of individuals belonging to identifiable social classes; the Judicial Clerkship Program, through which students act as law clerks to trial, appellate, juvenile and domestic relations, and federal bankruptcy judges; and the General Externship Program, through which students may pursue individual placements.

■ Special Programs

JD/MHA. With Virginia Commonwealth University (VCU) in Richmond, W&L Law offers a program through which students can receive a JD and a Master in Health Administration on an accelerated basis. Dual-degree candidates must be accepted for the program by both VCU and W&L; a portion of the degree requirements are taken on the campus of each university.

LLM in United States Law. W&L Law offers a one-year program in United States law to attorneys who hold a foreign law degree.

■ Student Activities

Students have three journal opportunities: the *Washington and Lee Law Review*, a quarterly journal for scholarly discussion of legal issues; the *Journal of Civil Rights and Social Justice*, focusing on legal issues having an impact on racial and ethnic minorities; and the *Journal of Energy, Climate, and the Environment*, devoted to environmental and natural resources issues and state and federal environmental legislation and regulation. A variety of moot court and advocacy competitions allow upper-level students to hone advocacy, counseling, negotiation, and trial skills.

W&L Law students have established numerous groups such as the Black Law Students Association, Asian Pacific American Law Students Association, Women Law Students Organization, LGBT Equality Project, Jewish Law Students Association, Christian Legal Society, Rationalist Society, Law Families, Federalist Society, American Constitution Society, National Lawyers Guild, and chapters of three national professional fraternities. Practice-oriented groups include the Environmental Law Society, International Law Society, Tax Law Society, Sports and Entertainment Law Society, Public Interest Law Students Association, Students for an Innocence Project, and Intellectual Property and Tech Law Society. Student groups foster a rich intellectual environment at the School of Law by presenting programs that address issues of special concern to their members.

■ Admission and Financial Aid

W&L Law actively seeks a diverse student body whose members are of different religious, racial, ethnic, economic, and geographic backgrounds. The admission process is highly individualized. Students are not ranked by any numerical

index, nor is there an assigned weight given to any objective or subjective factor presented in the application. The Admissions Committee considers not only the cumulative undergraduate grade-point average, but also trends in grades, the rigor of an applicant's academic program, the quality of the school attended, the LSAT score, extracurricular activities, community service, evidence of leadership, graduate study, work experience, assessments of recommenders, and any information presented in the applicant's personal statement. Admission officers will interview applicants upon request. Applicants are encouraged to visit the school to sit in on classes, tour the facility, and talk with students and faculty. A generous scholarship endowment allows W&L Law to assist a large percentage of its students with merit-based grant funds.

■ Career Planning and Professional Development

W&L Law graduates practice in every state and throughout the world. More than 70 percent of recent graduates practice outside Virginia. The two counseling professionals in the Office of Career Planning and Professional Development (OCP) hold JD degrees and work with each student individually to develop a unique career plan. OCP provides instruction in résumé and cover letter writing, networking, and other career development skills. It also provides programming on a wide variety of practice specialties and settings, and acts as a liaison between students and legal employers. Law students interview with prospective employers on campus, at a satellite location in Charlottesville, and at programs throughout the United States. An active alumni network assists students with contacts in every state.

■ Law Library and Physical Facilities

Sydney Lewis Hall, home of the School of Law, was built in 1976 and expanded in 1991 with the addition of the Lewis F. Powell Jr. Archives, which house the Supreme Court and professional papers of retired Supreme Court Justice Powell, a graduate of the university's college and law school. Wireless Internet access is available throughout the building. Every classroom has been renovated within the past five years and is equipped with state-of-the-art technology; the moot courtroom was completely renovated in 2006. The building, including the law library, is open 24 hours a day, 365 days a year. Students have access to the library collection on an open-stack basis.

Applicant Profile

Washington and Lee University School of Law
This grid includes only applicants who earned 120–180 LSAT scores under standard administrations.

LSAT Score	3.75 +		3.50–3.74		3.25–3.49		3.00–3.24		2.75–2.99		2.50–2.74		2.25–2.49		2.00–2.24		Below 2.00		No GPA		Total	
	Apps	Adm	Apps	Adm	Apps	Adm	Apps	Adm	Apps	Adm	Apps	Adm	Apps	Adm	Apps	Adm	Apps	Adm	Apps	Adm	Apps	Adm
175–180	2	2	7	6	7	7	6	6	3	1	2	0	0	0	1	0	0	0	0	0	28	22
170–174	29	26	28	24	26	19	24	15	15	8	6	1	4	0	1	0	1	0	0	0	134	93
165–169	138	125	187	144	136	101	94	52	36	12	15	0	8	0	1	0	0	0	5	0	620	434
160–164	342	105	373	65	287	31	163	23	40	2	17	0	5	0	2	0	0	0	26	0	1255	226
155–159	150	31	231	19	149	12	97	6	34	0	20	0	9	0	3	0	1	0	19	0	713	68
150–154	54	4	71	12	111	3	79	7	25	0	18	0	5	0	0	0	0	0	8	0	371	26
145–149	19	1	40	0	41	2	37	0	15	0	12	0	5	0	2	0	0	0	8	0	179	3
140–144	7	0	6	0	11	1	10	0	12	0	9	0	5	0	0	0	0	0	5	0	66	1
135–139	1	0	1	0	2	0	3	0	2	0	7	0	3	0	0	0	0	0	3	0	22	0
130–134	0	0	0	0	0	0	0	0	5	0	2	0	0	0	1	0	0	0	2	0	10	0
125–129	0	0	0	0	0	0	0	0	0	0	0	0	0	0	1	0	0	0	0	0	1	0
120–124	0	0	0	0	0	0	0	0	0	0	0	0	0	0	0	0	0	0	0	0	0	0
Total	742	294	944	270	770	176	513	109	187	23	108	1	44	0	12	0	3	0	76	0	3399	873

Apps = Number of Applicants
Adm = Number Admitted
Reflects 99% of the total applicant pool; average LSAT data reported.

Washington University School of Law

Campus Box 1120, One Brookings Drive
St. Louis, MO 63130-4899
Phone: 314.935.4525; Fax: 314.935.8778
E-mail: admiss@wulaw.wustl.edu; Website: http://law.wustl.edu

ABA
Approved
Since
1923

The Basics

Type of school	Private
Term	Semester
Application deadline	3/1
Application fee	$70
Financial aid deadline	3/1
Can first year start other than fall?	No
Student to faculty ratio	10.7 to 1
# of housing spaces available restricted to law students	
graduate housing for which law students are eligible	1,636

Faculty and Administrators

	Total		Men		Women		Minorities	
	Spr	Fall	Spr	Fall	Spr	Fall	Spr	Fall
Full-time	63	66	31	29	32	37	6	5
Other full-time	0	0	0	0	0	0	0	0
Deans, librarians, & others who teach	9	11	5	5	4	6	1	2
Part-time	87	77	73	63	13	14	8	8
Total	159	154	109	97	49	57	15	15

Curriculum

		Full-Time	Part-Time
Typical first-year section size		96	0
Is there typically a "small section" of the first-year class, other than Legal Writing, taught by full-time faculty		Yes	No
If yes, typical size offered last year		49	
# of classroom course titles beyond first-year curriculum		154	
# of upper division courses, excluding seminars, with an enrollment:	Under 25	114	
	25–49	48	
	50–74	20	
	75–99	5	
	100+	2	
# of seminars		25	
# of seminar positions available		407	
# of seminar positions filled		349	0
# of positions available in simulation courses		1,469	
# of simulation positions filled		1,267	0
# of positions available in faculty supervised clinical courses		89	
# of faculty supervised clinical positions filled	89		0
# involved in field placements		113	0
# involved in law journals		263	0
# involved in moot court or trial competitions	65		0
# of credit hours required to graduate		86	

JD Enrollment and Ethnicity

	Men		Women		Full-Time		Part-Time		1st-Year		Total		JD Degs. Awd.
	#	%	#	%	#	%	#	%	#	%	#	%	
African Amer.	39	7.8	51	14.2	90	10.6	0	0.0	32	12.3	90	10.5	19
Amer. Indian	5	1.0	1	0.3	6	0.7	0	0.0	1	0.4	6	0.7	3
Asian Amer.	45	9.0	48	13.4	90	10.6	3	60.0	25	9.6	93	10.9	19
Mex. Amer.	4	0.8	0	0.0	4	0.5	0	0.0	0	0.0	4	0.5	1
Puerto Rican	2	0.4	1	0.3	3	0.4	0	0.0	0	0.0	3	0.4	1
Hispanic	5	1.0	6	1.7	11	1.3	0	0.0	7	2.7	11	1.3	2
Total Minority	100	20.1	107	29.9	204	24.0	3	60.0	65	24.9	207	24.2	45
For. Nation.	34	6.8	23	6.4	57	6.7	0	0.0	8	3.1	57	6.7	25
Caucasian	263	52.8	161	45.0	422	49.6	2	40.0	144	55.2	424	49.5	143
Unknown	101	20.3	67	18.7	168	19.7	0	0.0	44	16.9	168	19.6	78
Total	498	58.2	358	41.8	851	99.4	5	0.6	261	30.5	856		291

Transfers

Transfers in	46
Transfers out	12

Tuition and Fees

	Resident	Nonresident
Full-time	$42,330	
Part-time		
Tuition Guarantee Program		N

Living Expenses

Estimated living expenses for singles

Living on campus	Living off campus	Living at home
N/A	$19,600	$16,110

Washington University School of Law

ABA
Approved
Since
1923

GPA and LSAT Scores

	Total	Full-Time	Part-Time
# of apps	3,690	3,690	0
# of offers	987	987	0
# of matrics	261	261	0
75% GPA	3.80	3.80	0.00
Median GPA	3.70	3.70	0.00
25% GPA	3.30	3.30	0.00
75% LSAT	168	168	0
Median LSAT	167	167	0
25% LSAT	161	161	0

Grants and Scholarships (from prior year)

	Total		Full-Time		Part-Time	
	#	%	#	%	#	%
Total # of students	839		831		8	
Total # receiving grants	517	61.6	517	62.2	0	0.0
Less than 1/2 tuition	241	28.7	241	29.0	0	0.0
Half to full tuition	199	23.7	199	23.9	0	0.0
Full tuition	52	6.2	52	6.3	0	0.0
More than full tuition	25	3.0	25	3.0	0	0.0
Median grant amount			$20,000		$0	

Informational and Library Resources

Total amount spent on library materials	$1,279,329
Study seating capacity inside the library	486
# of full-time equivalent professional librarians	9
Hours per week library is open	120
# of open, wired connections available to students	814
# of networked computers available for use by students	69
Has wireless network?	Y
Require computer?	N

JD Attrition (from prior year)

	Academic	Other	Total	
	#	#	#	%
1st year	0	15	15	5.6
2nd year	0	5	5	1.7
3rd year	0	0	0	0.0
4th year	0	0	0	0.0

Employment (9 months after graduation)

	Total	Percentage
Employment status known	259	97.4
Employment status unknown	7	2.6
Employed	246	95.0
Pursuing graduate degrees	4	1.5
Unemployed (seeking, not seeking, or studying for the bar)	8	3.1
Type of Employment		
# employed in law firms	152	61.8
# employed in business and industry	25	10.2
# employed in government	26	10.6
# employed in public interest	5	2.0
# employed as judicial clerks	26	10.6
# employed in academia	5	2.0
Geographic Location		
# employed in state	56	22.8
# employed in foreign countries	9	3.7
# of states where employed	30	

Bar Passage Rates

First-time takers	248	Reporting %	87.50
Average school %	91.21	Average state %	88.52
Average pass difference	2.69		

Jurisdiction	Takers	Passers	Pass %	State %	Diff %
Missouri	53	53	100.00	92.33	7.67
New York	50	46	92.00	88.98	3.02
Illinois	43	39	90.70	90.94	−0.24
California	21	12	57.14	78.07	−20.93
Others (10)	50	48	96.00		

Washington University School of Law

Campus Box 1120, One Brookings Drive
St. Louis, MO 63130-4899
Phone: 314.935.4525; Fax: 314.935.8778
E-mail: admiss@wulaw.wustl.edu; Website: http://law.wustl.edu

■ Introduction

Washington University School of Law offers its students an outstanding legal education in an intellectually challenging and collegial environment. Our faculty members are recognized for their excellent teaching and scholarship, and they are highly accessible to our students. The School of Law curriculum blends traditional theory with opportunities to participate in a wide variety of lawyering skills courses and cocurricular activities that encourage the development of practical skills and interdisciplinary learning.

■ Curriculum

Washington University law school offers a broad-based curriculum that highlights applied lawyering skills. A three-year, full-time course of study leads to the JD degree. All first-year students have half their courses in small sections of 45 students or less. These small classes increase the opportunities for participation in class discussions and individualized teacher-student contact. Second- and third-year students choose their own classes and can tailor them to fit their own particular interests. Students may also opt to enroll in courses from other graduate programs at the university and apply up to six credit hours toward the JD requirements. In addition, our Center for Interdisciplinary Studies, the Whitney R. Harris World Law Institute, and other school-sponsored conferences and symposia expose our students to a wide range of nationally and internationally renowned legal scholars.

■ Library and Physical Facilities

The law school moved into its state-of-the-art facility, Anheuser-Busch Hall, in 1997, and recently expanded into the newly constructed Seigle Hall. Anheuser-Busch Hall also underwent significant renovations in 2008, and both buildings provide well-functioning, vibrant spaces which enhance the law school's sense of community and collaboration. Although the buildings appear traditional, the latest computing and multimedia technologies are incorporated in their design. Cutting-edge information technology provides students with quick access to the Internet where they can register for courses, view grades, order transcripts, view a photo directory of classmates, access their e-mail, and enhance their legal research capabilities. Wireless connections and digital signage are available throughout. The law library is the focal point for much of the intellectual activity in the law school. It has a collection of over 675,000 volumes and access to a rich collection of online databases. The library has particularly strong collections in the areas of international law, environmental law, land use planning, urban law, tax law, Chinese law, and Japanese law.

■ Clinical Opportunities

The School of Law's exceptional Clinical Education Program provides law students with opportunities to learn professional skills and values by working with clients, attorneys, judges, and legislators under the close supervision of experienced and expert faculty. While offering a diverse array of experiences for students, the program also benefits the larger community—

locally, nationally, and internationally. The program includes the Civil Justice, Interdisciplinary Environmental, Civil Rights and Community Justice, Government Lawyering, Criminal Justice, Appellate, Judicial Clerkship, and Intellectual Property and Nonprofit Organizations Clinics. The Congressional and Administrative Law Clinic, founded in 1977, offers students the opportunity to spend a semester working in Washington, DC, for a member of the United States Congress, a congressional committee, or a federal administrative agency. Washington University has established an academic partnership with the Brookings Institution in Washington, DC. This affiliation provides research collaborations, internships for students, faculty exchanges, and other mutually beneficial projects in which students may be involved.

■ Special Degree Programs

Washington University complements its outstanding JD program with many different joint-degree opportunities. In addition to our formal joint-degree programs, students may design their own joint degrees, combining law and another course of study that leads to a master's degree. Joint degrees offered include a JD/MBA, JD/MSW, and JD/PhD-Political Science. We are one of only a very few joint-degree programs in the nation combining law with an MA in East Asian Studies. The School of Law offers LLM programs in Intellectual Property and Technology Law, Taxation, and US Law for International Students. A combined JD/LLM-Taxation may be completed in six semesters. The law school also offers a unique Trans-Atlantic Law Program in conjunction with Utrecht University School of Law (UULS) in the Netherlands. In this program, Washington University students will spend five semesters at the law school, then three semesters at UULS. At the conclusion, each student will receive a JD from Washington University and an LLM from UULS.

■ Study-Abroad Opportunities

The School of Law offers students the opportunity to study abroad for a semester and for international law students to study at our law school. Our students take regular courses in leading international institutions, studying under the legal scholars of the country. Washington University has exchange or study-abroad agreements in place with each of the following law schools: Utrecht University in the Netherlands, University of Pretoria in South Africa, Universidade Católica Portuguesa in Portugal, Fudan University in China, National University of Singapore, University of KwaZulu-Natal in South Africa, Korea University in the Republic of Korea, and National Taiwan University. The law school also offers the Summer Institute for Global Justice, a six-week, intensive course in Utrecht, the Netherlands, focusing on international and comparative law and the Trans-Atlantic Law Program with Utrecht University.

■ Student Activities

The School of Law publishes three student-edited law review periodicals, the *Washington University Law Review*, the *Washington University Journal of Law and Policy*, and the *Washington University Global Studies Law Review*. The Trial

and Advocacy Program includes a very active moot court program, mock trial competitions, and competitions in negotiation and client counseling. Students are actively involved in over 40 student organizations, including the Women's Law Caucus, Student Bar Association, Black Law Students Association, Latin American Law Students Association, Asian American Law Students Association, Native American Law Students Association, and OUTLAW (gay and lesbian alliance). Students also participate in a number of volunteer public service projects through student organizations or the school's Public Service Project program.

■ Public Interest

The School of Law has a long-standing commitment to public service and lawyering in the public interest. In addition to its nine clinics, public interest law is supported in a number of different ways: the Webster Society Scholarship provides full tuition for three years and an annual stipend to entering JD students with exemplary academic credentials and an established commitment to public service, summer stipends provide funding for students who work in summer internships in public interest law, the Mel Brown Family Loan Repayment Assistance Program (LRAP) assists graduates beginning their careers in public service positions, the assistant dean of student services coordinates the law school's many public service projects, the director of career services and public interest assists students interested in pursuing careers in the public sector, and the popular Public Interest Law and Policy Speakers Series is offered.

■ Career Services

Our Career Services Office is committed to matching students with outstanding employment opportunities from

around the country. The priority is to connect students to the jobs they desire and employers with the students they seek. In addition to hosting extensive fall on-campus and off-campus recruiting programs, the CSO offers a wide range of services throughout the year including workshops, a mock interview program, and other programming activities. The CSO offers programs on networking and skill development, clerkships, fellowships, researching employers, and a variety of informational sessions on different practice areas. Our graduates move on to many different locations to practice: the Class of 2008 relocated to 30 different states, the District of Columbia, and four foreign countries. Summer employment is equally diverse. Typically 30 or more states are represented, as well as summer internships in Africa and Asia.

■ Housing

Students find that the cost of living in St. Louis is much less than in other large metropolitan areas. There is a wide range of affordable housing available near the School of Law. The admission office hosts two "housing days" each summer to assist students in locating housing.

■ Scholarship and Financial Aid

The school offers merit- and merit/need-based scholarships. Most student aid is in the form of government and privately sponsored loans. Over half the students receive some scholarship assistance; two thirds receive loans. (Virtually all of those receiving scholarships also receive loans.) The school also offers loan repayment assistance for students who choose qualifying public interest law jobs upon graduation.

Applicant Profile

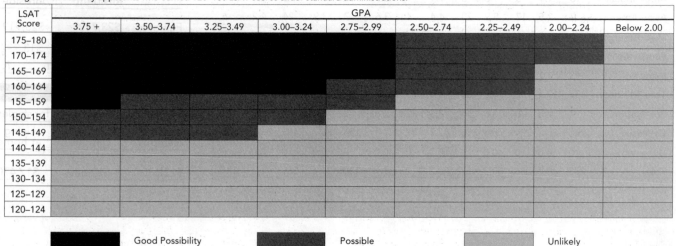

Washington University School of Law
This grid includes only applicants who earned 120–180 LSAT scores under standard administrations.

LSAT Score	GPA								
	3.75 +	3.50–3.74	3.25–3.49	3.00–3.24	2.75–2.99	2.50–2.74	2.25–2.49	2.00–2.24	Below 2.00
175–180									
170–174									
165–169									
160–164									
155–159									
150–154									
145–149									
140–144									
135–139									
130–134									
125–129									
120–124									

Good Possibility   Possible   Unlikely

Average LSAT data reported.

Wayne State University Law School

Admissions Office, 471 West Palmer
Detroit, MI 48202
Phone: 313.577.3937; Fax: 313.993.8129
E-mail: lawinquire@wayne.edu; Website: www.law.wayne.edu

ABA
Approved
Since
1937

The Basics

Type of school	Public
Term	Semester
Application deadline	3/15
Application fee	$50
Financial aid deadline	3/1
Can first year start other than fall?	No
Student to faculty ratio	14.4 to 1
# of housing spaces available restricted to law students	32
graduate housing for which law students are eligible	618

Faculty and Administrators

	Total		Men		Women		Minorities	
	Spr	Fall	Spr	Fall	Spr	Fall	Spr	Fall
Full-time	28	34	17	20	11	14	2	5
Other full-time	5	5	0	0	5	5	1	1
Deans, librarians, & others who teach	4	4	3	3	1	1	1	1
Part-time	26	24	18	21	8	3	1	0
Total	63	67	38	44	25	23	5	7

Curriculum

	Full-Time	Part-Time
Typical first-year section size	90	43
Is there typically a "small section" of the first-year class, other than Legal Writing, taught by full-time faculty	Yes	No
If yes, typical size offered last year	30	
# of classroom course titles beyond first-year curriculum	75	
# of upper division courses, excluding seminars, with an enrollment: Under 25	63	
25–49	20	
50–74	11	
75–99	2	
100+	0	
# of seminars	18	
# of seminar positions available	332	
# of seminar positions filled	229	26
# of positions available in simulation courses	330	
# of simulation positions filled	239	36
# of positions available in faculty supervised clinical courses	44	
# of faculty supervised clinical positions filled	41	1
# involved in field placements	113	4
# involved in law journals	85	7
# involved in moot court or trial competitions	118	3
# of credit hours required to graduate	86	

JD Enrollment and Ethnicity

	Men		Women		Full-Time		Part-Time		1st-Year		Total		JD Degs. Awd.
	#	%	#	%	#	%	#	%	#	%	#	%	
African Amer.	19	6.7	25	8.7	28	6.1	16	14.3	8	4.4	44	7.7	20
Amer. Indian	3	1.1	3	1.0	5	1.1	1	0.9	2	1.1	6	1.1	0
Asian Amer.	7	2.5	17	5.9	20	4.4	4	3.6	7	3.9	24	4.2	6
Mex. Amer.	3	1.1	2	0.7	5	1.1	0	0.0	2	1.1	5	0.9	5
Puerto Rican	0	0.0	0	0.0	0	0.0	0	0.0	0	0.0	0	0.0	4
Hispanic	3	1.1	5	1.7	6	1.3	2	1.8	2	1.1	8	1.4	2
Total Minority	35	12.4	52	18.2	64	14.0	23	20.5	21	11.7	87	15.3	37
For. Nation.	7	2.5	10	3.5	15	3.3	2	1.8	3	1.7	17	3.0	1
Caucasian	241	85.2	224	78.3	378	82.7	87	77.7	156	86.7	465	81.7	146
Unknown	0	0.0	0	0.0	0	0.0	0	0.0	0	0.0	0	0.0	0
Total	283	49.7	286	50.3	457	80.3	112	19.7	180	31.6	569		184

Transfers

Transfers in	4
Transfers out	8

Tuition and Fees

	Resident	Nonresident
Full-time	$23,713	$25,919
Part-time	$12,815	$13,992
Tuition Guarantee Program	N	

Living Expenses

Estimated living expenses for singles

Living on campus	Living off campus	Living at home
$22,680	$22,680	$12,470

Wayne State University Law School

ABA
Approved
Since
1937

GPA and LSAT Scores

	Total	Full-Time	Part-Time
# of apps	1,510	1,364	146
# of offers	568	537	31
# of matrics	185	163	22
75% GPA	3.69	3.69	3.70
Median GPA	3.51	3.53	3.36
25% GPA	3.17	3.25	3.11
75% LSAT	159	159	160
Median LSAT	156	156	156
25% LSAT	153	153	154

Grants and Scholarships (from prior year)

	Total		Full-Time		Part-Time	
	#	%	#	%	#	%
Total # of students	593		459		134	
Total # receiving grants	344	58.0	319	69.5	25	18.7
Less than 1/2 tuition	241	40.6	226	49.2	15	11.2
Half to full tuition	54	9.1	50	10.9	4	3.0
Full tuition	26	4.4	22	4.8	4	3.0
More than full tuition	23	3.9	21	4.6	2	1.5
Median grant amount			$4,000		$5,200	

Informational and Library Resources

Total amount spent on library materials	$1,432,327
Study seating capacity inside the library	400
# of full-time equivalent professional librarians	3
Hours per week library is open	97
# of open, wired connections available to students	203
# of networked computers available for use by students	30
Has wireless network?	Y
Require computer?	N

JD Attrition (from prior year)

	Academic	Other	Total	
	#	#	#	%
1st year	3	6	9	4.0
2nd year	0	11	11	8.3
3rd year	0	0	0	0.0
4th year	0	0	0	0.0

Employment (9 months after graduation)

	Total	Percentage
Employment status known	222	96.9
Employment status unknown	7	3.1
Employed	191	86.0
Pursuing graduate degrees	5	2.3
Unemployed (seeking, not seeking, or studying for the bar)	23	10.4
Type of Employment		
# employed in law firms	126	66.0
# employed in business and industry	25	13.1
# employed in government	22	11.5
# employed in public interest	11	5.8
# employed as judicial clerks	4	2.1
# employed in academia	3	1.6
Geographic Location		
# employed in state	171	89.5
# employed in foreign countries	0	0.0
# of states where employed	9	

Bar Passage Rates

First-time takers	198	Reporting %	98.48
Average school %	95.90	Average state %	82.13
Average pass difference	13.77		

Jurisdiction	Takers	Passers	Pass %	State %	Diff %
Michigan	195	187	95.90	82.13	13.77

Wayne State University Law School

Admissions Office, 471 West Palmer
Detroit, MI 48202
Phone: 313.577.3937; Fax: 313.993.8129
E-mail: lawinquire@wayne.edu; Website: www.law.wayne.edu

■ Introduction

Wayne State University Law School, founded in 1927, is the only public law school in Detroit, Michigan. Located in the heart of Detroit's historic cultural center, Wayne Law offers a unique urban experience. Detroit's vibrant legal market—including government offices, state and federal courts, multinational corporations, unions and major law firms—provides students with a wide range of opportunities for employment and internships. Our students are bright, mature, conscientious, and altruistic. They come from unique backgrounds and professions, some having previously served as doctors, musicians, actors, engineers, and law enforcement officers before pursuing the law. Wayne Law also offers a network of more than 11,000 living alumni, including established leaders of the legal community, practicing in every state of the nation and in more than a dozen foreign countries. Our expert faculty's nationally and internationally recognized scholarship adds depth to our students' understanding of legal theory, doctrine, and practice. Wayne Law students, faculty, and alumni are deeply engaged in the community and profession.

■ The Law School's Setting and Facilities

The Law School is a flagship unit of Wayne State University, a major metropolitan research university located in the Cultural Center about four miles from downtown Detroit. Within blocks of the Law School are the Detroit Public Library, the Detroit Institute of Arts, the Charles H. Wright Museum of African American History, the Detroit Science Center, and other cultural attractions. The City of Detroit shares an international border with Windsor, Ontario, and offers access to Michigan's largest concentration of law firms and state and federal courts.

■ The Arthur Neef Law Library

The Arthur Neef Law Library is the second largest academic law library in Michigan and houses one of the nation's fortieth largest legal collections. With over 620,000 volumes, it serves as a major center of legal research in the Detroit and Michigan legal communities and is a designated federal government depository.

The majority of the study space in the recently renovated law library makes use of natural light. The Law School, including the library, is served by a wireless network. In addition, many library study spaces are equipped with communication ports and electrical outlets for the convenient use of notebook computers.

The law library also houses a computer laboratory, featuring personal computers available for the exclusive use of Wayne State law students.

■ Clinical and Internship Programs

Wayne State University Law School offers its students a broad range of opportunities for practical legal training through its client clinics and its internship programs. The Law School operates seven clinics: a Child Advocacy Clinic, a Criminal Appellate Practice Clinic, a Disability Law Clinic, an Environmental Law Clinic, a Free Legal Aid Clinic, an Immigration and Asylum Clinic, and a Small Business Enterprises and Nonprofit Corporations Clinic. These clinical offerings give students a chance to take first-chair responsibility in a choice of settings while serving the needs of Detroit's urban community. Students also have the chance to serve as interns for state and federal judges, public prosecutors, the State Appellate Defender's Office, and many nonprofit organizations.

■ Joint-Degree Programs

Students may pursue joint-degree programs in one of five different areas: business administration, dispute resolution, history, political science, and economics. Joint-degree students must be admitted separately to the Law School and to the appropriate master's degree program at the university. Each joint-degree program requires a student to spend his or her first year taking exclusively law courses, followed by two and one-half to three years of concurrent studies.

■ Intellectual Property Law Institute

Intellectual property (IP) law and related fields, such as the emerging area of electronic commerce, are among the strengths of the Wayne State law faculty. The Law School offers a tremendous variety of courses and seminars on IP-related subjects. Wayne State law students may take courses at the University of Detroit Mercy and the University of Windsor, just across the river in Canada, through the Intellectual Property Law Institute (IPLI). IPLI, which was created in 1987 as a cooperative effort of these three law schools, offers a rich curriculum for IP-focused students, including courses and seminars in patent, copyright, trademark, computer and related technology, communications and media, and entertainment law.

■ Program for International Legal Studies

International law cuts across all aspects of a Wayne State legal education. Fully one third of Wayne Law's tenured and tenure-track faculty teaches and writes on international subjects. Those faculty members enjoy world-wide reputations as innovative and prolific scholars. Students can take classes on a remarkable range of international topics, from international commercial transactions to international environmental law, to the use of military force, and the protection of human rights. Study-abroad programs give students a first-hand view of other nations' legal systems and their approaches to legal education. The Law School also boasts a broad array of internationally oriented student organizations, including a highly successful Jessup International Law Moot Court Competition Team.

■ Student Activities

Student-Edited Law Journals—Wayne State University Law School publishes two student-edited law journals. The *Wayne Law Review*, a scholarly legal journal with a nationwide circulation, has been published since 1954 by upper-class law students selected on the basis of superior academic achievement and writing ability. The *Journal of Law in Society* publishes articles drawn from an annual spring symposium on

topics such as affirmative action, environmental justice, reparations for slavery, school vouchers, and gentrification. Both journals offer an opportunity for students to enhance their research and writing skills, and further their knowledge of the law, while earning law school course credit.

Moot Court—Founded in 1949, Wayne State University's Moot Court program, which helps students hone their written and oral advocacy skills, has evolved into one of the most competitive appellate advocacy programs in the country. Wayne State Moot Court teams compete in many national moot court competitions and have won many competitions, including the National Moot Court Championship in 2003.

Student Trial Advocacy Program—The Student Trial Advocacy Program (STAP) complements Wayne State's extensive offering of skills courses by providing students with instruction and experience in the techniques of trial litigation. Wayne State STAP members have successfully competed in trial advocacy competitions across the country.

Student Organizations—More than 30 student organizations add greatly to the quality of life at the Law School by sponsoring speakers and debates on topics of current interest or in specialized areas of law, jointly sponsoring outreach events for the needy, volunteering their time to public service, and collaborating to produce programs with area practitioners.

■ Scholarships

Wayne State University Law School is committed to attracting and retaining highly credentialed students while maintaining economic accessibility to legal education and the legal profession. We offer substantial scholarships, and award over $2.8 million in WSU and privately endowed scholarships and grants to students. The Dean's Scholars Program awards 50 percent, 75 percent, and 100 percent tuition scholarships to top students of each incoming class. These awards are renewable yearly if students maintain a GPA above an established minimum. We also offer one-year awards to incoming students and provide scholarships for continuing students based on first-year performance. More than 70 additional scholarships are awarded each year at Honors Convocation based on academic merit, future career plans, or participation in law-related activities.

■ Housing

As a Wayne Law student, you can live on campus and pay special reduced rates, either in the University Towers Apartments or in the Towers Residential Suites. The top floors of the high-rise tower are reserved for graduate students. The majority of the rooms are suite style. There are also studio rooms available. Within the building are a café-style dining hall, a mini bookstore, and multiple fitness rooms. The Towers feature free Internet access, cable connections, multiple social and study lounges, laundry rooms, and a 24-hour staffed reception area. Students interested in living off campus have many affordable options in the metropolitan Detroit area.

■ Career Services

Our Career Services Office provides Wayne Law students and alumni with tools, resources, and expertise needed to identify the ideal career path, launch a successful job search, and develop a fulfilling career in, around, or outside of the law. Three professional career counselors help students navigate job searches and offer guidance on balancing the demands of finding a job while in law school. Each of our counselors has a JD, has practiced law, and specializes in counseling students interested in working in government, law firms, courts, corporations, and public interest organizations, as well as pursuing alternative careers.

Applicant Profile

Wayne State University Law School
This grid includes only applicants who earned 120–180 LSAT scores under standard administrations.

LSAT Score	3.75 +		3.50–3.74		3.25–3.49		3.00–3.24		2.75–2.99		2.50–2.74		2.25–2.49		2.00–2.24		Below 2.00		No GPA		Total	
	Apps	Adm	Apps	Adm	Apps	Adm	Apps	Adm	Apps	Adm	Apps	Adm	Apps	Adm	Apps	Adm	Apps	Adm	Apps	Adm	Apps	Adm
175–180	1	1	0	0	1	0	0	0	0	0	0	0	0	0	0	0	0	0	0	0	2	1
170–174	2	2	0	0	1	1	0	0	0	0	0	0	0	0	0	0	0	0	0	0	3	3
165–169	7	7	11	11	4	3	1	1	3	3	3	2	1	1	1	0	0	0	0	0	31	28
160–164	25	24	35	35	21	20	25	23	13	11	3	3	0	0	0	0	1	1	4	3	127	120
155–159	35	31	49	48	41	32	41	30	30	19	9	1	6	3	3	1	2	1	6	4	222	170
150–154	42	34	74	57	87	41	86	26	47	10	33	4	16	1	2	0	1	0	8	4	396	177
145–149	23	11	54	12	66	13	81	5	49	4	33	2	15	0	5	0	1	0	14	1	341	48
140–144	11	3	30	3	45	3	55	2	46	1	25	0	19	0	4	0	3	0	8	2	246	14
135–139	6	0	9	0	9	0	16	1	14	0	20	0	16	0	2	0	2	0	6	0	100	1
130–134	1	0	3	1	5	0	5	0	9	0	11	0	2	0	6	0	3	0	5	0	50	1
125–129	0	0	0	0	0	0	0	0	3	0	5	0	2	0	1	0	2	0	1	0	14	0
120–124	0	0	0	0	0	0	0	0	0	0	0	0	0	0	0	0	0	0	0	0	0	0
Total	153	113	265	167	280	113	310	88	214	48	142	12	77	5	24	1	15	2	52	14	1532	563

Apps = Number of Applicants   Adm = Number Admitted   Reflects 99% of the total applicant pool; average LSAT data reported.

West Virginia University College of Law

101 Law Center Drive, PO Box 6130
Morgantown, WV 26506-6130
Phone: 304.293.5301; Fax: 304.293.8102
E-mail: wvulaw.admissions@mail.wvu.edu; Website: http://law.wvu.edu/

ABA
Approved
Since
1923

The Basics

Type of school	Public
Term	Semester
Application deadline	3/1
Application fee	$50
Financial aid deadline	3/1
Can first year start other than fall?	No
Student to faculty ratio	12.9 to 1
# of housing spaces available restricted to law students	
graduate housing for which law students are eligible	2

Faculty and Administrators

	Total		Men		Women		Minorities	
	Spr	Fall	Spr	Fall	Spr	Fall	Spr	Fall
Full-time	26	28	22	23	4	5	2	6
Other full-time	0	0	0	0	0	0	0	0
Deans, librarians, & others who teach	4	5	0	0	4	5	0	0
Part-time	27	25	16	14	11	11	0	0
Total	57	58	38	37	19	21	2	6

Curriculum

	Full-Time	Part-Time
Typical first-year section size	70	70
Is there typically a "small section" of the first-year class, other than Legal Writing, taught by full-time faculty	No	No
If yes, typical size offered last year		

# of classroom course titles beyond first-year curriculum		79
# of upper division courses, excluding seminars, with an enrollment:	Under 25	50
	25–49	32
	50–74	9
	75–99	3
	100+	0
# of seminars		14
# of seminar positions available		210
# of seminar positions filled	169	0
# of positions available in simulation courses		465
# of simulation positions filled	372	0
# of positions available in faculty supervised clinical courses		49
# of faculty supervised clinical positions filled	49	0
# involved in field placements	7	0
# involved in law journals	21	0
# involved in moot court or trial competitions	68	0
# of credit hours required to graduate		91

JD Enrollment and Ethnicity

	Men		Women		Full-Time		Part-Time		1st-Year		Total		JD Degs. Awd.
	#	%	#	%	#	%	#	%	#	%	#	%	
African Amer.	12	4.8	12	7.1	23	5.6	1	16.7	6	3.9	24	5.7	13
Amer. Indian	1	0.4	0	0.0	1	0.2	0	0.0	0	0.0	1	0.2	0
Asian Amer.	3	1.2	4	2.4	7	1.7	0	0.0	1	0.6	7	1.7	4
Mex. Amer.	0	0.0	0	0.0	0	0.0	0	0.0	0	0.0	0	0.0	0
Puerto Rican	0	0.0	0	0.0	0	0.0	0	0.0	0	0.0	0	0.0	0
Hispanic	1	0.4	0	0.0	1	0.2	0	0.0	1	0.6	1	0.2	1
Total Minority	17	6.8	16	9.5	32	7.8	1	16.7	8	5.2	33	7.9	18
For. Nation.	0	0.0	0	0.0	0	0.0	0	0.0	0	0.0	0	0.0	0
Caucasian	232	93.2	153	90.5	380	92.2	5	83.3	146	94.8	385	92.1	129
Unknown	0	0.0	0	0.0	0	0.0	0	0.0	0	0.0	0	0.0	2
Total	249	59.6	169	40.4	412	98.6	6	1.4	154	36.8	418		149

Transfers

Transfers in	1
Transfers out	4

Tuition and Fees

	Resident	Nonresident
Full-time	$10,644	$24,010
Part-time		
Tuition Guarantee Program		N

Living Expenses

Estimated living expenses for singles

Living on campus	Living off campus	Living at home
$12,525	$12,525	$12,525

West Virginia University College of Law

ABA
Approved
Since
1923

GPA and LSAT Scores

	Total	Full-Time	Part-Time
# of apps	648	648	0
# of offers	327	327	0
# of matrics	153	153	0
75% GPA	3.70	3.70	0.00
Median GPA	3.41	3.41	0.00
25% GPA	3.12	3.12	0.00
75% LSAT	156	156	0
Median LSAT	153	153	0
25% LSAT	151	151	0

Grants and Scholarships (from prior year)

	Total		Full-Time		Part-Time	
	#	%	#	%	#	%
Total # of students	428		426		2	
Total # receiving grants	205	47.9	205	48.1	0	0.0
Less than 1/2 tuition	114	26.6	114	26.8	0	0.0
Half to full tuition	44	10.3	44	10.3	0	0.0
Full tuition	23	5.4	23	5.4	0	0.0
More than full tuition	24	5.6	24	5.6	0	0.0
Median grant amount			$5,322		$0	

Informational and Library Resources

Total amount spent on library materials	$895,706
Study seating capacity inside the library	383
# of full-time equivalent professional librarians	4
Hours per week library is open	106
# of open, wired connections available to students	140
# of networked computers available for use by students	64
Has wireless network?	Y
Require computer?	N

JD Attrition (from prior year)

	Academic	Other	Total	
	#	#	#	%
1st year	0	12	12	8.3
2nd year	0	0	0	0.0
3rd year	0	0	0	0.0
4th year	0	0	0	0.0

Employment (9 months after graduation)

	Total	Percentage
Employment status known	144	99.3
Employment status unknown	1	0.7
Employed	132	91.7
Pursuing graduate degrees	7	4.9
Unemployed (seeking, not seeking, or studying for the bar)	2	1.4
Type of Employment		
# employed in law firms	60	45.5
# employed in business and industry	30	22.7
# employed in government	10	7.6
# employed in public interest	7	5.3
# employed as judicial clerks	21	15.9
# employed in academia	4	3.0
Geographic Location		
# employed in state	96	72.7
# employed in foreign countries	0	0.0
# of states where employed		16

Bar Passage Rates

First-time takers	149	Reporting %	71.14
Average school %	75.47	Average state %	79.97
Average pass difference	−4.50		

Jurisdiction	Takers	Passers	Pass %	State %	Diff %
West Virginia	92	70	76.09	78.95	−2.86
Pennsylvania	14	10	71.43	86.69	−15.26

West Virginia University College of Law

101 Law Center Drive, PO Box 6130
Morgantown, WV 26506-6130
Phone: 304.293.5301; Fax: 304.293.8102
E-mail: wvulaw.admissions@mail.wvu.edu; Website: http://law.wvu.edu/

■ Introduction

The College of Law, established in 1878, is the oldest professional school at West Virginia University. The university is located in Morgantown, West Virginia. Within a 500-mile radius of Morgantown is half of the population of the United States and one third of the population of Canada. The College of Law has been a member of the AALS since 1914 and was fully accredited by the ABA in 1923. The college has had a chapter of the Order of the Coif since 1925.

■ Library and Physical Facilities

The College of Law facility measures 131,966 square feet and provides a spacious learning community for law students. The law center is home to six classrooms, two courtrooms, a distance learning center, financial aid, career services, and a law bookstore. Ample parking at the law center is available by permit for all law students.

The George R. Farmer Jr. Law Library, a three-story, 32,476-square-foot facility with 40,386 feet of shelving space, is home to the largest law library in the state of West Virginia. The law library is comprehensive in scope with a collection of over 300,000 volumes and equivalents. As part of a sustainable strategy the library replaced its 42 outmoded computers with virtual desktops that significantly reduced power consumption and facilitates more efficient IT maintenance. This system also enhances network security and includes an additional 17 virtual desktops in the library's Carlin Computer Lab.

The Student Recreation Center is a $34 million, 177,000-square-foot facility complete with two swimming pools and a massive 50-foot climbing wall that stretches up through the center of the three-story building. The center also houses a wellness center, a resource library, a study area, a food-service operation, a small classroom, a meeting/conference room, and socialization areas.

■ Curriculum

Subject to modification, 91 hours are required for graduation. The 31-hour first-year curriculum is specified. The second- and third-year programs offer a number of course options and possibilities for concentration.

Students have the option, after being admitted, to request enrollment in the part-time program that offers daytime courses congruently with the full-time program. There is not a separate nighttime track.

■ Student Activities

West Virginia University College of Law has over 30 student organizations. The Student Bar Association is the student government of the school. The *West Virginia Law Review* (http://wvlawreview.wvu.edu) is the fourth oldest student-governed law review in the nation, and selects members on the basis of performance during their first year in law school and a writing competition. An active Moot Court Program is conducted at the law school.

■ Opportunities for Minority Students

The College of Law is committed to maintaining a diverse student body by welcoming students who are members of groups traditionally underrepresented in the legal profession. The Meredith Career Services Center assists minority students with securing summer employment through a Minority Clerkship Program. The College of Law also participates in the Southeast Minority Job Fair in Atlanta, a regional job fair that brings together employers and minority students. Student organizations, such as the Black Law Students Association, provide additional opportunities for minority students.

■ Career Services

The Career Services office provides career counseling, professional development workshops, interview programs, and job-search strategy sessions as part of a comprehensive career services program. Our graduates work in diverse settings throughout the United States and abroad, including law firms, courts, government agencies, public service organizations, corporations, and colleges and universities. The goals of the Career Services office are to educate students about possible careers in the law, encourage them to identify and set career goals, and assist them in achieving those goals. Please visit *http://law.wvu.edu/career_services* for more information.

■ Admission

The College of Law admits first-year students only in the first (fall) semester. No specific prelaw curriculum is required for admission. The college subscribes to the suggestions on prelaw study in this book and stresses the value of college courses that require extensive analytic skills and writing assignments.

Students are admitted to the College of Law on the basis of previous academic performance, scores on the Law School Admission Test, personal statements, letters of recommendation, and such other factors that bear upon the potential professional qualifications of the applicant as determined by the College of Law.

Applications are accepted beginning September 1 of each year for the class to be admitted to begin their studies the following August. Those accepted are required to make a seat deposit within a designated period, but not before April 1. The required seat deposit amount for residents is $200 and $400 for nonresidents, which is credited toward your tuition and fees for the fall semester.

■ Expenses and Financial Aid

Although WVU's reasonable tuition and fees are an excellent value, the College of Law recognizes that many students may not be able to afford the full cost of a legal education without financial assistance. Limited funds in the form of tuition waivers, scholarships, and college work-study are available each year through the university. Even if the student has not been accepted to the College of Law, he or she should apply for financial aid by March 1. The Free Application for Federal

Student Aid (FAFSA) must be completed in order to receive any financial assistance, including all need-based scholarships. Students must complete the FAFSA each year in order to be considered for financial aid.

More information may be obtained by contacting Eric Meadows, Financial Aid Counselor, PO Box 6130, Morgantown, WV 26506-6130; phone: 304.293.5302; e-mail: *eric.meadows@mail.wvu.edu*.

■ Housing

The majority of our students live off campus in private housing. The university's Student Life office assists students by providing information about off-campus housing options. You may contact them at 304.293.5611 or visit their website at *www.studentlife.wvu.edu*.

■ Clinic Programs

Hands-on training is a key component of our Advanced Lawyering curriculum. Clinical experience prepares students for the practical challenges of legal practice and hones the skills they need to best serve their clients, the profession, and society.

Clinic programs offered include:
- **Civil Clinic**—providing eligible individuals with legal services focused on family law, social security and supplemental security income, and consumer debt relief.
- **The Child, Family, and Health Advocacy Clinic**—offering legal assistance in collaboration with physicians from the WVU Robert C. Byrd Health Sciences Center.
- **Entrepreneurship Law Clinic**—offers start-up companies, small businesses, nonprofits, and individuals legal services in areas of counseling for a product plan or business organization, licensing, employee and contractor agreements, intellectual property, financing and venture capital, planning and negotiation, dispute resolution, and generalized assistance in business formation, planning, and strategy.
- **Immigration Clinic**—provides legal assistance and representation to foreign citizens across the region who are facing deportation, asylum, and other immigration proceedings.
- **Tax Clinic**—offers legal services to taxpayers residing in West Virginia who need to resolve a tax controversy with the Internal Revenue Service.

Applicant Profile

West Virginia University College of Law
This grid includes only applicants who earned 120–180 LSAT scores under standard administrations.

LSAT Score	3.75 + Apps	3.75 + Adm	3.50–3.74 Apps	3.50–3.74 Adm	3.25–3.49 Apps	3.25–3.49 Adm	3.00–3.24 Apps	3.00–3.24 Adm	2.75–2.99 Apps	2.75–2.99 Adm	2.50–2.74 Apps	2.50–2.74 Adm	2.25–2.49 Apps	2.25–2.49 Adm	2.00–2.24 Apps	2.00–2.24 Adm	Below 2.00 Apps	Below 2.00 Adm	No GPA Apps	No GPA Adm	Total Apps	Total Adm
175–180	0	0	0	0	0	0	0	0	0	0	0	0	0	0	0	0	0	0	0	0	0	0
170–174	0	0	0	0	0	0	0	0	0	0	0	0	1	0	0	0	0	0	0	0	1	0
165–169	3	3	1	1	0	0	0	0	1	1	0	0	0	0	0	0	0	0	0	0	5	5
160–164	3	3	6	5	6	6	3	3	5	4	2	1	2	1	0	0	0	0	1	0	28	23
155–159	18	18	14	13	26	25	13	13	11	9	7	6	1	1	0	0	0	0	0	0	90	85
150–154	32	29	47	35	48	40	41	23	26	13	11	3	8	2	1	0	0	0	4	0	218	145
145–149	19	11	44	18	46	13	32	6	27	7	9	1	4	1	4	0	0	0	5	0	190	57
140–144	7	1	12	0	20	4	16	3	19	3	13	1	3	0	6	0	1	0	3	0	100	12
135–139	0	0	2	0	8	0	7	0	8	0	2	0	0	0	1	0	0	0	1	0	33	0
130–134	0	0	1	0	1	0	1	0	1	0	1	0	2	0	0	0	0	0	0	0	9	0
125–129	0	0	0	0	0	0	0	0	0	0	0	0	0	0	0	0	0	0	1	0	1	0
120–124	0	0	0	0	0	0	0	0	0	0	0	0	0	0	0	0	0	0	0	0	0	0
Total	82	65	127	72	155	88	113	48	98	37	45	12	25	5	14	0	1	0	15	0	675	327

Apps = Number of Applicants
Adm = Number Admitted
Reflects 99% of the total applicant pool; average LSAT data reported.

Western New England College School of Law

Office of Admissions, 1215 Wilbraham Road
Springfield, MA 01119-2684
Phone: 800.782.6665, 413.782.1406; Fax: 413.796.2067
E-mail: admissions@law.wnec.edu; Website: www.law.wnec.edu

ABA
Approved
Since
1974

The Basics

Type of school	Private
Term	Semester
Application deadline	3/15
Application fee	$50
Financial aid deadline	4/15
Can first year start other than fall?	No
Student to faculty ratio	12.7 to 1
# of housing spaces available restricted to law students	65
graduate housing for which law students are eligible	

Faculty and Administrators

	Total		Men		Women		Minorities	
	Spr	Fall	Spr	Fall	Spr	Fall	Spr	Fall
Full-time	31	34	15	15	16	19	5	5
Other full-time	6	5	3	2	3	3	1	1
Deans, librarians, & others who teach	9	9	7	7	2	2	0	0
Part-time	21	17	15	14	6	3	0	0
Total	67	65	40	38	27	27	6	6

Curriculum

		Full-Time	Part-Time
Typical first-year section size		46	40
Is there typically a "small section" of the first-year class, other than Legal Writing, taught by full-time faculty		No	No
If yes, typical size offered last year			
# of classroom course titles beyond first-year curriculum		95	
# of upper division courses, excluding seminars, with an enrollment:	Under 25	42	
	25–49	35	
	50–74	12	
	75–99	2	
	100+	0	
# of seminars		17	
# of seminar positions available		295	
# of seminar positions filled		214	63
# of positions available in simulation courses		373	
# of simulation positions filled		284	85
# of positions available in faculty supervised clinical courses		76	
# of faculty supervised clinical positions filled		40	16
# involved in field placements		87	7
# involved in law journals		38	10
# involved in moot court or trial competitions		19	2
# of credit hours required to graduate		88	

JD Enrollment and Ethnicity

	Men		Women		Full-Time		Part-Time		1st-Year		Total		JD Degs. Awd.
	#	%	#	%	#	%	#	%	#	%	#	%	
African Amer.	6	2.4	11	3.9	9	2.3	8	5.4	6	3.3	17	3.2	4
Amer. Indian	1	0.4	1	0.4	2	0.5	0	0.0	0	0.0	2	0.4	0
Asian Amer.	11	4.3	13	4.6	21	5.4	3	2.0	6	3.3	24	4.5	4
Mex. Amer.	0	0.0	0	0.0	0	0.0	0	0.0	0	0.0	0	0.0	0
Puerto Rican	0	0.0	0	0.0	0	0.0	0	0.0	0	0.0	0	0.0	0
Hispanic	11	4.3	8	2.8	14	3.6	5	3.4	4	2.2	19	3.5	4
Total Minority	29	11.4	33	11.7	46	11.8	16	10.7	16	8.8	62	11.5	12
For. Nation.	1	0.4	2	0.7	3	0.8	0	0.0	0	0.0	3	0.6	9
Caucasian	192	75.3	205	72.4	289	74.3	108	72.5	155	85.2	397	73.8	158
Unknown	33	12.9	43	15.2	51	13.1	25	16.8	11	6.0	76	14.1	50
Total	255	47.4	283	52.6	389	72.3	149	27.7	182	33.8	538		229

Transfers

Transfers in	4
Transfers out	14

Tuition and Fees

	Resident	Nonresident
Full-time	$35,612	$35,612
Part-time	$26,328	$26,328
Tuition Guarantee Program	N	

Living Expenses

Estimated living expenses for singles

Living on campus	Living off campus	Living at home
$22,163	$19,201	$8,716

Western New England College School of Law

ABA
Approved
Since
1974

GPA and LSAT Scores

	Total	Full-Time	Part-Time
# of apps	1,696	1,423	273
# of offers	901	769	132
# of matrics	181	131	50
75% GPA	3.51	3.55	3.40
Median GPA	3.22	3.23	3.19
25% GPA	2.99	2.94	3.09
75% LSAT	155	156	151
Median LSAT	152	153	148
25% LSAT	150	151	147

Grants and Scholarships (from prior year)

	Total		Full-Time		Part-Time	
	#	%	#	%	#	%
Total # of students	573		405		168	
Total # receiving grants	319	55.7	261	64.4	58	34.5
Less than 1/2 tuition	170	29.7	116	28.6	54	32.1
Half to full tuition	139	24.3	136	33.6	3	1.8
Full tuition	10	1.7	9	2.2	1	0.6
More than full tuition	0	0.0	0	0.0	0	0.0
Median grant amount			$13,000		$4,000	

Informational and Library Resources

Total amount spent on library materials	$1,136,909
Study seating capacity inside the library	482
# of full-time equivalent professional librarians	8
Hours per week library is open	103
# of open, wired connections available to students	18
# of networked computers available for use by students	49
Has wireless network?	Y
Require computer?	N

JD Attrition (from prior year)

	Academic	Other	Total	
	#	#	#	%
1st year	3	19	22	12.2
2nd year	1	2	3	1.7
3rd year	0	0	0	0.0
4th year	0	0	0	0.0

Employment (9 months after graduation)

	Total	Percentage
Employment status known	126	90.6
Employment status unknown	13	9.4
Employed	103	81.7
Pursuing graduate degrees	6	4.8
Unemployed (seeking, not seeking, or studying for the bar)	16	12.7
Type of Employment		
# employed in law firms	50	48.5
# employed in business and industry	17	16.5
# employed in government	10	9.7
# employed in public interest	8	7.8
# employed as judicial clerks	16	15.5
# employed in academia	2	1.9
Geographic Location		
# employed in state	36	35.0
# employed in foreign countries	1	1.0
# of states where employed	16	

Bar Passage Rates

First-time takers	179	Reporting %	87.15
Average school %	75.64	Average state %	89.79
Average pass difference	–14.15		

Jurisdiction	Takers	Passers	Pass %	State %	Diff %
Connecticut	64	49	76.56	88.28	–11.72
Massachusetts	51	43	84.31	92.33	–8.02
New York	41	26	63.41	88.98	–25.57

Western New England College School of Law

Office of Admissions, 1215 Wilbraham Road
Springfield, MA 01119-2684
Phone: 800.782.6665, 413.782.1406; Fax: 413.796.2067
E-mail: admissions@law.wnec.edu; Website: www.law.wnec.edu

■ Introduction

For more than three-quarters of a century, Western New England College School of Law has been preparing men and women to succeed in the legal profession. Fully accredited by the ABA and a member of the AALS, our 7,000 alumni live and work in all 50 states and many foreign countries. They include judges, attorneys practicing in small and large firms, and lawyers for corporations, businesses, nonprofit organizations, and all levels of government. We are located in the heart of the beautiful and vibrant Pioneer Valley on a suburban campus, 90 miles from Boston and 150 miles from New York City.

Western New England College School of Law offers both full-time and part-time programs, each providing a strong, well-rounded curriculum that will enable you to succeed in your career. A distinctive feature of our law school is our personalized, student-centered approach to legal education and professional development. Our first-year section size, purposely among the smallest in the country, promotes effective learning in a challenging but collegial and supportive setting. Our accessible and dedicated faculty create a learning environment that helps every student succeed and reach his or her full potential. It is a wonderful place to begin your legal career.

■ Admission and Scholarships

Every application is read by members of the Admissions Committee. All facets of the application are carefully considered, including race, gender, language, and educational, social, and economic obstacles overcome in the applicant's pursuit of higher education. We seek candidates with well-developed writing ability and analytical skills who will contribute to classroom discussions and the law school community.

Each year partial-tuition scholarships are awarded to applicants whose credentials and backgrounds suggest they are likely to enrich the life of the School of Law. Partial-tuition scholarships are also awarded on the basis of academic merit. Partial scholarships are available for applicants who demonstrate potential for success and who have overcome cultural, economic, societal, physical, or educational obstacles. All admitted applicants receive automatic scholarship consideration. Typically, at least 50 percent of the entering class receives scholarship assistance.

In addition, several students are awarded full-tuition Oliver Wendell Holmes Jr. Scholarships. The Holmes Scholars usually score in the top 20 percent of the LSAT nationally and finish very near the top of their undergraduate classes. Holmes Scholars receive full-tuition scholarships, with an additional $3,500 research stipend.

The School of Law also offers six Public Interest Scholarships to full-time students, ranging from $15,000 to full tuition, with an additional $3,500 summer stipend. Public Interest Scholars take special public interest courses, have regular meetings with public interest practitioners to discuss current issues in public interest practice, and are mentored in the public interest careers by faculty and members of the Public Interest Advisory Board. The $3,500 stipend supports the required public interest summer internship. The Public Interest Scholars program provides an exceptional opportunity to offset the cost of law school while preparing for a career in public interest lawyering.

■ Faculty

The 12.7:1 student-to-faculty ratio, the strong commitment to student learning, and the outstanding credentials of the 38 faculty members provide an outstanding learning environment dedicated to your professional success. The faculty have been educated at many of the nation's most prestigious law schools, and all have practiced law prior to joining our faculty. They all share a love of teaching and take pride in their ability to engage students in rigorous law study in a collaborative, collegial environment. They are productive scholars who are consistently praised by our students for their accessibility.

■ Curriculum

All required courses, both day and evening, are taught by full-time faculty members. Some upper-level courses are taught through classroom discussions of judicial decisions and statutes. Others are taught through simulations in which students perform the roles of lawyers in lifelike situations and through clinics in which students represent actual clients. Part-time day and evening programs are also available.

Our broad-based curriculum allows students the opportunity to focus their legal studies in many different areas of the law, including tax, public interest, and corporate law. To assist students in preparing for their careers, and selecting among electives, the School of Law offers six concentrations (Business Law, Criminal Law, Estate Planning, International and Comparative Law, Public Interest Law, and Real Estate Law), along with several specializations. For a full list, please reference our website.

We also offer three joint-degree programs:
- JD/MBA (Master of Business Administration) with Western New England College
- JD/MSW (Master of Social Work) with Springfield College
- JD/MRP (Master of Regional Planning) with the University of Massachusetts at Amherst

Western New England College School of Law offers a Master of Laws (LLM) degree in Estate Planning and Elder Law. The part-time evening program will prepare both new and established attorneys to meet the growing demand for estate planning and taxation counseling resulting from the aging baby boomer generation.

■ Experiential Learning: Clinics, Simulations, and Externships

Clinics and simulation courses are integral components of the curriculum at Western New England College School of Law. Each type of course offers an opportunity to put theory into practice, thereby enhancing advocacy skills and enriching the understanding of core course materials. Students also apply their legal skills through externships.

Clinics provide an opportunity for upper-class students to represent clients with actual legal problems. Currently, the School of Law offers five different clinics in which students can gain valuable lawyering skills, such as legal writing,

interviewing, and negotiating. The following clinical opportunities are offered:

- Criminal Law Clinic—students prosecute cases for the Hampden County District Attorney's Office.
- Legal Services Clinic—students work in the office of Western Massachusetts Legal Services, Inc.
- Consumer Law Clinic—students work in the City of Springfield's Consumer Protection Program.
- Real Property Practicum—students work with practitioners in the real estate area.
- Small Business Clinic—students help start-up businesses at the Springfield Enterprise Center's business incubator.

Simulation courses allow students to represent hypothetical clients with challenging legal problems drawn from the experiences of practicing lawyers. Students perform research, prepare legal documents, and negotiate with and argue against role-playing students and faculty.

Externships enable students to work with judges or alongside attorneys in public interest organizations or government agencies. Externs are called upon to perform research and prepare legal documents. Externships allow students to refine their lawyering skills and provide interaction with professionals who can offer advice and career insights. Students receive two or three hours of academic credit for one nonpaying externship.

Western New England College School of Law students compete in many trial, appellate, and negotiation competitions, honing their research, writing, and advocacy skills, and gaining valuable experience. Our teams have won national championships in 2009, 2008, 2006, 2004, and 2001, and numerous regional titles.

▪ Library, Facilities, and the Area

The recently renovated S. Prestley Blake Law Center has a spacious law library, excellent classrooms, and comfortable student study and social space. With a collection of over 400,000 volumes, the Law Library also provides comprehensive access to numerous electronic resources. The School of Law's robust wireless network facilitates research and communication.

The Law Center is located in a residential section of Springfield, on Western New England College's 215-acre campus, with ample, free parking for all students. Springfield is a small city, located in the Pioneer Valley, with a wide array of recreational, social, and cultural attractions. There is a range of affordable off-housing options, as well as some on-campus housing options.

Attending the only law school in western Massachusetts, students have access to a host of externship and clinical opportunities throughout the Massachusetts/Connecticut/New York region, including state and federal courts, the attorney generals of several states, district attorney and state's attorney offices, public defender offices, public interest organizations, and small, medium, and large firms.

▪ Student Activities

Western New England College School of Law students enjoy a strong sense of community and support, strengthened and nurtured by numerous and varied student organizations and cocurricular activities. The Student Bar Association plays a leading role, with elected officers and appointed members to faculty/student committees. There are many other active student organizations, including the Multi-Cultural Law Students Association, the Women's Law Association, OUTlaw, and a variety of groups formed around interests in particular areas of law and practice, including the Health Law Association, the Family Law Association, the Criminal Law Society, and the Real Estate Guild. There is also a productive *Western New England Law Review*, many active moot court teams, and a student newspaper, *Lex Brevis*.

Applicant Profile

Western New England College School of Law
This grid includes only applicants who earned 120–180 LSAT scores under standard administrations.

LSAT Score	3.75 +		3.50–3.74		3.25–3.49		3.00–3.24		2.75–2.99		2.50–2.74		2.25–2.49		2.00–2.24		Below 2.00		No GPA		Total	
	Apps	Adm	Apps	Adm	Apps	Adm	Apps	Adm	Apps	Adm	Apps	Adm	Apps	Adm	Apps	Adm	Apps	Adm	Apps	Adm	Apps	Adm
175–180	0	0	0	0	0	0	0	0	0	0	0	0	0	0	0	0	0	0	0	0	0	0
170–174	1	0	0	0	0	0	2	2	0	0	0	0	1	0	0	0	0	0	1	0	5	2
165–169	4	4	3	3	4	4	4	3	1	1	0	0	0	0	0	0	0	0	0	0	16	15
160–164	9	8	7	7	12	12	13	13	9	8	4	4	2	2	3	2	2	2	0	0	61	58
155–159	21	21	34	34	46	44	40	39	31	28	15	15	7	7	7	6	1	0	3	3	205	197
150–154	31	31	84	82	92	81	90	79	88	65	53	40	27	15	11	6	2	1	5	4	483	404
145–149	28	18	71	38	121	63	122	52	89	20	58	9	22	3	7	2	1	0	7	0	526	205
140–144	8	1	17	2	43	6	55	2	54	0	31	0	14	0	8	0	3	1	5	0	238	12
135–139	2	0	4	1	13	0	15	0	15	0	15	0	18	0	7	0	2	0	3	0	94	1
130–134	1	0	3	0	6	0	3	0	7	0	6	0	0	0	1	0	1	0	4	0	32	0
125–129	0	0	0	0	1	0	0	0	0	0	2	0	1	0	0	0	1	0	1	0	6	0
120–124	0	0	0	0	0	0	0	0	0	0	0	0	0	0	0	0	1	0	0	0	1	0
Total	105	83	223	167	338	210	344	190	294	122	184	68	92	27	44	16	14	4	29	7	1667	894

Apps = Number of Applicants   Adm = Number Admitted   Reflects 98% of the total applicant pool; average LSAT data reported.

Western State University—College of Law

1111 North State College Boulevard
Fullerton, CA 92831
Phone: 800.WSU.4LAW, 714.459.1101; Fax: 714.441.1748
E-mail: adm@wsulaw.edu; Website: www.wsulaw.edu

ABA Approved Since 2006

The Basics

Type of school	Private
Term	Semester
Application deadline	6/1 12/1
Application fee	$50
Financial aid deadline	3/2 9/15
Can first year start other than fall?	Yes
Student to faculty ratio	22.6 to 1
# of housing spaces available restricted to law students	
graduate housing for which law students are eligible	

Faculty and Administrators

	Total Spr	Total Fall	Men Spr	Men Fall	Women Spr	Women Fall	Minorities Spr	Minorities Fall
Full-time	11	14	9	10	2	4	2	2
Other full-time	2	2	1	1	1	1	0	0
Deans, librarians, & others who teach	13	13	6	6	7	7	0	1
Part-time	21	20	12	13	9	7	3	7
Total	47	49	28	30	19	19	5	10

JD Enrollment and Ethnicity

	Men #	Men %	Women #	Women %	Full-Time #	Full-Time %	Part-Time #	Part-Time %	1st-Year #	1st-Year %	Total #	Total %	JD Degs. Awd.
African Amer.	2	1.0	14	6.7	7	2.5	9	6.4	6	3.3	16	3.8	6
Amer. Indian	2	1.0	1	0.5	1	0.4	2	1.4	2	1.1	3	0.7	1
Asian Amer.	34	16.3	37	17.8	46	16.7	25	17.7	27	14.9	71	17.0	15
Mex. Amer.	11	5.3	15	7.2	20	7.2	6	4.3	11	6.1	26	6.2	2
Puerto Rican	0	0.0	0	0.0	0	0.0	0	0.0	0	0.0	0	0.0	0
Hispanic	10	4.8	16	7.7	18	6.5	8	5.7	16	8.8	26	6.2	4
Total Minority	59	28.2	83	39.9	92	33.3	50	35.5	62	34.3	142	34.1	28
For. Nation.	5	2.4	2	1.0	7	2.5	0	0.0	5	2.8	7	1.7	2
Caucasian	126	60.3	110	52.9	156	56.5	80	56.7	104	57.5	236	56.6	50
Unknown	19	9.1	13	6.3	21	7.6	11	7.8	10	5.5	32	7.7	8
Total	209	50.1	208	49.9	276	66.2	141	33.8	181	43.4	417		88

Curriculum

		Full-Time	Part-Time
Typical first-year section size		52	35
Is there typically a "small section" of the first-year class, other than Legal Writing, taught by full-time faculty		No	No
If yes, typical size offered last year			
# of classroom course titles beyond first-year curriculum		48	
# of upper division courses, excluding seminars, with an enrollment:	Under 25	66	
	25–49	14	
	50–74	9	
	75–99	0	
	100+	0	
# of seminars		9	
# of seminar positions available		195	
# of seminar positions filled		44	17
# of positions available in simulation courses		365	
# of simulation positions filled		121	67
# of positions available in faculty supervised clinical courses		30	
# of faculty supervised clinical positions filled	18	2	
# involved in field placements	40	6	
# involved in law journals	20	6	
# involved in moot court or trial competitions	17	9	
# of credit hours required to graduate		88	

Transfers

Transfers in	4
Transfers out	5

Tuition and Fees

	Resident	Nonresident
Full-time	$32,870	$32,870
Part-time	$22,070	$22,070
Tuition Guarantee Program	N	

Living Expenses

Estimated living expenses for singles

Living on campus	Living off campus	Living at home
N/A	$23,022	$12,757

Western State University—College of Law

ABA
Approved
Since
2006

GPA and LSAT Scores

	Total	Full-Time	Part-Time
# of apps	1,629	1,266	374
# of offers	794	663	131
# of matrics	188	130	58
75% GPA	3.38	3.40	3.36
Median GPA	3.16	3.16	3.18
25% GPA	2.81	2.83	2.81
75% LSAT	154	154	154
Median LSAT	151	151	150
25% LSAT	149	149	148

Grants and Scholarships (from prior year)

	Total		Full-Time		Part-Time	
	#	%	#	%	#	%
Total # of students	387		260		127	
Total # receiving grants	200	51.7	134	51.5	66	52.0
Less than 1/2 tuition	131	33.9	83	31.9	48	37.8
Half to full tuition	39	10.1	25	9.6	14	11.0
Full tuition	23	5.9	20	7.7	3	2.4
More than full tuition	7	1.8	6	2.3	1	0.8
Median grant amount		$12,000		$6,475		

Informational and Library Resources

Total amount spent on library materials	$789,098
Study seating capacity inside the library	336
# of full-time equivalent professional librarians	12
Hours per week library is open	109
# of open, wired connections available to students	0
# of networked computers available for use by students	42
Has wireless network?	Y
Require computer?	N

JD Attrition (from prior year)

	Academic	Other	Total	
	#	#	#	%
1st year	38	22	60	33.3
2nd year	6	2	8	9.2
3rd year	2	0	2	2.2
4th year	0	0	0	0.0

Employment (9 months after graduation)

	Total	Percentage
Employment status known	104	99.0
Employment status unknown	1	1.0
Employed	72	69.2
Pursuing graduate degrees	0	0.0
Unemployed (seeking, not seeking, or studying for the bar)	29	27.9
Type of Employment		
# employed in law firms	55	76.4
# employed in business and industry	9	12.5
# employed in government	4	5.6
# employed in public interest	1	1.4
# employed as judicial clerks	0	0.0
# employed in academia	3	4.2
Geographic Location		
# employed in state	58	80.6
# employed in foreign countries	0	0.0
# of states where employed	12	

Bar Passage Rates

First-time takers	105	Reporting %	96.19
Average school %	67.32	Average state %	78.23
Average pass difference	−10.91		

Jurisdiction	Takers	Passers	Pass %	State %	Diff %
California	94	61	64.89	78.07	−13.18
Nevada	4	4	100.00	76.94	23.06
New Jersey	3	3	100.00	84.69	15.31

Western State University—College of Law

1111 North State College Boulevard
Fullerton, CA 92831
Phone: 800.WSU.4LAW, 714.459.1101; Fax: 714.441.1748
E-mail: adm@wsulaw.edu; Website: www.wsulaw.edu

■ Introduction

Western State University (WSU) College of Law, founded in 1966, is the oldest law school in Orange County, Southern California. Our 10,000 graduates have distinguished themselves as jurists, lawmakers, district attorneys, public defenders, and civil practitioners; they constitute a strong alumni network that mentors and enables an enviable job placement record for WSU graduates.

Located in the college town of Fullerton, in the heart of the vibrant economy and healthy legal market of Orange County, the WSU campus is about 30 miles south of Los Angeles and 100 miles north of San Diego. It is within commuting distance of the greater Los Angeles/Orange County metropolitan areas, the fast-growing Inland Empire, and the Southland's beach cities and high technology, finance, and business centers.

A private law school of fewer than 450 students, WSU offers small class sizes, personal interaction with faculty, and an extraordinary, supportive learning environment. Repeatedly cited as one of the most ethnically diverse law school student bodies in the country, WSU is also known for giving students practical hands-on lawyering experience as well as a strong academic foundation.

■ Faculty

WSU prides itself on a faculty of excellent professors whose first priority is teaching and student success. Most bring extensive real-world legal experience to the classroom in addition to their strong academic and teaching credentials. The full-time faculty is supplemented by an outstanding adjunct faculty of practicing attorneys and judges. With a student-to-faculty ratio of 20 to 1, and a highly accessible faculty, students benefit from individualized attention and mentoring.

■ Curriculum and Special Programs

WSU offers a full-time program that is normally completed in three years and part-time day or evening programs that take four years. Students may start in any of the programs in the fall. WSU also offers a January-start, part-time evening program; students in good standing may transition to full time in the fall.

The Business Law Center and Criminal Law Practice Center programs give students the option to focus their electives to earn a Certificate in Business Law or Criminal Law with a notation on their transcript indicating their special study emphasis. About 25 percent of students choose to earn a certificate in Business Law or Criminal Law. In addition to required and elective coursework, the centers also bring distinguished speakers to campus, arrange student visits to criminal justice facilities or business venues, and provide connections to practitioners, including internship and externship opportunities and career networking.

The on-site Legal Clinic functions as a small family and civil law practice, where student attorneys under supervision of the clinic director represent clients in the community, managing the cases from start to finish, including all court proceedings.

In the externship program, students receive placements in courts or in the offices of district attorneys, public defenders, practicing attorneys, corporate legal departments, or public interest organizations where they gain hands-on experience and academic credit.

■ Student Body and Organizations

WSU's total student body is roughly 425 students, with an entering class of approximately 180 students. Minority enrollment constitutes over a third of the total, with close to even enrollment of men and women. The fall 2009 class entered from 71 different undergraduate institutions and about 25 percent came from 14 different states outside California.

About 15 active student-led organizations enrich and complement the academic program with their cocurricular educational, networking, philanthropic, and social activities for students. These include the Student Bar Association, Asian Pacific American Law Student Association, Black Law Student Association, Latino Student Bar Association, Christian Legal Society, Business Law Association, Entertainment Sports Law Society, Criminal Law Association, and Trial Lawyers Association. Students who qualify for the law review and moot court team gain high-visibility legal writing and advocacy experience.

■ Library and Physical Facilities

The library has over 200,000 volumes housed on three levels as well as access to electronic resources on campus and remotely. Students may use the library's 45 computers, including 25 located in a large computer classroom, or the wireless network. The library has 16 study rooms that may be used by students for group or individual study. The library maintains long hours to service the needs of our students. Our librarians provide extensive reference services and training in legal research, online research, and software.

WSU's campus is located in the heart of Fullerton's university district and consists of a main building and the library, with on-site parking. Most areas of both buildings are covered by wireless Wi-Fi. The main building contains 11 classrooms, the modern Frank and Marleen Darras Moot Court Room, an administrative suite, faculty offices, and a student lounge and café.

■ Admission

All applicants are assigned to an admission advisor who assists in the admission process, may conduct a personal or telephone informational interview, and arranges for visits to the campus and contact with professors, students, or alumni. Each applicant's entire file is reviewed; admission decisions are made by a faculty committee. A bachelor's degree is required for admission. A personal statement and two letters of recommendation are required, and a résumé is encouraged. Details of the applicant's undergraduate record and LSAT score, writing ability, and maturing life and work experiences are key indicators of potential for success in law school. When there are multiple LSAT scores, the highest, most recent score may be accorded significant weight.

Western State University—College of Law

Admission is on a rolling basis, but application by April 1 for fall and October 1 for spring is highly encouraged.

■ Scholarships and Financial Aid

WSU offers generous merit-based scholarships; in the 2009 entering class, over 50 percent of new students received scholarships. No separate application is required; admitted students are automatically considered for merit scholarships based on academic predictors. After the first year, law students are eligible to compete for merit scholarships provided they rank within the top 30 percent. A full range of loan programs is available to complement students' financial needs, including Stafford loans, Perkins loans, and private loans. All students receiving scholarship funds and/or loans should plan to file the FAFSA and a preliminary financial aid application.

■ Career Services and Placement

With a 44-year history in Southern California and an influential alumni network of over 10,000 graduates, WSU has a strong placement track record and the connections to assist students in their job search. The most recent class found employment as follows: 76 percent private practice, 13 percent business and industry, 6 percent government, 1 percent public service, and 4 percent academia.

The active Career Services Office arranges on-campus interviews, career-related workshops, speaker panels, networking events, and individual counseling to help educate students about the many possible areas of practice and how to secure employment. The office serves as a liaison with legal employers, both public and private; it solicits job listings from alumni and local practitioners; and assists students with permanent and summer employment.

The Career Resource Center provides students with reference materials and counseling on résumé writing, job-search techniques, and study-abroad programs. Online job and résumé posting is provided by WSU to facilitate employment searches by students and alumni from the convenience of their home or office.

WSU alumni mentor students and recent graduates. In addition, the alumni assist with on-campus career fairs and networking events.

■ Contact Us

We encourage you to visit our website, speak to an admission advisor, and arrange to visit WSU in person, so you can sit in on a class and meet with students, alumni, and professors. Experience first hand the personal attention, supportive environment, and dedication to student success which set WSU apart.

Applicant Profile

Western State University—College of Law
This grid includes only applicants who earned 120–180 LSAT scores under standard administrations.

LSAT Score	3.75 +		3.50–3.74		3.25–3.49		3.00–3.24		2.75–2.99		2.50–2.74		2.25–2.49		2.00–2.24		Below 2.00		No GPA		Total	
	Apps	Adm	Apps	Adm	Apps	Adm	Apps	Adm	Apps	Adm	Apps	Adm	Apps	Adm	Apps	Adm	Apps	Adm	Apps	Adm	Apps	Adm
175–180	0	0	0	0	0	0	0	0	0	0	0	0	0	0	0	0	0	0	0	0	0	0
170–174	0	0	0	0	0	0	0	0	0	0	1	1	0	0	0	0	0	0	0	0	1	1
165–169	0	0	2	1	1	1	1	1	0	0	1	1	0	0	0	0	0	0	0	0	5	4
160–164	5	4	6	6	2	2	7	7	1	1	6	6	0	0	2	1	0	0	0	0	29	27
155–159	7	6	24	22	28	28	19	17	20	20	17	16	12	8	7	1	1	0	4	4	139	122
150–154	19	17	39	37	60	59	61	56	66	60	49	32	24	12	13	1	2	0	6	4	339	278
145–149	21	20	40	32	109	83	126	79	116	50	58	15	31	5	19	0	1	0	8	2	529	286
140–144	11	0	17	4	39	4	59	2	73	1	41	2	28	0	18	0	3	0	13	1	302	14
135–139	2	0	4	0	10	0	14	0	15	0	25	0	9	0	3	0	1	0	1	0	84	0
130–134	1	0	1	0	0	0	4	0	8	0	2	0	2	0	6	0	2	0	4	0	30	0
125–129	0	0	0	0	0	0	0	0	0	0	2	0	3	0	0	0	1	0	1	0	7	0
120–124	0	0	0	0	0	0	0	0	0	0	0	0	0	0	1	0	0	0	1	0	2	0
Total	66	47	133	102	249	177	291	162	299	132	202	73	109	25	69	3	11	0	38	11	1467	732

Apps = Number of Applicants
Adm = Number Admitted
Reflects 98% of the total applicant pool; average LSAT data reported.

Whittier Law School

3333 Harbor Boulevard
Costa Mesa, CA 92626
Phone: 714.444.4141 ext. 123; Fax: 714.444.0250
E-mail: info@law.whittier.edu; Website: www.law.whittier.edu

ABA
Approved
Since
1978

ABA AMERICAN BAR ASSOCIATION
Section of Legal Education
and Admissions to the Bar

The Basics

Type of school	Private
Term	Semester
Application deadline	7/15
Application fee	$60
Financial aid deadline	5/1
Can first year start other than fall?	No
Student to faculty ratio	17.6 to 1
# of housing spaces available restricted to law students	
graduate housing for which law students are eligible	

Faculty and Administrators

	Total		Men		Women		Minorities	
	Spr	Fall	Spr	Fall	Spr	Fall	Spr	Fall
Full-time	23	23	16	16	7	7	3	3
Other full-time	12	12	1	1	11	11	1	1
Deans, librarians, & others who teach	9	9	3	2	6	7	0	0
Part-time	11	12	7	6	4	6	5	4
Total	55	56	27	25	28	31	9	8

Curriculum

	Full-Time	Part-Time
Typical first-year section size	85	55
Is there typically a "small section" of the first-year class, other than Legal Writing, taught by full-time faculty	No	No
If yes, typical size offered last year		
# of classroom course titles beyond first-year curriculum		112
# of upper division courses, excluding seminars, with an enrollment: Under 25		163
25–49		32
50–74		7
75–99		2
100+		0
# of seminars		31
# of seminar positions available		830
# of seminar positions filled	268	179
# of positions available in simulation courses		629
# of simulation positions filled	287	102
# of positions available in faculty supervised clinical courses		100
# of faculty supervised clinical positions filled	29	17
# involved in field placements	100	23
# involved in law journals	68	21
# involved in moot court or trial competitions	57	8
# of credit hours required to graduate		87

JD Enrollment and Ethnicity

	Men		Women		Full-Time		Part-Time		1st-Year		Total		JD Degs. Awd.
	#	%	#	%	#	%	#	%	#	%	#	%	
African Amer.	4	1.5	12	3.7	11	2.4	5	3.5	10	3.3	16	2.7	5
Amer. Indian	0	0.0	2	0.6	2	0.4	0	0.0	2	0.7	2	0.3	0
Asian Amer.	35	13.0	45	14.0	67	14.9	13	9.2	27	8.8	80	13.5	27
Mex. Amer.	16	5.9	15	4.7	22	4.9	9	6.4	17	5.6	31	5.2	11
Puerto Rican	0	0.0	1	0.3	0	0.0	1	0.7	0	0.0	1	0.2	0
Hispanic	9	3.3	24	7.5	24	5.3	9	6.4	15	4.9	33	5.6	5
Total Minority	64	23.8	99	30.7	126	28.0	37	26.2	71	23.2	163	27.6	48
For. Nation.	1	0.4	1	0.3	2	0.4	0	0.0	2	0.7	2	0.3	0
Caucasian	99	36.8	105	32.6	143	31.8	61	43.3	70	22.9	204	34.5	79
Unknown	105	39.0	117	36.3	179	39.8	43	30.5	163	53.3	222	37.6	27
Total	269	45.5	322	54.5	450	76.1	141	23.9	306	51.8	591		154

Transfers

Transfers in	4
Transfers out	28

Tuition and Fees

	Resident	Nonresident
Full-time	$37,060	
Part-time	$24,720	
Tuition Guarantee Program		N

Living Expenses

Estimated living expenses for singles

Living on campus	Living off campus	Living at home
N/A	$20,280	$20,280

Whittier Law School

ABA
Approved
Since
1978

GPA and LSAT Scores

	Total	Full-Time	Part-Time
# of apps	2,284	1,914	370
# of offers	1,040	906	134
# of matrics	306	245	61
75% GPA	3.35	3.35	3.40
Median GPA	3.10	3.10	3.09
25% GPA	2.83	2.82	2.85
75% LSAT	153	153	153
Median LSAT	151	151	151
25% LSAT	149	149	149

Grants and Scholarships (from prior year)

	Total #	Total %	Full-Time #	Full-Time %	Part-Time #	Part-Time %
Total # of students	506		364		142	
Total # receiving grants	209	41.3	158	43.4	51	35.9
Less than 1/2 tuition	121	23.9	91	25.0	30	21.1
Half to full tuition	42	8.3	31	8.5	11	7.7
Full tuition	37	7.3	33	9.1	4	2.8
More than full tuition	9	1.8	3	0.8	6	4.2
Median grant amount			$15,000		$8,000	

Informational and Library Resources

Total amount spent on library materials	$890,683
Study seating capacity inside the library	386
# of full-time equivalent professional librarians	6
Hours per week library is open	102
# of open, wired connections available to students	223
# of networked computers available for use by students	109
Has wireless network?	Y
Require computer?	N

JD Attrition (from prior year)

	Academic #	Other #	Total #	Total %
1st year	20	29	49	31.4
2nd year	6	13	19	12.2
3rd year	2	4	6	4.5
4th year	1	2	3	5.6

Employment (9 months after graduation)

	Total	Percentage
Employment status known	160	99.4
Employment status unknown	1	0.6
Employed	147	91.9
Pursuing graduate degrees	5	3.1
Unemployed (seeking, not seeking, or studying for the bar)	5	3.1
Type of Employment		
# employed in law firms	91	61.9
# employed in business and industry	33	22.4
# employed in government	12	8.2
# employed in public interest	4	2.7
# employed as judicial clerks	3	2.0
# employed in academia	4	2.7
Geographic Location		
# employed in state	113	76.9
# employed in foreign countries	5	3.4
# of states where employed	17	

Bar Passage Rates

First-time takers	166	Reporting %	79.52
Average school %	82.58	Average state %	78.07
Average pass difference	4.51		

Jurisdiction	Takers	Passers	Pass %	State %	Diff %
California	132	109	82.58	78.07	4.51

Whittier Law School

3333 Harbor Boulevard
Costa Mesa, CA 92626
Phone: 714.444.4141 ext. 123; Fax: 714.444.0250
E-mail: info@law.whittier.edu; Website: www.law.whittier.edu

■ Introduction

Whittier Law School was founded in 1966 as Beverly Law School. In 1975, the Law School became part of Whittier College, established by Quakers in 1887. The Law School is located in Costa Mesa, Orange County. Orange County, ranked among the top business centers in the United States, is home to over 10,000 lawyers, more lawyers than half the states in the nation. The Law School is 30 miles south of downtown Los Angeles, 100 miles north of San Diego, and minutes away from the local beach cities such as Huntington Beach and Newport Beach. Ideally situated, the Law School enjoys the vibrant economies produced within each area as well as within Orange County. The Whittier tradition stresses concern for individual student's intellectual and ethical development. This tradition is reflected in admission practices stressing diversity, a small student-to-faculty ratio, small elective classes, and individual student counseling and placement services.

■ Part-Time Programs

In addition to the traditional three-year, full-time program, the JD can also be completed in four years, including two summer sessions, in the flexible day or evening programs. First- and second-year, part-time students generally attend classes three days a week. Standards for admission and retention are identical for all students, and the full-time faculty serves both programs.

■ Admission and Scholarships

In addition to the LSAT score and undergraduate GPA, subjective factors such as undergraduate school, major, graduate work, ethnic and economic background, work experience, and personal accomplishments are considered. Applicants are encouraged to discuss these factors in their written personal statements. The admission office automatically considers all applicants for merit-based scholarships.

■ Special Programs

Center for Children's Rights—The center enrolls up to 20 students yearly who receive fellowships and summer stipends to prepare for careers in children's rights advocacy. Fellows participate in special classes, colloquiums, symposiums, and externships. The center also sponsors the National Juvenile Law Moot Court Competition and the *Whittier Journal of Children and Family Advocacy*. The center also awards CCR Fellowships.

Center for Intellectual Property Law—The center provides students and practitioners with academic instruction in intellectual property law. The cornerstones of the center are the Certificate Program, the Summer Institute, and the Distinguished Speaker Series. The center also awards IP Fellowships.

Center for International and Comparative Law—The center allows students to participate in a specialized legal writing course, attend the International Law Symposium and Colloquia series, and receive a certificate by enrolling in

courses offered through the center. The center also awards CICL Fellowships.

Clinics—Whittier Law School boasts four clinics: the Children's Advocacy Clinic, the Special Education Clinic, the Family Violence Clinic, and the "clientless" Legal Policy Clinic.

Exchange Programs in France and Spain—Students with some knowledge of French or Spanish can spend one semester at the University of Paris X in Nanterre, France; the University of Cantabria in Santander, Spain; or the University of Seville, Spain.

Summer-Abroad Programs—The Law School offers five summer study-abroad programs approved by the ABA. Students from around the country can choose to study at the prestigious Bar-Ilan University in Tel Aviv, Israel; the University of Cantabria in Santander, Spain; the University of Toulouse in Toulouse, France; the University of Nanjing in China; or Iberoamericana University in Mexico City.

Institute of Student and Graduate Academic Support—Six full-time professors provide a comprehensive program of instruction and individual attention—the academic support students need to succeed in their courses, on the bar examination, and in the practice of law. The institute provides a year-long program, Student Academic Support Center, nationally recognized bar preparation program, and true open door policy. From the first day of orientation, through graduation and beyond, the institute is committed to making our students' law school experience a success.

Institute of Legal Writing and Professional Skills—The staff, composed of eight full-time professors and twelve part-time professors, teaches students how to write and conduct themselves well as lawyers. With this institute, our students have proven to be more prepared to perform at summer jobs, as well as to enter practice generally, than students from many schools throughout the state. The institute also offers three specialized writing courses in the first-year curriculum for the Center for Children's Rights, Center for Intellectual Property Law, and the Center for International and Comparative Law.

Concentrations in business and criminal law are also offered.

■ Library and Physical Facilities

Whittier Law School is located in the city of Costa Mesa on a beautiful 15-acre campus with exceptional facilities, including one of the largest academic law research libraries in the region. The Law School is composed of four buildings that are completely accessible to people with disabilities, totaling 130,000 square feet, and offers plentiful on-site parking. With over 380,000 volumes, the library has a rapidly growing legal research collection and serves as a state and federal depository. Three student computer labs support a variety of software to aid students with computer-assisted instruction, online legal research, and Internet access. Numerous conference rooms are available for group study. The entire facility is equipped with wireless Internet access for individual study.

Student Activities

The *Whittier Law Review* is open to students on the basis of grades and a writing competition, and members participate in the annual Health Law and International Law Symposia.

The *Whittier Journal of Child and Family Advocacy*, a student-run scholarly publication focusing on topics related to juvenile and family law, is one of the few journals of its kind in the nation.

Members of the Moot Court Honors Board and the Trial Advocacy Honors Board utilize written and oral advocacy skills to represent the Law School in regional and national trial and appellate advocacy competitions.

The Student Bar Association's activities include support of various social functions and participation in student-faculty committees for school governance. Numerous other student organizations represent various ethnic groups and legal specialties.

Externships and Career Services

Whittier Law School provides assistance to students and alumni in obtaining clerkships, externships, and attorney positions. The Law School offers a variety of externships with trial and appellate judges, governmental agencies, private firms, and public interest organizations. The Career Services Office assists in résumé-building exercises, career goal identification, and career-planning strategies. Additional services include on-campus interviews, a mentor program, panels and symposia on career-related topics, a comprehensive library of career resources, and a mock interview program.

Applicant Profile

Whittier Law School
This grid includes only applicants who earned 120–180 LSAT scores under standard administrations.

LSAT Score	3.75 +		3.50–3.74		3.25–3.49		3.00–3.24		2.75–2.99		2.50–2.74		2.25–2.49		2.00–2.24		Below 2.00		No GPA		Total	
	Apps	Adm	Apps	Adm	Apps	Adm	Apps	Adm	Apps	Adm	Apps	Adm	Apps	Adm	Apps	Adm	Apps	Adm	Apps	Adm	Apps	Adm
175–180	0	0	0	0	0	0	1	1	0	0	0	0	0	0	0	0	0	0	0	0	1	1
170–174	0	0	0	0	0	0	0	0	0	0	1	0	0	0	0	0	0	0	0	0	1	0
165–169	2	2	1	1	2	2	0	0	1	1	4	2	2	2	1	1	0	0	1	0	14	11
160–164	6	6	15	12	11	11	11	10	8	8	13	11	7	6	4	3	0	0	0	0	75	67
155–159	14	13	30	29	45	41	65	57	57	53	34	30	19	14	15	7	2	1	6	4	287	249
150–154	30	28	75	70	116	105	134	121	155	129	81	46	47	12	31	4	3	0	11	9	683	524
145–149	21	15	57	27	133	61	138	39	152	20	99	9	67	4	32	0	4	0	12	4	715	179
140–144	4	0	18	0	37	2	61	1	74	2	50	1	22	0	20	0	5	0	16	2	307	8
135–139	1	0	5	0	14	0	28	0	30	0	26	0	22	0	17	0	2	0	6	0	151	0
130–134	1	0	2	0	2	0	5	0	9	0	9	0	5	0	6	0	3	0	4	0	46	0
125–129	0	0	0	0	0	0	0	0	0	0	0	0	1	0	1	0	2	0	0	0	4	0
120–124	0	0	0	0	0	0	0	0	0	0	0	0	0	0	0	0	0	0	2	0	2	0
Total	79	64	203	139	360	222	443	229	486	213	317	99	192	38	127	15	21	1	58	19	2286	1039

Apps = Number of Applicants
Adm = Number Admitted
Reflects 99% of the total applicant pool; average LSAT data reported.

Widener University School of Law

4601 Concord Pike, PO Box 7474
Wilmington, DE 19803-0474
Phone: 302.477.2162; Fax 302.477.2224
E-mail: lawadmissions@widener.edu; Website: http://law.widener.edu

ABA
Approved
Since
1975

The Basics

Type of school	Private
Term	Semester
Application deadline	5/15
Application fee	$60
Financial aid deadline	
Can first year start other than fall?	No
Student to faculty ratio	18.6 to 1
# of housing spaces available	
restricted to law students	185
graduate housing for which law students are eligible	185

Faculty and Administrators

	Total		Men		Women		Minorities	
	Spr	Fall	Spr	Fall	Spr	Fall	Spr	Fall
Full-time	34	40	28	28	6	12	3	4
Other full-time	11	12	2	2	9	10	3	3
Deans, librarians, & others who teach	9	9	3	3	6	6	1	1
Part-time	48	46	35	26	13	19	3	3
Total	102	107	68	59	34	47	10	11

Curriculum

		Full-Time	Part-Time
Typical first-year section size		65	55
Is there typically a "small section" of the first-year class, other than Legal Writing, taught by full-time faculty		Yes	Yes
If yes, typical size offered last year		52	53
# of classroom course titles beyond first-year curriculum		126	
# of upper division courses, excluding seminars, with an enrollment:	Under 25	118	
	25–49	28	
	50–74	25	
	75–99	5	
	100+	1	
# of seminars		30	
# of seminar positions available		450	
# of seminar positions filled		203	112
# of positions available in simulation courses		700	
# of simulation positions filled		284	203
# of positions available in faculty supervised clinical courses		80	
# of faculty supervised clinical positions filled		49	29
# involved in field placements		77	29
# involved in law journals		134	36
# involved in moot court or trial competitions		75	52
# of credit hours required to graduate		88	

JD Enrollment and Ethnicity

	Men		Women		Full-Time		Part-Time		1st-Year		Total		JD Degs. Awd.
	#	%	#	%	#	%	#	%	#	%	#	%	
African Amer.	25	4.6	31	7.2	28	4.6	28	7.7	27	7.1	56	5.7	11
Amer. Indian	4	0.7	1	0.2	1	0.2	4	1.1	3	0.8	5	0.5	0
Asian Amer.	17	3.1	35	8.1	34	5.6	18	5.0	24	6.3	52	5.3	10
Mex. Amer.	1	0.2	1	0.2	2	0.3	0	0.0	1	0.3	2	0.2	0
Puerto Rican	4	0.7	2	0.5	3	0.5	3	0.8	0	0.0	6	0.6	0
Hispanic	5	0.9	7	1.6	9	1.5	3	0.8	5	1.3	12	1.2	4
Total Minority	56	10.3	77	17.9	77	12.6	56	15.4	60	15.9	133	13.6	25
For. Nation.	0	0.0	1	0.2	1	0.2	0	0.0	1	0.3	1	0.1	1
Caucasian	410	75.4	288	66.8	444	72.5	254	70.0	301	79.6	698	71.6	175
Unknown	78	14.3	65	15.1	90	14.7	53	14.6	16	4.2	143	14.7	36
Total	544	55.8	431	44.2	612	62.8	363	37.2	378	38.8	975		237

Transfers

Transfers in	1
Transfers out	39

Tuition and Fees

	Resident	Nonresident
Full-time	$33,540	$33,540
Part-time	$24,620	$24,620
Tuition Guarantee Program	N	

Living Expenses

Estimated living expenses for singles

Living on campus	Living off campus	Living at home
$16,475	$16,475	$11,075

Widener University School of Law

ABA
Approved
Since
1975

GPA and LSAT Scores

	Total	Full-Time	Part-Time
# of apps	2,173	2,055	534
# of offers	1,379	1,139	240
# of matrics	383	249	134
75% GPA	3.46	3.42	3.53
Median GPA	3.13	3.11	3.16
25% GPA	2.82	2.83	2.79
75% LSAT	154	154	152
Median LSAT	152	153	150
25% LSAT	150	151	148

Grants and Scholarships (from prior year)

	Total		Full-Time		Part-Time	
	#	%	#	%	#	%
Total # of students	950		611		339	
Total # receiving grants	268	28.2	209	34.2	59	17.4
Less than 1/2 tuition	198	20.8	160	26.2	38	11.2
Half to full tuition	59	6.2	39	6.4	20	5.9
Full tuition	10	1.1	10	1.6	0	0.0
More than full tuition	1	0.1	0	0.0	1	0.3
Median grant amount			$6,750		$7,500	

Informational and Library Resources

Total amount spent on library materials	$1,103,659
Study seating capacity inside the library	335
# of full-time equivalent professional librarians	10
Hours per week library is open	107
# of open, wired connections available to students	75
# of networked computers available for use by students	141
Has wireless network?	Y
Require computer?	N

JD Attrition (from prior year)

	Academic	Other	Total	
	#	#	#	%
1st year	55	50	105	28.2
2nd year	8	1	9	3.2
3rd year	0	0	0	0.0
4th year	0	0	0	0.0

Employment (9 months after graduation)

	Total	Percentage
Employment status known	215	78.8
Employment status unknown	58	21.2
Employed	193	89.8
Pursuing graduate degrees	4	1.9
Unemployed (seeking, not seeking, or studying for the bar)	15	7.0
Type of Employment		
# employed in law firms	84	43.5
# employed in business and industry	41	21.2
# employed in government	13	6.7
# employed in public interest	5	2.6
# employed as judicial clerks	46	23.8
# employed in academia	4	2.1
Geographic Location		
# employed in state	48	24.9
# employed in foreign countries	0	0.0
# of states where employed	12	

Bar Passage Rates

First-time takers	229	Reporting %	72.05
Average school %	86.06	Average state %	86.69
Average pass difference	−0.63		

Jurisdiction	Takers	Passers	Pass %	State %	Diff %
Pennsylvania	165	142	86.06	86.69	−0.63

Widener University School of Law

3800 Vartan Way, PO Box 69381
Harrisburg, PA 17106-9381
Phone: 717.541.3903; Fax 717.541.3999
E-mail: lawadmissions@widener.edu; Website: http://law.widener.edu

ABA Approved Since 1988

The Basics

Type of school	Private
Term	Semester
Application deadline	5/15
Application fee	$60
Financial aid deadline	4/1
Can first year start other than fall?	No
Student to faculty ratio	19.4 to 1
# of housing spaces available	
restricted to law students	
graduate housing for which law students are eligible	

Faculty and Administrators

	Total		Men		Women		Minorities	
	Spr	Fall	Spr	Fall	Spr	Fall	Spr	Fall
Full-time	16	19	11	13	5	6	1	2
Other full-time	7	8	1	1	6	7	2	2
Deans, librarians, & others who teach	6	5	1	1	5	4	1	1
Part-time	23	15	16	11	7	4	2	0
Total	52	47	29	26	23	21	6	5

Curriculum

		Full-Time	Part-Time
Typical first-year section size		73	34
Is there typically a "small section" of the first-year class, other than Legal Writing, taught by full-time faculty		No	No
If yes, typical size offered last year			
# of classroom course titles beyond first-year curriculum		72	
# of upper division courses, excluding seminars, with an enrollment:	Under 25	92	
	25-49	18	
	50-74	12	
	75-99	1	
	100+	1	
# of seminars		11	
# of seminar positions available		194	
# of seminar positions filled		72	52
# of positions available in simulation courses		233	
# of simulation positions filled		125	108
# of positions available in faculty supervised clinical courses		35	
# of faculty supervised clinical positions filled	19	16
# involved in field placements		19	28
# involved in law journals		34	6
# involved in moot court or trial competitions	29	13
# of credit hours required to graduate		88	

JD Enrollment and Ethnicity

	Men		Women		Full-Time		Part-Time		1st-Year		Total		JD Degs. Awd.
	#	%	#	%	#	%	#	%	#	%	#	%	
African Amer.	3	1.3	10	4.5	10	2.8	3	2.9	4	2.2	13	2.8	1
Amer. Indian	1	0.4	1	0.5	1	0.3	1	1.0	1	0.6	2	0.4	0
Asian Amer.	4	1.7	9	4.1	13	3.6	0	0.0	8	4.4	13	2.8	3
Mex. Amer.	2	0.8	0	0.0	2	0.6	0	0.0	0	0.0	2	0.4	0
Puerto Rican	1	0.4	2	0.9	2	0.6	1	1.0	2	1.1	3	0.7	0
Hispanic	8	3.3	7	3.2	14	3.9	1	1.0	9	5.0	15	3.3	3
Total Minority	19	7.9	29	13.1	42	11.7	6	5.8	24	13.3	48	10.4	7
For. Nation.	0	0.0	0	0.0	0	0.0	0	0.0	0	0.0	0	0.0	0
Caucasian	189	78.8	168	76.0	275	76.8	82	79.6	139	76.8	357	77.4	91
Unknown	32	13.3	24	10.9	41	11.5	15	14.6	18	9.9	56	12.1	21
Total	240	52.1	221	47.9	358	77.7	103	22.3	181	39.3	461		119

Transfers

Transfers in	1
Transfers out	13

Tuition and Fees

	Resident	Nonresident
Full-time	$33,540	$33,540
Part-time	$24,620	$24,620
Tuition Guarantee Program		N

Living Expenses

Estimated living expenses for singles

Living on campus	Living off campus	Living at home
$16,475	$16,475	$11,075

Widener University School of Law

ABA
Approved
Since
1988

GPA and LSAT Scores

	Total	Full-Time	Part-Time
# of apps	852	1,442	249
# of offers	914	800	114
# of matrics	183	143	40
75% GPA	3.47	3.44	3.67
Median GPA	3.20	3.18	3.38
25% GPA	2.80	2.78	2.83
75% LSAT	152	151	154
Median LSAT	150	150	151
25% LSAT	148	148	148

Grants and Scholarships (from prior year)

	Total		Full-Time		Part-Time	
	#	%	#	%	#	%
Total # of students	457		345		112	
Total # receiving grants	133	29.1	106	30.7	27	24.1
Less than 1/2 tuition	105	23.0	84	24.3	21	18.8
Half to full tuition	22	4.8	16	4.6	6	5.4
Full tuition	6	1.3	6	1.7	0	0.0
More than full tuition	0	0.0	0	0.0	0	0.0
Median grant amount		$5,000		$6,983		

Informational and Library Resources

Total amount spent on library materials	$770,464
Study seating capacity inside the library	335
# of full-time equivalent professional librarians	5
Hours per week library is open	105
# of open, wired connections available to students	10
# of networked computers available for use by students	68
Has wireless network?	Y
Require computer?	N

JD Attrition (from prior year)

	Academic	Other	Total	
	#	#	#	%
1st year	30	26	56	29.2
2nd year	0	0	0	0.0
3rd year	0	0	0	0.0
4th year	0	0	0	0.0

Employment (9 months after graduation)

	Total	Percentage
Employment status known	121	98.4
Employment status unknown	2	1.6
Employed	109	90.1
Pursuing graduate degrees	2	1.7
Unemployed (seeking, not seeking, or studying for the bar)	3	2.5
Type of Employment		
# employed in law firms	43	39.4
# employed in business and industry	18	16.5
# employed in government	24	22.0
# employed in public interest	7	6.4
# employed as judicial clerks	15	13.8
# employed in academia	2	1.8
Geographic Location		
# employed in state	84	77.1
# employed in foreign countries	0	0.0
# of states where employed		10

Bar Passage Rates

First-time takers	127	Reporting %	80.31
Average school %	91.17	Average state %	86.53
Average pass difference	4.64		

Jurisdiction	Takers	Passers	Pass %	State %	Diff %
Pennsylvania	94	86	91.49	86.69	4.80
New Jersey	8	7	87.50	84.69	2.81

Widener University School of Law

4601 Concord Pike, PO Box 7474, Wilmington, DE 19803-0474; Phone: 302.477.2162; Fax 302.477.2224
3800 Vartan Way, PO Box 69381, Harrisburg, PA 17106-9381; Phone: 717.541.3903; Fax 717.541.3999
E-mail: lawadmissions@widener.edu; Website: http://law.widener.edu

■ Introduction

Widener University School of Law is unique among American law schools. Widener has two campuses—one in Wilmington, Delaware, the corporate and banking center of the United States, and the other in Harrisburg, Pennsylvania, the state capital and a major center of government and commerce. Each campus offers a comprehensive curriculum of basic and advanced courses complemented by one of the most extensive clinical and skills programs in the country. The Harrisburg campus features a unique admission and academic cooperative program with the Pennsylvania State System of Higher Education.

The rich curriculum is taught by a faculty committed to personal attention and individual counseling so that all students will be encouraged to fulfill their potential. The full-time faculty is supplemented by a distinguished group of adjuncts, including two justices of the Delaware Supreme Court, US Vice President Joseph Biden, and numerous lower court judges from Pennsylvania, Delaware, and New Jersey. The school is a member of the AALS and is accredited by the ABA.

■ Library and Physical Facilities

The Legal Information Center houses one of the most significant legal collections in the region. The combined collections of the Delaware and Harrisburg campuses exceed 600,000 volumes. The library is a selective depository for United States government documents.

The attractive 34-acre Delaware campus is located in the heart of the beautiful Brandywine River Valley. The law building houses the Legal Information Center, state-of-the-art computer facilities, faculty offices, clinics, traditional and technologically enhanced classrooms, and three moot courtrooms. The scenic 19-acre Harrisburg campus is located in a contemporary complex within minutes of the state capital.

■ Special Programs and Institutes

Widener is a leader in developing a coordinated lawyering skills program. The program includes clinical practice, externship placements, and comprehensive simulations.

Clinics are designed to permit students to represent actual clients under the supervision of the clinic director before courts and administrative boards. Widener operates Environmental Law, Criminal Defense, Delaware Civil, Pennsylvania Civil, Harrisburg Civil, and Veterans Affairs clinics. A large number of supervised externships permit students to work as lawyers-in-training with state and county government agencies and nonprofit corporations. An extensive judicial externship program places students with state and federal courts at both the trial and appellate levels in Washington, DC; Delaware; Maryland; New Jersey; Pennsylvania; and Virginia. Additional public interest service opportunities are also available.

The Public Interest Resource Center on the Delaware campus and the Public Interest Initiative on the Harrisburg campus cultivate pro bono volunteer opportunities for students in public interest agencies and government offices throughout Delaware, Pennsylvania, and New Jersey; offer counseling and guidance to students who seek careers in public interest law; and recognize students and faculty for exceptional contributions to public service.

Widener offers certificate programs for specialized study in health law, law and government, business organizations law, advocacy and technology, criminal law, and environmental law.

The Health Law Institute on the Delaware campus provides research, policy analysis, and specialty education for those seeking a career in the area of health law. The Law and Government Institute on the Harrisburg campus provides hands-on experience with the operation and structure of government as well as practice before government agencies. The Institute of Delaware Corporate and Business Law on the Delaware campus provides a fundamental knowledge of business law through the Business Organizations Law concentration, which serves as a predicate to advanced practice in business and corporate law. The Advocacy and Technology Institute on the Delaware campus provides the extensive litigation skills that are essential to being a competent, professionally responsible trial advocate. The Environmental Law Center on both campuses harnesses the expertise of seven nationally and internationally recognized environmental law faculty members to provide students with extensive opportunities to engage in environmental law through coursework, externships, and training skills. Additionally, both campuses offer a seven-day Intensive Trial Advocacy Program supervised by outstanding local trial lawyers and judges.

Widener offers five joint-degree programs. The JD/MBA is offered in conjunction with the university's School of Business Administration. The JD/PsyD is offered in conjunction with the university's Institute for Graduate Clinical Psychology. The JD/MPH is offered in conjunction with Thomas Jefferson University. The JD/MSLS is offered in conjunction with Clarion University of Pennsylvania. The JD/MMP is offered in conjunction with the University of Delaware.

■ Study-Abroad Opportunities

Widener students have the opportunity to study international and comparative law while living abroad. Widener offers study-abroad programs in Nairobi, Kenya; Lausanne, Switzerland; Sydney, Australia; Venice, Italy; and Chongqing, China.

■ Student Activities

Selected Delaware students publish the *Delaware Journal of Corporate Law* and the *Widener Law Review*. Selected Harrisburg students publish the *Widener Law Journal*. Delaware and Harrisburg students may also be eligible to participate in our online journal, the *Widener Journal of Law, Economics and Race*. Students on both campuses compete in regional and national interschool moot court and trial competitions. Student organizations provide opportunities for intrascholastic and interscholastic competitions, public service, and association with others who share the same interests.

■ Admission

While there are no fixed admission criteria, great weight is given to the applicant's LSAT score and undergraduate grade-point average. The Admissions Committee carefully considers an applicant's personal statement. Graduate degrees, writing samples, extracurricular activities, and community and professional service may enhance the application. The law school encourages those with diverse backgrounds to apply.

Applications for admission must be received by May 15. Admission decisions are made on a rolling basis, and applicants are encouraged to apply early.

Each summer, Widener conducts the Trial Admissions Program (TAP) for a small number of carefully selected applicants who show potential for success in law school despite a relatively low score on the LSAT or a lower undergraduate grade-point average. TAP is a conditional admittance program. Participants who successfully complete the six-week program are offered admission to the fall entering class.

■ Financial Aid

The Office of Financial Aid works with any student wishing assistance in finding appropriate sources of funding. Additionally, all applicants are considered for Widener's merit- and need-based scholarships.

■ Career Development

The Career Development Office is strongly committed to helping students obtain the positions that best suit their individual needs and ambitions.

Widener's placement statistics evidence its success in helping graduates find a niche in the contemporary job market. Widener alumni have become judges in Delaware, New Jersey, New York, and Pennsylvania; members of the legislature; partners in major regional law firms; hospital administrators; legal educators; and broadcast journalists.

Applicant Profile

Widener University School of Law
This grid includes only applicants who earned 120–180 LSAT scores under standard administrations.

LSAT Score	GPA																						
	3.75 +		3.50–3.74		3.25–3.49		3.00–3.24		2.75–2.99		2.50–2.74		2.25–2.49		2.00–2.24		Below 2.00		No GPA		Total	
	Apps	Adm	Apps	Adm	Apps	Adm	Apps	Adm	Apps	Adm	Apps	Adm	Apps	Adm	Apps	Adm	Apps	Adm	Apps	Adm	Apps	Adm
175–180	0	0	0	0	1	0	1	0	0	0	0	0	0	0	0	0	0	0	0	0	2	0
170–174	2	1	0	0	0	0	0	0	0	0	0	0	1	0	0	0	0	0	0	0	3	1
165–169	2	2	4	2	1	1	6	5	0	0	1	1	0	0	0	0	0	0	0	0	14	11
160–164	12	11	16	13	15	13	24	23	13	12	6	6	6	6	2	0	0	0	0	0	94	84
155–159	40	37	55	51	61	55	68	61	41	37	42	36	13	11	7	5	1	1	2	0	330	294
150–154	69	63	130	110	160	136	173	152	125	110	77	67	52	46	25	21	6	4	10	2	827	711
145–149	43	21	121	53	192	85	221	87	174	66	118	45	65	28	21	12	3	1	19	4	977	402
140–144	20	2	61	5	80	4	111	9	103	5	73	3	32	1	22	0	9	0	19	0	530	29
135–139	4	0	19	1	33	0	36	0	53	0	40	0	35	0	15	0	1	0	18	0	254	1
130–134	1	0	1	0	13	0	14	0	17	0	15	0	10	0	3	0	3	0	9	0	86	0
125–129	0	0	0	0	1	0	4	0	4	0	3	0	1	0	4	0	1	0	2	0	20	0
120–124	0	0	0	0	0	0	0	0	0	0	1	0	0	0	0	0	0	0	2	0	3	0
Total	193	137	407	235	557	294	658	337	530	230	376	158	215	92	99	38	24	6	81	6	3140	1533

Apps = Number of Applicants
Adm = Number Admitted
Reflects 98% of the total applicant pool; average LSAT data reported.

The grid includes applicants admitted based upon successful completion of our Trial Admissions Program, rather than upon their LSAT score and undergraduate grade-point average. Additionally, nonnumerical factors are strongly considered for all applicants.

Willamette University College of Law

Truman Wesley Collins Legal Center, 245 Winter Street SE
Salem, OR 97301
Phone: 503.370.6282; Fax: 503.370.6087
E-mail: law-admission@willamette.edu; Website: www.willamette.edu/wucl

ABA
Approved
Since
1938

American Bar Association
Section of Legal Education
and Admissions to the Bar

The Basics

Type of school	Private
Term	Semester
Application deadline	3/1
Application fee	$50
Financial aid deadline	6/1
Can first year start other than fall?	No
Student to faculty ratio	15.0 to 1
# of housing spaces available restricted to law students	
graduate housing for which law students are eligible	26

Faculty and Administrators

	Total		Men		Women		Minorities	
	Spr	Fall	Spr	Fall	Spr	Fall	Spr	Fall
Full-time	24	22	19	14	5	8	1	4
Other full-time	4	4	1	1	3	3	1	1
Deans, librarians, & others who teach	12	11	4	3	8	8	2	2
Part-time	12	13	9	10	3	3	1	1
Total	52	50	33	28	19	22	5	8

Curriculum

	Full-Time	Part-Time
Typical first-year section size	80	0
Is there typically a "small section" of the first-year class, other than Legal Writing, taught by full-time faculty	Yes	No
If yes, typical size offered last year	35	
# of classroom course titles beyond first-year curriculum	110	
# of upper division courses, excluding seminars, with an enrollment: Under 25	62	
25–49	16	
50–74	13	
75–99	0	
100+	1	
# of seminars	21	
# of seminar positions available	313	
# of seminar positions filled	227	0
# of positions available in simulation courses	288	
# of simulation positions filled	227	0
# of positions available in faculty supervised clinical courses	56	
# of faculty supervised clinical positions filled	44	0
# involved in field placements	40	0
# involved in law journals	50	0
# involved in moot court or trial competitions	131	0
# of credit hours required to graduate	90	

JD Enrollment and Ethnicity

	Men		Women		Full-Time		Part-Time		1st-Year		Total		JD Degs. Awd.
	#	%	#	%	#	%	#	%	#	%	#	%	
African Amer.	4	1.6	3	1.6	7	1.7	0	0.0	1	0.7	7	1.6	0
Amer. Indian	4	1.6	2	1.1	6	1.4	0	0.0	2	1.4	6	1.4	2
Asian Amer.	15	6.1	17	9.3	32	7.6	0	0.0	11	7.5	32	7.5	5
Mex. Amer.	5	2.0	6	3.3	10	2.4	1	20.0	2	1.4	11	2.6	1
Puerto Rican	1	0.4	3	1.6	4	1.0	0	0.0	1	0.7	4	0.9	0
Hispanic	8	3.3	3	1.6	11	2.6	0	0.0	4	2.7	11	2.6	2
Total Minority	37	15.2	34	18.7	70	16.6	1	20.0	21	14.3	71	16.7	10
For. Nation.	2	0.8	0	0.0	2	0.5	0	0.0	1	0.7	2	0.5	0
Caucasian	180	73.8	136	74.7	313	74.3	3	60.0	111	75.5	316	74.2	101
Unknown	25	10.2	12	6.6	36	8.6	1	20.0	14	9.5	37	8.7	19
Total	244	57.3	182	42.7	421	98.8	5	1.2	147	34.5	426		130

Transfers

Transfers in	2
Transfers out	8

Tuition and Fees

	Resident	Nonresident
Full-time	$29,680	$29,680
Part-time		
Tuition Guarantee Program	N	

Living Expenses

Estimated living expenses for singles

Living on campus	Living off campus	Living at home
$16,630	$16,630	$16,630

Willamette University College of Law

ABA
Approved
Since
1938

GPA and LSAT Scores

	Total	Full-Time	Part-Time
# of apps	1,532	1,532	0
# of offers	598	598	0
# of matrics	148	148	0
75% GPA	3.51	3.51	0.00
Median GPA	3.23	3.23	0.00
25% GPA	3.05	3.05	0.00
75% LSAT	157	157	0
Median LSAT	154	154	0
25% LSAT	153	153	0

Grants and Scholarships (from prior year)

	Total #	Total %	Full-Time #	Full-Time %	Part-Time #	Part-Time %
Total # of students	428		423		5	
Total # receiving grants	233	54.4	233	55.1	0	0.0
Less than 1/2 tuition	150	35.0	150	35.5	0	0.0
Half to full tuition	83	19.4	83	19.6	0	0.0
Full tuition	0	0.0	0	0.0	0	0.0
More than full tuition	0	0.0	0	0.0	0	0.0
Median grant amount			$12,000		$0	

Informational and Library Resources

Total amount spent on library materials	$691,989
Study seating capacity inside the library	492
# of full-time equivalent professional librarians	5
Hours per week library is open	168
# of open, wired connections available to students	104
# of networked computers available for use by students	64
Has wireless network?	Y
Require computer?	N

JD Attrition (from prior year)

	Academic #	Other #	Total #	Total %
1st year	6	12	18	11.5
2nd year	4	8	12	8.7
3rd year	0	0	0	0.0
4th year	0	0	0	0.0

Employment (9 months after graduation)

	Total	Percentage
Employment status known	101	94.4
Employment status unknown	6	5.6
Employed	95	94.1
Pursuing graduate degrees	1	1.0
Unemployed (seeking, not seeking, or studying for the bar)	5	5.0
Type of Employment		
# employed in law firms	46	48.4
# employed in business and industry	18	18.9
# employed in government	17	17.9
# employed in public interest	6	6.3
# employed as judicial clerks	6	6.3
# employed in academia	1	1.1
Geographic Location		
# employed in state	63	66.3
# employed in foreign countries	0	0.0
# of states where employed	14	

Bar Passage Rates

First-time takers	102	Reporting %	84.31
Average school %	84.89	Average state %	78.20
Average pass difference	6.69		

Jurisdiction	Takers	Passers	Pass %	State %	Diff %
Oregon	77	65	84.42	78.64	5.78
Washington	9	8	88.89	74.40	14.49

Willamette University College of Law

Truman Wesley Collins Legal Center, 245 Winter Street SE
Salem, OR 97301
Phone: 503.370.6282; Fax: 503.370.6087
E-mail: law-admission@willamette.edu; Website: www.willamette.edu/wucl

■ Introduction

From the time the first student entered the classroom in 1883, Willamette University College of Law has been a pioneer of legal education in the western United States. Located across the street from the state capitol complex, the College of Law is situated in the epicenter of Oregon law, government, and business.

Willamette University is one of the nation's oldest academic institutions. It is situated in the historic riverfront capital city of Salem, Oregon. The university is an independent institution historically related to the United Methodist Church. College of Law students are members of a distinguished university community of 2,500 students enrolled in the undergraduate College of Liberal Arts and in graduate programs offered by the School of Education and the Atkinson Graduate School of Management.

The College of Law is an intimate, highly selective, and intellectually challenging school and a widely recognized leader in legal education. The college is committed to the pursuit of academic and professional excellence in a supportive environment that maximizes each student's unique potential. Selective enrollment of approximately 430 full-time students creates an intellectual intimacy unmatched by most law schools in the United States.

For more than 125 years, Willamette has trained talented, skilled lawyers who stand on equal footing with the very best legal practitioners in the country. Among the College of Law's distinguished alumni are numerous heads of Fortune 500 companies and more than a dozen state Supreme Court justices and members of the US Senate and House of Representatives.

■ Faculty

A law school faculty serves as both the brain and heart of the institution. Willamette's diverse law faculty includes some of the most respected legal minds in the country, including former federal judicial clerks, officers of the American Society of Comparative Law, First Amendment specialists and Fulbright scholars, as well as two former justices of the Oregon Supreme Court and the current chief justice.

These scholars and master teachers are nationally recognized for their research, publications, and contributions to the law, particularly in the areas of constitutional law, commercial and business law, international and comparative law, environmental law, and dispute resolution. Yet it is their authentic, deep dedication—both as educators and as mentors—that distinguishes them from others.

■ Academic Programs

The Doctor of Jurisprudence program (JD) requires three years of full-time study. After successfully completing the first year, in which all courses but one are prescribed, students may choose to create an individual program, electing courses from Willamette's broad-based curriculum.

The College of Law also offers a four-year, joint-degree program that leads to the JD and MBA for Business, Government, and Not-for-Profit Management. Managed in concert with Willamette's Atkinson Graduate School of Management, the joint-degree program saves students one

additional year of study. Students must apply separately for admission to each degree program and may begin the program either in the College of Law or in the Atkinson School. Students may apply prior to matriculating to Willamette or while in their first year of either the JD or MBA program.

Willamette's nationally recognized certificate programs further solidify the strong educational foundation provided at the College of Law. These specialized programs prepare students for exceptional legal careers and further distinguish them from other law school graduates. The five certificate programs are International and Comparative Law, Business Law, Law and Government, Dispute Resolution, and Sustainability Law.

Willamette's College of Law also offers the LLM in Transnational Law, an advanced degree available to those who have completed the JD at an ABA-accredited American law school or its equivalent from a foreign law school. For more information, visit *www.willamette.edu/wucl/programs/llm/*.

■ Facility

The College of Law is housed in the award-winning Truman Wesley Collins Legal Center on the beautifully landscaped 65-acre campus of the university. The school offers all the cutting-edge amenities a student would expect from a top law school. Bright, modern classrooms provide comfortable, professional environments for learning and include a state-of-the-art wireless network.

The J.W. Long Law Library anchors the north end of the Collins Legal Center. Its 296,000 volumes and microform equivalents include state and federal primary law sources, as well as the leading treatises, periodicals, and other secondary sources. Through a library consortium, an online shared catalog gives Willamette students access to a remarkably vast array of resources. The library, a selective federal government depository, houses special collections in public international law, tax law, and labor law.

Both the Collins Legal Center and the law library are accessible to law students 24 hours a day, 7 days a week.

■ International Study Programs

Willamette's College of Law students have the opportunity to deepen their international experience by participating in study-abroad programs in Germany, Ecuador, and China. The summer China Program acquaints students with Chinese law and Pacific Rim legal issues. It is based in Shanghai at the East China University of Politics and Law. The Ecuador Program provides students with an intensive semester immersion in the fundamentals of a civil law system and Latin American legal institutions. Students take courses at the Pontifical Catholic University of Ecuador in Quito. Proficiency in Spanish is required. The semester-long Germany Program is held at the Bucerius Law School in Hamburg, the first private institution for legal study in Germany.

■ Academic Centers and Other Resources

The Clinical Law Program at Willamette University provides students with hands-on, professional experience in the actual practice of law. The Clinical Law Program comprises six

Willamette University College of Law

advanced legal education courses, including specialized clinics in business law, trusts and estates, sustainability law, child and family advocacy, law and government, and international human rights. Clients are primarily nonprofit corporations and people of modest economic means.

The Externship Program immerses students in the fast-paced work of the practicing lawyer. Students participate in legal work in may different contexts, under the constraints of a real-life practice in the wider legal community. The program provides an experiential learning environment that helps students develop their skills and values as novice lawyers. It also enables students to "test the water" in a specific area of legal practice and improves their prospects for obtaining satisfying, permanent employment after graduation.

The nationally recognized Center for Dispute Resolution produces research on conflict theory and problem solving. The center teaches the theory and practice of negotiation, mediation, arbitration, and other methods of resolving disputes. It also administers the Certificate Program in Dispute Resolution.

The Willamette Center for Law and Government provides an impartial forum for the study, discussion, and improvement of government and public policy. It also administers the Certificate Program in Law and Government.

The Oregon Law Commission, which is housed at Willamette's College of Law, was established by legislative statute to provide academic and practical support for ongoing law revision, reform, and improvement. The commission is led by a member of the College of Law faculty.

Admission

Applicants are urged to apply in the fall prior to the year they intend to enter the law school. Willamette enrolls a first-year law class with a wide range of goals and backgrounds distinguished by academic achievements. Applications are reviewed closely and in their entirety to ensure an informed and fair decision. Although March 1 is the priority deadline for applications, students begin receiving admission decisions from Willamette in January.

Scholarships

The fiscal stability of Willamette University enables the College of Law to offer a strong program of financial aid to its students. Generous merit-based scholarships reward applicants whose accomplishments suggest continuing success in law school. Scholarships are renewable with a 2.90 cumulative law GPA. Every student is automatically considered for a scholarship when the application for admission is initially reviewed. All applicants to the College of Law should also complete and submit the Free

Application for Federal Student Aid (FAFSA) prior to March 1. Federal and private loan monies also may be available.

Employment and Career Services

The College of Law maintains an active Office of Career Services, which provides comprehensive career counseling services to current Willamette law students and law alumni. Career Services oversees a busy on-campus interview program, bringing legal employers directly to the College of Law. A wide range of workshops, panels, and speakers also are made available to students throughout the academic year. In addition, the Career Services library contains countless resources to assist with career planning and job searches.

Historically, most Willamette graduates choose careers in private practice. Graduates in government-related practice, including judicial clerkships, compose the next largest group. Business and industry attract the third largest group. Most graduates remain in the Pacific Northwest because of the region's unique lifestyle and natural environment. While the Willamette alumni network is strongest in Oregon and Washington, Career Services provides a comprehensive national job-search service. Thus, Willamette graduates practice nationwide, from Hawaii to Washington, DC; from Alaska to Florida; and internationally, as well.

Location

Willamette University is situated in the heart of Salem, Oregon's capital. Salem is home to a large, active legal community that readily employs and actively mentors Willamette law students. With 150,000 residents, Salem is neither a small college town nor a big city. This historic riverfront city offers all the amenities of a larger city, but has successfully maintained its hometown charm. A welcoming and affordable city, Salem boasts a vibrant downtown area, beautiful city parks, an innovative children's museum and popular community theater, great pubs and cafés, fine dining, numerous coffeehouses and microbreweries, and a wide range of small boutiques and department stores.

Salem is surrounded by award-winning vineyards and orchards that support countless wine and food festivals. The city is only a short drive from numerous beautiful state parks that provide wilderness hiking, fishing, camping, and winter sports. The desert is a little farther east, and Oregon's spectacular coast is an hour's drive to the west. Metropolitan Portland is just 45 minutes to the north, offering easy access to national sporting events and premier music and art venues.

Applicant Profile Not Available

William & Mary Law School

613 South Henry Street
Williamsburg, VA 23185
Phone: 757.221.3785; Fax: 757.221.3261
E-mail: lawadm@wm.edu; Website: http://law.wm.edu

ABA
Approved
Since
1932

The Basics

Type of school	Public
Term	Semester
Application deadline	3/1
Application fee	$50
Financial aid deadline	2/15
Can first year start other than fall?	No
Student to faculty ratio	15.7 to 1
# of housing spaces available restricted to law students	
graduate housing for which law students are eligible	117

Faculty and Administrators

	Total		Men		Women		Minorities	
	Spr	Fall	Spr	Fall	Spr	Fall	Spr	Fall
Full-time	31	35	19	23	12	12	5	7
Other full-time	4	5	1	2	3	3	0	0
Deans, librarians, & others who teach	10	10	6	6	4	4	0	0
Part-time	60	43	45	31	14	12	3	4
Total	105	93	71	62	33	31	8	11

Curriculum

		Full-Time	Part-Time
Typical first-year section size		70	0
Is there typically a "small section" of the first-year class, other than Legal Writing, taught by full-time faculty		Yes	No
If yes, typical size offered last year		16	
# of classroom course titles beyond first-year curriculum		129	
# of upper division courses, excluding seminars, with an enrollment:	Under 25	127	
	25–49	33	
	50–74	12	
	75–99	1	
	100+	6	
# of seminars		33	
# of seminar positions available		564	
# of seminar positions filled		458	0
# of positions available in simulation courses		613	
# of simulation positions filled		613	0
# of positions available in faculty supervised clinical courses		66	
# of faculty supervised clinical positions filled	61		0
# involved in field placements		147	0
# involved in law journals		249	0
# involved in moot court or trial competitions	92		0
# of credit hours required to graduate		86	

JD Enrollment and Ethnicity

	Men		Women		Full-Time		Part-Time		1st-Year		Total		JD Degs. Awd.
	#	%	#	%	#	%	#	%	#	%	#	%	
African Amer.	23	7.2	53	17.2	76	12.1	0	0.0	24	11.3	76	12.1	21
Amer. Indian	0	0.0	0	0.0	0	0.0	0	0.0	0	0.0	0	0.0	0
Asian Amer.	10	3.1	8	2.6	18	2.9	0	0.0	9	4.2	18	2.9	6
Mex. Amer.	0	0.0	0	0.0	0	0.0	0	0.0	0	0.0	0	0.0	0
Puerto Rican	0	0.0	0	0.0	0	0.0	0	0.0	0	0.0	0	0.0	0
Hispanic	3	0.9	2	0.6	5	0.8	0	0.0	1	0.5	5	0.8	3
Total Minority	36	11.3	63	20.5	99	15.8	0	0.0	34	16.0	99	15.8	30
For. Nation.	3	0.9	3	1.0	6	1.0	0	0.0	3	1.4	6	1.0	1
Caucasian	207	65.1	197	64.0	404	64.5	0	0.0	129	60.6	404	64.5	125
Unknown	72	22.6	45	14.6	117	18.7	0	0.0	46	21.6	117	18.7	36
Total	318	50.8	308	49.2	626	100.0	0	0.0	213	34.0	626		192

Transfers

Transfers in	3
Transfers out	6

Tuition and Fees

	Resident	Nonresident
Full-time	$21,646	$31,846
Part-time		
Tuition Guarantee Program	N	

Living Expenses

Estimated living expenses for singles

Living on campus	Living off campus	Living at home
$14,950	$14,950	$14,950

William & Mary Law School

ABA
Approved
Since
1932

GPA and LSAT Scores

	Total	Full-Time	Part-Time
# of apps	4,980	4,980	0
# of offers	1,109	1,109	0
# of matrics	209	209	0
75% GPA	3.77	3.77	0.00
Median GPA	3.66	3.66	0.00
25% GPA	3.42	3.42	0.00
75% LSAT	166	166	0
Median LSAT	165	165	0
25% LSAT	161	161	0

Grants and Scholarships (from prior year)

	Total		Full-Time		Part-Time	
	#	%	#	%	#	%
Total # of students	628		626		2	
Total # receiving grants	255	40.6	255	40.7	0	0.0
Less than 1/2 tuition	242	38.5	242	38.7	0	0.0
Half to full tuition	13	2.1	13	2.1	0	0.0
Full tuition	0	0.0	0	0.0	0	0.0
More than full tuition	0	0.0	0	0.0	0	0.0
Median grant amount			$6,000		$0	

Informational and Library Resources

Total amount spent on library materials	$1,069,221
Study seating capacity inside the library	568
# of full-time equivalent professional librarians	9
Hours per week library is open	168
# of open, wired connections available to students	68
# of networked computers available for use by students	43
Has wireless network?	Y
Require computer?	N

JD Attrition (from prior year)

	Academic	Other	Total	
	#	#	#	%
1st year	0	9	9	4.1
2nd year	0	1	1	0.5
3rd year	0	1	1	0.5
4th year	0	0	0	0.0

Employment (9 months after graduation)

	Total	Percentage
Employment status known	209	99.5
Employment status unknown	1	0.5
Employed	193	92.3
Pursuing graduate degrees	5	2.4
Unemployed (seeking, not seeking, or studying for the bar)	6	2.9
Type of Employment		
# employed in law firms	116	60.1
# employed in business and industry	13	6.7
# employed in government	29	15.0
# employed in public interest	8	4.1
# employed as judicial clerks	27	14.0
# employed in academia	0	0.0
Geographic Location		
# employed in state	71	36.8
# employed in foreign countries	1	0.5
# of states where employed	25	

Bar Passage Rates

First-time takers	201	Reporting %	71.14
Average school %	90.91	Average state %	83.55
Average pass difference	7.36		

Jurisdiction	Takers	Passers	Pass %	State %	Diff %
Virginia	99	88	88.89	82.70	6.19
New York	27	27	100.00	88.98	11.02
California	10	9	90.00	78.07	11.93
North Carolina	7	6	85.71	82.61	3.10

William & Mary Law School

613 South Henry Street
Williamsburg, VA 23185
Phone: 757.221.3785; Fax: 757.221.3261
E-mail: lawadm@wm.edu; Website: http://law.wm.edu

■ Introduction

Established in 1779 at the request of Thomas Jefferson, William & Mary Law School is the nation's oldest law school. William & Mary combines rich historic roots, a strong national reputation, and a wealth of programs at a cost rated to be "a very good buy." William & Mary is concerned for students' intellectual development as well as for helping them develop character and values as constructive citizens who will do their part in society. Many assume William & Mary is a private school—it is not. The Law School is small enough for people to know one another by name and large enough to form a critical mass for learning and scholarship.

Members of the 2009–2010 student body earned undergraduate degrees from 264 colleges and universities and represent 46 states, DC, and 12 other countries. The Law School is located a few blocks from Colonial Williamsburg and within short driving distance of the metropolitan areas of Washington, DC; Richmond; and Norfolk. Visits and student tours are encouraged.

■ Library and Physical Facilities

The Wolf Law Library's collection of nearly 400,000 volumes and its service-oriented staff provide an excellent setting for study and research. Legal materials are available in all formats, including an extensive treatise collection covering all areas of law. A major library expansion and renovation project was recently completed and has resulted in a new modern facility with cutting-edge technology. Features of the library include two reading rooms offering ample views of the outdoors, six lounges, abundant seating with Internet access, 12 group-study rooms, two computer labs, a rare book room, and a game room. The entire building is Wi-Fi compatible.

The McGlothlin Courtroom at the Law School is the nation's most technologically advanced trial and appellate chamber. The courtroom is designed to permit trials with multiple remote appearances and Web-based evidence, and offers students hands-on training in the use of state-of-the-art courtroom technology. It has a wide variety of features, including all available major court record systems, evidence presentation technologies, assistive and foreign language interpretation technologies, and critical infrastructure technologies.

The Law School is located between the National Center for State Courts and William & Mary's graduate apartment complex, where 20 percent of law students live. A wide variety of off-campus housing options are available in the Williamsburg area.

■ Curriculum

The required first-year curriculum includes constitutional law, contracts, torts, civil procedure, property, criminal law, and legal skills. The Legal Skills Program utilizes simulated law offices, client representation, and mock trials to teach the skills necessary for the practice of law as well as legal research, writing, and professional responsibility. To earn a Juris Doctor degree, students must successfully complete 86 credit hours through full-time study, all required courses, and a significant paper of publishable quality. Students may choose yearly from more than 100 upper-level courses covering a broad range of contemporary and traditional areas of law. The Law School offers seven clinical programs (legal aid clinic, domestic violence clinic, federal tax practice clinic, innocence project clinic, appellate litigation clinic, special education advocacy clinic, and the veterans' benefits clinic) and a wide variety of externships, including externships at the Virginia Attorney General's Office, the Virginia Court of Appeals, and the Virginia General Assembly. Students also can extern with federal and state judges; federal, state, and local government agencies; private nonprofit organizations; law firms; and in-house corporate law departments.

■ Joint-Degree Programs

There are three joint-degree programs: JD/MBA, JD/MPP, and JD/MA in American Studies. The JD/MBA and the JD/MPP combine traditional five-year programs into four years of study. Students may complete the JD/MA in either three or four years.

■ International Programs

A summer session in Madrid, Spain, offers a five-week program in which students can earn up to six credits. William & Mary professors and prominent Spanish professors and practitioners teach the courses in English. JD students may also study abroad in Beijing, China; Vienna, Austria; Madrid, Spain; Auckland, New Zealand; Tokyo, Japan; Luxembourg; and Hong Kong during their third academic year.

The Law School also offers an LLM in the American Legal System for students from outside the United States who take courses with the JD students and bring the richness of their legal traditions to the classroom.

■ Special Programs

Through the Institute of Bill of Rights Law, the Law School has become one of the preeminent institutions studying the Constitution's Bill of Rights. The Institute sponsors lectures, symposia, and publications that entice scholars to examine important constitutional issues. The programs and initiatives of the Center for Legal and Court Technology seek to improve the administration of justice through the use of technology. The Center puts the latest technology to the test each year in a laboratory trial conducted by students in the McGlothlin Courtroom.

Exciting new cocurricular programs at the Law School include the Human Security Law Program, which offers students the opportunity to learn about the interplay between national defense and the protection of civil rights; the Program in Comparative Legal Studies and Post-Conflict Justice, which serves as a focal point for research and study on comparative legal practices and the mechanisms used to reestablish justice after war and internal strife; the Property Rights Project, which encourages scholarship on the role that property rights plays in society and also facilitates the exchange of ideas between scholars and practitioners; the Election Law Program, which seeks to provide assistance to judges who are called upon to resolve difficult election law

disputes; and the George Wythe Society of Citizen Lawyers, a program that focuses on constructive citizenship.

The Loan Repayment Assistance Program provides up to $5,000 in loan forgiveness annually for a maximum of three years to selected graduates working full time for civil legal service organizations, public defenders or prosecutors, government agencies, or other 501(c)(3) organizations with a public service mission.

■ Student Activities

Scholars and practitioners frequently cite articles from our student-managed academic journals. These publications include *William and Mary Law Review, William & Mary Bill of Rights Journal, William & Mary Business Law Review, William & Mary Environmental Law and Policy Review,* and *William & Mary Journal of Women and the Law.* The Law School also has a highly competitive Moot Court Program and National Trial Team. In 2009, William & Mary students won first place at the Tulane Sports Law Appellate Moot Court Competition and first place in the Gourley Trial Competition in Pittsburgh, PA. More than 40 student organizations reflect the diverse interests of the student body. For more information about

William & Mary's student organizations, visit the Student Life section of the website.

■ Career Services

The Office of Career Services (OCS) provides students and alumni with comprehensive professional services, including individual counseling, speakers, workshops, and programs. Employers from 40 states, the District of Columbia, and 12 other countries conducted on-campus interviews during 2008–2009. Students also use our video conference technology for employment interviews. Nearly 2,000 nonvisiting employers from 50 states, the District of Columbia, and several other countries listed jobs through OCS. In 2008, William & Mary students also had the opportunity to participate in 34 off-campus job fairs with a national employer base, including events in Atlanta, Boston, Chicago, Dallas, Los Angeles, and New York, as well as specialized programs for intellectual property law, public interest and governmental positions, and regional firms.

The Law School awarded 105 fellowships to assist students working in low-paying or nonpaying public service positions during the summer of 2009.

Applicant Profile

William & Mary Law School
This grid includes only applicants who earned 120–180 LSAT scores under standard administrations.

LSAT Score	3.75 +		3.50–3.74		3.25–3.49		3.00–3.24		2.75–2.99		2.50–2.74		2.25–2.49		2.00–2.24		Below 2.00		No GPA		Total	
	Apps	Adm	Apps	Adm	Apps	Adm	Apps	Adm	Apps	Adm	Apps	Adm	Apps	Adm	Apps	Adm	Apps	Adm	Apps	Adm	Apps	Adm
175–180	7	7	5	5	4	4	5	4	2	1	0	0	0	0	1	0	0	0	0	0	24	21
170–174	48	48	22	18	42	32	23	12	17	1	7	0	1	0	0	0	1	0	1	1	162	112
165–169	225	220	221	197	181	93	101	20	57	5	18	1	17	0	1	0	0	0	12	3	833	539
160–164	473	184	526	101	427	26	244	11	85	3	35	1	19	0	6	0	1	0	42	2	1858	328
155–159	219	19	335	18	259	9	136	6	56	1	30	0	12	0	4	0	0	0	35	0	1086	53
150–154	86	2	132	10	125	8	83	9	48	3	23	0	14	0	4	1	0	0	10	0	525	33
145–149	28	2	58	4	51	4	57	3	32	0	20	0	13	1	3	0	1	0	14	0	277	14
140–144	8	1	21	1	21	1	16	0	29	0	15	0	6	0	2	0	0	0	6	0	124	3
135–139	1	0	5	0	7	0	8	0	3	0	6	0	5	0	4	0	1	0	1	0	41	0
130–134	0	0	0	0	3	0	0	0	5	0	1	0	2	0	2	0	0	0	0	0	15	0
125–129	0	0	0	0	0	0	0	0	2	0	0	0	0	0	0	0	0	0	0	0	2	0
120–124	0	0	0	0	0	0	0	0	1	0	0	0	0	0	0	0	0	0	0	0	1	0
Total	1095	483	1325	354	1120	177	675	65	334	14	158	2	89	1	27	1	4	0	121	6	4948	1103

Apps = Number of Applicants
Adm = Number Admitted
Reflects 99% of the total applicant pool; average LSAT data reported.

William Mitchell College of Law

Office of Admissions, 875 Summit Avenue
St. Paul, MN 55105
Phone: 651.290.6476; Toll-free: 888.WMCL.LAW; Fax: 651.290.7535
E-mail: admissions@wmitchell.edu; Website: www.wmitchell.edu

ABA
Approved
Since
1938

The Basics

Type of school	Private
Term	Semester
Application deadline	5/1
Application fee	$50
Financial aid deadline	3/15
Can first year start other than fall?	No
Student to faculty ratio	20.1 to 1
# of housing spaces available restricted to law students	
graduate housing for which law students are eligible	

Faculty and Administrators

	Total		Men		Women		Minorities	
	Spr	Fall	Spr	Fall	Spr	Fall	Spr	Fall
Full-time	34	36	20	18	14	18	6	5
Other full-time	1	1	0	0	1	1	0	0
Deans, librarians, & others who teach	9	9	4	4	5	5	1	1
Part-time	234	229	132	134	102	95	56	60
Total	278	275	156	156	122	119	63	66

Curriculum

		Full-Time	Part-Time
Typical first-year section size		80	80
Is there typically a "small section" of the first-year class, other than Legal Writing, taught by full-time faculty		Yes	Yes
If yes, typical size offered last year		12	12
# of classroom course titles beyond first-year curriculum		149	
# of upper division courses, excluding seminars, with an enrollment:	Under 25	123	
	25–49	54	
	50–74	23	
	75–99	5	
	100+	0	
# of seminars		99	
# of seminar positions available		1,969	
# of seminar positions filled		794	559
# of positions available in simulation courses		1,789	
# of simulation positions filled		1,056	510
# of positions available in faculty supervised clinical courses		367	
# of faculty supervised clinical positions filled		226	112
# involved in field placements		125	63
# involved in law journals		50	26
# involved in moot court or trial competitions		88	36
# of credit hours required to graduate		86	

JD Enrollment and Ethnicity

	Men		Women		Full-Time		Part-Time		1st-Year		Total		JD Degs. Awd.
	#	%	#	%	#	%	#	%	#	%	#	%	
African Amer.	10	2.0	12	2.5	11	1.8	11	2.9	5	1.7	22	2.3	14
Amer. Indian	4	0.8	6	1.2	6	1.0	4	1.1	3	1.0	10	1.0	1
Asian Amer.	22	4.5	25	5.1	20	3.3	27	7.2	16	5.3	47	4.8	15
Mex. Amer.	4	0.8	1	0.2	4	0.7	1	0.3	2	0.7	5	0.5	1
Puerto Rican	0	0.0	1	0.2	0	0.0	1	0.3	0	0.0	1	0.1	0
Hispanic	4	0.8	5	1.0	5	0.8	4	1.1	6	2.0	9	0.9	8
Total Minority	44	9.0	50	10.3	46	7.6	48	12.8	32	10.6	94	9.6	39
For. Nation.	4	0.8	0	0.0	1	0.2	3	0.8	0	0.0	4	0.4	3
Caucasian	342	69.7	361	74.3	444	73.6	259	69.3	234	77.7	703	72.0	242
Unknown	101	20.6	75	15.4	112	18.6	64	17.1	35	11.6	176	18.0	43
Total	491	50.3	486	49.7	603	61.7	374	38.3	301	30.8	977		327

Transfers

Transfers in	1
Transfers out	9

Tuition and Fees

	Resident	Nonresident
Full-time	$32,340	$32,340
Part-time	$23,400	$23,400
Tuition Guarantee Program		N

Living Expenses

Estimated living expenses for singles

Living on campus	Living off campus	Living at home
N/A	$16,850	N/A

William Mitchell College of Law

ABA
Approved
Since
1938

GPA and LSAT Scores

	Total	Full-Time	Part-Time
# of apps	1,395	1,268	424
# of offers	792	602	190
# of matrics	300	197	103
75% GPA	3.60	3.67	3.48
Median GPA	3.40	3.49	3.26
25% GPA	3.19	3.29	2.95
75% LSAT	158	159	154
Median LSAT	155	156	150
25% LSAT	150	154	147

Grants and Scholarships (from prior year)

	Total		Full-Time		Part-Time	
	#	%	#	%	#	%
Total # of students	1,031		644		387	
Total # receiving grants	343	33.3	249	38.7	94	24.3
Less than 1/2 tuition	160	15.5	110	17.1	50	12.9
Half to full tuition	169	16.4	133	20.7	36	9.3
Full tuition	14	1.4	6	0.9	8	2.1
More than full tuition	0	0.0	0	0.0	0	0.0
Median grant amount			$19,923		$9,143	

Informational and Library Resources

Total amount spent on library materials	$1,186,993
Study seating capacity inside the library	671
# of full-time equivalent professional librarians	8
Hours per week library is open	109
# of open, wired connections available to students	175
# of networked computers available for use by students	69
Has wireless network?	Y
Require computer?	N

JD Attrition (from prior year)

	Academic	Other	Total	
	#	#	#	%
1st year	8	21	29	9.1
2nd year	0	3	3	1.0
3rd year	0	0	0	0.0
4th year	0	0	0	0.0

Employment (9 months after graduation)

	Total	Percentage
Employment status known	317	99.7
Employment status unknown	1	0.3
Employed	289	91.2
Pursuing graduate degrees	3	0.9
Unemployed (seeking, not seeking, or studying for the bar)	9	2.8
Type of Employment		
# employed in law firms	147	50.9
# employed in business and industry	75	26.0
# employed in government	22	7.6
# employed in public interest	10	3.5
# employed as judicial clerks	27	9.3
# employed in academia	4	1.4
Geographic Location		
# employed in state	244	84.4
# employed in foreign countries	0	0.0
# of states where employed	15	

Bar Passage Rates

First-time takers	310	Reporting %	96.77
Average school %	90.33	Average state %	91.13
Average pass difference	−0.80		

Jurisdiction	Takers	Passers	Pass %	State %	Diff %
Minnesota	284	255	89.79	91.09	−1.30
Wisconsin	16	16	100.00	91.79	8.21

William Mitchell College of Law

Office of Admissions, 875 Summit Avenue
St. Paul, MN 55105
Phone: 651.290.6476; Toll-free: 888.WMCL.LAW; Fax: 651.290.7535
E-mail: admissions@wmitchell.edu; Website: www.wmitchell.edu

■ Introduction

William Mitchell College of Law, founded in 1900, is an independent, private law school in St. Paul, Minnesota. Named for one of the state's most respected judges, William Mitchell has pioneered a legal education that integrates practical skills with legal theory. William Mitchell welcomes both traditional and nontraditional law students from all walks of life, and students have an option of attending on a full- or part-time basis. William Mitchell College of Law's clinical, legal writing, and trial advocacy programs are nationally recognized. The college has produced many distinguished leaders at the bench and bar and in the business and civic arenas, among them the 15th Chief Justice of the United States, Warren E. Burger, and the first woman to serve on the Minnesota Supreme Court, Rosalie E. Wahl. The largest law school in Minnesota, William Mitchell has approximately 1,000 students, 39 full-time faculty members, and more than 11,000 alumni. William Mitchell has more alumni serving in the Minnesota judiciary than any other law school.

The college is accredited by the ABA, is a member of the AALS, and is approved by the US Veterans Administration.

■ Faculty

From day one, William Mitchell faculty members treat students as future colleagues. Faculty members are known for their teaching, scholarship, and practice. Faculty members have served on the bench, worked in the region's top law firms, and have had careers in public service, government, and corporations. William Mitchell professors have written many of the books used by law school professors and legal practitioners throughout the country. Faculty briefs and research have been accessed thousands of times by legal scholars, and professors are regularly quoted by national and international media. Many professors are exploring new ground on issues such as cyber law, intellectual property, national security, elder law, family law, and food safety. Adjunct professors, who practice at 18 of the top 25 law firms in the state, bring real-world practice to the classroom and connection to the practice of law.

■ Academics

William Mitchell students graduate with the practical wisdom to put the law to work. For 109 years, William Mitchell has pioneered a legal education that integrates practical skills with legal theory. William Mitchell requires students to take practical skills courses, including clinics, practicum, legal writing and research, and advocacy. In fact, William Mitchell was one of the first schools to develop a clinical program more than 30 years ago. Our clinical, legal writing, and trial advocacy programs are highly rated on a national level.

In addition to more than 200 law school courses, William Mitchell has several programs designed to help law students transition to lawyers. Keystone courses, generally taken in the final year of law school, address real-world challenges, building on previous courses, and enable students to produce substantial, concrete manifestations of their learning. The Fellows Program links exceptional students with a faculty member whose research and activities are changing the law itself. Students receive specialized training beyond the regular curriculum and have access to a range of special intellectual opportunities and networking events. And, Pathways to the Profession of Law™ is an innovative Web application that helps law students customize their course schedules, integrate their learning, and build experiences toward legal practice.

To focus faculty scholarship, spur collaboration between legal education and the profession, and continue its tradition of innovative teaching, William Mitchell has developed academic centers in critical areas of the legal profession, including the Intellectual Property Institute, Center for Negotiation and Justice, Center for Elder Justice and Policy, Rosalie Wahl Legal Practice Center, Public Health Law Center, and National Security Forum.

■ Enrollment Options

William Mitchell was started as a night law school by working attorneys more than a century ago to provide legal training for people of modest means. If not for the part-time, evening tradition at William Mitchell, many successful lawyers practicing today would not have been able to pursue their law school dreams. William Mitchell is the only law school in the region with a night school program, allowing students to continue to work to help pay for school, gain work experience, and balance family life. After the first year, students have the option to switch between full- and part-time enrollment as often as each semester to accommodate work experience and family life. Regardless of enrollment status, you achieve the same high-quality education. Advanced and elective classes are typically offered in the evening, so part-time and full-time students take classes together and have equal access to full-time and adjunct faculty. Although classes meet at set times, William Mitchell offers you enough flexibility to build your law school schedule around a clerkship, continue in your current career track or day job, or take care of other responsibilities.

■ Library and Physical Facilities

The Minneapolis-St. Paul region is home to 20 Fortune 500 companies and is frequently cited as one of the top 10 places to live and work in the United States. William Mitchell's campus is located in St. Paul, the state capital, along the historic and elegant Summit Avenue. The campus is a short walk to the lively Grand Avenue with restaurants and shopping, and many students find housing in the neighborhood.

The physical design of the campus as a whole mirrors the William Mitchell philosophy that practical skills are inseparable from legal doctrine. Our Rosalie Wahl Legal Practice Center, home to our top-rated clinical and skills programs, is located in the same building as classrooms and faculty offices. The campus is also equipped with technologically advanced moot courtrooms, computer labs, seminar rooms, student lounge and cafeteria, and offices for student organizations.

The Warren E. Burger Library's extensive in-house and online collection, customer service-oriented staff, and welcoming design make it the preferred choice for alumni,

legal professionals, and faculty. Nearly all of our professional librarians have JD degrees, in addition to master's of library and information science degrees. Several have law practice experience. Our librarians help plan research strategies, locate and use legal and nonlegal resources, do computer-assisted research, and find items that are not available at William Mitchell. You'll also find our librarians in the classroom. Extended reference desk hours reflect our commitment to the needs of our students, faculty, and alumni.

■ Public Service Opportunities

William Mitchell's heritage is rooted in public service. Students volunteer more than 6,000 hours of supervised pro bono service each year to our partner, the Minnesota Justice Foundation, which matches interested law students with volunteer opportunities. Students also perform approximately 14,000 hours of pro bono service annually through our for-credit legal clinical program.

■ Special Programs

In addition to hosting **Mitchell in London** in 2010, William Mitchell is a member of the Consortium for Innovative Legal Education, a consortium of four independent law schools, which provides students with the opportunity to enroll in 10 summer and semester study-abroad programs, as well as the opportunity to study as visiting students at any of the participating schools. The **Academic Achievement Program** is designed to help students work up to their potential by teaching the skills required to solve problems effectively. Individual academic advising and Academic Achievement Workshops are available throughout the year for all students. The workshops include study strategies, time and stress management, critical reading, case briefing, legal analysis, outlining, and exam taking.

■ Student Body

William Mitchell attracts students with a diversity of life and work experiences. That's what we call the "Mitchell Mix." Our students have all kinds of educational, professional, and cultural backgrounds. For example, students range in age from 20 to 56 and include recent college grads and students who bring professional work experience. Twenty-seven of our entering class hold graduate degrees, and 11 percent are people of color. Our student body represents 23 states and 22 foreign countries. Students can participate in more than 30 student organizations, including the Student Bar Association and the *William Mitchell Law Review*.

■ Career Development

William Mitchell's brand of legal education has earned the school a reputation for graduating lawyers who are prepared to practice. That's why 96.98 percent of the class of 2008 was employed within nine months of graduation. Career development is woven into each year of a student's legal education, helping students polish presentation, networking, and interviewing skills. Our alumni network of more than 11,000 offers students extensive opportunities to gather advice, meet attorneys, and learn about job opportunities both during school and upon graduation.

■ Scholarships/Financial Aid

Financial aid is available from William Mitchell in the form of merit-based scholarships, federal and alternative loans, and federal work-study. Approximately 90 percent of all William Mitchell students receive some type of financial aid.

Applicant Profile

William Mitchell College of Law
This grid includes only applicants who earned 120–180 LSAT scores under standard administrations.

LSAT Score	GPA																					
	3.75 +		3.50–3.74		3.25–3.49		3.00–3.24		2.75–2.99		2.50–2.74		2.25–2.49		2.00–2.24		Below 2.00		No GPA		Total	
	Apps	Adm	Apps	Adm	Apps	Adm	Apps	Adm	Apps	Adm	Apps	Adm	Apps	Adm	Apps	Adm	Apps	Adm	Apps	Adm	Apps	Adm
175–180	0	0	0	0	0	0	0	0	0	0	1	1	0	0	0	0	0	0	0	0	1	1
170–174	2	2	1	1	1	1	0	0	1	1	0	0	0	0	0	0	0	0	0	0	5	5
165–169	7	6	7	7	7	6	8	7	3	3	2	2	0	0	1	1	0	0	0	0	35	32
160–164	31	31	35	35	26	26	18	18	10	9	2	2	5	4	1	0	0	0	0	0	128	125
155–159	38	37	51	51	76	74	44	40	29	23	15	9	9	5	2	1	2	2	4	1	270	243
150–154	46	46	88	74	79	53	79	45	41	14	27	13	13	2	5	0	0	0	3	3	381	250
145–149	21	16	47	30	71	29	74	16	42	8	33	2	14	0	7	0	0	0	2	0	311	101
140–144	11	5	13	8	39	16	43	4	25	0	21	0	13	0	1	0	1	0	5	0	172	33
135–139	4	2	3	0	15	0	7	0	13	0	10	0	5	0	2	0	0	0	5	0	64	2
130–134	0	0	1	0	2	1	2	0	2	0	2	0	3	0	0	0	0	0	4	0	16	1
125–129	0	0	0	0	1	0	0	0	0	0	3	0	0	0	1	0	0	0	2	0	7	0
120–124	0	0	0	0	0	0	0	0	0	0	0	0	0	0	1	0	0	0	1	0	2	0
Total	160	145	246	206	317	206	275	130	166	58	116	29	62	11	21	2	3	2	26	4	1392	793

Apps = Number of Applicants   Adm = Number Admitted   Reflects 99% of the total applicant pool; average LSAT data reported.

University of Wisconsin Law School

975 Bascom Mall
Madison, WI 53706
Phone: 608.262.5914; Fax: 608.263.3190
E-mail: admissions@law.wisc.edu; Website: www.law.wisc.edu

ABA
Approved
Since
1923

The Basics

Type of school	Public
Term	Semester
Application deadline	3/1
Application fee	$56
Financial aid deadline	3/1
Can first year start other than fall?	No
Student to faculty ratio	12.8 to 1
# of housing spaces available restricted to law students graduate housing for which law students are eligible	974

Faculty and Administrators

	Total		Men		Women		Minorities	
	Spr	Fall	Spr	Fall	Spr	Fall	Spr	Fall
Full-time	52	50	30	28	22	22	13	12
Other full-time	7	8	2	2	5	6	1	1
Deans, librarians, & others who teach	6	6	4	5	2	1	0	1
Part-time	66	59	42	31	24	28	20	13
Total	131	123	78	66	53	57	34	27

JD Enrollment and Ethnicity

	Men		Women		Full-Time		Part-Time		1st-Year		Total		JD Degs. Awd.
	#	%	#	%	#	%	#	%	#	%	#	%	
African Amer.	26	5.8	32	8.4	58	7.3	0	0.0	23	8.1	58	7.0	22
Amer. Indian	11	2.5	9	2.4	20	2.5	0	0.0	5	1.8	20	2.4	9
Asian Amer.	32	7.2	29	7.6	56	7.1	5	15.2	22	7.7	61	7.4	18
Mex. Amer.	15	3.4	19	5.0	34	4.3	0	0.0	15	5.3	34	4.1	9
Puerto Rican	2	0.4	9	2.4	11	1.4	0	0.0	4	1.4	11	1.3	5
Hispanic	7	1.6	5	1.3	12	1.5	0	0.0	4	1.4	12	1.5	14
Total Minority	93	20.9	103	27.1	191	24.1	5	15.2	73	25.6	196	23.8	77
For. Nation.	7	1.6	15	3.9	22	2.8	0	0.0	11	3.9	22	2.7	6
Caucasian	310	69.7	249	65.5	532	67.2	27	81.8	183	64.2	559	67.8	177
Unknown	35	7.9	13	3.4	47	5.9	1	3.0	18	6.3	48	5.8	15
Total	445	53.9	380	46.1	792	96.0	33	4.0	285	34.5	825		275

Curriculum

	Full-Time	Part-Time
Typical first-year section size	71	0
Is there typically a "small section" of the first-year class, other than Legal Writing, taught by full-time faculty	Yes	No
If yes, typical size offered last year	21	
# of classroom course titles beyond first-year curriculum	167	

# of upper division courses, excluding seminars, with an enrollment:		
	Under 25	123
	25–49	48
	50–74	15
	75–99	6
	100+	6

# of seminars	86	
# of seminar positions available	1,295	
# of seminar positions filled	916	0
# of positions available in simulation courses	606	
# of simulation positions filled	484	0
# of positions available in faculty supervised clinical courses	402	
# of faculty supervised clinical positions filled	375	0
# involved in field placements	198	0
# involved in law journals	183	0
# involved in moot court or trial competitions	172	0
# of credit hours required to graduate	90	

Transfers

Transfers in	26
Transfers out	6

Tuition and Fees

	Resident	Nonresident
Full-time	$16,426	$36,350
Part-time	$1,372	$3,032
Tuition Guarantee Program	N	

Living Expenses

Estimated living expenses for singles

Living on campus	Living off campus	Living at home
$16,990	$16,990	$9,832

*Part-time tuition and fees per credit.

University of Wisconsin Law School

ABA Approved Since 1923

GPA and LSAT Scores

	Total	Full-Time	Part-Time
# of apps	2,936	2,936	0
# of offers	697	697	0
# of matrics	278	278	0
75% GPA	3.76	3.76	0.00
Median GPA	3.60	3.60	0.00
25% GPA	3.31	3.31	0.00
75% LSAT	163	163	0
Median LSAT	162	162	0
25% LSAT	156	156	0

Grants and Scholarships (from prior year)

	Total #	Total %	Full-Time #	Full-Time %	Part-Time #	Part-Time %
Total # of students	811		788		23	
Total # receiving grants	218	26.9	218	27.7	0	0.0
Less than 1/2 tuition	89	11.0	89	11.3	0	0.0
Half to full tuition	86	10.6	86	10.9	0	0.0
Full tuition	4	0.5	4	0.5	0	0.0
More than full tuition	39	4.8	39	4.9	0	0.0
Median grant amount			$12,000		$0	

Informational and Library Resources

Total amount spent on library materials	$1,143,321
Study seating capacity inside the library	613
# of full-time equivalent professional librarians	11
Hours per week library is open	104
# of open, wired connections available to students	526
# of networked computers available for use by students	74
Has wireless network?	Y
Require computer?	Y

JD Attrition (from prior year)

	Academic #	Other #	Total #	Total %
1st year	2	9	11	4.2
2nd year	1	0	1	0.4
3rd year	0	0	0	0.0
4th year	0	0	0	0.0

Employment (9 months after graduation)

	Total	Percentage
Employment status known	290	100.0
Employment status unknown	0	0.0
Employed	279	96.2
Pursuing graduate degrees	2	0.7
Unemployed (seeking, not seeking, or studying for the bar)	5	1.7
Type of Employment		
# employed in law firms	162	58.1
# employed in business and industry	34	12.2
# employed in government	43	15.4
# employed in public interest	19	6.8
# employed as judicial clerks	16	5.7
# employed in academia	5	1.8
Geographic Location		
# employed in state	142	50.9
# employed in foreign countries	8	2.9
# of states where employed	26	

Bar Passage Rates

First-time takers	288	Reporting %	100.00
Average school %	99.31	Average state %	91.79
Average pass difference	7.52		

Jurisdiction	Takers	Passers	Pass %	State %	Diff %
Wisconsin	288	286	99.31	91.79	7.52

University of Wisconsin Law School

975 Bascom Mall
Madison, WI 53706
Phone: 608.262.5914; Fax: 608.263.3190
E-mail: admissions@law.wisc.edu; Website: www.law.wisc.edu

■ A Preeminent Law School, A World-Class University, A Beautiful City

The UW Law School is one of the most intellectually exciting law schools in the country, attracting students from around the world. These students represent a variety of backgrounds, ages, interests, races, nationalities, and life experiences; encouraging a robust exchange of ideas.

Top applicants are drawn to the UW Law School because of its tradition of excellence, its beautiful setting in the heart of one of the world's leading research universities, and its *law-in-action* philosophy, an approach that differentiates it from other law schools.

The UW Law School is located in Madison, an affordable city strategically and conveniently situated in the middle of a triangle formed by Chicago, Minneapolis, and Milwaukee. As the state capital, Madison is home to many courts and state and federal government agencies—all within walking distance of the Law School.

■ A Commitment to Diversity and Community

A major indicator of the strength of any law school is its student body. The fall 2009 entering class of 278 students represents 29 states and 115 undergraduate institutions. Annually, approximately 40 percent of our students are from outside of Wisconsin, close to half are women, and approximately 30 percent are students of color. The UW Law School's admission policies enhance the diversity, vigor, social concern, and academic ability of the student body. There is a special feeling of community in the school and an informal, supportive atmosphere, reflecting a strong commitment by faculty and administrators to student learning, morale, and well-being.

■ The Faculty: Leading Scholars and Outstanding Teachers

The UW Law School's nationally recognized faculty come from a wide range of backgrounds and offer students strong role models and a variety of experiences. They are leading scholars who are also actively involved in the law. They advise on stem cell issues, represent clients on death row, work with congressional staffers to draft legislation, and provide legal advice to poor farmers in the South. They are interesting lawyers doing interesting things, but first and foremost, they are excellent teachers who are committed to their students. A superb clinical faculty and an experienced adjunct faculty provide additional teaching resources.

■ The Curriculum: Law in Action

Students at the UW Law School have many opportunities to experience *law-in-action*. An extensive curriculum places an emphasis on the dynamics of the law (how the law relates to social change and to society as a whole) while at the same time emphasizing skill development, particularly legal analysis and writing. The first-year small-section program teaches the fundamentals of legal analysis and reasoning in a supportive setting. In the first semester, two out of five classes—a substantive law class and a legal research and writing class—are small sections. These small sections allow for individual feedback on students' work, facilitate the formation of study groups, and foster collegiality.

In the second and third year of law school, there is time both to explore the curriculum and develop the lawyering skills needed to practice. The UW Law School is a national law school that prepares future lawyers to work wherever they choose. Students select courses from an extraordinary breadth and depth of offerings, affording them the opportunity to explore cutting-edge legal issues in the classroom and/or to apply their knowledge in one of the many clinical programs.

■ Dual-Degree Programs

Renowned for its interdisciplinary approach, the UW Law School offers many opportunities for students to combine the study of law with a graduate degree in another subject. There are many existing dual-degree programs. If one of the existing programs does not meet a student's academic needs, the Law School will help create an individualized curriculum.

■ Clinicals and Skills Training: Hands-on Learning

The UW Law School is committed to practical experience as a part of legal education. With one of the largest clinical programs in the country, the UW Law School offers a wide variety of hands-on lawyering experiences with real clients and excellent supervision. From representing low-income clients, to teaming up with medical students as advocates for newly diagnosed cancer patients, or assisting inmates in state and federal prisons, these experiences are invaluable opportunities. Judicial internships, externships, and our innovative lawyering skills program provide additional hands-on learning experiences.

■ Going Global: International Law and Study Abroad

Ten professors devote their scholarship and teaching primarily to international or comparative law, and many others integrate analysis of foreign legal developments into their domestic law courses. The Law School hosts international students and professors, bringing diverse international perspectives to the classroom, and the university has one of the largest groups of international students in the country. Students can also study with one of the nine foreign law faculties with which the Law School has exchange agreements or participate in foreign study programs of other US law schools. Additional international opportunities are available through the Law School's East Asian Legal Studies Center, established to formalize and increase the Law School's interaction in East and Southeast Asia.

■ Student Activities

More than 30 organizations provide outstanding opportunities for students to pursue their talents and interests. Several moot court competitions at the UW Law School enable students to gain experience with brief writing and oral advocacy, and three student journals—*Wisconsin Law Review, Wisconsin International Law Journal*, and *Wisconsin Journal of Law, Gender & Society*—give students an opportunity to gain invaluable training in legal research and writing.

■ Career Opportunities

Leading law firms, government agencies, businesses, and public interest organizations seek to hire UW Law School graduates. A broad range of legal employers from many major cities participate in the on-campus interview program. The Law School also participates in nine off-campus job fairs each year in New York; Washington, DC; Los Angeles; Chicago; and Minneapolis. Our students receive assistance from many of our more than 12,000 alumni throughout the country, and our graduates typically accept jobs in more than 20 different states from New York to California.

Applicant Profile

Admission to the University of Wisconsin Law School is competitive. The most recent entering class had a median LSAT score of 162 and a median GPA of 3.60. The Law School does not provide a profile chart because its admission decisions involve many factors that are not represented by undergraduate GPA and LSAT scores. The UW Law School

Admissions Committee looks at an applicant's credentials taken as a whole. While candidates with higher grades and scores tend to be admitted at higher rates, GPA and LSAT scores alone are not necessarily good predictors of admission decisions on individual applications.

University of Wyoming College of Law

Dept. 3035, 1000 E. University Avenue
Laramie, WY 82071
Phone: 307.766.6416; Fax: 307.766.6417
E-mail: lawadmis@uwyo.edu; Website: www.uwyo.edu/law

The Basics

Type of school	Public
Term	Semester
Application deadline	3/1
Application fee	$50
Financial aid deadline	3/1
Can first year start other than fall?	No
Student to faculty ratio	12.4 to 1
# of housing spaces available restricted to law students	
graduate housing for which law students are eligible	230

Faculty and Administrators

	Total		Men		Women		Minorities	
	Spr	Fall	Spr	Fall	Spr	Fall	Spr	Fall
Full-time	15	15	10	11	5	4	3	2
Other full-time	2	1	1	1	1	0	0	0
Deans, librarians, & others who teach	6	5	2	2	4	3	1	0
Part-time	8	5	4	1	4	4	0	0
Total	31	26	17	15	14	11	4	2

Curriculum

		Full-Time	Part-Time
Typical first-year section size		75	0
Is there typically a "small section" of the first-year class, other than Legal Writing, taught by full-time faculty		No	No
If yes, typical size offered last year			
# of classroom course titles beyond first-year curriculum		61	
# of upper division courses, excluding seminars, with an enrollment:	Under 25	43	
	25–49	10	
	50–74	8	
	75–99	0	
	100+	0	
# of seminars		4	
# of seminar positions available		40	
# of seminar positions filled		37	0
# of positions available in simulation courses		117	
# of simulation positions filled		111	0
# of positions available in faculty supervised clinical courses		70	
# of faculty supervised clinical positions filled	66		0
# involved in field placements		35	0
# involved in law journals		27	0
# involved in moot court or trial competitions	14		0
# of credit hours required to graduate		89	

Transfers

Transfers in	5
Transfers out	2

Tuition and Fees

	Resident	Nonresident
Full-time	$9,966	$21,156
Part-time		
Tuition Guarantee Program	N	

Living Expenses

Estimated living expenses for singles

Living on campus	Living off campus	Living at home
$14,319	$14,319	$6,794

JD Enrollment and Ethnicity

	Men		Women		Full-Time		Part-Time		1st-Year		Total		JD Degs. Awd.
	#	%	#	%	#	%	#	%	#	%	#	%	
African Amer.	1	0.9	1	0.9	2	0.9	0	0.0	1	1.2	2	0.9	2
Amer. Indian	1	0.9	1	0.9	2	0.9	0	0.0	2	2.4	2	0.9	0
Asian Amer.	3	2.6	4	3.7	7	3.1	0	0.0	1	1.2	7	3.1	1
Mex. Amer.	6	5.1	6	5.6	12	5.3	0	0.0	6	7.2	12	5.3	9
Puerto Rican	0	0.0	0	0.0	0	0.0	0	0.0	0	0.0	0	0.0	0
Hispanic	0	0.0	0	0.0	0	0.0	0	0.0	0	0.0	0	0.0	0
Total Minority	11	9.4	12	11.1	23	10.2	0	0.0	10	12.0	23	10.2	12
For. Nation.	0	0.0	1	0.9	1	0.4	0	0.0	0	0.0	1	0.4	0
Caucasian	83	70.9	83	76.9	166	73.8	0	0.0	62	74.7	166	73.8	57
Unknown	23	19.7	12	11.1	35	15.6	0	0.0	11	13.3	35	15.6	2
Total	117	52.0	108	48.0	225	100.0	0	0.0	83	36.9	225		71

University of Wyoming College of Law

ABA
Approved
Since
1923

GPA and LSAT Scores

	Total	Full-Time	Part-Time
# of apps	583	583	0
# of offers	198	198	0
# of matrics	83	83	0
75% GPA	3.68	3.68	0.00
Median GPA	3.44	3.44	0.00
25% GPA	3.25	3.25	0.00
75% LSAT	157	157	0
Median LSAT	153	153	0
25% LSAT	150	150	0

Grants and Scholarships (from prior year)

	Total		Full-Time		Part-Time	
	#	%	#	%	#	%
Total # of students	223		223		0	
Total # receiving grants	126	56.5	126	56.5	0	0.0
Less than 1/2 tuition	111	49.8	111	49.8	0	0.0
Half to full tuition	14	6.3	14	6.3	0	0.0
Full tuition	1	0.4	1	0.4	0	0.0
More than full tuition	0	0.0	0	0.0	0	0.0
Median grant amount			$2,000		$0	

Informational and Library Resources

Total amount spent on library materials	$814,201
Study seating capacity inside the library	282
# of full-time equivalent professional librarians	3
Hours per week library is open	107
# of open, wired connections available to students	326
# of networked computers available for use by students	54
Has wireless network?	Y
Require computer?	N

JD Attrition (from prior year)

	Academic	Other	Total	
	#	#	#	%
1st year	1	3	4	5.1
2nd year	0	0	0	0.0
3rd year	0	0	0	0.0
4th year	0	0	0	0.0

Employment (9 months after graduation)

	Total	Percentage
Employment status known	70	98.6
Employment status unknown	1	1.4
Employed	59	84.3
Pursuing graduate degrees	3	4.3
Unemployed (seeking, not seeking, or studying for the bar)	7	10.0
Type of Employment		
# employed in law firms	24	40.7
# employed in business and industry	9	15.3
# employed in government	10	16.9
# employed in public interest	4	6.8
# employed as judicial clerks	8	13.6
# employed in academia	1	1.7
Geographic Location		
# employed in state	35	59.3
# employed in foreign countries	0	0.0
# of states where employed	9	

Bar Passage Rates

First-time takers	73	Reporting %	84.93
Average school %	75.81	Average state %	73.28
Average pass difference	2.53		

Jurisdiction	Takers	Passers	Pass %	State %	Diff %
Wyoming	38	29	76.32	66.96	9.36
Colorado	24	18	75.00	83.29	–8.29

University of Wyoming College of Law

Dept. 3035, 1000 E. University Avenue
Laramie, WY 82071
Phone: 307.766.6416; Fax: 307.766.6417
E-mail: lawadmis@uwyo.edu; Website: www.uwyo.edu/law

■ Introduction

The University of Wyoming College of Law, founded in 1920, is a member of the AALS and is accredited by the ABA. An excellent faculty of 26 full-time professors and several highly qualified lecturers instructs a student body of approximately 225. The limited size of the student body and the favorable student-to-faculty ratio create an atmosphere of friendliness and informality, and students enjoy a degree of access to faculty that students would rarely find at a larger institution.

The College of Law is located on the campus of the University of Wyoming in Laramie. The university, the only four-year institution of higher learning in Wyoming, comprises seven colleges, a graduate school, and several organized research units. The university has a student body of 13,000 and boasts of being one of the best-valued schools in the nation.

Laramie is a town of 30,000 located in the southeastern part of Wyoming at an altitude of 7,200 feet on the high plains between two mountain ranges. Often referenced as "Law at its Highest Point," the College of Law's proximity to the mountains provides a variety of recreational activities, including skiing, backpacking, rock climbing, hiking, mountain biking, camping, fishing, and hunting. Laramie is situated in the wide open spaces of the West, just two hours north of Denver, Colorado.

■ Faculty

The faculty has a proven record of excellence in teaching and research. Particular areas of strength include environmental and natural resource law, water law, constitutional law, international, business, and transactional law. Faculty members are actively engaged in public service and university functions. Because of our small student body, the University of Wyoming College of Law faculty has instructional and research opportunities that are often not available in larger institutions. Students regularly converse with their professors both inside and outside the classroom.

■ Curriculum

The first year consists entirely of required courses. During the second year, students take two additional required courses: Evidence and Professional Responsibility. Students must also complete an advanced writing requirement and one skills course prior to graduation. In both the second and third years, practical legal training is available through courses in alternative dispute resolution, advanced legal research, legal skills and problems, trial practice, externships, and clinical work. Numerous externship opportunities are available in state and federal courts, the US Attorney's Office, various governmental agencies, and other nonprofit entities. The College has only limited nonclassroom offerings in its summer session; however, graduation may be accelerated one semester by attending study-abroad summer sessions at other ABA-accredited law schools.

■ Special Programs

The College of Law has a strong program of elective courses in natural resources law. Courses are regularly offered in environmental law, oil and gas, mining law, public lands, water rights, and energy law. The college offers a joint JD/MA in Environment and Natural Resources and joint degrees in JD/MPA and JD/MBA. Other electives include coverage of trial and appellate practice, business planning, estate planning, corporate and commercial law, administrative law, consumer law, international law, Indian law, health law, and education law.

Students may obtain practical experience and receive academic credit for work in four clinical programs: (1) a defender aid program in which students brief and argue criminal appeals on behalf of indigent persons, and assist penitentiary inmates in post-conviction cases; (2) a prosecution assistance program in which students work directly with prosecuting attorneys in criminal cases; (3) a legal services program in which students provide legal assistance to economically disadvantaged persons; and (4) a clinic dealing with victims of domestic violence. All clinical programs operate under faculty supervision. Under a special state rule, students working in the clinics frequently brief and argue cases before the Wyoming Supreme Court, an opportunity that is rare—if not unique—among law schools.

■ Admission Standards

The College of Law generally restricts the entering class to 75–80 students. The school does not discriminate on the basis of race, color, religion, sex, national origin, disability, age, veteran status, sexual orientation, or political belief in making admission decisions.

Students are admitted only for the fall semester. The college begins to accept applications on October 1 for the class entering the following August. An early admission program is available for those who apply before December 1. The entering class is selected from applications completed and on file by March 1. To meet the March 1 deadline, applicants should take the LSAT no later than February and should register with LSAC's Credential Assembly Service and arrange for forwarding of official transcripts no later than mid-January.

As a general rule, applicants must have received an undergraduate degree from an accredited undergraduate institution prior to registration. Applicants may submit up to three letters of recommendation. Selection of the entering class is based on consideration of applicants' undergraduate records, LSAT scores, a personal statement, and other criteria relevant to success in the study and practice of law including leadership and community service.

■ Student Activities

The College of Law publishes the *Wyoming Law Review*, a student-edited journal. Other student organizations include Potter Law Club, which provides student government and social activities with the Law Student Division of the ABA; three law fraternities; Students for Equal Justice; Intellectual

Property Club; International Law Students Association; Natural Resources Law Forum; Women's Law Forum; J. Reuben Clark Society; and the Wyoming Student Trial Lawyers Association. Students represent the college each year in the National Moot Court Competition, National Environmental Law Moot Court Competition, National Client Counseling Competition, and the ATLA National Student Trial Advocacy Competition. The college also participates in two law school honorary societies, the Order of the Coif and Excellence in Advocacy.

■ Career Services

About 75 percent of graduates remain in the Rocky Mountain region, but the College of Law has alumni around the globe. The curriculum is broad in scope, providing a core foundation of legal knowledge to prepare graduates to practice in a wide range of legal and geographic areas.

Graduates of the UW College of Law practice primarily in small private firms or are employed by state, local, tribal, and the federal government. Students also find work in public service, public interest organizations, and many alternative careers related to law. A high percentage of graduates consistently work in state and federal judicial clerkships following law school.

As with other aspects of the college's operation, the small size of the student body permits the Career Services Office to provide students with a level of personal attention that may not be feasible at larger institutions. Students receive one-on-one career counseling and job-search assistance for permanent or summer employment. Career Services also works with students and alumni to develop insightful career panels and résumé/cover letter workshops. A network of loyal alumni hires, often exclusively, at the University of Wyoming College of Law. Fall and spring on-campus interviews also provide many firms and students with a chance to interview one another. An online posting system allows national and local organizations to post legal positions for UW students across the country.

■ Financial Aid

State and privately funded scholarships are available. Scholarship awards are based upon merit, need, and diversity. Students should file the FAFSA prior to March 1. Scholarship applications are submitted directly to the College of Law but student loans and other financial resources are administered through the University of Wyoming Office of Student Financial Aid.

Applicant Profile

University of Wyoming College of Law
This grid includes only applicants who earned 120–180 LSAT scores under standard administrations.

LSAT Score	3.75 +		3.50–3.74		3.25–3.49		3.00–3.24		2.75–2.99		2.50–2.74		2.25–2.49		2.00–2.24		Below 2.00		No GPA		Total	
	Apps	Adm	Apps	Adm	Apps	Adm	Apps	Adm	Apps	Adm	Apps	Adm	Apps	Adm	Apps	Adm	Apps	Adm	Apps	Adm	Apps	Adm
175–180	0	0	0	0	0	0	0	0	0	0	0	0	0	0	0	0	0	0	0	0	0	0
170–174	0	0	1	1	0	0	0	0	0	0	0	0	0	0	0	0	0	0	0	0	1	1
165–169	2	2	1	1	1	1	1	0	0	0	1	1	0	0	0	0	0	0	0	0	6	5
160–164	8	6	4	4	6	5	7	7	4	3	4	1	2	1	1	0	0	0	0	0	36	27
155–159	12	11	27	25	24	19	18	9	13	6	8	2	3	0	1	0	2	0	1	0	109	72
150–154	16	12	31	21	52	27	35	10	25	3	11	2	5	0	2	0	2	0	0	0	179	75
145–149	15	10	32	5	39	7	36	5	27	3	17	0	5	0	2	0	0	0	4	0	177	30
140–144	5	0	9	3	15	4	15	1	11	0	12	0	2	0	3	0	0	0	3	1	75	9
135–139	1	0	2	0	6	0	5	0	4	0	1	0	6	0	3	0	0	0	1	0	29	0
130–134	0	0	3	0	0	0	1	0	0	0	2	0	2	0	0	0	1	0	1	0	10	0
125–129	0	0	0	0	0	0	0	0	0	0	0	0	0	0	0	0	0	0	0	0	0	0
120–124	0	0	0	0	0	0	0	0	0	0	1	0	0	0	0	0	0	0	0	0	1	0
Total	59	41	110	60	143	63	118	32	84	15	57	6	25	1	12	0	5	0	10	1	623	219

Apps = Number of Applicants
Adm = Number Admitted
Reflects 99% of the total applicant pool; average LSAT data reported.

Yale Law School

PO Box 208215
New Haven, CT 06520-8215
Phone: 203.432.4995
E-mail: admissions.law@yale.edu; Website: www.law.yale.edu

ABA
Approved
Since
1923

AMERICAN BAR ASSOCIATION
Section of Legal Education
and Admissions to the Bar

The Basics

Type of school	Private
Term	Semester
Application deadline	2/15
Application fee	$75
Financial aid deadline	3/15 4/15
Can first year start other than fall?	No
Student to faculty ratio	7.3 to 1
# of housing spaces available restricted to law students	
graduate housing for which law students are eligible	

Curriculum

	Full-Time	Part-Time
Typical first-year section size	58	0
Is there typically a "small section" of the first-year class, other than Legal Writing, taught by full-time faculty	Yes	No
If yes, typical size offered last year	15	
# of classroom course titles beyond first-year curriculum	163	
# of upper division courses, excluding seminars, with an enrollment: Under 25	52	
25–49	22	
50–74	12	
75–99	4	
100+	3	
# of seminars	71	
# of seminar positions available	710	
# of seminar positions filled	536	0
# of positions available in simulation courses	75	
# of simulation positions filled	61	0
# of positions available in faculty supervised clinical courses	690	
# of faculty supervised clinical positions filled	682	0
# involved in field placements	84	0
# involved in law journals	464	0
# involved in moot court or trial competitions	97	0
# of credit hours required to graduate	83	

Faculty and Administrators

	Total		Men		Women		Minorities	
	Spr	Fall	Spr	Fall	Spr	Fall	Spr	Fall
Full-time	64	73	50	58	14	15	8	8
Other full-time	11	8	4	3	7	5	2	0
Deans, librarians, & others who teach	12	13	5	5	7	8	4	4
Part-time	48	55	36	37	12	15	5	8
Total	135	149	95	103	40	43	19	20

JD Enrollment and Ethnicity

	Men		Women		Full-Time		Part-Time		1st-Year		Total		JD Degs. Awd.
	#	%	#	%	#	%	#	%	#	%	#	%	
African Amer.	17	5.3	29	9.9	46	7.5	0	0.0	15	7.0	46	7.5	15
Amer. Indian	0	0.0	1	0.3	1	0.2	0	0.0	0	0.0	1	0.2	1
Asian Amer.	24	7.5	47	16.0	71	11.6	0	0.0	24	11.3	71	11.6	28
Mex. Amer.	8	2.5	7	2.4	15	2.4	0	0.0	6	2.8	15	2.4	1
Puerto Rican	8	2.5	1	0.3	9	1.5	0	0.0	5	2.3	9	1.5	0
Hispanic	12	3.8	15	5.1	27	4.4	0	0.0	10	4.7	27	4.4	9
Total Minority	69	21.6	100	34.1	169	27.6	0	0.0	60	28.2	169	27.6	54
For. Nation.	15	4.7	10	3.4	25	4.1	0	0.0	11	5.2	25	4.1	7
Caucasian	222	69.4	166	56.7	388	63.3	0	0.0	132	62.0	388	63.3	136
Unknown	14	4.4	17	5.8	31	5.1	0	0.0	10	4.7	31	5.1	13
Total	320	52.2	293	47.8	613	100.0	0	0.0	213	34.7	613		210

Transfers

Transfers in	15
Transfers out	1

Tuition and Fees

	Resident	Nonresident
Full-time	$48,340	$48,340
Part-time		
Tuition Guarantee Program		N

Living Expenses

Estimated living expenses for singles

Living on campus	Living off campus	Living at home
$18,900	$18,900	$18,900

Yale Law School

ABA
Approved
Since
1923

GPA and LSAT Scores

	Total	Full-Time	Part-Time
# of apps	3,363	3,363	0
# of offers	270	270	0
# of matrics	214	214	0
75% GPA	3.96	3.96	0.00
Median GPA	3.90	3.90	0.00
25% GPA	3.82	3.82	0.00
75% LSAT	176	176	0
Median LSAT	173	173	0
25% LSAT	170	170	0

Grants and Scholarships (from prior year)

	Total		Full-Time		Part-Time	
	#	%	#	%	#	%
Total # of students	588		588		0	
Total # receiving grants	315	53.6	315	53.6	0	0.0
Less than 1/2 tuition	170	28.9	170	28.9	0	0.0
Half to full tuition	145	24.7	145	24.7	0	0.0
Full tuition	0	0.0	0	0.0	0	0.0
More than full tuition	0	0.0	0	0.0	0	0.0
Median grant amount			$21,410		$0	

Informational and Library Resources

Total amount spent on library materials	$3,089,862
Study seating capacity inside the library	424
# of full-time equivalent professional librarians	15
Hours per week library is open	133
# of open, wired connections available to students	1,009
# of networked computers available for use by students	67
Has wireless network?	Y
Require computer?	Y

JD Attrition (from prior year)

	Academic	Other	Total	
	#	#	#	%
1st year	0	3	3	1.6
2nd year	0	1	1	0.5
3rd year	0	3	3	1.5
4th year	0	0	0	0.0

Employment (9 months after graduation)

	Total	Percentage
Employment status known	199	99.5
Employment status unknown	1	0.5
Employed	191	96.0
Pursuing graduate degrees	4	2.0
Unemployed (seeking, not seeking, or studying for the bar)	3	1.5
Type of Employment		
# employed in law firms	79	41.4
# employed in business and industry	14	7.3
# employed in government	10	5.2
# employed in public interest	16	8.4
# employed as judicial clerks	67	35.1
# employed in academia	5	2.6
Geographic Location		
# employed in state	12	6.3
# employed in foreign countries	6	3.1
# of states where employed		28

Bar Passage Rates

First-time takers	195	Reporting %	71.79
Average school %	97.15	Average state %	85.12
Average pass difference	12.03		

Jurisdiction	Takers	Passers	Pass %	State %	Diff %
New York	85	82	96.47	88.98	7.49
California	42	41	97.62	78.07	19.55
Virginia	13	13	100.00	82.70	17.30

Yale Law School

PO Box 208215
New Haven, CT 06520-8215
Phone: 203.432.4995
E-mail: admissions.law@yale.edu; Website: www.law.yale.edu

■ Introduction

Yale Law School is an extraordinary community in which to study law. Standing at the intersection of the worlds of thought and action, Yale seeks not only to promote an intellectual understanding of the law, but also to sustain the moral commitments that justice requires.

Extensive student-faculty interactions and institutional flexibility are hallmarks of the Yale Law School experience. Students enjoy countless opportunities for research and writing with professors. Our unmatched faculty-to-student ratio allows us to offer a wide range of courses and small classes, with an average class size of under 20 students.

The school is also part of one of the world's great research universities. Yale University is home to an abundance of intellectual, cultural, social, and athletic activities, all of which are accessible to Yale law students.

■ Students

The vitality of Yale Law School depends as much on the knowledge, experience, and interests of the students as it does on the faculty, the library, or the alumni. The school selects its entering class from applicants with the highest academic qualifications. Within this exceptional group, Yale seeks a diversity of backgrounds, experiences, and interests. This diversity is reflected in the many thriving student organizations and student-run journals found at the school.

■ Faculty

The faculty at Yale Law School is as broad-ranging in its interests and expertise as it is distinguished. It includes prominent scholars of economics, philosophy, and the social sciences as well as leading specialists in every area of law. More than 60 full-time professors are joined each year by visiting lecturers, adjunct professors from other parts of the university, and practicing lawyers. Additionally, dozens of guest lecturers from around the world—ranging from Madeleine Albright to Al Franken—help to make Yale Law School a vibrant intellectual community.

■ Facilities and Housing

The Sterling Law Building occupies one city block in the heart of Yale University and downtown New Haven. The recently renovated building was modeled on the English Inns of Court, with classrooms, a dining hall, faculty offices, and the law library surrounding three pleasant courtyards. All classrooms are Internet accessible, and a wireless network is available throughout the Law School. A day care center is located on site.

Yale campus housing is available, but most students live off campus, close to the Law School. Within a 10-minute walk of the school, students can find housing options ranging from high-rise apartments downtown to Victorian houses in quiet residential neighborhoods.

■ Curriculum and Grading

The Yale Law School curriculum is very flexible. Students are able to shape their own course of study to satisfy their unique intellectual interests and goals. In the fall semester, all first-year students take classes in constitutional law, contracts, procedure, and torts. One of these classes is a small group of about 16 students, which includes instruction in legal research and writing. After the first term, students may select any classes they wish, including independent studies, clinics, and courses outside the Law School. Two major writing projects and courses in criminal law and professional responsibility are required for graduation.

In order to allow students to concentrate on learning, rather than on GPAs, Yale Law School does not use grades in the traditional sense. During the fall of the first year, all classes are credit/fail. In subsequent terms, grades are honors, pass, low pass, and fail, with credit/fail options available. Yale Law School does not calculate class rankings.

■ Joint Degrees, Special Programs, and Clinical Opportunities

Yale Law School sees the study of law as interrelated with other intellectual disciplines and with practical experience. The Law School allows a number of joint degrees with other schools and departments at Yale, including JD/MBAs, JD/PhDs, and JD/MDs. Joint degrees with other universities and opportunities for intensive semester experiences outside the Law School are available.

Yale Law School also offers a number of clinical opportunities to all students beginning in the first year. For example, students gain real-world experience participating in the Lowenstein International Human Rights Clinic, Supreme Court Clinic, Environmental Protection Clinic, and the Community Development Financial Institutions Clinic. Other clinics, including advocacy for prisoners, children, immigrants, and people with disabilities, provide opportunities for Yale law students to work on behalf of clients who cannot afford private attorneys.

■ Transfer Students and Other Degrees

Students who have completed two semesters of study at another ABA-approved law school may apply to transfer to Yale Law School. Transfer students must complete at least two years of work at Yale Law School.

In addition to the JD, Yale Law School offers an LLM degree for foreign lawyers who are interested in teaching law. The Master of Studies in Law (MSL) is a one-year program designed for mid-career professionals and journalists who desire an intensive introduction to the law. Yale also offers a JSD program for the school's LLM students.

■ Financial Aid and Loan Forgiveness

Financial aid is awarded solely on the basis of need, and admission decisions are made independent of financial aid decisions. Approximately 80 percent of the student body receives some form of financial aid. A financial aid award may

consist of a portion in grant and a portion in loan; typically, the higher the total financial need, the higher the proportion of grant.

In addition to financial aid during law school, Yale has one of the most generous loan forgiveness programs in the country: the Career Options Assistance Program (COAP). COAP provides grants to help repay the educational loans of graduates who take relatively low-paying jobs. Unlike many loan forgiveness programs, Yale's COAP includes not only law school loans, but some undergraduate loans as well. Last year, COAP covered over $2.5 million worth of loan payments for almost 300 graduates.

■ Career Development

Yale Law School graduates occupy leadership positions in a tremendous range of endeavors. The Law School's Career Development Office helps students explore the unparalleled diversity of opportunities available to them. Most students work for public interest organizations, private firms, or government entities during summer breaks. After graduation, roughly half of each class obtain judicial clerkships. Others work for law firms or corporations, while still others take advantage of public service fellowships available to Yale Law

School graduates. In addition, many graduates pursue careers in academia.

■ The Admission Process

Yale Law School considers every application for admission in its entirety and no index or numerical cutoffs are used in the admission process. No single element in an application is decisive; the totality of available information about the applicant is taken into account. A personal statement and a 250-word essay on a subject of the applicant's choice are required. Applicants are encouraged to bring aspects of their personal background or other special characteristics to the attention of the admission committee. Two letters of recommendation are required; additional letters are also welcome.

Each application file is first reviewed by the dean of admissions. A group of the most highly rated files is then considered by faculty. Each faculty member rates applications on the basis of the faculty member's unique criteria; the weight given to various factors is within each reader's discretion.

The Law School issues decisions on a rolling basis, but most of its decisions are made at the beginning of April. Use of the wait list varies from year to year, and the list is not ranked until offers are made.

Applicant Profile

Yale Law School

| Undergraduate GPA | Average LSAT Score on the 120–180 Scale | | | | | | | | | | | | Total | |
| | Below 155 | | 155–159 | | 160–164 | | 165–169 | | 170–174 | | 175–180 | | | |
	Apps	Adm	Apps	Adm	Apps	Adm	Apps	Adm	Apps	Adm	Apps	Adm	Apps	Adm
3.75 +	78	0	89	1	195	6	455	37	408	87	214	101	1439	232
3.50–3.74	97	0	94	0	155	6	273	9	229	12	100	10	948	37
3.25–3.49	84	0	54	0	88	0	80	2	68	1	28	0	402	3
3.00–3.24	64	0	28	0	35	0	31	0	17	0	7	0	182	0
Below 3.00	112	0	17	0	20	0	20	0	11	0	7	0	187	0
No GPA	44	0	19	0	23	0	22	2	12	0	2	1	122	3
Total	479	0	301	1	516	12	881	50	745	100	358	112	3280	275

Totals reflect 99% of applicant pool.
Apps = Number of Applicants
Adm = Number Admitted

Appendix A: Legal Education Statistics

Law School Attendance Figures, Fall 2009

		Full-time	Part-time	Total
First Year	Total	43,379	8,267	51,646
	Women	20,324	3,981	24,305
Second Year	Total	40,007	5,522	45,529
	Women	18,813	2,645	21,458
Third Year	Total	39,385	5,038	44,423
	Women	18,652	2,385	21,037
Fourth Year	Total		3,641	3,641
	Women		1,702	1,702
JD Total	Total	122,771	22,468	145,239
	Women	57,789	10,713	68,502
Post-JD	Total	5,315	2,433	7,748
	Women	2,527	1,151	3,678
Other	Total	905	657	1,562
	Women	479	431	910
Grand Total	Total	128,991	25,558	154,549
	Women	60,795	12,295	73,090

Professional Degrees Conferred, 2009

		Full-time	Part-time	Total
JD/LLB	Total	39,143	4,861	44,004
	Women	17,979	2,212	20,191
LLM	Total	4,282	776	5,058
	Women	1,905	360	2,265
MCL/MCJ	Total	16	0	16
	Women	7	0	7
SJD/JSD	Total	96	9	105
	Women	45	1	46
Other	Total	478	200	678
	Women	244	131	375
Total	Total	44,015	5,846	49,861
	Women	20,180	2,704	22,884

Teachers in Law Schools, 2009–2010

	Women	Minorities	Total
Full-time	3,134	1,359	8,095
Part-time	2,455	777	7,729
Deans & Administrators	2,491	888	4,122
Librarians	1,174	315	1,800

Total Minority Enrollment

Academic Year	Number of Schools Reporting*	First Year	Second Year	Third Year	Fourth Year	Total
2009–10	197	11,840	10,227	9,629	809	32,505
2008–09	197	11,320	10,028	9,311	709	31,368
2007–08	194	10,992	9,639	9,203	764	30,598
2006–07	191	10,898	9,539	9,371	749	30,557
2005–06	190	10,462	9,644	9,061	818	29,985
2004–05	188	10,694	9,280	8,766	749	29,489
2003–04	187	10,468	9,144	8,062	721	28,318
2002–03	187	10,224	8,326	7,898	721	27,169
2001–02	184	9,557	8,172	7,785	743	26,257
2000–01	183	9,335	8,052	7,690	676	25,753
1999–00	182	9,079	7,876	7,547	751	25,253
1998–99	181	9,076	7,635	7,761	794	25,266
1997–98	178	8,493	7,740	7,705	747	24,685
1996–97	179	8,722	8,009	7,869	679	25,279
1995–96	178	9,119	8,402	7,411	622	25,554
1994–95	177	9,249	7,633	7,124	605	24,611
1993–94	176	8,595	7,244	6,409	551	22,799
1992–93	176	8,070	6,682	6,032	482	21,266
1991–92	176	7,575	6,155	5,255	425	19,410
1990–91	175	6,933	5,325	4,676	396	17,330
1989–90	175	6,172	4,890	4,264	394	15,720
1988–89	174	5,565	4,408	3,911	411	14,295

*Please note that the minority enrollment charts on pages 22 through 30 do not include students from the three Puerto Rico schools. JD enrollment for the law schools in Puerto Rico was 2,257 for fall 2009.

American Indian or Alaska Native Enrollment

Academic Year	Number of Schools Reporting	First Year	Second Year	Third Year	Fourth Year	Total
2009–10	197	451	410	383	29	1,273
2008–09	197	448	360	373	17	1,198
2007–08	194	436	374	367	38	1,215
2006–07	191	418	365	358	27	1,158
2005–06	190	399	369	360	33	1,161
2004–05	188	387	366	325	28	1,106
2003–04	187	396	341	291	20	1,048
2002–03	187	375	318	317	11	1,021
2001–02	184	365	323	275	27	990
2000–01	183	348	293	290	21	952
1999–00	182	342	294	312	30	978
1998–99	181	361	307	351	45	1,064
1997–98	178	355	348	355	27	1,085
1996–97	179	391	397	310	18	1,116
1995–96	178	436	338	294	17	1,085
1994–95	177	377	283	290	12	962
1993–94	176	336	280	243	14	873
1992–93	176	313	243	206	14	776
1991–92	176	286	219	176	11	692
1990–91	175	224	185	129	16	554
1989–90	175	220	147	143	17	527
1988–89	174	177	165	149	8	499

Asian or Pacific Islander Enrollment

Academic Year	Number of Schools Reporting	First Year	Second Year	Third Year	Fourth Year	Total
2009–10	197	3,987	3,581	3,476	283	11,327
2008–09	197	3,911	3,647	3,404	282	11,244
2007–08	194	3,875	3,489	3,523	269	11,156
2006–07	191	3,839	3,635	3,577	255	11,306
2005–06	190	3,941	3,650	3,432	278	11,301
2004–05	188	3,982	3,440	3,217	217	10,856
2003–04	187	3,881	3,279	2,685	195	10,040
2002–03	187	3,602	2,819	2,578	182	9,181
2001–02	184	3,052	2,646	2,541	182	8,421
2000–01	183	2,924	2,570	2,510	169	8,173
1999–00	182	2,772	2,519	2,401	191	7,883
1998–99	181	2,762	2,403	2,497	215	7,877
1997–98	178	2,562	2,463	2,394	180	7,599
1996–97	179	2,695	2,451	2,380	180	7,706
1995–96	178	2,773	2,572	2,225	149	7,719
1994–95	177	2,740	2,247	2,087	122	7,196
1993–94	176	2,432	2,101	1,789	136	6,458
1992–93	176	2,235	1,873	1,618	97	5,823
1991–92	176	2,019	1,621	1,306	82	5,028
1990–91	175	1,753	1,343	1,134	76	4,306
1989–90	175	1,501	1,151	946	78	3,676
1988–89	174	1,282	954	825	72	3,133

African American Enrollment

Academic Year	Number of Schools Reporting	First Year	Second Year	Third Year	Fourth Year	Total
2009–10	197	3,791	3,165	2,955	262	10,173
2008–09	197	3,586	3,098	2,910	228	9,822
2007–08	194	3,475	3,037	2,708	273	9,493
2006–07	191	3,516	2,836	2,927	250	9,529
2005–06	190	3,132	3,040	2,735	288	9,195
2004–05	188	3,457	2,873	2,845	313	9,488
2003–04	187	3,300	3,007	2,786	342	9,435
2002–03	187	3,491	2,875	2,773	297	9,436
2001–02	184	3,474	2,867	2,737	334	9,412
2000–01	183	3,402	2,890	2,757	305	9,354
1999–00	182	3,353	2,903	2,700	316	9,272
1998–99	181	3,478	2,728	2,754	311	9,271
1997–98	178	3,126	2,752	2,887	367	9,132
1996–97	179	3,223	3,013	2,991	315	9,542
1995–96	178	3,474	3,161	2,855	289	9,542
1994–95	177	3,600	3,000	2,771	310	9,681
1993–94	176	3,455	2,846	2,573	282	9,156
1992–93	176	3,303	2,603	2,465	267	8,638
1991–92	176	3,169	2,556	2,196	228	8,149
1990–91	175	2,982	2,222	2,023	205	7,432
1989–90	175	2,628	2,128	1,816	219	6,791
1988–89	174	2,463	1,913	1,728	217	6,321

Mexican American Enrollment

Academic Year	Number of Schools Reporting	First Year	Second Year	Third Year	Fourth Year	Total
2009–10	197	972	862	697	61	2,592
2008–09	197	1,032	767	792	35	2,626
2007–08	194	888	805	760	45	2,498
2006–07	191	915	782	746	56	2,499
2005–06	190	866	757	787	47	2,457
2004–05	188	938	855	819	53	2,665
2003–04	187	923	831	738	47	2,539
2002–03	187	906	771	680	55	2,412
2001–02	184	896	705	686	47	2,334
2000–01	183	883	757	734	43	2,417
1999–00	182	901	772	750	60	2,483
1998–99	181	885	734	764	68	2,451
1997–98	178	859	766	777	50	2,452
1996–97	179	861	768	751	49	2,429
1995–96	178	896	820	743	36	2,495
1994–95	177	902	739	719	42	2,402
1993–94	176	838	698	639	28	2,203
1992–93	176	807	744	683	24	2,258
1991–92	176	770	644	584	29	2,027
1990–91	175	768	624	527	31	1,950
1989–90	175	640	531	469	23	1,663
1988–89	174	656	510	458	33	1,657

Puerto Rican Enrollment

Academic Year	Number of Schools Reporting	First Year	Second Year	Third Year	Fourth Year	Total
2009–10	197	246	166	195	19	626
2008–09	197	203	212	189	15	619
2007–08	194	213	183	177	16	589
2006–07	191	207	179	149	16	551
2005–06	190	203	154	175	16	548
2004–05	188	181	206	182	25	594
2003–04	187	228	204	194	29	655
2002–03	187	208	198	204	29	639
2001–02	184	221	216	222	30	689
2000–01	183	249	213	191	27	680
1999–00	182	243	188	192	23	646
1998–99	181	206	205	196	25	632
1997–98	178	224	198	188	26	636
1996–97	179	206	213	238	29	686
1995–96	178	236	238	214	17	705
1994–95	177	263	244	186	25	718
1993–94	176	275	195	177	17	664
1992–93	176	202	193	177	15	587
1991–92	176	208	177	140	14	539
1990–91	175	183	153	158	12	506
1989–90	175	171	150	156	6	483
1988–89	174	168	156	141	13	478

Other Hispanic American Enrollment

Academic Year	Number of Schools Reporting	First Year	Second Year	Third Year	Fourth Year	Total
2009–10	197	2,393	2,043	1,923	155	6,514
2008–09	197	2,140	1,944	1,643	132	5,859
2007–08	194	2,105	1,751	1,668	159	5,683
2006–07	191	2,003	1,742	1,624	145	5,514
2005–06	190	203	154	175	16	548
2004–05	188	1,749	1,540	1,378	113	4,780
2003–04	187	1,724	1,430	1,328	135	4,617
2002–03	187	1,642	1,345	1,346	147	4,480
2001–02	184	1,549	1,415	1,324	123	4,411
2000–01	183	1,529	1,329	1,208	111	4,177
1999–00	182	1,468	1,200	1,192	131	3,991
1998–99	181	1,384	1,258	1,199	130	3,971
1997–98	178	1,367	1,213	1,104	97	3,781
1996–97	179	1,346	1,167	1,199	88	3,880
1995–96	178	1,304	1,273	1,079	114	3,770
1994–95	177	1,367	1,120	1,071	94	3,652
1993–94	176	1,259	1,124	988	74	3,445
1992–93	176	1,210	966	883	65	3,124
1991–92	176	1,123	938	853	61	2,975
1990–91	175	1,023	798	705	56	2,582
1989–90	175	1,019	783	734	51	2,587
1988–89	174	819	710	610	68	2,207

Legal Education Statistics, 1983–2009

Academic Year	Number of Schools	Total LSAT Administrations	Applicants	First-year Enrollment	Total JD Enrollment	Total[1] Overall Enrollment	JD or LLB Awarded
2009–10	200	171,514	86,576	51,646	145,239	154,539	44,004
2008–09	200	151,398	83,371	49,414	142,922	152,033	43,588
2007–08	198	142,331	84,021	49,082	141,719	150,031	43,518
2006–07	195	140,048	88,662	48,937	141,031	148,698	43,920
2005–06	191	137,444	95,760	48,132	140,298	148,273	42,673
2004–05	188	145,258	100,604	48,239	140,376	148,169	40,023
2003–04	187	147,617	99,504	48,867	137,676	145,088	38,874
2002–03	186	148,014	90,853	48,433	132,885	140,612	38,605
2001–02	184	134,251	77,235	45,070	127,610	135,091	37,909
2000–01	183	109,030	74,550	43,518	125,173	132,464	38,157
1999–00	182	107,153	74,380	43,152	125,184	132,276	39,071
1998–99	181	104,236	71,726	42,804	125,627	131,833	39,455
1997–98	178[2]	103,991	72,340	42,186	125,886	131,801	40,114
1996–97	179	105,315	76,687	43,245	125,623	134,949	39,920
1995–96	178	114,756	84,305	43,676	129,397	135,595	39,271
1994–95	177	128,553	89,633	44,298	128,989	134,784	39,710
1993–94	176	132,028	91,892	43,644	127,802	133,339	40,213
1992–93	176	140,054	97,719	42,793	128,212	133,783	39,425
1991–92	176	145,567	99,377	44,050	129,580	135,157	38,800
1990–91	175	152,685	92,958	44,104	127,261	132,433	36,385
1989–90	175	138,865	87,288	43,826	124,471	129,698	35,520
1988–89	174	137,088	78,930	42,860	120,694	125,870	35,701
1987–88	175	115,988	68,804	41,055	117,997	123,198	35,478
1986–87	175	101,235	65,168	40,195	117,813	132,277	36,121
1985–86	175	91,848	60,338	40,796	118,700	124,092	36,829
1984–85	174	95,563	63,801	40,747	119,847	125,698	36,687
1983–84	173	105,076	71,755	41,159	121,201	127,195	36,389

Note: Enrollment is in American Bar Association-approved law schools as of October 1, 2009. The LSAT year begins in June and ends in February of the following year. JD or LLB degrees are those awarded by approved schools for the academic year ending in the first year stated. Total new admissions to the bar include those admitted by office study, diploma privilege, and examination and study at an unapproved law school. The great bulk of those admitted graduated from approved schools.

[1] Total overall enrollment includes post-JD and other.
[2] The District of Columbia School of Law is not included in this figure.

Appendix B: Post-JD and Non-JD Programs

Please note that it is the position of the Council of the ABA Section of Legal Education and Admissions to the Bar that no graduate degree in law is or should be a substitute for the first professional degree in law (JD) and should not serve as the same basis for bar admission purposes as the JD degree. The Council of the Section is licensed to accredit JD programs; it is not licensed to accredit post-JD and non-JD programs. For additional information about post-JD and non-JD programs, visit the Section's website at *www.abanet.org/legaled*.

For specific information about the programs listed below, you should contact the schools directly. In addition, if you have not obtained a JD from an ABA-approved law school, you may wish to contact the bar admission authorities in the state(s) in which you intend to practice for more information on whether graduation from a post-JD or non-JD program will qualify you to take the bar examination in that state.

The information contained in Appendix B was collected in fall 2009. Neither the ABA nor LSAC conducts an audit to verify the accuracy of the information submitted by the respective institutions.

■ Graduate Degrees Defined

While an individual law school's degree may differ slightly by name to similar programs elsewhere, most degrees offered through law schools fall into three general categories:

1) Academic master's degrees for nonlawyers, such as:
   MS   Master of Science or Master of Studies
   MPS   Master of Professional Studies

2) Post-JD law degrees for practicing lawyers and foreign lawyers seeking to practice in the US, such as:
   LLM   Master of Laws
   JM   Juris Master

MCL   Master of Comparative Law
MJ   Master of Jurisprudence
MLS   Master of Legal Studies

3) Research and academic-based doctorate level degrees, such as:
   JSD   Doctor of Jurisprudence
   SJD   Doctor of Juridical Science
   DCL   Doctor of Comparative Law

For questions regarding specific degree descriptions, contact the school directly.

■ Post-JD and Non-JD Programs by Law School

Akron
Intellectual Property, LLM

Alabama
Comparative Law, LLM
General, LLM
Taxation, LLM

Albany
Advanced Legal Studies, LLM; MS
Government Administration and Regulations, LLM
Health Law, LLM
Intellectual Property, LLM
International Law, LLM

American
General, SJD
International Legal Studies, LLM
Law and Government, LLM

Arizona
Indigenous People's Law & Policy, LLM; SJD
International Trade Law, LLM; SJD

Arizona State
Biotechnology and Genomics, LLM
General, LLM
Legal Studies, MLS
Tribal Policy, Law and Government, LLM

Arkansas (Fayetteville)
Agriculture Law, LLM

Baltimore
Law of the US, LLM
Taxation, LLM

Boston College
General, LLM

Boston
American Law (for international lawyers), LLM
Banking and Financial Law, LLM
Intellectual Property (LLM)
Taxation, LLM

Brigham Young
American Law (for international lawyers), LLM

Brooklyn Law
Information Law and Society, LLM

Buffalo
Criminal Law, LLM
General, LLM

California-Berkeley
General, JSD; LLM

California-Davis
US Legal System, LLM

California-Hastings
US Law (for international lawyers), LLM

California-Los Angeles
As Approved, LLM, SJD
Business Law, LLM
Entertainment and Media Law/Policy, LLM
Juridical Studies, SJD

California Western
Comparative Law (for international lawyers), LLM; MCL
Health Law, MAS
Trial Advocacy (specializing in federal criminal law), LLM

Capital
Business, LLM
Taxation, LLM, MT

Cardozo
Comparative Legal Thought, LLM
General, LLM
Intellectual Property, LLM

Case Western
US and Global Legal Studies, LLM

Catholic
American Law, LLM
Communications Law, LLM
National Security Law, LLM

Chapman
General, LLM
Prosecutorial Science, LLM
Taxation, LLM

Chicago
General, DCL; JSD; LLM; MCL

Chicago-Kent
Family Law, LLM
Financial Services Law, LLM
International and Comparative Law, LLM
International Intellectual Property, LLM
Taxation, LLM

Cleveland State
General, LLM

Colorado
General, LLM

Columbia
General, JSD; LLM

Connecticut
Insurance Law, LLM
US Legal Studies (for international lawyers), LLM

Cornell
General, JSD; LLM
International and Comparative Law, LLM

Dayton
Law and Technology, LLM; MSL

Denver
American and Comparative Law (for international lawyers), LLM
Legal Administration, MS
Natural Resources, LLM; MRLS
Taxation, LLM

DePaul
Health Law, LLM
Intellectual Property, LLM
International Law, LLM
Taxation, LLM

Drake
General, LLM; MJ
Health Law, LLM; MJ
Intellectual Property, LLM, MJ

Duke
General, MLS
International and Comparative Law, LLM
Research, SJD
US Law (for international lawyers), LLM

Duquesne
American Law (for international lawyers), LLM

Emory
General, LLM; SJD
Litigation, LLM
Taxation, LLM

Florida
Comparative Law, LLM
Environmental and Land Use Law, LLM
International Taxation, LLM
Taxation, LLM; SJD

Florida State
American Law (for international lawyers), LLM
Environmental Law and Policy, LLM

Fordham
Banking, LLM
Intellectual Property and Information Technology, LLM
International Business and Trade Law, LLM
International Law and Justice, LLM

Franklin Pierce
Commerce and Technology, LLM
Intellectual Property, LLM
Intellectual Property, Commerce and Technology Law, LLM
International Criminal Law and Justice LLM; MAS

George Mason
Intellectual Property, LLM
Law and Economics, LLM

George Washington
Environmental Law, LLM
General, LLM; SJD
Government and Procurement Law, LLM
Government Procurement and Environmental Law, LLM
Intellectual Property, LLM
International and Comparative Law, LLM
International Environmental Law, LLM
Litigation and Dispute Resolution, LLM
National Security and Foreign Relations, LLM

Georgetown
Advocacy, LLM
As Approved, SJD
General, LLM; MSL
Global Health Law, LLM
International Business and Economic Law, LLM
International and Comparative Law, LLM
International Legal Studies, LLM
Securities and Financial Regulation, LLM
Taxation, LLM

Georgia
General, LLM

Golden Gate
Environmental Law, LLM
Intellectual Property, LLM
International Legal Studies, LLM; SJD
Taxation, LLM
US Legal Studies (for international lawyers), LLM

Hamline
General (for international lawyers), LLM

Harvard
General, LLM; SJD

Hawaii
General (for international lawyers), LLM

Hofstra
American Legal Studies, LLM
Family Law, LLM
International Law, LLM

Houston
Energy, Environment, and Natural Resources, LLM
Foreign Scholars Program, LLM
Health Law, LLM
Intellectual Property and Information Law, LLM
International Law, LLM
Taxation, LLM

Howard
International Law (for international lawyers), LLM

Illinois
General, JSD; LLM

Indiana-Bloomington
As Approved, LLM; PhD
Comparative Law, MCL
Research, SJD

Indiana-Indianapolis
American Law (for international lawyers), LLM
General, SJD
Health Law and Bioethics, LLM
Intellectual Property Law, LLM
International and Comparative Law, LLM
International Human Rights Law, LLM

Iowa
International and Comparative Law, LLM

John Marshall (Chicago)
Employee Benefits, LLM, MS
Global Legal Studies, LLM
Information Technology Law, LLM; MS
Intellectual Property, LLM, MS
International Business and Trade Law, LLM
Real Estate, LLM
Taxation, LLM, MS

Judge Advocate General's School
Military Law, LLM

Kansas
Elder Law, LLM
General, SJD

Lewis & Clark
Environmental/Natural Resources, LLM

Louisiana State
As Approved, LLM; DCL

Loyola Marymount
American and International Legal Practice, LLM
Taxation, LLM

Loyola University-Chicago
Business Law, LLM; MJ
Child and Family Law, LLM; MJ
Health Law, LLM; MJ; SJD
Taxation, LLM

Loyola University-New Orleans
US Law, LLM

Marquette
Sports Law (for international lawyers), LLM

Maryland
General, LLM

Miami
Comparative Law, LLM
Estate Planning, LLM

Inter-American Law, LLM
International Law, LLM
Ocean and Coastal Law, LLM
Real Property, Land Development and Finance, LLM
Taxation, LLM

Michigan
As Approved, LLM; MCL; SJD
International Tax, LLM

Michigan State
American Legal System (for international lawyers), LLM
Intellectual Property and Communications, LLM; MJ

Minnesota
American Law (for international lawyers), LLM

Missouri
Dispute Resolution, LLM

Missouri-Kansas City
Estate Planning, LLM
General, LLM
Taxation, LLM
Urban Affairs, LLM

Nebraska
Law and Psychology, MLS
Space and Telecommunications, LLM

New York Law
Financial Services, LLM
Mental Disability Law, MS
Real Estate Law, LLM
Taxation, LLM

New York
Corporate Law, LLM
Environmental Law, LLM
General, LLM
International Business Regulation, Litigation and Arbitration, LLM
International Legal Studies, LLM
International Taxation, LLM
Juridical Science, JSD
Law and the Global Economy, LLM
Law and Jewish Civilization, MSL
Labor and Employment Law, LLM
Legal Theory, LLM
Taxation, LLM
Trade Regulation, LLM

Northwestern
As Approved, LLM; MSL; SJD
General, LLM
Taxation, LLM

Notre Dame
International and Comparative Law, LLM
International Human Rights, LLM; SJD

Nova Southeastern
Education Law, MSL
Employment Law, MSL
Health Law, MSL

Ohio Northern
Democratic Governance and Rule of Law, LLM

Ohio State
General, LLM; MSL

Oregon
Conflict and Dispute Resolution, MA; MS
Environmental and Natural Resources Law, LLM

Pace
Comparative Law (for international lawyers), LLM
Environmental Law, LLM; SJD
Real Estate Law, LLM

Pacific-McGeorge
Government and Public Policy, LLM
International Water Resources Law, JSD; LLM
Transnational Business Practice, LLM

Penn State
Comparative Law, LLM

Pennsylvania
As Approved, LLM; MCL; SJD

Pepperdine
Dispute Resolution, LLM; MDR

Pittsburgh
As Approved, JSD
General, MSL
International and Comparative Law, JSD; LLM

Puerto Rico
International Law, LLM

Quinnipiac
Health Law, LLM

Regent
American Legal Studies, LLM

St. John's
Bankruptcy Law, LLM
US Law (for international lawyers), LLM

Saint Louis
American Law (for international lawyers), LLM
Health Law, LLM

St. Mary's
American Legal Studies (for international lawyers), LLM
International and Comparative Law, LLM

St. Thomas (Florida)
Intercultural Human Rights, JSD; LLM
International Taxation, LLM

Samford
Business and Corporate Law, LLM
Comparative Law, LLM
General, LLM
International Law, LLM
Law, Religion, and Culture, LLM; SJD
Taxation, LLM

San Diego
Business and Corporate Law, LLM
Comparative Law (for international lawyers), LLM
General, LLM
International Law, LLM
Legal Studies, MSL
Taxation, LLM

San Francisco
Intellectual Property and Technology Law, LLM
International Transactions and Comparative Law (for international lawyers), LLM

Santa Clara
Intellectual Property Law, LLM
International and Comparative Law, LLM
US Law (for international lawyers), LLM

Seattle
American Legal Studies, LLM

Seton Hall
Health Law, LLM
Health Law, Science and Technology, MSJ
Intellectual Property, LLM

SMU Dedman
Comparative and International Law, LLM
General, LLM; SJD
Taxation, LLM

Southern California
Comparative Law, MCL
General (for international lawyers), LLM
Taxation, LLM

Southern Illinois
General, LLM; MLS
Health Law, LLM; MLS

Southwestern
Entertainment and Media Law, LLM
General, LLM

Stanford
As Approved, JSD; JSM; MLS
Corporate Governance and Practice, LLM
Law, Science and Technology, LLM

Stetson
Elder Law, LLM
International Law, LLM

Suffolk
General, SJD
Global Law and Technology, LLM
US and Global Business Law (for international lawyers), LLM

Temple
American Law (for international lawyers, LLM
General, LLM
Juridical Science, SJD
Taxation, LLM
Transnational Law, LLM
Trial Advocacy, LLM

Texas
General, LLM

Thomas M. Cooley (Lansing)
Corporate Law and Finance, LLM
General, LLM
Insurance Law, LLM
Intellectual Property, LLM*
Taxation, LLM*
US Legal Studies (for international lawyers, LLM)
*also offered at the Auburn Hills and Grand Rapids campuses

Thomas Jefferson
American Legal Studies, LLM
International Taxation and Financial Services, JSD; JSM; LLM
International Trade and Financial Services, LLM

Toledo
General, MSL

Touro
American Legal Studies (for international lawyers), LLM
General, LLM

Tulane
Admiralty, LLM
American Business Law, LLM
Comparative Law, MCL
Comparative Law and Latin American Studies, MCL
Energy and Environment, LLM
General, LLM; PhD; SJD
International and Comparative Law, LLM

Tulsa
American Indian and Indigenous Law, LLM
American Law (for international lawyers), LLM

Utah
Environmental and Natural Resources, LLM

Valparaiso
General, LLM

Vanderbilt
As Approved, LLM

Vermont
American Legal Studies, LLM
Environmental Law and Policy, LLM; MELP; MSEL

Villanova
Taxation, LLM

Virginia
General, LLM; SJD

Wake Forest
American Law (for international lawyers), LLM

Washington
Asian and Comparative Law, LLM; PhD
Health Law, LLM
Intellectual Property and Policy Law, LLM
Sustainable International Development, LLM
Taxation, LLM

Washington and Lee
US Law, LLM

Washington University
Intellectual Property and Technology Law, LLM
Juridical Studies, MJS
Research, JSD
Taxation, LLM

Urban Studies, LLM
US Law, LLM

Wayne State
Corporate and Finance, LLM
Labor Law and Employment, LLM
Taxation, LLM

Western New England
Closely Held Businesses, LLM
Estate Planning and Elder Law, LLM

Whittier
US Legal Studies (for international lawyers), LLM

Widener
Corporate and Business Law, DL; MJ; SJD
Corporate Law and Finance, LLM
Health Law, DL; LLM; MJ; SDJ

Willamette
Transnational Law, LLM

William & Mary
American Legal System (for international lawyers), LLM

Wisconsin
As Approved, LLM; MLI; SJD
Legal Institutions, LLM

Yale
General, JSD; LLM; MSL

■ Post-JD and Non-JD Programs by Category

Admiralty/Marine Affairs/Ocean and Coastal
Miami, LLM
Tulane, LLM

Advanced Legal Studies
Albany, LLM; MS
Arizona State, MLS
San Diego, MLS

Advocacy
Georgetown, LLM
Pacific McGeorge, LLM

Agriculture Law
Arkansas (Fayetteville), LLM

American Law
Boston, LLM
Brigham Young, LLM
Catholic, LLM
Denver, LLM
Duquesne, LLM
Florida State, LLM
Indiana-Indianapolis, LLM
Minnesota, LLM

Saint Louis, LLM
Temple, LLM
Tulsa, LLM
Wake Forest, LLM

American Legal Studies
Hofstra, LLM
Regent, LLM
St. Mary's, LLM
Seattle, LLM
Thomas Jefferson, LLM
Touro, LLM
Vermont, LLM

American Legal System
Michigan State, LLM
William and Mary, LLM

As Approved
California-Los Angeles, LLM; SJD
Georgetown, SJD
Indiana-Bloomington, LLM; PhD
Louisiana State, LLM; DCL
Michigan, LLM; MCL; SJD
Northwestern, LLM; MSL; SJD

Pennsylvania, LLM; MCL; SJD
Pittsburgh, JSD
Stanford, JSD; JSM; MLS
Vanderbilt, LLM
Wisconsin, LLM; MLI; SJD

Asian and Comparative Law
Washington, LLM; PhD

Banking and Finance Law
Boston, LLM
Chicago-Kent, LLM
Fordham, LLM
Thomas M. Cooley, LLM
Wayne State, LLM
Widener, LLM

Bankruptcy Law
St. John's, LLM

Biotechnology and Genomics
Arizona State, LLM

Business Law
California-Los Angeles, LLM
Capital, LLM
Loyola-Chicago, LLM; MJ
Samford, LLM
San Diego, LLM
Suffolk, LLM
Tulane, LLM
Widener, DL; MJ; SJD

Child and Family Law
Chicago-Kent, LLM
Hofstra, LLM
Loyola-Chicago, LLM; MJ

Closely Held Businesses
Western New England, LLM

Commerce and Technology
Franklin Pierce, LLM

Communications Law
Catholic, LLM

Comparative Law/Comparative Legal Studies/Comparative Legal Thought
Alabama, LLM
California Western, LLM; MCL
Cardozo, LLM
Chicago-Kent, LLM
Cornell, LLM
Denver, LLM
Duke, LLM
Florida, LLM
George Washington, LLM
Georgetown, LLM
Indiana-Bloomington, MCL

Indiana-Indianapolis, LLM
Iowa, LLM
Loyola Marymount, LLM
Miami, LLM
Notre Dame, LLM
Pace University, LLM
Penn State, LLM
Pittsburgh, JSD; LLM
St. Mary's, LLM
Samford, LLM
San Diego, LLM
San Francisco, LLM
Santa Clara, LLM
SMU Dedman, LLM
Southern California, MCL
Tulane, MCL
Washington, LLM; PhD

Corporate Law/Corporate Governance
New York, LLM
Samford, LLM
San Diego, LLM
Stanford, LLM
Thomas M. Cooley, LLM
Wayne State, LLM
Widener, DL; LLM; MJ; SJD

Criminal Law
Buffalo, LLM
Franklin Pierce (international criminal law), LLM

Democratic Governance and Rule of Law
Ohio Northern, LLM

Dispute Resolution
George Washington, LLM
Missouri, LLM
Oregon, MA; MS
Pepperdine, LLM; MDR

Economic Law
George Mason, LLM
Georgetown, LLM
New York, LLM

Education Law
Nova Southeastern, MSL

Elder Law
Kansas, LLM
Stetson, LLM
Western New England, LLM

Employee Benefits
John Marshall (Chicago), LLM; MS

Employment Law
Nova Southeastern, MSL
Wayne State, LLM

Energy/Environment/Natural Resources
Denver, LLM, MRLS
Florida, LLM
Florida State, LLM
George Washington, LLM
Golden Gate, LLM
Houston, LLM
Lewis & Clark, LLM
New York, LLM
Oregon, LLM
Pace, LLM; SJD
Pacific-McGeorge, JSD; LLM
Tulane, LLM
Utah, LLM
Vermont, LLM; MELP; MSEL

Entertainment and Media Law
California-Los Angeles, LLM
Southwestern, LLM

Estate Planning
Miami, LLM
Missouri-Kansas City, LLM
Western New England, LLM

Financial Services Law
Chicago-Kent, LLM
New York Law, LLM
Thomas Jefferson, JSD; JSM; LLM

Foreign Scholars Program
Houston, LLM

General
Alabama, LLM
American, SJD
Arizona State, LLM
Boston College, LLM
Buffalo, LLM
California-Berkeley, JSD; LLM
Cardozo, LLM
Chapman, LLM
Chicago, DCL; JSD; LLM; MCL
Cleveland State, LLM
Colorado, LLM
Columbia, JSD; LLM
Cornell, JSD; LLM
Drake, LLM; MJ
Duke, MLS; MJ
Emory, LLM; SJD
George Washington, LLM; SJD
Georgetown, LLM; MSL
Georgia, LLM
Hamline, LLM
Harvard, LLM; SJD
Hawaii, LLM
Illinois, JSD; LLM
Indiana-Indianapolis, SJD
Kansas, SJD
Maryland, LLM

Missouri-Kansas City, LLM
New York, LLM
Northwestern, LLM
Ohio State, LLM; MSL
Pittsburgh, MSL
Samford, LLM
San Diego, LLM
SMU Dedman, LLM; SJD
Southern California, LLM
Southern Illinois, LLM; MLS
Southwestern, LLM
Suffolk, SJD
Temple, LLM
Texas, LLM
Thomas M. Cooley, LLM
Toledo, MSL
Touro, LLM
Tulane, LLM; PhD; SJD
Valparaiso, LLM
Virginia, LLM; SJD
Yale, JSD; LLM; MSL

Government/Public Policy/Law and Government
Albany, LLM
American, LLM
George Washington, LLM
Pacific-McGeorge, LLM

Health Law
Albany, LLM
California Western, MAS
DePaul, LLM
Drake, LLM; MJ
Georgetown, LLM
Houston, LLM
Indiana-Indianapolis, LLM
Loyola-Chicago, LLM; MJ; SJD
Nova Southeastern, MSL
Quinnipiac, LLM
Saint Louis, LLM
Seton Hall, LLM
Southern Illinois, LLM; MLS
Washington, LLM
Widener, DL; LLM; MJ; SDJ

Human Rights
Indiana-Indianapolis, LLM
Notre Dame, LLM; SJD
St. Thomas (Florida), JSD; LLM

Indigenous Law
Arizona, LLM; SJD
Tulsa, LLM

Information Law and Society
Brooklyn Law, LLM

Information Technology
Dayton, LLM; MSL
Fordham, LLM

Houston, LLM
John Marshall (Chicago), LLM; MS

Insurance Law
Connecticut, LLM
Thomas M. Cooley, LLM

Intellectual Property
Akron, LLM
Albany, LLM
Boston, LLM
Cardozo, LLM
Chicago-Kent, LLM
Dayton, LLM; MSL
DePaul, LLM
Drake, LLM; MJ
Fordham, LLM
Franklin Pierce, LLM
George Mason, LLM
George Washington, LLM
Golden Gate, LLM
Houston, LLM
Indiana-Indianapolis, LLM
John Marshall (Chicago), LLM; MS
Michigan State, LLM; MJ
San Francisco, LLM
Santa Clara, LLM
Seton Hall, LLM
Thomas M. Cooley, LLM
Washington, LLM
Washington University, LLM

Inter-American Law
Miami, LLM

International Business and Trade Law/Economic Law
Arizona, LLM; SJD
Fordham, LLM
Georgetown, LLM
John Marshall (Chicago), LLM
New York, LLM
Pacific-McGeorge, LLM
San Francisco, LLM
Suffolk, LLM
Thomas Jefferson, LLM

International Law/International Legal Studies/Comparative Law
Albany, LLM
American, LLM
Case Western, LLM
Chicago-Kent, LLM
Cornell, LLM
DePaul, LLM
Duke, LLM
Fordham, LLM
George Washington, LLM
Georgetown, LLM
Golden Gate, LLM; SJD
Hofstra, LLM
Houston, LLM

Howard, LLM
Indiana-Indianapolis, LLM
Iowa, LLM
John Marshall (Chicago), LLM
Loyola Marymount, LLM
Miami, LLM
New York, LLM
Notre Dame, LLM
Pittsburgh, JSD; LLM
Puerto Rico, LLM
St. Mary's, LLM
Samford, LLM
San Diego, LLM
Santa Clara, LLM
SMU Dedman, LLM
Stetson, LLM
Temple, LLM
Tulane, LLM
Willamette, LLM

International Taxation
Florida, LLM
Michigan, LLM
New York, LLM
St. Thomas (Florida), LLM
Thomas Jefferson, LLM

Juridical Studies
California-Los Angeles, SJD
New York, JSD
Temple, SJD
Washington University, MJS

Labor and Employment Law
New York, LLM
Wayne State, LLM

Law and Jewish Civilization
New York, MSL

Law and Psychology
Nebraska, MLS

Legal Administration
Denver, MS

Latin American Studies/Comparative Law
Tulane, MCL

Legal Institutions
Wisconsin, LLM

Legal Theory
New York, LLM

Litigation/Trial Advocacy
California Western, LLM
Emory, LLM
George Washington, LLM
Temple, LLM

Mental Disability Law
New York Law, MS

Military Law
Judge Advocate General's School, LLM

National Security Law
Catholic, LLM
George Washington, LLM

Prosecutorial Science
Chapman, LLM

Real Estate/Land Development
John Marshall (Chicago), LLM
Miami, LLM
New York Law, LLM
Pace, LLM

Religion and Culture
Samford, LLM; SJD

Research
Duke, SJD
Indiana-Bloomington, SJD
Washington University, JSD

Science and Technology
Seton Hall, MSJ
Stanford, LLM
Suffolk, LLM

Securities and Financial Regulation
Georgetown, LLM

Space and Telecommunications
Nebraska, LLM

Sports Law
Marquette (for international lawyers), LLM

Sustainable International Development
Washington, University of, LLM

Taxation
Alabama, LLM
Baltimore, LLM
Boston, LLM
Capital, LLM; MT
Chapman, LLM
Chicago-Kent, LLM
Denver, LLM
DePaul, LLM

Emory, LLM
Florida, LLM; SJD
Georgetown, LLM
Golden Gate, LLM
Houston, LLM
John Marshall (Chicago), LLM; MS
Loyola Marymount, LLM
Loyola-Chicago, LLM
Miami, LLM
Missouri-Kansas City, LLM
New York Law, LLM
New York, LLM
Northwestern, LLM
Samford, LLM
San Diego, LLM
SMU Dedman, LLM
Southern California, LLM
Temple, LLM
Thomas M. Cooley, LLM
Villanova, LLM
Washington, LLM
Washington University, LLM
Wayne State University, LLM

Trade Regulation
New York, LLM

Tribal Policy, Law, and Government
Arizona State, LLM

Urban Affairs/Urban Studies
Missouri-Kansas City, LLM
Washington University, LLM

US Law/US Legal System
Baltimore, LLM
California-Davis, LLM
California-Hastings, LLM
Case Western, LLM
Connecticut, LLM
Duke, LLM
Golden Gate, LLM
Loyola-New Orleans, LLM
St. John's LLM
Santa Clara, LLM
Thomas M. Cooley, LLM
Washington and Lee, LLM
Washington University, LLM
Whittier Law School, LLM

■ A Note to Graduates of Law Schools Located Outside the United States

Degrees Other Than a JD and Bar Admission

In order to obtain a license to practice law in the United States, all candidates must apply for bar admission through a state board of bar examiners. Although this board is ordinarily an agency of the highest court in the jurisdiction, occasionally the board is connected to the state's bar association. The criteria for eligibility to take the bar examination or to otherwise qualify for bar admission are set by each state, not by the ABA or the Council of the Section of Legal Education and Admissions to the Bar.

In order to sit for the bar examination, most states require an applicant to hold a Juris Doctor (JD) degree from a law school that meets established educational standards. A JD earned at an ABA-approved law school meets the educational requirements in every jurisdiction in the United States. For those individuals who have not earned a JD degree from an ABA-approved law school, bar admission authorities have developed varying requirements and criteria to ascertain if such individuals meet the minimum educational requirements for bar admission. In most jurisdictions, individuals who lack such a JD will find that they do not satisfy the minimum educational requirements for bar admission and are ineligible to take the bar exam. In some of the remaining states, graduates of foreign law schools will find that additional schooling such as an LLM is required, and a few others recognize with regularity the sufficiency of a specific foreign legal education. A number offer an alternative licensure mechanism known as a Foreign Legal Consultant, which is a limited license to practice. And finally, some jurisdictions will allow individuals to be eligible for admission without examination under certain conditions if they have been admitted to the bar in another US jurisdiction.

In the past few years, there has been a large increase in the number of graduates from schools located outside the United States enrolled in advanced degree programs (such as the LLM). Upon graduating, many of these individuals return to their home country without seeking or obtaining bar licensure in the United States. However, an increasing number of these individuals seek to be admitted to a state bar.

Unlike the JD degree bestowed by an ABA-approved law school, which carries the indicia that the holder of that degree has completed a course of study imparting standards entitling him or her to engage in the practice of law, advanced degree programs at ABA-approved law schools are not regulated, and thus, not "approved." As a result, such degrees vary in content and rigor. In other words, the American Bar Association does NOT accredit degrees of any kind other than the JD.

It is the position of the Council of the Section of Legal Education and Admissions to the Bar of the American Bar Association that no graduate degree in law (LLM, MCL, SJD, etc.) is or should be a substitute for the first professional degree in law (JD), and that no graduate degree should substitute for the JD in order to meet the legal education requirements for admission to the bar.

As a result of the variance in state bar admission rules, the ABA strongly encourages individuals to contact the state board of bar examiners in the state(s) in which they are interested in being admitted to ascertain its requirements to sit for the bar examination. Contact information for all the state board of bar examiners is available at *www.abanet.org/legaled* and in the *Comprehensive Guide to Bar Admission Requirements*, which is available at the website above or through the ABA Service Center at 800.285.2221, Product Code: 529008710ED.

Appendix C: Other Organizations

You may have questions concerning a variety of issues while you are applying to law school, once you are in law school, and even after you have your degree.

The following organizations may provide you with the answers you need.

American Association of Law Libraries (AALL)

The American Association of Law Libraries exists to provide leadership in the field of legal information, to foster the professional growth of law librarians, to develop the profession of law librarianship, and to enhance the value of law libraries to the legal community and to the public. AALL members come from all sizes and types of libraries: the Library of Congress, legislative libraries, academic law libraries, law firm libraries, bar association libraries, county law libraries, court libraries, and law libraries in business and industry. The association publishes a quarterly journal (*Law Library Journal*), a monthly magazine (*AALL Spectrum*), and an annual directory and handbook (which includes a minority law librarians directory).

For more information, contact:

American Association of Law Libraries
105 W. Adams Boulevard, Suite 3300
Chicago, IL 60603
Phone: 312.939.4764
URL: *www.aallnet.org*

American Bar Association (ABA)

With nearly 400,000 members, including more than 40,000 law student members, the American Bar Association is the largest professional membership organization in the world. As the national voice of the legal profession, the ABA works to improve the administration of justice; promotes programs that assist lawyers and judges in their work; accredits law schools; promotes competence, ethical conduct, and professionalism; provides continuing legal education; and works to build public understanding around the world of the importance of the rule of law.

The ABA's Section of Legal Education and Admissions to the Bar advances effective legal education to serve society, the legal profession, law students, and legal academia, helping legal education through a wide range of resources and activities. To assure effective legal education, the Section provides a fair and efficient law school accreditation system. The Council and the Accreditation Committee of the Section are identified by the US Department of Education as the nationally recognized accrediting agency for professional schools of law.

The ABA may be contacted for information on the accreditation of law schools and the role of lawyers in the legal profession:

American Bar Association
Section of Legal Education and Admissions to the Bar
321 North Clark Street
Chicago, IL 60654-7598
Phone: 312.988.6738
URL: *www.abanet.org/legaled*

Association of American Law Schools (AALS)

The AALS is a nonprofit educational association of 171 law schools representing over 10,000 law faculty in the United States. The purpose of the association is "the improvement of the legal profession through legal education." This goal is furthered in a number of ways, including professional development programs for law professors and administrators, and a membership process that is designed to further the core values of the association. The AALS core values relate to the importance of faculty governance; scholarship, academic freedom, and diversity of viewpoints; a rigorous academic program built upon strong teaching; diversity and nondiscrimination; and the selection of students based upon intellectual ability and personal potential for success.

The AALS serves as the academic society for law teachers with an Annual Meeting that constitutes the largest gathering of law faculty in the world. The AALS is legal education's principal representative to the federal government and to other national higher education organizations and learned societies. The AALS also encourages collaboration with law professors on a global level, and has provided seed funding and continuing staff support for the International Association of Law Schools, an independent organization created with the help and encouragement of the AALS.

The AALS may be contacted for specific information about the role of legal education in the profession:

Association of American Law Schools
1201 Connecticut Avenue, NW
Suite 800
Washington, DC 20036-2717
Phone: 202.296.8851
URL: *www.aals.org*

HEATH Resource Center

The HEATH Resource Center of The George Washington University, Graduate School of Education and Human Development, is an online clearinghouse on postsecondary education for individuals with disabilities. The web-based organization serves as an information exchange about educational support services, policies, procedures, adaptations, and opportunities at American campuses. The organization no longer offers telephone services, but it does respond to e-mailed inquiries. You can send questions to *AskHEATH@gwu.edu*. Publications are available at no charge online; HEATH also offers RSS subscription to each of its pages.

For more information:

The George Washington University
HEATH Resource Center
2134 G Street, NW
Washington, DC 20052-0001
URL: *www.heath.gwu.edu*
Phone service not available.

Law School Admission Council

The Law School Admission Council (LSAC) is a nonprofit corporation whose members are more than 200 law schools in the United States, Canada, and Australia. It was founded in

1947 to coordinate, facilitate, and enhance the law school admission process. The organization also provides programs and services related to legal education. All law schools approved by the American Bar Association are LSAC members. Canadian law schools recognized by a provincial or territorial law society or government agency are also included in the voting membership of the Council. Accredited law schools outside of the US and Canada are eligible for membership at the discretion of the LSAC Board of Trustees.

The services provided by LSAC include the Law School Admission Test (LSAT), the Credential Assembly Service (CAS), the Candidate Referral Service (CRS), and various publications and LSAT preparation tools. The LSAT, the CAS, and the CRS are provided to assist law schools in serving and evaluating applicants. LSAC does not engage in assessing an applicant's chances for admission to any law school; all admission decisions are made by individual law schools.

LSAC exists to serve both the law schools and their candidates for admission. Last year, LSAC administered 151,398 tests, and processed 177,650 transcripts, 615,165 law school report requests, 912,122 law school reports, and 238,685 letters of recommendation.

For more information on the LSAT, the Credential Assembly Service, and law school admission, contact:

Law School Admission Council
662 Penn Street
Box 2000
Newtown, PA 18940-0998
Phone: 215.968.1001
URL: www.LSAC.org

For information on minority opportunities in law, contact:

Law School Admission Council
Minority Opportunities in Law
662 Penn Street
Box 40
Newtown, PA 18940-0040
Phone: 215.968.1338
URL: www.LSAC.org

NALP—The Association for Legal Career Professionals

NALP is a professional association of law schools and legal employers dedicated to facilitating legal career counseling and planning, recruitment and retention, and the professional development of law students and lawyers. NALP's core objectives include providing vision and expertise in research and education for legal career counseling and planning, recruitment, employment, and professional development; cultivating ethical practices and fairness in legal career counseling and planning, recruitment, employment, and professional development; promoting the full range of legal career opportunities and fostering access to legal public interest and public sector employment; and advocating for diversity in the legal profession and within NALP's membership.

NALP offers information and resources related to law careers through its website and online bookstore at www.nalp.org.

In addition, NALP publishes an online directory of legal employers and their hiring criteria at www.nalpdirectory.com and also an online directory of Canadian legal employers at www.nalpcanada.com. It also offers an extensive database of public opportunities for law students and lawyers through www.pslawnet.org (NALP's Public Service Law Network Worldwide).

NALP is not an employment agency and does not offer placement or career counseling services. NALP believes that each law school offers unique programs and opportunities and, like the American Bar Association and the Law School Admission Council, does not rank law schools or career services offices. The NALP Directory of Law Schools, which summarizes information relevant to recruiters, is published online at www.nalplawschoolsonline.org.

For further information, contact:

NALP
1025 Connecticut Avenue, NW
Suite 1110
Washington, DC 20036-5413
Phone: 202.835.1001
URL: www.nalp.org

Appendix D: Canadian LSAC-member Law Schools

University of Alberta Faculty of Law
Admissions Office, Room 480
Edmonton, Alberta
CANADA T6G 2H5

University of British Columbia Faculty of Law
1822 East Mall
Vancouver, British Columbia
CANADA V6T 1Z1

University of Calgary Faculty of Law
Murray Fraser Hall
Calgary, Alberta
CANADA T2N 1N4

Dalhousie Law School
6061 University Avenue
Halifax, Nova Scotia
CANADA B0J 1N0

University of Manitoba Faculty of Law
330 Robson Hall, 224 Dysart Road
Winnipeg, Manitoba
CANADA R3T 2N2

Faculty of Law McGill University
3644 Peel Street
Montreal, Quebec
CANADA H3A 1W9

University of New Brunswick Law School
PO Box 44271
Fredericton, New Brunswick
CANADA E3B 6C2

Osgoode Hall Law School, York University
4700 Keele Street
North York, Ontario
CANADA M3J 1P3

University of Ottawa Faculty of Law
57 Louis Pasteur
Ottawa, Ontario
CANADA K1N 6N5

Queen's University Faculty of Law
Admissions Office, Room 200
Macdonald Hall
128 Union Street
Kingston, Ontario
CANADA K7L 3N6

University of Saskatchewan College of Law
Admissions Committee
15 Campus Drive
Saskatoon, Saskatchewan
CANADA S7N 5A6

University of Toronto Faculty of Law
78 Queen's Park
Toronto, Ontario
CANADA M5S 2C5

University of Victoria Faculty of Law
PO Box 2400, STN CSC
Victoria, British Columbia
CANADA V8W 3H7

The University of Western Ontario Faculty of Law
Josephine-Spencer Niblett Building
London, Ontario
CANADA N6A 3K7

University of Windsor Faculty of Law
401 Sunset Avenue
Windsor, Ontario
CANADA N9B 3P4

Publications Available From the ABA's Section

THE OFFICIAL GUIDE TO ABA-APPROVED LAW SCHOOLS, 2011 EDITION

The Official Guide is published in cooperation with the Law School Admission Council and pursuant to the Section's Standard 509, modeled after Department of Education regulations requiring law schools to "publish basic consumer information in a fair and accurate manner reflective of actual practice." Admission data, tuition, fees, living costs, financial aid, enrollment data, graduation rates, composition and number of faculty and administrators, curricular offerings, library resources, physical facilities, placement rates, bar passage data, and post-JD programs are only some of the many categories covered in this comprehensive guide. Also available at major bookstores.

Product Code: 529008511ED, Price: $26

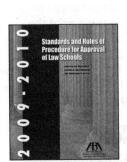

ABA STANDARDS AND RULES OF PROCEDURE FOR APPROVAL OF LAW SCHOOLS

ABA Standards and Rules of Procedure for Approval of Law Schools sets forth the standards that a law school must meet to obtain or retain ABA approval. Chapters include: Standards & Interpretations; Rules of Procedure; Keyword Index; Criteria for Approval of Summer Foreign Programs of ABA Approved Schools; Criteria for Student Study at a Foreign Institution; Criteria for Approval of Semester Abroad Programs; Statement of Ethical Practices in the Process of Law School Accreditation; Internal Operating Practices.

Product Code: 529008409ED, Price: $15

A SURVEY OF LAW SCHOOL CURRICULA—1992–2002

The result of a three-year project conducted by the Section's Curriculum Committee, this comprehensive survey of law school curricula at ABA-approved law schools highlights the changes, innovations, and trends in legal education that occurred from 1992 to 2002.

Available for free download at www.abanet.org/legaled/publications/pubs.html

COMPREHENSIVE GUIDE TO BAR ADMISSION REQUIREMENTS, 2010 EDITION

The Comprehensive Guide to Bar Admission Requirements is published each year by the Section and the National Conference of Bar Examiners. It sets out the rules and practices of all US jurisdictions for admission to the bar by examination and on motion; that is, legal education, character and fitness, bar examinations, and special licenses. Supplemental information follows each chart.

Product Code: 529008710ED, Price: $15

SOURCEBOOK ON LEGAL WRITING PROGRAMS

Establishes the parameters and common features that define successful programs for teaching legal writing skills in law school and to help improve the quality of legal writing programs across the country. *The Sourcebook* is the primary reference source for those designing, directing, and teaching in legal writing programs.

Product Code: 529009106ED, Price: $19

The Section publishes a number of books, reports, newsletters, and brochures to inform and educate its members and the public. All of the publications listed are available by calling the ABA Service Center at 1.800.285.2221 or through the Section website: www.abanet.org/legaled.

# of Legal Education & Admissions to the Bar

ADJUNCT FACULTY HANDBOOK

Published in 2005 by the Adjunct Faculty Committee of the ABA Section of Legal Education and Admissions to the Bar, this handbook covers a variety of topics and means of communication. Recognizing that schools differ in their use of adjunct faculty, it does not prescribe policy language. Rather, it covers topics the school might address and explains why they are important.
Available for free download at
www.abanet.org/legaled/publications/pubs.html

LAW SCHOOL BAR PREP PROGRAM DIRECTORY

The ABA Section of Legal Education and Admissions to the Bar and the Law School Admission Council sponsored a Bar Exam Passage Conference in October 2008 to assist law schools in addressing and improving the bar exam passage rates of their graduates. This directory (a PDF available for download) is a result of that conference. It contains pertinent information about bar prep courses at 61 law schools identified as having a bar prep program in place.

Key pieces of information in the directory include the law school name and title of bar prep program, the number of credits offered for the course, and if it is required for graduation. The directory also lists the name of the person at each law school to contact for further information.
Product Code: 2820001PDF, Price: $75

ANNUAL REPORT OF THE CONSULTANT ON LEGAL EDUCATION TO THE ABA

The Consultant's Office Annual Report is a brief overview of the events and activities of the Section and the Consultant's Office for the year. The current year edition is now available as are limited quantities of editions from previous years.
Product Code: 52900890809, Price: $10

LEGAL EDUCATION AND PROFESSIONAL DEVELOPMENT— AN EDUCATIONAL CONTINUUM ("MacCrate Report")

A comprehensive analysis of the role of law schools and the practicing bar in developing lawyering skills and values with recommendations for long-term change.
Product Code: 5290052, Price: $10

Call the ABA Service Center at 1.800.285.2221 to order Section Publications. Or visit the Section's website at www.abanet.org/legaled.

LAW SCHOOL FORUMS 2010
ADMISSION ADVICE
STRAIGHT FROM THE EXPERTS

Sponsored by the Law School Admission Council and Participating LSAC-Member Law Schools

If you're considering law school, come to a Law School Forum. Admission is free. At the forums you can ...

- talk with representatives of LSAC-member law schools from across the United States and Canada;

- attend workshops including financing a legal education, the law school application process, a panel discussion on being a lawyer, forum insider tips, and an LSAT overview;

- attend a panel presentation for diverse applicants;

- obtain admission materials, catalogs, and financial aid information;

- review LSAC publications and LSAT preparation materials; and

- visit the prelaw advisors' table if you want general advice about the law school admission process.

Registration is easy. Register at the forum or avoid the wait and register online at LSAC.org.

For more information about the forums visit LSAC.org.

Washington, DC
Saturday, June 19, 2010
10:00 AM–5:00 PM
Marriott Wardman Park
2660 Woodley Road NW
Washington, DC 20008

Miami, FL
Saturday, September 11, 2010
10:00 AM–4:00 PM
Hyatt Regency Miami
400 SE Second Avenue
Miami, FL 33131

Los Angeles, CA
Saturday, September 25, 2010
10:00 AM–4:00 PM
Millennium Biltmore Hotel
Los Angeles
506 S. Grand Avenue
Los Angeles, CA 90071

New York, NY
Friday, October 1, 2010
NOON–5:00 PM
Saturday, October 2, 2010
10:00 AM–4:00 PM
Hilton New York
1335 Avenue of the Americas
New York, NY 10019

Boston, MA
Saturday, October 16, 2010
10:00 AM–4:00 PM
Renaissance Boston
Waterfront Hotel
606 Congress Street
Boston, MA 02210

Chicago, IL
Saturday, October 30, 2010
10:00 AM–4:00 PM
Hyatt Regency
McCormick Place
2233 S. Martin Luther
King Drive
Chicago, IL 60616

Atlanta, GA
Saturday, November 6, 2010
10:00 AM–4:00 PM
Hyatt Regency Atlanta
265 Peachtree Street NE
Atlanta, GA 30303

Houston, TX
Saturday, November 20, 2010
10:00 AM–4:00 PM
JW Marriott Houston
5150 Westheimer
Houston, TX 77056

For directions, log in to
LSAC.org.

Aides for persons with visual or hearing impairments may be available with adequate advance notice. To make arrangements, call 215.968.1001.

Law School Admission Council
Box 40, Newtown, PA 18940-0040
P: 215.968.1001

The Law School Admission Council (LSAC) is a nonprofit corporation that provides services to the legal education community. Its members are more than 200 law schools in the US, Canada, and Australia. LSAT and LSAC are registered trademarks of Law School Admission Council, Inc. Law School Forums is a service mark of Law School Admission Council, Inc.

The Law School Admission Council (LSAC) is a nonprofit corporation whose members are more than 200 law schools in the United States, Canada, and Australia. Headquartered in Newtown, PA, USA, the Council was founded in 1947 to facilitate the law school admission process. The Council has grown to provide numerous products and services to law schools and to approximately 85,000 law school applicants each year.

All law schools approved by the American Bar Association (ABA) are LSAC members. Canadian law schools recognized by a provincial or territorial law society or government agency are also members. Accredited law schools outside of the US and Canada are eligible for membership at the discretion of the LSAC Board of Trustees; Melbourne Law School, the University of Melbourne is the first LSAC-member law school outside of North America.

The services provided by LSAC are the Law School Admission Test (LSAT); the Credential Assembly Service, which includes letters of recommendation, electronic applications, and domestic and international transcript processing for JD degrees; the LLM Credential Assembly Service; the Candidate Referral Service (CRS); the Admission Communication & Exchange System (ACES, ACES²); research and statistical reports; websites for law schools and prelaw advisors (LSACnet.org), law school applicants (LSAC.org), and undergraduates from minority groups (DiscoverLaw.org); testing and admission-related consultations with legal educators worldwide; and various publications, videos, and LSAT preparation tools. LSAC does not engage in assessing an applicant's chances for admission to any law school; all admission decisions are made by individual law schools.

LSAT, The Official LSAT PrepTest, The Official LSAT SuperPrep, ItemWise, and LSAC are registered marks of the Law School Admission Council, Inc. Law School Forums and LSAC Credential Assembly Service are service marks of the Law School Admission Council, Inc. 10 Actual, Official LSAT PrepTests; 10 More Actual, Official LSAT PrepTests; The Next 10 Actual, Official LSAT PrepTests; The New Whole Law School Package; ABA-LSAC Official Guide to ABA-Approved Law Schools; Whole Test Prep Packages; LLM Credential Assembly Service; ACES²; ADMIT-LLM; Law School Admission Test; and Law School Admission Council are trademarks of the Law School Admission Council, Inc.

LSAC fees, policies, and procedures relating to, but not limited to, test registration, test administration, test score reporting, misconduct and irregularities, Credential Assembly Service (CAS), and other matters may change without notice at any time. Up-to-date LSAC policies and procedures are available at LSAC.org, or you may contact our candidate service representatives.

Descriptive information about the law schools in this work, including such information and data published in electronic form, is provided by the individual law schools. Neither the ABA nor LSAC assumes any responsibility for inaccuracies or for changes in such information that may occur after publication. Questions regarding the accuracy or currency of any such descriptive information should be addressed to the specific law school.

Y0-BBY-912

ABA·LSAC
OFFICIAL GUIDE
TO ABA-APPROVED LAW SCHOOLS™

2011 EDITION

Produced by the Law School Admission Council and the
American Bar Association Section of Legal Education and
Admissions to the Bar